# THE NATURAL WORLD & YOU

Taken from:

*Environment: The Science behind the Stories*, Second Edition
by Jay Withgott and Scott Brennan

*Elements of Ecology*, Sixth Edition
by Thomas M. Smith and Robert Leo Smith

Cover images courtesy of Photodisc/Getty Images

Taken from:

*Environment: The Science Behind the Stories*, Second Edition
by Jay Withgott and Scott Brennan
Copyright © 2007 by Pearson Education, Inc.
Publishing as Benjamin Cummings
1301 Sansome St., San Francisco, California 94111

*Elements of Ecology*, Sixth Edition
by Thomas M. Smith and Robert Leo Smith
Copyright © 2006 by Pearson Education, Inc.
Publishing as Benjamin Cummings

This special edition published in cooperation with Pearson Custom Publishing.


Printed in the United States of America

10 V092 16 15 14


ISBN 0-536-29615-4

2006460117

AL

Please visit our web site at *www.pearsoncustom.com*

PEARSON CUSTOM PUBLISHING
75 Arlington Street, Suite 300, Boston, MA 02116
A Pearson Education Company

# Contents

## Chapter 24 | Aquatic Ecosystems 523

## Part Nine | Human Ecology 576

## Chapter 27 | Population Growth, Resource Use, and Sustainability 578

Taken from

# Elements of Ecology

## Sixth Edition

**Thomas M. Smith**

**Robert Leo Smith**

# Chapter 1 | The Nature of Ecology

Researcher Anker Nillsen taking morphological measurements from an Atlantic puffin chick (*Fratercula arctica*) as part of a study of this bird species being conducted in Rost, Norway.

Organisms interact with their environment at many levels. The physical conditions that surround an organism, such as ambient temperature, moisture, and light intensity, all influence basic physiological processes that are crucial to survival and growth. The organism must forage to acquire essential resources from the surrounding environment and in doing so must protect itself from becoming food for other organisms. It must recognize friend from foe, differentiating between potential mates and possible predators. All of this is in an attempt to succeed at the ultimate goal of all living organisms: to pass their genes on to successive generations.

The environment in which each organism carries out this "struggle for existence" is a place—a physical location in time and space. It can be as large and stable as an ocean or as small and transient as a puddle on the soil surface after a spring rain. This environment includes both the physical conditions and the array of organisms that coexist within its confines. This entity is what ecologists refer to as the ecosystem.

## 1.1 | Organisms Interact with the Environment in the Context of the Ecosystem

Organisms interact with the environment in the context of the **ecosystem.** The *eco* part of the word relates to the environment. The *system* part implies that the ecosystem functions as a collection of related parts that function as a unit. The automobile engine is an example of a system: components, such as the ignition and fuel pump, function together within the broader context of the engine. In a similar fashion, the ecosystem consists of interacting components that function as a unit. Broadly, the ecosystem consists of two basic interacting components: the living, or **biotic,** and the physical, or **abiotic.**

Consider a natural ecosystem, such as a forest (Figure 1.1). The physical (abiotic) component of the forest consists of the atmosphere, climate, soil, and water. The biotic component includes the many different organisms—plants, animals, and microbes—that inhabit the forest. Relationships are complex in that each organism not only responds to the physical environment but also modifies it and, in doing so, becomes part of the environment itself. The trees in the canopy of a forest intercept the sunlight and use this energy to fuel the process of photosynthesis. In doing so, the trees modify the environment of the plants below them, reducing the sunlight and lowering air temperature. Birds foraging on insects in the litter layer of fallen leaves reduce insect numbers and modify the environment for other organisms that depend on this shared food resource. By reducing the populations of insects upon which they feed, the birds are also indirectly influencing the interactions among different insect species that inhabit the forest floor. We will explore these complex interactions between the living and the physical environments in greater detail in succeeding chapters.

## 1.2 | Ecosystem Components Form a Hierarchy

The various kinds of organisms that inhabit our forest make up populations. The term *population* has many uses and meanings in other fields of study. In ecology, a **population** is a group of individuals of the same species

**Figure 1.1** | The interior of a forest ecosystem in coastal southeastern Alaska. Note the vertical structure within this forest. The Sitka spruce (*Picea sitchensis*) trees form the canopy, intercepting direct sunlight, and various species of mosses cover the surface of dead branches that extend from the canopy to the ground. A diversity of shrub and herbaceous plant species make up the understory, and another layer of mosses covers the forest floor, accessing the nutrients that are made available by the community of bacteria and fungi that function as decomposers at the soil surface. In addition, this forest is home to a wide variety of vertebrate and invertebrate animals, including larger species such as the bald eagle, black-tailed deer, and the Alaskan brown bear.

that occupy a given area. Populations of plants and animals in the ecosystem do not function independently of each other. Some populations compete with other populations for limited resources, such as food, water, or space. In other cases, one population is the food resource for another. Two populations may mutually benefit each other, each doing better in the presence of the other. All populations of different species living and interacting within an ecosystem are referred to collectively as a **community.**

We can now see that the ecosystem, consisting of the biotic community and the physical environment, has many levels. On one level, individual organisms, including humans, both respond to and influence the physical environment. At the next level, individuals of the same species form populations, such as a population of white oak trees or gray squirrels within a forest, which can be described in terms of number, growth rate, and age distribution. Further, individuals of these populations interact among themselves and with individuals of other species to form a community. Herbivores consume plants, predators eat prey, and individuals compete for limited resources. When individuals die, other organisms consume and break down their remains, recycling the nutrients contained in their dead tissue back into the soil. Ecology is the study of all these relationships—the complex web of interactions between organisms and their environment.

## 1.3 | Ecology Has a Rich History

The genealogy of most sciences is direct. Tracing the roots of mathematics, chemistry, and physics is relatively easy. The science of ecology is different. Its roots are complex and are intertwined with a wide array of scientific advances that have occurred in other disciplines within the biological and physical sciences. Although the term *ecology* did not appear until the mid-19th century, taking another century to enter the vernacular, the idea of ecology is much older.

One can argue that ecology goes back to the ancient Greek scholar Theophrastus, a friend of Aristotle, who wrote about the relations between organisms and the environment. On the other hand, ecology as we know it today has its early roots in plant geography and natural history.

In the 1800s, botanists began exploring and mapping the world's vegetation. Early plant geographers such as Carl Ludwig Willdenow (1765–1812) and Friedrich Heinrich Alexander von Humboldt (1769–1859) pointed out that regions of the world with similar climates supported vegetation that was similar in form, even though the species were different. The recognition that the form and function of plants within a region reflected the constraints imposed by the physical environment led the way for a new generation of scientists that explored the relationship between plant biology and plant geography (see Part Eight).

Among this new generation of scientists was Johannes Warming (1841–1924) at the University of Copenhagen who studied the tropical vegetation of Brazil. He wrote the first text on plant ecology, *Plantesamfund*. In this book, Warming integrated plant morphology, physiology, taxonomy, and biogeography into a coherent whole. This book had a tremendous influence on the early development of ecology.

Meanwhile, activities in other areas of natural history were assuming an important role. Developing his theory of evolution and the origin of species, Charles Darwin (see Chapter 2) came across the writings of Thomas Malthus (1766–1834). An economist, Malthus advanced the principle that populations grow in a geometric fashion, doubling at regular intervals until they outstrip the food supply. Ultimately, the population will be restrained by a "strong, constantly operating force such as sickness and premature death." From this concept, Darwin developed the idea of "natural selection" as a mechanism guiding the evolution of new species (see Chapter 2).

Meanwhile, unknown to Darwin, an Austrian monk, Gregor Mendel (1822–1884), was studying in his garden the transmission of characteristics from one generation of pea plants to another (see Chapter 2). Mendel's work on inheritance and Darwin's work on natural selection provided the foundation for the study of evolution and adaptation, the field of **population genetics.**

Darwin's theory of natural selection, combined with the new understanding of genetics, the means by which characteristics are transmitted from one generation to the next, provided the mechanism for understanding the link between organisms and their environment—the focus of ecology.

Early ecologists, particularly plant ecologists, were concerned with observing the patterns of organisms in nature, attempting to understand how patterns were formed and maintained by interactions with the physical environment. Some, notably Frederic E. Clements, sought some system of organizing nature. He proposed that the plant community behaves as a complex organism or superorganism that grows and develops through stages to a mature or climax stage (see Chapter 18). His idea was accepted and advanced by other ecologists. A few ecologists, however, notably Arthur G. Tansley (1871–1955), did not share this view. In its place he advanced a holistic and integrated ecological concept that combined living organisms and their physical environment into a system, which he called an ecosystem (see Chapter 20).

Whereas the early plant ecologists were mostly concerned with terrestrial vegetation, a group of European biologists was interested in the relationship between aquatic plants and animals and their environment. They advanced the ideas of organic nutrient cycling and feeding levels, using the terms *producers* and *consumers.* Their work influenced a young limnologist, Raymond A. Lindeman, at the University of Minnesota. He traced "energy-available" relationships within a lake community. Together with the writings of Tansley, Lindeman's 1942 paper, "The Trophic-Dynamic Aspects of Ecology," marked the beginning of **ecosystem ecology,** or the study of whole living systems.

Animal ecology initially developed largely independent of the early developments in plant ecology. The beginnings of animal ecology can be traced to two Europeans, R. Hesse of Germany and Charles Elton of England. Elton's *Animal Ecology* (1927) and Hesse's *Tiergeographie auf logischer grundlage* (1924), translated into English as *Ecological Animal Geography,* strongly influenced the development of animal ecology in the United States. Charles Adams and Victor Shelford were two pioneering U.S. animal ecologists. Adams published the first textbook on animal ecology, *A Guide to the Study of Animal Ecology* (1913). Shelford wrote *Animal Communities in Temperate America* (1913).

Shelford gave a new direction to ecology by stressing the interrelationship of plants and animals. Ecology became a science of communities. Some earlier European ecologists, particularly the marine biologist Karl Mobius, had developed the general concept of the community. In his essay *An Oyster Bank Is a Biocenose* (1877), Mobius explained that the oyster bank, although dominated by one animal, was really a complex community of many interdependent organisms. He proposed the word *biocenose* for such a community. The word comes from the Greek, meaning *life having something in common.*

The appearance in 1949 of the encyclopedic *Principles of Animal Ecology* by five second-generation ecologists from the University of Chicago (W. C. Allee, A. E. Emerson, Thomas Park, Orlando Park, and K. P. Schmidt) pointed to the direction modern ecology was to take. It emphasized feeding relationships and energy budgets, population dynamics, and natural selection and evolution.

The writings of the economist Thomas Malthus that were so influential in the development of Darwin's ideas about the origin of species also stimulated the study of natural populations. The study of populations in the early 20th century branched into two fields. One, **population ecology,** is concerned with population growth (including birth rates and death rates), fluctuation, spread, and interactions. The other, **evolutionary ecology,** is concerned with natural selection and the evolution of populations. Closely associated with population ecology and evolutionary ecology is **community ecology,** with its focus on species interactions. One of the major objectives of community ecology is to understand the origin, maintenance, and consequences of diversity within ecological communities.

At the same time, **physiological ecology** arose. It is concerned with the responses of individual organisms to temperature, moisture, light, and other environmental conditions.

Natural history observations also spawned **behavioral ecology.** Nineteenth-century behavioral studies included those on ants by William Wheeler and on South American monkeys by Charles Carpenter. Later, Konrad Lorenz and Niko Tinbergen gave a strong impetus to the field with their pioneering studies on the role of imprinting and instinct in the social life of animals, particularly birds and fish.

With advances in biology, physics, and chemistry throughout the latter part of the 20th century, new areas of study in ecology emerged. The development of aerial photography, and later the launching of satellites by the U.S. space program, provided scientists with a new perspective of the surface of Earth through the use of remotely sensed data. Ecologists began to explore spatial processes that linked adjacent communities and ecosystems through the newly emerging field of **landscape ecology.** A new appreciation for the impacts of changing land-use on natural ecosystems led to the development of **conservation ecology,** which applies principles of many different fields, from ecology to economics and sociology, to the maintenance of biological diversity. The application of principles of ecosystem development and function to the restoration and management of disturbed lands has given rise to **restoration ecology,** while understanding Earth as a system is the focus in the newest area of ecological study—**global ecology.**

## 1.4 | Ecology Has Strong Ties to Other Disciplines

The complex interactions taking place within the ecosystem involve all varieties of physical and biological processes. To study these interactions, ecologists have to draw on other sciences. This dependency makes ecology an interdisciplinary science.

Although in the chapters that follow, we will explore topics that are typically the subject of disciplines such as biochemistry, physiology, and genetics, we do so only in the context of understanding the interplay of organisms with their environment. The study of how plants take up carbon dioxide and lose water (see Chapter 6), for example, belongs to plant physiology. Ecology looks at how these processes respond to variations in rainfall and temperature. This information is crucial to understanding the distribution and abundance of plant populations and the structure and function of ecosystems on land. Likewise, we must draw upon many of the physical sciences, such as geology, hydrology, and meteorology. They will help us chart other ways organisms and environments interact. For instance, as plants take up water, they influence soil moisture and the patterns of surface water flow. As they lose water to the atmosphere, they increase atmospheric water content and influence regional patterns of precipitation. The geology of an area influences the availability of nutrients and water for plant growth. In each example, other scientific disciplines are crucial to understanding how individual organisms both respond to and shape their environment.

As we have made the transition from the 20th to the 21st century, ecology has entered a new frontier, one that requires expanding our view of ecology to include the dominant role of humans in nature. Among the many environmental problems facing humanity, four broad and interrelated areas can be identified as crucial: human population growth, biological diversity, sustainability, and global climate change. As the human population increased from approximately 500 million to more than

There is a tendency for ecologists to distinguish between the basic science of ecology—the study of the interaction of organisms with their environment—and the application of ecology to understand human interactions with the environment. The former is typically associated with the study of the "natural world," the environment apart from humans, whereas the focus of the latter is on the effects of human activities on the natural environment. This distinction even extends to the professional journals in which the results of research are reported. Studies of the natural world are reported in journals such as *Ecology* (Ecological Society of America) and the *Journal of Ecology* (British Ecological Society), whereas the influence of human activities on the environment appears in *Ecological Applications* (Ecological Society of America) and the *Journal of Applied Ecology* (British Ecological Society). This traditional distinction, however, is becoming more and more difficult to maintain, both in theory and practice. As this distinction becomes blurred, ecologists find themselves having to expand the very definition of what constitutes the "natural world."

Our species is having an ever-growing influence on Earth's environment. The human population now exceeds 6 billion, and, like our population, our collective impact on the planet's environment continues to grow. We use more than 50 percent of all freshwater resources, and our activities have transformed between 30 percent and 40 percent of the terrestrial surface to produce food, fuel, and fiber (see Chapter 27). Although air pollution has long been an issue of concern, changes in the atmosphere resulting from the burning of fossil fuels now have the potential to change Earth's climate (see Chapter 29).

In the title of his 1989 book, environmental writer Bill McKibben declared *The End of Nature*. The point of his declaration was that humans have so altered Earth's environment that nature, "the separate and wild province, the world apart from man," no longer exists. Although many of us may not agree with McKibben, it has become increasingly difficult to study the natural world without considering the influence of human activ-

ities, either past or present, on the ecological systems that are the focus of our research. For example, the forests of eastern North America were cleared for settlement and agricultural production (crops and/or pasture) by the latter part of the 19th century. It was not until the 1930s and 1940s that many of these lands were abandoned, as agricultural production moved westward, leading to the reforestation (regrowth of forests) of eastern North America. Ecologists cannot study these ecosystems without explicitly considering their history. We cannot understand the distribution and abundance of tree species across the region without an understanding of the past patterns of land use. We cannot study the cycling of nutrients within these forested watersheds without an understanding of the rate at which nitrogen and other nutrients are being deposited from atmospheric pollutants (see Chapter 22). Nor can we understand the causes of population decline in bird species that inhabit the forests of eastern North America without an understanding of how the fragmentation of forested lands from rural and urban development has restricted patterns of movement, susceptibility to predation, and the availability of habitat. Some of the leading questions facing ecologists today are directly related to the potential effects of human activities on terrestrial and aquatic ecosystems and the diversity of life that they support. Throughout the text, we will be highlighting these questions and topics in the feature Ecological Issues to illustrate the importance of the science of ecology in better understanding the human relationship with the environment—an environment of which we are a part. ●

1. How would you define nature? Does your definition include the human species? Why?

2. What would you consider as the most important environmental issue of our time? What role might the science of ecology (as you know it) play in helping us to understand this issue?

6 billion in the past two centuries, dramatic changes in land use altered Earth's surface. The clearing of forests for agriculture has destroyed many natural habitats, resulting in a rate of species extinction that is unprecedented in Earth's history. In addition, the expanding human population is exploiting natural resources at un-

sustainable levels. Due to growing demand for energy from fossil fuels that is needed to sustain economic growth, the chemistry of the atmosphere is changing in ways that may alter Earth's climate. These environmental problems are ecological in nature, and the science of ecology is essential to understanding their causes and identifying the means to mitigate their impacts (see Ecological Issues: The Human Factor and Part Nine: Human Ecology). Addressing these issues, however, requires a broader interdisciplinary framework to better understand their historical, social, legal, political, and ethical dimensions. That broader framework is known as environmental science. Environmental science examines the impact of humans on the natural environment and as such covers a wide range of topics including agronomy, soils, demography, agriculture, energy, and hydrology, to name but a few.

## 1.5 | Ecologists Use Scientific Methods

To investigate the relation of organisms to their environment, ecologists have to undertake experimental studies in the laboratory and in the field. All these studies have one thing in common, they involve the collection of data to test hypotheses (see Quantifying Ecology 1.1: Classifying Ecological Data). A **hypothesis** is an "educated guess" that a scientist poses to explain an ob-

served phenomenon; it should be a statement of cause and effect that can be tested. A hypothesis may be based on an observation in the field or laboratory or on previous investigations.

For example, an ecologist might hypothesize that the availability of the nutrient nitrogen is the major factor limiting growth and productivity of plants in the prairie grasslands of North America. To test this hypothesis, the ecologist can gather data in a number of ways. The first approach might be a field study. The ecologist would examine the relationship between available nitrogen and grassland productivity across a number of locations. Both factors vary across the landscape. If nitrogen is controlling grassland productivity, productivity should increase with nitrogen. The ecologist would measure nitrogen availability and grassland productivity at a number of sites in the region. Then, the relationship between these two variables, nitrogen and productivity, could be expressed graphically (see Quantifying Ecology 1.2: Displaying Ecological Data: Histograms and Scatter Plots). Go to QUANTIFYit! at www.ecologyplace.com to work with histograms and scatter plots.

## Quantifying Ecology 1.1 | *Classifying Ecological Data*

**A**ll ecological studies involve the collection of data—observations and measurements from which hypotheses can be tested and conclusions drawn about a population. The use of the term *population* in this context refers to a **statistical population**. It is highly unlikely that an investigator can gather observations on all members of a total population, so the part of the population that is actually observed is referred to as a **sample**. It is from this sample data that the investigator will draw his or her conclusions about the population as a whole. However, not all data are of the same type, and the type of data collected in a study directly influences the mode of presentation, types of analyses that can be performed, and the interpretations that can be made.

At the broadest level, data can be classified as either (1) categorical or (2) numerical. **Categorical data** are *qualitative*—observations that fall into separate and distinct categories. The resulting data are labels or categories, such as the color of hair or feathers, sex, or reproductive status (pre-reproductive, reproductive, postreproductive). Categorical data can be further subdivided into two categories: nominal and ordinal. **Nominal data** are categorical data in which objects fall into unordered categories, such as the previous examples of hair color or sex. In contrast, **ordinal data** are categori-

cal data in which order is important, such as the example of reproductive status. In the special case where only two categories exist, such as in the case of presence or absence of a trait, categorical data are referred to as **binary**. Both nominal and ordinal data can be binary.

With **numerical data**, objects are "measured" based on some *quantitative* trait. The resulting data are a set of numbers, such as height, length, or weight. Numerical data can be subdivided into two categories: discrete and continuous. For **discrete data**, only certain values are possible, such as with integer values or counts. Examples include the number of offspring, number of seeds produced by a plant, or number of visits to a flower by a hummingbird during the course of a day. With **continuous data**, theoretically, any value within an interval is possible, limited only by the ability of the measurement device. Examples of this type of data include height, weight, or concentration. ●

1. What type of data does the variable available nitrogen (the $x$-axis) represent in Fig. 1.2?

2. How might you transform this variable (available nitrogen) into categorical data? Would it be considered ordinal or nominal?

**W**hichever type of data an observer collects (see Quantifying Ecology 1.1), the process of interpretation typically begins with the graphical display of the set of observations. The most common method of displaying a single data-set is constructing a **frequency distribution**. A frequency distribution is a count of the number of observations (frequency) having a given score or value. For example, consider the following set of observations regarding flower color in a sample of 100 pea plants.

| Flower color | Purple | Pink | White |
|---|---|---|---|
| Frequency | 50 | 35 | 15 |

These data are categorical and nominal, as the categories have no inherent order.

Frequency distributions are likewise used to display continuous data. The following set of continuous data represents the body lengths (in centimeters) of 20 sunfish sampled from a pond.

8.83, 9.25, 8.77, 10.38, 9.31, 8.92, 10.22, 7.95, 9.74, 9.51, 9.66, 10.42, 10.35, 8.82, 9.45, 7.84, 11.24, 11.06, 9.84, 10.75

With continuous data, the frequency of each value is often a single instance, as it is unlikely that multiple measurements will be exactly the same. Therefore, continuous data are normally grouped into discrete categories, with each category representing a defined range

of values. Each category must be non-overlapping so that each observation belongs to only one category. For example, the body length data could be grouped into discrete categories as follows:

| Body length (intervals, cm) | Number of individuals |
|---|---|
| 7.00–7.99 | 2 |
| 8.00–8.99 | 4 |
| 9.00–9.99 | 7 |
| 10.00–10.99 | 5 |
| 11.00–11.99 | 2 |

Once the observations have been grouped into categories, the resulting frequency distribution can then be displayed as a **histogram** (type of bar graph) (Figure 1a). The *x*-axis represents the discrete intervals of body length, and the *y*-axis represents the number of individuals whose body length falls within each given interval.

In effect, the continuous data has been transformed into categorical data for the purposes of graphical display. Unless there are previous reasons for defining categories, defining intervals is part of the process of data interpretation—the search for pattern. For example, how would the pattern represented by the histogram in Figure 1a differ if the intervals were in units of 1 but starting with 7.50 (7.50–8.49, 8.50–9.49, etc.)?

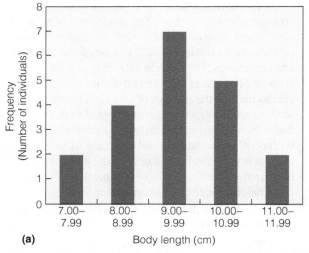

**(a)**

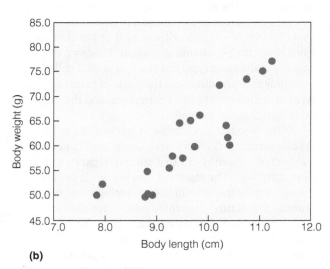

**(b)**

**Figure 1 | (a)** An example of a histogram relating the number of individuals belonging to different categories of body length from a sample of the sunfish population. **(b)** Scatter plot relating body length (*x*-axis) and body weight (*y*-axis) for the sample of sunfish presented in (a).

Often, however, the researcher is examining the relationship between two variables or sets of observations. When both variables are numerical, the most common method of graphically displaying the data is the use of a scatter plot. A **scatter plot** is constructed by defining two axes ($x$ and $y$), each representing one of the two variables being examined. For example, suppose the researcher that collected the observations of body length for sunfish netted from the pond also measured their weight in grams. The investigator might be interested in whether there is a relationship between body length and weight in sunfish.

In this example, body length would be the $x$-axis, or independent variable (Section 1.5), and body weight would be the $y$-axis, or dependent variable. Once the two axes are defined, each individual (sunfish) can be plotted as a point on the graph, with the position of the point being defined by its respective values of body length and weight (Figure 1b).

Scatter plots can be described as belonging to one of three general patterns represented by the three plots presented in Figure 2. In plot (a), there is a general trend for $y$ to increase with increasing values of $x$. In this case, the relationship between $x$ and $y$ is said to be positive (as with the example of body length and weight for sunfish). In plot (b), the pattern is reversed, and $y$ decreases with increasing values of $x$. In this case, the relationship between $x$ and $y$ is said to be negative, or inverse. In plot (c), there is no apparent relationship between $x$ and $y$.

Many types of graphs are presented throughout the text, but most will be histograms and scatter plots. No matter which type of graph is presented, you should ask yourself the same set of questions listed below to aid in the interpretation of the results. Review this set of questions by applying them to the graphs in Figure 1. What do you find out? ●

1. What type of data do the observations represent?

2. What variables do each of the axes represent, and what are their units (cm, g, color, etc.)?

3. How do values of $y$ (the dependent variable) vary with values of $x$ (the independent variable)?

Go to ɢʀᴀᴘʜɪt! and ǫᴜᴀɴᴛɪꜰʏɪt! at **www.ecologyplace.com** to further explore how to display data graphically.

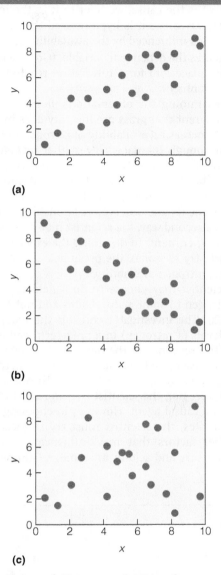

**(a)**

**(b)**

**(c)**

**Figure 2** | Three general patterns for scatter plots.

The graph of Figure 1.2 shows nitrogen availability on the horizontal or $x$-axis and plant productivity on the vertical or $y$-axis. The reason for this arrangement is important. The scientist is assuming that nitrogen is the cause and that plant productivity is the effect. Because nitrogen ($x$) is the cause, we refer to it as the independent variable. Because it is hypothesized that plant productivity ($y$) is influenced by the availability of nitrogen, we refer to it as the dependent variable. (Go to GRAPHit! at www.ecologyplace.com for a tutorial on reading and interpreting graphs.)

Upon examining the observations plotted in Figure 1.2, it is apparent that grass productivity does in fact increase with increasing availability of nitrogen in the soil. However, although the data suggest that nitrogen does control grassland production, they do not prove it. It might well be that some other factor that varies with nitrogen availability, such as moisture or acidity, is actually responsible for the observed relationship. To test the hypothesis a second way, the scientist may choose to undertake an experiment. In designing the experiment, the scientist will try to isolate the presumed causal agent—in this case, nitrogen availability.

The scientist may choose to do a field experiment, adding nitrogen to some natural sites and not to others (Figure 1.3). The investigator controls the independent variable (levels of nitrogen) in a predetermined way and monitors the response of the dependent variable (plant growth). By observing the differences in productivity between grasslands that were fertilized with nitrogen and those that were not, the scientist tries to test whether nitrogen is the causal agent. However, in choosing the experimental sites, the scientist must try to locate areas where other factors that may influence productivity, such as moisture and acidity, are similar. Otherwise, the

Figure 1.3 | Field experiment at the Cedar Creek Long Term Ecological Research (LTER) site in central Minnesota, operated by the University of Minnesota. Experimental plots such as those shown in the photograph are used to examine the effects of elevated nitrogen deposition, increased concentrations of atmospheric carbon dioxide, and the loss of biodiversity on ecosystem functioning.

scientist cannot be sure which factor is responsible for the observed differences in productivity among the sites.

Finally, the scientist might try a third approach: a series of laboratory experiments. The advantage of laboratory experiments is that the scientist has much more control over the environmental conditions. For example, the scientist can grow the native grasses in the greenhouse under conditions of controlled temperature, soil acidity, and water availability (Figure 1.4). If the plants exhibit increased growth under higher nitrogen fertilization, the scientist has evidence in support of the hypothesis. Nevertheless, the scientist faces a limitation common to all laboratory experiments; the results are not directly applicable in the field. The response of grass plants under controlled laboratory conditions may not be the same as their response under natural conditions in the field. In the field, the plants are part of the ecosystem and interact with other plants, animals, and the physical environment. Despite this limitation, the scientist now knows the basic growth response of the plants to nitrogen availability and goes on to design both laboratory and field experiments to explore new questions about the cause-and-effect relationship.

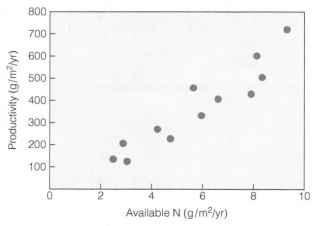

Figure 1.2 | The response of grassland production to nitrogen availability. Nitrogen, the independent variable, goes on the $x$-axis; grassland productivity, the dependent variable, goes on the $y$-axis.

Figure 1.4 | These *Eucalyptus* seedlings are being grown in the greenhouse as part of an experiment in which the response of plant growth to varying levels of nutrient availability is examined. The researcher shown in the picture is using a portable instrument to measure the rates of photosynthesis of plants that have received different levels of nitrogen during the period of their growth.

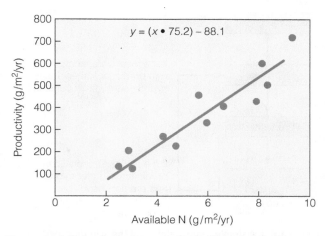

Figure 1.5 | A simple linear regression model to predict plant productivity (*y*-axis) from nitrogen availability (*x*-axis). The general form of the equation is $y = (x \times b) + a$, where *b* is the slope of the line (75.2) and *a* is the *y*-intercept (−88.1), or the value of *y* where the line intersects the *y*-axis.

## 1.6 | Experiments Can Lead to Predictions

Scientists use the understanding derived from observation and experiments to make models. Data are limited to the special case of what happened when the measurements were made. Like photographs, data represent a given place and time. Models use the understanding gained from the data to predict what will happen in some other place and time.

**Models** are abstract, simplified representations of real systems. They allow us to predict some behavior or response using a set of explicit assumptions. Models can be mathematical, like computer simulations, or they can be verbally descriptive, like Darwin's theory of evolution by natural selection. Hypotheses are models. Our hypothesis about nitrogen availability is a model. It predicts that plant productivity will increase with increasing nitrogen availability. However, this prediction is qualitative—it does not predict how much. In contrast, mathematical models offer quantitative predictions. For example, from the data in Figure 1.2, we can develop a regression equation, a form of statistical model that predicts the amount of plant productivity per unit of nitrogen in the soil (Figure 1.5). (See QUANTIFYit! at www.ecologyplace.com to review regression analysis.)

All of the approaches discussed above—observation, experimentation, hypothesis testing, and models—appear in the following chapters to illustrate basic concepts and relationships. They are the basic tools of science.

## 1.7 | Uncertainty Is an Inherent Feature of Science

Collecting observations, developing and testing hypotheses, and constructing predictive models all form the backbone of the scientific method (Figure 1.6). It is a continuous process of testing and correcting concepts in order to arrive at explanations for the variation we observe in the world around us, thus providing unity in observations that upon first inspection seem unconnected. The difference between science and art is that, although both involve the creation of concepts, in science their exploration is limited to the facts. In science, there is no test of concepts other than their empirical truth.

However, there is no permanence to scientific concepts because they are only our interpretations of natural phenomena. We are limited to inspecting only a part of nature because we have to simplify in order to understand. As discussed in Section 1.5, when we design experiments we control the pertinent factors and attempt to eliminate others that may confuse the results. Our intent is to focus on a subset of nature from which we can establish cause and effect. The trade-off is that whatever cause and effect we succeed in identifying represents only a partial connection to the nature we hope to understand. For that reason, when experiments and observations support our hypotheses, and when the predictions of the models are verified, our job is still not complete. We work to loosen the constraints imposed by the necessity to simplify in order to understand. We expand our hypothesis to cover a broader range of conditions and once again begin testing its ability to explain our new observations.

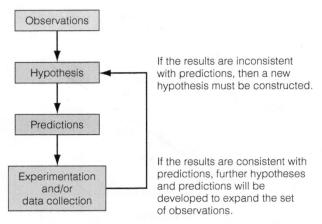

If the results are inconsistent with predictions, then a new hypothesis must be constructed.

If the results are consistent with predictions, further hypotheses and predictions will be developed to expand the set of observations.

**Figure 1.6** | A simple representation of the scientific method. Observations lead to the development of a conceptual model of how the system under study works. From the conceptual model, a hypothesis is constructed from which certain predictions follow. These predictions are tested through experimentation and/or further observations. If the results of the study are inconsistent with the predictions (negative result), the original conceptual model and hypothesis must be reevaluated and a new hypothesis constructed. If the results are consistent with the prediction (positive result), the conceptual model can be modified, relaxing previous assumptions. The hypothesis is then modified to include additional predictions, and the process of testing is repeated.

It may sound odd at first, but the truth is that science is a search for evidence that proves our concepts wrong. Rarely is there only one possible explanation for an observation. As a result, any number of hypotheses can be developed that may be consistent with an observation, so determining that observations are consistent with a hypothesis is not sufficient to prove that the hypothesis is true. The real goal of hypothesis testing is the elimination of incorrect ideas. Thus, we must follow a process of elimination, searching for evidence that proves a hypothesis wrong. Science is essentially a self-correcting activity, dependent on the continuous process of debate. Dissent is the activity of science, fueled by free inquiry and independence of thought. To the outside observer, this essential process of debate may appear to be a shortcoming. After all, we are dependent on science for the development of technology, and the ability to solve problems. In the case of current environmental issues, the solutions may well involve difficult ethical, social, and economic decisions. For that reason, the uncertainty that is inherent to science is discomforting. However, we must not mistake uncertainty for confusion, nor should we allow disagreement among scientists to become an excuse for inaction. Instead, we need to understand the uncertainty so that we may balance it against the costs of inaction.

## 1.8 | The Individual Is the Basic Unit of Ecology

As we noted in the previous discussion, ecology encompasses a broad area of investigation—from individuals to ecosystems. There are many points from which we can begin our study. We have chosen to begin with the individual organism, to examine the processes it uses and constraints it faces in maintaining life under varying environmental conditions. It is the individual organism that forms the basic unit in ecology. It is the individual that senses and responds to the prevailing physical environment. It is the collective properties of birth and death of individuals that drive the dynamics of populations, and it is individuals of different species that interact with each other in the context of the community. But perhaps most importantly, it is the individual through the process of reproduction that passes the genetic information to successive individuals, defining the nature of future individuals that will compose the populations, communities, and ecosystems in the future. It is with the individual that we can begin to understand the mechanisms that give rise to the diversity of life and ecosystems on Earth—mechanisms that are governed by the process of natural selection.

## Summary

### Ecosystems (1.1)

Organisms interact with their environment in the context of the ecosystem. Broadly, the ecosystem consists of two basic components, the living (biotic) and the physical (abiotic), interacting as a system.

### Hierarchical Structure (1.2)

The components of an ecosystem form a hierarchy. Organisms of the same kind that inhabit a given physical environment make up a population. Populations of different kinds of organisms interact with members of their own species as well as with individuals of other species. These interactions range from competition for shared resources to predation to mutual benefit. Interacting populations make up a biotic community. Community plus the physical environment make up an ecosystem.

### History of Ecology (1.3)

The origins of ecology are diverse, but a main root goes back to early natural history and plant geography. Those developed into the study of plant communities. Animal ecology developed later than plant ecology, eventually forming the foundations of population, evolutionary, and behavioral ecology.

Studies of the physiological response of plants and animals to features of the physical environment grew into physiological ecology.

The study of species interactions developed into the field of community ecology, and attempts to broaden the perspective of nature to include both physical environment and the biotic community gave rise to ecosystem ecology.

The development of modern technology and the growing influence of the human species on our planet have given rise to new areas of study within ecology. Landscape ecology involves the study of the spatial relationship between communities and ecosystems on the landscape. Conservation ecology and restoration ecology focus on the management and restoration of species diversity and natural ecosystems, and global ecology involves understanding Earth as a system.

### An Interdisciplinary Science (1.4)

Ecology is an interdisciplinary science because the interactions of organisms with their environment and with each other involve physiological, behavioral, and physical responses. The study of these responses draws upon such fields as physiology, biochemistry, genetics, geology, hydrology, and meteorology.

### Scientific Methods (1.5)

The study of patterns and processes within ecosystems involves field and laboratory studies or experiments. Experimentation begins with formulating a hypothesis. A hypothesis is a statement about a cause and effect that we can test experimentally.

### Models and Prediction (1.6)

From research data, ecologists develop models. Models are abstractions and simplifications of natural phenomena. Such simplification is necessary to understand natural processes.

### Uncertainty in Science (1.7)

Uncertainty is an inherent feature of scientific study, arising from the limitation that we can only focus on a small subset of nature, resulting in an incomplete perspective. Because any number of hypotheses can be developed that may be consistent with an observation, determining that observations are consistent with a hypothesis is not sufficient to prove that the hypothesis is true. The real goal of hypothesis testing is the elimination of incorrect ideas.

### Individuals (1.8)

The individual organism forms the basic unit in ecology. It is the individual that responds to the environment. It is the collective birth and death of individuals that define the dynamics of populations, and it is the interactions among individuals of the same and different species that define communities. It is the individual that passes genes to successive generations.

## Study Questions

1. How do ecology and environmentalism differ? In what way does environmentalism depend on the science of ecology?

2. Define the terms *population, community,* and *ecosystem.*

3. How might including the physical environment within the framework of the ecosystem help ecologists to achieve the basic goal of understanding the interaction of organisms with their environment?

4. What is a hypothesis? What is the role of hypotheses in science?

5. An ecologist observed that the diet of the bird species consisted primarily of large grass seeds (as opposed to smaller grass seeds or the seeds of other herbaceous plants that were found in the area). The ecologist hypothesized that the birds were choosing the larger seeds because they have a higher concentration of nitrogen than the other types of seeds present at the site. To test the hypothesis, the ecologist compared the large grass seeds with the other types of seeds, and the results clearly showed that the large grass seeds did indeed have a much higher concentration of nitrogen. Did the ecologist prove the hypothesis to be true? Can the ecologist conclude that the reason that the birds select the

larger grass seeds is because of their higher concentration of nitrogen? Why or why not?

6. What is a model? What is the relationship between hypotheses and models?

7. Given the importance of ecological research in making political and economic decisions regarding current environmental issues such as global warming, how do you think scientists should communicate uncertainties in their results to policymakers and the public?

## Further Readings

Bates, M. 1956. *The nature of natural history.* New York: Random House.

A lone voice in 1956, Bates shows us that environmental concerns have had a long history prior to the emergence of the modern environmental movement. A classic that should be read by all who are interested in current environmental issues.

Bronowski, J. 1956. *Science and human values.* New York: Harper & Row.

Written by a physicist and poet, this short book is a wonderful discussion of the scientific process as a human undertaking. The book explores the implication of science as a human endeavor. Highly recommended.

Cronon, W. 1996. "The trouble with wilderness; or, getting back to the wrong nature." In *Uncommon ground: Rethinking the human place in nature* (Cronon, W., ed.), 69–90. New York: W.W. Norton.

This is a great paper for students to read, which stirred up an incredible amount of debate among ecologists, environmentalists, and conservationists. Cronon describes how the idea of pristine nature is a human construct, and that, consequently, ecology is not natural without considering humans as an integral part of it.

McIntosh, R. P. 1985. *The background of ecology: Concept and theory.* Cambridge: Cambridge Univ. Press.

Provides an excellent history of the science of ecology from a scientific perspective.

Worster, D. 1994. *Nature's economy.* Cambridge: Cambridge Univ. Press.

A history of ecology written from the perspective of a leading figure in environmental history.

# Chapter 2 | Adaptation and Evolution

A cactus finch (*Geospiza scandens*) perches on an *Opuntia* cactus while feeding on the inner fruit in the Galápagos Islands.

Do you remember your first childhood visit to a zoo? You were probably amazed by the diversity of strange and wonderful animals: the giraffe with its long neck, the polar bear's snow-white coat, and the orangutan's exceedingly long arms. These animals seemed as if they were from another world, so unlike the animals that inhabit the environment we know. Among the widely dispersed, umbrella-shaped trees of the savannas of Africa, the ice flows of the Arctic, and the canopy of the tropical rain forest in Borneo, however, these animals look as natural as the birds at our backyard feeders or the deer that emerge from the forest's edge at dusk. What seem to be peculiarities in the context of one environment are advantages—characteristics that enable the organisms to thrive in another environment. The long neck of the giraffe allows it to feed in areas of a tree that are inaccessible to other browsing animals in the savanna. The white coat of the polar bear makes it virtually invisible to potential prey on the snowy landscape of the Arctic. The long arms of the orangutan are essential for life in the canopy, where balance requires more than a sure step. These characteristics that enable an organism to thrive in a given environment are called *adaptations*.

Figure 2.1 | Charles Darwin (1809–1882).

Prior to the mid-19th century, examples such as these served to illustrate the "wise laws that brought about the perfect adaptation of all organisms one to another and to their environment." Adaptation, after all, implied design, and design a designer. Natural history was the task of cataloging the creations of the divine architect. By the mid-1800s, however, a revolutionary idea emerged that would forever change our view of nature.

> In considering the origin of species, it is quite conceivable that a naturalist . . . might come to the conclusion that species had not been independently created, but had descended, like varieties, from other species. Nevertheless, such a conclusion, even if well founded, would be unsatisfactory, until it could be shown how the innumerable species, inhabiting this world, have been modified, so as to acquire that perfection of structure and coadaptation which justly excites our admiration.

The pages that followed in Charles Darwin's *The Origin of Species*, first published on November 24, 1859, altered the history of science and brought into question a view of the world that had been held for millennia (Figure 2.1). It affected not only the long-held view on the origin of the diversity of life on Earth but also the view on the very origin of the human species. What Charles Darwin put forward in those pages was the *theory of natural selection*. Its beauty lay in its simplicity; the mechanism of natural selection is the simple elimination of "inferior" individuals.

## 2.1 | Natural Selection Requires Two Conditions

Stated more precisely, natural selection is the differential success (survival and reproduction) of individuals within the population that results from their interaction with their environment. As outlined by Darwin, natural selection is a product of two conditions: (1) variation among individuals within a population in some "heritable" characteristic, and (2) that this variation results in differences among individuals in their survival and reproduction. Natural selection is a numbers game. Darwin wrote:

> Among those individuals that do reproduce, some will leave more offspring than others. These individuals are considered more fit than the others because they contribute the most to the next generation. Organisms that leave few or no offspring contribute little or nothing to the succeeding generations and so are considered less fit.

The **fitness** of an individual is measured by the proportionate contribution it makes to future generations. Under a given set of environmental conditions, individuals that possess certain characteristics that enable them to survive and reproduce, eventually passing those characteristics on to the next generation, are selected for. Individuals that do not are selected against.

The work of Peter and Rosemary Grant provides an excellent documented example of natural selection. The Grants have spent more than two decades studying the birds of the Galápagos Islands, the same islands whose diverse array of animals so influenced the young Charles Darwin when he was the naturalist aboard the expeditionary ship HMS *Beagle*. Among other events, their research documented a dramatic shift in a physical characteristic of finches inhabiting some of these islands during a period of extreme climate change (see Quantifying Ecology 2.1: Descriptive Statistics).

Figure 2.2 shows variation in beak size in Darwin's ground finch (*Geospiza fortis*) that inhabits the 40-ha islet of Daphne Major, one of the Galápagos Islands off the coast of Ecuador. Beak size is a trait that influences the feeding behavior of these seed-eating birds. Individuals with large beaks can feed on a wide range of seeds, from small to large, whereas those individuals with smaller beaks are limited to feeding on smaller seeds.

During the early 1970s, the island received regular rainfall (127–137 mm per year), supporting an abundance of seeds and a large finch population (1500 birds). In 1977, however, a periodic shift in the climate of the eastern Pacific Ocean called La Niña (see Chapter 3,

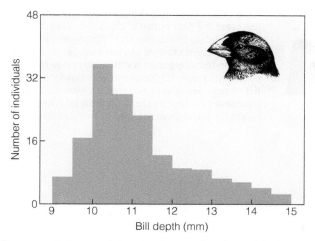

Figure 2.2 | Variation in bill size (as measured by depth) in the population of Galapagos ground finch (*Geospiza fortis*) on the island of Daphne Major. The histogram represents the number of individuals that were sampled (*y*-axis) in each category (0.5 mm) of bill depth (*x*-axis). Bill depth has a direct influence on the size of seeds that can be eaten by individual birds. (Adapted from Grant 1999.) Go to QUANTIFYit! at **www.ecologyplace.com** to work with histograms and scatter plots.

Section 3.9) altered weather patterns over the Galápagos, causing a severe drought. That season only 24 mm of rain fell. In the drought, seed production declined drastically. Small seeds declined in abundance faster than large seeds, increasing the average size and hardness of seeds available (see Quantifying Ecology 2.2: Confidence Intervals). The finches, which normally fed on small seeds, had to turn to larger ones. Small birds had difficulty finding food. Large birds, especially males with large beaks, survived best because they were able to crack large, hard seeds. Females suffered heavy mortality. Overall, the population declined 85 percent from mortality and possibly from emigration (Figure 2.3a).

The increased survival rate of larger individuals resulted in a dramatic shift in the distribution of beak size in the population (Figure 2.3b). This type of natural selection, where the mean value of the trait is shifted toward one extreme over another (Figure 2.4a), is called **directional selection.** In other cases, natural selection may favor individuals near the population mean at the expense of the two extremes, referred to as **stabilizing selection** (Figure 2.4b). When natural selection favors both extremes simultaneously, although not necessarily to the same degree, it can result in a bimodal distribution of the characteristic(s) in the population (Figure 2.4c). Such selection, known as **disruptive selection,** occurs when members of a population are subjected to different selection pressures. One of the few documented examples of disruptive selection in natural populations comes from the work of evolutionary ecologist Thomas B. Smith of San Francisco State University. Smith documented evidence of non-sex-related polymorphism (distinct

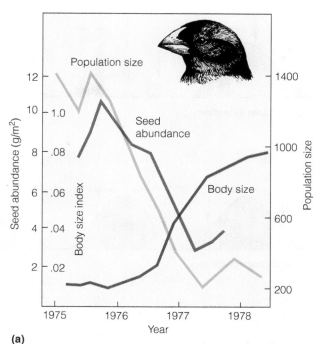

(a)

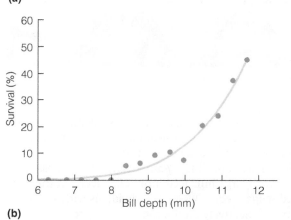

(b)

Figure 2.3 | Evidence of natural selection in the ground finch, *Geospiza fortis*. **(a)** The yellow line represents the population estimate on the island of Daphne Major based on the censuses of marked populations, and the green line estimates seed abundance, excluding two species of seeds never eaten by any Galapagos finches. Populations declined in the face of seed scarcity during a prolonged drought. The brown line plots changes in body size. Note how the body size of surviving birds increased during the drought period, suggesting that small-bodied birds were being selected against and large-bodied birds were being favored. The selection for larger body size is also reflected in the relationship between bill size and survival over this same period. **(b)** Results suggest that the most intense selection in a species occurs under unfavorable environmental conditions. (Adapted from Boag and Grant 1981.)

morphological types) in the black-bellied seedcracker (*Pyrenestes ostrinus*), found in Cameroon, West Africa. There is a distinct bimodal distribution in bill size for adult birds within both sexes (Figure 2.5; page 21) that results from disruptive selection.

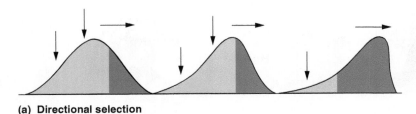

**(a) Directional selection**

Figure 2.4 | Three types of selection: The curves represent the distribution of characteristics within the population. **(a)** Directional selection moves the mean of the population toward one extreme. **(b)** Stabilizing selection favors organisms with values close to the population mean. **(c)** Disruptive selection increases the frequencies of both extremes. Downward arrows represent selection pressures; horizontal arrows represent the direction of change.

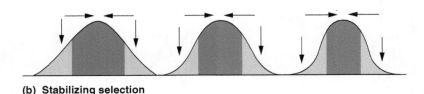

**(b) Stabilizing selection**

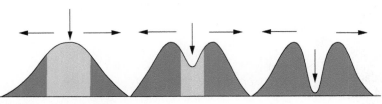

**(c) Disruptive selection**

In the case of the black-bellied seedcracker, disruptive selection is related to seed quality. Birds feed primarily on seeds of two species of sedge; these seeds are similar in size but differ dramatically in hardness. Individuals with large bills feed more effectively on the hard-seeded sedge species, whereas individuals with small bills feed more effectively on the soft-seeded species.

## 2.2 | Heritability Is an Essential Feature of Natural Selection

Two assumptions are basic to the theory that natural selection brings about the change of one species into another. The first is that an individual's characteristics are passed on from one generation to the next: from parent to offspring. This point was not controversial. For millennia, it had been observed that offspring resemble parents. How this inheritance occurred, however, remained a mystery. Not having an understanding of genetics when developing his theory of natural selection, Darwin accepted the hypothesis of inheritance that was in favor at his time—blending inheritance. It was thought that the characteristics of the parents were blended in their offspring, producing characteristics that were intermediate in form to the parents.

The second assumption, that the characteristics of a species could change through time, is where the controversy arose. The prevailing view was that species were independently created and invariable; the character of a species did not change from generation to generation—or at all for that matter.

When Charles Darwin proposed the theory of natural selection, the concept that species were mutable, subject to change, was an idea that, although not widely accepted, had existed for some time. Charles Darwin's own grandfather, Erasmus Darwin (1731–1802), published *The Laws of Organic Life (Zoonomia)* in 1794. Like his predecessor, the French philosopher Diderot, the elder Darwin believed that if an animal experienced a need, this need would provide for the formation of an "organ that satisfied the need." He believed that the modification of species was brought about by the "satisfaction of wants due to lust, hunger and danger" and "that many of these acquired forms or propensities are transmitted to their posterity" (offspring).

French soldier and natural historian Jean-Baptiste Lamarck (1744–1829) arrived at an independent and similar hypothesis to that of Erasmus Darwin. Lamarck supposed that as the environment imposed new "needs" upon an animal, its "inner feeling" set into motion (unknown) processes that produced new organs to satisfy

(a)

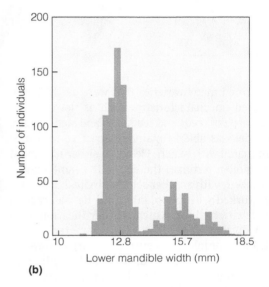

**Figure 2.5** | Bimodal distribution of bill size (as measured by the width of the lower section of bill, i.e., mandible: *x*-axis) for adult black-bellied seedcrackers (*Pyrenestes ostrinus*). **(a)** The bimodal distribution of bill size is found for both males and females and is a result of disruptive selection related to seed quality. Smaller billed individuals feed on soft-shelled seeds, whereas large-billed individuals are more successful at feeding on hard-shelled seeds, as shown in **(b)**. These two types of seeds are the primary food source for the species. (Adapted from Smith 1993.) (Nature Publishing Group.)

(b)

those needs; in other words, adapting the animal to its environment. These organs were then transmitted by heredity to the animal's offspring.

Such was the state of thinking when Charles Darwin wrote *The Origin of Species*. His theory of natural selection was a brilliant example of deductive reasoning. He had arrived at an explanation of how the characteristics of a species could change from generation to generation through the differential reproduction and survival of individuals within the population. There was no need to invoke the "inner feeling" or "living force" of his predecessors. Applying this mechanism to the origin of species, however, still required a huge leap of faith. Natural selection is bounded by the variation that is contained within the population. In the example of natural selection in Darwin's ground finch presented in Section 2.1, the shift in the distribution of beak size during the period of drought was still limited to the range of beak sizes present within the population. How does the range of characteristics get extended? How do new characteristics arise? For Darwin, mutation was the primary mechanism for maintaining variation within the

population: "the sudden and considerable deviation of structure" sometimes seen in offspring. Darwin also noted that, under domestication, mutations of an extreme type—"monstrosities"—sometimes arise, such as a two-headed calf or a "pig born with a sort of proboscis." The acceptance of blending inheritance required that Darwin invoke an unreasonably high mutation rate in order to maintain the patterns of variation that he observed in natural populations. Darwin was painfully aware of this limitation on his theory. What Darwin did not realize was that the answer to these questions regarding variation, as well as the means by which characteristics were transmitted from generation to generation, had already begun to unfold in the work of a contemporary.

Unknown to Darwin, an Austrian monk, Gregor Mendel (1822–1884), was studying in his garden the transmission of characteristics from one generation of pea plants to another. Mendel lived and worked in the abbey in Brunn, Austria (now the city of Brno in the Czech Republic). The pea plants that Mendel chose for his experiments had two characteristics that made them ideal for his work.

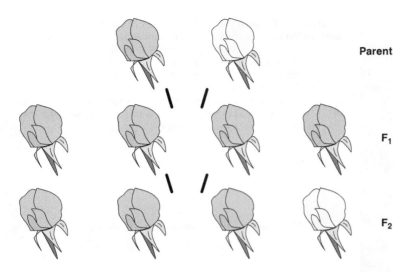

**Parent**

**F₁**

**F₂**

Figure 2.6 | Mendel tracked the heritable character of flower color for three generations. Purple and white parent plants that "bred true" were crossed to produce the F₁ generation, all of which had purple flowers. When individuals from the F₁ generation were crossed, the offspring in the resulting F₂ generation were a 3:1 ratio of purple:white flowered individuals.

First, they formed many varieties that were easily distinguishable based on characteristics such as flower color, the size and shape of seeds and seedpods, and stem length. Second, Mendel was able to maintain strict control over which plant mated with which. He could either let a plant self-fertilize (pollen fertilizes the egg of the same flower) or cross-fertilize it with another selected individual.

Mendel worked with his plants until he was certain that he had varieties for which self-fertilization produced offspring that were identical in characteristics to the parent. For example, he identified a purple-flowered variety that, when self-fertilized, produced plants with purple flowers only. In the terminology of plant breeders, these plants would "breed true." Mendel was then ready to examine what would happen when he crossed varieties with different characteristics. For example, what would happen if he crossed a plant with purple flowers with a plant having white flowers (Figure 2.6)? Mendel discovered that the plants produced by this crossing (mating), termed the F₁ *generation* (F referring to filial for the Latin word for son), all had purple flowers. The question Mendel faced was what had happened to the characteristic of white flowers?

When Mendel then crossed individuals from the F₁ generation, he had his answer. Out of the 929 plants produced by these crossings (termed the F₂ *generation*), 705 (approximately 75 percent) had purple flowers, and 224 (approximately 25 percent) had white flowers. From these experiments, Mendel concluded that the heritable factor for white flowers had not been lost in the F₁ generation, but rather that the heritable factor for purple flowers was controlling flower color. He also deduced that, because all of the F₁ plants had purple flowers yet were able to pass on the trait of white flowers to the next generation, the plants must carry two factors for the characteristic of flower color. From his experimental results, Mendel drew the following conclusions:

1. There are alternate forms of the units that control heritable traits (such as flower color).

2. For each inherited characteristic, an organism has two units, one from each parent (one each from the egg and sperm). These units may be the same (purple and purple or white and white) or different (purple and white).

3. When the two units are different, one is fully expressed, whereas the other has no noticeable effect on the organism's outward appearance. The unit that is expressed is called the **dominant** (purple), and the other is called the **recessive** (white).

By now it may be noticed that we have avoided using the term *gene* (or *allele*), choosing the word *unit* instead. This is intentional. Although Mendel's work had established a set of rules for the inheritance of characteristics, the nature of these units of transmission remained unknown. But as is often the case in science, although the landscape that lay ahead was unknown, the course of exploration had been set by the results of Mendel's experiments.

## 2.3 | Genes Are the Units of Inheritance

Mendel's experiments had provided the rules, but what was the unit of transmission? The search for the answer to this question left a trail of accumulated understanding that went on to form the basis of modern genetics. This trail finally ended in April 1953 when James Watson and Francis Crick published a two-page manuscript in the journal *Nature* that outlined their model for the structure of **DNA** (deoxyribonucleic acid).

At the root of all similarities and differences among organisms is the information contained within the molecules of DNA. All cells have DNA, and the manner in

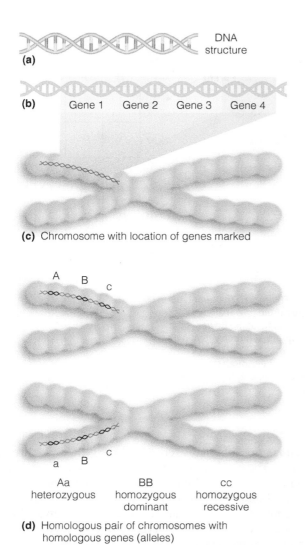

**(a)** DNA structure

**(b)** Gene 1  Gene 2  Gene 3  Gene 4

**(c)** Chromosome with location of genes marked

A    B    c

a    B    c

Aa
heterozygous

BB
homozygous
dominant

cc
homozygous
recessive

**(d)** Homologous pair of chromosomes with homologous genes (alleles)

**Figure 2.7** | **(a)** The double helix structure of DNA. **(b)** Genes are specific stretches of the DNA molecule that program the production and function of proteins. **(c)** Genes are contained in thread-like structures called chromosomes. **(d)** Chromosomes come in matched pairs, called homologous chromosomes. Because chromosomes are paired within the cells, alleles are also paired. Members of a pair of alleles occupy the same locus on homologous chromosomes.

which information is encoded is the same for all organisms. The structure of DNA is a double helix (Figure 2.7) composed of four kinds of chemical compounds called nucleotides. All DNA is composed of the same four nucleotides, with the blueprint of each species differing only in the sequence of these nucleotides. DNA is contained in threadlike structures called **chromosomes.**

Chromosomes come in matched pairs, called **homologous chromosomes.** Each chromosome carries DNA that is organized into discrete subunits, the **genes,** which form the informational units of the DNA molecule (see Figure 2.7). The alternate forms of a gene are called

alleles (originally termed allelomorphs; Greek, *different form*). For example, the unit of heredity that controlled the expression of flower color in Mendel's experiments was an allele. Because chromosomes are paired within the cells, alleles are also paired. The position an allele occupies on a chromosome is its **locus.** Members of the pair of alleles occupy the same locus on homologous chromosomes. If the alleles occupying the same locus on homologous chromosomes are the same, the individuals possessing them are called **homozygous.** If the alleles are different, the individual is called **heterozygous.** In this case, if one allele is fully expressed and the other has no noticeable effect, the allele fully expressed is referred to as the dominant allele, as was the allele for purple flowers in Mendel's experiment. The hidden, unexpressed allele is referred to as recessive (the allele for white flowers). If the physical expression of the heterozygous individual is intermediate between those of the homozygotes, the locus is said to display **incomplete dominance.**

We can now revisit the results of Mendel's experiments outlined in Figure 2.6, using the terminology of modern genetics (Figure 2.8). Because the initial parent plants "breed true," we know that they are both homozygous. Defining the dominant allele, the gene for purple flowers, as *P* and the recessive allele for white flowers as *w*, the white flower plants are *ww* and the purple flower plants are *PP*. This situation ensures that the offspring, which receive one allele from each parent, will all be heterozygous—*Pw*. The gene for purple flower being dominant, all of the resulting plants in the $F_1$ generation will have the physical expression of purple flowers.

When individuals of the $F_1$ generation are crossed, the possible outcome is different. Because both parents are heterozygous (*Pw*), each has an equal probability of contributing a gene for either purple (*P*) or white (*w*). The result of this crossing ($F_2$ generation), expressed in terms of proportion of total offspring, will be 0.5 heterozygous *Pw*, 0.25 homozygous dominant *PP*, and 0.25 homozygous *ww*. In terms of physical expression, this will translate into the proportions of 0.75 purple-flowered individuals and 0.25 white-flowered individuals, as was observed by Mendel (see Section 2.2, Figure 2.6).

The sum of hereditary information (genes) carried by the individual is the **genotype.** The total collection of genes across all individuals in the population at any one time is referred to as the **gene pool.** The genotype directs development and produces the individual's morphological, physiological, and behavioral makeup. The external, observable expression of the genotype is the **phenotype,** such as the flower color in Mendel's pea plants. The ability of a genotype to give rise to a range of phenotypic expressions under different environmental conditions is **phenotypic plasticity.** Some genotypes have a narrow range of reaction to environmental conditions and therefore give rise to fairly constant phenotypic expressions.

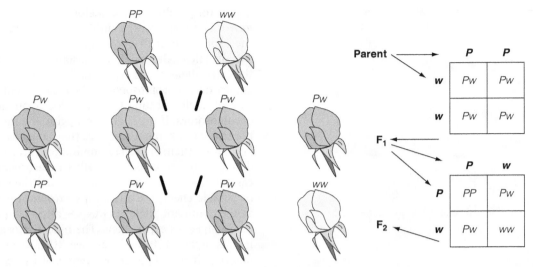

**Figure 2.8** | A more detailed depiction of Mendel's experiment outlined in Figure 2.6. The genotype of each plant is identified in the three generations (parent, $F_1$, and $F_2$). The purple flower allele is dominant, and the white flower allele is recessive. Each plant has two alleles controlling flower color. When two plants are crossed, each parent contributes one allele to the offspring. A homozygous parent can therefore only contribute one form of allele (*P* or *w*), whereas a heterozygous parent has an equal probability of contributing either a dominant or recessive allele. Note that although the proportion of different genotypes varies from generation to generation in this experiment, the gene frequency of each generation (the proportion of *P* and *w* alleles) is the same.

Some of the best examples of phenotypic plasticity occur among plants. The size of the plant, the ratio of reproductive tissue to vegetative tissue, and even the shape of the leaf may vary widely at different levels of nutrition, light, and moisture (Figure 2.9).

## 2.4 | Genetic Variation Is the Essential Ingredient for Natural Selection

One of Charles Darwin's many brilliant insights was his focus on variation among individuals within a species. Darwin's contemporaries viewed variation among individuals as an exception rather than the rule. Although the variation among individuals was used by breeders to create the many varieties of domestic plants and animals, these varieties were seen as more or less unstable—the product of careful selection and cross-breeding of individuals. Left to themselves, these varieties would return to the normal form of the parent species. In fact, the unstable nature of domestic varieties was used as an argument in support of the original and permanent distinctiveness of species. Darwin saw variation among individuals differently; it was not the exception but rather the norm. Variation was the essential ingredient of natural selection.

The major sources of genetic variation are mutation and genetic recombination in sexual reproduction. **Mu-**

**tations** are inheritable changes in a gene or a chromosome. The word *mutation* refers both to the process of alteration of a gene or chromosome and to the product, the altered state of the gene or chromosome. Most changes in phenotypic characters are attributable to changes in enzymes and proteins and therefore to changes in the DNA sequences that encode them.

Point mutations are chemical changes that occur in just one nucleotide in a single gene (see Figure 2.7). If a point mutation occurs in a gamete (egg or sperm), it can be transmitted to offspring and to a succession of future generations. Many mutations of a single gene have little or no apparent consequences on the phenotype. Mutations of single genes that produce large effects are often harmful. Gene mutations are important because they add variation to the gene pool. An example of a single gene mutation is albinism in mice. Albinism is the complete absence of pigment in the fur and the iris of eyes, causing a white coat and pink eyes. This gene is recessive and breeds true when albinos mate.

Chromosomal mutations may result from a change in the structure of a chromosome or a change in the number of chromosomes. Structural changes involve duplication, transposition (change in order or position), or deletion of part of a chromosome. Such changes result in abnormal phenotypic conditions. A change in chromosomal number can arise in two ways: (1) the complete or partial duplication of chromosomes or (2) the deletion of

**Figure 2.9** | Plasticity in leaf shape in response to environmental conditions. Pondweed (*Potamogeton*) has lance-shaped underwater leaves, responsive to underwater movements, and broad, heart-shaped leaves that float on the surface.

one or more chromosomes. Polyploidy, the duplication of entire sets of chromosomes, is discussed in Section 2.7.

By far, the greatest amount of genetic variation among individuals within a population occurs in species that reproduce sexually. In **sexual reproduction,** two individuals produce haploid (one-half the normal number of chromosomes) gametes—egg and sperm—that combine to form a diploid cell, or zygote, which has a full complement of chromosomes. Because the possible number of gene recombinations is enormous, recombination is an immediate and major source of genetic variability among offspring. In the case of humans, the number of possible unique combinations of chromosomes that could be produced in either a single egg or a single sperm is approximately 8 million. However, not all organisms reproduce sexually.

**Asexual reproduction** is the production of offspring by a single parent, without the participation of egg and sperm. Asexual reproduction takes many forms but in all cases creates offspring that are genetically identical to the parent (see Chapter 8 for further discussion and examples). In the absence of mutation, as the age-old saying goes, like really does beget like.

Although Darwin understood that heritable variation is what makes natural selection possible, an exact explanation for the mechanism that gave rise to the observable variations among individuals within a species eluded him. Although the work of Gregor Mendel was published only 6 years after the publication of *The Origin of Species*, his discovery went largely unknown until 1900, some 18 years after Darwin's death.

## 2.5 | Evolution Is a Change in Gene Frequency

Darwin did not use the word *evolution* in the original edition of *The Origin of Species*. Rather, he spoke of "descent with modification." Evolution (taken from the Latin word *evolvere* meaning "to unroll") had become a common English word in Darwin's time that implied the appearance of a series of events in an orderly succession. The term was tied to the concept of progress—directional change that represented the development from simple to complex. It implied the same concept of "directed purpose" that had been invoked by his predecessors, the very concept Darwin was intent on dispelling with his theory of natural selection (see Section 2.2).

Although the common application of the term *evolution* still implies directional change, the biological definition specifically applies to genetic change and does not imply direction or purpose. In the broadest sense, **evolution** is a change in gene frequencies within a population (or species) over time. Genes are transmitted from individual to individual, from parent to offspring, but individuals do not evolve—populations evolve. The focus of evolution is the gene pool, the collective. To illustrate this point, we can return to Mendel's experiments in Figure 2.8.

The proportion of individuals in each of the three possible genotypes (as represented by the trait of flower color) changes from generation to generation (parent, $F_1$, $F_2$). The gene frequencies (the proportion of $P$ and $w$ genes in the population), however, do not change. Both $P$ and $w$ remain in the same proportions from generation to generation: $0.5 P$ and $0.5 w$. No matter how many generations forward we calculate, the frequency of each gene ($P$ and $w$) will remain constant unless acted on by other agents. This rule is known as the **Hardy–Weinberg principle,** named for the two scientists who derived it in 1908. More specifically, the principle states that the gene frequencies will remain the same in successive generations of a sexually reproducing population if the following conditions hold: (1) mating is random, (2) mutations do not occur, (3) the population is large, so that changes by chance in gene frequencies are insignificant, (4) natural selection does not occur, and (5) migrations (movement of individuals and thus genes into or out of the population) do not occur. In the population of plants represented by Mendel's experiments, the frequencies of different genotypes changed through time (generations), as did the phenotypes, giving rise to a succession of colors—from purple and white to purple only and back again to purple and white. But as Mendel deduced, the change in the color of his garden did not imply a change in gene frequency (or units of inheritance in Mendel's terminology). In natural populations, however, the conditions required by the Hardy–Weinberg principle are never fully met. Mutations

**R**egardless of the trait being measured, individuals within a population typically exhibit some degree of variation. Quantifying that variation is central to any ecological study. So how does one characterize a population? What measures can be used to describe the variation that exists in a population or a set of observations? Two summary statistics are typically used to characterize a set of observations taken from a population: (1) an estimate of central tendency and (2) an estimate of variation. The actual statistics used, however, will depend on the type of data represented by the set of observations (see Quantifying Ecology 1.1: Classifying Ecological Data, p. 9).

Measures of central tendency describe the location of the middle or the center of a range of data values. The **arithmetic mean** (*m*), commonly referred to as the average, is the most generally used measure of central tendency for numerical data. It is simply the sum of the numbers (values of the observations) divided by the number of observations. For example, the following set of numbers represent the bill lengths (mm) of nine gold finches (*Carduelis tristis*) netted as part of a study to examine patterns of variation in the trait of bill size within a local population:

9.2, 8.7, 10.3, 9.3, 8.9, 10.2, 7.9, 9.7, 9.5

The arithmetic mean would be the sum of the lengths divided by 9 (the total number of observations being summed):

$$\frac{(9.2+8.7+10.3+9.3+8.9+10.2+7.9+9.7+9.5)}{9}$$

$$= \frac{83.7}{9} = 9.3$$

The mean bill length of finches sampled from the population is 9.3 mm.

Another measure of central tendency frequently used to summarize numerical data is the median. The **median** is the midpoint of a distribution: the same number of scores is above the median as below it. To calculate the median for the sample bill lengths presented above, we must first place them in rank order from smallest to largest:

7.9, 8.7, 8.9, 9.2, **9.3**, 9.5, 9.7, 10.2, 10.3

The median value (the midpoint of the distribution) is 9.3. In this example, the median has the same value as the mean. In the case where there is an even number of observations, selecting a midpoint is not possible, so the mean of the two mid-values is calculated to represent the median.

A third measure of central tendency, the mode, is commonly used to summarize discrete data. The **mode** is the most frequently occurring value. For example, consider the following data collected on the number of offspring produced per breeding pair (nest) of gold finch at our study site:

3, 2, 4, 2, 1, 3, 3, 4, 3, 5

The mode is 3 because more breeding pairs (4) had 3 offspring than any other number. The mode is easier to visualize when the data are represented as a histogram, as in Figure 1.

The mode of continuous data is normally computed from a grouped frequency distribution (see Quantifying Ecology 1.2: Displaying Ecological Data: Histograms and Scatterplots, p. 10), and the mode is represented as the midpoint of the interval with the highest frequency (9.5 for the interval 9.0–9.99 in Quantifying Ecology 1.2: Figure 1a).

Once an estimate of central tendency has been calculated, the next step is to characterize the variation about that estimate. The simplest measure of variation within a set of observations is the range. The **range** is simply the highest value minus the lowest value. In the example of bill length of finches presented above, the range is the difference between the highest value (maximum: 10.3 mm) and the lowest value (minimum: 7.9 mm), or 2.4 mm.

do occur. Mating is not random. Individuals move between populations, and natural selection does take place. All of these circumstances change gene frequencies from one generation to another, the result being evolution. Natural selection is in effect the selection (differential survival and reproduction) of one genotype over another, resulting in a change in gene frequencies.

The beauty of evolution by natural selection is that it does not require a direction or final cause. It is guided only by random changes in the sequence of the four nucleotides of the DNA that is the blueprint of each individual organism, constrained only by the necessity of survival and reproduction—the transmission of that DNA to succeeding generations.

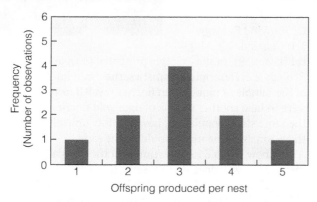

**Figure 1** | Histogram displaying the number of offspring produced per breeding pair (nest) of gold finch. The *x*-axis represents the number of offspring produced, while the *y*-axis represents the number of nests (frequency).

Because the range uses only the minimum and maximum values, it is greatly affected by extreme values that may not be representative of the sample (or population) as a whole. For this reason, a statistic that includes all of the observations is generally more desirable. A first attempt might be to estimate the deviation (difference) of each observation from a measure of central tendency such as the mean. We could estimate the "mean deviation" from the arithmetic mean ($m = 9.3$ mm) as follows.

First, subtract each value from the arithmetic mean:

$$(9.2 - 9.3) + (8.7 - 9.3) + (10.3 - 9.3)$$
$$+ (9.3 - 9.3) + (8.9 - 9.3) + (10.2 - 9.3)$$
$$+ (7.9 - 9.3) + (9.7 - 9.3) + (9.5 - 9.3)$$
$$= (-0.1) + (-0.6) + (1.0) + (0.0) + (0.4)$$
$$+ (0.9) + (-1.4) + (0.4) + (0.2) = 0.0$$

The problem with this approach is that the sum of the deviations from the mean is zero, and therefore the mean deviation will likewise be zero. This will always be the case for deviations from the arithmetic mean. (Can

you figure out why this is the case?) So to keep this from occurring, each deviation from the mean value is squared and called the "squared deviation from the mean." In this way, a deviation of 0.4, be it negative or positive, will have the same value (0.16).

If we now square the deviation from the overall mean, the sum of the deviations becomes:

$$(-0.1)^2 + (-0.6)^2 + (1.0)^2 + (0.0)^2 + (0.4)^2$$
$$+ (0.9)^2 + (-1.4)^2 + (0.4)^2 + (0.2)^2 = 4.5$$

and the average deviation is $4.5/9 = 0.5$. This "average squared deviation from the mean" is called the **variance** ($s^2$).

There is a problem with the variance. Because in its calculation the deviations are squared, the units are also squared. To return the units to the same as the original data values, the square root of the variance must be taken. This value ($s$) is called the **standard deviation**. For the variance of bill length, the standard deviation is $\sqrt{0.5}$, or 0.71.

Throughout this and other chapters in the text, results from studies are presented in summary form; often, this will include estimates of the sample means and variances (or standard deviations). In the case of categorical data, however, the use of mean and variance is not appropriate, as values represent only categories, and descriptive statistics will include frequency distributions and modes. ●

1. In the histogram of bill length of Darwin's ground finch that is shown in Figure 2.2, what is the mode (the bill depth intervals are 0.5 mm)?

2. Would it be appropriate to summarize the distribution of bill size for the sample of black-bellied seedcrackers presented in Figure 2.5 using the arithmetic mean as a measure of central tendency? Why or why not?

Go to QUANTIFYit! at www.ecologyplace.com to practice these quantitative tools with activities on summary statistics and standard deviation.

## 2.6 | The Concept of Species Is Based on Genetic Isolation

The understanding of the genetic basis for heredity altered the concept of species. Field guide in hand, we can distinguish a robin from a wood thrush or a white oak from a red oak. Each has physical characteristics that set

it apart. Each is an entity, a discrete unit, to which a name has been given. That is the way Carl von Linné (Linnaeus; 1707–1778), who gave us our system of binomial classification, saw plants and animals. He, like others of his day, regarded the many different organisms as fixed and unchanging units, the so-called products of special creation. They differed in color, pattern, structure,

In Quantifying Ecology 2.1: Descriptive Statistics (pp. 26–27), we examined the use of the mean and standard deviation to characterize a set of observations. The standard deviation is a particularly informative estimate of variation when the data conform to a **normal distribution**. Normal distributions are a family of distributions that have the same general shape. They are symmetric with scores more concentrated in the middle than in the tails, as shown in Figure 1. Normal distributions are sometimes described as bell-shaped. Any given normal distribution can be specified mathematically in terms of two parameters: the mean ($\mu$) and the standard deviation ($\sigma$). The mean defines the central point of the distribution, and although there are many normal curves, they all share an important property that allows us to treat them in a uniform fashion. All normal density curves satisfy the following property, which is often referred to as the *Empirical Rule*.

> 68 percent of the observations fall within 1 standard deviation of the mean.
>
> 95 percent of the observations fall within 2 standard deviations of the mean.
>
> 99.7 percent of the observations fall within 3 standard deviations of the mean.

Thus, for a normal distribution, almost all values lie within 3 standard deviations of the mean, as shown in Figure 1. The normal distribution is a central concept in statistics, in that an entire class of statistics (known as parametric statistics) is based on the assumption that the data being analyzed conform to the normal distribution.

Notice that in the above description of the normal distribution, we use the symbols $\mu$ and $\sigma$ for the mean and standard deviation (respectively), whereas in Quantifying Ecology 2.1: Descriptive Statistics, we used the symbols $m$ and $s$. The reason for this difference is that $\mu$ and $\sigma$ represent the mean and standard deviation of the entire population, whereas the values of $m$ and $s$ are estimates of $\mu$ and $\sigma$ based on our sample of the population, the subset of the population that we actually observed (see Quantifying Ecology 1.1: Classifying Ecological Data, p. 9). In the example presented in Quantifying Ecology 2.1: Descriptive Statistics, the mean bill length of the sample of nine golden finches was 9.3 mm. If we were to take another sample of nine gold finches from the same study population, however, it is unlikely that the estimate of the mean would be the same.

So how reliable is our estimate of the population mean? How well does $m$ represent the true population mean $\mu$? If the population of bill lengths is normally distributed (approximates a normal distribution), then the estimates of the population mean (values of $m$) will also be normally distributed. That is to say, if we were to take 100 different samples of nine gold finches from the population and calculate the means for those 100 samples, the values of $m$ would form a normal distribution, and the mean of that distribution would be the population mean, $\mu$. The standard deviation of the distribution

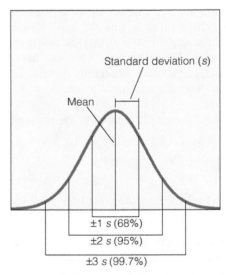

**Figure 1** | Normal distribution, showing the proportion of the population within 1, 2, and 3 standard deviations of the mean.

proportion, and other characteristics. By these criteria, naturalists such as Charles Darwin described, separated, and arranged species into groups. Each species was discrete. Some variation was permissible, but those variants were considered accidental. This classic **morphological species** concept is still alive, useful, and necessary for classifying the vast number of plants and animals. It is the basis of the descriptions of organisms found in field guides (Figure 2.10). However, if the observed differences in physical characteristics that are used to distinguish species are a result of genetic differences between the populations, the definition of species should recognize how these genetic differences are maintained.

of sample means would be $\sigma_m$, referred to as the **standard error** (of the mean). It would be calculated by summing the squared differences between the sample means and the population mean $(m - \mu)$. Under the normal distribution, the expected value of $\sigma_m = \sigma/\sqrt{n}$, where $n$ is the sample size (the number of observations used in calculating the means). Because we do not know the true standard deviation of the population $(\sigma)$, our best estimate is $s$, the sample standard deviation. Our best estimate of $\sigma_m$, the standard error, is therefore $s_m = s/\sqrt{n}$.

We can now use the standard error to provide us with an estimate of reliability of our sample mean $(m)$. Because the sample means follow a normal distribution, given the *Empirical Rule* stated above, the region $2.0\, s/\sqrt{n}$ below and $2.0\, s/\sqrt{n}$ above $\mu$ will include 95 percent of the estimates of $m$ of sample size $n$. Another way of expressing this statement symbolically is:

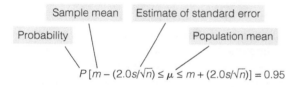

$$P[m - (2.0s/\sqrt{n}) \leq \mu \leq m + (2.0s/\sqrt{n})] = 0.95$$

For the example of bill length in the sample of nine golden finches presented in Quantifying Ecology 2.1: Descriptive Statistics, the calculation is as follows:

$$m = 9.3, s = 0.71, n = 9$$

$$s_m = \frac{s}{\sqrt{n}} = \frac{0.71}{3} = 0.237$$

$$P\big[9.3 - (2.0 \times 0.237) \leq \mu \leq 9.3$$
$$+ (2.0 \times 0.237)\big] = 0.95$$
$$P(8.826 \leq \mu \leq 9.774) = 0.95$$

There is a 95 percent probability (chance) that the true population mean $(\mu)$ lies between the values of 8.826 and 9.977 mm. This range of values is called the **confidence interval**. In this example, it is the 95 percent confidence interval. We could just as easily have calculated the 68 percent ($\pm 1$ standard error) or the 99.7 percent ($\pm 3$ standard error) confidence interval using the *Empirical Rule* stated above.

Note from the equation for the estimate of the standard error $(s/\sqrt{n})$ that the standard error decreases with increasing sample size $(n)$. One can therefore improve the estimate of the sample error, and decrease the range of the confidence interval, by increasing the number of observations (sample) taken in estimating the mean and standard deviation of the population being studied.

In reality, the *Empirical Rule* stated above holds only for the true population standard deviation $(\sigma)$ and standard error $(\sigma_m)$. When we estimate these values from our sample, the distribution can deviate slightly from the standard normal distribution. The expected distribution based on the sample estimate of the standard error $(s_m)$ is called a ***t*-distribution**. Like the normal distribution, the *t*-distribution is symmetric about the mean, but it differs in that it assumes different shapes depending on the number of degrees of freedom. By degrees of freedom (abbreviated *df*) we mean the quantity $n - 1$, where $n$ is the size of the sample from which the estimate of the standard deviation is based. The value of $t$ for our sample size of 9 $(df = 8)$ and a confidence interval of 95 percent is actually 2.31 rather than the value of 2.0 used above. Values of $t$ for differing degrees of freedom (sample sizes) can be found in any introductory statistics text or online (search: *t*-distribution table). ●

1. The standard deviation of the sample of 20 sunfish body lengths presented in Quantifying Ecology 1.2: Displaying Ecological Data is 4.11. What is the standard error of the mean for this sample?

2. Using a value of $t = 2.09$, calculate the 95 percent confidence interval for the population mean of golden finch bill length.

Go to **QUANTIFYit!** www.ecologyplace.com to review confidence intervals and comparing samples using the *t*-test.

---

The evolutionary biologist Ernst Mayr advanced the idea of the **biological species,** a group of populations whose individuals have the potential to interbreed and produce fertile offspring. This definition of species implies reproductive isolation; and as reproduction is the means of transmitting genetic information (DNA), it also implied genetic isolation.

Each spring, there is a rush of courtship and mating activity in woods and fields. Fish move to spawning areas, amphibians migrate to breeding pools, and birds sing. During this frenzy of activity, each species remains distinct. Song sparrows mate with song sparrows, brook trout with brook trout, wood frogs with wood frogs, and few mistakes occur, even between species similar in

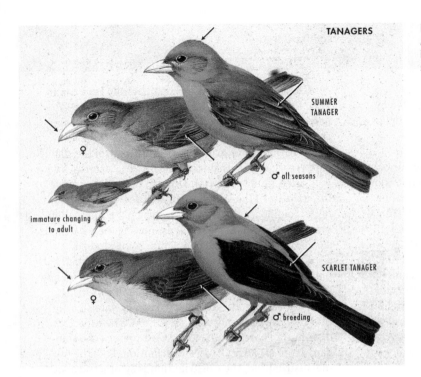

**Figure 2.10** | Illustration from *Field Guide to the Birds* by Roger Tory Peterson that identifies the physical characteristics used to distinguish various species of tanagers (Thraupidae).

appearance. But what maintains reproductive isolation among populations, giving rise to distinct species?

The means by which diverse species remain distinct are called **isolating mechanisms** (or **reproductive barriers**)—mechanisms that restrict the exchange of genes between populations. They include morphological characteristics, behavioral traits, ecological conditions, and genetic incompatibility. Isolating mechanisms may be premating or postmating. **Premating mechanisms**—those that prevent mating between individuals of different species—include habitat selection, temporal isolation, behavior, and mechanical or structural incompatibility. **Postmating mechanisms** reduce the survival or reproductive success of those offspring that may arise from the mating of individuals of two different species.

If two potential mates in breeding condition have little opportunity to meet, they are not likely to interbreed. Such is the case when two closely related species coexist in the same geographic area but use different habitats (local environments). Isolation through differences in habitat is common among frogs and toads. Different calling and mating sites among concurrently breeding frogs and toads tend to keep the species separated. The upland chorus frog (*Pseudoacris triseriata feriarum*) and the closely related southern chorus frog (*Pseudoacris nigrata*) breed in the same pools, but calling males tend to segregate themselves in different locations in the pond (Figure 2.11). The southern chorus frog calls from a concealed position at the base of grass clumps or among vegetation debris, whereas the upland chorus frog calls from a more open location.

Temporal isolation (differences in the timing of breeding and flowering seasons) can function to isolate species that occur in the same geographic area of habitat. The American toad (*Bufo americanus*) breeds early in the spring, whereas Fowler's toad (*Bufo woodhousei fowleri*) breeds a few weeks later.

Behavioral barriers (differences in courtship and mating behavior) are important isolating mechanisms. The males of many animals have specific courtship displays, to which, in most instances, only females of the same species respond. These displays may involve visual, auditory, and chemical stimuli. Some insects, such as certain species of butterflies and fruit flies, and some mammals possess species-specific scents. Birds, frogs, and toads, some fish, and such singing insects as crickets, grasshoppers, and cicadas have specific calls that attract the "correct" species. Visual signals are highly developed in birds and some fish. Among insects, the flight patterns and flash patterns of fireflies on a summer night are most unusual visual stimuli. The light signals emitted by various species differ in timing, brightness, and color, which may be white, blue, green, yellow, orange, or red.

Mechanical isolating mechanisms make copulation or pollination between closely related species impossible. Although such mechanical isolation is seldom a barrier to gene exchange among animals, differences in floral structure and intricate mechanisms for cross-pollination are common among plants.

Even when two individuals of differing species are able to mate, genetic differences generally do not allow fertilization to occur. Should fertilization occur, how-

(a)

(b)

Figure 2.11 | The **(a)** upland chorus frog (*Pseudoacris triseriata feriarum*) and **(b)** the closely related southern chorus frog (*Pseudoacris nigrata*) breed in the same pools, but calling males tend to segregate themselves in different locations in the pond.

ever, other genetic barriers may function as postmating mechanisms, maintaining isolation between the two gene pools. The offspring that result from the mating of two different species are called **hybrids.** In most cases, hybrid individuals are inviable and do not survive. In other situations, offspring survive, but are sterile—unable to produce offspring of their own. Such is the case with the mule, which is a cross between a female horse and a male donkey (Figure 2.12). Because the mule cannot reproduce, it is not able to transmit its genetic information to future generations.

Another additional factor is a key element of reproductive isolation and the maintenance of distinct species: geographic isolation. Species may be sympatric or allopatric. **Sympatric** species occupy the same area at the same time, so they have an opportunity to interbreed. **Allopatric** species occupy areas separated by time or space. Because individuals of allopatric species do not come into physical contact with each other, there is no indication whether they are capable of interbreeding. Only if the barriers are broken, allowing them to come together, can reproductive isolation be tested. Often, geographic isolation is the only mechanism of reproductive isolation for two similar but allopatric species, and without barriers the two species function as one. Such is the case, for example, with the red-shafted flicker (*Colaptes cafer*) and the yellow-shafted flicker (*Colaptes auratus*) (Figure 2.13). If you were to refer to early guides to birds, such as the Audubon or Peterson series (about 1940 through the 1960s), you would find pictures and descriptions of both species. If you were to refer to the current editions, however, you would see that the two species have now been lumped into a single species referred to as the northern flicker (*Colaptes auratus*). Historically, the two species had different geographic ranges, with the

Figure 2.12 | A mule is an example of a hybrid. It is a cross between a female horse and a male donkey.

red-shafted flicker's range being to the west of the yellow-shafted flicker. With time, the distributions of the two species expanded and overlapped (became sympatric), and the two species interbred and produced viable offspring (hybrids). As a result, they are now classified as a single species. As well as being a mechanism for maintaining reproductive isolation among closely related species, geographic isolation is also an important factor in the process through which new species arise.

## 2.7 | The Process of Speciation Involves the Development of Reproductive Isolation

As Darwin had hypothesized in *The Origin of Species*, speciation involves the divergence of existing species through natural selection. The crucial step in the origin

(a)

(b)

**Figure 2.13** | Flickers: **(a)** the eastern form of the yellow-shafted flicker has yellowish wing linings and undertail surfaces and a brown face with a black mustache. **(b)** The western form of the red-shafted flicker has pinkish-red wing linings and undertail surfaces and a gray face with a red mustache. Once considered separate species, they are now regarded as one species because they intergrade and interbreed.

of a species is the point at which the gene pool of a population becomes isolated from other populations of the parent species and the exchange of genes no longer occurs. Once the gene pool of the subpopulation is isolated, it will follow its own independent course as genetic changes occur due to natural selection and mutation. The process of speciation can be classified into two models based on the geographic relationship of the subpopulation to its parent population. If the subpopulation is geographically isolated from the original population by an extrinsic, physical barrier such as topography, water (or land), or unfavorable habitat, it is termed **allopatric speciation.** If the subpopulation becomes reproductively isolated in the presence of the parent population, it is termed **sympatric speciation.**

The first step in allopatric speciation, or geographic speciation as it is sometimes called, is the splitting of a single interbreeding population into two spatially isolated populations, each taking its own evolutionary route (Figure 2.14a). Imagine a piece of land, warm and dry, occupied by species A. At some point in geological time, mountains uplift and land sinks and floods with water. That action splits the piece of land and physically separates a segment of species A from the rest of the population. The newly isolated population will become subpopulation A'. It now occupies an area with a cool, moist climate.

Because it represents only a subset of the gene pool for species A, population A' will be slightly different genetically. The climatic conditions and the selective forces under which this population now lives are different. Natural selection will favor individuals best adapted to a cool, moist climate. Similar selection for a warm, dry climate will continue in population A on the original landmass. With different selection forces acting on them, the two populations will diverge. Accompanying the genetic divergence will be possible changes in physiology, morphology, color, and behavior resulting in ever-increasing external differences.

If the geological barrier breaks down and the two populations rejoin before natural selection has resulted in differences that cause reproductive isolation, the two populations may simply intermingle and merge once again into a single gene pool (Figure 2.14b). But if sufficient differences occur to inhibit interbreeding, the two populations will function as separate (sympatric) species even if they come together again (Figure 2.14c).

Sympatric speciation occurs without geographic isolation. Many species of plants appear to have arisen from a form of sympatric speciation in which a new species arises spontaneously. The most common method of abrupt speciation is a form of chromosomal mutation called *polyploidy*, the doubling of the number of chromosomes. An organism that has a double number of chromosomes in its gametes (egg or sperm) cannot produce fertile offspring with a member of its parent population,

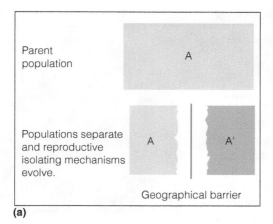

**(a)**

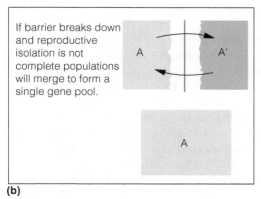

**(b)**

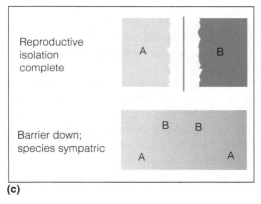

**(c)**

Figure 2.14 | Types of speciation: **(a)** Allopatric or geographic speciation takes place when two populations are isolated from each other over a long period of time. The first step in speciation comes about when species A becomes divided into two populations by a geographical barrier: A and A'. Over time under different selection pressures, A' diverges from A. **(b)** At this point, if sufficient differences evolve before the barrier breaks down but isolating mechanisms are incomplete, hybrids form. **(c)** When reproductive isolating mechanisms are complete, population A' has evolved into a new species B. If the barrier should break down, species A and B can exist sympatrically.

but it can do so by mating with another polyploid. Thus, a polyploid has already achieved reproductive isolation.

Many of our common cultivated plants—potatoes, wheat, alfalfa, coffee, and grasses, to mention a few—are

polyploids. Polyploidy is widespread among native plants, in which it produces a complex of species, such as blackberries (*Rubus*), willows (*Salix*), and birches (*Betula*). The common blue flag (*Iris versicolor*) of northern North America is a polyploid that probably originated from two other species, *I. virginica* and *I. setosa*, when the two, once widely distributed, met during the retreat of the Wisconsin ice sheet (see Chapter 18). The sequoia (*Sequoiadendron giganteum*) (see Figure 5.1) is a relict polyploid, its parent species having become extinct.

Sympatric speciation also may occur as a result of disruptive selection that favors divergent phenotypes within a population. When trade-offs exist in the characteristics required to forage effectively for different food resources or use different microhabitats, natural selection may favor divergent phenotypes within a population (see Figure 2.5 and also the example of the evolution of the stickleback species in Researcher Profile: Beren Robinson).

## 2.8 | Geographic Variation Within Species Provides Insight into the Process of Speciation

As we have seen from the discussion thus far, two fundamental processes are necessary to understand how evolution by natural selection results in speciation: (1) how a species changes through time and (2) how a single species becomes two (or more) species. The first process, evolution through natural selection, has been extensively documented and studied in a variety of species, including the examples presented of beak size in Darwin's finches (see Figure 2.3) and the development of antibiotic resistance in bacterial populations (see Ecological Issues: The Ecology of Antibiotic Resistance). The second process, speciation, is more difficult to observe directly because it occurs over much longer timescales. As a result, much of our understanding of the process of speciation has been developed from examining patterns of geographic variation within species.

Species having a wide geographic distribution often encounter a broader range of environmental conditions than those species whose distribution is more restricted. The variation in environmental conditions often gives rise to a corresponding variation in morphological, physiological, and behavioral characteristics. Significant differences often exist among populations of a single species inhabiting different regions. The greater the distance between populations, the more pronounced the differences often become with each population adapting to the locality it inhabits. Geographic variation within a species can result in clines, ecotypes, and geographic isolates.

A **cline** is a measurable, gradual change over a geographic region in the average of some phenotypic character, such as size and coloration, or a gradient in genotypic

Most of the lakes scattered over the northern regions of North America were formed after the immense ice sheets that covered the region retreated about 15,000 years ago. One group of fish inhabiting these new environments, the threespine sticklebacks (*Gasterosteus* spp.), have undergone a rapid period of speciation, with the species inhabiting the lakes of coastal British Columbia being among the youngest species on Earth. No more than two species occur in any one lake, and pairs of species in different lakes seem to have evolved completely independently of other pairs.

In every lake where a pair of threespine stickleback species is found, the two species have different patterns of habitat use and diet. One of the species feeds on plankton in the open-water zone (limnetic form), whereas the other species exploits larger prey from the sediments and submerged vegetation of the shallower, near-shore waters (benthic form). Morphological differences between the species correlate with these differences in habitat use and diet (Figure 1). Whether constraints imposed by these distinct environments are responsible in part for the evolution of the pairs of species is a central question in the research of Beren Robinson of the Department of Zoology at the University of Guelph.

In lakes where only a single species is found, the species of threespine stickleback tend to be intermediate in morphology and habit to the limnetic and benthic species. In sampling the population of one such species, *Gasterosteus aculeatus,* which occurs in Cranby Lake in the coastal region of British Columbia, Robinson found that individuals sampled from the open-water habitat differed morphologically from those individuals sampled from the shallower near-shore waters. In addition, these differences in morphology parallel the differences observed between species that occupy these two habitats in lakes where species pairs are found (Figure 1). Robinson hypothesized that these individuals represented distinct phenotypes that are products of natural selection promoting divergence within the population. Divergent (or disruptive) selection can potentially occur when individuals within a population face trade-offs involving the performance of different tasks. Trade-offs can occur when performance on one task (such as feeding on plankton in the open water) results in a cost to performance and fitness on a second task (feeding on the sediments in the shallow water of the shoreline). Severe trade-offs can result in divergent selection that favors resource specialization.

To test his hypothesis, Robinson needed to establish that two conditions were met. First, that morphological differences between the two forms were heritable, rather than an expression of phenotypic plasticity in response to the two different habitats or diets. Second, that the observed morphological differences between the two forms influence their foraging efficiency—that they do in fact represent a trade-off.

To test the first condition, Robinson reared offspring of the two forms under identical laboratory conditions (environmental conditions and diet). The results showed that although there was some degree of phenotypic plasticity, differences in most characteristics remained between the two forms when raised under identical conditions. On average, the benthic form had (1) shorter overall body length, (2) deeper body, (3) wider mouth, (4) more dorsal spines, and (5) fewer gill rakers than did the limnetic form. Therefore, the phenotypic difference in morphology between these two forms is indeed heritable.

To test the second condition, Robinson conducted a number of feeding trials in the laboratory to test for trade-offs in the foraging efficiency of the two forms. The foraging success of individual fish was assessed in two artificial habitats, mimicking conditions in the limnetic and benthic environments.

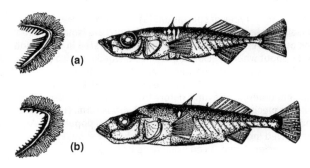

**Figure 1** | **Morphological differences in the gill rakers of the stickleback species based on (a) limnetic form and (b) benthic form feeding habits.** Illustration by Laura Nagel, Queen's University. (From Schulter 1993.)

Two food types were used in the trials. Brine shrimp larvae (*Artemia*), a common prey found in open water, were placed in the artificial limnetic habitats. Larger amphipods, fast-moving arthropods with hard exoskeletons that forage on dead organic matter on the sediment surface, were placed in the artificial benthic habitats.

An experimental trial consisted of releasing a single fish into the test aquarium and observing it for a period of time. At the end of the observation period, the total number of prey items eaten was determined and the data were converted into two measures of foraging success: intake rate (number of prey items consumed per minute) and capture effort (mean number of bites per prey item).

Results of the foraging trials revealed distinct differences in the foraging success of the two morphological forms (phenotypes) (Figure 2). Individuals of the limnetic form were most successful at foraging on the brine shrimp larvae, having both a higher consumption rate as well as requiring only half the number of bites to consume as compared to individuals of the benthic form. In contrast, individuals of the benthic form had a higher intake rate for amphipods and on average consumed larger amphipods than did individuals of the limnetic form.

Robinson was able to determine that the higher intake rate of brine shrimp larvae by the limnetic form was related to this form's greater number of gill rakers, and greater mouth width was related to the higher intake rate of amphipods by individuals of the benthic form. Therefore, foraging efficiency was found to be related to morphological differences between the two forms, suggesting trade-offs in characteristics related to the successful exploitation of these two distinct habitats and associated food resources.

These and other experiments by Robinson strongly suggest that divergent natural selection is occurring in these populations and may represent the early stages of speciation. Previous studies of divergent species of sticklebacks (species pairs) inhabiting the lakes of British Columbia have suggested that opposing selective pressures in open-water and near-shore (shallow water) environments have been a major factor in the evolution of these species. Yet, Beren Robinson's work is unique in its illustration that natural selection is at work within a single population, resulting in different morphological phenotypes that inhabit these two distinct environments. It is one of few studies that have actually quantified the nature of trade-offs faced by individuals within a

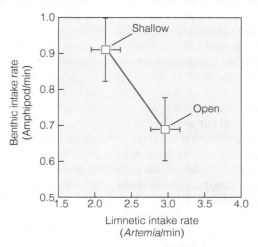

**Figure 2** | Mean intake rate (and standard errors) of limnetic (open) and benthic (shallow) forms in open-water (food source: *Artemia* [brine shrimp larvae]) and shallow-water (food source: amphipod) feeding trials. (Adapted from Robinson 2000.)

population, relating to the exploitation of different resources. Robinson's work provides us with important insights into the mechanisms at work in the evolution of diversity in this closely related group of fishes. ●

### Bibliography
Robinson, B. W. 2000. Trade offs in habitat-specific foraging efficiency and the nascent adaptive divergence of sticklebacks in lakes. *Behaviour* 137:865–88.
Robinson, B. W., and S. Wardrop. 2002. Experimentally manipulated growth rate in threespine sticklebacks: assessing trade offs with developmental stability. *Environmental Biology of Fishes* 63:67–78.

1. How do you think that the differences in morphology, diet, and habitat of the two phenotypic forms within the population of fish might possibly lead to reproductive isolation and eventual speciation?

2. Suppose that an intermediate phenotype (intermediate in characteristics) was present in the population and that this intermediate was equally capable of feeding in both the open-water and near-shore environments (and as efficient as both of the other phenotypes). How would this change the interpretation of the results?

See QUANTIFY it! at www.ecologyplace.com to calculate summary statistics using stickleback data.

When we think of adaptation and evolution, we typically think of timescales involving millions of years. Yet, as we have seen from examples such as the shift in bill size in Darwin's ground finch (see Figure 2.3), evolution by natural selection can occur over relatively short periods of time when populations are exposed to sudden shifts in the environment. In one group of organisms, evolution by natural selection has been accelerated by our attempts at eradication, with potentially grave consequences to our own species.

Antibiotics are a class of compounds, natural or synthetic, that destroy or inhibit the growth of microorganisms. Their discovery and successful use against disease-causing bacteria is one of modern medicine's greatest success stories. Since these compounds (drugs) first became widely used in the mid-20th century, they have saved countless lives though their ability to fight infections and disease-causing bacteria. But just 4 years after drug companies began mass-producing penicillin—the first of these compounds—microbes began appearing that could resist it.

Antibiotic resistance spreads fast. Between 1979 and 1987, for example, a survey by the U.S. Centers for Disease Control and Prevention (CDC) found that only 0.02 percent of bacterial strains that cause pneumonia were penicillin-resistant. Today, 6.6 percent of these bacterial strains are resistant. The CDC also reports that in 1992, more than 13,000 hospital patients died of bacterial infections that were resistant to antibiotic treatment.

The increased prevalence of antibiotic resistance is an outcome of evolution, specifically the accelerated process of natural selection in bacterial populations brought about by the widespread use of antibiotics. All populations of organisms, including bacteria, exhibit genetic variations that influence traits among individuals: in this case, the ability of the bacterium to withstand the effects of the antibiotic. Whenever antibiotics are used, there is selective pressure for resistance to occur. When a person takes an antibiotic, the drug kills the vast majority of bacteria that are defenseless. If any of the bacteria are resistant, however, they will survive. These resistant bacteria then multiply, increasing their numbers—up to a million-fold in a day. This process builds upon itself, with more and more bacteria developing resistance to more and more antibiotic compounds. Natural selection favors those individuals (bacteria) that are resistant to the antibiotic. The increased fitness of antibiotic-resistant individuals results in a greater proportion of the population being antibiotic-resistant in each succeeding generation.

An individual can develop an antibiotic-resistant infection either by becoming initially infected with a resistant strain of bacteria or by having a resistant bacterial strain emerge in the body once antibiotic treatment begins. The development of antibiotic resistance by a bacterium is a result of acquiring genes that confer resistance to the action caused by the compound (i.e., the actual effects of the drug). Bacteria acquire genes that confer resistance in one of three ways. Bacterial DNA may mutate spontaneously, which is likely the most common cause of resistance. In a process called *transformation,* one bacterium may take up DNA from another bacterium. The third means is resistance acquired from a small circle of DNA called a *plasmid,* which can be transmitted from one type of bacterium to another. A single plasmid can provide a variety of different resistances. In 1968, more than 12,000 people in Guatemala died in an epidemic of bacteria-caused diarrhea. The strain of bacteria harbored a plasmid that carried resistances to four different antibiotics.

Although bacterial antibiotic resistance is a natural phenomenon, a number of societal factors also contribute to the problem; namely, inappropriate antibiotic use. For example, doctors sometimes prescribe antibiotics for a cold, cough, or the flu, all of which are viral and do not respond to antibiotics. Also, patients who are prescribed antibiotics but do not take the complete course (correct dose for the entire period of the prescription) can contribute to resistance.

Another much-publicized concern is the use of antibiotics in livestock, where the drugs are used in healthy animals to prevent disease or administered at low levels in feed for long durations to increase the rate of weight gain. Although the U.S. Food and Drug Administration's (FDA's) Center for Veterinary Medicine limits the amount of antibiotic residue allowed in poultry and other meats, these drugs can cause bacteria to become resistant to drugs used to treat humans, ultimately making some human illnesses harder to treat. •

1. In the treatment of potentially deadly bacterial infections, patients are often given a series of different types of antibiotics. Can you think why this treatment might be utilized?

2. Why does the development of antibiotic resistant populations of bacteria represent an example of evolution by natural selection?

frequency. Clines are usually associated with an environmental gradient such as temperature, moisture, light, or altitude. Continuous variation results from gene flow from one population to another along the gradient. Because environmental constraints influencing natural selection vary along the gradient, any one population along the gradient will differ genetically to some degree from another, the difference increasing with the distance between the populations.

Clinal differences exist in size, body proportions, coloration, and physiological adaptations among animals. For example, the white-tailed deer in North America exhibit a clinal variation in body weight. White-tailed deer in Canada and the northern United States are heaviest, weighing on the average more than 136 kg. Individuals of the species weigh on average 93 kg in Kansas, 60 kg in Louisiana, and 46 kg in Panama. The smallest individuals of this species, the Key deer in Florida, weigh less than 23 kg.

Clinal variations can show marked discontinuities. Such abrupt changes, or step clines, often reflect abrupt changes in local environments. Such variants are called **ecotypes.** An ecotype is a population adapted to its unique local environmental conditions. For example, a population inhabiting a mountaintop may differ from a population of the same species in the valley below. Often, ecotypes will be scattered like a mosaic across the landscape. That frequently is the situation when several habitats to which the species is adapted recur throughout the range of the species.

Yarrow, *Achillea millefolium*, is a plant species of the temperate and subarctic regions of the Northern Hemisphere with an exceptional number of ecotypes. It exhibits considerable variation, an adaptive response to different climates at various altitudes. Populations at lower altitudes are tall and have high seed production. Montane (high altitude) populations have a distinctive small size and low seed production.

In a classic study, plant ecologists J. Clausen, D. D. Keck, and W. M. Hiesey of Stanford University planted seeds of yarrows collected from different elevations in a transect across the Sierra Nevada in transplant gardens at several elevations from lowland to mountain. Yarrows from the high elevations retained their short stature no matter where planted. The other ecotypes showed some phenotypic plasticity in growth but were dwarfed at high elevations.

The southern Appalachian Mountains are noted for their diversity of salamanders, fostered in part by a rugged terrain, an array of environmental conditions, and the limited ability of salamanders to disperse (Figure 2.15). Populations become isolated from one another, preventing a free flow of genes. One species of salamander, *Plethodon jordani*, breaks into a number of semi-isolated populations, each characteristic of a particular part of the mountains. Groups of such populations make up

**geographic isolates,** prevented by some extrinsic barrier—in the case of the salamanders, rivers and mountain ridges—from effecting a free flow of genes with other subpopulations. The degree of isolation depends on the efficiency of the extrinsic barrier, but rarely is the isolation complete. These geographic isolates are often classified as **subspecies,** a taxonomic term for populations of a species that are distinguishable by one or more characteristics. Subspecies with little gene flow between them may be in the first stages of speciation. Unlike clines, we can draw a geographic line that separates the subpopulations into subspecies.

The pattern of geographic variation within species that has provided evolutionary ecologists with some of the best examples of how the process of speciation might unfold is the rare phenomenon known as "ring species." In a ring species, populations of a single species encircle an area of unsuitable habitat (such as a mountain range or a large body of water). As a result, the species becomes geographically distributed in a circular, or ring, pattern over a large geographic area. Immediately adjacent (neighboring) populations vary only slightly and interbreed. At the opposite ends of the distribution that link to form a circle, however, the difference between populations is great enough that they function as two noninterbreeding species.

A well-documented example of a ring species is the salamander *Ensatina escholtzii* of the Pacific coastal region of the United States (Figure 2.16; page 39). In southern California, two distinct forms of the species are found. These two forms differ dramatically in color and do not interbreed. A chain of populations to the north that encircles the Central Valley of California, however, connects these two forms. Through this ring of populations, the color pattern of the salamanders changes gradually. The ecologist Robert Stebbins, who first described this pattern of geographic variation in 1949, hypothesized that it arose when an ancestral population in northern California expanded southward, one to the west along the Sierra Nevada and the other to the east along the coastal range. The two populations then gradually became different as they expanded southward, adapting to their local environments. By the time they met once again in southern California, they had evolved sufficient differences that they no longer interbred. Recent genetic studies of these populations confirm Stebbins's hypothesis, providing us with a picture of the ongoing process of speciation.

## 2.9 | Adaptations Reflect Trade-offs and Constraints

The heritable characteristics possessed by an organism are owed to past generations. Its ancestors, in effect, experienced the process of natural selection that produced the heritable characteristics owned by present individuals.

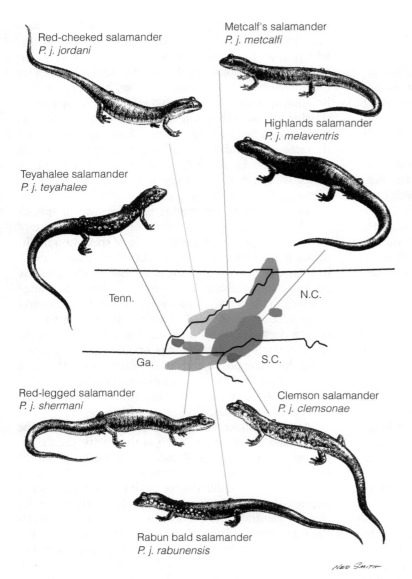

Red-cheeked salamander
*P. j. jordani*

Metcalf's salamander
*P. j. metcalfi*

Highlands salamander
*P. j. melaventris*

Teyahalee salamander
*P. j. teyahalee*

Tenn.

N.C.

Ga.

S.C.

Red-legged salamander
*P. j. shermani*

Clemson salamander
*P. j. clemsonae*

Rabun bald salamander
*P. j. rabunensis*

NED SMITH

**Figure 2.15** | Geographical isolates in *Plethodon jordani* of the Appalachian highlands. These salamanders originated when a population of the salamander *P. yonahlossee* became separated by the French Broad River valley. The eastern population developed into Metcalf's salamander, which spread northward, the only direction in which any group member could find suitable ecological conditions. South, southwest, and northwest the mountains end abruptly, limiting the remaining *jordani*. Metcalf's salamander is the most specialized and ecologically divergent and the least competitive. Next, the red-cheeked salamander became isolated from the red-legged and the rest of the group by the deepening of the Little Tennessee River. Remaining members are still somewhat connected.

The possession of these characteristics enables an organism to match the features of its environment. As long as environmental conditions under which individuals of the current generation exist are similar to those experienced by past generations, the organism is adapted to the environment. If environmental conditions change significantly, then the fitness and even the survival of individuals will be in jeopardy (see Figure 2.3, Section 2.1). **Adaptation,** then, is any heritable behavioral, morphological, or physiological trait that maintains or increases the fitness of an organism under a given set of environmental conditions.

If Earth were one large homogeneous environment, perhaps a single genotype, a single set of characteristics, might bestow upon all living organisms the ability to survive, grow, and reproduce. But this is not the case; environmental conditions that directly influence life vary in both space and time. Therefore, natural selection will favor different characteristics as environmental conditions change—in both space and time. The response of an organism to its environment is not a repertoire of infinite possibilities. It is bounded, constrained within a range of environmental tolerances—limits to the environmental conditions under which an organism can survive, grow, and reproduce (Figure 2.17). These tolerances are a function of trade-offs imposed by constraints that can ultimately be traced to the laws of physics and chemistry. Stated simply: the characteristics that enable an individual to do well under one set of conditions limit its performance under a different set of conditions. This general but important concept is obvious to sports fans. Figure 2.18 is a photograph of two great sports figures. Wilt Chamberlain was probably the greatest center in basketball. Willie Shoemaker was probably the best jockey

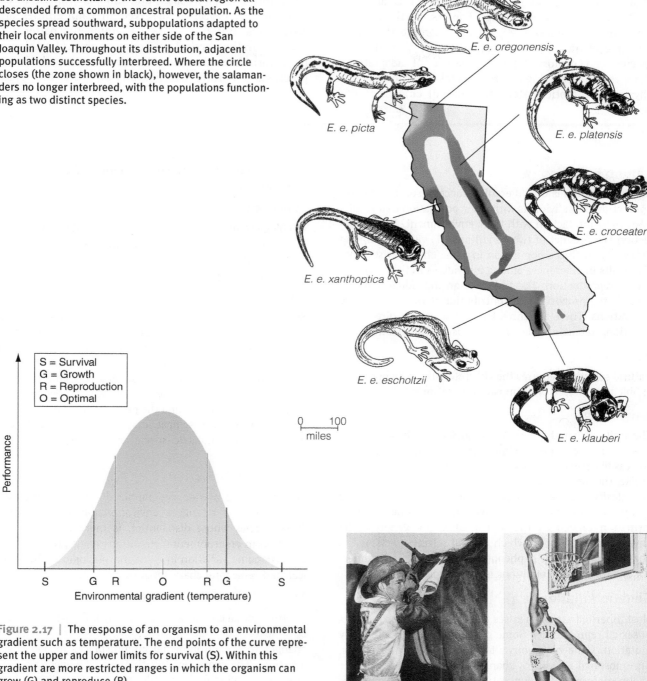

Figure 2.16 | The various subspecies of the salamander *Ensatina escholtzii* of the Pacific coastal region all descended from a common ancestral population. As the species spread southward, subpopulations adapted to their local environments on either side of the San Joaquin Valley. Throughout its distribution, adjacent populations successfully interbreed. Where the circle closes (the zone shown in black), however, the salamanders no longer interbreed, with the populations functioning as two distinct species.

E. e. oregonensis

E. e. picta

E. e. platensis

E. e. croceater

E. e. xanthoptica

E. e. escholtzii

E. e. klauberi

0    100
miles

S = Survival
G = Growth
R = Reproduction
O = Optimal

Performance

S    G   R    O    R   G    S

Environmental gradient (temperature)

Figure 2.17 | The response of an organism to an environmental gradient such as temperature. The end points of the curve represent the upper and lower limits for survival (S). Within this gradient are more restricted ranges in which the organism can grow (G) and reproduce (R).

to ride a racehorse. At the height of 1.49 m, Willie Shoemaker could never have played center for the Los Angeles Lakers, and at 2.15 m, Wilt Chamberlain could never have ridden to victory in the Kentucky Derby. The set of physical characteristics that enables an individual to excel at one of these sports precludes that individual's

(a)                       (b)

Figure 2.18 | (a) Willie Shoemaker and (b) Wilt Chamberlain each excelled in a sport for which the other was physically unsuited.

ability to do well at the other. So, too, the characteristics of organisms constrain them (see Figure 7.1, Chapter 7).

Throughout the following chapters, particularly in Part Three (Chapters 6–8), we will examine this basic principle of trade-offs as it applies to the adaptation of species and explore how the nature of adaptations changes with changing environmental conditions—both physical and biotic. Later chapters will emphasize the consequences of those adaptations as environmental conditions change in space and time, giving rise to the patterns and processes observed in communities and ecosystems. But first we will examine the patterns of variation in the physical environment across Earth's surface, variations that set the stage upon which the processes of natural selection and evolution take place.

---

## Summary

### Natural Selection (2.1)

Natural selection is the differential success (survival and reproduction) of individuals within the population that results from their interaction with their environment. Natural selection is a product of two conditions: (1) variation among individuals within a population in some characteristic that (2) results in differences among individuals in their survival and/or reproduction. The fitness of an individual is measured by the proportionate contribution it makes to future generations. There are three types of selection: directional selection, stabilizing selection, and disruptive selection.

### Heritability (2.2)

Natural selection requires the characteristic to be heritable, or able to be passed on from parent to offspring.

### Genes (2.3)

The units of heredity are genes carried on chromosomes. The alternative forms of a gene are alleles. Individuals that possess like pairs of alleles are homozygous. If the alleles are unlike, the individuals are heterozygous. In the case of heterozygosity, the allele that is expressed is the dominant, and that not expressed is the recessive. The sum of heritable information carried by the individual is the genotype. Its physical expression, on which natural selection acts, is the phenotype. The range of phenotypic expression under different environmental conditions is phenotypic plasticity.

### Genetic Variation (2.4)

Most inherited variation arises from recombination of genes in sexual reproduction. Some genetic material is altered by mutation. Gene mutations alter sequences of nucleotides. Chromosomal mutations change the structure or number of chromosomes. The duplication of entire sets of chromosomes is polyploidy, which is most common in plants. Single gene mutations rarely are visible. Most gene mutations are neutral and maintain genetic variability in a population.

### Evolution (2.5)

The outcome of natural selection is evolution, a change in gene frequency through time. Speciation by natural selection is a form of evolution. The process of speciation requires changes in the gene frequencies of a population that result in reproductive isolation: the evolution of characteristics that sever the exchange of genes with the parent population.

### Concept of Species (2.6)

A biological species is a group of interbreeding individuals living together in a similar environment in a given region. Species may be sympatric or allopatric. Species maintain their identities by means of isolating mechanisms.

### Speciation (2.7)

Species arise by the interaction of heritable variations, by natural selection, and by barriers to gene flow between populations. The most widely accepted mechanism of speciation is allopatric or geographic speciation. A single interbreeding population splits into spatially isolated populations, which diverge into distinct species. When reproductive isolation precedes differentiation and the process takes place within a population, we have sympatric speciation. The most common form of sympatric speciation is polyploidy among plants.

### Geographic Variation (2.8)

Species having a wide geographic distribution often encounter a broader range of environmental conditions than those species whose distribution is more restricted. The variation in environmental conditions often gives rise to a corresponding variation in many morphological, physiological, and behavioral characteristics.

### Trade-offs and Constraints (2.9)

Environmental conditions that directly influence life vary in both space and time; likewise, the objective of selection changes with environmental circumstances in both space and time. The characteristics that enable a species to survive, grow, and reproduce under one set of conditions limit its ability to do equally well under different environmental conditions.

## Study Questions

1. What is natural selection? What conditions are necessary for natural selection to occur?

2. David Reznick, an ecologist at the University of California at Riverside, studied the process of natural selection

in populations of guppies (small freshwater fish) on the island of Trinidad. Reznick found that populations at lower elevations face the assault of predatory fish, whereas the populations at higher elevations live in peace, because few predators can move upstream past the waterfalls. The average size of individuals in the higher elevation waters is larger than the average size of guppies in the lower elevation populations. Reznick hypothesized that the smaller size of individuals in the lower elevation populations was a result of increased rates of predation on larger individuals; in effect, predation was selecting for smaller individuals in the population. To test this hypothesis, Reznick moved individuals from the lower elevations to (unoccupied) pools upstream where predation was not a factor. Eleven years in these conditions produced a population of individuals that were on average larger than the individuals of the downstream populations. Is the study by Reznick an example of natural selection (does it meet the necessary conditions)? If so, what type of selection does it represent (directional, stabilizing, or disruptive)? Can you think of any alternative hypotheses to why the average size of individuals may have shifted through time as a result of moving the population to the upstream (higher elevation) environment?

3. Let's make the following assumptions: (1) the gene for blue eyes is recessive and (2) the gene for brown eyes is dominant. If a child is born with blue eyes, what can you conclude about the eye colors of her mother and father? What can you conclude about the genotypes (with respect to eye color) of her parents? What can you conclude about the child's genotype for eye color?

4. What are the two main sources of genetic variation in a sexually reproducing population?

5. An ecologist studying the diversity of lizard species on a small island off the west coast of Africa identified a species of lizard that was similar to one on the African mainland. The ecologist could identify only one difference between the island and mainland populations. Males of the mainland population have a red-colored head and bright green body, whereas males of the island population have the same bright green body, but their head is dark green. Females from both populations appear identical, being bright green over the entire body. In a series of experiments, the ecologist found that females from the mainland population did not recognize (respond to courtship behavior) males from the island population as potential mates. Likewise, females from the island population did not recognize the males from the mainland population as potential mates. Given this information, would you conclude that the island and mainland populations were different species?

The ecologist then continued his study by altering the physical appearance of males. The heads of male individuals from the island population were dyed red, and likewise, the heads of individual males from the mainland population were dyed dark green. When the experiments were repeated, females from the island population now recognized and mated with males from the mainland and *vice versa*. Assuming that the offspring from these matings survive and reproduce, does this new result change your answer regarding whether the two populations should be classified as separate species?

6. Distinguish between a genotype and a phenotype. What is phenotypic plasticity?

7. What is the gene pool?

8. What is the difference between the morphological and biological species concepts? Can you think of a set of conditions when one definition might apply but the other would not?

9. What is speciation? Distinguish between the allopatric and sympatric models of speciation.

10. How does evolution differ from natural selection?

## Further Readings

Desmond, A., and J. Moore. 1991. *Darwin: The life of a tormented evolutionist*. New York: W. W. Norton.

Written by two historians, this book functions as an anthology by providing an introduction to the man and his works.

Gould, S. J. 1992. *Ever since Darwin: Reflections in natural history*. New York: W.W. Norton.

A collection of Gould's essays written for scientific journals. The first in a series of humorous and fun reading. See other collections, including *The panda's thumb*, *The flamingo's smile*, and *Dinosaur in a haystack*.

Gould, S. J. 2002. *The structure of evolutionary theory*. Cambridge, MA: Belknap Press of Harvard University Press.

The last book written by Gould, the best, most-respected popular science writer in evolution. Although the book is more technical than others, Chapter 1 provides an excellent overview of current thinking in evolutionary theory.

Grant, P. R., and B. R. Grant. 2000. "Non-random fitness variation in two populations of Darwin's finches." *Proceedings of the Royal Society of London Series B* 267:131–8.

An excellent source of additional information for those intrigued by the example of natural selection in Darwin's ground finch in Section 2.1.

Mayr, E. 2001. *What evolution is*. New York: Basic Books.

An excellent primer on the topics of natural selection and evolution by a leading figure in evolution. Wonderfully written, like literature, for the general reader.

Reznick, D. N., F. H. Shaw, F. H. Rodd and R. G. Shaw 1997. "Evaluation of the rate of evolution in natural populations of guppies (*Poecilia reticulata*)." *Science* 275:1934–1937.

A beautifully designed experiment to evaluate the role of natural selection in the evolution of life history characteristics.

Weiner, J. 1994. *The beak and the finch: A story of evolution in our time*. New York: Alfred A. Knopf.

Winner of the Pulitzer Prize. Provides the reader with a first-hand view of scientific research in action.

# Part Two | The Physical Environment

In January 2004, two small, robotic vehicles named the Mars Exploration Rovers landed on the Martian surface. Their mission was to explore the surface for evidence of whether life ever arose on Mars. The rovers were not looking for living organisms or even for fossils within the rocks that litter the Martian surface. These robotic vehicles were exploring the geology of the Martian surface. Their task was to determine the history of water on Mars. Although there is no liquid water on the surface of Mars today, the record of past water activity on Mars can be found in the planet's rocks, minerals, and geologic landforms, particularly in those that can only form in the presence of water.

Why search for water as evidence of life? Because life as we understand it is impossible without conditions that allow for the existence of water in a liquid form. The history of water on Mars is therefore crucial to determining if the Martian environment was ever conducive to life. The mission of the Mars Exploration Rovers was not to search for direct evidence for life, but rather to provide us with information on the "habitability" of the environment.

Although the study of the physical environment is the central mission of disciplines such as geology, meteorology, and hydrology, it is this concept of **habitability**—the ability of the physical environment to support life—that links the physical sciences with the discipline of ecology. To illustrate this connection between ecology and the study of the physical environment, let us move from the surface of Mars to the small chain of islands off the western coast of South America that so influenced the thinking of the young Charles Darwin—the Galápagos Islands.

When one thinks of penguins, it is the frozen landscape of the Antarctic that generally comes to mind. Yet the Galápagos Islands, which lie on the Equator, are home to the smallest of the penguin species: *Spheniscus mendiculus*, or the Galapagos penguin. They stand only 16 to 18 inches (40 to 45 cm) tall and weigh only 5 pounds (2 to 2.5 kg). Found only on the Galápagos Islands, these penguins live the farthest north of all the penguin species.

The Galapagos penguins eat mostly small fish such as mullet and sardines and are dependent on the ocean currents flowing from the cooler waters of the south to bring these fish to their feeding grounds. The young Darwin himself made note of the importance of the currents that flow north from the South Pacific Ocean to the Galápagos environment: "Considering that these islands are placed directly under the equator, the climate is far from being excessively hot; this seems chiefly caused by the singularly low temperature of the surrounding water, brought here by the great southern Polar current" (*Voyage of the Beagle*). However, the prevailing winds that give rise to the cool waters that bathe these tropical islands are not always predictable. Periodically, the trade winds that flow westward in this region stall, and the waters around the Galápagos Islands warm. The warm waters result in a dramatic reduction in the fish populations upon which the penguins depend. Such an occurrence caused a severe shortage of food about 20 years ago. At that time, more than 70 percent of the Galapagos penguins died. Since that time their numbers have increased, with the population currently estimated at about 800 breeding pairs. Fishermen in the region as far back as the 16th century have recorded periods of

The Galápagos penguin (*Spheniscus mendiculus*).

small body size (smallest of all penguin species) enables it to dissipate heat easily to the surrounding air: an important characteristic in this tropical environment (see Chapter 7). Second, unlike most other penguins, Galapagos penguins have no particular breeding season and may have as many as three clutches in a single year. This is an adaptation that allows them to cope with their variable and unreliable food resource; a direct result of the unpredictable changes in the patterns of prevailing winds and ocean currents. An understanding of these characteristics requires an understanding of the physical environment that has shaped this species over evolutionary time through the process of natural selection.

Over the short term, year-to-year variations in the currents and water temperatures around the islands are crucial to understanding the population dynamics of this species. Periodic increases and decreases in the population of Galapagos penguins are a direct response to variations in the availability of food resources.

In the following chapters that make up Part Two, we will look at those features of Earth's physical environment that directly influence its habitability. We will explore features of the two dominant environments that characterize our planet: land and water. We begin by examining Earth's climate (Chapter 3); the broad-scale patterns of temperature, winds, precipitation, seasonality, and ocean currents. We then turn our attention to the dominant physical characteristics of aquatic (Chapter 4) and terrestrial (Chapter 5) environments. These chapters will set the stage for our discussion in Part Three of the adaptations of plants and animals to these physical environments.

warming such as the one that occurred 20 years ago, and these periods of severe food shortage no doubt have affected the penguin population since their ancestors first arrived on the islands.

Even from the short description provided above, it should be apparent that understanding the ecology of the Galapagos penguins very much depends on an understanding of the physical environment of these islands; namely, features of the environment that influence their habitability for the penguin population. Ecologists view the interaction between organisms and their surrounding physical environment at two very different timescales. Over the period of many generations, the physical environment represents a guiding force in the process of natural selection, favoring individuals with certain characteristics over others (see Chapter 2). Over a shorter period, the physical environment influences both the physiological performance of individuals and the availability of essential resources, both of which directly influence the survival, growth, and reproduction of individuals within the population. The example of the Galapagos penguin presented above can be used to illustrate both of these timescales.

Over evolutionary time, the physical environment of the Galápagos Islands has influenced the characteristics and behavior of the Galapagos penguins through the process of natural selection. First, its

# Chapter 3 | Climate

As the sun rises, warming the morning air in this tropical rainforest on the island of Borneo, fog that has formed in the cooler night air begins to evaporate.

What determines whether a particular geographic region will be a tropical forest, a grassy plain, or a barren landscape of sand dunes? The aspect of the physical environment that most influences a particular ecosystem by placing the greatest constraint on organisms is climate. *Climate* is one of those terms we tend to use loosely. In fact, people sometimes confuse climate with weather. **Weather** is the combination of temperature, humidity, precipitation, wind, cloudiness, and other atmospheric conditions occurring at a specific place and time. **Climate** is the long-term average pattern of weather and may be local, regional, or global.

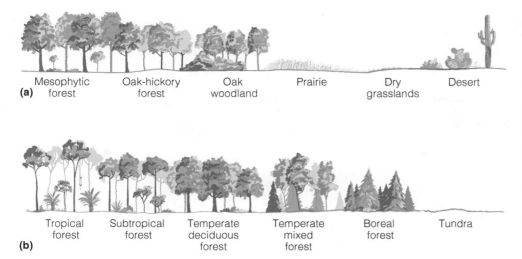

**Figure 3.1 |** Gradients of vegetation in North America from east to west and south to north. **(a)** The east-west gradient reflects a decrease in annual precipitation (does not cut across the Rocky Mountains). **(b)** The south-north gradient reflects a decrease in mean annual temperature. Note that with both decreasing precipitation and temperatures, the stature of the vegetation decreases. See Chapter 23 for a detailed discussion of the characteristics and distribution of terrestrial ecosystems.

The structure of terrestrial ecosystems is largely defined by the dominant plants, which in turn are a reflection of the prevailing physical environmental conditions, namely climate (see Chapter 23). Geographic variations in climate, primarily temperature and precipitation, govern the large-scale distribution of plants and therefore the nature of terrestrial ecosystems (Figure 3.1). In this chapter, we learn how climate determines the availability of heat and water on Earth's surface and influences the amount of solar energy that plants can harness.

## 3.1 | Earth Intercepts Solar Radiation

Earth's atmosphere intercepts solar radiation on its outer edge. The resulting molecular interactions create heat and cause thermal patterns that, coupled with Earth's rotation and movement, generate the prevailing winds and ocean currents. These movements of air and water in turn influence Earth's weather patterns, including the distribution of rainfall.

Solar radiation, the electromagnetic energy emanating from the Sun, travels more or less unimpeded through the vacuum of space until it reaches Earth's atmosphere. Scientists conceptualize solar radiation as a stream of photons, or packets of energy, which—in one of the great paradoxes of science—behave either as waves or as particles, depending on the manner in which they are observed. Scientists characterize waves of energy in terms of their wavelength ($\lambda$), or the physical distances between successive crests, and frequency ($\nu$), or the number of crests that pass a given point per second. All objects emit radiant energy (see Quantifying Ecology 3.1: Energy Transfer Through Radiation), typically across a wide range of wavelengths. The exact nature of the energy emitted, however, depends on the object's temperature (Figure 3.2). The hotter the object is, the more

energetic the emitted photons and the shorter the wavelength. A very hot surface such as that of the Sun (~5800°C) gives off primarily **shortwave radiation.** In contrast, cooler objects such as Earth's surface (average temperature of 15°C) emit radiation of longer wavelengths, or **longwave radiation.**

Of the solar radiation that reaches the top of Earth's atmosphere, only 51 percent makes it to the surface. What happens to all the incoming energy? If you take the amount of solar radiation that reaches the atmosphere as 100 units, on average, clouds and the atmosphere reflect and scatter 26 units, and Earth's surface reflects an additional 4 units, giving a total of 30 units being reflected back to space (Figure 3.3). Together the atmosphere and clouds absorb another 19 units (giving a total of 49 units), leaving 51 units of direct and indirect solar radiation to be absorbed by Earth's surface.

Of the 51 units that reach the surface, 23 units are used to evaporate water and another 7 units heat the air adjacent to the surface, leaving 21 units to heat the planet's landmasses and oceans. The landmasses and oceans in turn emit radiation back to the atmosphere in the form of longwave (thermal) radiation. The amount of longwave radiation emitted by Earth's surface exceeds the 21 units of solar radiation that are absorbed. Actually, some 117 units in total are emitted. How is this possible? It does so because, although the surface receives solar (shortwave) radiation only during the day, it constantly emits longwave radiation during both day and night. Additionally, the atmosphere above only allows a small fraction of this energy (6 units) to pass through into space. The majority (111 units) is absorbed by the water vapor and $CO_2$ in the atmosphere and by clouds. Much of this energy (96 units) is radiated back to Earth, producing the greenhouse effect (see Chapter 29), which is crucial to maintaining the surface warmth of Earth. As a result, Earth's surface receives nearly twice as much longwave radiation from the

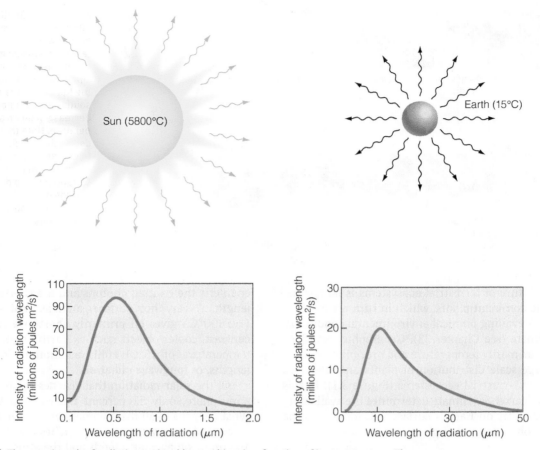

Figure 3.2 | The wavelength of radiation emitted by an object is a function of its temperature. The Sun, with an average surface temperature of 5800°C, emits relatively shortwave radiation as compared to Earth, with an average surface temperature of 15°C, which emits relatively longwave radiation. When comparing these two graphs, note the difference in scale ($1 \text{ J/s} = 1 \text{ W}$).

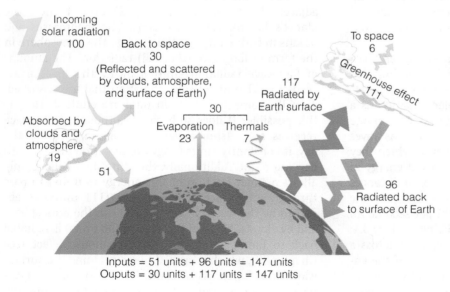

Figure 3.3 | Disposition of solar energy reaching Earth's atmosphere. Inputs include incoming solar (shortwave) radiation and longwave radiation radiated back to Earth as a function of the greenhouse effect. Outputs include heat from surface evaporation and thermals and longwave energy radiated by Earth's surface.

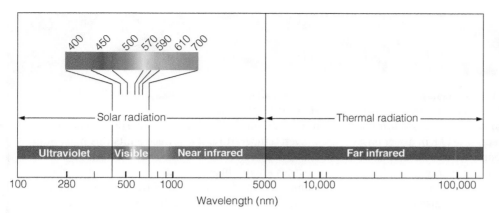

**Figure 3.4 | A portion of the electromagnetic spectrum, separated into solar and thermal radiation. Ultraviolet, visible, and infrared light waves represent only a small portion of the spectrum. To the left of ultraviolet radiation are X rays and gamma rays (not shown).** (Adapted from Halverson and Smith 1979.)

atmosphere as it does shortwave radiation from the Sun. In all of these exchanges, the energy lost at Earth's surface (30 units + 117 units = 147 units) is exactly balanced by the energy gained (51 units + 96 units = 147 units) (see Figure 3.3). The radiation budget of Earth is in balance.

The electromagnetic radiation emitted by the Sun covers a wide range of wavelengths. Of the total range of solar radiation reaching Earth's atmosphere, the wavelengths of approximately 400 to 700 nm (a nanometer is one-billionth of a meter) make up **visible light** (Figure 3.4). Collectively, these wavelengths are also known as **photosynthetically active radiation (PAR),** because they include the wavelengths that plants use as a source of energy in the process of photosynthesis (see Chapter 6). Wavelengths shorter than the visible range are ultraviolet (UV) light. There are two types of ultraviolet light: UV-A, with wavelengths from 315 nm to 380 nm; and UV-B, with wavelengths from 280 to 315 nm. Radiation with wavelengths longer than the visible range is infrared. Near infrared includes wavelengths of approximately 740 to 4000 nm, and far infrared or thermal radiation includes wavelengths from 4000 to 100,000 nm.

## 3.2 | Intercepted Solar Radiation Varies Seasonally

The amount of solar energy intercepted at any point on Earth's surface varies markedly with latitude (Figure 3.5). Two factors influence this variation. First, at higher latitudes, radiation hits the surface at a steeper angle, spreading sunlight over a larger area. Second, radiation that penetrates the atmosphere at a steep angle must travel through a deeper layer of air. In the process, it encounters more particles in the atmosphere, which reflect more of it back into space.

Although the variation in solar radiation reaching Earth's surface with latitude can explain the gradient of decreasing temperature from the Equator to the poles, it does not explain the systematic variation that occurs

over the course of a year. What gives rise to the seasons on Earth? Why do the hot days of summer give way to the changing colors of fall, or the freezing temperatures and snow-covered landscape of winter to the blanket of green with the onset of spring? The explanation is quite simple. It is because Earth does not stand up straight but rather tilts on its side.

Earth, like all planets, is subjected to two distinct motions. While it orbits around the Sun, Earth rotates about an axis that passes through the North and South Poles, giving rise to the brightness of day followed by the darkness of night (the diurnal cycle). Earth travels about the Sun in a plane called the ecliptic (a plane traveled by all other planets with the exception of Pluto). As chance would have it, Earth's axis of spin is not perpendicular to the ecliptic but is tilted at an angle of 23.5° (Figure 3.6). It is this tilt (inclination) that is responsible for the seasonal variations in temperature and daylength. Only at the Equator are there exactly 12 hours of daylight and darkness every day of the year. At the vernal equinox (approximately March 21) and autumnal

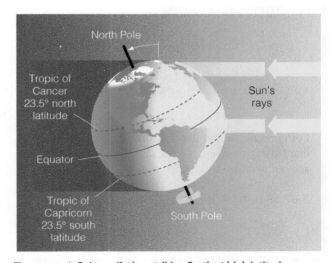

**Figure 3.5 | Solar radiation striking Earth at high latitudes arrives at an oblique angle and spreads over a wide area. Therefore, it is less intense than energy arriving vertically at the Equator.**

There are three mechanisms by which energy is transferred between objects. **Conduction** is the transfer of energy (heat) through molecular motion. For this form of transfer to occur, the two objects must be in direct physical contact. Conduction accounts for the transfer of energy through solids. The transfer of energy through the mass movement of a fluid, either gas or liquid, is called **convection**. The third form of energy transfer is **radiation**, or the transfer of energy through electromagnetic rays.

It is transfer of energy through the electromagnetic radiation of the Sun (solar radiation) that provides the energy that drives Earth's climate system. All objects with a temperature greater than absolute zero (0 K), however, emit electromagnetic radiation, where the energy is carried by photons of light in the infrared and visible portions of the electromagnetic spectrum (see Figure 3.3). The transfer of radiant heat differs from that of conduction and convection in that it requires no medium, with energy being emitted in the form of photons that travel at the speed of light. It is radiant energy that warms one's face in the Sun and is the apparent heat that one feels when standing near a fire.

The amount of radiant energy emitted from any object to its surroundings is a function of its temperature and is described by the following equation:

Temperature of the object in degrees Kelvin raised to the power of four

Heat emitted in units of Watts (W) per m² per second

$$Q = \sigma T^4$$

Stefan–Boltzmann constant $(5.67 \times 10^8 \text{ W/m}^2 \cdot \text{K}^2)$

For example, we can use this formula to calculate the radiant energy per square meter emitted by the Sun (average temperature of 6000 K):

$5.67 \times 10^{-8} \ (\text{W/m}^2 \cdot \text{K}^4) \times 6000^4 \ (\text{K})$
$$= 7.3 \times 10^7 \ (\text{W/m}^2)$$

The calculation above is for the maximum amount of radiation that any surface can emit for a given temperature. If a surface emits this maximum amount of radiation, it is known as a *blackbody.* Most surfaces are not blackbody emitters and emit only some fraction of the amount of thermal radiation that a blackbody would. This fraction is known as **emissivity** ($e$). Values of emissivity range from 0 to 1.0. If a surface emits only half as much radiation as a blackbody, it is said to have an emissivity of 0.5. If it emits 1/10 or 0.1 as much as a blackbody, it has an emissivity of 0.1, and so on. Highly reflective objects have an emissivity near zero, dull or black objects have a value close to one. The Sun and Earth behave approximately as blackbodies. Taking the concept of emissivity ($e$) into consideration, we can modify the equation above to apply to all objects:

$$Q = e\sigma T^4$$

Objects generally emit radiation at many wavelengths (see Figure 3.2); however, there will be one wavelength where object emits the most. The dominant wavelength, termed $\lambda_{max}$, is a function of temperature, with the wavelength increasing as the temperature declines (see Figure 3.2). The dominant wavelength of an object can be determined based on Wein's law:

$$\lambda_{max} = 2897 \ \mu\text{m}/T(\text{K})$$

$T$ is the temperature of the object in degrees Kelvin ($K = °C + 273.15$). You can use this formula to solve for the differences in the dominant wavelengths emitted by the Sun and Earth presented in Figure 3.2. ●

1. The value of emissivity for the human body is $e = 0.7$. Calculate the transfer of radiant energy to the surrounding air from your body (per square meter of surface area), assuming that your body temperature is 98.6°F, or 310 K.

2. What is the dominant wavelength of electromagnetic radiation that your body is emitting? Using Figure 3.4, identify the type of radiation (far infrared, near infrared, visible, etc.). Note that the scale for Figure 3.4 is in nanometers (nm), whereas the units for the calculation above are in micrometers ($\mu$m). To make the units comparable, you must first convert (nm = $\mu$m × 1000).

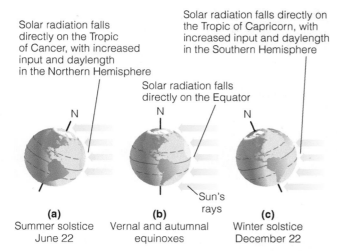

Solar radiation falls directly on the Tropic of Cancer, with increased input and daylength in the Northern Hemisphere

Solar radiation falls directly on the Tropic of Capricorn, with increased input and daylength in the Southern Hemisphere

Solar radiation falls directly on the Equator

N          N          N

Sun's rays

**(a)**          **(b)**          **(c)**
Summer solstice      Vernal and autumnal      Winter solstice
June 22          equinoxes          December 22

**Figure 3.6** | Angle of the Sun and circle of illumination at the equinoxes and the winter and summer solstices.

equinox (approximately September 22), solar radiation falls directly on the Equator (Figure 3.6b). At this time, the equatorial region is heated most intensely, and every place on Earth receives the same 12 hours each of daylight and night.

At the summer solstice (June 22) in the Northern Hemisphere, solar rays fall directly on the Tropic of Cancer (23.5° north latitude) (Figure 3.6a). This time is when days are longest in the Northern Hemisphere, and the Sun heats the surface most intensely. In contrast, the Southern Hemisphere experiences winter at this time. At winter solstice (December 22) in the Northern Hemisphere, solar rays fall directly on the Tropic of Capricorn (23.5° south latitude) (Figure 3.6c). This period is summer in the Southern Hemisphere, whereas the Northern Hemisphere is enduring shorter days and colder temperatures. Thus, the summer solstice in the Northern Hemisphere is the winter solstice in the Southern Hemisphere.

The seasonality of solar radiation, temperature, and daylength increases with latitude. At the Arctic and Antarctic Circles (66.5° north and south latitudes, respectively), daylength varies from 0 to 24 hours over the course of the year. The days shorten until the winter solstice, a day of continuous darkness. The days lengthen with spring, and on the day of the summer solstice, the Sun never sets.

Figure 3.7 shows how annual, seasonal, and daily solar radiation varies over Earth. Although in theory every location on Earth receives the same amount of daylight over the course of a year, in high latitudes where the Sun is never positioned directly overhead, the annual input of solar radiation is the lowest. This pattern of varying exposures to solar radiation controls mean annual temperature around the globe (Figure 3.8; page 51). Like annual solar radiation, mean annual tem-

peratures are highest in tropical regions and decline as one moves toward the poles.

## 3.3 | Air Temperature Decreases with Altitude

Whereas varying degree and length of exposure to solar radiation may explain changes in latitudinal, seasonal, and daily temperatures, they do not explain why air gets cooler with increasing altitude. Mount Kilimanjaro, for example, rises from the hot plain of tropical East Africa, but its peak is capped with ice and snow (Figure 3.9; page 52). The explanation of this apparent oddity of snow in the tropics lies in the physical properties of air.

The weight of all the air molecules surrounding Earth is a staggering 5600 trillion tons. The air's weight acts as a force upon Earth's surface, and the amount of force exerted over a given area of surface is called **atmospheric pressure,** or air pressure. Envision a vertical column of air. The pressure at any point in the column can be measured in terms of the total mass of air above that point. As we climb in elevation, the mass of air above us decreases, and therefore pressure declines. Although atmospheric pressure decreases continuously, the rate of decline slows with increasing altitude (Figure 3.10; page 52).

Because of the greater air pressure at Earth's surface, the density of air (the number of molecules per unit volume) is high, decreasing in parallel with air pressure as we climb in altitude. As altitude above sea level increases, both air pressure and density decrease. Although by an altitude of 50 km, air pressure is only 0.1 percent of that measured at sea level, the atmosphere continues to extend upward for many hundreds of kilometers, gradually becoming thinner and thinner until it merges into outer space.

Although both air pressure and density decrease systematically with height above sea level, air temperature has a more complicated vertical profile. Air temperature normally decreases from Earth's surface up to an altitude of approximately 11 km (nearly 36,000 feet). The rate at which temperature decreases with altitude is called the **environmental lapse rate.**

The decrease in air temperature as one moves farther from Earth's surface is caused by two factors. Because of the higher density of air at the surface, air molecules collide, generating heat. The decrease in air density with altitude results in fewer collisions, thus generating less heat. The primary reason for the decrease in air temperature with increasing altitude, however, is the corresponding decline in the "warming effect" of Earth's surface. The absorption of solar radiation functions to warm Earth's surface. Energy (longwave radiation) is emitted upward from the surface, heating the air above it. This process of transfer continues upward as heat

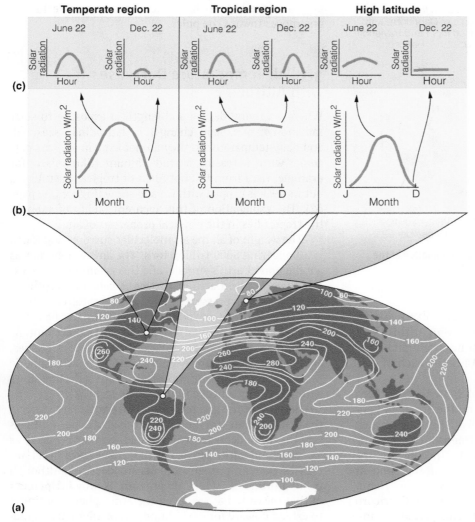

**Figure 3.7** | Annual variation in solar radiation on Earth. **(a)** Global mean solar radiation. **(b)** Variations in solar radiation from summer solstice to winter solstice at three locations: a temperate region, a tropical region, and a high-latitude region. **(c)** Diurnal variations in solar radiation on two days in the year: the summer solstice and the winter solstice. (Adapted from Barry and Chorley 1992.)

flows spontaneously from warmer to cooler areas but at a continuously declining rate as the energy emitted from the surface is dissipated.

Unlike air pressure and density, air temperature does not decline continuously with increasing height above Earth's surface. In fact, at certain heights in the atmosphere, a change in altitude can result in an abrupt change in temperature. Atmospheric scientists use these altitudes at which temperatures change abruptly to distinguish different regions in the atmosphere (Figure 3.11; page 52). Beginning at Earth's surface, the regions are called the troposphere, the stratosphere, the mesosphere, and the thermosphere. The boundary zones between these four regions of the atmosphere are the tropopause, stratopause, and mesopause, respectively. The two most important regions in terms of climate and, therefore, life on Earth are the troposphere and stratosphere.

So far, the discussion of the change in air temperature with increasing altitude has assumed no vertical movement of air from the surface to the top of the atmosphere. When a volume of air at the surface warms, however, it becomes buoyant and rises (just as does a hot-air balloon). As the volume of air (referred to as a parcel of air) rises, the decreasing pressure causes it to expand and cool. The decrease in air temperature through expansion, rather than through heat loss to the surrounding atmosphere, is called **adiabatic cooling.** The same process works in an air conditioner, where a coolant is compressed. As the coolant moves from the compressor to the coils, the drop in pressure causes it to expand and cool.

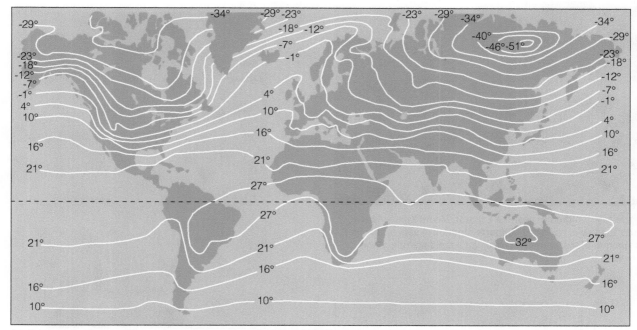

**(a) January isotherms (lines of equal temperature) around the Earth**

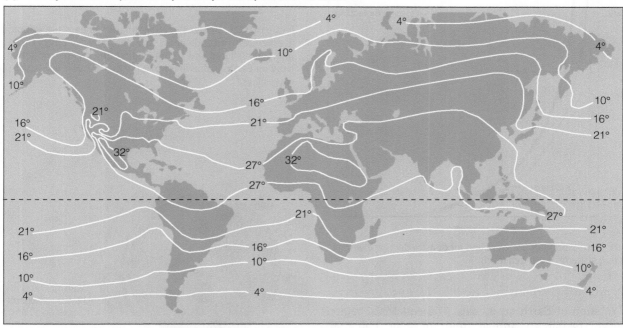

**(b) July isotherms (lines of equal temperature) around the Earth**

**Figure 3.8** | Mean annual global temperatures change with latitude and season. **(a)** Mean sea-level temperatures (°C) in January. **(b)** Mean sea-level temperatures (°C) in July. Note the colder temperatures during the Northern Hemisphere winter (January), warmer temperatures during the Southern Hemisphere summer, and the reversal in temperature patterns with the shift to summer in the Northern Hemisphere and winter in the Southern Hemisphere (July).

The rate of adiabatic cooling depends on how much moisture is in the air. The adiabatic cooling of dry air is approximately 10°C per 1000 m elevation. Moist air cools more slowly (~6°C per 1000 m). The rate of temperature change with elevation is called the **adiabatic lapse rate.**

## 3.4 | Air Masses Circulate Globally

The blanket of air that surrounds the planet—the atmosphere—is not static. It is in a constant state of movement, driven by the rising and sinking of air masses and

Figure 3.9 | Although near the Equator, Mount Kilimanjaro in Africa is snow-capped and supports tundra-like vegetation near its summit. Global warming is causing a rapid melting of this snowcap.

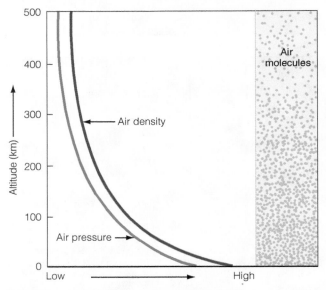

Figure 3.10 | Both air pressure and air density decrease with increasing altitude above sea level.

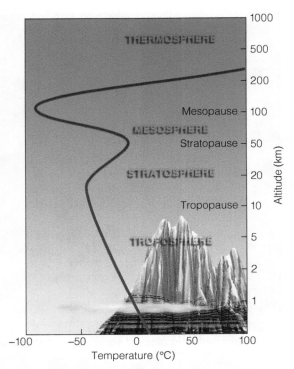

Figure 3.11 | Changes in atmospheric temperature (global average) with altitude above sea level. The regions of the atmosphere are labeled and Mount Everest (the highest mountain peak on Earth) is drawn for perspective. (Adapted from Graedel and Crutzen 1995.)

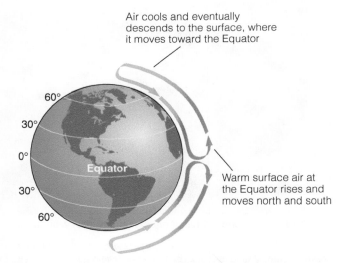

Figure 3.12 | Circulation of air cells and prevailing winds on an imaginary, nonrotating Earth. Air heated at the Equator rises and moves north and south. Cooling at the poles, it descends and moves back toward the Equator.

the rotation of Earth on its axis. The equatorial region receives the largest annual input of solar radiation. Warm air rises because it is less dense than the cooler air above it. Air heated at the equatorial region rises to the top of the atmosphere, establishing a zone of low pressure down at the surface (Figure 3.12). More air rising beneath it forces the air mass to spread north and south toward the poles. As air masses move poleward, they cool, become heavier, and sink. The sinking air raises surface air pressure (high-pressure zone). The cooled, heavier air then flows toward the Equator, replacing the warm air rising over the tropics.

If Earth were stationary and without irregular landmasses, the atmosphere would circulate as shown in Figure 3.12. Earth, however, spins on its axis from west to east. Although each point on Earth's surface makes a complete rotation every 24 hours, the speed of rotation varies with latitude (and circumference). At a point on the Equator (its widest circumference at 40,176 km), the speed of rotation is 1674 km per hour. In contrast, at 60° north or south, Earth's circumference is approximately half that at the Equator (20,130 km), and the speed of rotation is 839 km per hour. According to the law of angular motion, the momentum of an object moving from a greater circumference to a lesser circumference will deflect in the direction of the spin, and an object moving from a lesser circumference to a greater circumference will deflect in the direction opposite that of the spin. As a result, air masses and all moving objects in the Northern Hemisphere are deflected to the right (clockwise motion), and in the Southern Hemisphere to the left (counterclockwise motion). This deflection in the pattern of air flow is the **Coriolis effect,** named after a 19th-century French mathematician, G. C. Coriolis, who first analyzed the phenomenon (Figure 3.13).

As a result of the deflection of air masses, the Coriolis effect prevents a direct, simple flow of air from the Equator to the poles. Instead, it creates a series of belts of prevailing winds, named for the direction from which they come. These belts break the simple flow of surface air toward the Equator and the flow aloft to the poles into a series of six cells, three in each hemisphere. They produce areas of low and high pressure as air masses ascend from and descend toward the surface, respectively (Figure 3.14). To trace the flow of air as it circulates between the Equator and poles, we begin at Earth's equatorial region, which receives the largest annual input of solar radiation.

Air heated in the equatorial zone rises upward, creating a low-pressure zone near the surface: the equatorial low. This upward flow of air is balanced by a flow of air from the north and south toward the Equator. As the warm air mass rises, it begins to spread, diverging northward and southward toward the North and South Poles, cooling as it goes. In the Northern Hemisphere, the Cori-

olis effect forces air in an easterly direction, slowing its progress north. At about 30° north latitude, the now cool air sinks, closing the first of the three cells, the Hadley cells, named for the Englishman George Hadley who first

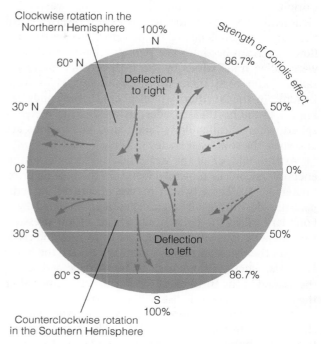

**Figure 3.13** | Effect of the Coriolis force on wind direction. The effect is absent at the Equator, where the linear velocity is the greatest, 465 m/s (1040 mi/h). Any object on the Equator is moving at the same rate. The Coriolis effect increases regularly toward the poles. If an object, including an air mass, moves northward from the Equator at a constant speed, it speeds up because Earth moves more slowly (403 m/s at 30° latitude, 233 m/s at 60° latitude, and 0 m/s at the poles). As a result, the path of the object appears to deflect to the right or east in the Northern Hemisphere and to the left or west in the Southern Hemisphere.

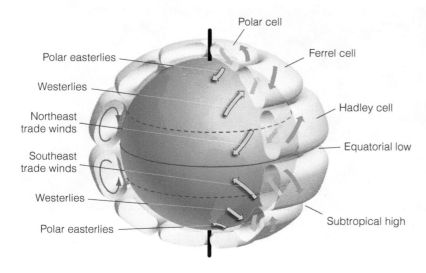

**Figure 3.14** | Belts and cells of air circulation about a rotating Earth. This circulation gives rise to the trade, westerly, and easterly winds.

described this pattern of circulation in 1735. The descending air forms a semipermanent high-pressure belt at the surface and encircling Earth: the subtropical high. Having descended, the cool air warms and splits into two currents flowing over the surface. One moves northward toward the pole, diverted to the right by the Coriolis effect to become the prevailing **westerlies.** Meanwhile, the other current moves southward toward the Equator. Also deflected to the right, this southward-flowing stream becomes the strong, reliable winds that were called **trade winds** by the 17th-century merchant sailors, who used them to reach the Americas from Europe. In the Northern Hemisphere, these winds are known as the northeast trades. In the Southern Hemisphere where similar flows take place, these winds are known as the southeast trades.

As the mild air of the westerlies moves poleward, it encounters cold air moving down from the pole (approximately 60°N). These two air masses of contrasting temperature do not readily mix. They are separated by a boundary called the polar front, a zone of low pressure (the subpolar low) where surface air converges and rises. Some of the rising air moves southward toward the horse latitudes, where it sinks back to the surface and closes the second of the three cells, the Ferrel cell, named after the American meteorologist William Ferrel.

As the northward-moving air reaches the pole, it slowly sinks to the surface and flows back (southward) toward the polar front, completing the last of the three cells: the polar cell. This southward-moving air is deflected to the right by the Coriolis effect, giving rise to

the **polar easterlies.** Similar flows take place in the Southern Hemisphere (see Figure 3.14).

## 3.5 | Solar Energy, Wind, and Earth's Rotation Create Ocean Currents

The global pattern of the prevailing winds plays a crucial role in determining major patterns of surface water flow in Earth's oceans. These systematic patterns of water movement are called **currents.** In fact, the major currents of the oceans generally mimic the movement of the wind currents above until they encounter one of the continents.

Each ocean is dominated by two great circular water motions, or **gyres.** Within each gyre, the ocean current moves clockwise in the Northern Hemisphere and counterclockwise in the Southern Hemisphere (Figure 3.15). Along the Equator, trade winds push warm surface waters westward. When these waters encounter the eastern margins of the continents, they split into north- and south-flowing currents along the coasts, forming north and south gyres. As the currents move farther from the Equator, the water cools. Eventually, they encounter the westerly winds at higher latitudes (30–60°N and 30–60°S), which produce eastward-moving currents. When these eastward-moving currents encounter the western margins of the continents, they form cool currents that flow along the coastline toward the Equator. Just north of the Antarctic continent, ocean waters circulate unimpeded around the globe.

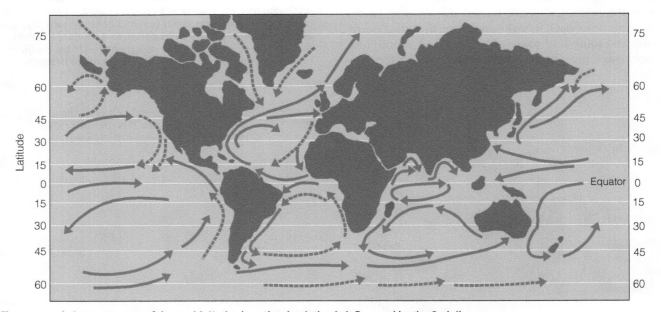

**Figure 3.15** | Ocean currents of the world. Notice how the circulation is influenced by the Coriolis force (clockwise movement in the Northern Hemisphere and counterclockwise movement in the Southern Hemisphere) and continental landmasses and how oceans are connected by currents. Dashed arrows represent cool water and solid arrows represent warm water.

## 3.6 | Temperature Influences the Moisture Content of Air

Air temperature plays a crucial role in the exchange of water between the atmosphere and Earth's surface. Whenever matter, including water, changes from one state to another, energy is either absorbed or released. The amount of energy released or absorbed (per gram) during a change of state is known as **latent heat** (from the Latin *latens*, hidden). In going from a more ordered state (liquid) to a less ordered state (gas), energy is absorbed. While going from a less ordered to a more ordered state, energy is released. The transformation of water from a liquid to a gaseous state is called **evaporation,** requiring 2260 joules (J) of energy per gram of liquid water converted to water vapor (1 J/s = 1 W). The transformation of water vapor to a liquid state is called **condensation,** releasing an equivalent amount of energy. When air comes into contact with liquid water, water molecules are freely exchanged between the air and the water's surface. When the rate of evaporation is equal to the rate of condensation, the air is said to be saturated.

In the air, water vapor acts as an independent gas that has weight and exerts pressure. The amount of pressure water vapor exerts independent of the pressure of dry air is called **vapor pressure.** Vapor pressure is typically defined in units of megapascals (MPa). The water vapor content of air at saturation is called the **saturation vapor pressure.** The saturation vapor pressure, also known as the water vapor capacity of the air, cannot be exceeded. If the vapor pressure exceeds the capacity, condensation occurs in order to reduce the vapor pressure. The saturation vapor pressure varies with temperature, increasing as air temperature increases (Figure 3.16). Warm air has a greater capacity for water vapor than does cold air.

The amount of water in a given volume of air is its absolute humidity. The most familiar measure is **relative humidity,** or the amount of water vapor in the air expressed as a percentage of the saturation vapor pressure. At saturation vapor pressure, the relative humidity is 100 percent. If air cools while the actual amount of moisture it holds (water vapor pressure) remains constant, then relative humidity increases as the value of saturation vapor pressure declines. If the air cools to a point where the actual vapor pressure exceeds the saturation vapor pressure, moisture in the air will condense and form clouds. As soon as particles of water or ice in the air become too heavy to remain suspended, precipitation falls.

For a given water content of a parcel of air (vapor pressure), the temperature at which saturation vapor pressure is achieved is called the **dew point temperature.** Think about finding dew or frost on a cool fall morning. As nightfall approaches, temperatures drop and relative humidity rises. If cool night air temperatures reach the dew point, water condenses and dew forms, lowering the amount of water in the air. As the sun rises, air tempera-

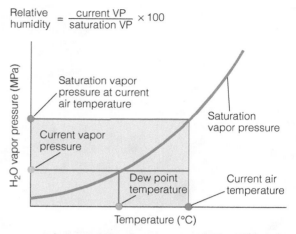

$$\text{Relative humidity} = \frac{\text{current VP}}{\text{saturation VP}} \times 100$$

**Figure 3.16** | Saturation vapor pressure as a function of air temperature (saturation VP increases with air temperature). For a given air temperature, the relative humidity is the ratio of current vapor pressure to saturation vapor pressure ([current VP/saturation VP] × 100). For a given vapor pressure, the temperature at which saturation vapor pressure occurs is called the dew point. (Go to QUANTIFYIT! at **www.ecology.place.com** to review functions.)

ture warms and the water vapor capacity (saturation vapor pressure) increases. As a result, the dew evaporates, increasing vapor pressure in the air.

## 3.7 | Precipitation Has a Distinctive Global Pattern

By bringing together patterns of temperature, winds, and ocean currents, we are ready to understand the global pattern of precipitation. Precipitation is not evenly distributed across Earth (Figure 3.17). At first inspection, the global map of annual precipitation presented in Figure 3.17 may appear to lack any discernible pattern or regularity. However, if we examine the simpler pattern of variation in average rainfall with latitude (Figure 3.18), a general pattern emerges. Precipitation is highest in the region of the Equator, declining as one moves north and south. The decline, however, is not continuous. Two peaks occur in the mid-latitudes followed by a further decline toward the poles. The sequence of peaks and troughs seen in Figure 3.18 corresponds to the pattern of rising and falling air masses associated with the belts of prevailing winds presented in Figure 3.14.

As the warm trade winds move across the tropical oceans, they gather moisture. Near the Equator, the northeasterly trade winds meet the southeasterly trade winds. This narrow region where the trade winds meet is the **intertropical convergence zone (ITCZ),** characterized by high amounts of precipitation (Figure 3.19; page 57). Where the two air masses meet, air piles up, and the warm humid air rises and cools. When the dew point is

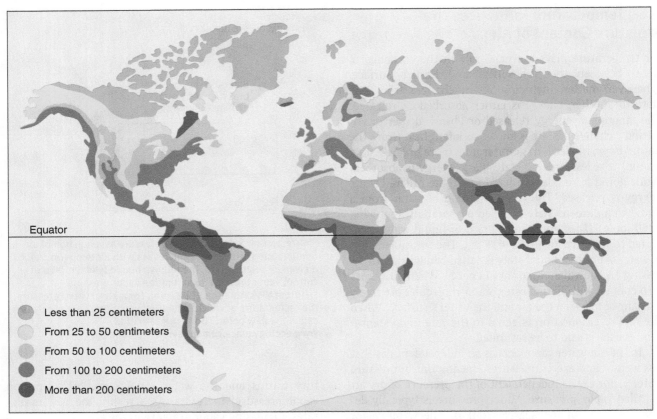

**Figure 3.17** | Annual world precipitation. Relate the wettest and driest areas to mountain ranges, ocean currents, and winds.

Legend:
- Less than 25 centimeters
- From 25 to 50 centimeters
- From 50 to 100 centimeters
- From 100 to 200 centimeters
- More than 200 centimeters

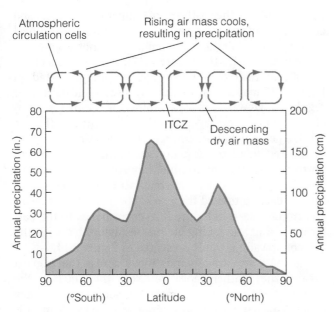

**Figure 3.18** | Variation in mean annual precipitation with latitude. The peaks in rainfall correspond to rising air masses, such as that of the intertropical convergence zone, whereas the troughs are associated with descending dry air masses.

reached, clouds form, and precipitation falls as rain. This pattern accounts for high precipitation in the tropical regions of eastern Asia, South America, and Africa, as well as relatively high precipitation in southeastern North America (see Figure 3.17).

Having lost much of its moisture, the ascending air mass continues to cool as it splits and moves northward and southward. In the horse latitudes (approximately 30° north and south), where the cool air descends, two belts of dry climate encircle the globe (the two troughs at the mid-latitudes seen in Figure 3.18). The descending air warms. Because the saturation vapor pressure rises, it draws water from the surface through evaporation, causing arid conditions. In these belts, the world's major deserts have formed (see Chapter 23).

As the air masses continue to move north and south, they once again draw moisture from the surface, but to a lesser degree as a result of the cooler surface conditions. Moving poleward, they encounter cold air masses originating at the poles (approximately 60° north and south). Where the surface air masses converge and rise, the ascending air mass cools and precipitation occurs (seen as the two peaks in precipitation between 50° and 60° north and south in Figure 3.18). From this point on to

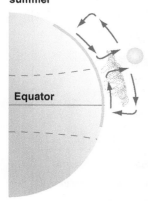

**Northern Hemisphere summer**

Equator

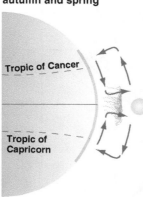

**autumn and spring**

Tropic of Cancer

Tropic of Capricorn

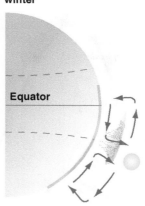

**Northern Hemisphere winter**

Equator

**Figure 3.19** | Shifts of the intertropical convergence zone, producing rainy seasons and dry seasons. Note that as the distance from the Equator increases, the dry season is longer and the rainfall is less. These oscillations result from changes in the altitude of the Sun between the equinoxes and the solstices as diagrammed in Figure 3.6. Patterns of air circulation are shown in Figure 3.14.

the poles, the cold temperature and associated low vapor saturation point function to restrict precipitation.

One other pattern is worth noting in Figure 3.18. In general, rainfall is greater in the Southern Hemisphere as compared to the Northern Hemisphere (note the southern shift in the rainfall peak associated with the ITCZ). This is because the oceans cover a greater proportion of the Southern Hemisphere, and water evaporates more readily from the water's surface than from the soil and vegetation. This is also the reason that the interior of continents generally experience less precipitation than the coastal regions (note the gradients of precipitation from the coast to the interiors of North America and Europe/Asia in Figure 3.17).

What is missing from our discussion thus far is the temporal variation of precipitation over Earth. The temporal variation is directly linked to the seasonal changes in the heating of Earth and its effect on the movement of global pressure systems and air masses. This is illustrated in seasonal movement north and south of the ITCZ, which follows the apparent migration of the direct rays of the Sun (Figure 3.19).

The ITCZ is not stationary but tends to migrate toward regions of the globe with the warmest surface temperature. Although tropical regions about the Equator are always exposed to warm temperatures, the Sun is directly over the geographical Equator only two times a year, at the spring and fall equinoxes. At the northern summer solstice, the Sun is directly over the Tropic of Cancer; at the winter solstice (which is summer in the Southern Hemisphere), it is directly over the Tropic of Capricorn. As a result, the ITCZ moves poleward and invades the subtropical highs in northern summer; in the winter it moves southward, leaving clear dry weather behind. As it migrates southward, it brings rain to the southern summer. Thus, as the ITCZ shifts north and south, it brings on the wet and dry seasons in the tropics (Figure 3.20).

## 3.8 | Topography Influences Regional and Local Patterns of Precipitation

Mountainous topography influences local and regional patterns of precipitation. Mountains intercept air flow. As an air mass reaches a mountain, it ascends, cools, becomes saturated with water vapor (because of lower saturation vapor pressure), and releases much of its moisture at upper altitudes of the windward side. This phenomenon is called a **rain shadow** (Figure 3.21). As the now cool, dry air descends the leeward side, it warms again and gradually picks up moisture. As a result, the windward side of a mountain supports denser, more vigorous vegetation and different species of plants and associated animals than does the leeward side, where in some areas dry, desert-like conditions exist. Thus in North America, the westerly winds that blow over the Sierra Nevada and the Rocky Mountains, dropping their moisture on west-facing slopes, support vigorous forest growth. By contrast, the eastern slopes exhibit semidesert or desert conditions.

Some of the most pronounced effects of this same phenomenon occur in the Hawaiian Islands. There, plant cover ranges from scrubby vegetation on the leeward side of an island to moist, forested slopes on the windward side (Figure 3.22; page 59).

## 3.9 | Irregular Variations in Climate Occur at the Regional Scale

The patterns of temporal variation in climate that we have discussed thus far occur at regular and predictable intervals: seasonal changes in temperature with the rotation of Earth about the Sun, and the migration of the intertropical convergence zone with the resulting seasonality of rainfall in the tropics and monsoons in southeast Asia. Not all features of the climate system, however, occur with such regularity. Earth's climate system is

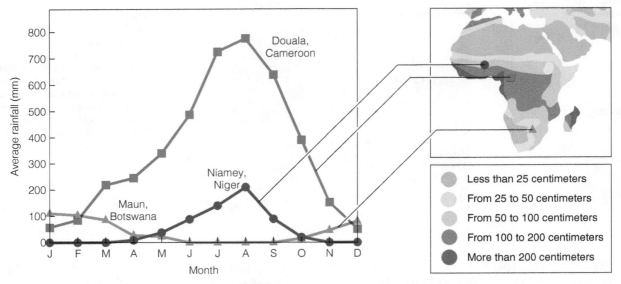

**Figure 3.20** | Seasonal variations in precipitation at three sites within the intertropical convergence zone. Although site **(a)** shows a seasonal variation, precipitation exceeds 50 mm each month. Sites **(b)** and **(c)** are within the regions of the ITCZ that experience a distinct wet (summer) and dry (winter) season. Note that the rainy season is 6 months out of phase for these two sites, reflecting the difference in the timing of the summer month in the two hemispheres.

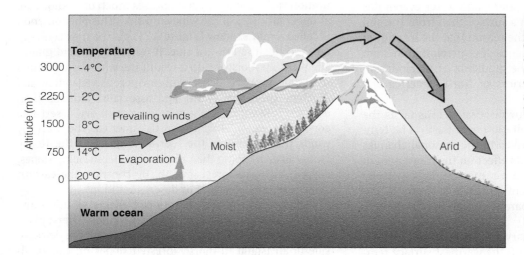

**Figure 3.21** | Formation of a rain shadow. Air is forced to go over a mountain. As it rises, the air mass cools and loses its moisture as precipitation on the windward side. The descending air, already dry, picks up moisture from the leeward side.

characterized by variability at both the regional and global scales.

The Little Ice Age, a period of cooling that lasted from approximately the mid-14th to the mid-19th century, brought bitterly cold winters to many parts of the Northern Hemisphere, affecting agriculture, health, politics, economics, emigration, and even art and literature. In the mid-17th century, glaciers in the Swiss Alps advanced, gradually engulfing farms and crushing entire villages. In 1780, New York Harbor froze, allowing people to walk from Manhattan to Staten Island. In fact, the image of a white Christmas evoked by Charles Dickens and the New England poets of the 18th and 19th centuries is largely a product of the cold and snowy winters of the Little Ice Age. But the climate has since warmed to a point at which a white Christmas in these regions is an anomaly.

The Great Plains region of central North America has undergone periods of drought dating back to the mid-Holocene period some 5000 to 8000 years ago, but the homesteaders of the early 20th century settled the Great Plains at a time of relatively wet summers. They assumed these moisture conditions were the norm, and they employed the agricultural methods they had used in the East. So they broke the prairie sod for crops, but the cycle of drought returned, and the prairie grasslands became a dust bowl.

**(a)**

**(b)**

Figure 3.22 | Rain shadow on the mountains of Maui, Hawaiian Islands. **(a)** The windward, east-facing slopes, intercepting the trade winds, are cloaked with wet forest. **(b)** Low-growing shrubby vegetation on the dry side.

These examples reflect the variability in Earth's climate systems, which operate on timescales ranging from decadal to tens of thousands of years, driven by changes in the input of energy to Earth's surface. Earth's orbit is not permanent. Changes occur in the tilt of the axis and the shape of the yearly path about the Sun. These variations affect climate by altering the seasonal inputs of solar radiation. These variations, which occur on a timescale of tens of thousands of years, are associated with the glacial advances and retreats throughout Earth's history.

Variations in the level of solar radiation to Earth's surface are also associated with sunspot activity—huge magnetic storms on the Sun. These storms are associated with strong solar emissions and occur in cycles, with the number and size reaching a maximum approximately every 11 years. Among other occurrences, researchers have related sunspot activity to periods of drought and winter warming in the Northern Hemisphere.

Interaction between two components of the climate system, the ocean and the atmosphere, are associated with a number of major climatic variations that occur at a regional scale. As far back as 1525, historic documents record that fishermen off the coast of Peru made note of periods of unusually warm water. The Peruvians referred to these periods of unusually warm water as El Niño, because it commonly appears at Christmas time, the season of the Christ Child (Spanish: *El Niño*). El Niño is the phenomenon in the waters of the Galápagos Islands described in the introduction of Part Two (pp. 42–43). Now referred to by scientists as the **El Niño–Southern Oscillation (ENSO),** this phenomenon is a global event arising from large-scale interaction between the ocean and the atmosphere. The Southern Oscillation, a more recent discovery, refers to an oscillation in the surface pressure (atmospheric mass) between the southeastern tropical Pacific and the Australian–Indonesian regions. When the waters of the eastern Pacific are abnormally warm (an El Niño event), sea level pressure drops in the eastern Pacific and rises in the west. The reduction in the pressure gradient is accompanied by a weakening of the low-latitude easterly trades.

Although the cause of the ENSO phenomenon is still not completely understood by scientists, the mechanism has been well documented. Recall from Section 3.4, the trade winds blow westward across the tropical Pacific (see Figure 3.14). As a consequence, the surface currents within the tropical oceans flow westward (see Figure 3.15), bringing cold, deeper waters to the surface off the coast of Peru, a process known as upwelling (see Section 4.8). This pattern of upwelling together with the cold-water current that flows from south to north along the western coast of South America results in this region of the ocean being normally colder than one would expect given its equatorial location (Figure 3.23a).

As the surface currents move westward, the water warms, giving the water's destination, the western Pacific, the warmest ocean surface on Earth. The warmer water of the western Pacific causes the moist maritime air to rise and cool, bringing abundant rainfall to the region (Figure 3.23a; also see Figure 3.17). In contrast, the cooler waters of the eastern Pacific result in relatively dry conditions along the Peruvian coast.

During an El Niño event, the trade winds slacken, reducing the westward flow of the surface currents (Figure 3.23b). The result is a reduced upwelling and a warming of the surface waters in the eastern Pacific. Rainfall follows the warm water eastward, with associated flooding in Peru and drought in Indonesia and Australia.

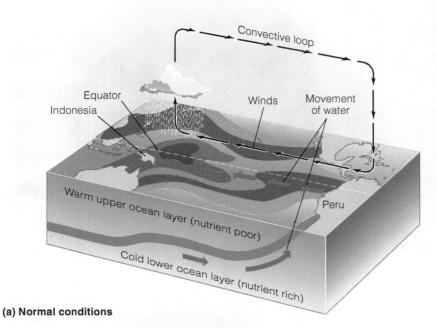

Convective loop
Equator
Indonesia
Winds
Movement of water
Warm upper ocean layer (nutrient poor)
Peru
Cold lower ocean layer (nutrient rich)

**(a) Normal conditions**

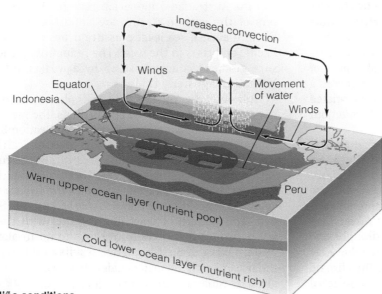

Increased convection
Equator
Indonesia
Winds
Movement of water
Winds
Warm upper ocean layer (nutrient poor)
Peru
Cold lower ocean layer (nutrient rich)

**(b) El Niño conditions**

**Figure 3.23** | Schematic of the El Niño–Southern Oscillation (ENSO) that occurs off the western coast of South America. **(a)** Under normal conditions, strong trade winds move surface waters westward. As the surface currents move westward, the water warms. The warmer water of the western Pacific causes the moist maritime air to rise and cool, bringing abundant rainfall to the region. **(b)** Under ENSO conditions, the trade winds slacken, reducing the westward flow of the surface currents. Rainfall follows the warm water eastward, with associated flooding in Peru and drought in Indonesia and Australia.

This eastward displacement of the atmospheric heat source (latent heat associated with the evaporation of water; see Section 4.2) overlaying the warm surface waters results in large changes in the global atmospheric circulation, which in turn influences weather in regions far removed from the tropical Pacific.

At other times, the injection of cold water becomes more intense than usual, causing the surface of the eastern Pacific to cool. This variation is referred to as **La Niña**

(Figure 3.24). It results in droughts in South America and heavy rainfall, even floods, in eastern Australia.

## 3.10 | Most Organisms Live in Microclimates

Most organisms live in local conditions that do not match the general climate profile of the larger region surrounding them. For example, today's weather report

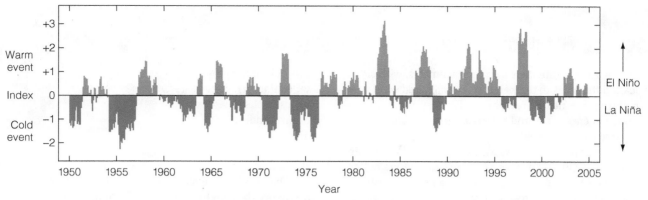

**Figure 3.24** | Record of El Niño–La Niña events during the second half of the 20th century. The numbers on the left side of the diagram represent the ENSO index, which includes a combination of six factors related to environmental conditions over the tropical Pacific Ocean: air temperature, surface water temperature, sea-level pressure, cloudiness, and wind speed and direction. Warm episodes are in red, cold episodes are in blue. An index value greater than $+1$ represents an El Niño. A value less than $-1$ represents a La Niña.

may state that the temperature is 28°C and the sky is clear. However, your weather forecaster is only painting a general picture. Actual conditions of specific environments will be quite different depending on whether they are underground versus on the surface, beneath vegetation or on exposed soil, on mountain slopes or at the seashore. Light, heat, moisture, and air movement all vary greatly from one part of the landscape to another, influencing the transfer of heat energy and creating a wide range of localized climates. These **microclimates** define the conditions in which organisms live (see Ecological Issues: Urban Microclimates).

On a sunny but chilly day in early spring, flies may be attracted to sap oozing from the stump of a maple tree. The flies are active on the stump in spite of the near-freezing air temperature because, during the day, the surface of the stump absorbs solar radiation, heating a thin layer of air above the surface. On a still day, the air heated by the tree stump remains close to the surface, and temperatures decrease sharply above and below this layer. A similar phenomenon occurs when the frozen surface of the ground absorbs solar radiation and thaws. On a sunny, late winter day, one walks on muddy ground, even though the air about is cold.

By altering soil temperatures, moisture, wind movement, and evaporation, vegetation moderates microclimates, especially areas near the ground. For example, areas shaded by plants have lower temperatures at ground level than do places exposed to the sun. On fair summer days in locations 25 mm (1 inch) above the ground, dense forest cover can reduce the daily range of temperatures by 7°C to 12°C below soil temperature in bare fields. Under the shelter of heavy grass and low plant cover, the air at ground level is completely calm. This calm is an outstanding feature of microclimates within

dense vegetation at Earth's surface. It influences both temperature and humidity, creating a favorable environment for insects and other ground-dwelling animals.

Topography, particularly aspect (the direction that a slope faces), influences the local climatic conditions. In the Northern Hemisphere, south-facing slopes receive the most solar energy, whereas north-facing slopes receive the least. At other slope positions, energy varies between these extremes, depending on their compass direction.

Different exposure to solar radiation at south- and north-facing sites has a marked effect on the amount of moisture and heat present. Microclimate conditions range from warm, dry, variable conditions on the south-facing slope to cool, moist, more uniform conditions on the north-facing slope. Because high temperatures and associated high rates of evaporation draw moisture from soil and plants, the evaporation rate at south-facing slopes is often 50 percent higher; the average temperature is higher; and soil moisture is lower. Conditions are driest on the top of south-facing slopes where air movement is greatest, and dampest at the bottom of north-facing slopes.

The same microclimatic conditions occur on a smaller scale on north-facing and south-facing slopes of large ant hills, mounds of soil, dunes, and small ground ridges in otherwise flat terrain, as well as on the north-facing and south-facing sides of buildings, trees, and logs. The south-facing sides of buildings are always warmer and drier than the north-facing sides, a consideration for landscape planners, horticulturists, and gardeners. North sides of tree trunks are cooler and moister than south sides, a fact reflected in more vigorous growth of moss. In winter, the temperature of the north-facing side of a tree may be below freezing while the south side,

Urban areas create their own microclimates, with significant differences in temperature, rainfall, and wind flow patterns than nearby rural areas. The result is an increase in energy use and a decrease in air quality, with adverse effects on public health.

On warm summer days with little or no wind, the air temperature in urban areas can be several degrees hotter than the surrounding countryside. As a result, scientists refer to these urban areas as "urban heat islands." The reason that urban areas are warmer than the surrounding rural environments is a result of their energy balance, or the difference between the amount of energy gained and lost. In rural environments, the solar energy absorbed by the vegetation and ground is in part dissipated by the evaporation of water from the vegetation and soil. In urban areas there is less vegetation, and so the buildings, streets, and sidewalks absorb the majority of solar energy. With narrow streets and tall buildings, the building walls radiate heat toward one another instead of skyward. In addition, because the man-made surfaces of asphalt, cement, and brick are not porous, most rainfall is lost as runoff to storm drains before evaporation can cool the air. Waste heat from cars, buses, and city buildings also contributes to the input of energy. Although this waste heat eventually makes its way into the atmosphere, it can contribute as much as one-third of that received from solar energy. Adding to the problem is that construction materials (asphalt, concrete, bricks, and tar) are better conduc-

tors of heat than the vegetation that dominates the landscapes of surrounding rural areas. At night, these structures slowly give off heat that was stored during the day.

The heat island effect can raise temperatures 6°C to 8°C above those in the surrounding countryside. In Baltimore, Phoenix, Tucson, and Washington, D.C., for example, scientific data show that July's maximum temperatures during the past 30 to 80 years have been steadily increasing at a rate of one-half to one degree Fahrenheit every decade. The highest temperatures are in areas of highest population density and activity, whereas temperatures decline markedly toward the periphery of the city. Although temperature differences are detectable throughout the year, the heat island effect is most pronounced during the summer and early winter, and particularly at night, when heat stored by pavement and buildings reradiates into the air.

The heat island effect also has an impact on air quality within urban areas. Throughout the year, urban areas are blanketed with particulate matter and pollutants from the combustion of fossil fuels and industrial activity. Smog is created by photochemical reaction of pollutants in the atmosphere. The rate at which these reactions occur increases with higher temperatures. In Los Angeles, for example, for every degree the temperature rises above 20°C, the incidence of smog increases by 3 percent (Figure 1). Smog contains ozone, a pollutant that can be harmful when there are elevated levels in the air we breathe. In addition, ozone adversely affects vegetation, both within the urban environment and surrounding rural areas. The heat island effect exacerbates these effects on air quality, as higher ambient temperatures during the summer months increase air-conditioning energy use. As power plants burn more fossil fuels, they increase both pollution levels and energy costs.

Particulate matter has other microclimatic effects. Because of a city's low evaporation rate and the lack of vegetation, relative humidity is lower in urban than in surrounding rural areas. However, the particulates act as condensation nuclei for water vapor in the air, producing fog and haze. Fog is much more frequent in urban areas than in the country, especially in winter. ●

1. What simple steps could be taken to decrease the heat island effect in urban areas?

2. How might the urban heat island effect influence surrounding rural environments?

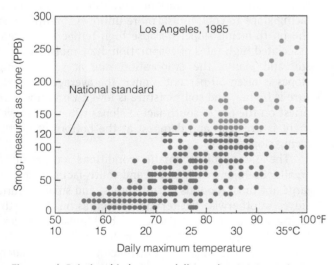

**Figure 1** | Relationship between daily maximum temperature and smog concentration (measured as ozone concentration in parts per billion-PPB) for the city of Los Angeles (1985). The dashed horizontal line at 120 PPB represents the national standard as defined by the US Environmental Protection Agency.

heated by the sun, is warm. This temperature difference may cause frost cracks in the bark as sap, thawed by day, freezes at night. Bark beetles and other wood-dwelling insects that seek cool, moist areas in which to lay their eggs prefer north-facing locations. Flowers on the south side of tree crowns often bloom sooner than those on the north side.

Microclimatic extremes also occur in depressions in the ground and on the concave surfaces of valleys where the air is protected from the wind. Heated by sunlight during the day and cooled by terrestrial vegetation at night, this air often becomes stagnant. As a result, these sheltered sites experience lower nighttime temperatures (especially in winter), higher daytime temperatures (es-

pecially in summer), and higher relative humidity. If the temperature drops low enough, frost pockets form in these depressions. The microclimates of the frost pockets often display the same phenomenon, supporting different kinds of plant life than found on surrounding higher ground.

Although the global and regional patterns of climate discussed in this chapter function to constrain the large-scale distribution and abundance of plants and animals, it is the localized patterns of microclimate that define the actual environmental conditions that are sensed by the individual organism. It is this localized microclimate that therefore determines the distribution and activities of organisms within a particular region.

---

## Summary

### Interception of Solar Radiation (3.1)

Earth intercepts solar energy in the form of shortwave radiation, which easily passes through the atmosphere, and emits much of it back as longwave radiation. However, energy of longer wavelengths cannot readily pass through the atmosphere and so is returned to Earth, producing the greenhouse effect.

### Seasonal Variation (3.2)

The amount of solar radiation intercepted by Earth varies markedly with latitude. Tropical regions near the Equator receive the greatest amount of solar radiation and high latitudes receive the least. Because Earth tilts on its axis, parts of Earth receive seasonal differences in solar radiation. These differences give rise to seasonal variations in temperature and rainfall. There is a global gradient in mean annual temperature; it is warmest in the tropics and declines toward the poles.

### Altitude and Temperature (3.3)

Heating and cooling, influenced by energy emitted from Earth's surface and by atmospheric pressure, cause air masses to rise and sink. This movement of air masses involves an adiabatic process in which heat is neither gained from nor lost to the outside.

### Atmospheric Circulation (3.4)

Vertical movements of air masses give rise to global patterns of atmospheric circulation. The spin of Earth on its axis deflects air and water currents to the right in the Northern Hemisphere and to the left in the Southern Hemisphere. Three cells of global air flow occur in each hemisphere.

### Ocean Currents (3.5)

The global pattern of winds and the Coriolis effect cause major patterns of ocean currents. Each ocean is dominated by great circular water motions, or gyres. These gyres move clockwise in the Northern Hemisphere and counterclockwise in the Southern Hemisphere.

### Atmospheric Moisture (3.6)

Atmospheric moisture is expressed in terms of relative humidity. The maximum amount of moisture the air can hold at any given temperature is called the saturation vapor pressure, which increases with temperature. Relative humidity is the amount of water in the air expressed as a percentage of the maximum amount the air could hold at a given temperature.

### Precipitation (3.7)

Wind, temperature, and ocean currents produce global patterns of precipitation. They account for regions of high precipitation in the tropics and belts of dry climate in the horse latitudes (~30° N and S).

### Topography (3.8)

Mountainous topography influences local and regional patterns of precipitation. As an air mass reaches a mountain, it ascends, cools, becomes saturated with water vapor, and releases much of its moisture at upper altitudes of the windward side.

### Irregular Variation (3.9)

Not all temporal variation in regional climate occurs at a regular interval. Irregular variations in the trade winds give rise to periods of unusually warm waters off the coast of western South America. Referred to by scientists as the El Niño, this phenomenon is a global event arising from large-scale interaction between the ocean and the atmosphere.

### Microclimates (3.10)

The actual climatic conditions under which organisms live vary considerably within one climate. These local variations, or microclimates, reflect topography, vegetative cover, exposure, and other factors on every scale. Angles of solar radiation cause marked differences between north-facing and south-facing slopes, whether on mountains, sand dunes, or ant mounds.

## Study Questions

1. Why does the Equator receive more solar radiation than the polar regions? What is the consequence of latitudinal patterns of temperature?

2. What is the greenhouse effect and how does it influence the energy balance (and temperature) of Earth?

3. The 23.5° tilt of Earth on its north–south axis gives rise to the seasons (review Figure 3.5). How would the pattern of seasons differ if the tilt of Earth were 90°? How would this influence the diurnal (night–day) cycle?

4. Why are the coastal waters of the southeastern United States warmer than the coastal waters off the southwestern coast (assume the same latitude)?

5. The air temperature at noon on January 20 was 45°F, and the air temperature at noon on July 20 at the same location was 85°F. The relative humidity on both days was 75 percent. On which of these two days was there more water vapor in the air?

6. How might the relative humidity of a parcel of air change as it moves up the side of a mountain? Why?

7. What is the intertropical convergence zone (ITCZ) and why does it give rise to a distinct pattern of seasonality in precipitation in the tropical zone?

8. What feature of global atmospheric circulation gives rise to the desert zones of the mid-latitudes?

9. Which aspect, south-facing or north-facing slopes, would receive the most solar radiation in the mountain ranges of the Southern Hemisphere?

10. Spruce Knob (latitude 38.625°N) in eastern West Virginia is named for the spruce trees that dominate the forests at this site. Spruce trees are typically found in the colder forests of the more northern latitudes (northeastern United States and Canada). What does the presence of spruce trees at Spruce Knob tell you about this site?

## Further Readings

Ahrens, C. D. 2003. *Meteorology today: An introduction to weather, climate, and the environment*. 6th ed. Belmont, CA: Brooks/Cole.

    An excellent introductory text on climate, clearly written and well illustrated.

Fagen, B. 2001. *The Little Ice Age: How climate made history, 1300–1850*. New York: Basic Books.

    An enjoyable book to read that provides an overview of the effects of the Little Ice Age on human history.

Graedel, T. E. and P. J. Crutzen. 1997. *Atmosphere, climate and change*. New York: Scientific American Library.

    A short introduction to climate written for the general public. Provides an excellent background for those interested in topics relating to air pollution and climate change.

Philander, G. 1989. El Niño and La Niña. *American Scientist* 77:451–9.

Suplee, C. 1999. El Niño, La Niña. *National Geographic* 195:73–95.

    These two articles provide a general introduction to the El Niño–La Niña climate cycle.

# Chapter 4 | The Aquatic Environment

A rainstorm over the ocean—a part of the water cycle.

**W**ater is the essential substance of life; the dominant component of all living organisms. About 75–95 percent of the weight of all living cells is water, and there is hardly a physiological process in which water is not of fundamental importance.

Covering some 75 percent of the planet's surface, water is also the dominant environment on Earth. One of the major features influencing the adaptations of organisms that inhabit aquatic environments is water salinity (see Section 4.5). For this reason, aquatic ecosystems are divided into two major categories: saltwater (or marine) and freshwater. These two major categories are further divided into a variety of aquatic ecosystems based on the depth and flow of water, substrate, and the type of organisms (typically plants) that dominate. We will explore the diversity of aquatic environments and the organisms that inhabit them later in Chapters 24 and 25. In this chapter, we will examine the unique physical and chemical characteristics of water and how those characteristics interact to define the nature of different aquatic environments and function as constraints on the evolution of organisms that inhabit them.

## 4.1 | Water Cycles Between Earth and the Atmosphere

All marine and freshwater aquatic environments are linked, either directly or indirectly, as components of the **water cycle** (also referred to as the **hydrologic cycle**) (Figure 4.1)—the process by which water travels in a sequence from the air to Earth and returns to the atmosphere.

Solar radiation, which heats Earth's atmosphere (see Chapter 3) and provides the energy for the evaporation of water, is the driving force behind the water cycle. **Precipitation** sets the water cycle in motion. Water vapor, circulating in the atmosphere, eventually falls in some form of precipitation. Some of the water falls directly on the soil and bodies of water. Some is intercepted by vegetation, dead organic matter on the ground, and urban structures and streets.

Because of **interception,** which can be considerable, various amounts of water never infiltrate the ground but evaporate directly back to the atmosphere. Precipitation that reaches the soil moves into the ground by **infiltration.** The rate of infiltration depends on the type of soil (see Section 5.8), slope, vegetation, and the intensity of the precipitation. During heavy rains when the soil is saturated, excess water flows across the surface of the ground as surface runoff or overland flow. At places, it concentrates into depressions and gullies, and the flow changes from sheet to channelized flow, a process one can observe on city streets as water moves across the pavement into gutters. Because of low infiltration, runoff from urban areas might be as much as 85 percent of the precipitation.

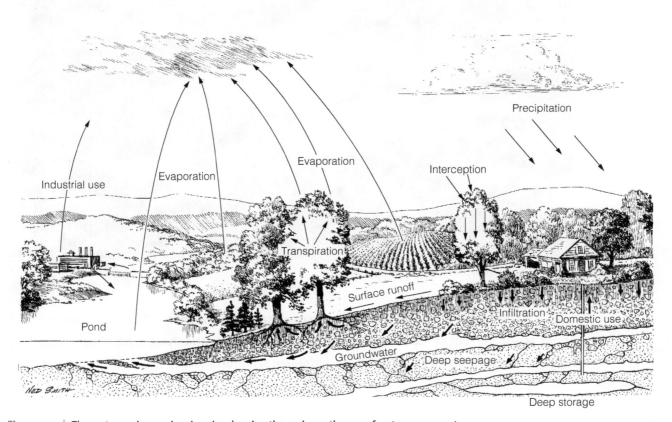

**Figure 4.1** | The water cycle on a local scale, showing the major pathways of water movement.

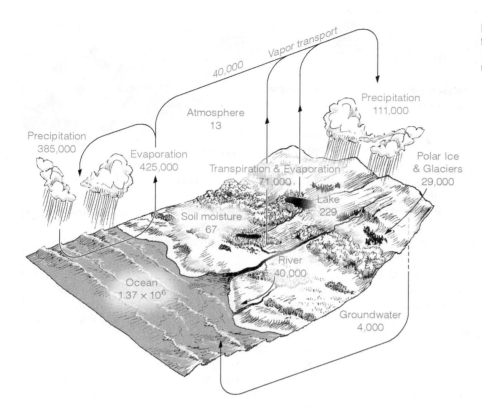

**Figure 4.2** | Global water cycle. Values for reservoirs (shown in blue) are in $10^8$ km³. Values for fluxes (shown in red) are in km³ per year.

Some water entering the soil seeps down to an impervious layer of clay or rock to collect as **groundwater** (see Figure 4.1 and see Ecological Issues: Groundwater Resources). From here, water finds its way into springs and streams. Streams coalesce into rivers as they follow the topography of the landscape. In basins and floodplains, lakes and wetlands form. Rivers eventually flow to the coast, forming the transition from freshwater to marine.

Water remaining on the surface of the ground, in the upper layers of the soil, and collected on the surface of vegetation, as well as water in the surface layers of streams, lakes, and oceans, returns to the atmosphere by evaporation. The rate of evaporation is governed by how much water vapor is in the air relative to the saturation vapor pressure (see Section 3.6). Plants cause additional water loss from the soil. Through their roots, they take in water from the soil and lose it through the leaves and other organs in a process called **transpiration.** Transpiration is the evaporation of water from internal surfaces of leaves, stems, and other living parts (see Chapter 6). The total amount of evaporating water from the surfaces of the ground and vegetation is called **evapotranspiration.**

A diagram of the global water cycle is presented in Figure 4.2, which shows the various reservoirs (bodies of water) and fluxes (exchanges between reservoirs). The total volume of water on Earth is approximately 1.4 billion cubic kilometers (km³), of which more than 97 percent resides in the oceans. Another 2 percent of the total

resides in the polar ice caps and glaciers, while the third largest active reservoir is groundwater (0.3 percent). Over the oceans, evaporation exceeds precipitation by some 40,000 km³. A significant proportion of the water evaporated from the oceans is transported by winds over the land surface in the form of water vapor, where it is deposited as precipitation. Of the 111,000 km³ of water that falls as precipitation on the land surface, only some 71,000 km³ is returned to the atmosphere as evapotranspiration. The remaining 40,000 km³ is carried as runoff by rivers, eventually returning to the oceans. This amount balances the net loss of water from the oceans to the atmosphere through evaporation (Figure 4.2).

The relatively small size of the atmospheric reservoir (only 13 km³) does not reflect its importance in the global water cycle. Note the large fluxes between the atmosphere and the oceans and land surface relative to the amount of water that resides in the atmosphere at any given time (reservoir size). The importance of the atmosphere in the global water cycle is better reflected by the turnover time of this reservoir. The turnover time is calculated by dividing the size of the reservoir by the rate of output (flux out). For example, the turnover time for the ocean is the size of the reservoir ($1.37 \times 10^6$ km³) divided by the rate of evaporation (425 km³ per year), or more than 3000 years. In contrast, the turnover time of the atmospheric reservoir is approximately 0.024 years. That is to say, the entire water content of the atmosphere is replaced on average every 9 days.

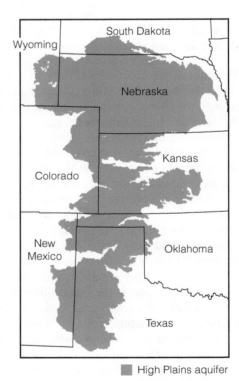

The addition of water to agricultural fields, known as the process of irrigation, is an ancient and important practice. In dry environments, irrigation is essential. However, even in regions where average precipitation is adequate for agricultural production, irrigation is often used to provide a steady supply of water to fields, making plant growth less dependent on the effects of weather. Although only 15 percent of the world's cultivated land is irrigated, it accounts for 35–40 percent of the global food harvest.

In most cases, groundwater supplies the necessary water for irrigation. Approximately 30 percent of the groundwater used for irrigation in the United States comes from a single source: the Ogallala–High Plains Aquifer (see Figure 1). An aquifer is a layer of water-bearing permeable rock, sand, or gravel capable of providing significant amounts of water. The buried sand and gravel that hold the aquifer water originated from rivers that have flowed eastward from the Rockies over the past several million years. The thickness of the aquifer, averaging 65 m, varies from more than 1000 m in Nebraska to less than 20 m in New Mexico. The water it contains dates back to the last ice age, more than 10,000 years ago.

The high permeability of the Ogallala–High Plains Aquifer enables a large volume of water to be pumped from the ground but also means that the cumulative effect of pumping at any location is that the water level is drawn down over an extensive area of the aquifer. The rate at which water is now being pumped from more than 200,000 wells in the region is as much as 50 times the rate at which water in the aquifer is being recharged. For decades, it was assumed that the aquifer's water supply was endless. Intensive pumping since the 1940s, however, has steadily lowered the water level in many areas. Withdrawals in 1990 for irrigation alone exceeded 14 billion gallons per day. During the period of drought in the western states that extended from mid-1992 to late 1996, the decline in the water level (depth) of the aquifer averaged 40 cm per year.

One consequence of the decreased water levels within the aquifer is that the costs of pumping have risen sharply, becoming prohibitively expensive in some places. Pumping has also decreased the volume of water discharged out of the aquifer into streams and springs. For example, pumping from the aquifer in Colorado decreased flow in the Arkansas River, which flows through Kansas.

In addition to the impacts on agriculture, the decline of the Ogallala–High Plains Aquifer also affects the supply of drinking water in the region. Although 95 percent of the water pumped from the aquifer is used for irrigation, upwards of 80 percent of the people in the region depend on the aquifer for drinking water. Water in some areas of the aquifer does not meet the U.S. Environmental Protection Agency's (EPA) standards for human consumption, and declining water levels reduce the quality of remaining waters as the concentrations of salts and other solutes increase. ●

1. In many areas of the Ogallala–High Plains Aquifer, there is no possibility of developing additional water sources and supplies. In these areas, what steps could possibly be taken to help conserve the existing water supplies?

2. Because the use of water in one state can influence the long-term availability of water throughout the region (other states), how would you propose the management of these water resources?

■ High Plains aquifer

**Figure 1** | The Ogallala–High Plains aquifer underlies an area of approximately 174,000 square miles that extends through eight states. This aquifer is the principle source of water in one of the major agricultural regions of the United States.

## 4.2 | Water Has Important Physical Properties

Because of the physical arrangement of its component molecules, water is a unique substance. A molecule of water consists of two atoms of hydrogen (H) joined to one atom of oxygen (O), represented by the chemical symbol $H_2O$. The H atoms are bonded to the O atoms asymmetrically, such that the two H atoms are at one end of the molecule and the O at the other (Figure 4.3a). The bonding between the two hydrogen atoms and the oxygen atom is via shared electrons (called a covalent bond), with each H atom sharing a single electron with the oxygen. The shared hydrogen atoms are closer to the oxygen atom than they are to each other. As a result, the side of the water molecule on which the H atoms are located has a positive charge, and the opposite side where the oxygen atom is located has a negative charge, thus polarizing the water molecule (termed a *polar covalent bond*) (Figure 4.3b).

Because of its polarity, each water molecule becomes weakly bonded with its neighboring molecules (Figure 4.3c). The positive (hydrogen) end of one molecule attracts the negative (oxygen) end of the other. The angle between the hydrogen atoms encourages an open tetrahedral-like arrangement of water molecules. This situation, in which hydrogen atoms act as connecting links between water molecules, is **hydrogen bonding.** The simultaneous bonding of a hydrogen atom to the oxygen atoms of two different water molecules gives rise to a lattice arrangement of molecules (Figure 4.3d). These bonds, however, are weak in comparison to the bond between the hydrogen and oxygen atoms and as a result are easily broken and reformed.

Water has a number of unique properties related to its hydrogen bonds. One property is high **specific heat;** that is, the number of calories necessary to raise 1 gram of water 1 degree Celsius. The specific heat of water is defined as a value of 1, and other substances are given a value relative to water. Water can store tremendous quantities of heat energy with a small rise in temperature. As a result, great quantities of heat must be absorbed before the temperature of natural waters, such as ponds, lakes, and seas, rises just 1°C. They warm up slowly in spring and cool off just as slowly in the fall. This behavior prevents the wide seasonal fluctuations in the temperature of aquatic habitats so characteristic of air temperatures and moderates the temperatures of local and worldwide environments (see Chapter 3). The high specific heat of water also is important in the thermal regulation of organisms. Because 75–95 percent of the weight of all living cells is water, temperature variation is also moderated relative to changes in ambient temperature.

Because of the high specific heat of water, large quantities of heat energy are required to change the state between solid (ice), liquid, and gaseous (water vapor) phases. Collectively, the energy released or absorbed in the transformation of water from one state to another is called latent heat (see Section 3.6). It takes the removal of only 1 calorie (4.184 joules) of heat energy to lower the temperature of a gram of water from 2°C to 1°C, but it requires the removal of approximately 80 times as much heat energy (80 calories per gram) to convert that same quantity of water at 1°C to ice (freezing point of 0°C). Likewise, it takes 536 calories to overcome the attraction between molecules and convert 1 g of water at 100°C into vapor, the same amount of heat needed to raise 536 g of water 1°C.

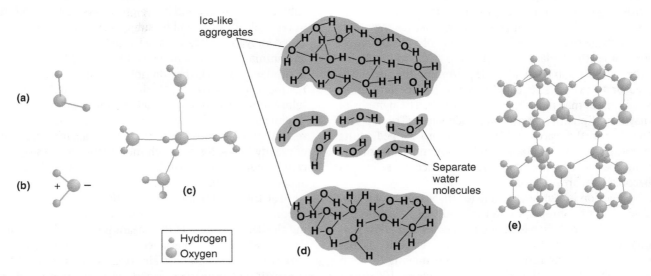

**Figure 4.3** | The structure of water. **(a)** An isolated water molecule, showing the angular arrangement of the hydrogen atoms. **(b)** Polarity of water. **(c)** Hydrogen bonds to one molecule of water in ice. **(d)** The structure of liquid water. **(e)** The open lattice structure of ice.

The nature of the lattice arrangement of molecules gives water a peculiar density–temperature relationship. Most liquids become denser as they are cooled. If cooled to their freezing temperature they become solid, and the solid phase is denser than the liquid. This is not true for water. Pure water becomes denser as it is cooled until it reaches 4°C. Cooling below this temperature results in a decrease in density. When 0°C is reached, freezing occurs and the lattice structure is complete with each oxygen atom connecting to four other oxygen atoms by means of hydrogen atoms. The result is a lattice with large open spaces, and therefore decreased density (see Figure 4.3e). Water molecules so structured occupy more space than they would in liquid form. As a result of the reduced density, ice is lighter than water and floats on it. This property is crucially important to life in aquatic environments. The presence of ice on the surface of water bodies functions to insulate the waters below, helping to keep larger bodies of water from freezing solid during the winter months.

As a result of the hydrogen bonding, water molecules tend to stick firmly to each other, resisting external forces that would break these bonds. This property is called **cohesion.** Within a body of water, these forces of attraction are the same on all sides. At the water's surface, however, there is a different set of conditions. Below the surface, molecules of water are strongly attracted to one another. Above is the much weaker attraction between water molecules and air. Therefore, molecules on the surface are drawn downward, resulting in a surface that is taut like an inflated balloon. This condition, called **surface tension,** is important in the lives of aquatic organisms.

For example, the surface of water is able to support small objects and animals, such as the water strider (Gerridae) and water spiders (*Dolomedes* spp.) that run across a pond's surface (Figure 4.4). To other small organisms, surface tension is a barrier, whether they wish to penetrate the water below or escape into the air above. For some, the surface tension is too great to break; for others, it is a trap to avoid while skimming the surface to feed or to lay eggs. If caught in the surface tension, a small insect may flounder on the surface. The nymphs of mayflies (Ephemeroptera) and caddisflies (Trichoptera) that live in the water and transform into winged adults find surface tension a handicap in their efforts to emerge from the water. Slowed down at the surface, these insects become easy prey for fish.

Cohesion is also responsible for the viscosity of water. **Viscosity** is the property of a material that measures the force necessary to separate the molecules and allow passage of an object through the liquid. Viscosity is the source of frictional resistance to objects moving through water. This frictional resistance of water is 100 times greater than that of air. The streamlined body shape of many aquatic organisms, for example most fish and ma-

Figure 4.4 | The water strider (Gerridae) is able to glide across the water surface as a result of the property of surface tension.

rine mammals, helps to reduce this frictional resistance. Replacement of water in the space left behind by the moving animal adds additional drag on the body. An animal streamlined in reverse, with a short, rounded front and a rapidly tapering body, meets the least resistance in the water. The perfect example of such streamlining is the sperm whale (*Physeter catodon*) (Figure 4.5).

The high viscosity of water relative to air is due largely to its greater density. The density of water is about 860 times greater than that of air (pure water has a density of $1000 \text{ kg/m}^3$). Although the resulting viscosity of water functions as a constraint on the mobility of aquatic organisms, it also provides a benefit. If a body is submerged in water and its weight is less than that of the water it displaces, it will be subjected to an upward force called **buoyancy.** Because most aquatic organisms (plants and animals) are close to neutral buoyancy (their density is similar to water), they do not require a significant investment in structural material such as skeletons or cellulose in order to hold themselves erect against the force of gravity. Similarly, when movement is concerned, terrestrial animals must raise their mass against the force of gravity for each step. Such movement requires significantly more energy than swimming movements do for aquatic organisms.

But the greater density of water can have profound effects on the metabolism of marine organisms inhabiting the deeper waters of the ocean. Because of its greater density, water also experiences greater changes in pressure with depth than does air. At sea level, the weight of the vertical column of air from the top of the atmosphere to the sea surface is $1 \text{ kg/cm}^2$, or 1 atmosphere (atm). In contrast, pressure increases 1 atm for each 10 m in depth.

Figure 4.5 | The body of the sperm whale (*Physeter catodon*) is streamlined in reverse, with a short, rounded front and a rapidly tapering body. This shape meets the least resistance in the water.

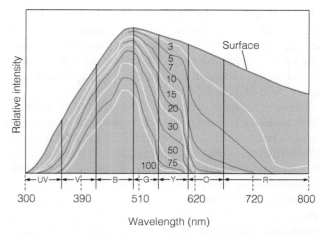

Figure 4.6 | The spectral distribution of solar energy at Earth's surface and after it has been modified by passage through varying depths, measured in meters, of pure water. Note how rapidly red wavelengths are attenuated. At approximately 10 m, red light is depleted; but at 100 m, blue wavelengths still retain nearly one-half their intensity. (Adapted from Clark 1939.)

Because the deep ocean varies from a few hundred meters down to the deep trenches at more than 10,000 m, the range of pressure at the ocean bottom is from 20 to more than 1000 atm. Recent research has shown that both proteins and biological membranes are strongly affected by pressure and must be modified to work in animals living in the deep ocean.

## 4.3 | Light Varies with Depth in Aquatic Environments

When light strikes the surface of the water, a certain amount is reflected back to the atmosphere. The amount of light reflected from the surface depends on the angle at which the light strikes the surface. The lower the angle, the larger the amount of light that will be reflected. As a result, the amount of light that is reflected from the water surface will vary both diurnally and seasonally as one moves from the Equator to the poles (see Section 3.2 for a complete discussion).

The amount of light that enters the water surface is subjected to further reduction by two additional processes. First, suspended particles, both alive and dead, intercept the light and either absorb or scatter it. The scattering of light increases its path of travel through the water and results in further attenuation. Second, water itself absorbs light (Figure 4.6). Even in perfectly clean, clear water, only about 40 percent of shortwave radiation reaches a depth of 1 meter. Moreover, water absorbs some wavelengths more than others. First to be absorbed are visible red light and infrared radiation in wavelengths greater than 750 nm. This absorption reduces solar energy by one-half. Next, in clear water yellow disappears, followed by green and violet, leaving only blue wavelengths to penetrate deeper water. A fraction of blue light is lost with increasing depth. In the clearest of seawater, only about 10 percent of blue light reaches to more than 100 m in depth.

These changes in the quantity and quality of light have important implications to life in aquatic environments, both directly by influencing the quantity and distribution of productivity (see Section 20.4 and Chapter 24) and indirectly by influencing the vertical profile of temperature with water depth. The lack of light in the deeper waters of the oceans has resulted in a number of adaptations. Organisms of the deeper ocean, between 200 and 1000 m, are typically silvery gray or deep black, and organisms living in even deeper waters (below 1000 m) often lack pigment. Another adaptation is large eyes, giving them maximum light-gathering ability, and many organisms have adapted organs with the ability to produce light through chemical reactions, referred to as bioluminescence (see Section 24.10).

## 4.4 | Temperature Varies with Water Depth

As we discussed in Chapter 3 (Section 3.1), surface temperatures reflect the balance of incoming and outgoing radiation. The exponential decline in solar radiation with water depth (as shown by the vertical light profile in Figure 4.6) also gives rise to a corresponding decline in water temperature. The region of the vertical depth profile where the most rapid decline in temperature occurs is called the **thermocline.** The depth of the thermocline will depend on the input of solar radiation and temperature of the surface water. Below the thermocline, water temperatures continue to fall with depth but at a much slower rate. The result is a distinct pattern of temperature zonation with depth. The thermocline demarcates an upper layer of warm, lighter (less dense) water called the **epilimnion** and a deeper layer of cold, denser water called the **hypolimnion** (Figure 4.7; also see Section 21.8 and Figure 21.18).

Just as seasonal variation in the input of solar radiation to Earth's surface results in seasonal changes in surface temperatures (see Section 3.2), likewise seasonal changes in the input of solar radiation to the water surface give rise to seasonal changes in the vertical profile of temperature in aquatic environments. The relatively constant input of solar radiation to the water surface throughout the year results in the thermocline being a permanent feature of tropical waters. In the waters of the temperate zone, a distinct thermocline exists during the summer months. By fall, conditions begin to change, and a turnabout takes place. Air temperatures and sunlight decrease, and the surface water starts to cool. As it does, the water becomes denser and sinks, displacing the warmer water below to the surface, where it cools in turn. This cooling continues until the temperature is uniform throughout the basin (see Figure 4.7). Now, pond and lake water circulate throughout the basin. This process of vertical circulation, called the fall turnover, is an important component of nutrient dy-

namics in open-water ecosystems (see Chapter 21). Stirred by wind, the process of vertical mixing may last until ice forms.

Then comes winter, and as the surface water cools to below 4°C, it becomes lighter again and remains on the surface. (Remember, water becomes lighter above and below 4°C; see Section 4.2 for discussion). If the winter is cold enough, surface water freezes; otherwise, it remains close to 0°C. Now the warmest place in the pond or lake is on the bottom. With the spring breakup of ice and the heating of surface water, the water again becomes stratified.

Not all bodies of water experience such seasonal changes in stratification, and you should not consider this phenomenon as characteristic of all deep bodies of water. In shallow lakes and ponds, temporary stratification of short duration may occur; in others, stratification may exist, but the depth is not sufficient to develop a distinct thermocline. In some very deep lakes and the oceans, the thermocline simply descends during periods of turnover and does not disappear at all. In such bodies of water, the bottom water never becomes mixed with the top layer. However, some form of thermal stratification occurs in all open bodies of water.

The temperature of a flowing body of water (stream or river) on the other hand is variable (Figure 4.8). Small, shallow streams tend to follow, but lag behind, air temperatures. They warm and cool with the seasons but rarely fall below freezing in winter. Streams with large areas exposed to sunlight are warmer than those shaded by trees, shrubs, and high banks. That fact is ecologically important because temperature affects the stream community, influencing the presence or absence of cool-water and warm-water organisms. For example, the dominant predatory fish shift from cooler water, higher oxygen demanding species such as trout and small-mouthed bass to warmer water, lower oxygen demanding species such as suckers and catfish (see Figure 24.13).

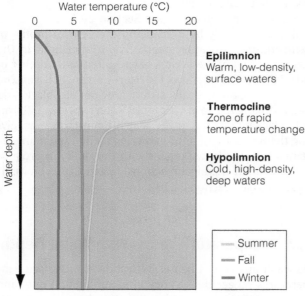

**Figure 4.7** | Temperature profile with water depth for an open body of water such as a lake or pond. The vertical profile can be divided into three distinct zones: epilimnion, thermocline, and hypolimnion. As the air temperatures decline during the fall months, the surface water cools and sinks. At this time, the temperature is uniform with depth. With the onset of winter, surface water further cools and ice may form on the surface. With the arrival of spring, the process reverses and the thermocline once again forms.

## 4.5 | Water Functions as a Solvent

As you stir a spoon of sugar into a glass of water, it dissolves, forming a homogeneous or uniform mixture. A liquid that is a homogeneous mixture of two or more substances is called a **solution.** The dissolving agent of a solution is the **solvent,** and the substance that is dissolved is referred to as the **solute.** A solution in which water is the solvent is called an **aqueous solution.**

Water is an excellent solvent with the ability to dissolve more substances than any other liquid. It is this extraordinary ability to function as a solvent that makes water such a biologically crucial substance. It provides a fluid in which molecules of nutrients and waste products can be dissolved and transported, helps to regulate tem-

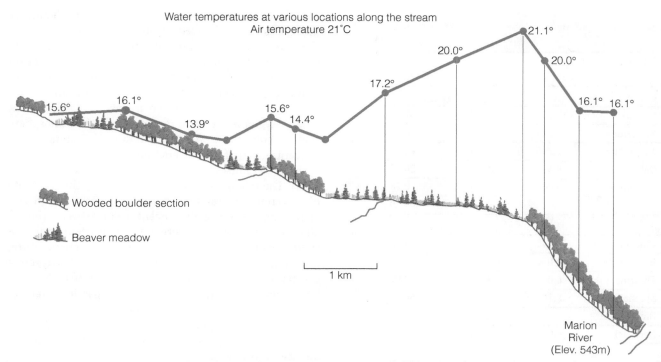

Water temperatures at various locations along the stream
Air temperature 21°C

21.1°
20.0°
20.0°
17.2°
16.1°  16.1°
15.6°    16.1°
13.9°
15.6°  14.4°

Wooded boulder section

Beaver meadow

1 km

Marion
River
(Elev. 543m)

**Figure 4.8** | Profile of Bear Brook (Adirondack Mountains, New York) and a graph of its water temperatures. Note that water temperatures rise as the stream moves through the open beaver meadows, once again declining as it flows into the shaded cover of the wooded forest.

perature, and preserves chemical equilibrium within living cells.

The solvent ability of water is due largely to the bonding discussed in Section 4.2. As a result of the H atom being bonded to the O atoms asymmetrically (see Figure 4.3), one side of every water molecule has a permanent positive charge, and the other side has a permanent negative charge; such a situation is called a permanent dipole (dipole referring to oppositely charged poles). Because opposite charges attract, in addition to water molecules being strongly attracted to each other, they also attract other molecules carrying a charge.

Compounds that consist of electrically charged atoms or groups of atoms are called **ions.** Sodium chloride (table salt), for example, is composed of positively charged sodium ions ($Na^+$) and negatively charged chloride ions ($Cl^-$) arranged in a crystal lattice. When placed in water, the attractions between negative (oxygen atom) and positive (hydrogen atoms) charges on the water molecule (see Figure 4.3) and those of the sodium and chloride atoms are greater than the forces (ionic bonds) that hold the salt crystals together. The result is that the salt crystals readily dissociate into their component ions when placed into contact with water; that is, they dissolve.

The solvent properties of water are responsible for most of the minerals (elements and inorganic compounds) that are found in aquatic environments. When

water condenses to form clouds it is nearly pure, with the exception of some dissolved atmospheric gases. As water falls to the surface as precipitation, it acquires additional substances from particulates and dust particles suspended in the atmosphere. Water that falls on land flows over the surface and percolates into the soil, obtaining more solutes. Surface waters, such as streams and rivers, pick up more solvents from the substances through and over which they flow. The waters of most rivers and lakes contain 0.01–0.02 percent dissolved minerals. The relative concentrations of minerals in these waters reflect the substrates over which they flow. For example, waters that flow through areas where the underlying rocks consist largely of limestone (composed primarily of calcium carbonate; $CaCO_3$) will have high concentrations of calcium ($Ca^{2+}$) and bicarbonate ($HCO_3^-$).

In contrast to freshwaters, the oceans have a much higher concentration of solutes. In effect, the oceans function as a large still. The flow of freshwaters into the oceans continuously adds to the solute content of the waters, as pure water evaporates from the surface to the atmosphere. The concentration of solutes, however, cannot continue to increase indefinitely. When the concentration of specific elements reaches the limit set by the maximum solubility of the compounds they form (grams per liter), the excess amounts will precipitate and be deposited as sediments. Calcium, for example, readily forms

| Table 4.1 | Composition of Seawater of 35 practical salinity units (psu) | | |
|---|---|---|---|
| Elements | g/kg | Milli-moles/kg | Milli-equivalents/kg |
| *Cations* | | | |
| Sodium | 10.752 | 467.56 | 467.56 |
| Potassium | 0.395 | 10.10 | 10.10 |
| Magnesium | 1.295 | 53.25 | 106.50 |
| Calcium | 0.416 | 10.38 | 20.76 |
| Strontium | 0.008 | 0.09 | 0.18 |
| | | | 605.10 |
| *Anions* | | | |
| Chlorine | 19.345 | 545.59 | 545.59 |
| Bromine | 0.066 | 0.83 | 0.83 |
| Fluorine | 0.0013 | 0.07 | 0.07 |
| Sulphate | 2.701 | 28.12 | 56.23 |
| Bicarbonate | 0.145 | 2.38 | — |
| Boric acid | 0.027 | 0.44 | — |
| | | | 602.72 |

calcium carbonate ($CaCO_3$) in the waters of the oceans. The maximum solubility of calcium carbonate, however, is only 0.014 grams per liter of water, a concentration that was reached early in the history of the oceans. As a result, calcium ions continuously precipitate out of solution and are deposited as limestone sediments on the ocean bottom.

In contrast, the solubility of sodium chloride is very high (360 grams per liter). In fact, these two elements, sodium and chlorine, make up some 86 percent of sea salt. These, along with other major elements such as sulfur, magnesium, potassium, and calcium, whose relative proportions vary little, compose 99 percent of sea salts (Table 4.1). Determination of the most abundant element, chlorine, is used as an index of salinity. Salinity is expressed in **practical salinity units (PSU)** (represented as ‰), measured as grams of chlorine per kilogram of water. The salinity of the open sea is fairly constant, averaging about 35‰. In contrast, the salinity of freshwater ranges from 0.065 to 0.30‰. However, over geologic timescales (hundreds of millions of years), the salinity of the oceans has increased and continues to do so.

## 4.6 | Oxygen Diffuses from the Atmosphere to the Surface Waters

The role of water as a solvent is not limited to the dissolution of solids. The surface of a body of water defines a boundary with the atmosphere. It is across this boundary that gases are exchanged through the process of diffusion. **Diffusion** is the general tendency of molecules to move from a region of high concentration to one of lower concentration (see Quantifying Ecology 4.1: Diffusion and Osmosis). It is the process of diffusion that results in a net transfer of two metabolically important gases, oxygen and carbon dioxide, from the atmosphere (higher concentration) into the surface waters (lower concentration) of aquatic environments.

Oxygen diffuses from the atmosphere into the surface water. The rate of diffusion is controlled by the solubility of oxygen in water and the steepness of the diffusion gradient (the difference in concentration between the air and the surface waters where diffusion is occurring). The solubility of gases in water is a function of temperature, pressure, and salinity. The saturation value of oxygen is greater for cold water than warm water because the solubility (ability to stay in solution) of a gas in water decreases as the temperature rises. However, solubility increases as atmospheric pressure increases and it decreases as salinity increases, which is of little consequence in freshwater.

Once in the surface water, the process of diffusion continues, and oxygen diffuses from the surface to the waters below (lower concentration). The greater density and viscosity of water relative to air function to limit the rate at which gases diffuse through water. The diffusion of gases occurs some 10,000 times slower in water than in air. In addition to the process of diffusion, oxygen absorbed by surface water is mixed with deeper water by turbulence and internal currents. In shallow, rapidly flowing water and in wind-driven sprays, oxygen may reach and maintain saturation and even supersaturated levels because of the increase of absorptive surfaces at the air–water interface. Oxygen is lost from the water as temperatures rise, decreasing solubility, and through the uptake of oxygen by aquatic life.

During the summer, oxygen, like temperature (see Section 4.4), may become stratified in lakes and ponds. The amount of oxygen usually is greatest near the surface, where an interchange between water and atmosphere, further stimulated by the stirring action of the wind, takes place (Figure 4.9). In addition to oxygen entering the water by diffusion from the atmosphere, it is also a product of photosynthesis, which is largely restricted to the surface waters due to the limitations of available light (see Figure 4.7 and Chapter 6). The quantity of oxygen decreases with depth because of the oxygen demand by decomposer organisms living in the bottom sediments (Chapter 21). During spring and fall turnover, when water recirculates through the lake, oxygen becomes replenished in deep water. In winter, the reduction of oxygen in unfrozen water is slight, because the demand for oxygen by organisms is reduced by the cold,

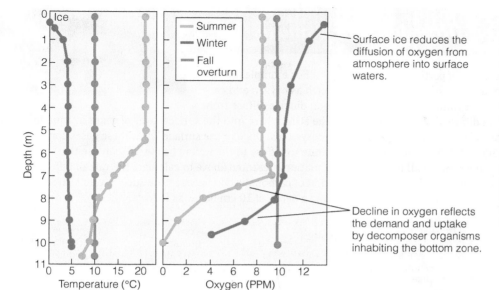

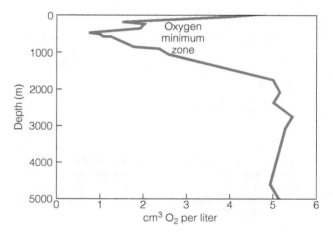

Figure 4.9 | Oxygen stratification in Mirror Lake, New Hampshire, in winter, summer, and late fall. The late fall turnover results in both a uniform temperature and a uniform distribution of oxygen throughout the lake basin. In summer, a pronounced stratification of both temperature and oxygen exists. Oxygen declines sharply in the thermocline and is nonexistent on the bottom because of the uptake by decomposer organisms taking place in the sediments. In winter, oxygen is also stratified, but it is present at a low concentration in deep water. (Adapted from Likens 1985.)

and the solubility of oxygen is greater at low temperatures. Under ice, however, oxygen depletion may be serious because of the lack of diffusion from the atmosphere to the surface waters.

As with ponds and lakes, oxygen is not distributed uniformly within the depths of the oceans (Figure 4.10). A typical oceanic oxygen profile shows a maximum amount in the upper 10–20 m, where photosynthetic activity and diffusion from the atmosphere often lead to saturation. With increasing depth, the oxygen content declines. In the open waters of the ocean, concentrations reach a minimum value somewhere between 500 and 1000 m, a region referred to as the *oxygen minimum zone*. Unlike lakes and ponds, where the seasonal breakdown of the thermocline and resulting mixing of surface and deep waters result in a dynamic gradient of temperature and oxygen content, the limited depth of surface mixing in the deep oceans maintains the vertical gradient of oxygen availability year round.

The availability of oxygen in aquatic environments characterized by flowing water is quite different. The constant churning and swirling of stream water over riffles and falls gives greater contact with the atmosphere; therefore, the oxygen content of the water is high, often near saturation for the prevailing temperature. Only in deep holes or in polluted waters does dissolved oxygen show any significant decline.

Even under ideal conditions, however, the solubility of gases in water is not great. For example, rarely is oxygen limited in terrestrial environments. In aquatic environments, however, the supply of oxygen, even at saturation levels, is meager and problematic. Compared with its concentration of 0.21 liters per liter in the atmosphere (21% by volume), the solubility of oxygen in

Figure 4.10 | Vertical profile of oxygen with depth in the tropical Atlantic Ocean. The oxygen content of the waters decline to a depth known as the oxygen minimum zone. The oxygen increase below this zone is thought to be the result of the influx of cold, oxygen-rich waters that originally sank in the polar waters (see Section 4.8).

water reaches a maximum of 0.01 liters per liter (1%) in freshwater at a temperature of 0°C. As a result, the concentration of oxygen in aquatic environments often limits respiration and metabolic activity (see Section 6.1).

## 4.7 | Acidity Has a Widespread Influence on Aquatic Environments

The solubility of carbon dioxide is somewhat different from that of oxygen, as it reacts chemically with water. Water has a considerable capacity to absorb carbon

**D**iffusion is the net passive movement of particles (atoms, ions, or molecules) from a region of higher concentration to a region of lower concentration (Figure 1). In other words, any substance will diffuse down its concentration gradient. A substance will continue to do this until equilibrium is achieved (Figure 1c). Equilibrium occurs when the concentration is the same in all regions.

The flux (movement of the substance) is described by Fick's law:

Flux or movement of substance from one point to another in time. Units are moles per unit area per unit time. For example: $mol/cm^2/s$.

Diffusion coefficient. A constant that describes how quickly a substance diffuses through the medium. Units are area per unit time: $cm^2/s$.

$$J = -D \times \Delta C/\Delta z$$

Concentration gradient. Refers to the change in concentration (quantity per volume: $moles/cm^3$) from the region of higher concentration ($C_1$) to the region of lower concentration ($C_2$). $\Delta C = C_1 - C_2$

Distance that the substance is diffusing ($z_2 - z_1$). Units are length: cm.

For example, gases such as oxygen and carbon dioxide diffuse from the atmosphere into the surface layer of water in aquatic ecosystems. Once in the surface layer, these gases continue to diffuse to the waters below. We can use the equation presented above to calculate the rate of diffusion of carbon dioxide between the surface water layer and a depth of 10 cm below as follows:

Diffusion rate ($mol/cm^2/s$)

$CO_2$ concentration in surface water ($mol/cm^3$)

$CO_2$ concentration at 10 cm depth ($mol/cm^3$)

$$J = -(1.6 \times 10^{-5}) \times (5.6 \times 10^{-5} - 2.9 \times 10^{-5})/10 = 4.32 \times 10^{-11}$$

Diffusion coefficient for $CO_2$ ($cm^2/s$)

Distance (cm)

In addition to being an important process in the movement of substances in and between the atmosphere and aquatic environments (also the movement of substances in soil solution, see Chapter 5), diffusion also

**Figure 1** | **Substances diffuse from regions of higher concentration to regions of lower concentration. Carbon dioxide will diffuse from the air into the surface water (a-b) until the concentration in the surface water is equal to that of the air above—equilibrium achieved (c).**

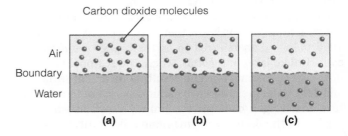

Carbon dioxide molecules

Air

Boundary

Water

(a)      (b)      (c)

dioxide, and it is therefore abundant in both freshwater and saltwater. Upon diffusion into the surface, carbon dioxide reacts with water to produce carbonic acid ($H_2CO_3$):

$$CO_2 + H_2O \longleftrightarrow H_2CO_3$$

Carbonic acid further dissociates into a hydrogen ion and a bicarbonate ion:

$$H_2CO_3 \longleftrightarrow HCO_3^- + H^+$$

Bicarbonate may further dissociate into another hydrogen ion and a carbonate ion:

$$HCO_3^- \longleftrightarrow H^+ + CO_3^{2-}$$

The carbon dioxide–carbonic acid–bicarbonate system is a complex chemical system that tends to stay in equilibrium. (Note that the arrows on the above equations go in both directions.) Therefore, if $CO_2$ is removed from the water, the equilibrium is disturbed and the above equations will shift to the left, with carbonic acid and bicarbonate producing more $CO_2$ until a new equilibrium is produced.

The above chemical reactions result in the production and absorption of free hydrogen ions ($H^+$). The abundance of hydrogen ions in solution is a measure of

occurs in biological processes. Much of the transport across cell membranes occurs by diffusion (see Chapters 6 and 7). When a substance is more concentrated on one side of the membrane than on the other, there is a tendency for the substance to diffuse across the membrane down its concentration gradient (assuming that the membrane is permeable to that substance). However, membranes are selectively permeable and therefore affect the rates of diffusion of various substances.

The diffusion of water across a selectively permeable membrane is a special case of passive transport called **osmosis**. Suppose we enclose a solute such as salt (sodium chloride) in high concentration (and water in low concentration) in a funnel sealed with a semipermeable membrane and lower it into a beaker of distilled water (Figure 2). The membrane is permeable to water but not to salt. The volume of the fluid within the funnel will increase and move up the tube as water moves across the membrane into the solution by a process called osmosis. Water continues to move across the membrane until the osmotic pressure of the solute—decreasing as the solute becomes more diluted by the pure water—is equal to the downward physical pressure exterted by the column of water in the funnel.

The tendency of solutes in a solution to cause water molecules to move from areas of high to low concentration is called osmotic potential. The osmotic potential of a solution depends on its concentration. The higher the concentration of solutes, the lower its osmotic potential and the greater its tendency to gain water.

Osmosis is of great importance in biological processes. The transport of water and other molecules across biological membranes is essential to many processes in living organisms. Osmosis and osmotic potential are involved in maintaining water balance in

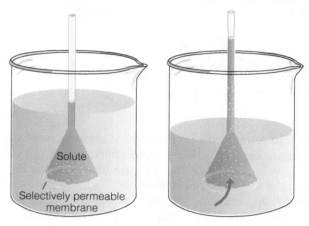

**Figure 2**

all living things, from single-cell protozoa to vertebrates. Osmosis plays a particularly important role in freshwater and marine organisms whose internal solute concentrations differ from the water around them. ●

1. How does the influence of osmosis differ for fish that live in freshwater and saltwater environments? Assume that the solute (salt) concentration of the fish tissues is intermediate between that of freshwater and saltwater.

2. In the example of carbon dioxide diffusion in water presented above, how would doubling the concentration of carbon dioxide in the surface water change the rate of diffusion (to the waters at 10 cm depth)?

**acidity.** The greater the number of $H^+$ ions, the more acidic the solution will be. **Alkaline** solutions are those that have a large number of $OH^-$ (hydroxyl ions) and few $H^+$ ions. The measurement of acidity and alkalinity is pH, calculated as the negative logarithm (base 10) of the concentration of hydrogen ions in solution. In pure water, a small fraction of molecules dissociates into ions: $H_2O \rightarrow H^+ + OH^-$, and the ratio of $H^+$ ions to $OH^-$ ions is 1:1. Because both occur in a concentration of $10^{-7}$ moles per liter, a neutral solution has a pH of 7 $[-\log(10^{-7}) = 7]$. A solution departs from neutral when one ion increases and the other decreases. Custom-

arily, we use the negative logarithm of the hydrogen ion to describe a solution as an acid or a base. Thus, a gain of hydrogen ions to $10^{-6}$ moles per liter means a decrease of $OH^-$ ions to $10^{-8}$ moles per liter, and the pH of the solution is 6. The negative logarithmic pH scale goes from 1 to 14. A pH greater than 7 denotes an alkaline solution (greater $OH^-$ concentration) and a pH of less than 7 an acidic solution (greater $H^+$ concentration).

Although pure water is neutral in pH, because the dissociation of the water molecule produces equal numbers of $H^+$ and $OH^-$ ions, the presence of $CO_2$ in the water will alter this relationship. The above chemical

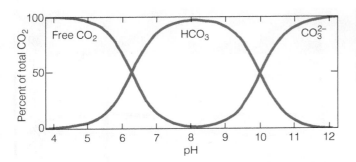

Figure 4.11 | Theoretical percentages of $CO_2$ in each of the three forms of water in relation to pH. At low values of pH (acidic conditions), the majority of $CO_2$ is in its free form. At intermediate values (neutral conditions) bicarbonate dominates, whereas under alkaline conditions most of the $CO_2$ is in the form of carbonate ions.

reactions result in the production and absorption of free hydrogen ions ($H^+$). Because the abundance of hydrogen ions in solution is the measure of acidity, the dynamics of the carbon dioxide–carbonic acid–bicarbonate system have a direct influence on the pH of aquatic ecosystems. In general, the carbon dioxide–carbonic acid–bicarbonate system functions as a buffer to keep the pH of water within a narrow range. It does this by absorbing hydrogen ions in the water when they are in excess (producing carbonic acid and bicarbonates) and producing them when they are in short supply (producing carbonate and bicarbonate ions). At neutrality (pH 7), most of the $CO_2$ is present as $HCO_3^-$ (Figure 4.11). At a high pH, more $CO_2$ is present as $CO_3^{2-}$ than at a low pH, where more $CO_2$ occurs in the free condition. Addition or removal of $CO_2$ affects pH, and a change in pH affects $CO_2$.

The pH of natural waters ranges between the extremes of 2 to 12. Waters draining from watersheds dominated geologically by limestone will have a much higher pH and be well buffered compared with waters from watersheds dominated by acid sandstone and granite. The presence of the strongly alkaline ions sodium, potassium, and calcium in ocean waters results in seawater being slightly alkaline, usually ranging from 7.5 to 8.4.

The pH of aquatic environments is a condition that can exert a powerful influence on the distribution and abundance of organisms. Increased acidity can affect organisms both directly, through its influence on physiological processes, and indirectly, by influencing the concentrations of toxic heavy metals. Tolerance limits for pH vary among plant and animal species, but most organisms are not able to survive and reproduce at a pH below about 4.5. A major contributing factor to the inability of aquatic organisms to tolerate low pH conditions is the high concentrations of aluminum found in acidic waters. Aluminum is highly toxic to many species of aquatic life and thus will lead to a general decline in aquatic populations.

Aluminum is insoluble when the pH is neutral or basic. Insoluble aluminum is present in very high concentrations in rocks, soils, and river and lake sediments. Under normal pH conditions, the aluminum concentrations of lake water are very low; however, as the pH drops

and becomes more acidic, aluminum begins to dissolve, raising the concentration in solution.

## 4.8 | Water Movements Shape Freshwater and Marine Environments

The movement of water, currents in streams and waves in an open body of water or breaking on a shore, determines the nature of many aquatic environments. The velocity of a current molds the character and the structure of a stream. The shape and steepness of the stream channel; its width, depth, and roughness of the bottom; and the intensity of rainfall and rapidity of snowmelt all affect velocity. Fast streams are those whose velocity of flow is 50 cm per second or higher (see Quantifying Ecology 24.1: Streamflow). At this velocity, the current will remove all particles less than 5 mm in diameter and will leave behind a stony bottom. High water volume increases the velocity; it moves bottom stones and rubble, scours the streambed, and cuts new banks and channels. As the gradient decreases and the width, depth, and volume of water increase, silt and decaying organic matter accumulate on the bottom. Thus, the character of a stream changes from fast water to slow (Figures 4.12a and 4.12b).

Wind generates waves on large lakes and on the open sea (Figure 4.13). The frictional drag of the wind on the surface of smooth water causes it to ripple. As the wind continues to blow, it applies more pressure to the steep side of the ripple, and wave size begins to grow. As the wind becomes stronger, short, choppy waves of all sizes appear; and as they absorb more energy, they continue to grow. When the waves reach a point at which the energy supplied by the wind is equal to the energy lost by the breaking waves, they become whitecaps. Up to a certain point, the stronger the wind, the higher the waves.

The waves that break on a beach are not composed of water driven in from distant seas. Each particle of water remains largely in the same place and follows an elliptical orbit with the passage of the wave form. As a wave moves forward, it loses energy to the waves behind and disappears, its place taken by another. The swells that break on a beach are distant descendants of waves generated far out at sea.

(a)

(b)

Figure 4.12 | **(a)** A fast mountain stream. The elevation gradient is steep, and fast-flowing water scours the stream bottom, leaving largely bedrock material. **(b)** In contrast, a slow-flowing stream meanders through a growth of willows. The relatively flat topography reduces the flow rate and allows for the buildup of finer sediments on the stream bottom. These two streams represent very different environmental conditions and subsequently support very different forms of aquatic life (see Chapter 24).

Figure 4.13 | Waves breaking on a rocky shore.

As the waves approach land, they advance into increasingly shallow water. The height of each wave rises until the wave front grows too steep and topples over. As the waves break on shore, they dissipate their energy, pounding rocky shores or tearing away sandy beaches in one location and building up new beaches elsewhere.

In Chapter 3, we discussed the patterns of ocean currents, influenced by the direction of the prevailing winds and the Coriolis effect (see Section 3.5). However, movement of the deep waters of the oceans is quite different from that of the surface currents. Because the deep waters are isolated from the wind, their motion cannot be dependent on it. Movement of deep waters does, however, result from changes occurring at the surface. As discussed above, seawater increases in density as a result of decreasing temperature and increasing salinity. When seawater increases in density, it sinks. As the warm, highly saline surface currents of the tropical waters move north and southward, they cool (see map of surface currents in Figure 3.15). As these waters cool, they increase in density and sink. Because these cold, dense waters originated at the surface, they contain high concentrations of oxygen. As these waters sink, they begin the return trip to the tropics, forming the deep-water currents. When these deep-water currents meet in the equatorial waters of the ocean, they form a region of **upwelling** where the deep waters move up to the surface, closing the pattern of ocean circulation (Figure 4.14a).

In coastal regions, winds blowing parallel to the coast cause surface waters to be blown offshore. Water moving upward from the deep replaces this surface water, creating a pattern of coastal upwelling (Figure 4.14b).

## 4.9 | Tides Dominate the Marine Coastal Environment

Tides profoundly influence the rhythm of life on ocean shores. Tides come about from the gravitational pulls of the Sun and the Moon. Each causes two bulges in the waters of the oceans. The two caused by the Moon occur at the same time on opposite sides of Earth on an imaginary line extending from the Moon through the center of

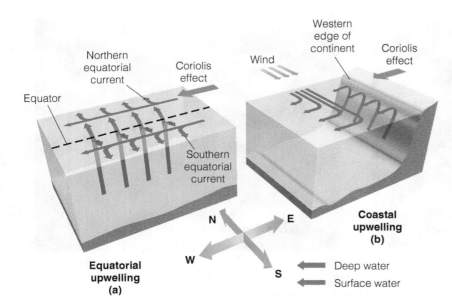

Figure 4.14 | **(a)** Along the Equator, the Coriolis effect acts to pull the westward-flowing currents to the north and south (solid arrows), resulting in an upwelling of deeper cold waters to the surface. **(b)** Along the western margins of the continents, the Coriolis effect causes the surface waters to move offshore (solid arrows). The movement of the surface waters offshore results in an upwelling of deeper, colder waters to the surface. Example shown is for the Northern Hemisphere.

Earth (Figure 4.15). The tidal bulge on the Moon side is due to gravitational attraction; the bulge on the opposite side occurs because the gravitational force there is less than at the center of Earth. As Earth rotates eastward on its axis, the tides advance westward. Thus, Earth will in the course of one daily rotation pass through two of the lunar tidal bulges, or high tides, and two of the lows, or low tides, at right angles (90° longitude difference) to the high tides.

The Sun also causes two tides on opposite sides of Earth, and these tides have a relation to the Sun like that of the lunar tides to the Moon. Because the gravitational pull of the Sun is less than that of the Moon, solar tides are partially masked by lunar tides except for two times during the month: when the Moon is full and when it is new. At these times, Earth, Moon, and Sun are nearly in line, and the gravitational pulls of the Sun and the Moon are additive. This combination causes the high tides of those periods to be exceptionally large, with maximum rise and fall. These are the fortnightly spring tides, a name derived from the Saxon *sprungen*, which refers to the brimming fullness and active movement of the water. When the Moon is at either quarter, its pull is at right angles to the pull of the Sun, and the two forces interfere with each other. At this time, the differences between high and low tides are exceptionally small. These are the neap tides, from an old Scandinavian word meaning "barely enough."

Tides are not entirely regular, nor are they the same all over Earth. They vary from day to day in the same place, following the waxing and waning of the Moon. They may act differently in several localities within the same general area. In the Atlantic, semidaily tides are the rule. In the Gulf of Mexico and the Aleutians of Alaska, the alternate highs and lows more or less cancel each other, and flood and ebb follow one another at about

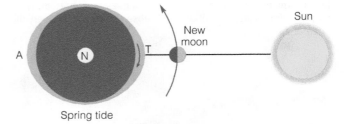

Spring tide

Figure 4.15 | Tides result from the gravitational pull of the Moon on Earth. Centrifugal force applied to a kilogram of mass is 3.38 mg. This centrifugal force on a rotating Earth is balanced by gravitational force, except at those (moving) points on Earth's surface that come into direct line with the moon. Thus the centrifugal force at point N, the center of the rotating Earth, is 3.38 mg. Point T on Earth is in direct line with the Moon. At this point the gravitational force of the Moon is 3.49 mg, a difference of 0.11 mg. Because the Moon's gravitational force is greater than the centrifugal force at T, the force is directed away from the Earth and causes a tidal bulge. At point A on the opposite side of the Earth from T, the Moon's gravitational force is 3.27 mg, 0.11 mg less than the centrifugal force at N. This difference causes a tidal bulge on the opposite side of Earth.

24-hour intervals to produce one daily tide. Mixed tides in which successive or low tides are of significantly different heights through the cycle are common in the Pacific and Indian oceans. These tides are combinations of daily and semidaily tides in which one partially cancels out the other.

Local tides around the world are inconsistent for many reasons. These reasons include variations in the gravitational pull of the Moon and the Sun due to the elliptical orbit of Earth, the angle of the Moon in relation to the axis of Earth, onshore and offshore winds, the depth of water, the contour of the shore, and wave action.

The area lying between the water lines of high and low tide, referred to as the **intertidal zone,** is an environment of extremes. The intertidal zone undergoes dramatic shifts in environmental conditions with the daily patterns of inundation and exposure. As the tide recedes, the uppermost layers of life are exposed to air, wide temperature fluctuations, intense solar radiation, and desiccation for a considerable period, whereas the lowest fringes on the tidal zone may be exposed only briefly before the high tide submerges them again. Temperatures on tidal flats may rise to 38°C when exposed to direct sunlight and drop to 10°C within a few hours when the flats are covered by water.

Organisms living within the sand and mud do not experience the same violent fluctuations in temperature as those on rocky shores. Although the surface temperature of the sand at midday may be 10°C or more higher than the returning seawater, the temperature a few centimeters below the surface of the sand remains almost constant throughout the year.

## 4.10 | The Transition Zone Between Freshwater and Saltwater Environments Presents Unique Constraints

Water from streams and rivers eventually drains into the sea. The place where this freshwater joins and mixes with the saltwater is called an estuary (see Chapter 24). Temperatures in estuaries fluctuate considerably, both daily and seasonally. Sun and inflowing and tidal currents heat the water. High tide on the mudflats may heat or cool the water, depending on the season. The upper layer of estuarine water may be cooler in winter and warmer in summer than the bottom, a condition that, as in a lake, will cause spring and autumn turnovers (see Section 4.4).

In the estuarine environment, where freshwater meets the sea, the interaction of inflowing freshwater and tidal saltwater influences its salinity of the estuarine environment. Salinity varies vertically and horizontally, often within one tidal cycle (Figure 4.16). Salinity may be the same from top to bottom or it may be completely stratified, with a layer of freshwater on top and a layer of dense, salty water on the bottom. Salinity is homogeneous when currents are strong enough to mix the water from top to bottom. The salinity in some estuaries is homogeneous at low tide, but at high tide a surface wedge of seawater moves upstream more rapidly than the bottom water. Salinity is then unstable, and density is inverted. The seawater on the surface tends to sink as lighter freshwater rises, and mixing takes place from the surface to the bottom. This phenomenon is known as **tidal overmixing.** Strong winds, too, tend to mix saltwater with freshwater in some estuaries; but when the winds are still, the river water flows seaward on a shallow surface over an upstream movement of seawater, more gradually mixing with the salt.

Horizontally, the least saline waters are at the river mouth and the most saline at the sea (see Figure 4.16). Incoming and outgoing currents deflect this configuration. In all estuaries of the Northern Hemisphere, outward-flowing freshwater and inward-flowing seawater are deflected to the right (relative to the axis of water flow from the river to ocean) because of Earth's rotation. As a result, salinity is higher on the left side; the concentration of metallic ions carried by rivers varies from drainage to drainage; and the salinity and chemistry of estuaries differ. The portion of dissolved salts in the estuarine waters remains about the same as that of seawater, but the concentration varies in a gradient from freshwater to sea.

To survive in estuaries, aquatic organisms must have evolved physiological or behavioral adaptations to changes in salinity. Many oceanic species of fish are able to move inward during periods when the flow of freshwater from rivers is low and the salinity of estuaries increases. Conversely, freshwater fish move into the estuarine environment during periods of flood when salinity levels drop. Due to the stressful conditions that organisms face in the mixed zones of estuaries, there is often a relatively low diversity of organisms despite the high productivity found in these environments (see Chapter 24).

**Figure 4.16 |** Vertical and horizontal stratification of salinity (‰; practical salinity units, see Section 4.5) from the river mouth to the estuary at both high tide (brown lines) and low tide (blue lines). At high tide, the incoming seawater increases the salinity toward the river mouth. At low tide, salinity is reduced. Note how salinity increases with depth, because the lighter freshwater flows over the denser saltwater.

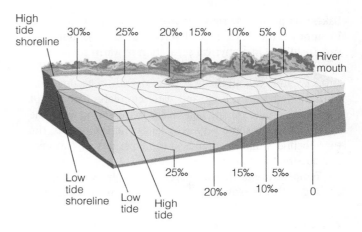

## Summary

### The Water Cycle (4.1)

Water follows a cycle traveling from the air to Earth and returning to the atmosphere. It moves through cloud formation in the atmosphere, precipitation, interception, and infiltration into the ground. It eventually reaches groundwater, springs, streams, and lakes from which evaporation takes place, bringing water back to the atmosphere in the form of clouds. The various aquatic environments are linked, either directly or indirectly, by the water cycle.

The largest reservoir in the global water cycle is the oceans, which contain more than 97 percent of the total volume of water on Earth. In contrast, the atmosphere is one of the smallest reservoirs but has a very fast turnover time.

### Properties of Water (4.2)

Water has a unique molecular structure. The side of the water molecule on which the hydrogen atoms are located has a positive charge, and the opposite side where the oxygen atom is located has a negative charge, thus polarizing the water molecule. Because of their polarity, water molecules become coupled with neighboring water molecules to produce a lattice-like structure with unique properties.

Depending on its temperature, water may be in the form of a liquid, solid, or gas. It absorbs or releases considerable quantities of heat with a small rise or fall in temperature. Water has a high viscosity that affects its flow. It exhibits high surface tension, caused by a stronger attraction of water molecules for each other than for the air above the surface. If a body is submerged in water and its weight is less than that of the water it displaces, it will be subjected to the upward force of buoyancy. These properties are important ecologically and biologically.

### Light (4.3)

Both the quantity and quality of light change with water depth. In pure water, red and infrared light are absorbed first, followed by yellow, green, and violet; blue penetrates the deepest.

### Temperature in Aquatic Environments (4.4)

Lakes and ponds experience seasonal shifts in temperature. In summer, there is a distinct vertical gradient of temperature, resulting in a physical separation of warm surface waters and the colder waters below the thermocline. When the surface waters cool in the fall, the temperature become uniform throughout the basin and water circulates throughout the lake. A similar mixing takes place in the spring when the water warms. In some very deep lakes and the oceans, the thermocline simply descends during periods of turnover and does not disappear at all.

Temperature of flowing water is variable, warming and cooling with the season. Within the stream or river, temperatures vary with depth, amount of shading, and exposure to sun.

### Water as a Solvent (4.5)

Water is an excellent solvent with the ability to dissolve more substances than any other liquid. The solvent properties of water are responsible for most of the minerals that are found in aquatic environments. The waters of most rivers and lakes contain a relatively low concentration of dissolved minerals, determined largely by the underlying bedrock over which the water flows. In contrast, the oceans have a much higher concentration of solutes. The flow of freshwaters into the oceans continuously adds to the solute content of the waters, as pure water evaporates from the surface to the atmosphere.

The solubility of sodium chloride is very high, and together with chlorine makes up some 86 percent of sea salt. The concentration of chlorine is used as an index of salinity. Salinity is expressed in practical salinity units or PSU (represented as ‰), measured as grams of chlorine per kilogram of water.

### Oxygen (4.6)

Oxygen enters the surface waters from the atmosphere through the process of diffusion. The amount of oxygen water can hold depends on temperature, pressure, and salinity. In lakes, oxygen absorbed by surface water mixes with deeper water by turbulence. During the summer, oxygen may become stratified, decreasing with depth because of decomposition in bottom sediments. During spring and fall turnover, oxygen becomes replenished in deep water. Constant swirling of stream water gives it greater contact with the atmosphere and thus maintains a high oxygen content.

### Acidity (4.7)

The measurement of acidity is pH, the negative logarithm of the concentration of hydrogen ions in solution. In aquatic environments, a close relationship exists between the diffusion of carbon dioxide into the surface waters and the degree of acidity and alkalinity. Acidity influences the availability of nutrients and restricts the environment of organisms sensitive to acid situations.

### Water Movement (4.8)

Both currents in streams and rivers and waves in open sea and breaking on ocean shores determine the nature of many aquatic and marine environments. Velocity of currents shapes the environment of flowing water. Waves pound rocky shores and tear away and build up sandy beaches. Movement of water in the surface currents of the ocean has an effect on the patterns of deep-water circulation. As the equatorial currents move northward and southward, deep waters move up to the surface, forming regions of upwelling. In coastal regions, winds blowing parallel to the coast create a pattern of coastal upwelling.

## Tides (4.9)

Rising and falling tides shape the environment and influence the rhythm of life of the coastal intertidal zones.

## Estuaries (4.10)

Water from all streams and rivers eventually drains into the sea. The place where this freshwater joins and mixes with the salt is called an estuary. Temperatures in estuaries fluctuate considerably, both daily and seasonally. The interaction of inflowing freshwater and tidal saltwater influences the salinity of the estuarine environment. Salinity varies vertically and horizontally, often within one tidal cycle.

## Study Questions

1. Draw a simple diagram and describe the water cycle.
2. How does the physical structure of water influence its ability to absorb and release heat energy?
3. What property of water allows aquatic organisms to function with far less supportive structures (tissues) than terrestrial organisms?
4. What is the fate of visible light in water?
5. What is the thermocline? What causes the development of a thermocline?
6. Explain why seasonal stratification of temperature and oxygen takes place in deep ponds and lakes.
7. Increasing the carbon dioxide concentration of water will have what effect on its pH?
8. The concentration of which element is used to define the salinity of water?
9. What causes the upwelling of deeper, cold waters in the equatorial zone of the oceans?
10. What causes the tides?

## Further Readings

Garrison, T. 2001. *Oceanography: An invitation to marine science*. Belmont, CA: Brooks-Cole.
> A clearly written and well illustrated introductory text for those that are interested in more detail on the subject matter.

Hutchinson, G. E. 1957–1967. *A treatise on limnology. Vol. 1, Geography, physics, and chemistry*. New York: Wiley.
> A classic reference.

Hynes, H. B. N. 2001. *The ecology of running waters*. Caldwell, NJ: Blackburn Press.
> Reprint of a classic and valuable work: a major reference that continues to be influential.

McLusky, D. S. 1989. *The estuarine ecosystem*, 2nd ed. New York: Chapman & Hall.
> Clearly describes the structure and function of estuarine ecosystems.

Nybakken, J. W. 2005. *Marine biology: An ecological approach*. 6th ed. San Francisco: Benjamin Cummings.
> Chapters 1 and 6 provide an excellent introduction to the physical environment of the oceans.

# Chapter 5 | The Terrestrial Environment

High surface temperatures, precipitation, and wind function as agents of soil erosion in this cornfield in Minnesota.

Our introduction of aquatic environments in the previous chapter was dominated by discussion of the physical and chemical properties of water, characteristics such as depth, flow rate, and salinity. When we think of the term *terrestrial environment*, however, it is typically not the physical and chemical characteristics of a place that first come to mind. What you most likely visualize is the vegetation: the tall, dense forests of the wet tropics; the changing colors of autumn in a temperate forest; or the broad expanse of grass that characterizes the prairies. Animal life depends on the vegetation within a region to provide the essential resources of food and cover, and as such, the structure and composition of plant life function to constrain the distribution and abundance of animal life. But ultimately, as with aquatic environments, it is the physical and chemical features of terrestrial environments that set the constraints for life. Plant life is a reflection of the climate and soils (as we shall discuss in Chapter 6), and regardless of the suitability of plant life to provide essential resources, the physical conditions within a region pose the primary constraints on animal life as well (Chapter 7).

In this chapter, we will explore key features of the terrestrial environment that directly influence life on land. Life emerged from the water to colonize the land more than a billion years ago. The transition to terrestrial environments posed a unique set of problems for organisms already adapted to an aquatic environment. In order to understand the "adaptive constraints" imposed by the terrestrial environment, we have to first look at the physical differences between the terrestrial and aquatic environments and what problems these differences impose on organisms making the transition from water to land.

## 5.1 | Life on Land Imposes Unique Constraints

The transition from life in aquatic environments to life on land brought with it a variety of constraints. Perhaps the greatest constraint imposed by terrestrial environments is desiccation. Living cells, both plant and animal, contain from about 75 percent to 95 percent water. Unless the air is saturated with moisture (see Section 3.6), water will readily evaporate from the surfaces of cells as a result of the process of diffusion. The water that is lost to the air is water that must be replaced if the cell is to remain hydrated and continue to function. Maintaining this balance of water between organisms and their surrounding environment (referred to as an organism's **water balance**) has been a major influence on the evolution of life on land. For example, as plants have adapted to the terrestrial environment, they have evolved extensively specialized cells for different functions. Aerial parts of most plants, such as stems and leaves, are coated with a waxy cuticle that prevents water loss. While it reduces the loss of water, the waxy surface also prevents gas exchange (carbon dioxide and oxygen) from occurring. As a result, terrestrial plants have evolved pores on the leaf surface (stomata; see Chapter 6) that allow for the diffusion of gases from the air into the interior of the leaf.

To not dry out, an organism must replace water that it has lost to the air. Terrestrial animals can acquire water by drinking and eating. For plants, however, the process is passive. Early in their evolution, land plants evolved vascular tissues consisting of cells joined into tubes that transport water and nutrients throughout the plant body. The topic of water balance and the array of adaptations that plants and animals have evolved to overcome the problems of water loss will be discussed in more detail in Chapters 6 and 7.

Desiccation is not the only constraint imposed by the transition from water to land. Because air is less dense than water, it results in a much lower drag (frictional resistance) on the movement of organisms, but it greatly increases the constraint imposed by gravitational forces.

The upward force of buoyancy due to the displacement of water helps organisms in aquatic environments overcome the constraints imposed by gravity (see Section 4.2). In contrast, the need to remain erect against the force of gravity in terrestrial environments results in a significant investment in structural materials such as skeletons (for animals) or cellulose (for plants). The giant kelp (*Macrocystis pyrifera*) inhabiting the waters off the coast of California provides an excellent example (Figure 5.1a). It grows in dense stands called kelp forests. Anchored to the bottom sediments, these kelp plants can grow 100 feet or more toward the surface. These kelp

(a)

(b)

Figure 5.1 | (a) The giant kelp (*Macrocystis pyrifera*) inhabits the waters off the coast of California. Anchored to the bottom sediments, these kelp plants can grow 100 feet or more toward the surface despite their lack of supportive tissues. These kelp plants are kept afloat aided by the buoyancy provided by gas-filled bladders attached to each blade, yet when the help plants are removed from the water, they collapse into a mass. (b) In contrast, a redwood tree (*Sequoia sempervirens*) of comparable height must allocate more than 80 percent of its biomass to supportive and conductive tissues as a result of gravitational forces.

plants are kept afloat by gas-filled bladders attached to each blade, yet when the kelp plants are removed from the water, they collapse into a mass. Lacking supportive tissues strengthened by cellulose and lignin, the kelp cannot support its own weight under the forces of gravity. In contrast, a tree of equivalent height inhabiting the coastal forest of California (Figure 5.1b) must allocate more than 80 percent of its total mass to supportive and conductive tissues in the trunk (bole), branches, leaves, and roots.

Another characteristic of terrestrial environments is their high degree of variability, both in time and space. Temperature variations on land (air) are much greater than in water. The high specific heat of water (see Section 4.2) prevents wide daily and seasonal fluctuations in the temperature of aquatic habitats, which are a characteristic of air temperatures (see Chapter 3). Likewise, the timing and quantity of precipitation received at a location constrain the availability of water for terrestrial plants and animals and their ability to maintain water balance. These fluctuations in temperature and moisture have both a short-term effect on metabolic processes and a long-term influence on the evolution and distribution of terrestrial plants and animals (see Chapters 6 and 7). Ultimately, it is the geographic variation in climate (see Chapter 3) that governs the large-scale distribution of plants and therefore the nature of terrestrial ecosystems (see Figure 3.1 and Chapter 23).

## 5.2 | Plant Cover Influences the Vertical Distribution of Light

In contrast to aquatic environments, where the absorption of solar radiation by the water itself results in a distinct vertical gradient of light, the dominant factor influencing the vertical gradient of light in terrestrial environments is the absorption and reflection of solar radiation by plants. A decrease in light is observed when one walks into a forest in summer (Figure 5.2a). Much the same effect would be observed if one examined the lowest layer in grassland or an old field (Figure 5.2b). The amount of light that does penetrate the canopy of vegetation to reach the ground varies with both the quantity and orientation of the leaves.

The amount of light at any depth in the canopy is a function of the number of leaves above. As we move down through the canopy, the number of leaves above increases, so the amount of light decreases. However, because leaves vary in size and shape, the number of leaves is not the best measure of quantity.

The quantity of leaves, or foliage density, is generally expressed in terms of leaf area. Because most leaves are flat, the leaf area is the surface area of one or both sides of the leaf. When the leaves are not flat, the entire surface area is sometimes measured. To quantify the changes in light environment with increasing area of leaves, we need to define the area of leaves per unit ground area ($m^2$ leaf area/$m^2$ ground area). This meas-

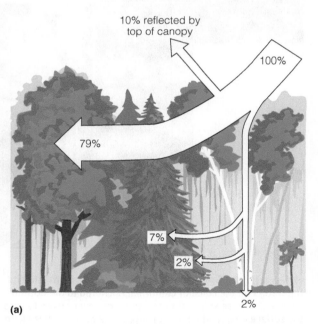

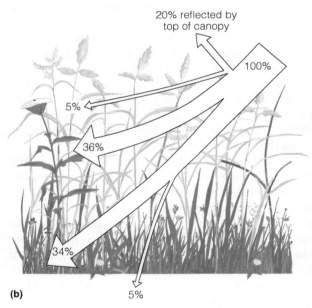

**Figure 5.2** | Absorption and reflection of light by the plant canopy. **(a)** A mixed conifer–deciduous forest reflects about 10 percent of the incident photosynthetically active radiation (PAR) from the upper crown, and it absorbs most of the remainder within the crown. **(b)** A meadow reflects 20 percent of the photosynthetically active radiation from the upper surface. The middle and lower regions, where the leaves are most dense, absorb most of the rest. Only 2–5 percent of PAR reaches the ground. (Adapted from Larcher 1980.)

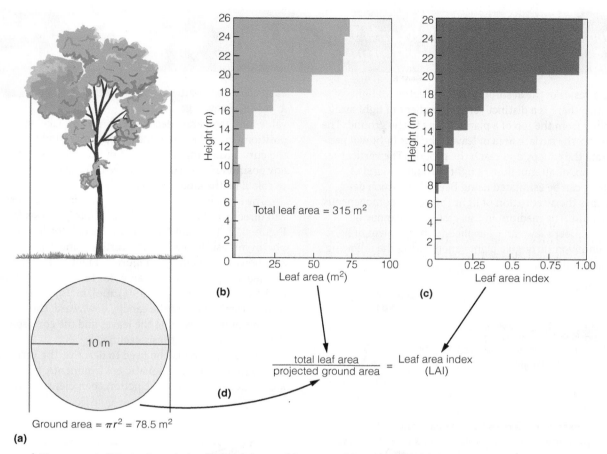

**(b)** Total leaf area = 315 m²

**(c)** Leaf area index

**(a)** Ground area = $\pi r^2$ = 78.5 m²

10 m

**(d)** $\dfrac{\text{total leaf area}}{\text{projected ground area}}$ = Leaf area index (LAI)

**Figure 5.3** | The concept of the leaf area index (LAI). **(a)** A tree with a 10-m-wide crown projects the same size circle on the ground. **(b)** The foliage density (area of leaves) at various heights above the ground. **(c)** The contributions of layers in the crown to the leaf area index. **(d)** Calculation of LAI. The total leaf area is 315 m². The projected ground area is 78.5 m². The LAI is 4.

ure is the **leaf area index (LAI)** (Figure 5.3). A leaf area index of 3 (LAI = 3) would mean that there are 3 m² of leaf area over each 1 m² of ground area.

The greater the leaf area index above any surface, the lower the quantity of light reaching that surface. As you move from the top of the canopy to the ground in a forest, the cumulative leaf area and LAI increase. Correspondingly, light decreases. The general relationship between available light and leaf area index is described by Beer's law (see Quantifying Ecology 5.1: Beer's Law and the Attenuation of Light).

In addition to the quantity of leaves, the orientation of leaves on the plant influences the attenuation of light through the canopy. The angle at which a leaf is oriented relative to the Sun changes the amount of light it absorbs. If a leaf that is perpendicular to the Sun absorbs 1.0 unit of light energy (per unit leaf area/time), the same leaf displayed at a 60-degree angle to the Sun will absorb only 0.5 unit. The reason is that the same leaf area represents only half the projected surface area and therefore intercepts only half as much light energy (Figure 5.4). Thus, leaf angle influences the vertical

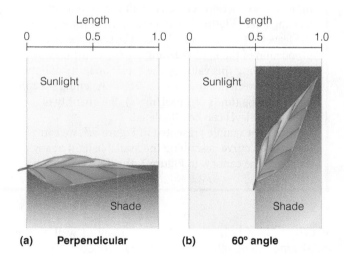

**Figure 5.4** | The influence of leaf orientation (angle) on the interception of light energy. If a leaf that is perpendicular to the source of light **(a)** intercepts 1.0 unit of light energy, the same leaf at an angle of 60° relative to the light source will only intercept 0.5 unit **(b)**. The reduction in intercepted light energy is a result of the angled leaf projecting a smaller surface area relative to the light source.

**A**s a result of the absorption and reflection of light by leaves, there is a distinct vertical gradient of light availability from the top of a plant canopy to the ground. The greater the surface area of leaves, the less light will penetrate the canopy and reach the ground. The vertical reduction, or attenuation, of light through a stand of plants can be estimated using Beer's law, which describes the attenuation of light through a homogeneous medium. The medium in this case is the canopy of leaves. Beer's law can be applied to the problem of light attenuation through a plant canopy using the following relationship:

Leaf area index above height $i$

Light reaching any vertical position $i$, expressed as a proportion of light reaching the top of the canopy

$$AL_i = e^{-LAI_i \times k}$$

Light extinction coefficient

The subscript $i$ refers to the vertical height of the canopy. For example, if $i$ were in units of meters, a value of $i = 5$ refers to a height of 5 m above the ground. The value $e$ is the natural logarithm (2.718). The light extinction coefficient, $k$, represents the quantity of light attenuated per unit of leaf area index (LAI) and is a measure of the degree to which leaves absorb and reflect light. The extinction coefficient will vary as a function of leaf angle (see Figure 5.5) and the optical properties of the leaves. Although the value of $AL_i$ is expressed as a proportion of the light reaching the top of the canopy, by multiplying this value by the actual quantity of light (or photosynthetically active radiation) reaching the top of the canopy (units of $\mu mol/m^2/s$), the quantity of light at any level can be calculated.

For the example presented in Figure 5.4, we can construct a curve describing the available light at any height in the canopy. In Figure 1, the light extinction coefficient has a value of $k = 0.6$, an average value for a temperate deciduous forest. We label vertical positions from the top of the canopy to ground level on the curve. Knowing the amount of leaves (LAI) above any position in the canopy ($i$), we can use the equation to calculate the amount of light there.

The availability of light at any point in the canopy will directly influence the levels of photosynthesis (see Figure 6.2). The light levels and rates of light-limited photosynthesis for each of the vertical canopy positions are shown in the curve in Figure 2. Light levels are expressed as a proportion of values for fully exposed leaves at the top of the canopy ($1500 \ \mu mol/m^2/s$). As one moves from the top of the canopy downward, the amount of light reaching the leaves and the corresponding rate of photosynthesis decline.

Beer's law can also be used to describe the vertical attenuation of light in aquatic environments, but the application of the light extinction coefficient ($k$) is

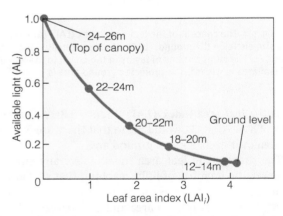

**Figure 1** | Relationship between leaf area index above various heights in the canopy ($LAI_i$) and the associated values of available light ($AL_i$), expressed as a proportion of PAR at the top of the canopy.

distribution of light through the canopy as well as the total amount of light absorbed and reflected. The sun angle varies, however, both geographically (see Section 3.1) and through time at a given location (over the course of the day and seasonally). The result is that different leaf angles are more effective at intercepting light at different locations and at different times. For example, in high-latitude environments, where sun angles are low

(see Figure 3.5), canopies having leaves that are displayed at an angle are more effective at absorbing light. Leaves that are displayed at an angle rather than perpendicular to the Sun are also typical of arid tropical environments. In these hot and dry environments, angled leaves function to reduce light interception during midday when temperatures and demand for water are at their highest.

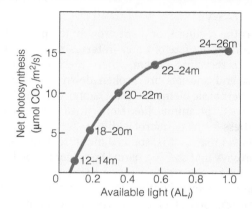

**Figure 2** | Relationship between available light (PAR) and rate of net photosynthesis at various heights in the canopy. Available light is expressed as the proportion of PAR at the top of the canopy (assumed to be $1500 \ \mu mol/m^2/s$).

Whereas the light extinction coefficient for leaf area expresses the attenuation of light per unit leaf area index, these values of $k$ are expressed as the attenuation of light per unit of water depth (such as centimeter, meter, inches, or feet). Beer's law can then be used to estimate the quantity of light reaching any depth ($z$) using the following equation:

$$AL_z = e^{-k_T z}$$

If the ecosystem supports submerged vegetation, such as kelp (see Figure 5.1), seagrass, or other plants that are rooted in the bottom sediments, the above equation can be used to calculate the available light at the top of the canopy. The equation describing the attenuation of light as a function of LAI can then be applied (combined) to calculate the further attenuation from the top of the plant canopy to the sediment surface. ●

1. If we assume that the value of $k$ used to calculate the vertical profile of light in Figure 1 ($k = 0.6$) is for a plant canopy where the leaves are positioned horizontally (parallel to the forest floor), how would the value of $k$ differ (higher or lower) for a forest where the leaves were oriented at a 60 degree angle (see example in Figure 5.4)?

2. In shallow-water ecosystems, storms and high wind can result in bottom sediments (particulates) being suspended in the water for a period of time before they once again settle to the bottom. How would this affect the value of $k_T$ and the attenuation of light in the water profile?

more complex. The reduction of light with water depth is a function of a variety of factors: (1) attenuation by the water itself (see Section 4.3, Figure 4.6); (2) attenuation by phytoplankton (microscopic plants suspended in water), typically expressed as the concentration of chlorophyll (the light-harvesting pigment of plants) per volume of water (see Section 6.1); (3) attenuation by dissolved substances; and (4) attenuation by suspended particulates. Each of these factors has an associated light extinction coefficient, and the overall light extinction coefficient ($k_T$) is the sum of the individual coefficients:

Chlorophyll     Particulates

$$k_T = k_w + k_c + k_d + k_p$$

Total     Water     Dissolved substance

Although light decreases downward through the plant canopy, some direct sunlight does penetrate openings in the crown and reaches the ground as sunflecks. Sunflecks can account for 70–80 percent of solar energy reaching the ground in forest environments (Figure 5.5).

In many environments, seasonal changes strongly influence leaf area. For example, in the temperate re-

gions of the world, many forest tree species are deciduous, shedding their leaves during the winter months. In these cases, the amount of light that penetrates a forest canopy varies with the season (Figure 5.6). In early spring in temperate regions, when leaves are just expanding, 20–50 percent of the incoming light may reach the forest floor. In other regions characterized by distinct wet and dry seasons (see Chapter 3), a similar pattern of

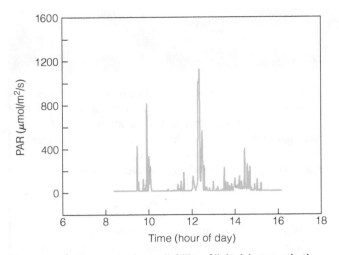

Figure 5.5 | Changes in the availability of light (photosynthetically active radiation; PAR) at ground level in a redwood forest in northern California over the course of a day. The spikes are a result of sunflecks in an otherwise low-light environment (average PAR of 30 $\mu$mol/m²/s). The median sunfleck length on this day was 2 seconds. (Adapted from Pfitsch and Pearcy 1989.)

increased light availability at the ground level occurs during the dry season.

## 5.3 | Soil Is the Foundation Upon Which All Terrestrial Life Depends

Soil is the medium for plant growth; the principle factor controlling the fate of water in terrestrial environments; nature's recycling system, where the waste products of plants and animals are broken down and transformed into their basic elements (see Chapter 21); and habitat to a diversity of animal life, from small mammals to the countless forms of microbial life.

As familiar as it is, soil is difficult to define. One definition says that soil is a natural product formed and synthesized by the weathering of rocks and the action of living organisms. Another states that soil is a collection of natural bodies of earth, composed of mineral and organic matter and capable of supporting plant growth. Indeed, one eminent soil scientist, Hans Jenny, a pioneer of modern soil studies, will not give an exact definition of soil. In his book *The Soil Resource*, he writes:

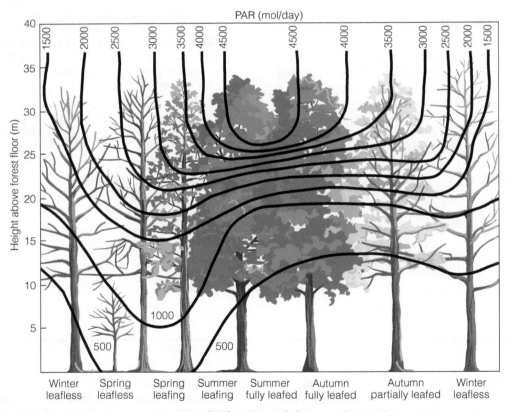

Figure 5.6 | Levels of photosynthetically active radiation (PAR), within and above a yellow-poplar (*Liriodendron tulipifera*) stand over a year. The lines (isopleths) define the gradient of PAR. The greatest intensity of solar radiation occurs in summer, but the canopy intercepts most of the PAR, thus little reaches the forest floor. The greatest values of PAR reach the forest floor in spring, when trees are still leafless. The forest receives the least PAR in winter with its lower solar elevations and shorter daylengths. As a result, the amount of PAR reaching the forest floor is little more than that of midsummer. (Adapted from Hutchinson and Matt 1977.)

Popularly, soil is the stratum below the vegetation and above hard rock, but questions come quickly to mind. Many soils are bare of plants, temporarily or permanently, or they may be at the bottom of a pond growing cattails. Soil may be shallow or deep, but how deep? Soil may be stony, but surveyors (soil) exclude the larger stones. Most analyses pertain to fine earth only. Some pretend that soil in a flowerpot is not a soil, but soil material. It is embarrassing not to be able to agree on what soil is. In this pedologists are not alone. Biologists cannot agree on a definition of life and philosophers on philosophy.

Of one fact we are sure. Soil is not just an abiotic environment for plants. It is teeming with life—billions of minute and not so minute animals, bacteria, and fungi. The interaction between the biotic and the abiotic makes the soil a living system.

Soil scientists recognize soil as a three-dimensional unit, or body, that possesses length, width, and depth. In most places on Earth's surface, exposed rock has crumbled and broken down to produce a layer of unconsolidated debris overlaying the hard, unweathered rock. This unconsolidated layer is called the **regolith** and varies in depth from virtually nonexistent to tens of meters. It is at this interface between rock and the air, water, and living organisms that characterize the surface environment that soil is formed.

## 5.4 | The Formation of Soil Begins with Weathering

The formation of soil begins with the weathering of rocks and their minerals. Weathering includes both the mechanical destruction of rock materials into smaller particles and their chemical modification. **Mechanical weathering** comes about through the interaction of several forces. Exposed to the combined action of water, wind, and temperature, rock surfaces flake and peel away. Water seeps into crevices, freezes, expands, and cracks the rock into smaller pieces. Wind-borne particles, such as dust and sand, wear away at the rock surface. Growing roots of trees split rock apart.

Without appreciably influencing their composition, physical weathering breaks down rock and minerals into smaller particles. Simultaneously, these particles are chemically altered and broken down through the process of **chemical weathering.** The presence of water, oxygen, and acids that results from the activities of soil organisms and the continual addition of organic matter (dead plant and animal tissues) enhance the chemical weathering process. Rainwater falling on and filtering through this organic matter and mineral soil sets up a chain of chemical reactions that transform the composition of the original rocks and minerals.

## 5.5 | Soil Formation Involves Five Interrelated Factors

Five interdependent factors are important in the formation of soils: parent material, climate, biotic factors, topography, and time.

**Parent material** is the material from which soil develops. The original parent material could originate from the underlying bedrock, glacial deposits (till), from sand and silt carried by the wind (eolian), and from sediments carried by flowing water (fluvial), including water in flood plains, or from gravity moving material down a slope. The physical character and chemical composition of the parent material play an important role in the determination of soil properties, especially during the early stages of development.

Biotic factors—plants, animals, bacteria, and fungi—all contribute to the formation of soil. Plant roots can function both to break up parent material, enhancing the process of weathering, and to stabilize the soil surface, thus reducing erosion. Plant roots pump nutrients up from soil depths and add them to the surface. In doing so, plants recapture minerals carried deep into the soil by weathering processes. Through photosynthesis, plants capture the Sun's energy and add a portion of this energy to the soil in the form of organic carbon. On the soil surface, remains of dead plants and animals are broken down by microorganisms and eventually become organic matter that is incorporated into the soil (see Chapter 21).

Climate influences the development of soils both directly and indirectly. Temperature, precipitation, and winds directly influence the physical and chemical reactions that are responsible for the breakdown of parent material and the subsequent **leaching** (movement of solutes through the soil) and movement of weathered materials. Water is essential for the process of chemical weathering, and the greater the depth of water percolation, the greater the depth of weathering and soil development. Temperature controls the rates of biochemical reactions, affecting the balance between the accumulation and breakdown of organic materials. The result is that under conditions of warm temperatures and abundant water, the processes of weathering, leaching, and plant growth (input of organic matter) will be maximized. In contrast, under cold, dry conditions, the influence of these processes will be much more modest. Indirectly, climate influences the plant and animal life in a region, both of which are important in soil development.

Topography, the contour of the land, can affect how climate influences the weathering process. More water runs off and less enters the soil on steep slopes than on level land, whereas water draining from slopes enters the soil on low and flat land. Steep slopes are also subject to soil erosion and soil creep—the downslope movement of soil material that accumulates on lower slopes and lowlands.

Time is a crucial element in soil formation. All of the above factors assert themselves through time. The weathering of rock material; the accumulation, decomposition, and mineralization of organic material; the loss of minerals from the upper surface; and the downward movement of materials through the soil all require considerable time. The formation of well-developed soils may require 2000 to 20,000 years.

## 5.6 | Soils Have Certain Distinguishing Physical Characteristics

Soils are distinguished by differences in their physical and chemical properties. Physical properties include color, texture, structure, moisture, and depth. All may be highly variable from one soil to another.

Color is one of the easily defined and most useful characteristics of soil. It has little direct influence on the function of a soil but can be used to relate chemical and physical properties. Organic matter (particularly humus) makes soil dark or black. Other colors can indicate the chemical composition of the rocks and minerals from which the soil was formed. Oxides of iron give a color to the soil ranging from yellowish-brown to red, whereas manganese oxides give the soil a purplish to black color. Quartz, kaolin, gypsum, and carbonates of calcium and magnesium give whitish and grayish colors to the soil. Blotches of various shades of yellowish-brown and gray indicate poorly drained soils or soils saturated by water. Soils are classified by color using standardized color charts.

Soil texture is the proportion of different-sized soil particles. Texture is partly inherited from parent material and partly a result of the soil-forming process. Particles are classified on the basis of size into gravel, sand, silt, and clay. Gravel consists of particles larger than 2.0 mm. They are not part of the fine fraction of soil. Soils are classified based on texture by defining the proportion of sand, silt, and clay.

Sand ranges from 0.05 to 2.0 mm, is easy to see, and feels gritty. Silt consists of particles from 0.002 to 0.05 mm in diameter, which can scarcely be seen by the naked eye and feels and looks like flour. Clay particles are less than 0.002 mm, too small to be seen under an ordinary microscope. Clay controls the most important properties of soils, including its water holding capacity (see Section 5.8), and the exchange of ions between soil particles and soil solution (see Section 5.9). A soil's texture is the percentage (by weight) of sand, silt, and clay. Based on proportions of these components, soils are divided into texture classes (Figure 5.7).

Soil texture affects pore space in the soil, which plays a major role in the movement of air and water in the soil and the penetration by roots. In an ideal soil, particles

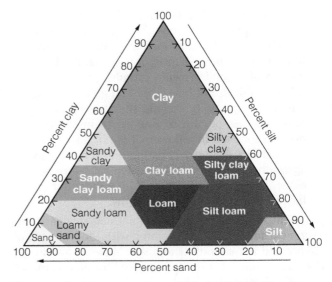

**Figure 5.7** | A soil texture chart, which shows the percentages of clay (below 0.002 mm), silt (0.002–0.05 mm), and sand (0.05–2.0 mm) in the basic soil texture classes. For example, a soil with 60 percent sand, 30 percent silt, and 10 percent clay would be classified as a sandy loam.

make up 50 percent of the total volume of the soil; the other 50 percent is pore space. Pore space includes spaces within and between soil particles, as well as old root channels and animal burrows. Coarse-textured soils possess large pore spaces that favor rapid water infiltration, percolation, and drainage. To a point, the finer the texture, the smaller the pores, and the greater the availability of active surface for water adhesion and chemical activity. Very fine textured or heavy soils, such as clays, easily become compacted if plowed, stirred, or walked on. They are poorly aerated and difficult for roots to penetrate.

Soil depth varies across the landscape, depending on slope, weathering, parent materials, and vegetation. In grasslands, much of the organic matter added to the soil is from the deep fibrous root systems of the grass plants. By contrast, tree leaves falling on the forest floor are the principle source of organic matter in forests. As a result, soils developed under native grassland tend to be several meters deep and soils developed under forests are shallow. On level ground at the bottom of slopes and on alluvial plains, soils tend to be deep. Soils on ridge tops and steep slopes tend to be shallow, with bedrock close to the surface.

## 5.7 | The Soil Body Has Horizontal Layers, or Horizons

Initially, soil develops from undifferentiated parent material. Over time, changes occur from the surface down, through the accumulation of organic matter near the surface and the downward movement of material. These changes result in the formation of horizontal layers that are differentiated by physical, chemical, and biological characteristics. Collectively, a sequence of horizontal layers constitutes a soil profile. This pattern of horizontal layering, or **horizons,** is easily visible where a recent cut has been made along a road bank or during excavation for a building site (Figure 5.8).

The simplest, general representation of a soil profile consists of four horizons: O, A, B, and C (Figure 5.9). The surface layer is the O horizon, or organic layer. This horizon is dominated by organic material, consisting of partially decomposed plant materials, such as leaves, needles, twigs, mosses, and lichens. This horizon is often subdivided into a surface layer composed of undecomposed leaves and twigs (Oi), a middle layer composed of partially decomposed plant tissues (Oe), and a bottom layer consisting of dark brown to black, homogeneous organic material—the humus layer (Oa). This pattern of

**Figure 5.8** | The pattern of horizontal layering or soil horizons is easily visible where a recent cut has been made along a road bank. This soil is relatively shallow, with the parent material close to the surface.

layering is easily seen by carefully scraping away the surface organic material on the forest floor. In temperate regions, it is thickest in the fall, when new leaf litter accumulates on the surface. It is thinnest in the summer after decomposition has taken place.

Below the organic layer is the A horizon, often referred to as the topsoil. This is the first of the layers that is largely composed of mineral soil derived from the parent materials. In this horizon, organic matter (humus) leached from above accumulates in the mineral soil. The accumulation of organic matter typically gives this horizon a darker color, distinguishing it from lower soil layers. The downward movement of water through this layer also results in the loss of minerals and finer soil particles, such as clay, to lower portions of the profile, sometimes giving rise to an E horizon, a zone or layer of maximum leaching, or eluviation (from Latin *ex* or *e*, out, and *lavere*, to wash) of minerals and finer soil particles to lower portions of the profile. Such E horizons are quite common in soils developed under forests, but because of lower precipitation, they rarely occur in soils developed under grasslands.

Below the A (or E) is the B horizon, also called the subsoil. Containing less organic matter than the A horizon, the B horizon shows accumulations of mineral particles such as clay and salts due to leaching from the topsoil. This process is called illuviation (from the Latin *il*, in, and *lavere*, to wash). The B horizon usually has a denser structure than the A horizon, making it more difficult for plants to extend their roots downward. B horizons are distinguished on the basis of color, structure, and the kind of material that has accumulated as a result of leaching from the horizons above.

The C horizon is the unconsolidated material that lies under the subsoil and is generally made of original material from which the soil developed. Because it is below the zones of greatest biological activity and weathering and has not been sufficiently altered by the soil-forming processes, it typically retains much of the characteristics of the parent materials from which it was formed. Below the C horizon lies the bedrock.

## 5.8 | Moisture-Holding Capacity Is an Essential Feature of Soils

If one digs into the surface layer of a soil after a soaking rain, a sharp transition between wet surface soil and the dry soil below should be discovered. As rain falls on the surface, it moves into the soil by infiltration. Water moves by gravity into the open pore spaces in the soil, and the size of the soil particles and their spacing determine how much water can flow in. Wide pore spacing at the soil surface increases the rate of water infiltration, so coarse soils have a higher infiltration rate than fine soils.

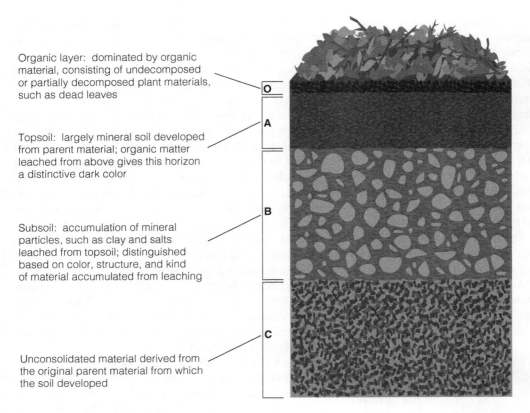

Organic layer: dominated by organic material, consisting of undecomposed or partially decomposed plant materials, such as dead leaves

**O**

**A**

Topsoil: largely mineral soil developed from parent material; organic matter leached from above gives this horizon a distinctive dark color

**B**

Subsoil: accumulation of mineral particles, such as clay and salts leached from topsoil; distinguished based on color, structure, and kind of material accumulated from leaching

**C**

Unconsolidated material derived from the original parent material from which the soil developed

**Figure 5.9** | A generalized soil profile. Over time, changes occur from the surface down, through the accumulation of organic matter near the surface and the downward movement of material. These changes result in the formation of horizontal layers, or horizons.

If the amount of water exceeds what the pore space can hold, we say that the soil is **saturated,** and excess water drains freely from the soil. If water fills all the pore spaces and is held there by internal capillary forces, the soil is at **field capacity.** Field capacity is generally expressed as the percentage of the weight or volume of soil occupied by water when saturated compared to the oven-dried weight of the soil at a standard temperature. The amount of water a soil holds at field capacity varies with the soil's texture—the proportion of sand, silt, and clay. Coarse, sandy soil has large pores; water drains through it quickly. Clay soils have small pores and hold considerably more water. Water held between soil particles by capillary forces is **capillary water.**

As plants and evaporation from the soil surface extract capillary water, the amount of water in the soil declines. When the moisture level decreases to a point at which plants can no longer extract water, the soil has reached the **wilting point.** The amount of water retained by the soil between field capacity and wilting point (or the difference between FC and WP) is the **available water capacity (AWC)** (Figure 5.10). The AWC provides an estimate of the water available for uptake by plants. Although water still remains in the soil—filling up to 25 percent of the pore spaces—soil particles hold it tightly, making it difficult to extract.

Both the field capacity and wilting point of a soil are heavily influenced by soil texture. Particle size of the soil

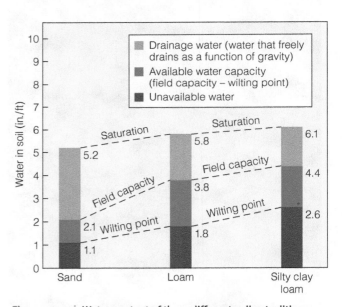

**Figure 5.10** | Water content of three different soils at wilting point (WP), field capacity (FC), and saturation. The three soils differ in texture from coarse-textured sand to fine-textured silty clay loam (see soil texture chart of Figure 5.7). Available water capacity (AWC) is defined as the difference between FC and WP. Note that both FC and WP increase from coarse- to fine-textured soils and that the highest AWC is in the intermediate-textured soils.

directly influences the pore space and surface area onto which water adheres. Sand has 30 percent to 40 percent of its volume in pore space, whereas clays and loams (see soil texture chart in Figure 5.7) range from 40 percent to 60 percent. As a result, fine-textured soils have a higher field capacity than sandy soils, but the increased surface area results in a higher value of the wilting point as well (see Figure 5.10). Conversely, coarse-textured soils (sands) have a low field capacity and a low wilting point. Thus, AWC is highest in intermediate clay loam soils.

The topographic position of a soil affects the movement of water both on and in the soil. Water tends to drain downslope, leaving soils on higher slopes and ridgetops relatively dry and creating a moisture gradient from ridgetops to streams.

## 5.9 | Ion Exchange Capacity Is Important to Soil Fertility

Chemical elements within the soil dissolve into the soil water to form a solution (see Section 4.5). Referred to as exchangeable nutrients, these chemical nutrients in solution are the most readily available for uptake and use by plants (see Chapter 6). They are held in soil by the simple attraction of oppositely charged particles and are in constant interchange with the soil solution.

As described in Chapter 4, an **ion** is a charged particle. Ions carrying a positive charge are **cations,** whereas ions carrying a negative charge are **anions.** Chemical elements and compounds exist in the soil solution as both cations, such as calcium ($Ca^{2+}$), magnesium ($Mg^{2+}$), and ammonium ($NH_4^+$), and anions, such as nitrate ($NO_3^-$) and sulfate ($SO_4^{2-}$). The ability of these ions in soil solution to bind to the surface of soil particles depends on the number of negatively or positively charged sites within the soil. The total number of charged sites on soil particles within a volume of soil is called the **ion exchange capacity.** In most soils of the temperate zone, cation exchange predominates over anion exchange because of the prevalence of negatively charged particles in the soil, referred to as **colloids.** The total number of negatively charged sites, located on the leading edges of clay particles and soil organic matter (humus particles), is called the **cation exchange capacity (CEC).** These negative charges enable a soil to prevent the leaching of its positively charged nutrient cations. Because in most soils there are far fewer positively charged than negatively charged sites, anions such as nitrate ($NO_3^-$) and phosphate ($PO_3^{4-}$) are not retained on exchange sites in soils but tend to leach away quickly if not taken up by plants. The CEC is a basic measure of soil quality and increases with higher clay and organic matter content.

Cations occupying the negatively charged particles in the soil are in a state of dynamic equilibrium with similar cations in the soil solution (Figure 5.11). Cations in soil solution are continuously being replaced by or exchanged with cations on the clay and humus particles. The relative abundance of different ions on exchange sites is a function of their concentration in the soil solution and the relative affinity of each for the sites. In general, the physically smaller the ion and the greater the positive charge on it, the more tightly it is held. The lyotropic

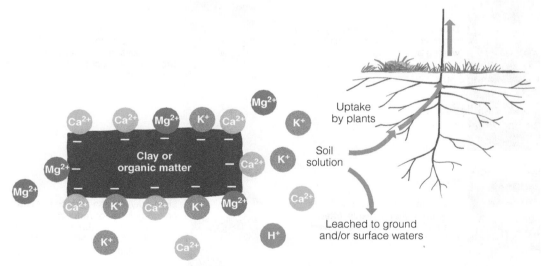

**Figure 5.11** | The process of cation exchange in soils. Cations occupying the negatively charged particles in the soil are in a state of dynamic equilibrium with similar cations in the soil solution. Cations in soil solution are continuously being replaced by or exchanged with cations on clay and humus particles. In addition, cations in the soil solution are also taken up by plants and leached to ground and surface waters.

series places the major cations in order of their strength of bonding to the cation exchange sites in the soil:

$$Al^{3+} > H^+ > Ca^{2+} > Mg^{2+} > K^+ = NH^{4+} > Na^+$$

However, higher concentrations in the soil solution can overcome these differences in affinity.

Hydrogen ions added by rainwater, by acids from organic matter, and by metabolic acids from roots and microorganisms increase the concentration of hydrogen ions in the soil solution and displace other cations, such as $Ca^{2+}$, on the soil exchange sites. As more and more hydrogen ions replace other cations, the soil becomes increasingly acidic (see Section 4.5). Acidity is one of the most familiar of all chemical conditions in the soil. Typically, soils range from pH 3 (extremely acid) to pH 9 (strongly alkaline). Soils just over pH 7 (neutral) are considered basic, and those of pH 5.6 or below are acid. As soil acidity increases, the proportion of exchangeable $Al^{3+}$ increases and $Ca^{2+}$, $Na^+$, and other cations decrease. High aluminum ($Al^{3+}$) concentrations in soil solution can result in toxicity to the plants. Aluminum toxicity damages the root system first, and roots become short, thick, and stubby. The result is reduced nutrient uptake.

## 5.10 | Basic Soil Formation Processes Produce Different Soils

Broad regional differences in geology, climate, and vegetation give rise to characteristically different soils. The broadest level of soil classification is the order. Each order has distinctive features, summarized in Figure 5.12, and its own distribution, mapped in Figure 5.13. Although a wide variety of processes are involved in soil formation (pedogenesis), soil scientists recognize five main soil-forming processes that give rise to these different classes of soils. These processes are laterization, calcification, salinization, podzolization, and gleization.

**Entisol**

Immature soils that lack vertical development of horizons; associated with recently deposited sediments.

**Aridisol**

Develop in very dry environments; low in organic matter; high in base content; prone to the process of salinization.

**Vertisol**

Dark clay soils that show significant expansion and contraction due to wetting and drying.

**Mollisol**

Surface horizons dark brown to black with soft consistency; rich in bases; soils of semi-humid regions; prone to the process of calcification.

**Inceptisol**

Young soils that are more developed than entisols; often shallow; moderate development of horizons.

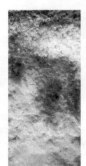

**Spodosol**

Light gray, whitish surface horizon on top of black or reddish B horizon; high in extractable iron and aluminum; formed through process of podzolization.

**Figure 5.12** | Profiles and general description of the 12 major soil orders of the world.

**Laterization** is a process common to soils found in humid environments within the tropical and subtropical regions. The hot, rainy conditions result in the rapid weathering of rocks and minerals. Movements of large amounts of water through the soil cause heavy leaching, and most of the compounds and nutrients made available by the weathering process are transported out of the soil profile if not taken up by plants. The two exceptions to this process are compounds of iron and aluminum. It is iron oxides that give tropical soils their unique reddish coloring (see Ultisol profile in Figure 5.12 as an example of soil formed through the process of laterization). Heavy leaching also causes these soils to be acidic due to the loss of other cations (other than $H^+$).

**Calcification** occurs when evaporation and water uptake by plants exceed precipitation. The net result is an upward movement of dissolved alkaline salts, typically calcium carbonate ($CaCO_3$), from the groundwater. At the same time, the infiltration of water from the surface causes a downward movement of the salts. The net result is the deposition and buildup of these deposits in the B horizon (subsoil). In some cases, these deposits can form a hard layer called caliche (Figure 5.14a).

**Salinization** is a process that functions in a way similar to calcification, only in much drier climates. It differs from calcification in that the salt deposits occur at or very near the soil surface (Figure 5.14b). Saline soils are common in deserts but may also occur in coastal regions as a result of sea spray. Salinization is also a growing problem in agricultural areas where irrigation is practiced (see Ecological Issues: Land Use and Soil Salinization).

**Podzolization** occurs in cool, moist climates of the mid-latitude regions where coniferous vegetation (e.g., pine forests) dominates. The organic matter of coniferous vegetation creates strongly acidic conditions. The acidic soil solution enhances the process of leaching, causing the removal of cations and compounds of iron and aluminum from the A horizon (topsoil). This process creates a sublayer in the A horizon that is composed of sand that is white to gray in color (see Spodosol profile in

**Alfisol**

Shallow penetration of humus; translocation of clay; well-developed horizons.

**Histosol**

High content of organic matter; formed in areas with poor drainage; bog and muck soils.

**Ultisol**

Intensely leached; strong clay translocation; low base content; humid warm climate; formed by process of laterization.

**Andisol**

Developed from volcanic parent material; not highly weathered; upper layers dark colored; low bulk density.

**Oxisol**

Highly weathered soils with nearly featureless profile; red, yellow or gray; rich in kalolinate, iron oxides, and often humus; in tropics and subtropics.

**Gelisol**

Presence of permafrost or soil temperature of 0°C or less within 2 meters of the surface; formed through the process of gleization.

**Figure 5.12** | continued

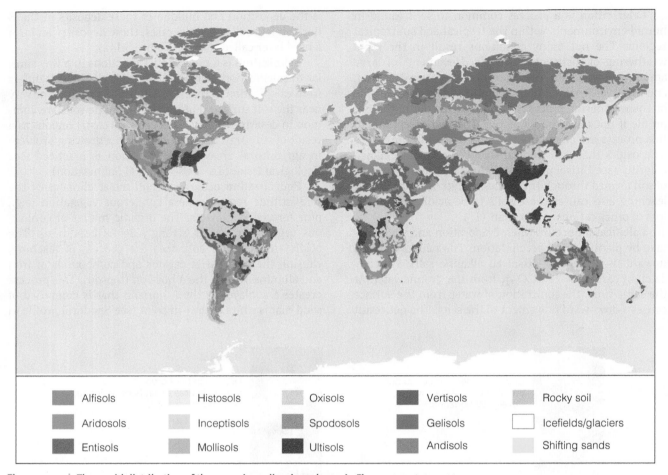

**Figure 5.13** | The world distribution of the 12 major soil orders shown in Figure 5.12. (Adapted from USGS, Soil Conservation Service.) Go to GRAPHit! at **www.ecologyplace.com** to graph global soil degradation.

Legend:
- Alfisols
- Aridosols
- Entisols
- Histosols
- Inceptisols
- Mollisols
- Oxisols
- Spodosols
- Ultisols
- Vertisols
- Gelisols
- Andisols
- Rocky soil
- Icefields/glaciers
- Shifting sands

**(a)**      **(b)**

**Figure 5.14** | **(a)** Salination is the process in arid regions where salts (the white crust at the center of the picture) accumulate near the soil surface as a result of surface evaporation. **(b)** Calcification is when calcium carbonates precipitate out from water moving downward through the soil or from capillary water moving upward from below. The result is an accumulation of calcium in the B horizon (seen as the white soil layer in the picture).

Salinization is a natural process that can occur in areas where surface evaporation and water uptake by plants exceed precipitation. The net result is an upward movement of dissolved salts from the groundwater toward the soil surface, often degrading soil conditions for plant growth. Agricultural practices have increased soil salinity in many regions of the world by changing the natural balance of the water cycle.

Groundwater used for irrigation contains soluble salts such as sodium, calcium, magnesium, potassium, sulfate, and chloride dissolved from the rocks and minerals with which the water has been in contact. Evaporation and transpiration (plant uptake) of irrigation water eventually cause excessive amounts of salts to accumulate in soils unless adequate leaching and drainage are provided. This process is referred to as irrigation salinization.

In regions of eastern Australia, another form of salinization is occurring that does not involve irrigation: dry land salinization. Groundwater recharge is the amount of water being added to the groundwater. If this is higher than discharge, which is the amount of water lost from the groundwater, then the water table (the top surface of the groundwater layer) rises. As it does, the water dissolves salt held in the soil profile, and the salt becomes more and more concentrated as the water moves upward. If the salty water keeps rising, it eventually reaches the surface and subsurface layers of the soil. The water evaporates, leaving the salt behind.

Dry land salinization is a very serious and worsening problem in Australia, posing a serious long-term threat to the sustainability of land and water resources. In preparing lands for agriculture, the trees of the *Eucalyptus* woodlands are cleared, yet these trees play a crucial role in maintaining the water balance of these soils. Introduced crops have different water-use characteristics than native vegetation and allow more rainfall to enter the groundwater. Scientists estimate that the amount of water that percolates below the root zone of crops and pastures can be 10 to 100 times the amount percolating below trees. If more water is being added than can be accommodated in the aquifer, the groundwater level will rise, bringing with it salts, as groundwater is saline in many areas. Currently, 10 percent of the agricultural area in Western Australia is classified as affected by salinization, reducing crop production on these lands by as much as 50 percent. If current landuse practices continue, the percentage of lands affected is expected to double by 2020.

Soil salinization, both irrigation and dry land, is a growing problem and threat to global agricultural production. Worldwide, 12–17 million acres of arable land are lost for production each year from soil degradation; of these, 5 million are directly attributable to salinization. In the United States alone, almost one-quarter of irrigated land exhibits some degree of salinization resulting in significant crop loss. ●

1. How does the process of salinization resulting from irrigation differ from the natural process of salinization that occurs in arid areas (see Section 5.10 for help)?

2. One possible solution to the problem of salinization from irrigation is the desalinization (removal of salts) of water used for irrigation, but this practice is extremely expensive. Can you think of any alternatives?

**Figure 1** | An example of soil salinization in New South Wales, Australia. The white crust on the surface is salt that has moved to the surface as a result of a rising water table within the region.

Figure 5.12 as an example of soil formed through the process of podzolization).

**Gleization** occurs in regions with high rainfall or low-lying areas associated with poor drainage (waterlogged). The constantly wet conditions slow the breakdown of organic matter by decomposers (bacteria and fungi), allowing the matter to accumulate in the upper layers of the soil. The accumulated organic matter releases organic acids that react with iron in the soil, giving the soil a black to bluish-gray color (see Gelisol profile in Figure 5.12 as an example of soil formed through the process of gleization).

These five processes represent the integration of climate and edaphic factors on the formation of soils, which gives rise to the geographic diversity of soils that influence the distribution, abundance, and productivity of terrestrial ecosystems, a topic we will explore further in Chapters 20, 21, and 23.

## Summary

### Life on Land (5.1)

Maintaining the balance of water between organisms and their surrounding environment has been a major influence on the evolution of life on land. The need to remain erect against the force of gravity in terrestrial environments results in a significant investment in structural materials. Variations in temperature and precipitation have both a short-term effect on metabolic processes and a long-term influence on the evolution and distribution of terrestrial plants and animals. The result is a distinct pattern of terrestrial ecosystems across geographic gradients of temperature and precipitation.

### Light (4.2)

Light passing through a canopy of vegetation becomes attenuated. The density and orientation of leaves in a plant canopy influence the amount of light reaching the ground. Foliage density is expressed as leaf area index (LAI), the area of leaves per unit of ground area. The amount of light reaching the ground in terrestrial vegetation varies with the season. In forests, only about 1–5 percent of light striking the canopy reaches the ground. Sunflecks on the forest floor enable plants to endure shaded conditions.

### Soil Defined (5.3)

Soil is a natural product of unconsolidated mineral and organic matter on Earth's surface. It is the medium for plant growth; the principle factor controlling the fate of water in terrestrial environments; nature's recycling system, where the waste products of plants and animals are broken down and transformed into their basic elements; and habitat to a diversity of animal life.

### Weathering (5.4)

Soil formation begins with the weathering of rock and minerals. In mechanical weathering, water, wind, temperature, and plants break down rock. In chemical weathering, the activity of soil organisms, the acids they produce, and rainwater break down primary minerals.

### Soil Formation (5.5)

Soil results from the interaction of five factors: parent material, climate, biotic factors, topography, and time. Parent material provides the substrate from which soil develops.

Climate shapes the development of soil through temperature, precipitation, and its influence on vegetation and animal life. Biotic factors—vegetation, animals, bacteria, and fungi—add organic matter and mix it with mineral matter. Topography influences the amount of water that enters the soil and rates of erosion. Time is required for full development of distinctive soils.

### Distinguishing Characteristics (5.6)

Soils differ in the physical properties of color, texture, and depth. Although color has little direct influence on the function of a soil, it can be used to relate chemical and physical properties. Soil texture is the proportion of different-sized soil particles—sand, silt, and clay. A soil's texture is largely determined by the parent material but is also influenced by the soil-forming process. Soil depth varies across the landscape, depending on slope, weathering, parent materials, and vegetation.

### Soil Horizons (5.7)

Soils develop in layers called horizons. Four horizons are commonly recognized, although all are not necessarily present in any one soil: the O or organic layer; the A horizon, or topsoil, characterized by accumulation of organic matter; the B horizon, or subsoil, in which mineral materials accumulate; and the C horizon, the unconsolidated material underlying the subsoil, extending downward to the bedrock.

### Moisture-Holding Capacity (5.8)

The amount of water a soil can hold is one of its important characteristics. When water fills all pore spaces, the soil is saturated. When a soil holds the maximum amount of water it can retain, it is at field capacity. Water held between soil particles by capillary forces is capillary water. When the moisture level is at a point at which plants cannot extract water, the soil has reached wilting point. The amount of water retained between field capacity and wilting point is the available water capacity. The available water capacity of a soil is a function of its texture.

### Ion Exchange (5.9)

Soil particles, particularly clay particles and organic matter, are important to nutrient availability and the cation exchange capacity of the soil—the number of negatively charged sites on soil particles that can attract positively charged ions. Cations occupying the negatively charged particles in the soil are in a state of dynamic equilibrium with similar cations in the soil solution. Percent base saturation is the percentage of sites occupied by ions other than hydrogen.

## Soil Formation Processes Form Different Soils (5.10)

Broad regional differences in geology, climate, and vegetation give rise to characteristically different soils. The broadest level of soil classification is the order. Each order has distinctive features. Soil scientists recognize five main soil-forming processes that give rise to these different classes of soils. These processes are laterization, podzolization, calcification, salinization, and gleization.

## Study Questions

1. Name two constraints imposed on organisms in the transition of life from aquatic to terrestrial environments.

2. Assume that two forests have the same quantity of leaves (leaf area index). In one forest, however, the leaves are oriented horizontally (parallel to the forest floor). In the other forest, the leaves are positioned at an angle of 60 degrees. How would the availability of light at the forest floor differ for these two forests at noon? In which forest would the leaves at the bottom of the canopy (lower in the tree) receive more light at mid-morning?

3. What is the general shape of the curve that describes the vertical attenuation of light through the plant canopy based on Beer's law? Why is it not a straight line (linear)?

4. What five major factors affect soil formation?

5. What role does weathering play in soil formation? What factors are involved in the process of weathering?

6. Use Figure 5.10 to answer this question: Which soil holds more moisture at field capacity: clay or sand? Which soil holds more moisture at wilting point: clay or sand? Which soil type has a greater availability of water for plant uptake when the water content of the soil is 3.0 in./ft (value on $y$-axis)?

7. What is the major factor distinguishing the O and A soil horizons?

8. Why do clay soils typically have a higher cation exchange capacity than do sandy soils?

9. How does pH influence the base saturation of a soil?

10. Why is the process of salinization more prevalent in arid areas? How does irrigation increase the process of salinization in agricultural areas?

11. What soil-forming process is dominant in the wet tropical regions? How does this process influence the availability of nutrients to plant roots in the A horizon?

## Further Readings

Brady, N. C., and R. W. Weil. 1999. *The nature and properties of soils*. 12th ed. Upper Saddle River, NJ: Prentice Hall.
   The classic introductory textbook on soils. Used for courses in soil science.

Jenny, H. 1994. *Factors of soil formation*. Mineola, NY.: Dover Publications.
   A well written and accessible book written by one of the pioneers in soil science.

Kohnke, H., and D. P. Franzmeier. 1994. *Soil science simplified*. Prospect Heights, IL: Wavelength Press.
   A well written and illustrated overview of concepts and principles of soil science for the general reader. Provides many examples and applications of basic concepts.

Patton, T. R. 1996. *Soils: A new global view*. New Haven, CT: Yale University Press.
   Presents a new view and approach to studying soil formation at a global scale.

# Part Three | The Organism and Its Environment

The Namib Desert, stretching 1200 miles in length along the southwest coast of Africa, is home to the highest sand dunes in the world. Although rainfall is a rare event in the Namib, each morning as the sun rises, the cool, moist air of this coastal desert begins to warm, and the Namib becomes shrouded in fog. And each morning, black thumbnail-size beetles perform one of nature's more bizarre behaviors (Figure 1). These tenebrionid beetles (*Stenocara* spp.) upend their bodies into a handstand position. While the beetle is in this position, fog droplets collect on its back and then gradually roll down the wing case (called the elytra) into its mouth. When the bumps on its back

**Figure 1** | A tenebrionid beetle (*Stenocara spp.*) perched upon a sand dune in the Namib Desert of southeastern Africa.

(Figure 2) are viewed through an electron microscope, a wax-coated carpet of tiny nodules covering the sides of the bumps and the valleys between them can be seen, which aid in the channeling of water from the back to the mouth.

The tenebrionid beetles of the Namib desert illustrate two important concepts: the relationship between structure and function and how that relationship reflects adaptations of the organism to its environment. The structure of the beetle's back and its behavior of standing on its head in the morning fog serve the function of acquiring water, a scarce and essential resource in this arid environment. This same set of characteristics, however, are unlikely to be efficient for acquiring water in the desert regions of the continental interior where morning fog does not form, or in wet environments, such as a tropical rain forest, where standing pools of water are readily available.

A fundamental question to the ecologist is, What controls the distribution and abundance of species? What enables a species to succeed in one environment but not another? To the ecologist, the link between structure and function provides the first clue. The characteristics that an organism exhibits—its physiology, morphology (physical structure), behavior, and lifetime pattern of development and reproduction (life history)—reflect adaptations to the particular environment it lives in, which are the product of natural selection (see Chapter 2). Each environment presents a different set of con-

Figure 2 | Fog droplets can be seen on the wing case (elytra) of this tenebrionid beetle.

straints on processes relating to survival, growth, and reproduction. The set of characteristics that enable an organism to succeed in one environment typically preclude it from doing equally well under a different set of environmental conditions. The different evolutionary solutions to life in various environments represent the products of trade-offs. In nature, one size does not fit all. There are 1.5 million known species that inhabit Earth's diverse environments, which is 1.5 million different ways in which life exists on this planet.

Despite the diversity of species, all organisms (from single-celled bacteria to the largest of all animals, the blue whale) represent solutions to the same three basic functions shared by all living organisms: assimilation, reproduction, and the ability to respond to external stimuli. Organisms must acquire energy and matter from the external environment for the synthesis of new tissue through the process of assimilation. To maintain the continuity of life, some of the assimilated resources (energy and matter) must be allocated to reproduction—the production of new individuals. Finally, organisms must be able to respond to external stimuli relating to both the physical (such as heat and humidity) and the biotic (such as recognition of potential mates or predators) environments.

Perhaps the most fundamental constraint on life is the acquisition of energy. The acquisition and assimilation of essential nutrients and the processes associated with life—synthesis, growth, reproduction, and maintenance—require energy. Chemical energy is generated in the breakdown of carbon compounds in all living cells, a process called respiration. But the ultimate source of energy for life on Earth is the Sun (solar energy; see Chapter 3). It is solar energy that fuels photosynthesis, the process of assimilation in green plants. Through the consumption of plant and animal tissues, all other organisms use energy that comes directly or indirectly from photosynthesis. The source from which an organism derives its energy is one of the most basic distinctions in ecology. Organisms that derive their energy from sunlight are referred to as **autotrophs,** or **primary producers.** Organisms that derive energy from consuming plant and animal tissues, breaking down assimilated carbon compounds, are called **heterotrophs,** or **secondary producers.** These two modes of acquiring energy impose fundamentally different evolutionary constraints, and for that reason, our discussion of adaptations to the environment in Part Three is divided into the subjects of autotrophs (Chapter 6: Plant Adaptations to the Environment) and heterotrophs (Chapter 7: Animal Adaptations to the Environment). These chapters will focus on adaptations relating to the exchange of energy and matter between organisms and their environment: the processes of energy, carbon, nutrient, and water balances that govern the survival and growth of individual organisms. The final chapter (Chapter 8: Life History Patterns) treats adaptations relating to reproduction; in other words, how resources are used to assure the continuity of life. The concept of trade-offs is a central theme in each of these discussions, linking the constraints imposed by different environments (and resources) and the "solutions" that are reflected in the traits that characterize each species—the products of natural selection.

# Chapter 6 | Plant Adaptations to the Environment

The use of the CAM photosynthetic pathway by these Kokerboom trees in the desert region of Bloedkoppie, Namibia, in southeastern Africa, functions to conserve water in this harsh environment.

All life on Earth is carbon-based. This means all living creatures are made up of complex molecules built on a framework of carbon atoms. The carbon atom is able to bond readily with other carbon atoms, forming long, complex molecules. The carbon atoms needed to construct these molecules—the building blocks of life—are derived from various sources. The means by which organisms acquire and use carbon represent some of the most basic adaptations required for life. Humans, like all other animals, gain their carbon by consuming other organisms. However, the ultimate source of carbon from which life is constructed is carbon dioxide ($CO_2$) in the atmosphere.

Not all living organisms can use this abundant form of carbon directly. Only one process is able to transform carbon in the form of $CO_2$ into organic molecules and living tissue. That process, carried out by green plants, algae, and some types of bacteria, is photosynthesis. Photosynthesis is essential for the maintenance of life on Earth. All other organisms derive their carbon (and most other essential nutrients) from the consumption of organic carbon compounds in the form of plant and animal tissues.

Although all green plants derive their carbon from photosynthesis, how organisms, from microscopic algae (phytoplankton) to the largest of trees, allocate the products of photosynthesis to the basic processes of growth and maintenance varies immensely. These differences represent a diversity of evolutionary solutions to the problem of being a plant—acquisition of the essential resources of carbon, light, water, and mineral nutrients necessary to support the process of photosynthesis. In this chapter, we will examine the variety of adaptations that plants have evolved that allow plant life to successfully survive, grow, and reproduce across virtually the entire range of environmental conditions found on Earth.

First, let us review the process so essential to life on Earth, or as the author John Updike so poetically phrased it, "the lone reaction that counterbalances the vast expenditures of respiration, that reverses decomposition and death."

## 6.1 | Photosynthesis Is the Conversion of Carbon Dioxide into Simple Sugars

**Photosynthesis** is the process by which energy from the Sun, in the form of shortwave radiation (photosynthetically active radiation, or PAR; see Section 3.1), is harnessed to drive a series of chemical reactions that result in the fixation of $CO_2$ into carbohydrates (simple sugars) and the release of oxygen ($O_2$) as a by-product.

The process can be expressed in the simplified form shown below:

$$6CO_2 + 12H_2O \longrightarrow C_6H_{12}O_6 + 6O_2 + 6H_2O$$

The net effect of the above chemical reaction is the utilization of six molecules of water ($H_2O$) and the production of six molecules of oxygen ($O_2$) for every six molecules of $CO_2$ that are transformed into one molecule of sugar ($C_6H_{12}O_6$). The synthesis of various other carbon-based compounds, such as proteins, fatty acids, and enzymes, from these initial products occurs in both the leaves and other parts of the plant.

Photosynthesis, a complex sequence of metabolic reactions, can be separated into two processes, often referred to as the light and dark reactions. The light reactions begin with the initial photochemical reaction

where chlorophyll (light-absorbing pigment) traps light energy within the chloroplast cells. The absorption of a photon of light raises the energy level of the chlorophyll molecule. The excited molecule is not stable, and the electrons rapidly return to their ground state, thus releasing the absorbed photon energy. This energy is transferred to another acceptor molecule, resulting in a process called photosynthetic electron transport. This process results in the synthesis of ATP (adenosine triphosphate) from ADP (adenosine diphosphate) and of NADPH (the reduced form of NADP) from $NADP^+$ (nicotinamide adenine dinucleotide phosphate). The high-energy substance ATP and the strong reductant NADPH produced in the light reactions are essential for the second step in photosynthesis: the dark reactions.

In the dark reactions, $CO_2$ is biochemically incorporated into simple sugars. The dark reactions do not directly require the presence of sunlight. They are, however, dependent on the products of the light reactions, and therefore ultimately depend on the essential resource of sunlight.

The process by which $CO_2$ is incorporated into simple sugars begins in most plants when the five-carbon molecule RuBP (ribulose biphosphate) combines with $CO_2$ to form two molecules of a three-carbon compound called 3-PGA (phosphoglycolate).

$$CO_2 \ + \ RuBP \longrightarrow 2 \ 3\text{-PGA}$$

| | | |
|:--:|:--:|:--:|
| 1-carbon molecule | 5-carbon molecule | 3-carbon molecule |

This reaction is called carboxylation and is catalyzed by the enzyme **rubisco** (ribulose biphosphate carboxylase-oxygenase). The plant quickly converts the 3-PGA formed in this process into the energy-rich sugar molecule G3P (glyceraldehyde 3-phosphate). The synthesis of G3P from 3-PGA requires both ATP and NADPH, the high-energy molecule and reductant that are formed in the light reactions. Some of this G3P is used to produce simple sugars ($C_6H_{12}O_6$), starches, and other carbohydrates required for the growth and maintenance of the plant, and the remainder is used to synthesize new RuBP to continue the process. The synthesis of new RuBP from G3P requires additional ATP. In this manner, the availability of light energy (solar radiation) can limit the dark reactions of photosynthesis through its control on the production of ATP and NADPH required for the synthesis of G3P and the regeneration of RuBP. This photosynthetic pathway involving the initial fixation of $CO_2$ into the 3-carbon PGAs is called the Calvin–Benson cycle, or $C_3$ cycle, and plants employing it are known as **$C_3$ plants** (Figure 6.1).

The $C_3$ pathway has one major drawback. The enzyme rubisco driving the process of carboxylation also acts as an oxygenase—rubisco can catalyze the reaction between $O_2$ and RuBP. The oxygenation of RuBP results in the eventual release of $CO_2$. This competitive reaction

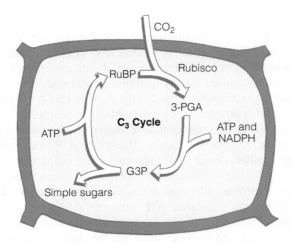

Figure 6.1 | A simple representation of the $C_3$ pathway, or Calvin–Benson cycle. Note the link between the light and dark reactions, as the products of the light reactions (ATP and NADPH) are required for the synthesis of the energy-rich sugar molecule G3P and the regeneration of RuBP.

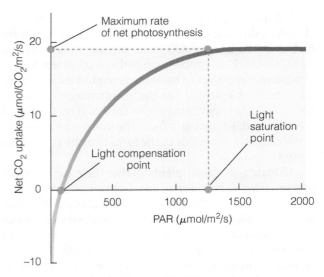

Figure 6.2 | Response of photosynthetic activity ($y$-axis) to available light ($x$-axis) (PAR: photosynthetically active radiation). The plant increases its rate of photosynthesis as the light level increases up to a maximum rate known as the light saturation point. The light compensation point is the value of PAR at which the uptake of $CO_2$ for photosynthesis equals the loss of $CO_2$ in respiration.

to the carboxylation process reduces the efficiency of $C_3$ photosynthesis.

Some of the carbohydrates produced in photosynthesis are used in the process of cellular respiration—the harvesting of energy from the chemical breakdown of simple sugars and other carbohydrates. Respiration involves the oxidation of carbohydrates to generate energy in the form of ATP and takes place exclusively in the mitochondria.

$$C_6H_{12}O_6 + 6O_2 \longrightarrow 6CO_2 + 6H_2O + ATP$$

Respiration occurs in all living cells, both plant and animal.

Because leaves both use $CO_2$ in the process of photosynthesis and produce $CO_2$ in the process of respiration, the difference in the rates of these two processes is the net gain, referred to as **net photosynthesis.**

Net photosynthesis = Photosynthesis − Respiration

The rates of photosynthesis and respiration, and therefore net photosynthesis, are typically measured in moles $CO_2$ per unit leaf area (or mass) per unit time.

## 6.2 | The Light a Plant Receives Affects Its Photosynthetic Activity

Solar radiation provides the energy required for the conversion of $CO_2$ into simple sugars. Thus, the availability of light (PAR) to the leaf will directly influence the rate at which photosynthesis proceeds (Figure 6.2). As the amount of light declines, the rate of carbon uptake in photosynthesis will eventually decline to a level at which it equals the rate of carbon loss in respiration. At this point, the rate of net photosynthesis is zero. The light

level (value of PAR) at which this occurs is called the **light compensation point.** At light levels below the compensation point, the rate of carbon loss due to respiration exceeds the rate of uptake in the process of photosynthesis, and as a result, there is a net loss of carbon dioxide from the leaf to the atmosphere.

As light levels exceed the light compensation point, the rate of photosynthesis increases with PAR, with the light reactions limiting the rate of photosynthesis. Eventually, photosynthesis becomes light saturated, and now the dark reactions limit the rate at which photosynthesis occurs. The value of PAR, above which no further increase in photosynthesis occurs, is referred to as the **light saturation point.** In some plants adapted to extremely shaded environments, photosynthetic rates decline as light levels exceed saturation. This negative effect of high light levels, called **photoinhibition,** can be the result of "overloading" the processes involved in the light reactions.

## 6.3 | Photosynthesis Involves Exchanges Between the Plant and Atmosphere

The process of photosynthesis occurs in specialized cells within the leaf that are called **mesophyll** cells. For photosynthesis to take place within the mesophyll cells, $CO_2$ must be transported from the outside atmosphere into the leaf. In terrestrial (land) plants, $CO_2$ enters through openings on the surface of the leaf that are called **stomata** (Figure 6.3) via the process of diffusion.

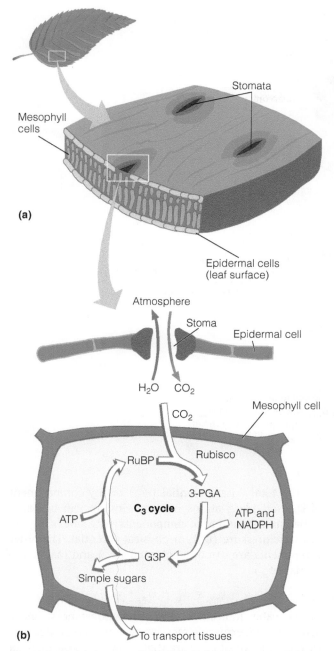

**Figure 6.3** | **(a)** Cross section of a leaf, showing stomata, mesophyll cells, and epidermal cells. **(b)** The $C_3$ pathway of photosynthesis. Carbon dioxide from the atmosphere diffuses into the leaf through the stoma to the mesophyll cells, where it is transformed into three-carbon molecules ($3 = $ PGA).

Diffusion is the movement of a substance from areas of higher to lower concentration (see Quantifying Ecology 4.1: Diffusion and Osmosis). Concentrations of $CO_2$ are often described in units of parts per million (ppm) of air. A $CO_2$ concentration of 355 ppm would be 355 molecules of $CO_2$ for every 1 million molecules of air. Substances flow from areas of high concentration to areas of low concentration until the concentrations in the two areas are equal. As long as the concentration of $CO_2$ in the air outside the leaf is greater than that inside the leaf, $CO_2$ will continue to diffuse through the stomata.

As $CO_2$ diffuses into the leaf through the stomata, why don't the concentrations of $CO_2$ inside and outside the leaf come into equilibrium? As $CO_2$ is transformed into sugar during the process of photosynthesis, the concentration inside the leaf declines. As long as photosynthesis occurs, the gradient remains. If photosynthesis was to stop and the stomata were to remain open, $CO_2$ would diffuse into the leaf until the internal $CO_2$ equaled the outside concentration.

When photosynthesis and the demand for $CO_2$ are reduced for any reason, the stomata tend to close, thus reducing flow into the leaf. The reason for this closure is that stomata play a dual role. As $CO_2$ diffuses into the leaf through the stomata, water vapor inside the leaf diffuses out through the same openings. This water loss through the stomata is called **transpiration.**

The rate at which water moves from inside the leaf, through the stomata, and into the surrounding outside air depends on the diffusion gradient of water vapor from inside to outside the leaf. Like $CO_2$, water vapor diffuses from areas of high concentration to areas of low concentration—from wet to dry. For all practical purposes, the air inside the leaf is saturated with water, so the outflow of water is a function of the amount of water vapor in the air—the relative humidity (see Section 3.6; Figure 3.16). The drier the air (lower the relative humidity), the more rapidly the water inside the leaf will diffuse through the stomata into the outside surrounding air. The leaf must replace the water lost to the atmosphere; otherwise, it will wilt and die.

## 6.4 | Water Moves from the Soil, Through the Plant, to the Atmosphere

The rate of growth of plant cells and the efficiency of their physiological processes are highest when the cells are at maximum turgor: that is, when they are fully hydrated. When the water content of the cell declines, turgor pressure drops, and water stress occurs, ranging from wilting to dehydration. For the leaves to maintain maximum turgor, the water lost to the atmosphere in transpiration must be replaced by water taken up from the soil through the root system of the plant and transported to the leaves. The dual role of stomata in $CO_2$ uptake and water loss (transpiration) leads to the inevitable conflict between the maintenance of turgor and high photosynthetic rates as water availability declines.

As the leaf loses water via transpiration, the turgor of the leaf cells drops, setting up a pressure gradient from the leaf to the root–soil surface, resulting in water movement from the soil into the root and from the root

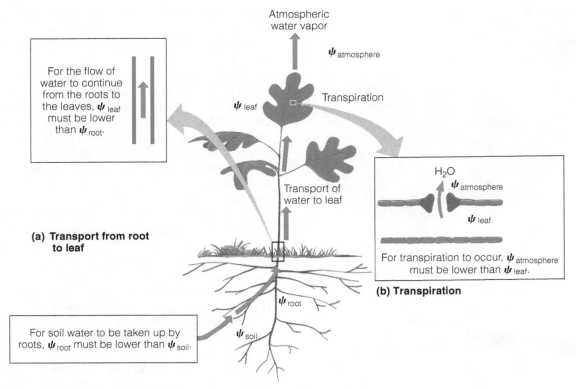

**Figure 6.4** | Transport of water along a water potential ($\psi$) gradient from soil to leaves to air. **(a)** As long as the osmotic potential of the roots is lower than that of the soil, $\psi_{\text{root}}$ will be lower than $\psi_{\text{soil}}$, and the roots will continue to take up water from the soil. **(b)** As long as the vapor pressure of the atmosphere (relative humidity) is lower than that of the air inside the leaf, $\psi_{\text{atmosphere}}$ will be lower than $\psi_{\text{leaf}}$, and transpiration will continue.

through the conductive tissue to the leaf (Figure 6.4). The movement of water through the soil–plant–atmosphere continuum is passive and in response to the pressure gradient. In the case of transpiration, the exchange of water from the leaf interior to the atmosphere is a function of the hydrostatic pressure gradient represented by the difference in the absolute water vapor pressure between the inside of the leaf and the outside air (see Section 6.3). However, in the various transfers of water from the soil to the root, and from the root to the leaf, forces other than hydrostatic pressure are involved. For this reason, the concept of water potential is used to describe the pressure gradient. The symbol used to represent water potential is $\psi$, and it is defined in pressure units, generally megapascals (MPa). As with hydrostatic pressure, water flows from areas of high to areas of low water potential. In nature, values of water potential typically range from zero, when water is freely available, to increasingly negative values. Therefore, for water to flow from the soil into the roots, through the conductive tissues into the leaf, and from the leaf to the atmosphere, the following condition must hold:

$$\psi_{\text{atmosphere}} < \psi_{\text{leaf}} < \psi_{\text{root}} < \psi_{\text{soil}}$$

The total water potential ($\psi_{\text{w}}$) of any compartment of the soil–plant–atmosphere continuum can be partitioned into a number of components, with one being hydrostatic pressure ($\psi_{\text{p}}$), or physical potential. The other components are osmotic potential ($\psi_{\pi}$) and matric potential ($\psi_{\text{m}}$).

$$\psi_{\text{w}} = \psi_{\text{p}} + \psi_{\pi} + \psi_{\text{m}}$$

As water molecules (and other substances) move across a semipermeable membrane, diffusion generates a certain amount of pressure that slows the movement of water across it. The amount of pressure needed to stop its movement across a membrane is called **osmotic pressure** (see Quantifying Ecology 4.1: Diffusion and Osmosis). Osmotic pressure accounts for the turgor achieved by plant cells when the water supply is adequate. As plants face internal water stress, the concentration of water molecules in the cells decreases, and water, when available, moves from the soil solution into the plant. The tendency of a solution to attract water molecules from areas of high to low concentration is called its **osmotic potential.** The osmotic potential of a solution depends on its concentration (see Section 4.5). The higher the concentration of solutes (and thus the lower the concentration of water molecules), the lower the solution's osmotic potential and the greater is its tendency to gain water. Osmotic potential is a major component of the total leaf and root water potentials.

Water in the soil moves along the potential gradient into the roots, which have a higher solute concentration and lower water potential. The water potential gradient from the soil to the atmosphere prevents the roots from achieving equilibrium with the soil water potential and draws the water up through the plant. Plants draw water from the soil, where the water potential is the highest, to the atmosphere, where water potential is the lowest (most negative). When the relative humidity of the atmosphere drops below 100 percent, the water potential of the atmosphere rapidly becomes negative, thus increasing the capacity of the air to evaporate water and drive transpiration. Drawn by the low water potential of the atmosphere, moisture from the surface of and between the mesophyll cells within the leaf evaporates and escapes through the stomata. To replace the water lost, more water is pulled from the xylem (hollow conducting tubes throughout the plant) in the leaf veins. Transpiration and replacement of water at the cell's surface make the surface water potential more negative. The negative water potential extends down to the fine rootlets in contact with soil particles and pores. This tension pulls water from the root and up through the stem to the leaf. The root water potential declines so that more water moves from the soil into the root.

The loss of water through transpiration continues as long as the amount of energy striking the leaf is enough to supply the necessary latent heat of evaporation, moisture is available for roots in the soil, and the roots are capable of removing water from the soil. At field capacity (see Section 5.8), water is freely available, and soil water potential is at or near zero. As water is drawn from the soil, the water content of the soil declines, and the soil water potential ($\psi_{soil}$) becomes more negative.

The tendency for water to adhere to surfaces is called **matric potential.** As the water content of the soil declines, the remaining water adheres more tightly to the surfaces of the soil particles, and the matric potential becomes more negative. For a given water content, the matric potential of soil is influenced strongly by its texture (see Figure 5.10). Soils composed of fine particles, such as clays, have a higher surface area (per soil volume) for water to adhere to than do sandy soils and therefore maintain more negative matric potentials for the same water content.

As soil water potential becomes more negative, the root and leaf water potentials must decline to maintain the potential gradient. If precipitation does not recharge soil water and soil potentials continue to decline, eventually the plant will not be able to maintain the potential gradient. At this point, the stomata will close to stop fur-

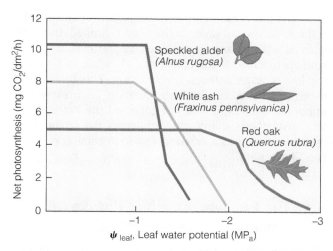

**Figure 6.5 |** Changes in net photosynthesis (*y*-axis) as a function of leaf water potential ($\psi_{leaf}$: *x*-axis) for three tree species from the northeastern United States. The decline in net photosynthesis with declining leaf water potentials (more negative values) results primarily from stomatal closure. As the water content of the soil declines, the plant must reduce the leaf water potential to maintain the gradient so that water can move from the soil to the roots and from the roots to the leaves. Eventually, a point is reached when the plant is no longer able to reduce leaf water potentials further and the stomata will close to reduce the loss of water.

ther loss of water through transpiration. However, this closure also results in stopping further uptake of $CO_2$. The soil water potential at which stomatal closure occurs is a function of the ability of the plant to reduce leaf water potentials further without disrupting basic physiological processes. The value of leaf water potential at which stomates close and net photosynthesis ceases varies among plant species (Figure 6.5) and reflects basic differences in their biochemistry, physiology, and morphology.

The rate of water loss varies with daily environmental conditions, such as humidity and temperature, and with the characteristics of plants. Opening and closing the stomata is probably the most important regulator of water loss through the plant. The trade-off between the uptake of $CO_2$ and the loss of water through the stomata results in a direct link between water availability in the soil and the ability of the plant to carry out photosynthesis. To carry out photosynthesis, the plant must open its stomata; but when it does, it will lose water, which it must replace. If water is scarce, the plant must balance the opening and closing of the stomata, taking up enough $CO_2$ while minimizing the loss of water. The ratio of carbon fixed (photosynthesis) per unit of water lost (transpiration) is called the **water-use efficiency.**

We can now appreciate the trade-off faced by terrestrial plants. To carry out photosynthesis, the plant must open the stomata to take up $CO_2$, but at the same time the plant will lose water through the stomata to the outside air; water that must be replaced through the plant's roots. If the availability of water to the plant is limited, the plant is faced with balancing the opening and closing of the stomata to allow for the uptake of $CO_2$ while minimizing the loss of water through transpiration. This balance between photosynthesis and transpiration is an extremely important constraint that has governed the evolution of terrestrial plants and directly influences the productivity of ecosystems under differing environmental conditions (see Chapter 20).

## 6.5 | The Process of Carbon Uptake Differs Between Aquatic and Terrestrial Plants

The major difference in $CO_2$ uptake and assimilation between aquatic and terrestrial plants is the lack of stomata in submerged aquatic plants. $CO_2$ diffuses from the atmosphere into the surface waters followed by mixing into the water column. Once dissolved, $CO_2$ reacts with the water to form bicarbonate ($HCO_3^-$). This reaction is reversible, and the concentrations of $CO_2$ and bicarbonate tend toward a dynamic equilibrium (see Section 4.7). In aquatic plants, there is a direct diffusion of $CO_2$ from the waters adjacent to the leaf across the cell membrane. Once inside, the process of photosynthesis proceeds in much the same manner as that outlined above for terrestrial plants.

One difference is that some aquatic plants can also use bicarbonate as a carbon source. However, the plants must first convert it to $CO_2$ using the enzyme carbonic anhydrase. This conversion can occur in two ways: (1) active transport of bicarbonate into the leaf followed by conversion to $CO_2$ or (2) excretion of the enzyme into adjacent waters and subsequent uptake of converted $CO_2$ across the membrane. As $CO_2$ is taken up, its concentration in the waters adjacent to the leaf will decline. Because the diffusion of $CO_2$ in water is $10^4$ times slower than in the air, it can easily become depleted (low concentrations) in the waters adjacent to the leaf, reducing rates of plant uptake and photosynthesis. This constraint can be particularly important in still waters such as dense seagrass beds or rocky intertidal pools.

## 6.6 | Plant Temperatures Reflect Their Energy Balance with the Surrounding Environment

Both photosynthesis and respiration respond directly to variations in temperature (Figure 6.6). As temperatures rise above freezing, both photosynthesis and respiration rates increase. Initially, photosynthesis increases faster than respiration. As temperatures continue to rise, the photosynthetic rate reaches a maximum related to the temperature response of the enzyme rubisco. As temper-

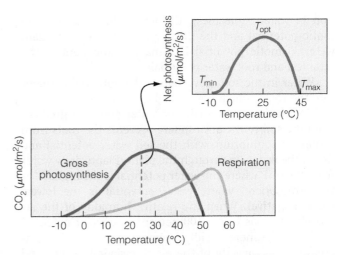

Figure 6.6 | The general response of the rates of photosynthesis and respiration to temperature. At any temperature, the difference between these two rates is the rate of net photosynthesis (net uptake rate of $CO_2$). Here, the optimal temperature for net photosynthesis is between 20°C and 30°C.

atures continue to rise, photosynthetic rate declines, and respiration rate continues to increase. As temperatures rise further, even respiration declines as temperatures reach critical levels. The temperature response of net photosynthesis is the difference between the rate of carbon uptake in photosynthesis and the rate of carbon loss in respiration (see Figure 6.6). Three values describe the temperature response curve: $T_{min}$, $T_{opt}$, and $T_{max}$. $T_{min}$ and $T_{max}$ are, respectively, the minimum and maximum temperatures at which net photosynthesis approaches zero, meaning no net carbon uptake. $T_{opt}$ is the temperature, or range of temperatures, over which net carbon uptake is at its maximum.

It is the temperature of the leaf, not the air, that controls the rate of photosynthesis and respiration, and leaf temperature is a function of the exchange of energy (radiation) between the leaf and its surrounding environment. Plants absorb both shortwave (solar) and longwave (thermal) radiation (see Section 4.1). Plants reflect some of this solar radiation and emit longwave radiation back to the atmosphere. The difference between the radiation a plant receives and the radiation it reflects and emits back to the surrounding environment is the net energy balance of the plant ($R_n$). The net energy balance of a plant is analogous to the concept of the energy balance of Earth presented in Chapter 3 (see Figure 3.3). Of the net radiation absorbed by the plant, some is used in metabolic processes and stored in chemical bonds; namely, in the processes of photosynthesis and respiration. This quantity is quite small, typically less than 5 percent of $R_n$. The remaining energy heats the leaves and the surrounding air. On a clear, sunny day, the amount of energy plants absorb can raise internal leaf temperatures well above ambient (air or water temperature). Internal leaf temperatures may go beyond the optimum for photosynthesis and possibly reach critical levels (Figure 6.6).

To maintain internal temperatures within the range of tolerance (positive net photosynthesis), plants must dissipate heat to the surrounding environment. Terrestrial plants lose heat by convection and evaporation and aquatic plants primarily by convection (see Quantifying Ecology 7.1: Heat Exchange and Temperature Regulation). Recall from Chapter 3 that convection is the transfer of heat energy between a solid and a moving fluid. Convective loss depends on the difference between the temperature of the leaf and the surrounding fluid (air or water). If the temperature of the leaf is higher than that of the surrounding air, the leaf loses heat to the air moving over it. Evaporation occurs in the process of transpiration. As plants transpire water from their leaves to the surrounding atmosphere through the stomata, the leaves lose energy, and their temperature declines through evaporative cooling (see Section 4.2).

The size and shape of their leaves influence the ability of plants to exchange heat through convection (see Quantifying Ecology 7.1: Heat Exchange and Temperature Regulation). Deeply lobed leaves, like those of some oaks, and small, compound leaves, lose heat more effectively than broad, unlobed leaves (Figure 6.7). They ex-

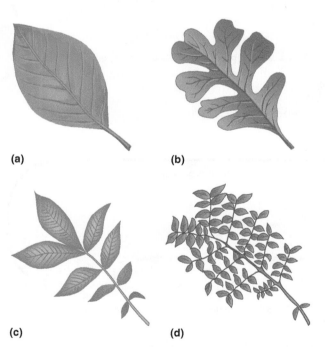

**Figure 6.7** | Four general categories of leaf shape: **(a)** entire, **(b)** lobed, **(c)** simple compound, and **(d)** double compound. For a given volume or mass of leaf, the greater the surface area exposed to the surrounding air, the greater the potential for the exchange of heat energy through convection (see Quantifying Ecology 7.1: Heat Exchange and Temperature Regulation).

pose more surface area per volume of leaf to the air for exchange of heat. The ability of terrestrial plants to dissipate heat by evaporation is dependent on the rate of transpiration, which is influenced by both the relative humidity of the air and the availability of water to the plant (see Section 6.2).

## 6.7 | Carbon Gained in Photosynthesis Is Allocated to the Production of Plant Tissues

Because leaves both take in carbon dioxide in the process of photosynthesis and produce carbon dioxide in the process of respiration, a simple economic approach can be used to explore the balance of these two processes. This approach is referred to as the **carbon balance.** Thus far, our discussion of plant carbon balance has focused on net photosynthesis: the balance between the processes of photosynthesis and respiration in the leaves of green plants. However, plants are not composed only of leaves but also have roots and supportive tissues such as stems. Keeping with our simple economic model, the net uptake of carbon by the whole plant will be the difference between the uptake of carbon in photosynthesis minus the loss of carbon in respiration (Figure 6.8a). The total carbon uptake or gain per unit time will be the product of the average rate of carbon uptake in photosynthesis per unit of leaf area (photosynthetic surface) multiplied by the total surface area of leaves. Because all living cells respire, the total loss of carbon in respiration per unit time will be a function of the total mass of living tissue; that is, the sum of leaf, stem, and root tissues. The net carbon gain for the whole plant per unit time is the difference between these two values (carbon gain and carbon loss). This net carbon gain is then allocated to a variety of processes. Some of the carbon will be used in maintenance and the rest in the synthesis of new tissues in plant growth and reproduction.

How the net carbon gain is allocated will have a major influence on the survival, growth, and reproduction of the plant. The acquisition of essential resources necessary to support photosynthesis and growth involves different plant tissues. Leaf tissue is the photosynthetic surface, providing access to the essential resources of light and $CO_2$. The root tissue provides access to belowground resources such as water and nutrients in the soil, as well as serving to anchor the plant to the soil. Stem tissue provides vertical support, elevating leaves above the ground and increasing access to light by reducing the chance of being shaded by taller plants (see Section 5.2). It also provides the conductive tissue necessary to move water and nutrients from the roots to other parts of the plant. As we discuss in the following sections, the availability of these essential resources for plant growth influences the allocation of carbon to the production of various tissues.

Under ideal conditions (no resource limitations), the allocation of carbon to the further production of leaf tissue will promote the fastest growth. Increased allocation to leaf tissue increases the photosynthetic surface, which increases the rate of carbon uptake as well as carbon loss due to respiration. Allocation to all other tissues, such as stem and root, increases the respiration rate but does not directly increase the capacity for carbon uptake through photosynthesis. The consequence is the reduction of net carbon gain by the plant (Figure 6.8b). However, the allocation of carbon to the production of stem and root tissue is essential for acquiring the key resources necessary to maintain photosynthesis and growth. As these resources become scarce, it becomes increasingly necessary to allocate carbon to the production of these tissues at the trade-off of leaf production. The implications of these shifts in patterns of carbon allocation will be addressed in the following sections.

## 6.8 | Constraints Imposed by the Physical Environment Have Resulted in a Wide Array of Plant Adaptations

In Part Two (Chapters 3–5), we explored variation in the physical environment over Earth's surface: the salinity, depth, and flow of water; spatial and temporal patterns in climate (precipitation and temperature); variations in geology and soils. In all but the most extreme of these environments, autotrophs—green plants—harness the energy of the Sun to fuel the conversion of carbon dioxide into glucose in the process of photosynthesis. To survive, grow, and reproduce, plants must maintain a positive carbon balance, converting enough carbon dioxide into glucose to offset the expenses of respiration (photosynthesis > respiration). To accomplish this, a plant must acquire the essential resources of light, carbon dioxide, water, and mineral nutrients and tolerate other features of the environment that have a direct influence on basic plant processes, such as temperature, salin-

**Figure 6.8** | The net carbon gain of a plant is the difference between carbon gain in photosynthesis and carbon loss in respiration. Because leaves (or more generally, photosynthetic tissues) are responsible for carbon gain, while all plant tissues respire (leaves, stem, and roots), the net carbon gain will be directly influenced by the pattern of carbon allocation to the production of different plant tissues. **(a)** Increased allocation to leaves will increase carbon gain (photosynthesis) relative to carbon loss (respiration) and therefore increase net carbon gain. **(b)** Increased allocation to roots will have the opposite effect, decreasing carbon gain relative to carbon loss. The result is a lower net carbon gain by the plant.

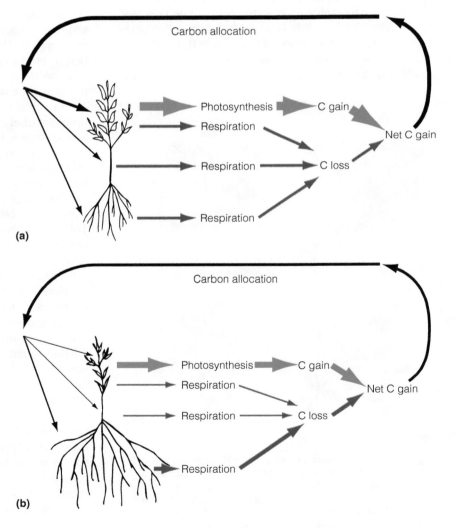

ity, and pH. Although often discussed and even studied as though they are independent of each other, the adaptations exhibited by plants to these features of the environment are not independent, for reasons relating to both the physical environment and the plants themselves.

Many features of the physical environment that have a direct influence on plant processes are interdependent. For example, the light, temperature, and moisture environments are all linked through a variety of physical processes discussed in Chapters 3–5. The amount of solar radiation not only influences the availability of light (PAR) required for photosynthesis but also has a direct influence on the temperature of the leaf and its surroundings. In addition, air temperature has a direct influence on the relative humidity, a key feature influencing the rate of transpiration and evaporation of water from the soil (see Section 3.6, Figure 3.17). For this reason, we see a correlation in the adaptations of plants to variations in these environmental factors. Plants adapted to dry, sunny environments must be able to deal with the higher demand for water associated with higher temperatures and lower relative humidity and have characteristics such as smaller leaves and increased production of roots.

In other cases, there are trade-offs in the ability of plants to adapt to limitations imposed by multiple environmental factors, particularly resources. One of the most important of these trade-offs is in the acquisition of above- and below-ground resources. Allocation of carbon to the production of leaves and stems provides increased access to the resources of light and carbon dioxide but at the expense of allocation of carbon to the production of roots. Likewise, allocation to the production of roots increases access to water and soil nutrients but limits the production of leaves and therefore the rate of carbon gain in photosynthesis. The set of characteristics (adaptations) that allow a plant to successfully survive, grow, and reproduce under one set of environmental conditions inevitably limits its ability to do equally well under different environmental conditions. We explore the consequences of this simple premise in the following sections.

## 6.9 | Species of Plants Are Adapted to Either High or Low Light

Although the amount of solar radiation reaching Earth's surface varies diurnally, seasonally, and geographically (Section 3.2), one of the major factors influencing the amount of light (PAR) a plant receives is the presence of other plants through shading (see Section 5.2, and Quantifying Ecology 5.1: Beer's Law and the Attenuation of Light). Although the amount of light that reaches an individual plant varies continuously as a function of the area of leaves above it, plants live in one of two qualitatively different light environments—sun or shade—depending on whether they are overtopped by other plants. Plants have evolved a range of physiological and morphological adaptations that allow individuals to survive, grow, and reproduce in these two different light environments.

The relationship between the availability of light and the rate of photosynthesis varies among plants (Figure 6.9). Plants growing in shaded environments tend to have a lower light compensation point, a lower light saturation point, and a lower maximum rate of photosynthesis than plants growing in high-light environments.

These differences relate in part to lower concentrations of the photosynthetic enzyme rubisco (see Section 6.1) found in shade-grown plants. Plants must expend a large amount of energy and nutrients to produce rubisco and other components of the photosynthetic apparatus. In shaded environments, low light, not the availability of rubisco to catalyze the fixation of $CO_2$, limits the rate at which photosynthesis can proceed. The plant produces less rubisco as a result. By contrast, production of chlorophyll, the light-harvesting pigment in the leaves, often increases. The reduced energy cost of producing rubisco and other compounds involved in photosynthesis functions to lower the rate of leaf respiration. Because the light compensation point is the value of PAR necessary to maintain photosynthesis at a rate that exactly offsets the loss of $CO_2$ in respiration (net photosynthesis = 0), the lower rate of respiration is offset by a lower rate of photosynthesis, requiring less light. The result is a lower light compensation point. However, the same reduction in enzyme concentrations limits the maximum rate at which photosynthesis can occur when light is abundant (high PAR). Thus, it lowers the light saturation point and maximum rate of photosynthesis.

The work of ecologist Stuart Davies of Harvard University illustrates this trade-off in leaf respiration rate, light compensation point, and maximum rate of net photosynthesis under conditions of high and low light. Davies examined the response of nine tree species of the genus *Macaranga* that inhabit the rain forests of Borneo (Malaysia) to variations in the light environment. Davies grew seedlings of the nine species in a greenhouse under two light regimes: high light (total daily PAR of 21.4 mol/m$^2$/day), and low light (7.6 mol/m$^2$/day). The shaded (low light) treatment was created using shade cloth. After a period of approximately 6 months, he took measurements of net photosynthesis under varying light levels (values of PAR) for seedlings of each species grown under high and low light. The resulting light response curves, such as the one presented in Figure 6.2, were used to estimate values of leaf respiration, light compensation point, and the maximum rate of net photosynthesis at light saturation. A comparison of the nine species is presented in Figure 6.10; p. 115.

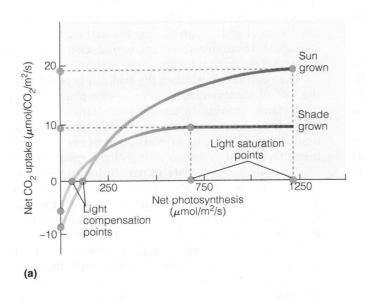

(a)

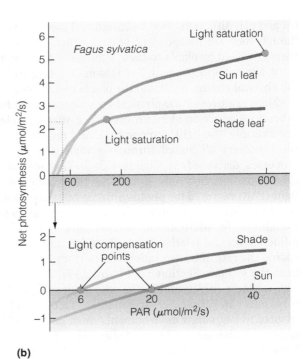

(b)

**Figure 6.9** | **(a)** General patterns of photosynthetic response to light availability (photosynthetically active radiation; PAR) for plants grown in sun and shade environments. Shade-grown plants typically have a lower light compensation point and a lower light saturation point than do sun-grown plants. These same differences in photosynthetic response to light are also seen when comparing shade-tolerant (shade-adapted) and shade-intolerant (sun-adapted) plant species. **(b)** Example of shift in photosynthetic characteristics of sun and shade leaves for *Fagus sylvatica*. Sun leaf is from the periphery of the canopy where leaves are exposed to full sunlight. Shade leaf is from the shaded interior of the canopy. Insert shows the regions of the response curves below 50 $\mu mol/m^2/s$, illustrating the differences in the light compensation points. (Adapted from Larcher 1995.)

The rate of leaf respiration for seedlings grown under low-light conditions was significantly lower than the corresponding value for individuals of the same species grown under high-light conditions (Figure 6.10a). This reduction in leaf respiration rate was accompanied by both a decrease in the light compensation point (Figure 6.10b) and the maximum rate of net photosynthesis at light saturation (Figure 6.10c). These shifts in the photosynthetic characteristics of leaves from plants grown in high- and low-light environments were also accompanied by changes in leaf morphology (structure).

The ratio of surface area ($cm^2$) to weight (g) for a leaf is called the specific leaf area (SLA; $cm^2/g$). The value of SLA represents the surface area of leaf produced per gram of biomass (or carbon) allocated to the production of leaves. Plants grown under low-light conditions typically produce leaves with a greater specific leaf area. In the experiment conducted by Davies, SLA increased for all nine species when grown under low-light conditions (Figure 6.10d). In general, leaves grown under reduced light conditions are larger (in surface area) and thinner than those grown under high-light levels

(Figure 6.11). The shift in leaf structure effectively increases the surface area for the capture of light (the limiting resource) per unit of biomass allocated to the production of leaves.

In addition to producing broader, thinner leaves, plants grown under shaded conditions allocate a greater proportion of their net carbon gain to leaf production and less to the roots (Figure 6.12; p.116). Just as with the changes in leaf morphology (thinner, broader leaves), this shift in allocation from roots to leaves increases the surface area for the interception of light. The increase in leaf area (photosynthetic surface area) can partially offset the decrease in photosynthetic rates per unit leaf area under low-light conditions, allowing the plant to maintain a positive carbon balance and continued growth (see Quantifying Ecology 6.1: Relative Growth Rate).

The patterns in photosynthetic and morphological response to variations in the light environment described above can occur among plants of the same species grown under different light conditions (as in Figures 6.11 and 6.12) and even among leaves on the same plant with different exposures to light (as in Figures 6.7b and 6.11). Such change in the physiology or form of an individual

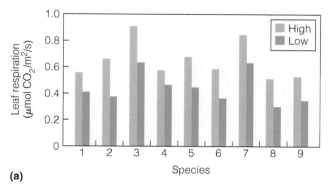

**(a)**

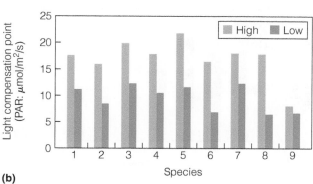

**(b)**

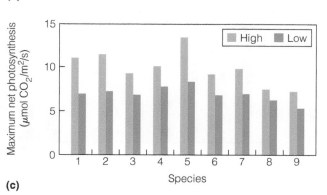

**(c)**

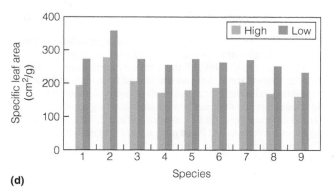

**(d)**

**Figure 6.10** | Variation in **(a)** leaf respiration rate, **(b)** light compensation point, **(c)** light saturated rate of net photosynthesis, and **(d)** specific leaf area for seedlings of nine tree species of the genus *Macaranga* grown in contrasting light environments (high light: 21.4 mol/m$^2$/day; low light: 7.6 mol/m$^2$/day). The nine species of *Macaranga* inhabit the forests of Borneo, Malaysia. Species codes: (1) *M. hosei*, (2) *M. winkleri*, (3) *M. gigantea*, (4) *M. hypoleuca*, (5) *M. beccariana*, (6) *M. triloba*, (7) *M. trachyphylla*, (8) *M. hullettii*, and (9) *M. lamellata*. (Adapted from Davies 1998.)

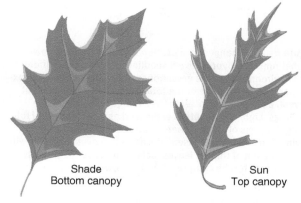

Shade
Bottom canopy

Sun
Top canopy

**Figure 6.11** | Example of the response of leaf shape (morphology) to the light environment under which it developed. Red oak (*Quercus rubra*) leaves vary in size and shape from the top to the bottom of the tree. Leaves at the top of the canopy receive higher levels of solar radiation and experience higher temperatures than those growing at the bottom. Upper leaves are smaller, thicker, and more lobed than those growing at the bottom. This morphology aids in heat loss through convection. Conversely, the larger, thinner leaves at the bottom increase the surface area for capture of light.

organism in response to changes in environmental conditions is a form of phenotypic plasticity (see Section 2.3). These differences, however, are most pronounced between species of plants adapted to high- and low-light environments (see Researcher Profile: Kaoru Kitajima). These adaptations represent genetic (genotypic) differences in the potential response of the plant species to the light environment. Plant species adapted to high-light environments are called **shade-intolerant** species, or sun-adapted species. Plant species adapted to low-light environments are called **shade-tolerant** species, or shade-adapted species.

The variations in photosynthesis, respiration, and growth rate that characterize plant species adapted to different light environments are illustrated in the work of plant ecologist Peter Reich and colleagues at the University of Minnesota. They examined the characteristics of nine tree species that inhabit the cool temperate forests of northeastern North America (boreal forest).

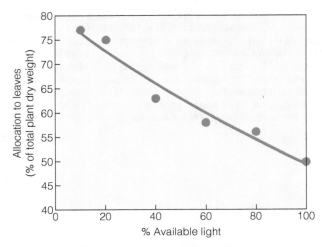

**Figure 6.12** | Changes in allocation to leaves for broadleaved peppermint (*Eucalyptus dives*) seedlings grown under different light environments in the greenhouse. Allocation to leaves is expressed as a percentage of the total dry weight of the plant at harvest. Each point represents the average response of five seedlings. Light availability is expressed as a percentage of full sunlight. Levels of shading were controlled by shade-cloth of varying density. The increased allocation to leaves, together with the production of thinner leaves, acts to increase the photosynthetic surface for the capture of light. (Adapted from Smith et al. 2002.)

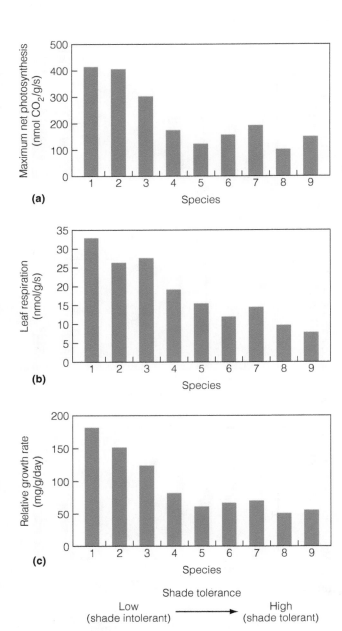

**Figure 6.13** | Differences in the rates of **(a)** light saturated photosynthesis, **(b)** leaf respiration, and **(c)** relative growth rate for nine tree species that inhabit the forests of northeastern North America (boreal zone). Species are ranked from highest (shade intolerant) to lowest (shade tolerant) in terms of shade tolerance. Species codes: (1) *Populus tremuloides* (quaking aspen), (2) *Betula papyrifera*, (3) *Betula allegheniensis*, (4) *Larix laricina*, (5) *Pinus banksiana*, (6) *Picea glauca*, (7) *Picea mariana*, (8) *Pinus strobus*, and (9) *Thuja occidentalis*. (Adapted from Reich et al. 1998.)

The species differ widely in shade tolerance from very tolerant of shaded conditions to very intolerant. Seedlings of the nine species were grown in the greenhouse, and measurements of maximum net photosynthetic rate at light saturation, leaf respiration rate, and relative growth rate (growth rate per unit plant biomass; see Quantifying Ecology 6.1: Relative Growth Rate) were made over the course of the experiment (Figure 6.13). Species adapted to lower light environments (shade tolerant) are characterized by lower maximum rates of net photosynthesis, leaf respiration, and relative growth rate than are species adapted to higher light environments (shade intolerant).

The difference in the photosynthetic characteristics between shade-tolerant and shade-intolerant species influences not only rates of net carbon gain and growth but also ultimately the ability of individuals to survive in low-light environments. This relationship is illustrated in the work of Caroline Augspurger of the University of Illinois. She conducted a series of experiments designed to examine the influence of light availability on seedling survival and growth for a variety of tree species, both shade tolerant and intolerant, that inhabit the tropical rain forests of Panama. Augspurger grew tree seedlings of each species under two levels of light availability. These two treatments mimic the conditions found either under the shaded environment of a continuous forest canopy (shade treatment) or in the higher light environment in openings or gaps in the canopy caused by the death of large trees (sun treatment). She continued the experiment for a year, monitoring the survival and growth of seedlings on a weekly basis. The results for two contrasting species, shade tolerant and a shade intolerant, are presented in Figure 6.14.

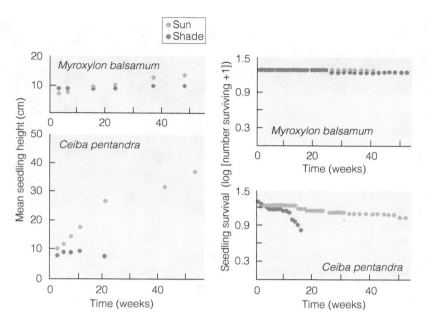

**Figure 6.14** | Seedling survival and growth over a period of 1 year for seedlings of two tree species on Barro Colorado Island, Panama, grown under sun and shade conditions. *Ceiba pentandra* is a shade-intolerant species; *Myroxylon balsamum* is shade tolerant. (Adapted from Augspurger 1982.)

The shade-tolerant species (*Ceiba pentandra*) showed little difference in survival and growth rates under sunlight and shade conditions. In contrast, both survival and growth rates of the shade-intolerant species (*Myroxylon balsamum*) were dramatically reduced under shade conditions. These observed differences are a direct result of the difference in the adaptations relating to photosynthesis and carbon allocation discussed earlier. The higher rate of light-saturated photosynthesis results in a high growth rate for the shade-intolerant species in the high-light environment. The associated high rate of leaf respiration and light compensation point, however, reduced rates of survival in the shaded environment. By week 20 of the experiment, all individuals had died. In contrast, the shade-tolerant species was able to survive in the low-light environment. The low rates of leaf respiration and light-saturated photosynthesis that allow for the low-light compensation point, however, limit rates of growth even in high-light environments.

The dichotomy in adaptations between shade-tolerant and shade-intolerant species reflects a trade-off between characteristics that enable a species to maintain high rates of net photosynthesis and growth under high-light conditions and the ability to continue survival and growth under low-light conditions. The changes in biochemistry, physiology, leaf morphology, and carbon allocation exhibited by shade-tolerant species enable them to reduce the amount of light required to survive and grow. However, these same characteristics limit their ability to maintain high rates of net photosynthesis and growth when light levels are high. In contrast, plants adapted to high-light environments (shade-intolerant species) can maintain high rates of net photosynthesis and growth under high-light conditions but at the expense of continuing photosynthesis, growth, and survival under shaded conditions.

## 6.10 | The Link Between Water Demand and Temperature Influences Plant Adaptations

As with the light environment, terrestrial plants have evolved a range of adaptations in response to variations in precipitation and soil moisture. As we saw in the earlier discussion of transpiration (see Section 6.3), however, the demand for water is linked to temperature (see Ecological Issues: Global Warming and Grapes). As air temperature rises, the saturation vapor pressure will likewise rise (see Section 3.6), increasing the gradient of water vapor between the inside of the leaf and the outside air and subsequently the rate of transpiration. As a result, the amount of water required by the plant to offset losses from transpiration will likewise increase with temperature.

When the atmosphere or soil is dry, plants respond by partially closing the stomata and opening them for shorter periods of time. In the early period of water stress, a plant closes its stomata during the hottest part of the day. It resumes normal activity in the afternoon. As water becomes scarcer, the plant opens its stomata only in the cooler, more humid conditions of morning. This closure reduces the loss of water through transpiration, but it also reduces $CO_2$ diffusion into the leaf and the dissipation of heat through evaporative cooling. As a result, the rate of photosynthesis declines, and leaf temperatures may rise. Some plant species, such as evergreen rhododendrons, respond to moisture stress by an inward curling of the leaves. Others show it in a wilted appearance caused by a lack of turgor in the leaves. Both leaf curling and wilting allow leaves to reduce water loss and heat gain by reducing the surface area exposed to solar radiation.

**A** major factor influencing the availability of light to a plant is its neighbors. By intercepting light, taller plants shade individuals below, influencing rates of photosynthesis, growth, and survival. Nowhere is this effect more pronounced than on the forest floor of a tropical rain forest (Figure 1), where light levels are often less than 1 percent of those recorded at the top of the canopy (see Section 5.2). With the death of a large tree, however, a gap is created in the canopy, giving rise to an "island" of light on the forest floor. With time, these gaps in the canopy will eventually close, as individuals grow up to the canopy from below or neighboring trees expand their canopies, once again shading the forest floor.

How these extreme variations in the availability of light at the forest floor have influenced the evolution of rain forest plant species has been the central research focus of plant ecologist Kaoru Kitajima of the University of Florida. Kitajima's work in the rain forests of Barro Colorado Island in Panama presents a story of plant adaptations to variations in the light environment that includes all life-stages of the individual, from seed to adult.

Within the rain forests of Barro Colorado Island, the seedlings of some tree species survive and grow only in the high-light environments created by the formation of canopy gaps, whereas the seedlings of other species can survive for years in the shaded conditions of the forest floor.

In a series of experiments designed to determine shade tolerance based on patterns of seedling survival in sun and shade environments (see Figure 6.10), Kitajima noted that seed mass (weight) is negatively correlated with seedling mortality rates. Interestingly, not only did large-seeded species have higher rates of survival in the shade, they also exhibited slower rates of growth after germination. Intuitively, one might think that larger reserves of energy and nutrients within the seed (larger mass) would allow for a faster rate of initial development, but this was not the case. What role does seed size (reserves) play in the survival and growth of species in different light environments? An understanding of these relationships requires close examination of how seed reserves are used.

The storage structure(s) within a seed are called the cotyledon. Upon germination, cotyledons transfer reserve materials (lipids, carbohydrates, mineral nutrients) into developing shoots and roots. The cotyledons of some species serve strictly as organs to store and transfer seed reserves throughout their life span and are typically positioned at or below the ground level (Figure 2a), whereas the cotyledons of other species develop a second function: photosynthetic carbon assimilation. In these species, the cotyledons function as "seed leaves" and are raised above the ground (Figure 2b). As Kitajima's research has revealed, the physiological function of cotyledons is of great importance in determining growth response of seedlings to the light environment.

Kitajima conducted an experiment involving tree species that differed in cotyledon function (photosynthetic and storage) and shade tolerance. Seedlings were raised from germination under two light levels: sun (23 percent full sun) and shade (1 percent full sun).

Change in biomass and leaf area were recorded during a period of 40 days postgermination to determine when light began to affect seedling growth (determined for each species by the difference between individuals grown in shade and sun environments).

The smaller seeds of the shade-intolerant species had photosynthetic cotyledons and developed leaves earlier than shade-tolerant species with their larger storage cotyledons. These differences reflect two different "strategies" in the use of initial seed reserves. Shade-intolerant species invested reserves into the production of leaves to bring about a rapid return (carbon uptake in photosynthesis), whereas shade-tolerant species kept seed reserves as storage for longer periods at the expense of growth rate.

**Figure 1** | The dense canopy and understory in a tropical rainforest results in little light reaching the forest floor.

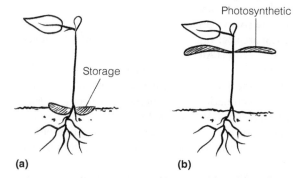

**Figure 2** | Two contrasting functional forms of cotyledons found in tropical rain forest trees: **(a)** storage and **(b)** photosynthetic.

Having used their limited seed reserves for the production of leaves, the shade-intolerant species responded to light availability earlier than did the shade-tolerant species. And in the absence of sufficient light, mortality was generally the outcome.

So the experiments revealed that larger seed storage in shade-tolerant species does not result in a faster initial growth under shaded conditions; rather, these species (shade tolerant) exhibit a conservative strategy of slow use of reserves over a prolonged period.

Whether shade tolerant or intolerant, once seedlings use up seed reserves, maintenance of a positive net carbon gain is a prerequisite for survival (see Section 6.7). What suites of seedling traits allow some species to survive better than others in the shade? To answer this question, Kitajima grew seedlings in the experimental sun and shade environments for an extended period beyond the reserve phase.

Individuals of both shade-tolerant and shade-intolerant species shifted allocation of carbon from the production of roots to the production of leaves as well as produced broader, thinner leaves under shaded conditions (higher specific leaf area: SLA, see Quantifying Ecology 6.1: Relative Growth Rate.)

Despite the similarity between shade-tolerant and shade-intolerant species in their phenotypic responses to reduced available light, these two types exhibit different overall patterns of morphology and carbon allocation. Under both sun and shade conditions, shade-tolerant species had a greater proportional allocation to roots (relative to leaves), thicker leaves (lower SLA), and, as a result, a lower photosynthetic surface area than did shade-intolerant species. As a result, the relative growth

rates of shade-intolerant species were consistently greater than those of the shade-tolerant species, both in sun and shaded conditions (Figure 3).

Whereas the characteristics exhibited by the shade-intolerant species reflect strong natural selection for fast growth within light gaps, shade-tolerant species appear adapted to survive for many years in the understory, where their ability to survive attacks by pathogens and herbivores is enhanced by their well-developed reserves within the root system. ●

### Bibliography

Kitajima, K. 1996. Ecophysiology of tropical tree seedlings. In *Tropical forest plant ecophysiology*, eds. S. Mulkey, R.L. Chazdon, and A.P. Smith, 559–96. New York: Chapman & Hall.

Kitajima, K. 2002. Do shade-tolerant tropical tree seedlings depend longer on seed reserves? *Functional Ecology* 16:433–44.

1. What processes might create gaps in the forest canopy?

2. How might seed size influence the method of seed dispersal from the parent plant?

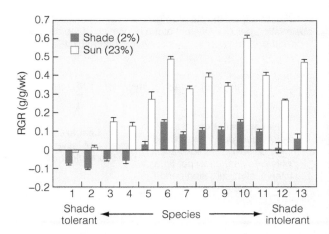

**Figure 3** | Relative growth rates (RGRs) of 13 tropical tree species grown as seedlings from germination to 10 weeks under controlled shade and sun conditions. Species are ranked based on their shade tolerance (survival in shade). Species codes: (1) *Aspidosperma cruenta*, (2) *Tachigalia versicolor*, (3) *Bombacopsis sessilis*, (4) *Platypodium elegans*, (5) *Lonchocarpus latifolius*, (6) *Lafoensia punicifolia*, (7) *Terminalia amazonica*, (8) *Cordia alliodora*, (9) *Pseudobombax septenatum*, (10) *Luehea seemannii*, (11) *Ceiba pentandra*, (12) *Cavanillesia platanifolia*, (13) *Ochroma pyramidale* (Adapted from Kitajima 1994.)

**W**hen we think of growth rate, what typically comes to mind is a measure of change in size during some period of time, such as change in weight during the period of a week (grams weight gain/week). However, this conventional measure of growth is often misleading when comparing individuals of different sizes or tracking the growth of an individual through time, because although larger individuals may have a greater absolute weight gain when compared with smaller individuals, this may not be the case when weight gain is expressed as a proportion of body weight (proportional growth). A more appropriate measure of growth is the mass specific or relative growth rate. **Relative growth rate (RGR)** expresses the growth during the observed period of time as a function of the size of the individual. This calculation is found by dividing the increment of growth during some observed time period (grams weight gain) by the size of the individual at the beginning of that time period (grams weight gain/total grams weight at the beginning of observation period) and then dividing the period of time to express the change in weight as a rate (g/g/time).

The use of RGR in evaluating the growth of plants has an additional value, in that it can be partitioned into components reflecting the influences of assimilation (photosynthesis) and allocation on growth: the assimilation of new tissues per unit leaf area (g/cm$^2$/time), called the **net assimilation rate (NAR)**, and the leaf area per unit of plant weight (cm$^2$/g), called the **leaf area ratio (LAR)**.

The NAR is a function of the total gross photosynthesis of the plant minus the total plant respiration. It is the net assimilation gain expressed on a per unit leaf area basis. The LAR is a function of the amount of that assimilation that is allocated to the production of leaves, more specifically leaf area, expressed on a per unit plant weight basis.

The LAR can be further partitioned into two components that describe the allocation of net assimilation to leaves, the **leaf weight ratio (LWR)**, and a measure of leaf density or thickness, the **specific leaf area (SLA)**. The LWR is the total weight of leaves expressed as a proportion of total plant weight (g leaves/g total plant weight), whereas the SLA is the area of leaf per gram of leaf weight. For the same tissue density, a thinner leaf would have a greater value of SLA.

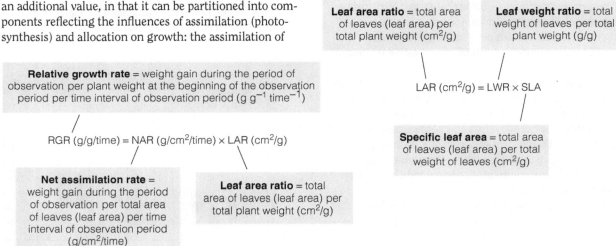

**Leaf area ratio** = total area of leaves (leaf area) per total plant weight (cm$^2$/g)

**Leaf weight ratio** = total weight of leaves per total plant weight (g/g)

LAR (cm$^2$/g) = LWR × SLA

**Relative growth rate** = weight gain during the period of observation per plant weight at the beginning of the observation period per time interval of observation period (g g$^{-1}$ time$^{-1}$)

RGR (g/g/time) = NAR (g/cm$^2$/time) × LAR (cm$^2$/g)

**Net assimilation rate** = weight gain during the period of observation per total area of leaves (leaf area) per time interval of observation period (g/cm$^2$/time)

**Leaf area ratio** = total area of leaves (leaf area) per total plant weight (cm$^2$/g)

**Specific leaf area** = total area of leaves (leaf area) per total weight of leaves (cm$^2$/g)

---

Prolonged moisture stress inhibits the production of chlorophyll, causing the leaves to turn yellow or, later in the summer, to exhibit premature autumn coloration. As conditions worsen, deciduous trees may prematurely shed their leaves, the oldest ones dying first. Such premature shedding can result in dieback of twigs and branches.

In tropical regions with distinct wet and dry seasons (see Section 3.7), some species of trees and shrubs have evolved the characteristic of dropping their leaves at the onset of the dry season. These plants are termed *drought deciduous*. In these species, leaf senescence occurs at the onset of the dry season, and new leaves are grown just prior to the onset of rains.

The real value of partitioning the estimate of RGR is for purposes of comparison, either among individuals of different species or among individuals of the same species grown under different environmental conditions. For example, the data presented in the table opposite are the results of a greenhouse experiment where seedlings of *Acacia tortilis* (a tree that grows on the savannas of southern Africa) were grown under two different light environments: full sun and shaded (50 percent full sun). Individuals were harvested at two times (4 and 6 weeks), and the total plant weight, total leaf weight, and total leaf area were measured. The mean values of these measures are shown in the table. From these values, estimates of RGR, LAR, LWR, and SLA were calculated. The values of RGR are calculated using the total plant weights at 4 and 6 weeks. NAR was then calculated by dividing the RGR by LAR. Because LAR varies through time (between weeks 4 and 6), the average of LAR at 4 and 6 weeks was used to characterize LAR in estimating RGR. Note that the average size (weight and leaf area) of seedlings grown in the high-light environment is approximately twice that of seedlings grown in the shade. Despite this difference in size, and the lower light levels to support photosynthesis, the difference in RGR between sun- and shade-grown seedlings is only about 20 percent. By examining the components of RGR, we can see how the shaded individuals are able to accomplish this task. Low-light conditions reduced rates of photosynthesis, subsequently reducing NAR for the individuals grown in the shade. The plants compensated, however, by increasing the allocation of carbon (assimilates) to the production of leaves (higher LWR) and producing thinner leaves (higher SLA) than the individuals grown in full sun. The result is that individuals grown in the shade have a greater LAR (photosynthetic surface area relative to plant weight), offsetting the lower NAR and maintaining comparable RGR.

| | week 4 | | week 6 | |
| --- | --- | --- | --- | --- |
| | sun | shade | sun | shade |
| leaf area (cm$^2$) | 18.65 | 12.45 | 42 | 24 |
| leaf weight (g) | 0.056 | 0.032 | 0.126 | 0.061 |
| stem weight (g) | 0.090 | 0.058 | 0.283 | 0.138 |
| root weight (g) | 0.099 | 0.043 | 0.239 | 0.089 |
| total weight (g) | 0.245 | 0.133 | 0.648 | 0.288 |
| LAR (cm$^2$/g) | 75.998 | 93.750 | 64.854 | 83.304 |
| SLA (cm$^2$/g) | 334 | 392 | | |
| LWR (g/g) | 0.228 | 0.239 | 0.194 | 0.213 |
| | | | | |
| RGR (g/g/week) | | | 0.471 | 0.382 |
| NAR (g/cm$^2$/week) | | | 0.007 | 0.004 |

These results illustrate the value of using the approach of RGR for examining plant response to varying environmental conditions, either among individuals of the same species or among individuals of different species adapted to different environmental conditions. By partitioning the components of plant growth into measures directly related to morphology, carbon allocation, and photosynthesis, we can begin to understand how plants both acclimate and adapt to differing environmental conditions. ●

1. When plants are grown under dry conditions (low water availability), there is an increase in the allocation of carbon to the production of roots at the expense of leaves. How would this shift in allocation influence the plant's leaf area ratio (LAR)?

2. Nitrogen availability can directly influence the rate of net photosynthesis. Assuming no change in the allocation of carbon or leaf morphology, how would an increase in the rate of net photosynthesis resulting from an increase in nitrogen availability influence relative growth rate? Which component of RGR would be influenced by the increase in net photosynthesis?

Some species of plants, referred to as C$_4$ and CAM plants, have evolved a modified form of photosynthesis that functions to increase water-use efficiency in warmer and drier environments. The modification involves an additional step in the conversion (fixation) of CO$_2$ into sugars.

In C$_3$ plants, the capture of light energy and the transformation of CO$_2$ into sugars occur in the meso- phyll cells. The products of photosynthesis move into the vascular bundles, part of the plant's transport system, where they can be transported to other parts of the plant. In contrast, plants possessing the **C$_4$ photosynthetic pathway** have a leaf anatomy different from that of C$_3$ plants (see Figure 6.11). C$_4$ plants have two distinct types of photosynthetic cells: the mesophyll cells and the

During the past century, Earth's climate has warmed. The mean global surface temperature has risen by as much as 1°C, and many scientists believe this warming is due largely to changes in the composition of the atmosphere brought about largely by the burning of fossil fuels (see Chapter 29). One of the key questions facing ecologists is how this warming will influence the growth of plants.

Two measures of available heat energy are typically associated with plant growth, the length of the growing season, and an index of integrated temperatures over the growing season. The growing season refers to the period of the year during which environmental conditions are suitable for plant growth. In the temperate zone, the growing season is generally defined by the time period, usually measured in days, between the last frost in the spring and the first frost in the fall.

During the growing season, the relative rates of photosynthesis and respiration vary over the course of the day and from day to day as temperatures vary. The accumulation of carbon and the growth of individual plants will reflect these variations in temperature over the course of the growing season. A measure that is commonly used to integrate temperature over a single growing season as it relates to plant growth is the index of growing degree-days (GDD).

Each plant species has its own minimum temperature requirement for photosynthesis and growth. Because of these differences, ecologists typically refer to an average minimum temperature of 5°C when characterizing the heat requirements of plants as a group. The index of GDD is calculated as the sum of the departures in temperatures above this minimum temperature. GDD for 1 day is calculated as the difference between average daily temperature and 5°C. So on a day when the average temperature is 12°C, the GDD is 7. GDD is calculated for only those days when the average temperature is higher than the minimum temperature (5°C). Annual GDD is calculated as the sum of GDD for the growing season or year and represents the heat energy available for plant growth.

The rise in mean global surface temperature during the past century has been characterized by a faster increase in minimum temperatures compared to maximum temperatures. Both the overall warming and the disproportionate increase in minimum temperatures have contributed to both a lengthening of the growing season and an overall increase in GDD, especially in mid to high latitudes. In the northeastern United States, the frost-free season now begins an average of 11 days earlier than in the 1950s. In regions of British Columbia, Canada, values of annual GDD have increased by as much as 16 percent during this same period.

A significant increase in available heat energy could have both positive and negative effects on crop species and agricultural production within the temperate zone. Warmer conditions (increased growing season and GDD) would allow farmers to succeed in introducing new varieties of crops that were previously marginal or not viable in their regions. In other areas, however, warming could have negative effects on agriculture. Warmer temperatures and greater evapotranspiration, for example, may mean less available soil moisture in some regions, requiring an increase in irrigation to maintain plant growth. For the wine industry, however, this increase in heat energy has been a positive.

Over the Napa and Sonoma Valleys of California, annual average temperatures have risen by 1.13°C during the period 1951–1997. Nearly all of this warming is due to an increase in nighttime (minimum) temperatures. In addition, the warming has been highly seasonal, with the average spring warming nearly twice that for the rest of the year. The result has been a 71 percent decline in the frost frequency and a corresponding 66-day increase in the growing season. For the vineyards of the Napa and Sonoma Valleys (one of the largest grape-producing regions of the world), this pattern of warming has been extremely positive. Both grape yield and the quality of wine that they produce have risen steadily during this period.

The benefits of global warming, however, might be short lived. Future predictions for California suggest a continued warming and drying, which would negatively affect agricultural production, including the wine industry, as atmospheric concentrations of greenhouse gases continue to rise into the future (see Chapter 29). •

1. Could the value of the growing-degree index for an area increase without changing the length of the growing season? How?
2. Minimum temperatures occur at night; therefore, the increase in minimum temperatures associated with global warming is largely an increase in nighttime temperatures. Because the rate of respiration increases with temperature, how might this influence the carbon balance of plants?

**bundle sheath cells.** The bundle sheath cells surround the veins or vascular bundles (Figure 6.15). $C_4$ plants divide photosynthesis between the two types of cells: the mesophyll and the bundle sheath cells.

In $C_4$ plants, $CO_2$ reacts with PEP (phosphoenolpyruvate), a three-carbon compound, within the mesophyll cells. This is in contrast to the initial reaction between RuBP in $C_3$ plants. This reaction is catalyzed by the enzyme **PEP carboxylase,** producing OAA (oxaloacetate) as the initial product. The OAA is then rapidly transformed into the four carbon molecules of malic and aspartic acids. These organic acids are then transported to the bundle sheath cells (see Figure 6.15). There, enzymes break down the organic acids to form $CO_2$, reversing the process that is carried out in the mesophyll cells. In the bundle sheath cells, the $CO_2$ is transformed into sugars using the $C_3$ pathway involving RuBP and rubisco.

The extra step in the fixation of $CO_2$ gives $C_4$ plants certain advantages. First, PEP does not interact with oxygen, as does RuBP. This eliminates the inefficiency that occurs in the mesophyll cells of $C_3$ plants when rubisco catalyzes the reaction between $O_2$ and RuBP, leading to the production of $CO_2$ and a reduction in the rate of net photosynthesis (see Section 6.1). Second, the conversion of malic and aspartic acids into $CO_2$ within the bundle sheath cells acts to concentrate $CO_2$. The concentration of $CO_2$ within the bundle sheath cells can reach much higher concentrations than in either the mesophyll cells or the surrounding atmosphere. The higher concentrations of $CO_2$ in the bundle sheath cells increases the efficiency of the reaction between $CO_2$ and RuBP catalyzed by rubisco. The net result is that the maximum rate of photosynthesis is generally higher in $C_4$ plants than in $C_3$ plants.

To understand the adaptive advantage of the $C_4$ pathway, we must go back to the trade-off in terrestrial plants between the uptake of $CO_2$ and the loss of water through the stomata. Due to the higher photosynthetic rate, $C_4$ plants exhibit greater water-use efficiency. That is, for a given degree of stomatal opening and water loss, $C_4$ plants typically fix more carbon. This increased water-use efficiency can be a great advantage in hot, dry climates where water is a major factor limiting plant growth. However, it comes at a price. The $C_4$ pathway has a higher energy expenditure because of the need to produce PEP and the associated enzyme, PEP carboxylase.

The $C_4$ photosynthetic pathway is not found in algae, bryophytes, ferns, gymnosperms (includes conifers, cycads, and ginkos), or the more primitive flowering plants (angiosperms). $C_4$ plants are mostly grasses native to tropical and subtropical regions and some shrubs characteristic of arid and saline environments, such as *Larrea* (creosote bush) and *Atriplex* (salt bush) that dominate

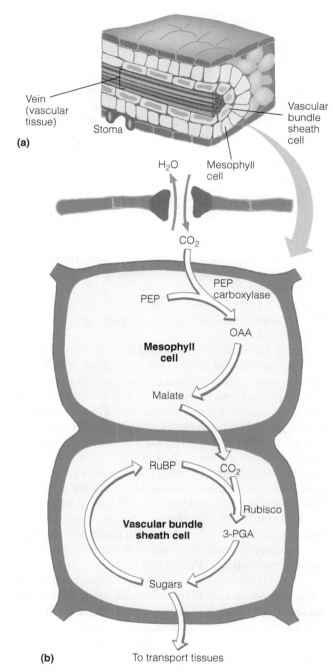

**Figure 6.15** | The $C_4$ pathway of photosynthesis. Different reactions take place in the mesophyll and bundle sheath cells. Compare to the $C_3$ pathway (see Figure 6.1). PEP, phosphoenolpyruvate; OAA, oxaloacetate.

regions of the desert southwest in North America. The distribution of $C_4$ grass species in North America reflects the advantage of the $C_4$ photosynthetic pathway under warmer and drier conditions (Figure 6.16). The proportion of total grass species within the community that are

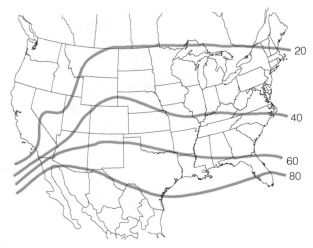

Figure 6.16 | Percentage of total grass species that are $C_4$. Values on isopleths (lines) represent percentages. (Adapted from Teeri and Stone 1976.)

$C_4$ increases from north to south, reaching a maximum in the southwest.

In the hot deserts of the world, environmental conditions are even more severe. Solar radiation is high, and water is scarce. To counteract these conditions, a small group of desert plants, mostly succulents in the families Cactaceae (cacti), Euphorbiaceae, and Crassulaceae, use a third type of photosynthetic pathway: the Crassulacean acid metabolism (CAM). The **CAM pathway** is similar to the $C_4$ pathway in that $CO_2$ is first transformed into the four-carbon compounds using the enzyme PEP carboxylase. The four-carbon compounds are later converted back into $CO_2$, which is transformed into glucose using the $C_3$ cycle. Unlike $C_4$ plants, however, in which these two steps are physically separate (in mesophyll and bundle sheath cells), both steps occur in the mesophyll cells but at separate times (Figure 6.17).

CAM plants open their stomata at night, taking up $CO_2$ and converting it to malic acid using PEP, which accumulates in large quantities in the mesophyll cells. During the day, the plant closes its stomata and reconverts the malic acid into $CO_2$, which it then fixes using the $C_3$ cycle. Relative to both $C_3$ and $C_4$ plants, the CAM pathway is slow and inefficient in the fixation of $CO_2$, but by opening their stomata at night when temperatures are lowest and relative humidity is highest, CAM plants dramatically reduce water loss through transpiration.

Plants may also respond to a decrease in available soil water by increasing the allocation of carbon to the production of roots while decreasing the production of leaves (Figure 6.18). The increased production of roots allows the plant to explore a larger volume and depth of soil from which to extract water, and the reduction in leaf area decreases the amount of solar radiation the plant intercepts and the surface area that is losing water

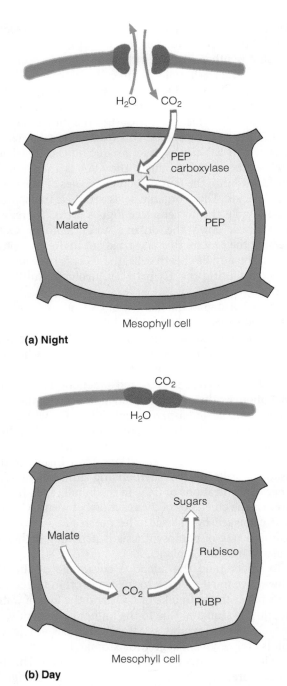

**(a) Night**

**(b) Day**

Figure 6.17 | Photosynthesis in CAM plants. **(a)** At night, the stomata open, the plant loses water through transpiration, and $CO_2$ diffuses into the leaf. $CO_2$ is stored as malate in the mesophyll, to be used in photosynthesis by day. **(b)** During the day, when stomata are closed, the stored $CO_2$ is refixed in the mesophyll cells using the $C_3$ cycle.

through transpiration. The combined effect is to increase the uptake of water per unit leaf area while reducing the total amount of water that is lost to the atmosphere through transpiration.

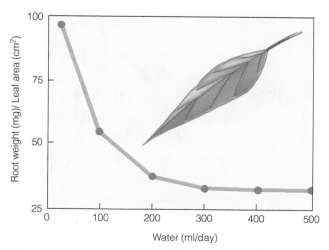

**Figure 6.18** | Relationship between plant water availability and the ratio of root mass (mg) to leaf area (cm²) for broadleaved peppermint (*Eucalyptus dives*) seedlings grown in the greenhouse. Each point on the graph represents the average value for plants grown under the corresponding water treatment. As water availability decreases, plants allocate more carbon to the production of roots relative to leaves. This increased allocation to roots increases the surface area of roots for the uptake of water, while the decline in leaf area decreases water loss through transpiration. (Adapted from Smith et al. 2002.)

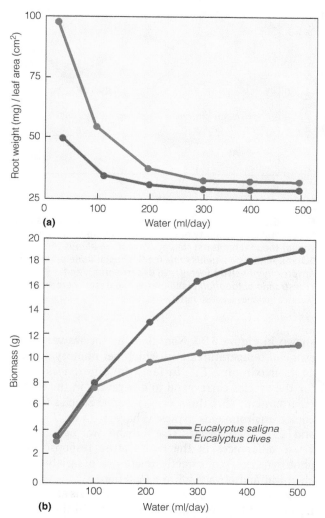

**Figure 6.19** | Comparison of patterns of carbon allocation and growth rate for two species of *Eucalyptus* along an experimental gradient of water availability. **(a)** Although both species exhibit the same patterns of response to declining water availability, the xeric species, *E. dives*, exhibits a consistently higher ratio of root mass (mg) to leaf area (cm²) than the mesic species, *E. saligna*, across the water gradient. **(b)** *E. saligna's* growth rate (biomass gain over period of experiment) continues to increase with increasing water availability. *E. dives* reaches maximum growth rate at intermediate water treatments. (Adapted from Smith et al. 2002.)

The decline in leaf area with decreasing water availability is actually a combined effect of both reduced allocation of carbon to the production of leaves and changes in leaf morphology (size and shape). The leaves of plants grown under reduced water conditions tend to be smaller and thicker (lower specific leaf area: see Section 6.9) than those of individuals growing in more mesic (wet) environments. In some plants, the leaves are small, the cell walls are thickened, the stomata are tiny, and the vascular system for transporting water is dense. Some species have leaves covered with hairs that scatter incoming solar radiation, whereas others have leaves coated with waxes and resins that reflect light and reduce its absorption. All these structural features reduce the amount of energy striking the leaf and thus the loss of water through transpiration.

Although the decrease in leaf area and corresponding increase in biomass allocated to roots (Figure 6.18) observed for plants growing under reduced water availability functions to reduce transpiration and increase the ability of the plant to acquire water from the soil, this shift in patterns of allocation has consequences to plant growth. The reduced leaf area decreases carbon gain from photosynthesis relative to the loss of carbon from respiration (see Figure 6.8). The result is a reduction in net carbon gain and growth rate of the plant.

As with the shifts in plant morphology under varying light environments (see Section 6.9), the observed changes in leaf shape and carbon allocation among indi-

viduals of the same species in response to the availability of water represent phenotypic plasticity (as in Figure 6.18). These differences, however, are most pronounced between species of plants adapted to wet (mesic) and dry (xeric) environments (Figure 6.19).

## 6.11 | Plants Vary in Their Response to Environmental Temperatures

The photosynthetic temperature response curves (see Figure 6.6) for a number of terrestrial plant species are

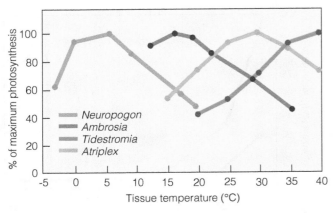

**Figure 6.20** | Relationship between net photosynthesis and temperature for a variety of terrestrial plant species from dissimilar thermal habitats: *Neuropogon acromelanus* (Arctic lichen), *Ambrosia chamissonis* (cool, coastal dune plant), *Atriplex hymenelytra* (evergreen desert shrub), and *Tidestromia oblongifolia* (summer-active desert perennial). (Adapted from Mooney et al. 1976.)

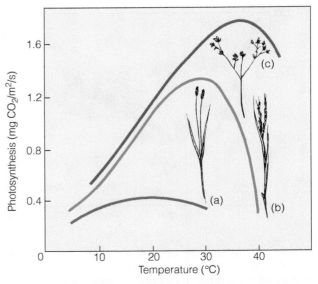

**Figure 6.21** | The effect of change in leaf temperature on the photosynthetic rates of $C_3$ and $C_4$ plants. **(a)** A $C_3$ plant, the north temperate grass *Sesleria caerulea*, exhibits a decline in the rate of photosynthesis as the temperature of the leaf increases. **(b)** A $C_4$ north temperate grass, *Spartina anglica*. **(c)** A $C_4$ shrub of the North American hot desert, *Tidestromia oblongifolia* (Arizona honeysweet). Note that the maximum rate of photosynthesis for the $C_4$ species occurs at higher temperatures than for the $C_3$ species. (Adapted from Bjorkman 1973.)

shown in Figure 6.20. Note that the species vary in the range of temperatures over which net photosynthesis is at its maximum, $T_{opt}$. In fact, the differences in $T_{opt}$ for the species correspond to differences in the thermal environments that the species inhabit. Species found in cooler environments typically have a lower $T_{min}$, $T_{opt}$, and $T_{max}$ than species that inhabit warmer climates. These differences in the temperature response of net photosynthesis are directly related to a variety of biochemical and physiological adaptations that act to shift the temperature responses of photosynthesis and respiration toward the prevailing temperatures in the environment. These differences are most pronounced between plants using the $C_3$ and $C_4$ photosynthetic pathways (see Section 6.10). $C_4$ plants inhabit warmer, drier environments and exhibit higher optimal temperatures for photosynthesis (generally between 30°C and 40°C) than do $C_3$ plants (Figure 6.21).

Although species from different thermal habitats exhibit different temperature responses for photosynthesis and respiration, these responses are not fixed. When two groups of individuals of the same species are grown under different thermal conditions in the laboratory or greenhouse, divergence in the temperature response of net photosynthesis is often observed (Figure 6.22). In general, the range of temperatures over which net photosynthesis is at its maximum shifts in the direction of the thermal conditions under which the plant is grown. That is to say, individuals grown under cooler temperatures exhibit a lowering of $T_{opt}$, whereas those individuals grown under warmer conditions exhibit an increase in $T_{opt}$. This same shift in the temperature response can be observed in individual plants in response to seasonal shifts in temperature (Figure 6.23).

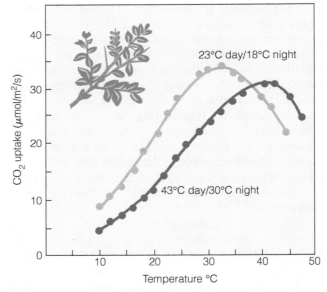

**Figure 6.22** | The relationship between temperature and net photosynthesis for cloned plants of big saltbush (*Atriplex lentiformis*) grown under two different day/night temperature regimes. Note that the shift in $T_{opt}$ corresponds to the temperature conditions under which the plants were grown. (Adapted from Pearcy 1977.)

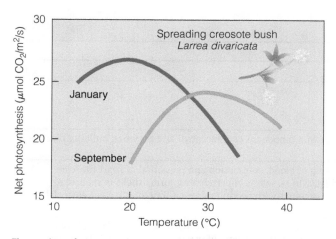

**Figure 6.23** | Seasonal shift in the relationship between net photosynthesis and temperature for creosote bush (*Larrea divacarta*) shrubs growing in the field. Note that $T_{opt}$ shifts to match the prevailing temperatures. (Adapted from Mooney et al. 1978.)

In addition to the influence of temperature on plant carbon balance, periods of extreme heat or cold can directly damage plant cells and tissues. Plants that inhabit seasonally cold environments, where temperatures drop below freezing for periods of time, have evolved a number of adaptations for survival. The leaves of some plant species can tolerate subzero ($<0°C$) temperatures if the temperature decreases slowly, allowing ice to form in the cell wall. The effect is dehydration, which the plant can reverse when the temperature rises. If the temperature falls too rapidly for dehydration to take place, ice crystals form within the cell. The crystals may puncture cell membranes. When the plant thaws, the cell contents spill out, giving the plant a cooked, wilted appearance.

The ability to tolerate extreme cold, referred to as frost hardening, is a genetically controlled characteristic that varies among species and among separated populations of the same species. In seasonally changing environments, plants develop frost hardening through the fall and achieve maximum hardening in winter. Plants acquire frost hardiness—the turning of cold-sensitive cells into hardy ones—through the formation or addition of protective compounds in the cells. Plants synthesize and distribute substances, such as sugars, amino acids, and other compounds, which function as antifreeze, lowering the temperature at which freezing occurs. Once growth starts in spring, plants lose this tolerance quickly and are susceptible to frost damage in late spring.

Producing the protective compounds that allow leaves to survive freezing temperatures requires a significant expenditure of energy and nutrients. Some species avoid these costs by shedding their leaves prior to the onset of the cold season. These plants are termed *winter deciduous*, and their leaves senesce during the fall. They are replaced during the spring, when conditions are once again favorable for photosynthesis. In contrast, needle-leaf evergreen species, such as pine (*Pinus* spp.) and spruce (*Picea* spp.) trees, contain a high concentration of these protective compounds, allowing the needles to survive the freezing temperatures of winter.

## 6.12 | Plants Exhibit Adaptations to Variations in Nutrient Availability

Both plants and animals require a variety of chemical elements to carry out their metabolic processes and to synthesize new tissues (Table 6.1). Thus, the availability of nutrients has many direct effects on plant survival, growth, and reproduction. Some of these elements, known as **macronutrients,** are needed in large amounts. Other elements are needed in lesser, often minute, quantities. These elements are called **micronutrients,** or trace elements. The prefixes micro and macro refer only to the quantity in which the nutrients are needed, not their importance to the organism. If micronutrients are lacking, plants fail as completely as if they lacked nitrogen, calcium, or any other macronutrient.

Of the macronutrients, carbon (C), hydrogen (H), and oxygen (O) form the majority of plant tissues. These elements are derived from $CO_2$ and $H_2O$ and are made available to the plant as glucose through photosynthesis. The remaining six macronutrients—nitrogen (N), phosphorus (P), potassium (K), calcium (Ca), magnesium (Mg), and sulfur (S)—exist in a variety of states in the soil, and their availability to plants is affected by different processes depending on their location in the physical environment (see Chapter 5). In the case of terrestrial environments, plants take up nutrients from the soil. In aquatic environments, plants take up nutrients from the substrate or directly from the water.

The best example of the direct link between nutrient availability and plant performance involves nitrogen. Nitrogen plays a major role in photosynthesis. In Section 6.1, we examined two important compounds in photosynthesis: the enzyme rubisco and the pigment chlorophyll. Rubisco catalyzes the transformation of carbon dioxide into simple sugars, and chlorophyll absorbs light energy. Nitrogen is a component of both compounds. In fact, more than 50 percent of the nitrogen content of a leaf is in some way involved directly with the process of photosynthesis, with much of it tied up in these two compounds. As a result, the maximum (light saturated) rate of photosynthesis for a species is correlated with the nitrogen content of its leaves (Figure 6.24).

The uptake of a nutrient depends on both supply and demand. Figure 6.25a illustrates the typical relationship between the uptake of a nutrient and its concentration in

Table 6.1   Some Essential Elements for Plant and Animal Growth

| Element | Role |
|---|---|
| *Macronutrients* | |
| Carbon (C) <br> Hydrogen (H) <br> Oxygen (O) | Basic constituents of all organic matter. |
| Nitrogen (N) | Used only in a fixed form: nitrates, nitrites, ammonium. Component of chlorophyll and enzymes; building block of protein. |
| Calcium (Ca) | In animals, needed for acid-base relationships, clotting of blood, contraction and relaxation of heart muscles. Controls movement of fluid through cells; gives rigidity to skeletons of vertebrates; forms shells of mollusks, arthropods, and one-celled Foraminifera. In plants, combines with pectin to give rigidity to cell walls; essential to root growth. |
| Phosphorus (P) | Necessary for energy transfer in living organisms; major component of nuclear material of cells. Animals require a proper ratio of Ca:P, usually 2:1 in the presence of vitamin D. Wrong ratio in vertebrates causes rickets. Deficiency in plants arrests growth, stunts roots, and delays maturity. |
| Magnesium (Mg) | In all living organisms, essential for maximum rates of enzymatic reactions in cells. Integral part of chlorophyll; involved in protein synthesis in plants. In animals, activates more than 100 enzymes. Deficiency in ruminants causes a serious disease, grass tetany. |
| Sulfur (S) | Basic constituent of protein. Plants use as much sulfur as they do phosphorus. Excessive sulfur is toxic to plants. |
| Sodium (Na) | Needed for maintenance of acid-base balance, osmotic homeostasis, formation and flow of gastric and intestinal secretions, nerve transmission, lactation, growth, and maintenance of body weight. Toxic to plants along roadsides when used to treat icy highways. |
| Potassium (K) | In plants, involved in osmosis and ionic balance; activates many enzymes. In animals, involved in synthesis of protein, growth, and carbohydrate metabolism. |
| Chlorine (Cl) | Enhances electron transfer from water to chlorophyll in plants. Role in animals similar to that of sodium, with which it is associated in salt (NaCl). |
| *Micronutrients* | |
| Iron (Fe) | In plants, involved in the production of chlorophyll; is part of the complex protein compounds that activate and carry oxygen and transport electrons in mitochondria and chloroplasts. In animals, iron-rich respiratory pigment hemoglobin in blood of vertebrates and hemolymph of insects transports oxygen to every organ and tissue. Synthesized into hemoglobin and hemolymph throughout life. Deficiency results in anemia. |
| Manganese (Mn) | In plants, enhances electron transfer from water to chlorophyll and activates enzymes in fatty-acid synthesis. In animals, necessary for reproduction and growth. |
| Boron (B) | Fifteen functions are ascribed to boron in plants, including cell division, pollen germination, carbohydrate metabolism, water metabolism, maintenance of conductive tissue, translation of sugar. Deficiency causes stunted growth in leaves and roots and yellowing of leaves. |
| Cobalt (Co) | Required by ruminants for the synthesis of vitamin $B_{12}$ by bacteria in the rumen. |
| Copper (Cu) | In plants, concentrates in chloroplasts, influences photosynthetic rates, activates enzymes. Excess interferes with phosphorus uptake, depresses iron concentration in leaves, reduces growth. Deficiency in vertebrates causes poor utilization of iron, resulting in anemia and calcium loss in bones. |
| Molybdenum (Mo) | In free-living nitrogen-fixing bacteria and cyanobacteria, a catalyst for the conversion of gaseous nitrogen to usable form. High concentration in ruminants causes a disease characterized by diarrhea, debilitation, and permanent fading of hair color. |
| Zinc (Zn) | In plants, helps form growth substances (auxins); associated with water relationships; component of several enzyme systems. In animals, functions in several enzyme systems, especially the respiratory enzyme carbonic anhydrase in red blood cells. Deficiency in animals causes dermatitis, parakeratosis. |
| Iodine (I) | Involved in thyroid metabolism. Deficiency results in goiter, hairlessness, and poor reproduction. |
| Selenium (Se) | Closely related to vitamin E in function. Prevents white-muscle disease in ruminants. Borderline between requirement level and toxicity is narrow. Excess results in loss of hair, sloughing of hooves, liver injury, and death. |

soil. Note that the uptake rate increases with the concentration until some maximum rate. No further increase occurs above this concentration because the plant meets its demands. In the case of nitrogen, low concentrations in the soil or water mean low uptake rates. A lower uptake rate decreases the concentrations of nitrogen in the leaf (Figure 6.25b) and, consequently, the concentrations of rubisco and chlorophyll. Therefore, lack of nitrogen

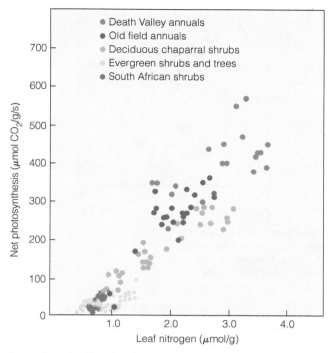

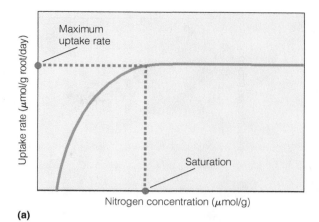

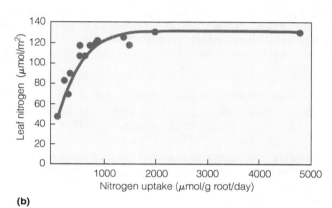

Figure 6.24 | Influence of leaf nitrogen concentrations on maximum observed rates of net photosynthesis for a variety of species from differing habitats. (Adapted from Field and Mooney 1983.) Go to QUANTIFY it! at **www.ecologyplace.com** to work with histograms and scatter plots.

Figure 6.25 | **(a)** Uptake of nitrogen by plant roots increases with concentration in soil until the plant arrives at maximum uptake. **(b)** Influence of root nitrogen uptake on leaf nitrogen concentrations. (Adapted from Woodward and Smith 1994.)

limits the growth of plants. A similar pattern holds for other essential nutrients.

We have seen that geology, climate, and biological activity alter the availability of nutrients in the soil (see Chapter 5). As a consequence, some environments are rich in nutrients, whereas others are poor. How do plants from low-nutrient environments succeed? Because plants require nutrients for the synthesis of new tissue, a plant's rate of growth influences its demand for a nutrient. In turn, the plant's uptake rate of the nutrient also influences growth. This relationship may seem circular, but the important point is that not all plants have the same inherent (maximum potential) rate of growth. In Section 6.9 (see Figure 6.13), we saw how shade-tolerant plants have an inherently lower rate of photosynthesis and growth than shade-intolerant plants, even under high-light conditions. This lower rate of photosynthesis and growth means a lower demand for resources, including nutrients. The same pattern of reduced photosynthesis occurs among plants that are characteristic of low-nutrient environments. Figure 6.26 shows the growth responses of two grass species when soil is enriched with nitrogen. The species that naturally grows in a high-nitrogen environment keeps increasing its rate of growth with increasing nitrogen. The species native to a low-nitrogen environment reaches its maximum rate of growth at low to medium nitrogen availability. It does not respond to further additions of nitrogen.

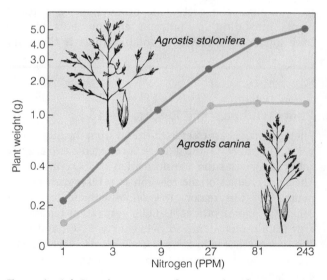

Figure 6.26 | Growth responses of two species of grass—carpet bent grass (*Agrostis stolonifera*), found in high-nutrient environments, and velvet bent grass (*Agrostis canina*), found in low-nutrient environments—to the addition of different levels of nitrogen fertilizer. Note that *A. canina* responds to nitrogen fertilizer up to a certain level only. (Adapted from Bradshaw et al. 1974.)

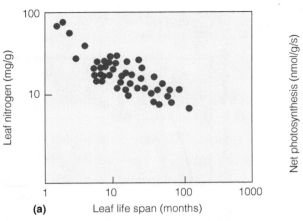
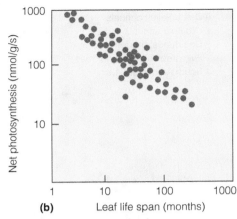

**Figure 6.27** | Relationship between **(a)** leaf longevity (life span) and leaf nitrogen concentration and **(b)** leaf longevity and net photosynthetic rate (maximum) for a wide variety of plants from different environments. Each data point represents a single species. Species having longer lived leaves tend to have lower leaf nitrogen concentrations and subsequently lower rates of photosynthesis. (Adapted from Reich et al. 1996.)

Some plant ecologists suggest that a low natural growth rate is an adaptation to a low-nutrient environment. One advantage of slower growth is that the plant can avoid stress under low-nutrient conditions. A slow-growing plant can still maintain optimal rates of photosynthesis and other processes crucial for growth under low-nutrient availability. In contrast, a plant with an inherently high rate of growth will show signs of stress.

A second adaptation to low-nutrient environments is leaf longevity (Figure 6.27). The production of a leaf has a cost to the plant. This cost can be defined in terms of the carbon and other nutrients required to grow the leaf. At a low rate of photosynthesis, a leaf needs a longer time to "pay back" the cost of its production. As a result, plants inhabiting low-nutrient environments tend to have longer lived leaves. A good example is the domi-

nance of pine species on poor, sandy soils in the coastal region of the southeastern United States. In contrast to deciduous tree species, which shed their leaves every year, these pines have needles that live for up to 3 years.

Like water, nutrients are a below-ground resource of terrestrial plants. Their ability to exploit this resource is related to the amount of root mass. One means by which plants growing in low-nutrient environments compensate is to increase the production of roots. This increase is one cause of their low growth rates. Just as was the case with water limitation, carbon is allocated to the production of roots at the cost of the production of leaves. The reduced leaf area reduces the rate of carbon uptake in photosynthesis relative to the rate of carbon loss in respiration. The result is a lower net carbon gain and growth rate by the plant.

## Summary

### Photosynthesis and Respiration (6.1)

Photosynthesis harnesses light energy from the Sun to convert $CO_2$ and $H_2O$ into glucose. A nitrogen-based enzyme, rubisco, catalyzes the transformation of $CO_2$ into sugar. The first product of the reaction is a three-carbon compound. For this reason, this photosynthetic pathway is called $C_3$ photosynthesis. Cellular respiration releases energy from carbohydrates to yield energy, $H_2O$, and $CO_2$. The energy released in this process is stored as the high-energy compound ATP. Respiration occurs in the living cells of all organisms.

### Photosynthesis and Light (6.2)

The amount of light reaching a plant influences its photosynthetic rate. The light level at which the rate of carbon

dioxide uptake in photosynthesis is equal to the rate of carbon dioxide loss due to respiration is called the light compensation point. The light level at which a further increase in light no longer produces an increase in the rate of photosynthesis is the light saturation point.

### $CO_2$ Uptake and Water Loss (6.3)

Photosynthesis involves two key physical processes: diffusion and transpiration. $CO_2$ diffuses from the atmosphere to the leaf through leaf pores, or stomata. As photosynthesis slows down during the day and demand for $CO_2$ lessens, stomata close to reduce loss of water to the atmosphere. Water loss through the leaf is called transpiration. The amount of water lost depends on the humidity. Water lost through transpiration must be replaced by water taken up from the soil.

## Water Movement (6.4)

Water moves from the soil into the roots, up through the stem and leaves, and out to the atmosphere. Pressure differences along a water gradient move water along this route. Plants draw water from the soil, where the water potential is the highest, and release it to the atmosphere, where it is the lowest. Water moves out of the leaves through the stomata in transpiration and this reduces water potential in the roots, so more water moves from the soil through the plant. This process continues as long as water is available in the soil. This loss of water by transpiration creates moisture conservation problems for plants. Plants need to open their stomata to take in $CO_2$, but they can conserve water only by closing the stomata.

## Aquatic Plants (6.5)

The major difference between aquatic and terrestrial plants in $CO_2$ uptake and assimilation is the lack of stomata in submerged aquatic plants. In aquatic plants, there is a direct diffusion of $CO_2$ from the waters adjacent to the leaf across the cell membrane.

## Plant Energy Balance (6.6)

Leaf temperatures affect both photosynthesis and respiration. Plants have optimal temperatures for photosynthesis beyond which photosynthesis declines. Respiration increases with temperature. The internal temperature of all plant parts is influenced by heat gained from and lost to the environment. Plants absorb longwave and shortwave radiation. They reflect some of it back to the environment. The difference is the plant's net radiation balance. The plant uses some of the absorbed radiation in photosynthesis. The remainder must be either stored as heat in the plant and surrounding air or dissipated through the processes of evaporation (transpiration) and convection.

## Net Carbon Gain and Carbon Allocation (6.7)

The net carbon gain (per unit time) of a plant is the difference between carbon uptake in photosynthesis and carbon loss through respiration. The net carbon gain is then allocated to a variety of plant processes, including the production of new tissues. Because, in general, only leaves (photosynthetic tissues) are able to photosynthesize, yet all living tissues respire, the net carbon gain (and subsequently the growth) of a plant is influenced by the patterns of carbon allocation.

## Interdependence of Plant Adaptations (6.8)

Plants have evolved a wide range of adaptations to variations in environmental conditions. The adaptations exhibited by plants to these features of the environment are not independent for reasons relating to both the physical environment and the plants themselves.

## Plant Adaptations to High and Low Light (6.9)

Plants are either sun plants (shade intolerant) or shade plants (shade tolerant). Shade-adapted plants have low photosynthetic, respiratory, metabolic, and growth rates. Sun plants generally have higher photosynthetic, respiratory, and growth rates but have lower survival rates under shaded conditions. The leaves of some species of plants change structure and shape in response to light conditions. Leaves in sun plants tend to be smaller, lobed, and thick. Shade-plant leaves tend to be larger and thinner.

## Plant Response to Water Limitation (6.10)

Plants of warm environments can use a $C_4$ pathway of photosynthesis. It involves two steps and is made possible by leaf anatomy that differs from $C_3$ plants. $C_4$ plants have vascular bundles surrounded by chlorophyll-rich bundle sheath cells. $C_4$ plants transport carbon in the form of malate and aspartate in the mesophyll cells. They transfer these acids to the bundle sheath cells, where they release the $CO_2$ they contain. Photosynthesis then follows the $C_3$ pathway. $C_4$ plants have a high water-use efficiency (the amount of carbon fixed per unit of water transpired). Succulent desert plants, such as cacti, have a third type of photosynthetic pathway, called CAM. CAM plants open their stomata to take in $CO_2$ at night, when the humidity is high. They convert $CO_2$ to a four-carbon compound: malate. During the day, CAM plants close their stomata, convert malate back to $CO_2$, and follow the $C_3$ photosynthetic pathway.

## Adaptations to Heat and Cold (6.11)

Plants exhibit a variety of adaptations to both extremely cold and hot environments. Cold tolerance is mostly genetic and varies among species. Plants acquire frost hardiness through the formation or addition of protective compounds in the cell, which function as antifreeze. The ability to tolerate high air temperatures is related to plant moisture balance.

## Plant Adaptations to Nutrient Availability (6.12)

Terrestrial plants take up nutrients from soil through the roots. As roots deplete nearby nutrients, diffusion of water and nutrients through the soil replaces them. Availability of nutrients has a direct effect on a plant's survival, growth, and reproduction. Nitrogen is important because rubisco and chlorophyll are nitrogen-based compounds essential to photosynthesis. Uptake of nitrogen and other nutrients depends on availability and demand. Plants with high nutrient demands grow poorly in low-nutrient environments. Plants with lower demands survive and grow, if slowly, in low-nutrient environments. Plants adapted to low-nutrient environments exhibit lower rates of growth and increased longevity of leaves. The lower nutrient concentration in their tissues means lower quality food for decomposers.

## Study Questions

1. What does it mean to say that life on Earth is carbon-based?

2. Distinguish between photosynthesis and assimilation. How are they related?

3. What is the function of respiration?

4. What is the role of light (PAR) in the process of photosynthesis?

5. In the relationship between net photosynthesis and available light (PAR) shown in Figure 6.2, there is a net loss of carbon dioxide by the leaf at levels of light below the light compensation point. Why does this occur? Based on this relationship, how do you think net photosynthesis varies over the course of the day?

6. How does diffusion control the uptake of carbon dioxide and the loss of water from the leaf?

7. How does the availability of water to a plant constrain the rate of photosynthesis?

8. What is the advantage of the $C_4$ photosynthetic pathway as compared to the conventional $C_3$ pathway? How might these advantages influence where these plant species are found?

9. What is the advantage of a lower light compensation point (LCP) for plant species adapted to low-light environments? What is the cost of maintaining a low LCP?

10. How do plants growing in shaded environments respond to increase their photosynthetic surface area?

11. How does a decrease in water availability influence the allocation of carbon (photosynthates) in the process of growth?

12. What is the basis for the relationship between leaf nitrogen concentration and rate of net photosynthesis shown in Figure 6.24?

13. How could increased leaf longevity (longer lived leaves) function as an adaptation to low-nutrient environments?

## Further Readings

Dale, J. E. 1992. How do leaves grow? *Bioscience* 42:423–32.
How do environmental conditions influence leaf development? This paper provides the reader with a basic understanding of the processes involved in leaf growth and the background necessary to answer this question.

Grime, J. 1971. *Plant strategies and vegetative processes*. New York: Wiley.
An excellent integrated overview of plant adaptations to the environment. This book describes how the various features of a plant's life history, from seed to adult, reflect adaptations to different habitats and the constraints imposed on plant survival, growth, and reproduction.

Lambers, H., F. S. Chapin III, and T. L. Pons, 1998. *Plant physiological ecology*. New York: Springer.
For more information, read this technical (but well written), illustrated, and organized book that delves further into the processes presented in this chapter.

Larcher, W. 1996. *Physiological plant ecology*. 3rd ed. New York: Springer-Verlag.
Excellent reference on plant ecophysiology. Like the above text, this is an excellent reference book for more information on the materials presented in the chapter. Less technical but also less comprehensive.

Schulze, E. D., R. H. Robichaux, J. Grace, P. W. Randel, and J. R. Ehleringer, 1987. Plant water balance. *Bioscience* 37:30–7.
A good introduction to plant water balance that is well written, illustrated, and not too technical. For those students who wish to expand their understanding of the topic, it complements the materials presented in this chapter.

Walker, D. 1992. *Energy, plants and man*. East Sussex, UK: Packard Publishing.
This book is a humorous, well-written presentation of plant biology. The sections on photosynthesis are easy to read, well illustrated, and present an excellent introduction to the topic. Highly recommended.

Woodward, F. I. 1987. *Climate and plant distribution*. Cambridge, UK: Cambridge University Press.
An excellent overview of plant energy and water balance, as well as plant adaptations to climate. It is easy to read, well referenced, and concise.

# Chapter 7 | Animal Adaptations to the Environment

A male white-fronted brown lemur (*Eulemur fulvus albifrons*) feeds on fruits in the canopy of a rainforest in Madagascar (Africa). This omnivore feeds of fruits, leaves, and insects in the forest canopy, where it lives in small, cohesive groups of from 3 to 12 individuals.

All green plants, whether the smallest of violets or the giant sequoia trees of the western United States, derive their energy from the same process—photosynthesis. The story is quite different for animals. Because heterotrophic organisms derive their energy, and the majority of their nutrients, from the consumption of organic compounds contained in plants and animals, they encounter literally hundreds of thousands of different types of potential food items that are

133

packaged as the diversity of plant and animal species inhabiting Earth. For this reason alone, the adaptation of animals to the environment is a much more complex and diverse topic than the adaptation of plants, which was presented in Chapter 6. However, there are a number of key processes that are common to all animals: the acquisition and digestion of food, the maintenance of body temperature, the maintenance of water balance, and the adaptation to systematic variation in light and temperature (the diurnal and seasonal cycles). In addition, there are a number of fundamentally different constraints imposed by aquatic and terrestrial environments. In this chapter, we will examine the variety of adaptations that animals have evolved, allowing them to successfully survive, grow, and reproduce in the diversity of environments that exist on Earth. In doing so, we will focus on both the benefits and constraints imposed by specific adaptations and how the trade-offs involved influence the success of the organisms under different environmental conditions.

## 7.1 | Animals Have Various Ways of Acquiring Energy and Nutrients

Carbon fixed by plants in the process of photosynthesis, directly or indirectly, provides the nutritional resources for animals. Whatever the means by which animals obtain their energy from organic carbon compounds contained in a wide array of potential food items, the ultimate source of these organic compounds is plants. Because plants and animals have different chemical compositions, the problem facing animals is the conversion of this plant tissue to animal tissue. Animals are high in fat and proteins, which they use as structural building blocks. Plants are low in proteins and high in carbohydrates, much in the form of cellulose and lignin in cell walls, which are complex in structure and difficult to break down (see Chapter 21). Nitrogen is a major constituent of protein. In plants, the ratio of carbon to nitrogen is about 50 to 1. In mammals, the ratio is about 14 to 1. The task of converting cellulose and a limited supply of plant protein into animal tissue is carried out by herbivores.

The diversity of potential sources of energy in the form of plant and animal tissues requires an equally diverse array of physiological, morphological, and behavioral characteristics that enable animals to acquire (Figure 7.1) and assimilate these resources. There are many ways to classify animals based on the resources they use and the means by which they exploit them. The most general of these classifications is the division based on how animals use plant and animal tissues as sources

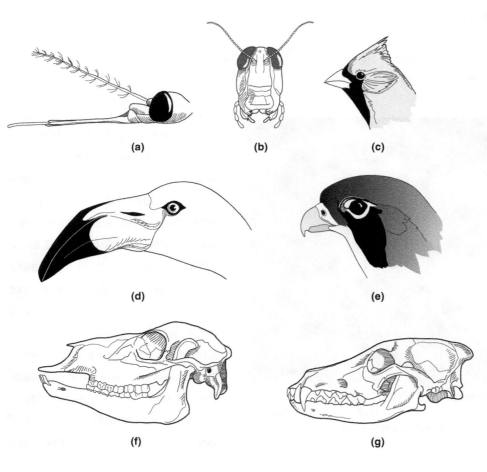

(a)  (b)  (c)

(d)  (e)

(f)  (g)

**Figure 7.1** | Mouthparts reflect how organisms obtain their food. **(a)** Piercing mouthparts of a mosquito. **(b)** Chewing mouthparts of a grasshopper. **(c)** The strong conical bill of a seed-eating bird. **(d)** The straining bill of a flamingo. **(e)** Tearing beak of a hawk. **(f)** The grinding molars of an herbivore, a deer. **(g)** The canine and shearing teeth of a carnivorous mammal, the coyote.

of food. Those that feed exclusively on plant tissues are classified as **herbivores.** Animals that feed exclusively on the tissues of other animals are classified as **carnivores,** whereas those that feed on both plant and animal tissues are called **omnivores.** In addition, animals that feed on dead plant and animal matter, called detritus, are detrital feeders, or **detritivores** (see Chapter 21). Each of these four feeding groups has characteristic adaptations that allow it to exploit the different diet.

## Herbivory

Herbivores are categorized by the type of plant material they eat. Grazers feed on leafy material, especially grasses. Browsers feed mostly on woody material. Granivores feed on seeds, and frugivores eat fruit. Other types of herbivorous animals such as avian sapsuckers (*Sphyrapicus* spp.) and sucking insects such as aphids feed on plant sap; and hummingbirds, butterflies, and a variety of moth and ant species feed on plant nectar (nectivores).

Grazing and browsing herbivores, with some exceptions, live on diets high in cellulose. In doing so, they face several dietary problems. Their diets are rich in carbon, but low in protein. Most of the carbohydrates are locked in indigestible cellulose, and the proteins exist in chemical compounds. Lacking the enzymes needed to digest cellulose, herbivores depend on specialized bacteria and protozoa living in their digestive tracts. These bacteria and protozoans digest cellulose and proteins, and they synthesize fatty acids, amino acids, proteins, and vitamins. For most vertebrates, bacteria and protozoans concentrate in the foregut (from mouth to intestines) or hindgut (intestines) (Figure 7.2a). In this anaerobic (oxygen free) environment, aerobic respiration (see Section 6.1) is replaced

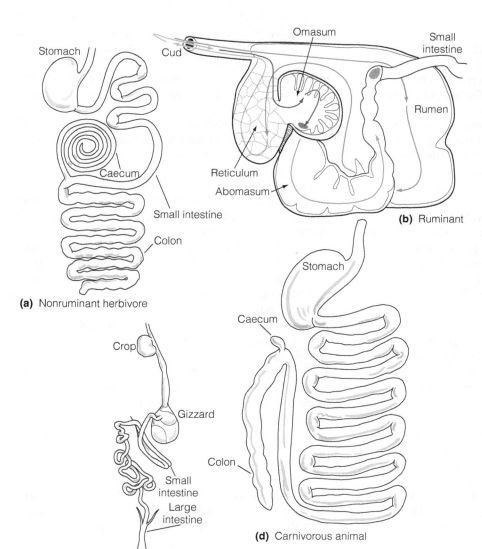

**(a)** Nonruminant herbivore

**(b)** Ruminant

**(c)** Bird

**(d)** Carnivorous animal

**Figure 7.2** | **(a)** Digestive tract of a nonruminant herbivore, which is characterized by a long intestine and well-developed caecum. **(b)** The ruminant stomach. The four-compartment stomach consists of the rumen, reticulum, omasum, and abomasum. Food enters the rumen and the reticulum. The ruminant regurgitates fermented material (cud) and rechews it. Finer material enters the reticulum and then the omasum and abomasum. Coarser material reenters the rumen for further fermentation. **(c)** The digestive tract of a bird with a crop, the stomach, or the gizzard. **(d)** The relatively simple digestive tract of a carnivorous mammal, which consists of the esophagus, stomach (collectively the foregut), small intestine, and a small caecum and large intestine (collectively the hindgut).

by fermentation. **Fermentation,** which converts sugars to inorganic acids and alcohols in the absence of oxygen, is a less efficient process than aerobic respiration.

In herbivorous insects, bacteria and protozoans inhabit the hindgut. Some species of cellulose-consuming wood beetles and wasps depend on fungi. These insects carry fungal spores with them externally when they invade new wood.

Ruminants, such as cattle and deer, are exemplary cases of herbivores anatomically specialized for the digestion of cellulose. They possess a highly complex digestive system that consists of a four-compartment stomach—the rumen (from which the group gets its name), reticulum, omasum, and abomasum (or true stomach) (Figure 7.2b)—and a long intestine. The rumen and reticulum, inhabited by anaerobic bacteria and protozoans, function as fermentation vats. These microbes break down the cellulose into usable nutrients. Ruminants have highly developed salivary glands that excrete substances that allow the regulation of acidity (pH) and chemistry in the rumen.

As ruminants graze, they chew their food hurriedly. The food material descends to the rumen and reticulum, where it is softened to a pulp by the addition of water, kneaded by muscular action, and fermented by bacteria. At leisure, the animals regurgitate the food, chew it more thoroughly to reduce plant particle size, thus making it more accessible to microbes, and swallow it again. The mass again enters the rumen. Finer material moves into the reticulum. Contractions force it into the third compartment, or omasum, where the material is further digested and finally forced into the abomasum, or true glandular stomach.

The digestive process carried on by the microorganisms in the rumen produces fatty acids. These acids rapidly absorb through the wall of the rumen into the bloodstream, providing the ruminant with a major source of food energy. Part of the material in the rumen converts to methane, which is expelled from the body, and part is converted into compounds that can be used directly as food energy. The ruminant digests many of the microbial cells in the abomasum to recapture still more of the energy and nutrients. Further bacterial action breaks down complex carbohydrates into sugars. In addition to carrying on fermentation, the bacteria also synthesize B-complex vitamins and amino acids.

Most of the digestion in ruminants takes place in the foregut. Among nonruminants, such as rabbits and horses, digestion takes place less efficiently in the hindgut. Nonruminant vertebrate herbivores, such as horses, have simple stomachs, long intestinal tracts that slow the passage of food through the gut, and a well-developed caecum, which is a pouch attached to the colon of the intestine and is where fermentation takes place (Figure 7.2a).

Lagomorphs—rabbits, hares, and pikas—resort to a form of coprophagy, the ingestion of fecal material for further extraction of nutrients. Part of ingested plant material enters the caecum (see Figure 7.2a), and part enters the intestine to form dry pellets. In the caecum, microorganisms process the ingested material and expel it into the large intestine and then out of the body as soft, green, moist pellets. Lagomorphs reingest the soft pellets, which are much higher in protein and lower in crude fiber than the hard fecal pellets. The coprophagy recycles 50 to 80 percent of feces. The reingestion is important because the pellets, functioning as "external rumen," provide bacterially synthesized B vitamins and ensure a more thorough digestion of dry material and better use of protein. Coprophagy is widespread among the detritus-feeding animals, such as wood-eating beetles and millipedes that ingest pellets after they have been enriched by microbial activity.

Seed-eating birds—gallinaceous (chicken-like) birds, pigeons, doves, and many species of song birds—have three separate chambers. The first chamber is a pouch in the esophagus called the crop, which is a reservoir for food that passes on to the stomach (Figure 7.2c). The stomach secretes enzymes to begin digestion. The food then passes to the gizzard, which functions as a powerful grinding organ. Birds assist the grinding action of the gizzard by swallowing small pebbles and gravel, or grit.

Among marine fish, herbivorous species are small and typically inhabit coral reefs. Characterized by high diversity (many different species), they make up about 25 percent to 40 percent of the fish biomass about the reefs. These herbivorous fish feed on algal growth that, unlike the food of terrestrial herbivores, lacks lignin and other structural carbon compounds that are more difficult to digest. They gain access to the nutrients inside the algal cells by means of one or more of four basic types of digestive mechanisms. In some fish with thin-walled stomachs, low stomach pH (acidic) weakens algal cell walls and allows digestive enzymes access to the cell contents. Fish that possess gizzard-like stomachs ingest inorganic material that mechanically breaks down algal cells to release nutrients. Some reef fish possess specialized jaws that shred or grind algal material before it reaches the intestine. Other fish depend on microbial fermentation in the hindgut to assist in the breakdown of algal cells. These four types are not mutually exclusive. Some marine herbivores may combine low stomach pH or grinding and shredding with microbial fermentation in the hindgut.

## Carnivory

Herbivores are the energy source for carnivores—the flesh eaters. Unlike herbivores, carnivores are not faced with the problems relating to the digestion of cellulose or the quality of food. Because little difference exists in the chemical composition between the flesh of prey and the flesh of predators, carnivores encounter no problem in digestion and assimilation of nutrients from their prey. Their major problem is obtaining a sufficient quantity of food.

Lacking the need to digest complex cellulose compounds, carnivores have short intestines and simple stomachs (Figure 7.2d). In mammalian carnivores, the stomach is little more than an expanded hollow tube with muscular walls. It stores and mixes foods, adding mucus, enzymes, and hydrochloric acid to speed digestion. In carnivorous birds such as hawks and owls, the gizzard is little more than an extendable pocket with reduced muscles in which digestion, started in the anterior stomach, con-

tinues. In hawks and owls, the gizzard acts as a barrier against hair, bones, and feathers, which these birds regurgitate and expel as pellets by way of the mouth.

## Omnivory

Omnivory includes animals that feed on both plants and animals. The food habits of many omnivores vary with the seasons, stages in the life cycle, and their size and growth rate. The red fox (*Vulpes vulpes*), for example, feeds on berries, apples, cherries, acorns, grasses, grasshoppers, crickets, beetles, and small rodents (Figure 7.3). The black bear (*Ursus americanus*) feeds heavily on vegetation—buds, leaves, nuts, berries, tree

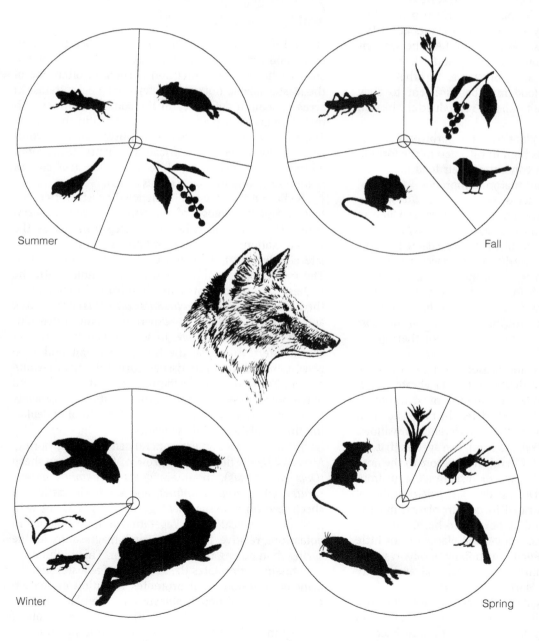

**Figure 7.3** | The red fox is an example of an omnivore. It feeds on both plant and animal tissues. Its diet varies with the seasons. Note the prominence of fruits and insects in summer and fall and of rodents and rabbits in winter and spring.

bark—supplemented with bees, beetles, crickets, ants, fish, and small- to medium-sized mammals.

## 7.2 | Animals Have Various Nutritional Needs

Animals require mineral elements (see Table 6.1) and 20 amino acids, 14 of which are essential ones that the body cannot synthesize and therefore have to be supplied by the diet. These nutritional needs differ little among vertebrates and invertebrates. Insects, for example, have the same dietary requirements as vertebrates, although they need more potassium, phosphorus, and magnesium and less calcium, sodium, and chlorine than vertebrates. The ultimate source of most of these nutrients is plants. For this reason, the quantity and quality of plants affect the nutrition of herbivorous consumers. When the amount of food is insufficient, consumers may suffer from acute malnutrition, leave the area, or starve. In other situations, the quantity of food may be sufficient to allay hunger, but its low quality affects reproduction, health, and longevity.

The highest quality plant food for herbivores, vertebrate and invertebrate, is high in nitrogen in the form of protein. As the nitrogen content of their food increases, their assimilation of plant material improves, increasing growth, reproductive success, and survival. Nitrogen is concentrated in the growing tips, new leaves, and buds of plants. Its content declines as leaves and twigs mature and become senescent. Herbivores have adapted to this period of new growth. Herbivorous insect larvae are most abundant early in the growing season, and these complete their growth before the leaves mature. Many vertebrate herbivores, such as deer, give birth to their young at the start of the growing season, when the most protein-rich plant foods will be available for their growing young.

Although availability and season strongly influence food selection, both vertebrate and invertebrate herbivores do show some preference for the most nitrogen-rich plants, which they probably detect by taste and odor. For example, beaver show a strong preference for willows (*Salix* spp.) and aspen (*Populus* spp.), two species that are high in nitrogen content. Chemical receptors in the nose and mouth of deer encourage or discourage consumption of certain foods. During drought, nitrogen-based compounds are concentrated in certain plants, making them more attractive and vulnerable to herbivorous insects. However, preference for certain plants means little if they are unavailable. Food selection by herbivores is an interaction among quality, preference, and availability (see Researcher Profile: Martin Wikelski).

The need for quality foods differs among herbivores. Ruminant animals, as already pointed out, can subsist on rougher or lower quality plant materials because bacteria in the rumen can synthesize such requirements as vitamin $B_1$ and certain amino acids from simple nitrogen-based compounds. Therefore, the caloric content and the nutrients in a certain food might not reflect its real nutritive value for the ruminant. Nonruminant herbivores require a larger amount of complex proteins in their foods. Seed-eating herbivores exploit the concentration of nutrients in the seeds. Among the carnivores, quantity is more important than quality. Carnivores rarely have a dietary problem because they consume animals that have resynthesized and stored protein and other nutrients from plants in their tissues.

## 7.3 | Mineral Availability Affects Growth and Reproduction of Animals

Mineral availability also appears to influence the abundance and fitness of some animals. One essential nutrient that has received attention is sodium, often one of the least available nutrients in terrestrial ecosystems. In areas of sodium deficiency in the soil, herbivorous animals face an inadequate supply of sodium in their diets. The problem has been noted in Australian herbivores such as kangaroos, in African elephants (*Loxodonta africana*), in rodents, in white-tailed deer (*Odocoileus virginianus*), and in moose (*Alces alces*).

Sodium deficiency can influence the distribution, behavior, and physiology of mammals, especially herbivores. The spatial distribution of elephants across the Wankie National Park in central Africa appears to correlate closely with the sodium content of drinking water. The most elephants are found at water holes with the highest sodium content. Three herbivorous mammals—the European rabbit (*Oryctolagus cuniculus*), the moose, and the white-tailed deer—experience sodium deficiencies in parts of their range. In sodium-deficient areas in southwestern Australia, the European rabbit builds up reserves of sodium in its tissues during the nonbreeding season. These reserves become exhausted near the end of the breeding season, forcing the rabbits to graze selectively on sodium-rich plants, often to the point of depleting the populations of these plants.

Ruminants face severe mineral deficiencies in spring. Attracted by the flush of new growth, deer, bighorn sheep (*Ovis canadensis*), mountain goats (*Oreamnos americanus*), elk (*Cervus elaphus*), and domestic cattle and sheep feed on new succulent growth of grass, but with high physiological costs. Vegetation is much higher in potassium relative to calcium and magnesium in the spring than during the rest of the year. This high intake of potassium stimulates the secretion of aldosterone, the principal hormone that promotes retention of sodium by the kidney. Although aldosterone stimulates the retention of sodium, it also facilitates the excretion of potassium and magnesium. Because concentrations of

Figure 7.4 | A mineral lick used by white-tailed deer.

magnesium in soft tissues and skeletal stores are low in herbivores, these animals experience magnesium deficiency. This deficiency results in a rapid onset of diarrhea and often muscle spasms (tetany). The deficiency comes late in gestation for females and at the beginning of antler growth for male deer and elk, a time when mineral demands are high.

To counteract this mineral imbalance in the spring, large herbivores seek mineral licks—places in the landscape where animals concentrate to satisfy their mineral needs by eating mineral-rich soil (Figure 7.4). Although sodium chloride is associated with mineral licks, animal physiologists hypothesize that it is not sodium the animals seek but magnesium, and in the case of bighorn sheep, mountain goats, and elk, calcium as well.

The size of deer, their antler development, and their reproductive success all relate to nutrition. Other factors being equal, only deer obtaining high-quality foods grow large antlers. Deer on diets low in calcium, phosphorus, and protein show stunted growth, and males develop only thin spike antlers.

## 7.4 | Animals Require Oxygen to Release Energy Contained in Food

Animals obtain their energy from the organic compounds in the food they eat. They release this energy primarily through aerobic respiration, which requires oxygen (see Section 6.1). Oxygen is easily available in the atmosphere for terrestrial animals. However, for aquatic animals, oxygen may be limiting and its acquisition problematical (see Section 4.6).

Differences in the means of oxygen acquisition between terrestrial and aquatic animals reflect the availability of oxygen in the two environments. Minute terrestrial organisms take in oxygen by diffusion across the body surface. Insects possess tracheal tubes that open to the outside through openings (or spiracles) on the body wall (Figure 7.5a). The tracheal tubes carry oxygen directly to the body cells.

Unable to meet demands through the direct diffusion of oxygen across the body surface, larger terrestrial animals (mammals, birds, and reptiles) have some form of lungs. Unlike tracheal systems that branch throughout the insect body, lungs are restricted to one location. Structurally, lungs have innumerable small sacs that increase surface area across which oxygen readily diffuses into the bloodstream. Amphibians take in oxygen through a combination of lungs and vascularized skin. Lungless salamanders are an exception; they live in a moist environment and take in oxygen directly through the skin.

In addition to lungs, birds have accessory air sacs that act as bellows that keep air flowing through the lungs as they inhale and exhale (Figure 7.5b). Airflow is one way only, forming a continuous circuit through the interconnected system, whether the bird is inhaling or exhaling. During inhalation, most of the air bypasses the lungs and enters the posterior air sac. Air then passes through the lungs to the anterior air sac, while at the same time, the posterior air sac draws in more air.

In aquatic environments, organisms have to take in oxygen from the water or gain oxygen from the air by some means. Marine mammals such as whales and dolphins come to the surface to expel carbon dioxide and take in air containing oxygen to the lungs. Some aquatic insects rise to the surface to fill the tracheal system with air. Others, like diving beetles, carry a bubble of air with them when submerged. Held beneath the wings, the air bubble contacts the spiracles of the abdomen.

Fish, the major aquatic vertebrates, pump water through their mouth. The water passes through slits in the pharynx, flows over gills, and exits through the back of the gill covers (Figure 7.5c). The close contact with and the rapid flow of water over the gills allows for exchanges of oxygen and carbon dioxide between water and the gills (Figure 7.5d). Water passing over the gills flows in a direction opposite to that of blood, setting up a countercurrent exchange. As the blood flows through capillaries, it becomes more and more loaded with oxygen. It also encounters water more and more concentrated with oxygen because water is just beginning to pass over the gills. As water continues its flow, it encounters blood with lower oxygen concentration, aiding the uptake of oxygen through the process of diffusion (Figure 7.5e).

## 7.5 | Regulation of Internal Conditions Involves Homeostasis and Feedback

In an ever-changing physical environment, organisms must maintain a fairly constant internal environment within the narrow limits required by their cells, organs,

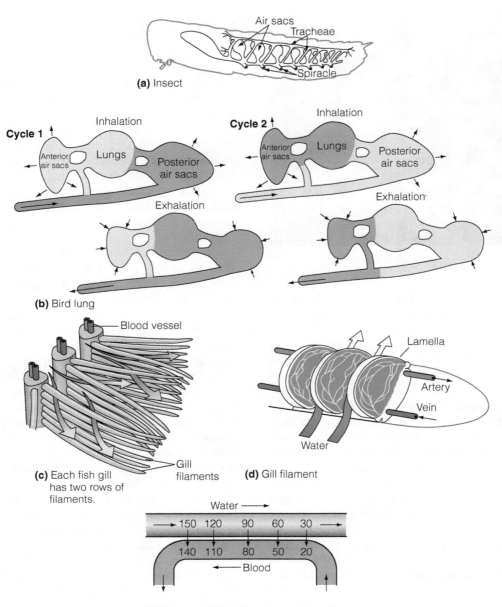

**Figure 7.5** | Respiratory systems. **(a)** The tracheal system and the spiracles of an insect (grasshopper). Airs enters the tracheal tubes through spiracles, openings on the body wall. **(b)** Gas exchange in the bird lung requires two cycles involving both inhalation and exhalation. During the first inhalation, most of the air flows past the lungs into a posterior air sac. That air passes through the lungs upon exhalation and the next inhalation ends up in the anterior air sac. At the same time, the posterior sacs draw in more air. This flow pattern allows oxygenated blood to leave the lungs with the highest possible amount of oxygen. **(c)** Fish obtain oxygen from water by the way of gills. Gill filaments have flattened plates called lamellae. **(d)** Blood flowing through capillaries within the lamella pick up oxygen from the water through a countercurrent exchange. Water flows across the lamellae in a direction opposite to the blood flow. The blood enters the gill low in oxygen. As it flows through the lamellae, it picks up more and more oxygen from the water. The water flowing in the opposite direction gradually loses more and more of its oxygen. Numbers refer to $O_2$ concentration.

and enzyme systems. They need some means of regulating their internal environment relative to external conditions including body temperature, water balance, pH, and the amounts of salts in fluids and tissues. For exam-

ple, the human body must maintain internal temperatures within a narrow range around 37°C. An increase or decrease of only a few degrees from this value or point could prove fatal. The maintenance of a relatively constant internal environment in a varying external environment is called **homeostasis.**

Whatever the processes involved in regulating an organism's internal environment, homeostasis depends on negative feedback, meaning that when a system deviates from the normal or desired state, mechanisms function to restore the system to that state. The thermostat that controls the temperature in your home is an example of a negative feedback system. If we wish the temperature of the room to be 20°C (68°F), we set that point on the thermostat. When the temperature of the room air falls below that point, a temperature-sensitive device within the thermostat trips the switch that turns on the furnace. When the room temperature reaches the set point, the thermostat responds by shutting off the furnace. Should the thermostat fail to function properly and not shut the furnace off, then the furnace would continue to heat, the temperature would continue to rise, and the furnace would ultimately overheat, causing either a fire or a mechanical breakdown.

A key difference between mechanical and living systems is that in living systems, the set point is not firmly fixed as it often is in mechanical systems. Instead, organisms have a limited range of tolerances, called **homeostatic plateaus.** Homeostatic systems work within minimum and maximum values by using negative feedback to regulate activity above or below the set point. If the system deviates from that set point, a negative feedback response ensues—a control mechanism inhibits any strong movement away from the set point. Among animals, the control of homeostasis is both physiological and behavioral.

An example is temperature regulation in humans (Figure 7.6). The normal temperature, or set point, for humans is 37°C. When the temperature of the environment rises, sensory mechanisms in the skin detect the change. They send a message to the brain, which automatically relays the message to receptors that increase blood flow to the skin, induce sweating, and stimulate behavioral responses. Water excreted through the skin

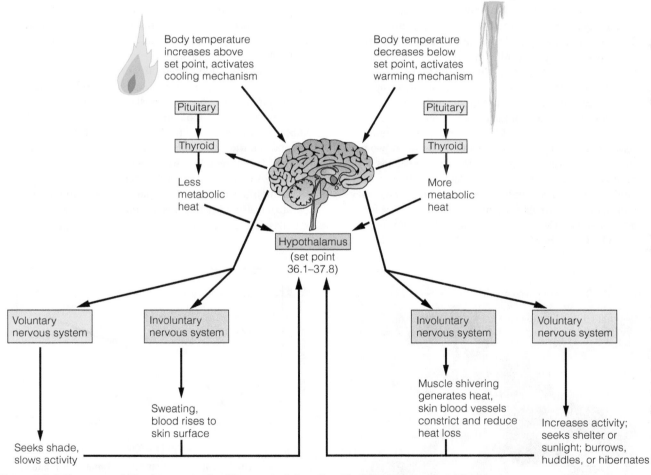

**Figure 7.6** | Thermoregulation is an example of homeostasis in action. The hypothalamus in one's brain receives feedback or senses the temperature of blood arriving from the body core. If body core temperature rises, it responds accordingly in two ways, activating the autonomic (or involuntary) and voluntary nervous systems and the endocrine system.

The isolated archipelago of the Galápagos Islands off the western coast of South America is known for its amazing diversity of animal and plant life. It was the diversity of life on these islands that so impressed the young Charles Darwin and laid the foundations for his theory of natural selection (see Chapter 2). However, one inhabitant of the Galápagos fauna has consistently been met with revulsion by historic visitors: the marine iguana, *Amblyrhynchus cristatus* (Figure 1). Indeed, even Darwin himself commented on this: "hideous-looking creature."

Marine iguanas are widely distributed throughout the Galápagos Islands, and different populations vary dramatically in size (both length and weight). Due to these variations, many of the iguana populations were long considered separate species, yet modern genetic studies have confirmed that all of the populations are part of a single species. What could possibly account for this marked variation in body size among populations? This question has been central to the research of Princeton University ecologist Martin Wikelski. The studies of Wikelski and his colleagues during the past decade have revealed an intriguing story of the constraints imposed by variations in the environment of the Galápagos on the evolution of these amazing creatures.

In a series of studies, Wikelski and his colleagues have examined differences in body size between two populations of marine iguanas that inhabit the islands of Santa Fe and Genovesa. The populations of these two islands differ markedly in body size, with an average body length of 25 cm (maximum body weight of 900 g) for adult males on Genovesa as compared to 40 cm (maximum body weight of 3500 g) for adult males on the is-

land of Santa Fe. Wikelski hypothesized that these differences reflected energetic constraints on the two populations in the form of food supply.

Marine iguanas are herbivorous reptiles that feed on submerged intertidal and subtidal algae (seaweed) along the rocky island shores, referred to as algae pastures. To quantify the availability of food for iguana populations, Wikelski and colleagues quantified the standing biomass and productivity of pastures in the tidal zones of these two islands. Their results show that the growth of algae pastures correlates with sea surface temperatures. The waters in the tidal zone off Santa Fe (the more southern island) are cooler than those off Genovesa, and as a result both the length of algae plants and the productivity of pastures are much higher off Santa Fe.

By examining patterns of food intake and growth of marked individuals on the two islands, Wikelski was able to demonstrate that food intake limits growth rate and subsequent body size in marine iguanas, which in turn depends on the availability of algae (Figure 2). Body size differences between the two island populations can be explained by differences in food availability.

Temporal variations in climate and sea surface temperatures also influence food availability for the marine iguanas across the Galápagos Islands. Marine iguanas

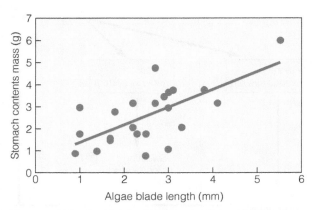

Figure 2 | The food intake (dry mass in stomach) for iguanas of a given length (200–250 mm) from both study islands increased with increasing length of the algae pasture in the intertidal zone. (Adapted from Wikelski et al. 1997.)

Figure 1 | The Galápagos marine iguana.

can live for up to 30 years, and environmental conditions can change dramatically within an individual's lifetime. El Niño events (see Section 3.8) usually recur at intervals of 3–7 years, but more were prevalent in the decade of the 1990s. During El Niño years in the Galápagos, sea surface temperatures increase from an average of 18°C to a maximum of 32°C as cold ocean currents and cold-rich upwellings are disrupted. As a result, green and red algal species, which are the preferred food of marine iguanas, disappear and are replaced by the brown algae, which the iguanas find hard to digest. Up to 90 percent of marine iguana populations on islands can die of starvation as a result of these environmental changes.

In a study of patterns of mortality during the El Niño events of the 1990s, Wikelski observed the highest mortality rate for larger individuals. This higher mortality rate directly related to observed differences in foraging efficiency with body size. Wikelski and colleagues determined that although larger individuals have a higher daily intake of food, smaller individuals have a higher food intake per unit body mass, a result of higher foraging efficiency (food intake per bite per gram body mass). Large iguanas on both islands showed a marked decline in body mass during the El Niño events. The result is a strong selective pressure against large body size during these periods of food shortage (Figure 3).

Perhaps the most astonishing result of Wikelski's research is that the marine iguanas exhibit an unusual adaptation to the environmental variations that occur as a result of El Niño.

Change in body length is considered to be unidirectional in vertebrates, but Wikelski repeatedly observed

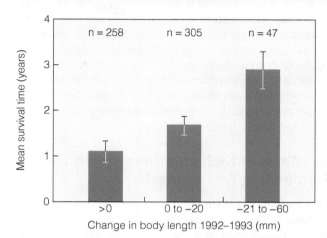

**Figure 4** | Relation between change in body length and survival time for adult iguanas on the island of Santa Fe during the 1997–1998 El Niño (ENSO) cycle. Values of *n* refer to sample size. (Adapted from Wikelski 2000.) (Nature Publishing Group.)

shrinkage of up to 20 percent in the length of individual adult iguanas. This shrinking coincided with low food availability resulting from El Niño events.

Shrinking did not occur equally across all size classes. Wikelski found an inverse relationship between the initial body size of individuals and the observed change in body length during the period of food shortage.

Shrinkage was found to have an influence on survival. Large adult individuals that shrank more survived longer because their foraging efficiency increased and their energy expenditure decreased (Figure 4). ●

### Bibliography

Wikelski, M. and C. Thom. 2000. Marine iguanas shrink to survive El Niño. *Nature* 403:37–38.

Wikelski, M., V. Carrillo, and F. Trillmich. 1997. Energy limits on body size in a grazing reptile, the Galápagos marine iguana. *Ecology* 78:2204–2217.

1. Does the mortality of iguanas during El Niño events represent a case of natural selection? Which of the three models of selection best describe the pattern of natural selection?

2. If the iguanas did not have the ability to "shrink" during the period of resource shortage, how do you think the El Niño events would influence natural selection?

Go to QUANTIFY it! at **www.ecologyplace.com** to explore how to use a scatterplot to display data.

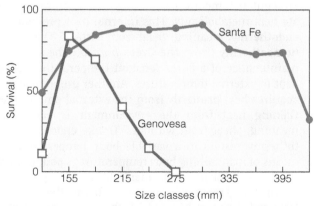

**Figure 3** | **Survival of individually marked animals on Genovesa (squares) and Santa Fe (dots).** (Adapted from Wikelski and Trillmich 1997.)

evaporates, cooling the body. When the environmental temperature falls below a certain point, another reaction takes place. This time, it reduces blood flow and causes shivering, an involuntary muscular exercise that produces more heat.

If the environmental temperature becomes extreme, the homeostatic system breaks down. When it gets too warm, the body cannot lose heat fast enough to maintain normal temperature. Metabolism speeds up, further raising body temperature, until death results from heatstroke. If the environmental temperature drops too low, metabolic processes slow down, further decreasing body temperature, until death by freezing ensues.

## 7.6 | Animals Exchange Energy with Their Surrounding Environment

Animals differ significantly from plants in their thermal relations with the environment. Animals can produce heat by metabolism, and their mobility allows them to seek out or escape heat and cold.

Body structure influences the exchange of heat between animals and the external environment. Consider a simple thermal model of an animal body (Figure 7.7). The interior or core of the body must be regulated within a defined range of temperature. In contrast, the temperature of the environment surrounding the animal's body varies. The temperature at the surface of the body, however, is not the same as the air or water temperature in which the animal lives, but rather is the temperature at a thin layer of air (or water) called the **boundary layer** that lies at the surface, just above and within hair, feathers, and scales. Therefore, body surface temperature differs from both the air (or water) and the core body temperatures. Separating the body core from the body surface are layers of muscle tissue and fat, across which the temperature gradually changes from the core temperature to the body surface temperature. This layer of insulation influences the organism's thermal **conductivity;** that is, the ability to exchange heat with the surrounding environment.

To maintain the core body temperature, the animal has to balance gains and losses of heat to the environment. It does so by changes in metabolic rate and by heat exchange. The core area exchanges heat (produced by metabolism and stored in the body) with the surface area by conduction, the transfer of heat through a solid. Influencing this exchange are the thickness and conductivity of fat and the movement of blood to the surface. The surface layer exchanges heat with the environment by convection, conduction, radiation, and evaporation (see Quantifying Ecology 7.1: Heat Exchange and Thermal Regulation for a quantitative discussion of heat exchange and thermal regulation), all influenced by the characteristics of skin and body covering.

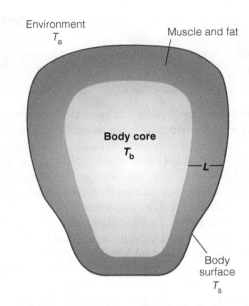

**Figure 7.7** | Temperatures in an animal body. Body core temperature is $T_b$, the environmental temperature is $T_a$, the surface temperature is $T_s$, and $L$ is the thickness of the outer layer of the body.

External environmental conditions heavily influence how animals confront thermal stress. Because air has a lower specific heat and absorbs less solar radiation than water, terrestrial animals face more radical and dangerous changes in their thermal environment than aquatic animals. Incoming solar radiation can produce lethal heat. The loss of radiant heat to the air, especially at night, can result in deadly cold. Aquatic animals live in a more stable energy environment (see Chapter 4), but they have a lower tolerance for temperature changes.

## 7.7 | Animals Fall into Three Groups Relative to Temperature Regulation

To regulate temperature, some groups of animals generate heat metabolically. This internal heat production is **endothermy,** meaning, "heat from within." The result is **homeothermy** (from the Greek *homeo,* "the same"), or maintenance of a fairly constant temperature independent of external temperatures. Another group of animals acquires heat primarily from the external environment. Gaining heat from the environment is **ectothermy,** meaning, "heat from without." Unlike endothermy, ectothermy results in a variable body temperature. This means of maintaining body temperature is **poikilothermy** (from the Greek *poikilos,* "manifold" or "variegated").

Birds and mammals are notable **homeotherms,** popularly called "warm-blooded." Fish, amphibians, reptiles, insects, and other invertebrates are **poikilotherms,** often called "cold-blooded" because they can be cool to the touch. A third group regulates body temperature by endothermy at some times and ectothermy at other times. These animals are **heterotherms** (from *hetero*, "different"). Heterotherms employ both endothermy and ectothermy, depending on environmental situations and metabolic needs. Bats, bees, and hummingbirds belong to this group.

The terms homeotherm and endotherm are often used synonymously, as are poikilotherm and ectotherm, but there is a difference. Ectotherm and endotherm emphasize the mechanisms that determine body temperature. The other two terms, homeotherm and poikilotherm, represent the nature of body temperature (either constant or variable).

## 7.8 | Poikilotherms Depend on Environmental Temperatures

Poikilotherms, such as amphibians, reptiles, and insects, gain heat easily from the environment and lose it just as fast. Environmental sources of heat control the rates of metabolism and activity among most poikilotherms. Rising temperatures increase the rate of enzymatic activity, which controls metabolism and respiration (Figure 7.8). For every 10°C rise in temperature, the rate of metabolism in poikilotherms approximately doubles. They become active only when the temperature is sufficiently warm. Conversely, when ambient temperatures fall, metabolic activity declines, and poikilotherms become sluggish.

Poikilotherms have an upper and lower thermal limit that they can tolerate. Most terrestrial poikilotherms can maintain a relatively constant daytime body temperature by behavioral means, such as seeking sunlight or shade. Lizards and snakes, for example, may vary their body temperature by no more than 4°C to 5°C (Figure 7.9) and amphibians by 10°C when active. The range of body temperatures at which poikilotherms carry out their daily activities is the **operative temperature range.**

Poikilotherms have a low metabolic rate and a high ability to exchange heat between body and environment (high conductivity). During normal activities, poikilotherms carry out aerobic respiration. Under stress and while pursuing prey, the inability to supply sufficient oxygen to the body requires that much of their energy production come from anaerobic respiration, in which oxygen is not used. This process depletes stored energy and accumulates lactic acid in the muscles. (Anaerobic respiration takes place in the muscles of marathon runners and other athletes, causing leg cramps.) Anaerobic respiration metabolism limits poikilotherms to short bursts of activity and results in rapid physical exhaustion.

Aquatic poikilotherms, completely immersed, do not maintain any appreciable difference between their body temperature and the surrounding water. Aquatic poi-

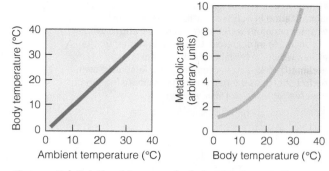

**Figure 7.8** | Relationship among body temperature, resting metabolic rate, and ambient temperature in poikilotherms. **(a)** Body temperature is a function of ambient temperature. **(b)** Resting metabolism is a function of body temperature. (Adapted from Hill and Wyse 1989.)

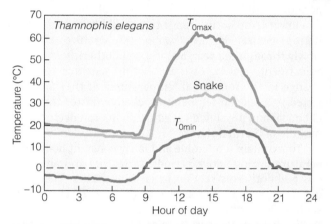

**Figure 7.9** | Daily temperature variation in the western terrestrial garter snake (*Thamnophis elegans*), within its operative temperature range ($T_{0min}$ and $T_{0max}$). Note that the snake maintains a fairly constant temperature during the day. (Adapted from Peterson, et al. 1993.)

kilotherms are poorly insulated. Any heat produced in the muscles moves to the blood and on to the gills and skin, where heat transfers to the surrounding water by convection. Exceptions are sharks and tunas that possess a **rete,** a blood circulation system that allows them to keep internal temperatures higher than external ones (see Section 7.13). Because seasonal water temperatures are relatively stable, fish and aquatic invertebrates maintain a constant temperature within any given season. They adjust seasonally to changing temperatures by **acclimatization,** or physiological adjustment to a change in environmental conditions (Figure 7.10). They undergo these physiological changes over a period of time. Poikilotherms have an upper and lower limit of tolerance to temperature that varies with the species. If they live at the upper end of their tolerable thermal range, poikilotherms will adjust their physiology at the expense of being able to tolerate the lower range. Similarly, during

**Figure 7.10** | A diagrammatic representation of acclimatization in bullhead catfish. Tolerance for warmer or colder water shifts as temperatures gradually increase or decrease. Exposure to higher temperatures would be lethal when the organism is acclimatized to a colder temperature. Response over period shown as dashed line is an estimate (no direct observation). (Adapted from Frye 1947.)

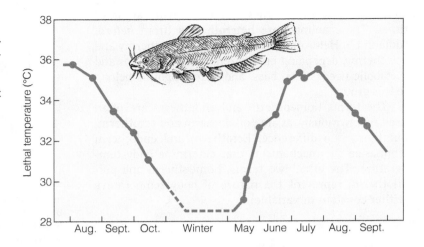

periods of cold, the animals shift physiological functions to a lower temperature range that would have been debilitating before. Because water temperature changes slowly through the year, aquatic poikilotherms can make adjustments slowly. Fish are highly sensitive to rapid change in environmental temperatures. If they are subjected to a sudden temperature change (faster than biochemical and physiological adjustments can occur), they may die of thermal shock.

To maintain a tolerable and fairly constant body temperature during active periods, terrestrial and amphibious poikilotherms rely on behavioral means. They seek out appropriate microclimates (Figure 7.11). Insects such as butterflies, moths, bees, dragonflies, and damselflies bask in the sun to raise their body temperature to the level necessary to become highly active. When they become too warm, these animals seek the shade. Semiterrestrial frogs, such as bullfrogs and green frogs, exert considerable control over their body temperature. By basking in the sun, frogs can raise their body temperature as much as 10°C above ambient temperature. Because of associated evaporative water losses, such amphibians must either be near or partially submerged in water. By changing position or location or by seeking a warmer or cooler substrate, amphibians can maintain body temperatures within a narrow range.

Most reptiles are terrestrial and exposed to widely fluctuating surface temperatures. The simplest way for a reptile to raise body temperature is to bask in the sun. Snakes, for example, heat up rapidly in the morning sun (see Figure 7.9). When they reach the preferred temperature, the animals move on to their daily activities, retreating to the shade to cool when necessary. In this manner, they maintain a stable body temperature during the day. In the evening, the reptile experiences a slow cooling. Its body temperature at night depends on its location.

Lizards raise and lower their bodies and change body shape to increase or decrease the conduction of heat between themselves and the rocks or soil on which they rest. They also seek sunlight or shade or burrow into the soil to adjust their temperatures. Desert beetles, locusts, and scorpions exhibit similar behavior. They raise their legs to reduce contact between their body and the ground, minimizing conduction and increasing convection by exposing body surfaces to the wind. Thus, body temperatures of poikilotherms do not necessarily follow the general ambient temperature.

## 7.9 | Homeotherms Escape the Thermal Restraints of the Environment

Homeothermic birds and mammals meet the thermal constraints of the environment by being endothermic. They maintain body temperature by oxidizing glucose and other energy-rich molecules in the process of respiration. The process of oxidation is not 100 percent efficient, and in addition to the production of chemical energy in the form of ATP (see Section 6.1), some energy is converted to heat energy. Because oxygen is used in the process of respiration, the basal metabolic rate of an organism is typically measured by the rate of oxygen consumption. Recall from Section 6.1 that all living cells respire, therefore, the rate of respiration for homeothermic animals is proportional to their body mass (grams body mass$^{0.75}$).

For homeotherms, the **thermoneutral zone** is a range of environmental temperatures within which the metabolic rates are minimal (Figure 7.12). Outside this zone, marked by upper and lower **critical temperatures,** metabolic rate increases.

Maintenance of a high body temperature is associated with specific enzyme systems that operate optimally within a high temperature range, with a set point about 40°C. Because efficient cardiovascular and respiratory systems bring oxygen to their tissues, homeotherms can maintain a high level of energy production through aerobic respiration (high metabolic rates). Thus, they can sustain a high level of physical activity for long periods.

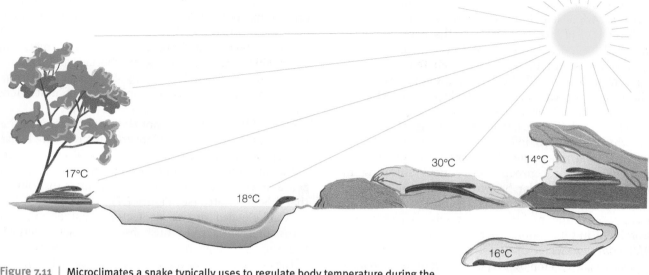

Figure 7.11 | Microclimates a snake typically uses to regulate body temperature during the summer. (Adapted from Pearson et al. 1993.)

Figure 7.12 | General resting metabolic response of homeotherm to changes in ambient temperature. For temperatures within the thermal neutral zone, resting metabolic rate changes little with a change in ambient temperature. Beyond these limits, however, metabolic rate increases markedly with either an increase or decrease in ambient temperature as a result of feedback mechanisms (see Section 7.5 and Figure 7.6).

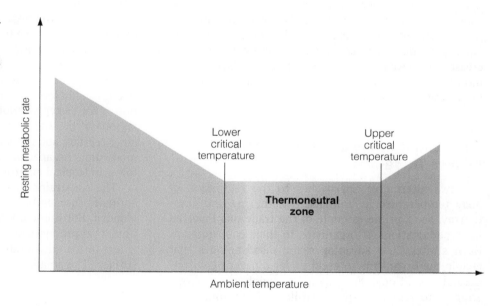

Independent of external temperatures, homeotherms can exploit a wider range of thermal environments. They can generate energy rapidly when the situation demands, escaping from predators or pursuing prey.

To regulate the exchange of heat between the body and the environment, homeotherms use some form of insulation—a covering of fur, feathers, or body fat (see Figure 7.7). For mammals, fur is a major barrier to heat flow, but its insulation value varies with thickness, which is greater on large mammals than on small ones. Small mammals are limited in the amount of fur they can carry, because a thick coat could reduce their ability to move. Mammals change the thickness of their fur with the season. Aquatic mammals, especially of Arctic regions, and such Arctic and Antarctic birds as auklets

(Alcidae) and penguins, have a heavy layer of fat beneath the skin. Birds reduce heat loss by fluffing the feathers and drawing the feet into them, making the body a round, feathered ball. Some Arctic birds, such as ptarmigan (*Lagopus* spp.), have feathered feet, unlike most birds, which have scaled feet that function to lose heat.

Although the major function of insulation is to keep body heat in, it also keeps heat out. In a hot environment, an animal has to either rid itself of excess body heat or prevent heat from being absorbed in the first place. One means is to reflect solar radiation from light-colored fur or feathers. Conversely, many birds of desert regions have dark feathers that absorb heat and then radiate it off again. Another means is to grow a heavy coat of fur that heat does not penetrate. Large mammals of the desert, notably the camel, employ this method. The outer layers of hair absorb heat and return it to the environment.

A number of insects, notably moths, bees, and bumblebees, have a dense, fur-like coat over the thoracic region, which serves to retain the high temperature of flight muscles during flight. The long, soft hairs of caterpillars, together with changes in body posture, act as insulation, reducing convective heat exchange.

When insulation fails, many animals resort to shivering, which is a form of involuntary muscular activity that increases heat production. Many species of small mammals increase heat production without shivering by burning highly vascular brown fat with a high rate of oxygen consumption. Brown fat, found about the head, neck, thorax, and major blood vessels, is particularly prominent in hibernators, such as bats and groundhogs (*Marmota monax*).

Many species employ evaporative cooling to reduce the body heat load. Birds and mammals lose some heat by evaporation of moisture from the skin. Above the upper critical temperature, they accelerate evaporative cooling by sweating and panting. Only certain mammals have sweat glands, in particular horses and humans. Panting in mammals and gular fluttering in birds increase the movement of air over moist surfaces in the mouth and pharynx. Many mammals, such as pigs, wallow in water and wet mud to cool down.

## 7.10 | Endothermy and Ectothermy Involve Trade-offs

The two alternative approaches to the regulation of body temperature in animals, endothermy and ectothermy, are a prime example of the trade-offs involved in the adaptations of organisms to their environment. Each strategy has advantages and disadvantages that enable the organisms to excel under different environmental conditions. For example, endothermy allows animals to remain active regardless of environmental temperatures, whereas environmental temperatures largely dictate the activity of poikilotherms. However, the freedom of activity enjoyed by homeotherms comes at a great energy cost. To generate heat through respiration, homeotherms must take in calories (food). Of the food energy that is assimilated, a minimum goes to growth (the majority going to respiration).

The metabolic heat that is produced by homeothermy can be lost to the surrounding environment (see Quantifying Ecology 7.1: Heat Exchange and Temperature Regulation), and this heat must be replaced by additional heat generated through respiration. As a result, metabolic costs weigh heavily against homeotherms. In contrast, ectotherms can allocate more of their energy intake to biomass production than to metabolic needs.

Not needing to burn calories to provide metabolic heat, ectotherms require fewer calories (food) per gram of body weight. Because they do not depend on internally generated body heat, ectotherms can curtail metabolic activity in times of food and water shortage and temperature extremes. Their low energy demands enable some terrestrial poikilotherms to colonize areas of limited food and water.

One of the most important features of an animal that influences its ability to regulate body temperature is size. A body exchanges heat with the external environment (either air or water) in proportion to the surface area exposed. In contrast, it is the entire body mass (or volume) that is being heated (see Figure 7.7).

Cold-blooded organisms (ectotherms) absorb heat across their surface but must absorb sufficient energy to heat the entire body mass (volume). Therefore, the ratio of the surface area to the volume is a key factor in controlling the uptake of heat and the maintenance of body temperature. As the size of an organism increases, the ratio of the surface area to volume decreases (Figure 7.13). Because the organism has to absorb sufficient energy across its surface to warm the entire body mass, the amount of energy and/or the period of time required to raise body temperature likewise increases. For this reason, ectothermy imposes a constraint on maximum body size for cold-blooded animals and restricts the distribution of the larger poikilotherms to the warmer, aseasonal regions of the subtropics and tropics. For example, the large reptiles, such as alligators, crocodiles, iguanas, komodo dragons, anacondas, and pythons, are all restricted to warm tropical environments.

The constraint that size imposes on warm-blooded animals (homeotherms) is opposite that for cold-blooded. For homeotherms, it is the body mass (or volume) that produces heat through respiration, while heat is lost to the surrounding environment across the body surface. The smaller the organism, the larger the ratio

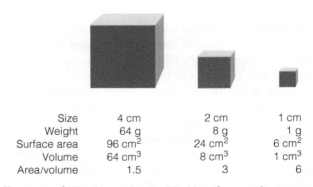

| | | | |
|---|---|---|---|
| Size | 4 cm | 2 cm | 1 cm |
| Weight | 64 g | 8 g | 1 g |
| Surface area | 96 cm² | 24 cm² | 6 cm² |
| Volume | 64 cm³ | 8 cm³ | 1 cm³ |
| Area/volume | 1.5 | 3 | 6 |

**Figure 7.13** | The three cubes—with sides of 4, 2, and 1 cm— point out the relationship between surface area and volume. A small object has more surface area in proportion to its volume than a larger object of similar shape.

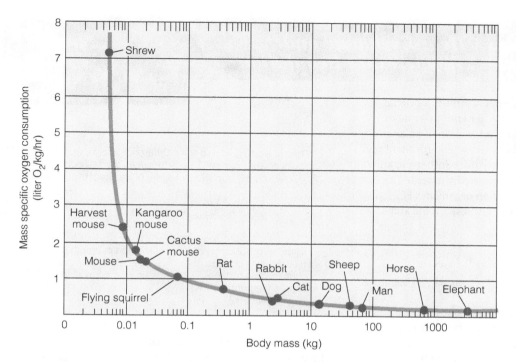

**Figure 7.14** | Observed relationship between metabolic rate (oxygen consumption) per unit body mass (mass-specific metabolic rate) and body mass for a variety of mammal species. Mass-specific metabolic rate increases with decreasing body mass. Note that body mass is plotted on a logarithmic scale. (Adapted from Schmidt-Nielson 1979.)

of surface area to volume, and therefore, the greater the relative heat loss to the surrounding environment. To maintain a constant body temperature, the heat loss must be offset by increased metabolic activity (respiration). Thus, small homeotherms have a higher mass-specific metabolic rate (metabolic rate per unit body mass; Figure 7.14) and consume more food energy per unit of body weight than large ones. Small shrews (*Sorex* spp.), for example, ranging in weight from 2 to 29 g, require daily an amount of food (wet weight) equivalent to their own body weight. It is as if a 150-pound human needed 150 pounds of food daily to stay alive. Therefore, small animals are forced to spend most of their time seeking and eating food. The mass-specific metabolic rate (respiration rate per gram of body weight) of small endotherms rises so rapidly that below a certain size, they could not meet their energy demands. On the average, 2 g is about as small as an endotherm can be and still maintain a metabolic heat balance, although this minimum constraint is dependent on the thermal environment. Some shrews and hummingbirds undergo daily torpor (see Section 7.12) to reduce their metabolic needs. Because of the conflicting metabolic demands of body temperature and growth, most young birds and mammals are born in an altricial state (see Section 8.8), meaning they are blind, naked, and helpless, and begin life as ectotherms. They depend on the body heat of their parents to maintain their body temperature, which allows young animals to allocate most of their energy to growth.

## 7.11 | Heterotherms Take on Characteristics of Ectotherms and Endotherms

Species that sometimes regulate their body temperature and sometimes do not are called *temporal heterotherms*. At different stages of their daily and seasonal cycle or in certain situations, these animals take on characteristics of endotherms or ectotherms. They can undergo rapid, drastic, repeated changes in body temperature.

Insects are ectothermic and poikilothermic; yet in the adult stage, most species of flying insects are heterothermic. When flying, they have high rates of metabolism, with heat production as great as or greater than homeotherms. They reach this high metabolic state in a simpler fashion than do homeotherms because they are not constrained by the uptake and transport of oxygen through the lungs and vascular system. Insects take in oxygen by demand through openings in the body wall and transport it throughout the body in a tracheal system (see Section 7.4).

Temperature is crucial to the flight of insects. Most cannot fly if the temperature of the body muscles is below 30°C; nor can they fly if muscle temperature is above 44°C. This constraint means that an insect has to warm up before it can take off, and it has to get rid of excess heat in flight. With wings beating up to 200 times per second, flying insects can produce a prodigious amount of heat.

Some insects, such as butterflies and dragonflies, warm up by orienting their bodies and spreading their wings to the sun. Most warm up by shivering their flight

The regulation of internal temperatures is a crucial process in all animals, and whether endothermic or ectothermic, this regulation is a function of balancing inputs of heat, from both the external environment and metabolic processes (particularly in endothermic animals), with losses to the external environment. The total heat stored by the body of an organism ($H_{stored}$) can be represented by the sum of these inputs and losses:

$$H_{stored} = H_{metabolism} + H_{conduction} + H_{convection} + H_{radiation} + H_{evaporation}$$

The value of heat energy from metabolic processes ($H_{metabolism}$) will always be positive, representing a gain of heat energy from respiration. In contrast, the transfer of heat between the organism and the external environment through the processes of conduction, convection, radiation, and evaporation can be either positive (gain of heat energy) or negative (loss of heat energy). The physical laws that govern the transfer of energy determine these inputs and outputs of heat energy, which energy always travels from hot to cold—regions of higher energy to regions of lower energy content.

The transfer of heat through the process of evaporation (latent heat exchange) is discussed in Chapter 4 (see Section 4.2), and the process of radiative heat transfer is covered in Chapter 3 (see Quantifying Ecology 3.1: Energy Transfer Through Radiation). The other two forms of energy transfer, conduction and convection, are particularly important in the energy balance and thermal regulation of animals in both terrestrial and aquatic environments.

**Conductive heat transfer** is the movement of heat through solids or between two solids that are in direct contact. Conduction is the process through which heat is transferred between the core and the surface of an organism's body (see Section 7.6 and Figure 7.8). As with all forms of heat transfer, energy will flow from the region of high temperature to the region of low temperature. The rate of conductive heat transfer ($H_{conduction}$) through a solid is described by the following equation:

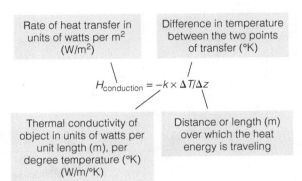

Rate of heat transfer in units of watts per m² (W/m²)

Difference in temperature between the two points of transfer (°K)

$$H_{conduction} = -k \times \Delta T / \Delta z$$

Thermal conductivity of object in units of watts per unit length (m), per degree temperature (°K) (W/m/°K)

Distance or length (m) over which the heat energy is traveling

The symbol $\Delta$ refers to "a difference." Therefore, $\Delta T$ is the difference in temperature between the two regions (such as the body core and surface), and $\Delta z$ is the difference in position ($z$)—the length or distance between the two points of transfer. The **thermal conductivity** of an object ($k$) describes its ability to transfer heat. A variety of factors including its density and specific heat will influence the thermal conductivity of an object. Forms of insulation, such as fat, fur, or feathers, function to decrease an organism's thermal conductivity with the surroundings.

As an example of conduction, consider the transfer of heat energy through an organism. In the case of an endothermic animal, the core body temperature is maintained by metabolic processes, and heat will be transferred from the core to the body surface, where temperatures are lower. If we assume that the thermal conductivity ($k$) of the body is 1.25 (W/m/°K) and the distance ($\Delta z$) from the core to the surface is 10 cm, we can calculate the heat transfer between the core and the surface in Figure 1.

If the value of $H_{conduction}$ is positive, then the direction of flow is outward. If the value is negative, the flow of heat would be inward, from the surface to the body core. This would be the case for a reptile basking on a warm surface such as a rock heated by the Sun. We can use the same approach to calculate the transfer of heat between two objects in contact, such as the reptile and the rock.

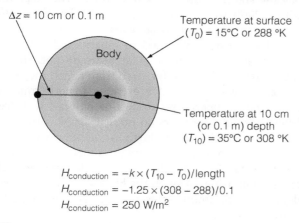

$\Delta z = 10$ cm or 0.1 m

Body

Temperature at surface
$(T_0) = 15°C$ or 288 °K

Temperature at 10 cm
(or 0.1 m) depth
$(T_{10}) = 35°C$ or 308 °K

$H_{conduction} = -k \times (T_{10} - T_0)/\text{length}$
$H_{conduction} = -1.25 \times (308 - 288)/0.1$
$H_{conduction} = 250$ W/m$^2$

Figure 1

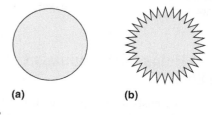

(a)          (b)

Figure 2

The transfer of heat energy between a solid and a moving fluid (air or water) is called **convection**. As with conduction, the rate of convective heat transfer ($H_{convection}$) is a function of the temperature gradient between the object and the surrounding environment, in this case the fluid:

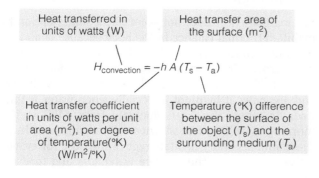

Heat transferred in units of watts (W)

Heat transfer area of the surface (m$^2$)

$H_{convection} = -h\, A\, (T_s - T_a)$

Heat transfer coefficient in units of watts per unit area (m$^2$), per degree of temperature(°K) (W/m$^2$/°K)

Temperature (°K) difference between the surface of the object ($T_s$) and the surrounding medium ($T_a$)

The **heat transfer coefficient** represents how easily heat can move through the fluid. The value will depend on the type of fluid (gas or liquid) and its flow (velocity and viscosity) and thermal (specific heat) properties. For example, for a given gas or liquid, the heat transfer coefficient increases with the flow rate (such as wind speed).

The surface area of an object relative to its volume plays an important role in convective heat transfer. Because heat energy being emitted by an object is transferred to the surrounding fluid across its surface area, the greater the surface area per volume (or mass), the greater will be the rate at which heat is transferred. As discussed in Section 7.10, the result is that smaller bodies with their greater surface area to volume will exchange heat more readily than larger bodies having a lower surface area per volume. Shape as well as size, however, will influence the exchange of heat between a body and the surrounding environment. For example, the cross sections of the two objects (Figure 2) shown above are of the same size when measured as volume, yet object (2b) has a much greater surface area, and will therefore have a greater capacity for exchanging heat energy with the surrounding fluid. As discussed in both Chapters 6 and 7, this relationship between shape and heat transfer is important in the energy and thermal balance of organisms, especially poikilotherms, and represents an important adaptive constraint in the evolution of both plants and animals. ●

1. Figure 6.11 illustrates the differences observed in the size and shape of leaves on the same plant that are exposed to full sunlight and shade. How might the differences in leaf morphology shown in Figure 6.11 influence the ability of these two leaves to dissipate heat through convection?

2. Given the importance of conduction and convection in regulating the body temperature of poikilotherms, how do you think general patterns of body shape might differ between homeotherms and poikilotherms of the same body mass (size)?

muscles in the thorax. Moths and butterflies vibrate their wings to raise thoracic temperatures above ambient. Bumblebees pump their abdomens without any external wing movements. They do not maintain any physiological set point, and they cool down to ambient temperatures when not in flight.

## 7.12 | Torpor Helps Some Animals Conserve Energy

To reduce metabolic costs during periods of inactivity, a number of small homeothermic animals become heterothermic and enter into torpor daily. Daily **torpor** is the dropping of body temperature to approximately ambient temperature for a part of each day, regardless of season.

A number of birds, such as hummingbirds (Trochilidae) and poorwills (*Phalaenoptilus nuttallii*), and small mammals, such as bats, pocket mice, kangaroo mice, and white-footed mice, experience daily torpor. Such daily torpor seems to have evolved as a means of reducing energy demands over that part of the day in which the animals are inactive. Nocturnal mammals, such as bats, go into torpor by day; and diurnal animals, such as hummingbirds, go into torpor by night. As the animal goes into torpor, its body temperature falls steeply. With the relaxation of homeothermic responses, the body temperature declines to within a few degrees of ambient. Arousal returns the body temperature to normal rapidly as the animal renews its metabolic heat production.

To escape the rigors of long, cold winters, many terrestrial poikilotherms and a few heterothermic mammals go into a long seasonal torpor, called **hibernation.** Hibernation is characterized by the cessation of activity. Hibernating poikilotherms experience such physiological changes as decreased blood sugar, increased liver glycogen, altered concentration of blood hemoglobin, altered carbon dioxide and oxygen content in the blood, altered muscle tone, and darkened skin.

Hibernating homeotherms become heterotherms and invoke controlled hypothermia (reduction of body temperature). They relax homeothermic regulation and allow the body temperature to approach ambient temperature. Heart rate, respiration, and total metabolism fall, and body temperature sinks below 10°C. Associated with hibernation are high levels of $CO_2$ in the body and acid in the blood. This state, called acidosis, lowers the threshold for shivering and reduces the metabolic rate. Hibernating homeotherms, however, are able to rewarm spontaneously using only metabolically generated heat.

Among homeotherms, entrance into hibernation is a controlled process difficult to generalize from one species to another. Some hibernators, such as the groundhog (*Marmota monax*), feed heavily in late summer to store large fat reserves, from which they will draw energy dur-

ing hibernation. Others, like the chipmunk (*Tamias striatus*), lay up a store of food instead. All hibernators, however, convert to a means of metabolic regulation different from that of the active state. Most hibernators rouse periodically and then drop back into torpor. The chipmunk, with its large store of seeds, spends much less time in torpor than species that store large amounts of fat.

Although popularly said to hibernate, black bears, grizzly bears, and female polar bears do not. Instead, they enter a unique winter sleep from which they easily rouse. They do not enter extreme hypothermia but allow body temperatures to decline only a few degrees below normal. The bears do not eat, drink, urinate, or defecate, and females give birth to and nurse young during their sleep; yet they maintain a metabolism that is near normal. To do so, the bears recycle urea, normally excreted in urine, through the bloodstream. The urea is degraded into amino acids that are reincorporated in plasma proteins.

Hibernation provides selective advantages to small homeotherms. For them, maintaining a high body temperature during periods of cold and limited food supply is too costly. It is far less expensive to reduce metabolism and allow the body temperature to drop. Doing so eliminates the need to seek scarce food resources to keep warm.

## 7.13 | Some Animals Use Unique Physiological Means for Thermal Balance

Storing body heat does not seem like a sound option to maintain thermal balance in the body because of an animal's limited tolerance for heat. However, certain mammals, especially the camel, oryx, and some gazelles, do just that. The camel, for example, stores body heat by day and dissipates it by night, especially when water is limited. Its temperature can fluctuate from 34°C in the morning to 41°C by late afternoon. By storing body heat, these animals of dry habitats reduce the need for evaporative cooling and thus reduce water loss and food requirements.

Many ectothermic animals of temperate and Arctic regions withstand long periods of below-freezing temperatures in winter through supercooling and developing a resistance to freezing. **Supercooling** of body fluids takes place when the body temperature falls below the freezing point without actually freezing. The presence of certain solutes in the body that function to lower the freezing point of water (see Chapter 4) influences the amount of supercooling that can take place. Some Arctic marine fish, certain insects of temperate and cold climates, and reptiles exposed to occasional cold nights employ supercooling by increasing solutes, notably glycerol, in body fluids. Glycerol protects against freezing damage, increasing the degree of supercooling. Wood frogs (*Rana*

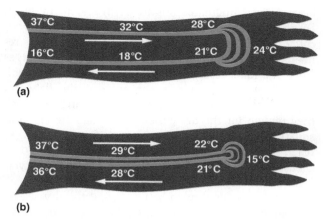

**(a)**

**(b)**

Figure 7.15 | A model of countercurrent flow in the limb of a mammal, showing hypothetical temperature changes in the blood **(a)** in the absence and **(b)** in the presence of countercurrent heat exchange.

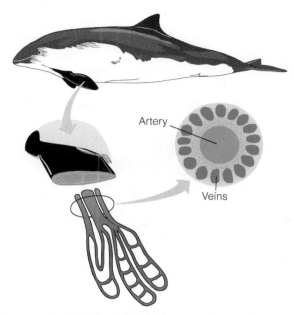

Figure 7.16 | The porpoise and its relatives, the whales, use flippers and flukes as a temperature-regulating device. Several veins in the appendages surround the arteries. Venous blood returning to the body core is warmed through heat transfer, retaining body heat. (Adapted from Schmidt-Nielson 1977.)

*sylvatica*), spring peepers (*Hyla crucifer*), and gray tree frogs (*Hyla versicolor*) can successfully overwinter just beneath the leaf litter because they accumulate glycerol in their body fluids.

Some intertidal invertebrates of high latitudes and certain aquatic insects survive the cold by freezing and then thawing out when the temperature moderates. In some species, more than 90 percent of the body fluids may freeze, and the remaining fluids contain highly concentrated solutes. Ice forms outside the shrunken cells, and muscles and organs are distorted. After thawing, they quickly regain normal shape.

To conserve heat in a cold environment and to cool vital parts of the body under heat stress, a number of animals have evolved **countercurrent heat exchange** (Figure 7.15). For example, the porpoise (*Phocaena* spp.), swimming in cold Arctic waters, is well insulated with blubber. It could experience an excessive loss of body heat, however, through its uninsulated flukes and flippers. The porpoise maintains its body core temperature by exchanging heat between arterial (coming from the lungs) and venous (returning to the lungs) blood in these structures (Figure 7.16). Veins completely surround arteries, which carry warm blood from the heart to the extremities. Warm arterial blood loses its heat to the cool venous blood returning to the body core. As a result, little body heat passes to the environment. Blood entering the flippers cools, whereas blood returning to the deep body warms. In warm waters, where the animals need to get rid of excessive body heat, blood bypasses the heat exchangers. Venous blood returns unwarmed through veins close to the skin's surface to cool the body core. Such vascular arrangements are common in the legs of mammals and birds and the tails of rodents, especially the beaver (*Castor canadensis*).

Many animals have arteries and veins divided into small, parallel, intermingling vessels that form a discrete vascular bundle or net known as a rete. In a rete, the principle is the same as in the blood vessels of the porpoise's flippers. Blood flows in opposite directions, and heat exchange takes place.

Countercurrent heat exchange can also keep heat out. The oryx (*Oryx besia*), an African desert antelope exposed to high daytime temperatures, can experience elevated body temperatures yet keep the highly heat-sensitive brain cool by a rete in the head. The external carotid artery passes through a cavernous sinus filled with venous blood that is cooled by evaporation from the moist mucous membranes of the nasal passages (Figure 7.17). Arterial blood passing through the cavernous sinus cools on the way to the brain, reducing the temperature of the brain 2°C to 3°C lower than that of the body core.

Countercurrent heat exchangers are not restricted to homeotherms. Certain poikilotherms that assume some degree of endothermism employ the same mechanism. The swift, highly predaceous tuna (*Thunnus* spp.) and the mackerel shark (*Isurus tigris*) possess a rete in a band of dark muscle tissue used for sustained swimming effort. Metabolic heat produced in the muscle warms the venous blood, which gives up heat to the adjoining newly oxygenated blood returning from the gills. Such a countercurrent heat exchange increases the power of the muscles because warm muscles contract and relax more rapidly. Sharks and tuna maintain fairly constant body temperatures, regardless of water temperatures.

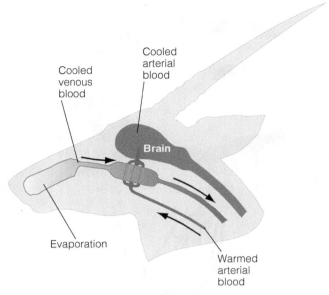

**Figure 7.17** | A desert gazelle can keep a cool head in spite of a high body core temperature by means of a rete. Arterial blood passes in small arteries through a pool of venous blood cooled by evaporation as it drains from the nasal region.

## 7.14 | Maintenance of Water Balance for Terrestrial Animals Is Constrained by Uptake and Conservation

Living cells, both plant and animal, contain from about 75 percent to 95 percent water. Water not only is the essential for virtually all biochemical reactions within the body, but it also functions as a medium for the excretion of metabolic wastes and for the dissipation of excess heat through evaporative cooling. This loss of water must be offset by the uptake from the external environment if the organism is to remain properly hydrated.

Terrestrial animals have three major means of gaining water and solutes: directly by drinking and eating and indirectly by producing metabolic water in the process of respiration (see Section 6.1). They lose water and solutes through urine, feces, evaporation from the skin, and in the moist air that is exhaled. Some birds and reptiles have a salt gland, and all birds and reptiles have a cloaca, a common receptacle for the digestive, urinary, and reproductive tracts. They reabsorb water from the cloaca back into the body proper. Mammals possess kidneys capable of producing urine with high osmotic pressure and ion concentrations.

In arid environments, animals, like plants, face a severe problem of water balance. They can solve the problem in one of two ways: either by evading the drought or by avoiding its effects. Animals of semiarid and desert regions may evade drought by leaving the area during the dry season and moving to areas where permanent water is available. That is the strategy employed by many of the

large African ungulates (Figure 7.18) and many birds. During hot, dry periods the spadefoot toad (*Scaphiopus couchi*) of the southern deserts of the United States remains below ground in a state of dormancy and emerges when the rains return. Some invertebrates that inhabit ponds that dry up in summer, such as the flatworm *Phagocytes vernalis*, develop hardened casings in which they remain for the dry period. Other aquatic or semi-aquatic animals retreat deep into the soil until they reach the level of groundwater. Many insects undergo diapause, a stage of arrested development in their life cycle from which they emerge when conditions improve.

Other animals remain active during the dry season but reduce respiratory water loss. Some small desert rodents lower the temperature of the air they breathe out. Moist air from the lungs passes over cooled nasal membranes, leaving condensed water on the walls. As the rodent inhales, this water humidifies and cools the warm, dry air.

There are other approaches to the problem. Some small desert mammals reduce water loss by remaining in burrows by day and emerging by night. Many desert mammals, from the kangaroo to camels, extract water from the food they eat, either directly from the moisture content of the plants or from metabolic water produced in the process of respiration, and produce highly concentrated urine and dry feces. In addition, some desert mammals can tolerate a certain degree of dehydration. Desert rabbits may withstand water losses of up to 50 percent and camels of up to 27 percent of their body weight.

## 7.15 | Animals of Aquatic Environments Face Unique Problems in Maintaining Water Balance

Aquatic animals face the constant exchange of water with the external environment through the process of osmosis (see Quantifying Ecology 4.1: Diffusion and Osmosis). Osmotic pressure moves water through cell membranes from the side of greater water concentration to the side of lesser water concentration. Aquatic organisms living in freshwater are **hyperosmotic,** having a higher salt concentration in their bodies than in the surrounding water. Their problem is to prevent uptake or to rid themselves of excess water. Freshwater fish maintain osmotic balance by absorbing and retaining salts in special cells in the gills and by producing copious amounts of watery urine. Amphibians balance the loss of salts through the skin by absorbing ions directly from the water and transporting them across the skin and gill membranes. In the terrestrial phase, they store water from the kidneys in the bladder. If circumstances demand it, they can reabsorb the water through the bladder wall.

Marine fish face problems opposite to those in freshwater. These organisms are **hypoosmotic,** having a lower

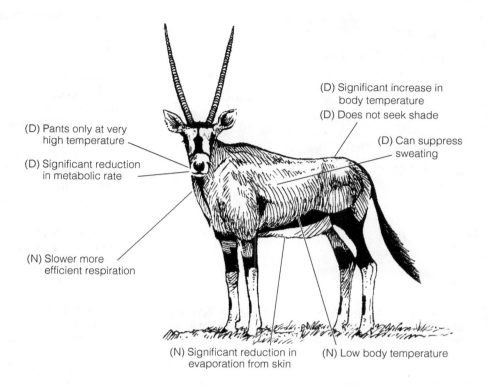

**Figure 7.18** | The physiological adaptation to aridity and heat of an African ungulate, the oryx. D = day; N = night.

(D) Pants only at very high temperature

(D) Significant reduction in metabolic rate

(N) Slower more efficient respiration

(D) Significant increase in body temperature

(D) Does not seek shade

(D) Can suppress sweating

(N) Significant reduction in evaporation from skin

(N) Low body temperature

salt concentration in their bodies than in the surrounding water. When the concentration of salts is greater outside the body than within, organisms tend to dehydrate. Osmosis draws water out of the body into the surrounding environment. In marine and brackish environments, organisms have to inhibit the loss of water by osmosis through the body wall and prevent an accumulation of salts in the body.

There are many solutions to this problem. Invertebrates get around it by possessing body fluids that have the same osmotic pressure as seawater. Marine bony (teleost) fish absorb saltwater into the gut. They secrete magnesium and calcium through the kidneys and pass these ions off as a partially crystalline paste. In general, fish excrete sodium and chloride, major ions in seawater, by pumping the ions across special membranes in the gills. This pumping process is one type of active transport, moving salts against the concentration gradient. This type of transport comes at a high energy cost. Sharks and rays retain a sufficient amount of urea to maintain a slightly higher concentration of solute in the body than in surrounding seawater. Birds of the open sea and sea turtles can consume seawater because they possess special salt-secreting nasal glands. Gulls, petrels, and other seabirds excrete fluids in excess of 5 percent salt from these glands. Petrels forcibly eject the fluids through the nostrils; other species drip the fluids out of the internal or external nares. In marine mammals, the kidney is the main route for the elimination of salt. Porpoises have highly developed kidneys to eliminate salt loads rapidly.

## 7.16 | Buoyancy Aids Aquatic Organisms to Stay Afloat

Aquatic animals have adapted a variety of mechanisms to stay afloat in water. Most aquatic animals inhabiting the oceans have densities very close to that of seawater. Because living tissues are generally denser (heavier) than water, the ability of larger animals to maintain buoyancy means that they have lower density areas of their bodies that counter the higher density of most tissues.

Most fish have a gas or swim bladder (Figure 7.19a), which typically accounts for 5 percent to 10 percent of total body volume. Most can control the degree of buoyancy by regulating the amount of gas in the bladder. Lungs in air-breathing animals sustain neutral buoyancy.

Some marine animals such as the squid maintain neutral buoyancy by replacing heavy chemical ions in the body fluids with lighter ones. Squids have body cavities in which lighter ammonium ions replace the heavier sodium ions. As a result, an equal amount of body fluid is less dense than the same volume of seawater. Another mechanism is increased storage of lipids (fats and oils). Lipids are less dense than seawater. Large amounts of lipids are present in fishes that lack air bladders (such as sharks, mackerels, bluefish, and bonito). Lipid deposits are located in muscles, internal organs, and the body cavity (Figure 7.19b). In marine mammals, lipids are typically deposited as a layer of fat just below the skin (blubber) (Figure 7.19c). Blubber not only aids in buoyancy but also functions as insulation and energy storage.

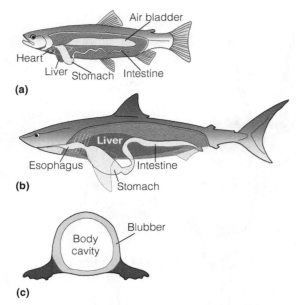

**Figure 7.19** | Buoyancy adaptation in fish and seal: **(a)** gas bladder in a fish, **(b)** large fat-filled liver of a shark, **(c)** blubber surrounding the body of a seal.

The maintenance of neutral buoyancy in open-water environments releases organisms from many of the structural constraints imposed by gravity in terrestrial environments. Organisms such as the jellyfish, squid, and octopus quickly lose their graceful forms when removed from the water. Beached whales die from suffocation when they are no longer able to support their body weight through neutral buoyancy. It is no coincidence that the largest vertebrate and invertebrate organisms on Earth inhabit the oceans.

## 7.17 | Daily and Seasonal Light and Dark Cycles Influence Animal Activity

The major influence of light on animals is its role in timing daily and seasonal activities including feeding, food storage, reproduction, and migratory movements. Animals react to changing light through the response of their **internal biological clocks.** An internal biological clock is fundamental to all living organisms, influencing hormones that play a role in sleep and wakefulness, metabolic rate, and body temperature.

Physiological functions fluctuate in cycles, or rhythms, that range from minutes to months. The main physiological functions of animals, however, are governed by a 24-hour clock, known as **circadian rhythm** (Latin *circa*, about; and *dia*, day) (see Ecological Issues: Humans and the Diurnal Cycle). The circadian rhythm and its sensitivity to light and dark are the major mechanisms that operate the biological clock—that time-keeper of physical and physiological activity in living

things. Where is such a clock located in organisms? Its position must expose it to its time-setter: light. In single-celled protists and plants, the clock appears to be located in individual cells. Light acts directly on photosensitive chemicals that activate cellular pathways. In multicellular animals, however, the clock is within the nervous system.

Skillful surgical procedures have allowed circadian physiologists to discover the location of the physiological clock in some mammals, birds, and insects. In most insects studied, the photoreceptors—located in cells at the base of the compound eye—are connected by axons to the clock, which is located in the optic lobe of the brain or in the tissues between the optic lobes. In birds and reptiles, the clock is located in the pineal gland, functioning as a third eye resting close to the surface of the brain. In mammals, including humans, the clock is in two clumps of neurons (suprachiasmatic nuclei) just above the optic chiasm. The optic chiasm is the place where the optic nerves from the eyes intersect. Operation of the clock in mammals involves a special hormone, melatonin, produced by the pineal gland, which serves to measure time. More melatonin is produced in the dark than in the light. The amount produced is a measure of changing daylength.

How and why circadian rhythms and biological clocks function is the domain of the physiologist. Ecologists are more interested in the adaptive value of biological clocks. One adaptive value is that the biological clock provides the organism with a time-dependent mechanism. It enables the organism to prepare for periodic changes in the environment ahead of time. Circadian rhythms help organisms with physical aspects of the environment other than light or dark. For example, a rise in humidity and a drop in temperature accompany the transition from light to dark. Wood lice, centipedes, and millipedes, which lose water rapidly in dry air, spend the day in the darkness and damp under stones, logs, and leaves. At dusk they emerge, when the humidity of the air is more favorable. These animals show an increased tendency to escape from light as the length of time they spend in darkness increases. On the other hand, the strength of their response to low humidity decreases with darkness. Thus, these invertebrates come out at night into places too dry for them during the day, and they quickly retreat to their dark hiding places as light comes.

The circadian rhythms of many organisms relate to biotic aspects of their environment. Predators such as insectivorous bats must match their feeding activity to the activity rhythm of their prey. Moths and bees must seek nectar when flowers are open. Flowers must open when insects that pollinate them are flying. The circadian clock lets insects, reptiles, and birds orient themselves by the position of the sun. Organisms make the most economical use of energy when they adapt to the periodicity of their environment.

Humans are by nature diurnal (as opposed to nocturnal) beings, meaning that our physiological functions are geared toward daytime activity and nighttime rest. Like other animals, our main physiological functions such as core body temperature, hormone production, heart rate, blood pressure, gastric activity, and the sleep/wake cycle all have circadian rhythms (see Section 7.17) of approximately 25 hours. Normally, these cycles are synchronized to one another by the internal biological clock and reset daily to the 24-hour day/night cycle by external time cues, such as variations in sunlight and the patterns of environmental activity around us.

A typical cycle of core body temperature for a human (see Figure 1) normally has two peaks (around 11:30 A.M. and 7:00 P.M.) and two troughs (around 4:00 A.M. and 2:00 P.M.). Between 3:00 A.M. and 5:00 A.M., the core body temperature is falling to its lowest. During this period, the desire to sleep is the strongest and an individual tends to feel cooler even if the external temperature remains the same.

Between 1:00 P.M. and 4:00 P.M., the core body temperature again dips. In many cultures, this midday fatigue is recognized, and periods of rest are an accepted part of daily activities (such as the siesta in many Latin American and Mediterranean countries or afternoon tea in Britain).

Throughout most of human history, our diurnal patterns of activity have been in tune with these internal cycles. In our modern society, however, many factories and businesses continue to function around the clock, requiring workers to alter their normal daily cycle of activity. However, our circadian rhythms do not adjust immediately, and different cycles adjust at different rates. Changing to a night shift causes the greatest disruption to our circadian rhythms as we attempt to remain active and alert when our cycles (such as core body temperature; see Figure 1) are at their lowest and to sleep when they are at their highest. ●

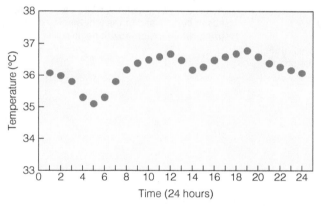

**Figure 1** | Daily variation in human body temperature.

1. Recall from Chapter 3 that the daylength varies seasonally, with daylength decreasing from the summer solstice (longest day) to the winter solstice (shortest day). How do you think humans adjust to the extreme differences in daylength that occur in the far north, such as Alaska or Scandinavia?

2. How does "jet lag" relate to circadian rhythm?

## 7.18 | Critical Daylengths Trigger Seasonal Responses

In the middle and upper latitudes of the Northern and Southern Hemispheres, the daily periods of light and dark lengthen and shorten with the seasons (see Section 3.2). The activities of animals are geared to the changing seasonal rhythms of night and day. The flying squirrel (*Glaucomys volans*), for example, starts its daily activity with nightfall, regardless of the season. As the short days of winter turn to the longer days of spring, the squirrel begins its activity a little later each day (Figure 7.20).

Most animals of temperate regions have reproductive periods that closely follow the changing daylengths of the seasons. For most birds, the height of the breeding

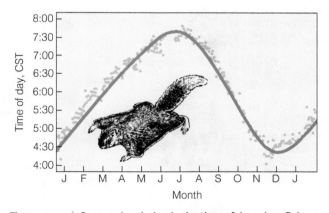

**Figure 7.20** | Seasonal variation in the time of day when flying squirrels become active. (Adapted from Decoursey 1960.)

season is the lengthening days of spring; for deer, the mating season is the shortening days of fall.

The signal for these responses is **critical daylength.** When the duration of light (or dark) reaches a certain proportion of the 24-hour day, it inhibits or promotes a photoperiodic response. Critical daylength varies among organisms, but it usually falls somewhere between 10 and 14 hours. Through the year, plants and animals compare critical daylength with the actual length of day or night and respond appropriately. Some organisms can be classified as **day-neutral;** they are not controlled by daylength but by some other influence such as rainfall or temperature. Others are short-day or long-day organisms. **Short-day** organisms are those whose reproductive or other seasonal activity is stimulated by daylengths shorter than their critical daylength. **Long-day** organisms are those whose seasonal responses, such as flowering and reproduction, are stimulated by daylengths longer than the critical daylength.

Many organisms possess both long-day and short-day responses. Because the same duration of dark and light occurs two times a year, in spring and fall, the organisms could get their signals mixed. For them, the distinguishing cue is the direction from which the critical daylength comes. In one situation, the critical daylength is reached as long days move into short, and at the other time, as short days move into long.

**Diapause,** a stage of arrested growth over winter in insects of the temperate regions, is controlled by photoperiod. The time measurement in such insects is precise, usually between 12 and 13 hours of light. A quarter-hour difference in the light period can determine whether an insect goes into diapause or not. The shortening days of late summer and fall forecast the coming of winter and call for diapause. The lengthening days of late winter and early spring are signals for the insect to resume development, pupate, emerge as an adult, and reproduce.

**Figure 7.21** | Seasonal reproductive cycle of the white-tailed deer. The cycle is attuned to the decreasing daylength of fall, when the breeding season begins, and to the lengthening days of spring, when antler growth begins.

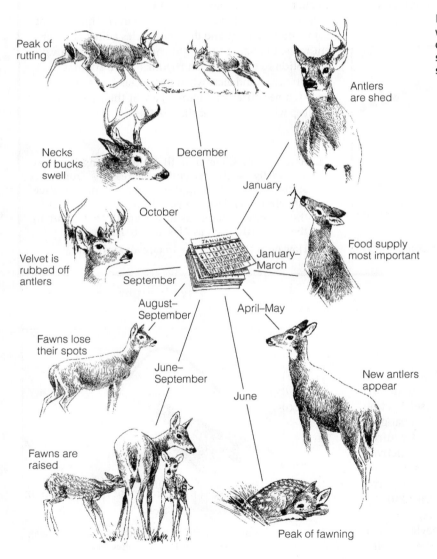

Increasing daylength induces spring migratory behavior, stimulates gonadal development, and brings on the reproductive cycle in birds. After the breeding season, the gonads of birds regress spontaneously. During this time, light cannot induce gonadal activity. The short days of early fall hasten the termination of this period. The progressively shorter days of winter then become stimulatory. The lengthening days of early spring bring the birds back into the reproductive stage.

In mammals, photoperiod influences activity such as food storage and reproduction, too. Consider, for example, such seasonal breeders as sheep and deer. Melatonin initiates their reproductive cycle. More melatonin is produced when it is dark, so these animals receive a higher concentration of melatonin as the days become shorter in the fall. This increase in melatonin reduces the sensitivity of the pituitary gland to negative feedback effects of hormones from the ovaries and testes. Lacking this feedback, the anterior pituitary releases pulses of another hormone (called *luteinizing hormone*) that stimulates growth of ova in the ovaries and sperm production in the testes.

Activities of animals through the year reflect this seasonal response to changing daylength. The reproductive cycle of the white-tailed deer (*Odocoileus virginianus*; Figure 7.21), for example, begins in fall, and the young are born in spring when the highest quality food for lactating mother and young is available. In tropical Central America, home of numerous species of fruit-eating (frugivorous) bats, the reproductive periods track the seasonal production of food. The birth periods of frugivorous bats coincide with the peak period of fruiting. Young are born when both females and young will have adequate food. Insects and other arthropods reach their greatest biomass early in the rainy season in the Costa Rican forests. At this time, the insectivorous bats give birth to their young.

## 7.19 | Activity Rhythms of Intertidal Organisms Follow Tidal Cycles

Along the intertidal marshes, fiddler crabs (*Uca* spp.; the name refers to the enormously enlarged claw of the male, which he waves incessantly) swarm across the exposed mud of salt marshes and mangrove swamps at low tide. As high tide inundates the marsh, fiddler crabs retreat to their burrows, where they await the next low tide. Other intertidal organisms—from diatoms, green algae, sand beach crustaceans, and salt marsh periwinkles to intertidal fish such as blennies (*Malacoctenus*) and cottids (*Cottidae*)—also obey both daily and tidal cycles.

Fiddler crabs brought into the laboratory and held under constant temperature and light devoid of tidal cues exhibit the same tidal rhythm in their activity as they show back in the marsh (Figure 7.22). This tidal

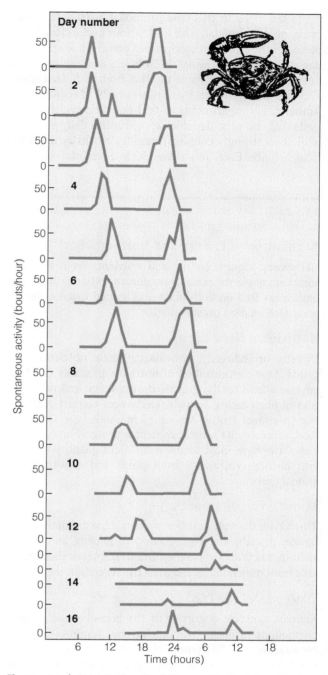

**Figure 7.22** | Tidal rhythm of a fiddler crab in the laboratory in constant light at a constant temperature of 22°C for 16 days. Because the lunar day is 51 minutes longer than the solar day, the tides occur 51 minutes later each solar day; thus, peaks of activity appear to move to the right. (Adapted from Palmer 1990.)

rhythm mimics the ebb and flow of tides every 12.4 hours, one-half of the lunar day of 24.8 hours, the interval between successive moonrises. Under the same constant conditions, fiddler crabs exhibit a circadian rhythm of color changes, turning dark by day and light by night.

Is the clock in this case unimodal, with a 12.4-hour cycle, or is it bimodal, with a 24.8-hour cycle, close to the period of the circadian clock? Does one clock keep a solar-day rhythm of approximately 24 hours and another clock keep a lunar-day rhythm of 24.8 hours? J. D. Palmer and his associates at the University of Massachusetts, Amherst, did experiments to find out. The evidence suggests that one solar-day clock synchronizes daily activities, while two strongly coupled lunar-day clocks synchronize tidal activity. Each lunar-day clock drives its own tidal peak. If one clock quits running in the absence of environmental cues, the other one still runs. This feature enables tidal organisms to synchronize their activities in a variable tidal environment. Day–night cycles reset solar-day rhythms, and tidal changes reset tidal rhythms. Even at the cellular level, organisms do not depend on one clock any more than most of us keep a single clock at home. Organisms have built-in redundancies. Such redundancies enable the various clocks to run at different speeds, governing different processes with slightly differing periods.

## Summary

### Acquisition of Energy and Nutrients (7.1)

Herbivores acquire energy and nutrients from the consumption of plants; carnivores consume other animals; and omnivores feed on both plant and animal tissues. Detritivores feed on dead organic matter.

### Nutritional Needs (7.2)

Directly or indirectly, animals get their nutrients from plants. Low concentration of nutrients in plants can have adverse effects on the growth, development, and reproduction of plant-eating animals. Herbivores convert plant tissue to animal tissue. Among plant eaters, the quality of food, especially its protein content and digestibility, is crucial. Carnivores must secure a sufficient quantity of nutrients already synthesized from plants and converted into animal flesh.

### Mineral Requirements (7.3)

Three essential nutrients that influence the distribution, behavior, growth, and reproduction of grazing animals are sodium, calcium, and magnesium. Grazers seek these nutrients from mineral licks and from the vegetation they eat.

### Oxygen Uptake (7.4)

Animals generate energy from the breakdown of organic compounds primarily through aerobic respiration, which requires oxygen. Differences in the means of oxygen acquisition between terrestrial and aquatic animals reflect the availability of oxygen in the two environments. Most terrestrial animals have some form of lungs, whereas most aquatic animals use gills for the transfer of gases between the body and the surrounding water.

### Regulation of Internal Conditions (7.5)

To confront daily and seasonal environmental changes, organisms must maintain some equilibrium between their internal environment and the external one. Homeostasis is the maintenance of a relatively constant internal environment in a variable external environment through negative feedback responses. Through various sensory mechanisms, an organism responds physiologically and/or behaviorally to maintain an optimal internal environment relative to its external environment. Doing so requires an exchange between the internal and external environments.

### Energy Exchange (7.6)

Animals maintain a fairly constant internal body temperature, known as the body core temperature. They use behavioral and physiological means to maintain their heat balance in a variable environment. Layers of muscle fat and surface insulation of scales, feathers, and fur insulate the animal body core against environmental temperature changes. Terrestrial animals face a more changeable and often more threatening thermal environment than do aquatic animals.

### Thermal Regulation (7.7)

Animals fall into three major groups relative to temperature regulation: poikilotherms, homeotherms, and heterotherms. Poikilotherms, so named because they have variable body temperatures influenced by ambient temperatures, are ectothermic. Animals that depend on internally produced heat to maintain body temperatures are endothermic. They are called homeotherms because they maintain a rather constant body temperature independent of the environment. Many animals are heterotherms that function either as endotherms or ectotherms, depending on external circumstances.

### Poikilotherms (7.8)

Poikilotherms gain heat from and lose heat to the environment. Poikilotherms have low metabolic rates and high thermal conductance. Environmental temperatures control their rates of metabolism. Poikilotherms are active only when environmental temperatures are moderate and are sluggish when temperatures are cool. They have, however, upper and lower limits of tolerable temperatures. Most aquatic poikilotherms do not maintain any appreciable difference between body temperature and water temperature.

Poikilotherms resort to behavioral means to regulate body temperature. They exploit variable microclimates by moving into warm, sunny places to heat up and by seeking shaded places to cool. Many amphibians move in and out of water. Insects and desert reptiles raise and lower their bodies to reduce or increase conductance from the ground or convective cooling. Desert animals resort to shade or spend the heat of day in underground burrows.

## Homeotherms (7.9)

Homeotherms maintain high internal body temperature by oxidizing glucose and other energy-rich molecules. They have high metabolic rates and low thermal conductance. Body insulation of fat, fur, feathers, scales, and furlike covering on many insects reduces heat loss from the body. A few desert mammals employ heavy fur to keep out desert heat and cold. When insulation fails during cold, many homeotherms resort to shivering and burning fat reserves. For homeotherms, evaporative cooling by sweating, panting, and wallowing in mud and water is an important way of dissipating body heat.

## Trade-offs in Thermal Regulation (7.10)

The two approaches to maintaining body temperature, ectothermy and endothermy, involve trade-offs. Unlike poikilotherms, homeotherms are able to remain active regardless of environmental temperatures. For homeotherms, a high rate of aerobic metabolism comes at a high energy cost. This cost places a lower limit on body size. Because of the low metabolic cost of ectothermy, poikilotherms can curtail metabolic activity in times of food and water shortage and temperature extremes. Their low energy demands enable some terrestrial poikilotherms to colonize areas of limited food and water.

## Heterotherms (7.11)

Depending on environmental and physiological conditions, heterotherms take on the characteristics of endotherms or ectotherms. Some normally homeothermic animals become ectothermic and drop their body temperature under certain environmental conditions. Many poikilotherms, notably insects, need to increase their metabolic rate to generate heat before they can take flight. Most accomplish this feat by vibrating their wings or wing muscles or by basking in the sun. After flight, their body temperatures drop to ambient temperatures.

## Torpor (7.12)

During environmental extremes, some animals enter a state of torpor to reduce the high energy costs of staying warm or cool. They slow their metabolism, heartbeat, and respiration and lower their body temperature. Birds such as hummingbirds and mammals such as bats undergo daily torpor, the equivalent of deep sleep, without the extensive metabolic changes of seasonal torpor. Hibernation (seasonal torpor over winter) involves a whole rearrangement of metabolic activity to run at a very low level. Heartbeat, breathing, and body temperature are all greatly reduced.

## Unique Physiological Means to Maintain Thermal Balance (7.13)

Many homeotherms and heterotherms employ countercurrent circulation, the exchange of body heat between arterial and venous blood reaching the extremities. This exchange reduces heat loss through body parts or cools blood flowing to such vital organs as the brain.

Some desert mammals use hyperthermia to reduce the difference between body and environmental temperatures. They store up body heat by day, then release it to the cool desert air by night. Hyperthermia reduces the need for evaporative cooling and thus conserves water. Some cold-tolerant poikilotherms use supercooling, the synthesis of glycerol in body fluids, to resist freezing in winter. Supercooling takes place when the body temperature falls below freezing without freezing body fluids. Some intertidal invertebrates survive the cold by freezing, then thawing with warmer temperatures.

## Water Balance for Terrestrial Animals (7.14)

Terrestrial animals must offset the loss of water from evaporation, respiration, and the excretion of wastes by consuming and/or conserving water. Terrestrial animals gain water by drinking, eating, and producing metabolic water. Animals of arid regions may reduce water loss by becoming nocturnal, producing highly concentrated urine and feces, becoming hyperthermic during the day, using only metabolic water, and tolerating dehydration.

## Water Balance in Aquatic Animals (7.15)

Aquatic animals need to prevent the uptake of or rid themselves of excess water. Freshwater fish maintain osmotic balance by absorbing and retaining salts in special cells in the body and by producing copious amounts of watery urine. Many marine invertebrates maintain the same osmotic pressure as seawater in their body cells. Marine fish secrete excess salt and other ions through kidneys or across gill membranes.

## Buoyancy (7.16)

Aquatic animals use a wide variety of mechanisms to maintain buoyancy, including gas-filled bladders, lungs, and lipid deposits.

## Daily and Seasonal Changes in Daylength (7.17)

Living organisms, except bacteria, have an innate circadian rhythm of activity and inactivity. Under natural conditions, the circadian rhythm is set to the 24-hour day by external time cues, notably light and dark (day and night). This setting synchronizes the activity of plants and animals with the environment. The onset and cessation of activity depend on whether the organisms are light-active or dark-active.

Circadian rhythms operate the biological clocks in the cells of plants and in the brains of multicelled animals. Animals produce more of a special hormone, melatonin, in the dark than in the light. Thus, melatonin becomes a device for measuring daylength.

## Critical Daylength (7.18)

Seasonal changes in activity are based on daylength. Lengthening days of spring and the shortening days of fall stimulate migration in animals and reproduction and food storage as well. These seasonal rhythms bring living organisms into a reproductive state at the time of year when the probability of survival of offspring is the highest. The rhythms synchronize within a population such activities as mating and migration.

## Tidal Cycles (7.19)

Intertidal organisms are under the influence of two environmental rhythms: daylength and tidal cycles of 12.4 hours. Intertidal organisms appear to have two lunar-day clocks that set tidal rhythms and one solar-day clock that sets circadian rhythms.

## Study Questions

1. What constraints are imposed by a diet of plants as compared to one of animal tissues?

2. What is homeostasis?

3. In Figure 7.14, why does mass specific metabolic rate (metabolic rate per unit weight) of mammals increase with decreasing body mass?

4. Why are the largest species of poikilotherms found in the tropical and subtropical regions?

5. How might you expect the average size of mammal species to vary from the tropics to the polar regions? Why?

6. Why might it be easier to capture a snake in the early morning rather than the afternoon?

7. Why do homeotherms typically have a greater amount of body insulation than do poikilotherms?

8. What behaviors help poikilotherms maintain a fairly constant body temperature during their season of activity?

9. How does the size and shape of an animal's body influence its ability to exchange heat with the surrounding environment?

10. Contrast the problem of maintaining water balance for freshwater and marine fishes.

11. How does supercooling enable some insects, amphibians, and fish to survive freezing conditions?

12. How does countercurrent circulation work, and what function does it serve?

13. Distinguish between hibernation and torpor.

14. Consider a population of fish that lives below a power plant that is discharging heated water. The plant shuts down for 3 days in the winter. What effect would that have on the fish?

15. Define circadian rhythm.

16. How does daylength influence the seasonal activity of plants and animals?

17. What is the adaptive value of seasonal synchronization of animal activity?

## Further Readings

French, A. R. 1988. The patterns of mammalian hibernation. *American Scientist* 76:569–575.

This article provides an excellent, easy to read, and well-illustrated overview of the concept of hibernation.

Heinrich, B. 1996. *The thermal warriors: Strategies of insect survival*. Cambridge: Harvard Univ. Press.

This enjoyable book describes the variety of strategies insects use to heat their bodies. It is full of strange and wonderful examples of evolution in the world of insects.

Johnson, C. H., and J. W. Hastings. 1986. The elusive mechanisms of the circadian clock. *American Scientist* 74:29–36.

This article discusses the history of the search for the mechanisms controlling circadian rhythm and gives an easily understood overview of our current understanding.

Lee, R. E., Jr. 1989. Insect cold-hardiness: To freeze or not to freeze. *Bioscience* 39:308–313.

This article provides an excellent overview of the diversity of adaptations that represent evolutionary solutions to the problems faced by insects in dealing with seasonal variations in temperature. It includes a good discussion of supercooling and cold hardening in insects.

Palmer, J. D. 1996. Time, tide, and living clocks of marine organisms. *American Scientist* 84:570–578.

Easy to read and well-illustrated article on the adaptation of marine organisms to the tidal cycle.

Schmidt-Neilsen, K. 1997. *Animal physiology: Adaptation and environment*. 5th ed. New York: Cambridge Univ. Press.

This comprehensive text will provide you with more information regarding the physiology of animals and the range of adaptations that allow animals to cope with the variety of terrestrial and aquatic environments.

Storey, K. B., and J. M. Storey. 1996. Natural freezing survival in animals. *Annual Review of Ecology and Systematics* 27:365–386.

An excellent, if somewhat technical, review of the adaptations that allow animals to cope with freezing temperatures.

Takahashi, J. S., and M. Hoffman. 1995. Molecular biological clocks. *American Scientist* 83:158–165.

A great, readable article that provides an overview of the mechanisms involved in biological clocks.

# Chapter 8 | Life History Patterns

A female Alaskan brown bear (*Ursus arctos*) with her three cubs. Litter sizes range from 1 to 4 cubs, born between the months of January and March. The cubs remain with their mothers for at least 2 1/2 years, so the most frequently females can breed is every 3 years.

An organism's life history is its lifetime pattern of growth, development, and reproduction. Life histories combine a rich array of adaptations relating to physiology, morphology, and behavior. They involve adaptations to the prevailing physical environment, such as those discussed in Chapters 6 and 7. Perhaps most importantly, life histories involve adaptations relating to the organism's interactions with other organisms—the biological environment. Without question, the most important of these life history characteristics are those adaptations relating to reproduction. The true measure of an organism's reproductive success is fitness (see Chapter 2). Evolution is the product of differential reproduction of individuals and the process of natural selection.

If reproductive success (the number of offspring that survive to reproduce) is the measure of fitness, imagine designing an organism with the objective of maximizing its fitness. It would reproduce as soon as possible after birth, it would reproduce continuously, producing large numbers of large offspring, which it would nurture and protect. Yet such an organism is not possible. Each individual has a limited amount of resources that can be allocated to specific tasks, and allocation to one task reduces the resources available for the others. Allocation to reproduction reduces the amount of resources available for growth. Should an individual reproduce early in life or delay reproduction? For a given allocation of resources to reproduction, should an individual produce many small or fewer, but larger offspring? Thus, organisms face trade-offs in life history characteristics related to reproduction, just as they do in the adaptations related to carbon, water, and energy balance discussed in Chapters 6 and 7. These trade-offs involve modes of reproduction; age at reproduction; allocation to reproduction; timing of reproduction; number and size of eggs, young, or seeds produced; and parental care. These trade-offs are imposed by constraints of physiology, energetics, and the prevailing physical and biotic environment—the organism's habitat. In this chapter, we will explore these trade-offs and the diversity of solutions that have evolved to assure success at the one task that is essential for the continuation of life on our planet: reproduction.

## 8.1 | Reproduction May Be Sexual or Asexual

In Chapter 2, we explored how genetic variation among individuals within a population arises from the shuffling of genes and chromosomes in sexual reproduction. In sexual reproduction between two diploid individuals, the individuals produce haploid (one-half the normal number of chromosomes) gametes—egg and sperm—that combine to form a diploid cell, or zygote, that has a full complement of chromosomes. Because the possible number of gene recombinations is enormous, recombination is an immediate and major source of genetic variability among offspring. However, not all reproduction is sexual. Many organisms reproduce asexually. Asexual reproduction produces offspring without the involvement of egg and sperm. It takes many forms, but in all cases, the new individuals are genetically the same as the parent. Strawberry plants spread by rhizomes: underground stems from which new roots and vertical stems sprout. The one-celled paramecium reproduces by dividing in two. Hydras, coelenterates that live in freshwater (Figure 8.1), reproduce by budding, a process by which a bud pinches off as a new individual. In spring, wingless female aphids emerge from eggs

Figure 8.1 | The freshwater hydra reproduces asexually by budding.

that have survived the winter and give birth to wingless females without fertilization, a process called **parthenogenesis** (Greek *parthenos*, "virgin"; Latin *genesis*, "to be born").

Organisms that rely heavily on asexual reproduction revert on occasion to sexual reproduction. Many of these reversions to sexual reproduction are induced by an environmental change at some time in their life cycle. During warmer parts of the year, hydras turn to sexual reproduction to produce eggs that lay dormant over the winter and from which young hydras emerge in the spring to mature and reproduce asexually. After giving birth to several generations of wingless females, aphids produce a generation of winged females. These winged females migrate to different food plants, become established, and reproduce parthenogenetically. Later in the summer, these same females move back to the original food plants and give birth to true sexual forms, winged males and females that lay eggs rather than give birth to young. After mating, each female lays one or more overwintering eggs. Because the males produce sperm with the X chromosome only, the eggs that hatch in spring will produce wingless females that give birth to female young.

Each form of reproduction, asexual and sexual, has its trade-offs. The ability to survive, grow, and reproduce indicates that an organism is well adapted to the prevailing environmental conditions. Asexual reproduction produces offspring that are genetically identical to the parent and are therefore well adapted to the local environment. Because all individuals are capable of reproducing, asexual reproduction results in a potential for high population growth. However, the cost of asexual reproduction is the loss of genetic recombination that increases variation among offspring. Low genetic variability among individuals in the population means that the population responds more uniformly to a change in environmental conditions than does a sexually reproducing population. If a change in environmental conditions is detrimental, the effect on the population can be catastrophic.

In contrast, the mixing of genes and chromosomes that occurs in sexual reproduction produces genetic variability to the degree that each individual in the population is genetically unique. This genetic variability produces a broader range of potential responses to the environment, increasing the probability that some individuals will survive environmental changes. But this variability comes at a cost. Each individual can contribute only one-half of its genes to the next generation. It requires specialized reproductive organs that, aside from reproduction, have no direct relationship to an individual's survival. Production of gametes (egg and sperm), courtship activities, and mating are energetically expensive. The expense of reproduction is not shared equally by both sexes. The eggs (ovum) produced by females are much larger and energetically much more expensive than sperm produced by males. As we shall examine in the following sections, this difference in energy investment in reproduction between males and females has important implications in the evolution of life history characteristics.

## 8.2 | Sexual Reproduction Takes a Variety of Forms

Sexual reproduction takes a variety of forms. The most familiar involves separate male and female individuals. It is common to most animals. Plants with that characteristic are called **dioecious** (Greek *di*, "two," and *oikos*, "home"); examples are holly trees (*Ilex* spp.) and stinging nettle (*Urtica* spp.) (Figure 8.2a).

In some species, individual organisms possess both male and female organs. They are **hermaphroditic** (Greek *hermaphroditos*). In plants, individuals can be hermaphroditic by possessing bisexual flowers with both male organs (stamens) and female organs (ovaries), such as lilies and buttercups (Figure 8.2b). Such flowers are termed *perfect*. Asynchronous timing of the maturation of pollen and ovules reduces the chances of self-fertilization. Other plants are **monoecious** (Greek *mon*, "one," and *oikos*, "house"). They possess separate male and female flowers on the same plant, as do birch (*Betula* spp.) and hemlock (*Tsuga* spp.) trees (Figure 8.2c). Such flowers are called *imperfect*. This strategy of sexual reproduction can be an advantage in the process of colonization. A single self-fertilized hermaphroditic plant can colonize a new habitat and reproduce, establishing a new population, as do self-fertilizing annual weeds that colonize disturbed sites.

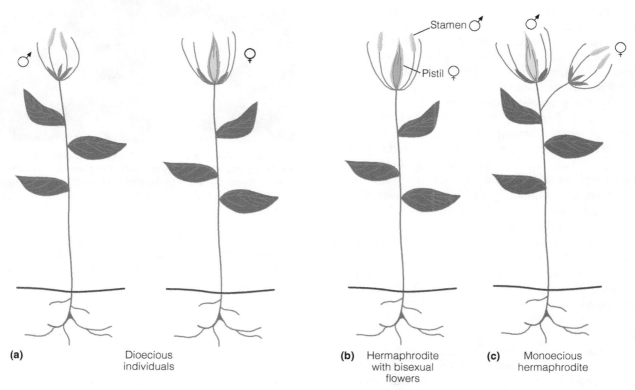

(a) Dioecious individuals

(b) Hermaphrodite with bisexual flowers

(c) Monoecious hermaphrodite

**Figure 8.2** | Floral structure in **(a)** dioecious plant (separate male and female individuals), **(b)** hermaphroditic plant possessing bisexual flowers, and **(c)** monoecious plant possessing separate male and female flowers.

Figure 8.3 | Hermaphroditic earthworms mating.

Figure 8.4 | Parrotfishes (Scaridae) that inhabit coral reefs exhibit sex change. When a large dominant male mating with a harem of females is removed (by a predator or experimenter), within days, the largest female in the harem becomes a dominant male and takes over the missing male's function.

Among animals, hermaphroditic individuals possess the sexual organs of both males and females (both testes and ovaries), a condition common in invertebrates such as earthworms (Figure 8.3). In these species, referred to as **simultaneous hermaphrodites,** the male organ of one individual is mated with the female organ of the other and vice versa. The result is that a population of hermaphroditic individuals is able to produce two times as many offspring as a population of unisexual individuals.

Other species are **sequential hermaphrodites.** Animals—such as some mollusks and echinoderms—and some plants may be males first during one part of their life cycle and females in another part. Some fish may be females first, then males. Sex change usually takes place as individuals mature or grow larger. A change in the sex ratio of the population stimulates sex change among some animals. Removing individuals of the other sex initiates sex reversal among some species of marine fish (Figure 8.4). Among some coral reef fish, removal of females from a social group stimulates males to change sex and become females. In other species, removal of males stimulates a one-to-one replacement of males by sex-reversing females. Among the mollusks, the Gastropoda (snails and slugs) and Bivalvia (clams and mussels) have sex-changing species. Almost all of these species change from male to female.

Plants also can undergo sex change. One such plant is jack-in-the-pulpit (*Arisaema triphyllum*), a clonal herbaceous plant found in the woodlands of eastern North America (Figure 8.5). Jack-in-the-pulpit may produce male flowers one year, an asexual vegetative shoot the next, and female flowers the next. Over its life span, a jack-in-the-pulpit may produce both sexes as well as an asexual vegetative shoot, but in no particular sequence. Usually an asexual stage follows a sex change. Sex change in jack-in-the-pulpit appears to be triggered by the large energy cost of producing female flowers. Jack-in-the-

Figure 8.5 | The jack-in-the-pulpit becomes asexual, male, or female depending on energy reserves. The plant gets its name from the flower stem, or spadix, enclosed in a hood-like sheath. This fruiting plant is the female stage.

pulpit plants generally lack sufficient resources to produce female flowers in successive years; male flowers and pollen are much cheaper to produce than female flowers and subsequent fruits.

## 8.3 | Mating Systems Describe the Pairing of Males and Females

On a brushy rise of ground at the edge of a forest, a pair of red foxes (*Vulpes vulpes*) has dug a deep burrow. Inside are the female and her litter of pups. Outside at the burrow entrance are scattered bits of fur and bones, the leftovers of meals carried to the den by the male for his mate and pups. Back in the woods, a female deer has hidden a young dappled fawn in a patch of ferns on the forest floor. The fawn's father is gone and has no knowledge of this offspring's existence. His only interaction with the mother was during the previous fall, when she was one of a number of females with which he mated during a short period of several days.

The fox and the deer represent two extremes in what is referred to as the **mating system,** the pattern of mating between males and females in a population. The structure of mating systems ranges from **monogamy,** which involves the formation of a lasting pair bond between one male and one female, to **promiscuity,** in which males and females mate with one or many of the opposite sex and form no pair bond.

Monogamy is most prevalent among birds and rare among mammals, with the exception of several carnivores such as foxes and weasels, and a few herbivores such as the beaver, muskrat (*Ondatra zibethica*), and prairie vole (*Microtus ochrogaster*). It exists mostly among species in which cooperation by both parents is needed to raise the young successfully. Most species of birds are seasonally monogamous (during the breeding season), because most young birds are helpless at hatching and need food, warmth, and protection. The avian mother is no better suited to provide these needs than the father. Instead of seeking other mates, the male can increase his fitness more by continuing his investment in the young. Without him, the young carrying his genes may not survive. Among mammals, the situation is different. The females lactate (produce milk), providing food for the young. Males often can contribute little or nothing to the survival of the young, so it is to their advantage to mate with as many females as possible. Among the exceptions are the foxes, wolves, and other canids among which the male provides for the female and young and defends the territory. Both males and females regurgitate food for the weaning young.

Monogamy, however, has another side. Among numerous species of monogamous birds, the female or male may "cheat" by engaging in extra-pair copulations while maintaining the reproductive relationship with the primary mate and caring for the young. By engaging in extra-pair relationships, the female may increase her fitness by rearing young sired by two or more males. The male increases his fitness by producing offspring with several females.

**Polygamy** is the acquisition by an individual of two or more mates, none of which is mated to other individuals. It can involve one male and several females or one female and several males. A pair bond exists between the individual and each mate. The individual having multiple mates (be it male or female) is generally not involved in caring for the young. Freed from parental duty, the individual can devote more time and energy to competition for more mates and resources. The more unevenly such crucial resources as food or quality habitat are distributed, the greater the opportunity for a successful individual to control the resource and several mates.

The number of the opposite sex an individual can monopolize depends on the degree of synchrony in sexual receptivity. For example, if females in the population are sexually active for only a brief period, as with the white-tailed deer, the number a male can monopolize is limited. However, if females are receptive over a long period of time, as with elk (*Cervus elaphus*), the size of a harem a male can control depends on the availability of females and the number of mates the male has the ability to defend.

Environmental and behavioral conditions result in various types of polygamy. In **polygyny,** an individual male pairs with two or more females. In **polyandry,** an individual female pairs with two or more males. Polyandry is interesting because it is the exception rather than the rule. This system is best developed in three groups of birds, the jacanas (Figure 8.6), phalaropes, and sandpipers. The female competes for and defends resources essential for the male. In addition, females compete for available males. As in polygyny, this mating system depends on the distribution and defensibility of resources, especially quality habitat. The female produces multiple clutches of eggs, each with a different male. After the female lays a clutch, the male begins incubation and becomes sexually inactive.

The nature and evolution of male–female relationships are influenced by environmental conditions, especially the availability and distribution of resources and the ability of individuals to control access to resources. If the male has no role in the feeding and protection of young and defends no resources available to them, the female gains no advantage by remaining with him; and likewise, the male gains no increase in fitness

**Figure 8.6 |** An example of polyandry. The male African Jacana (*Actophilornis africanus*) is shown defending the young. After the female lays a clutch, the male incubates the eggs and cares for the young while the female seeks additional mates.

by remaining with the female. If the habitat were sufficiently uniform so that little difference exists in the quality of territories held by individuals, selection would favor monogamy because female fitness in all habitats would be nearly the same. However, if the habitat is diverse, with some parts more productive than others, competition may be intense, and some males will settle on poorer territories. Under such conditions, a female may find it more advantageous to join another female in the territory of the male defending a rich resource than to settle alone with a male on a poorer territory. Selection under those conditions will favor a polygamous relationship, even though the male may provide little aid in feeding the young.

## 8.4 | Acquisition of a Mate Involves Sexual Selection

The flamboyant plumage of the peacock (Figure 8.7) presented a troubling problem for Charles Darwin. Its tail feathers are big and clumsy and require a considerable allocation of energy to grow. In addition, they are very conspicuous and present a hindrance when a peacock is trying to escape predators. In the theory of natural selection (see Chapter 2), what could account for the peacock's tail? Of what possible benefit could it be?

In his book *The Descent of Man and Selection in Relation to Sex*, published in 1871, Darwin observed that the elaborate and often outlandish plumage of birds as well as the horns, antlers, and large size of polygamous males seemed incompatible with natural selection. To explain why males and females of the same species often differ greatly in body size, ornamentation, and color (referred to as *sexual dimorphism*), Darwin developed a theory of sexual selection. He proposed two processes to

Figure 8.8 | This bull elk is bugling a challenge to other males in a contest to control a harem.

account for these differences between the sexes: intrasexual selection and intersexual selection.

**Intrasexual selection** involves male-to-male (or female-to-female, in the case of polyandry) competition for the opportunity to mate. It leads to exaggerated secondary sexual characteristics, such as large size, aggressiveness, and organs of threat such as antlers and horns (Figure 8.8) that aid in competition for access to mates.

**Intersexual selection** involves the differential attractiveness of individuals of one sex to another (see Researcher Profile: Alexandra L. Basolo). Intersexual selection leads to characteristics in males such as bright or elaborate plumage used in sexual displays, as well as the elaboration of some of the same characteristics related to intrasexual selection (such as horns and antlers). There is intense rivalry among males for female attention. In the end, the female determines the winner, selecting an individual as a mate. But do such characteristics as bright coloration, elaborate plumage, and size really influence the selection of males by females of the species?

Marion Petrie of the University of Newcastle, England, conducted a number of experiments to examine intersexual selection in peacocks (*Pavo cristatus*). She measured the tail length of male peacocks chosen by females as mates over the breeding season. Her results show that females selected males with larger tail feathers. She then removed tail feathers from a group of large-tailed males and found that reduced tail size led to a reduction in mating success. In the case of the peacock's tail, size does matter.

However, tail size in and of itself is not what is important; it is what tail size implies about the individual. The large, colorful, and conspicuous tail makes the male more vulnerable to predation, or in many other ways reduces the male's probability of survival. The fact that a male can carry these handicaps and survive is an honest

Figure 8.7 | Male peacock in courtship display.

appraisal of his health, strength, and genetic superiority. Females showing preference for males with large tail feathers will produce offspring that will carry genes for high viability. Thus, the driving force behind the evolution of exaggerated secondary sexual characteristics in males is selection by females. In fact, the offspring of female peacocks paired with males having large tail feathers had higher rates of survival and growth than the offspring of those paired with males having short tails. A similar mechanism may be at work in the selection of male birds with bright plumage. One hypothesis proposes that only healthy males can develop bright plumage. There is evidence from some species that males with low parasitic infection have the brightest plumage. Females selecting males based on differences in the brightness of plumage are in fact selecting males that are the most disease resistant, therefore increasing their fitness (see Section 15.7).

## 8.5 | Females May Acquire Mates Based on Resources

A female exhibits two major approaches in choosing a mate. In the sexual selection discussed above, the female selects for characteristics such as exaggerated plumage or displays that are indirectly related to the health and quality of the male as a mate. The second approach is that the female can base her choice on resources such as habitat or food that will improve her fitness.

For monogamous females, the criterion for mate selection appears to be acquisition of a resource, usually a defended high-quality habitat or territory (see Section 11.10). Does the female select the male and accept the territory that goes with him, or does she select the territory and accept the male that goes with it? There is some evidence from laboratory and field studies that female songbirds base their choice, in part, on the variety of the male's song. In aviary studies, female great tits (*Parus major*) were more receptive of males with more varied or elaborate songs. In the field, male sedge warblers (*Acrocephalus schoenobaenus*) with more complex song repertoires appear to hold the higher quality territories, so the more complex song may convey that fact to the female. None of these studies, however, determined the fitness of females attracted to these males.

Among polygamous species, the question becomes more complex. In those cases in which females acquire a resource along with the male, the situation is similar to that of monogamous relationships. Among polygamous birds, for example, the females show strong preference for males with high-quality territories. On territories with superior nesting cover and an abundance of food, females can attain reproductive success even if they share the territory and the male with other females.

When polygamous males offer no resources, it would seem that the female has limited information upon which to act. She might select a winner from among males that best others in combat—as in bighorn sheep, elk, and seals. She might select mates by intensity of courtship display or some morphological feature that may reflect a male's genetic superiority and vitality.

Among some polygamous species, it is hard to see female choice at work. In elk and seals, a dominant male takes charge of a harem of females (see Figure 8.8). Nevertheless, the females express some choice. Protestations by female elephant seals over the attention of a dominant male may attract other large males nearby, who attempt to replace the male. Such behavior ensures that females will mate only with the highest ranking male.

In other situations, females seem clearly in control. Males put on an intense display for them. Such advertising can be costly for courting polygamous males. Because of conspicuous behavior and inattention, they may be subject to intense predation. Outstanding examples of female choice appear in lek species. These animals aggregate into groups on communal courtship grounds called **leks** or arenas. Males on the lek defend small territories that hold no resources and advertise their presence by colorful vocal and visual displays. Females visit the leks of displaying males, select a male, mate, and move on. Although few species engage in this type of mating system, it is widespread in the animal world, from insects to frogs to birds and mammals. Males defend small, clustered mating territories, whereas females have large overlapping ranges that the males cannot economically defend. Leks provide an unusual opportunity for females to choose a mate among the displaying males. Congregating about dominant males with the most effective displays, subdominant and satellite males may steal mating opportunities. A majority of matings on the lek, however, are done by a small percentage of the males in a dominance hierarchy formed in the absence of females.

## 8.6 | Organisms Budget Time and Energy to Reproduction

Organisms spend their energy, like income in a household or a business, to meet many needs. Some energy must go to growth, to maintenance, to acquiring food, to defending territory, and to escaping predators. Energy must also be allocated to reproduction. The time and energy allocated to reproduction make up an organism's **reproductive effort.**

The more energy an organism spends on reproduction, the less it can allocate for growth and maintenance. For example, reproducing females of the terrestrial isopod *Armadillidium vulgare* have a lower rate of growth than nonreproducing females. Nonreproducing females

The elaborate and often flamboyant physical traits exhibited by males of many animal species—bright coloration, exceedingly long feathers or fins—have always presented a dilemma to the traditional theory of natural selection. Because females in the process of mate selection often favor these male traits, sexual selection (see Section 8.4) will function to reinforce these characteristics. However, male investment in these traits may also function to reduce the amount of energy available for other activities that are directly related to individual fitness, such as reproduction, foraging, defense, predator avoidance, and growth. The role of such trade-offs in energy allocation on the evolution of animal traits is the central focus of ecologist Alexandra Basolo's research, which is changing the way that behavioral ecologists think about the evolution of mate selection.

Basolo's research focuses on the small freshwater fishes of the genus *Xiphophorus* that inhabit Central America. One group of species within this genus, the swordtail fish, exhibits a striking sexual dimorphism in the structure of the caudal fin. Males have a colorful, elongated caudal appendage, termed the *sword* (Figure 1), which is absent in females. This appendage appears to play no role other than as a visual signal to females in the process of mate selection. To test the hypothesis that this trait is in part a consequence of female choice (intersexual selection) Basolo undertook a series of laboratory experiments to determine if females exhibited a preference for male sword length. Her test subject was the green swordtail, *Xiphophorus hellerim,* shown in Figure 1. In these experiments, females were given a choice between a pair of males differing in sword length.

Five tests with different pairs of males were conducted in which the sword differences between paired males varied. Female preference was measured by scoring the amount of time a female spent in association with each male.

Results of the experiments revealed that females preferred males with longer swords. The greater the difference in sword length between two males, the greater was the difference in time that the female spent with them (Figure 2). The results suggest that sexual selection through female choice will influence the relative fitness of males. The benefit of having a long sword is the increased probability of mating. But what is the cost? Locomotion accounts for a large part of the energy budget of fish, and the elongated caudal fin (sword) of the male swordtails may well influence the energetic cost of swimming. The presence of the sword increases mating success (via female choice) but may well negatively affect swimming activities.

To evaluate the costs associated with sword length, Basolo undertook a series of experiments using another species of swordtail, the Montezuma swordtail (*X. montezumae*) found in Mexico. Like the green swordtail, males have an asymmetric caudal fin as a result of an extended sword, and the presence of this sword increases mating success. The experiments were designed to quantify the metabolic costs of the sword fins during two types of swimming—routine and courtship—for males with and without sword fins. Males were chosen from the population having average length sword fins. For some of these males, the sword was surgically removed (excised). Comparisons were then made between males with and without swords for both routine (no female present) and courtship (female present) swimming. Male courtship behavior involves a number of active maneuvers. Routine swimming by males occurs in the absence of females, whereas the presence of females elicits courtship-swimming behavior.

Basolo placed test males into a respirometric chamber—a glass chamber instrumented to measure the

**Figure 1** | The green swordtail, *Xiphophorus hellerim*. Males (shown in the photo) have a colorful, elongated appendage on the lower caudal fin (tail), termed the *sword*, which functions as a visual cue to attract females during courtship.

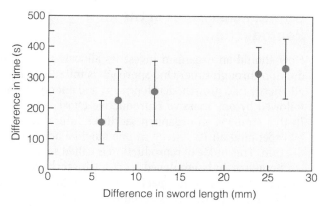

**Figure 2** | Relationship between the difference in sword length between the two test males and the difference in the time spent with the male having the longer sword. (Adapted from Basolo 1990b.)

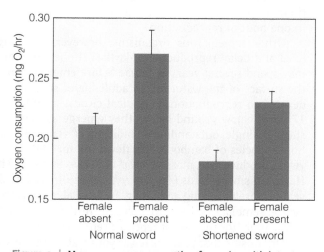

**Figure 3** | Mean oxygen consumption for males with intact (normal) swords and shortened (excised) swords in the absence and presence of females. Female-absence results represent routine swimming. Female-present results represent male courtship swimming. (Adapted from Basolo 2003.)

oxygen content of the water continuously. For a trial where a female was present, the female was suspended in the chamber in a cylindrical glass tube having a separate water system. During each trial, water was sampled from the chamber for oxygen content to determine the rate of respiration. Higher oxygen consumption is indicative of a higher metabolic cost (respiration rate).

Results of the experiments show a significant energy cost associated with courtship behavior (Figure 3).

A 30 percent increase in net cost was observed when females were present for both groups (males with and without swords) as a result of increased courtship behavior. However, the energy cost for males with swords was significantly higher than that for males without swords for both routine and courtship swimming behavior (Figure 3). Thus, although sexual selection via female choice favors long swords, males with longer swords experience higher metabolic costs during swimming, suggesting that sexual and natural selection have opposing effects on sword evolution.

The cost of a long sword to male swordtails extends beyond the energetics of swimming. Other studies have shown that more conspicuous males are more likely to be attacked by predators than less conspicuous individuals. In fact, in green swordtail populations that occur sympatrically (together) with predatory fish, the average sword length of males in the population is significantly shorter than populations where predators are not present.

Despite the cost, both in energy and probability of survival, the sword fin of the male swordtails confer an advantage in the acquisition of mates that must offset these costs in terms of natural selection. ●

## Bibliography

Basolo, A. L. 1990a. Female preference predates the evolution of the sword in swordtail fish. *Science* 250:808–810.

Basolo, A. L. 1990b. Female preference for male sword length in the green swordtail, *Xiphophorus helleri*. *Animal Behaviour* 40:332–338.

Basolo, A. L., and G. Alcaraz. 2003. The turn of the sword: length increases male swimming costs in swordtails. *Proceedings of the Royal Society of London* 270:1631–1636.

1. In her experiments examining the costs and benefits of swords on the caudal fins of male fish, did Prof. Basolo actually quantify differences in fitness associated with this characteristic?

2. Often, sexual selection favors characteristics that appear to reduce the probability of survival for the individual. Doesn't this run counter to the idea of natural selection presented in Chapter 2?

Go to **QUANTIFYit!** at **www.ecologyplace.com** to perform regression analysis.

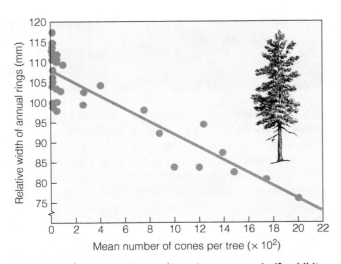

**Figure 8.9** | Douglas-fir trees (*Pseudotsuga menziesii*) exhibit an inverse relationship between the allocation to reproduction (number of cones produced) and annual growth (as measured by radial growth). (Adapted from Eis 1965.)

devote as much energy to growth as reproducing females devote to both growth and reproduction. Likewise, there is a negative relationship between annual growth and the size of the cone crop for Douglas-fir trees (*Pseudotsuga menziesii*) (Figure 8.9). The greater the number of cones produced per tree, the smaller the increment of radial growth. Life histories represent trade-offs; compromises between competing objectives. By increasing the current allocation to reproduction, the organism—isopod or fir tree—is decreasing its growth, which may have consequences for its ability to compete for resources, survive, or reproduce in the future.

The amount of energy organisms invest in reproduction varies. Herbaceous perennials invest between 15 percent and 20 percent of annual net production to reproduction, including vegetative propagation. Wild annuals that reproduce only once expend 15 percent to 30 percent; most grain crops, 25 percent to 30 percent; and corn and barley, 35 percent to 40 percent. The lizard *Lacerta vivipara* invests 7 percent to 9 percent of its annual energy assimilation to reproduction. The female Allegheny Mountain salamander (*Desmognathus ochophaeus*) spends 48 percent of its annual energy budget on reproduction.

The investment by an organism in reproduction includes not only the production of offspring, but also the costs of care and nourishment. It is this investment in reproduction that will ultimately determine the fitness of an individual (see Chapter 2). The fitness of an individual, however, is not defined by the number of offspring produced over their lifetime, but rather by the number of offspring that survive to reproduce. How a given investment in reproduction is allocated, the timing of repro-

duction, the number and size of offspring produced, and the care and defense provided will all interact in the context of the environment to determine the return (see Quantifying Ecology 8.1: Interpreting Trade-offs).

## 8.7 | Species Differ in the Timing of Reproduction

How should an organism invest its allocation in reproduction through time? One approach is initially to invest all energy into growth, development, and energy storage, followed by one massive reproductive effort, and death. In this strategy, an organism sacrifices future prospects by expending all its energy in one suicidal act of reproduction. This mode of reproduction is called **semelparity.**

Semelparity is employed by most insects and other invertebrates, by some species of fish, notably salmon, and by many plants. It is common among annuals, biennials, and some species of bamboos. Many semelparous plants, such as ragweed (*Ambrosia* spp.), are small, short-lived, and found in ephemeral or disturbed habitats. For them, it would not pay to hold out for future reproduction, for the chances are slim. They gain their maximum fitness by expending all their energies in one bout of reproduction.

Other semelparous organisms, however, are long-lived and delay reproduction. Mayflies (Ephemeroptera) may spend several years as larvae before emerging from the surface of the water for an adult life of several days devoted to reproduction. Periodical cicadas spend 13 to 17 years below ground before they emerge as adults to stage a single outstanding exhibition of reproduction. Some species of bamboo delay flowering for 100 to 120 years, produce one massive crop of seeds, and die. The Hawaiian silverswords (*Argyroxiphium* spp.) live 7 to 30 years before flowering and dying. In general, species that evolve semelparity have to increase fitness enough to compensate for the loss of repeated reproduction.

Organisms that produce fewer young at one time and repeat reproduction throughout their lifetime are called **iteroparous.** Iteroparous organisms include most vertebrates, perennial herbaceous plants, shrubs, and trees. For an iteroparous organism, the problem is timing reproduction—early in life or later. Whatever the choice, it involves trade-offs. Early reproduction means less growth, earlier maturity, reduced survivorship, and reduced potential for future reproduction. Later reproduction means increased growth, later maturity, and increased survivorship, but less time for reproduction. In effect, if an organism is to make a maximum contribution to future generations, it has to balance the profits of immediate reproduction against future prospects, including the cost to fecundity (total offspring produced) and its own survival.

## 8.8 | Parental Investment Depends on the Number and Size of Young

In theory, a given allocation to reproduction can potentially produce many small young or fewer large ones. The number of offspring affects the parental investment each receives. If the parent produces a large number of young, it can afford only minimal investment in each one. In such cases, animals provide no parental care, and plants store little food energy in seeds (Figure 8.10). Such organisms usually inhabit disturbed sites, unpredictable environments, or places such as the open ocean where opportunities for parental care are difficult at best. By dividing energy for reproduction among as many young as possible, these parents increase the chances that some young will successfully settle somewhere and reproduce in the future.

Parents that produce few young are able to expend more energy on each individual. The amount of energy will vary with the number of young, their size, and their maturity at birth. Some organisms expend less energy during incubation. The young are born or hatched in a helpless condition and require considerable parental care. These animals, such as young mice or nestling robins (*Turdus migratorius*), are **altricial.** Other animals have longer incubation or gestation, so the young are born in an advanced stage of development. They are able to move about and forage for themselves shortly after birth. Such young are called **precocial.** Examples are gal-

linaceous birds, such as chickens and turkeys, and ungulate mammals, such as cows and deer.

The degree of parental care varies widely. Some species of fish, such as cod (*Gadus morhua*), lay millions of floating eggs that drift freely in the ocean with no parental care. Other species, such as bass, lay eggs in the hundreds and provide some degree of parental care. Among amphibians, parental care is most prevalent among tropical toads and frogs and some species of salamanders. Among reptiles, crocodiles are an exception. They actively defend the nest and young for a considerable time. Invertebrates exhibit parental care to varying degrees. Octopus; crustaceans such as lobsters, crayfish, and shrimp; and certain amphipods such as millipedes brood and defend eggs. Parental care developed best among the social insects: bees, wasps, ants, and termites. Social insects perform all functions of parental care, including feeding, defense, heating and cooling, and sanitation.

## 8.9 | Fecundity Depends on Age and Size

For many species, the number of offspring produced varies with the age and size of the parent. Many plants and ectothermic (cold-blooded) animals (fish, reptiles, amphibians, and invertebrates) do not have a characteristic adult size. These species can continue to grow throughout their adult lives (although typically at a continuously declining relative rate). This condition is referred to as **indeterminate growth.**

Among plants, perennials delay flowering until they have attained a sufficiently large size (and leaf area) to support seed production. Many biennials in poor environments also delay flowering beyond the usual 2-year life span until environmental conditions become more favorable. Annuals show no relationship between size and the percentage of energy devoted to reproductive output; as a result, size differences among annuals result in differences in the number of seeds produced. Small plants produce fewer seeds, even though the plants may be contributing the same proportion of energy to reproduction as larger plants.

Similar patterns exist among poikilothermic (cold-blooded) animals. The production of offspring (fecundity) in fish increases with size, which increases with age. Because early fecundity reduces both growth and later reproductive success, fish obtain a selective advantage by delaying sexual maturation until they grow larger. Gizzard shad (*Dorosoma cepedianum*) reproducing at 2 years of age produce about 59,000 eggs. Those delaying reproduction until the third year produce about 379,000 eggs. Among the gizzard shad, only about 15 percent spawn at 2 years of age and about 80 percent at 3 years. The number of eggs produced by loggerhead sea

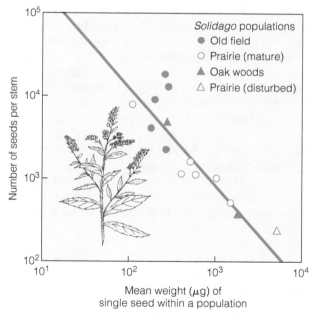

**Figure 8.10** | Inverse relationship between mean weight of individual seeds and the number of seeds produced per stem for populations of goldenrod (*Solidago*) in a variety of habitats. (Adapted from Werner and Platt 1976.)

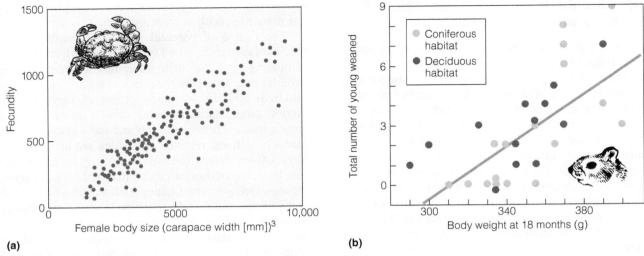

**(a)**

**(b)**

Figure 8.11 | **(a)** The annual production of young (fecundity) by female big-handed crabs (native to New Zealand) increases with female body size (as measured by the width of the carapace, or shell). (Adapted from Jones 1978.) **(b)** Lifetime reproductive success of the European red squirrel is correlated with body weight in the first winter as an adult. (Adapted from Wauters and Dhondf 1989.)

turtles (*Caretta caretta*) is constrained by the female's egg-carrying capacity, which is related to body size. Similarly, there is a positive relationship between body size and the number of young produced for female big-handed crabs (*Heterozius rohendifrons*) inhabiting the coastal environments of New Zealand (Figure 8.11a).

An apparent relationship also exists between body size and fecundity for some endothermic (warm-blooded) animals. Heavier females are more successful in reproduction, and more of their young survive. For example, the body weight of female European red squirrels (*Sciurus vulgaris*) in Belgian forests is strongly correlated with lifetime reproductive success (Figure 8.11b). Few squirrels weighing less than 300 g reproduce.

## 8.10 | Food Supply Affects the Production of Young

Within a given region, production of young may reflect the abundance of food. In the case of species with indeterminate growth, the availability of food can have a direct influence on body size and therefore reproductive effort (see the Chapter 7 Researcher Profile).

In environments where the availability of food resources is highly variable through time, the number of offspring that can physiologically be produced may be greater than the number that can be provided for during certain years. Under these circumstances, it may be necessary to reduce the number of young. In many species of birds, asynchronous hatching and **siblicide,** the killing of one sibling by another, function to reduce the number of offspring.

In asynchronous hatching, the young are of several ages. The older siblings beg more vigorously for food, forcing the harried parents to ignore the calls of the younger, smaller sibling, which perishes. For example, the common grackle (*Quiscalus quiscula*) begins incubation before the entire clutch of five eggs has been laid. The eggs laid last are heavier, and the young from them grow fast. However, if food is scarce, the parents fail to feed these late offspring because of more vigorous begging by the larger, older siblings. The last-hatched young then die of starvation. Thus, asynchronous hatching favors the early-hatched young, ensuring the survival of some siblings under adverse conditions.

In other situations, the older or more vigorous young simply kill their weaker siblings. A number of birds, including raptors, herons, egrets, gannets, boobies, and skuas, practice siblicide. The parents normally lay two eggs, possibly to insure against infertility of a single egg. The larger of the two hatchlings kills the smaller sibling, or runt, and the parents redirect all resources to the surviving chick (Figure 8.12). These birds are not alone in siblicidal tendencies. The females of some parasitic wasps lay two or more eggs in a host, and the larvae fight each other until only one survives.

## 8.11 | Reproductive Effort May Vary with Latitude

Birds in temperate regions have larger clutch sizes (the number of eggs produced) than do those in the tropics (Figure 8.13), and mammals at higher latitudes have larger litters than those at lower latitudes. Lizards ex-

Figure 8.12 | Example of siblicide in the Masked Booby, in which the larger of two offspring kills the smaller sibling. Masked Booby parents collaborate by ignoring the battle between the offspring.

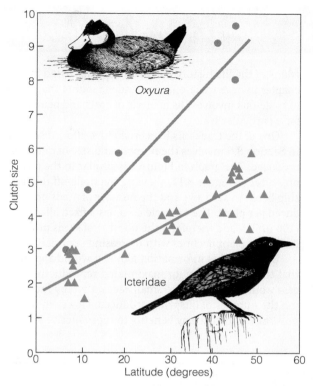

Figure 8.13 | The relationship between clutch size and latitude in birds. Represented are the subfamily Icteridae (blackbirds, orioles, and meadowlarks) in North and South America and the worldwide genus *Oxyura* (ruddy and masked ducks) of the subfamily Anatinae. (Adapted from Cody 1966.)

hibit a similar pattern. Those living at lower latitudes have smaller clutches, reproduce at an earlier age, and experience higher adult mortality than those living at higher latitudes.

Insects, too, such as the milkweed beetle (*Oncopeltus* spp.), exhibit a latitudinal pattern in reproductive effort. Temperate and tropical milkweed beetles have a similar duration of the egg stage, egg survivorship, developmental rate, and age at sexual maturity. Although the clutch sizes are the same, the temperate species lay more clutches and therefore a greater number of eggs. Total egg production of the tropical species is only 60 percent of that of the temperate species.

Plants also follow the general principle of allocation on a latitudinal basis. For example, three species of cattail grow in North and Central America. The common cattail (*Typha latifolia*) grows under a broad range of climates, with a distribution extending from the Arctic Circle to the Equator. The narrow-leaved cattail (*T. angustifolia*) is restricted to the northern latitudes. The southern cattail (*T. domingensis*) grows only in the southern latitudes. These three cattails show a climatic gradient in the allocation of energy to vegetative (asexual) reproduction. *T. angustifolia* and the northern populations of *T. latifolia* grow earlier and faster than *T. domingensis* and produce a greater number of rhizomes (ramets). The southern populations produce fewer but larger rhizomes.

Why might this pattern of geographic variation in reproductive allocation occur? David Lack, an English ornithologist, proposed that clutch size in birds has evolved to equal the largest number of young the parents can feed. Thus, clutch size is an adaptation to food supply. Temperate species, he argued, have larger clutches because increasing daylength during the spring provides

a longer time to forage for food to support large broods. In the tropics, where daylength is roughly 12 hours, foraging time is more limited.

Martin Cody at University of California at Los Angeles modified Lack's ideas by proposing that clutch size results from different allocations of energy to egg production, avoidance of predators, and competition. In temperate regions, periodic local climatic catastrophes (such as a very harsh winter or summer drought) can hold a population below the level that the resources could support. Organisms respond with larger clutches and a higher rate of population increase. In tropical regions, with predictable climates and increased probability of survival, there is no need for extra young.

A third hypothesis, proposed by N. Philip Ashmole of the University of Edinburg (Scotland), states that clutch size varies in direct proportion to the seasonal variation in resources, especially food. Population density is regulated primarily by mortality in winter, when resources are scarce. Greater winter mortality means more food for the survivors during the breeding season. This abundance is reflected in larger clutches. Thus, geographical variation in mean clutch size and the size of the breeding population is inversely related to winter food supply.

**M**any of the life history characteristics discussed in this chapter involve trade-offs, and understanding the nature of trade-offs involves the analysis of costs and benefits for a particular trait.

One of the trade-offs in reproductive effort discussed in Section 8.6 involves the number and size of offspring produced. The graph in Figure 1 is similar to the one presented in Figure 8.11, showing the trade-off relationship between seed size and the number of seeds produced per plant. The example assumes a fixed allocation (100 units), and therefore, the number of seeds produced per plant declines with increasing seed size.

Based on this information alone, it would appear that the best strategy for maximizing reproductive success would be to produce small seeds, thereby increasing the number of offspring produced. However, we must also consider any benefits to reproductive success

that might vary as a function of seed size. The reserves of energy and nutrients associated with large seed size have been shown to increase the probability of successful establishment, particularly for seedlings in low-resource environments (see example of the relationship between seed size and seedling survival in shade in the Chapter 6 Researcher Profile, Kaoru Kitajima). A generalized relationship between seed size and seedling survival for two different environments (wet and dry) is plotted in Figure 2. In both environments, survival increases with seed size; however, in dry environments, the probability of survival declines dramatically with decreasing seed size.

By multiplying the number of seeds produced by the probability of survival, we can now calculate the expected

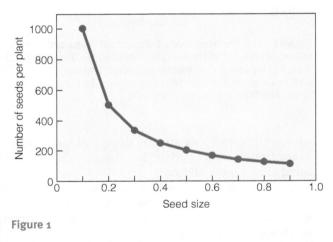

Figure 1

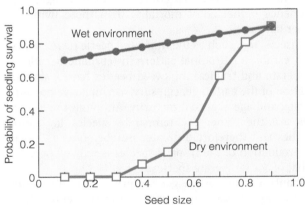

Figure 2

Although reproductive output among organisms does appear to be greater at higher latitudes, the number of comparable species for which there are data is too small to confirm any of these hypotheses. Many more studies along a latitudinal gradient are needed.

## 8.12 | Habitat Selection Influences Reproductive Success

Reproductive success depends heavily on choice of habitat. Settling on a less-than-optimal habitat can result in reproductive failure. The process in which organisms actively choose a specific location to inhabit is called **habitat selection.** Given the importance of habi-

tat selection on an organism's fitness, how are they able to assess the quality of an area in which they settle? What do they seek in a living place? Such questions have been intriguing ecologists for many years. Understanding the relationship between habitat selection, reproductive success, and population dynamics has become particularly important in light of the loss of habitats for many species as a result of human impacts on the landscape (see Chapter 28).

Habitat selection has been most widely studied in birds, particularly those species that defend breeding territories (see Section 11.10). Territories can be delineated, and features of the habitat can be described and contrasted with the surrounding environment. Of particular importance is the ability to contrast those areas

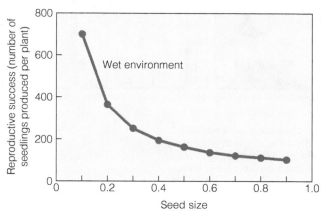

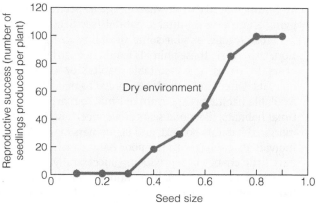

**Figure 3**

reproductive success (the number of surviving offspring produced per plant) for plants producing seeds of a given size in both the wet and dry environments (Figure 3).

In wet environments, where all seed sizes have comparable probabilities of survival, the strategy of producing many small seeds results in the highest reproductive success and fitness. In contrast, the greater probability of survival makes the strategy of producing large seeds the most successful in dry environments, even though far fewer seeds are produced.

Interpreting the trade-offs observed in life history characteristics, such as the one illustrated between seed size and the number of seeds produced, requires understanding how those trade-offs function in the context of the environment (both biotic and abiotic) in which the species lives. Both costs and benefits of a trait can change as the environmental conditions change. The diversity of life history traits exhibited by species is testimony to the fact that there is no single "best" solution for all environmental conditions. •

1. In the example presented above, natural selection should favor plants producing small seeds in wet environments and plants that produce larger seeds in dry environments, resulting in a difference in average seed size in these two environments. What might you expect in an environment where annual rainfall is relatively high during most years (wet) but in which periods of drought (dry), which persist for several years, are common?

2. The seeds of shade-tolerant plant species are typically larger than those of shade-intolerant species. How might this difference reflect a trade-off in life history characteristics relating to successful reproduction in sun and shade environments? See the discussion of shade tolerance in Chapter 6 and also the Researcher Profile in that chapter.

that have been chosen as habitats with adjacent areas that have not. Using this approach, a wide variety of studies examining the process of habitat selection in birds have demonstrated a strong correlation between the selection of an area as habitat and structural features of the vegetation. These studies suggest that habitat selection most likely involves a hierarchical approach. Birds appear initially to assess the general features of the landscape: the type of terrain; presence of lakes, ponds, streams, and wetlands; gross features of the vegetation such as open grassland, shrubby areas, and types and extent of forests. Once in a broad general area, the birds respond to more specific features, such as the structural configuration of vegetation, particularly the presence or absence of various vertical layers such as shrubs, small

trees, tall canopy, and degree of patchiness (Figure 8.14). Frances James, an avian ecologist at Florida State University, coined the term *niche gestalt* to describe the vegetation profile associated with the breeding territory of a particular species.

In addition to the physical structure of the vegetation, the actual plant species present can also be important. Certain species of plants might produce preferred food items, such as seeds and fruits, or influence the type and quantity of insects available as prey for insectivorous birds.

The structural features of the vegetation that define its suitability for a given species may be related to a variety of specific needs, such as food, cover, and nesting sites. The lack of song perches may prevent some birds

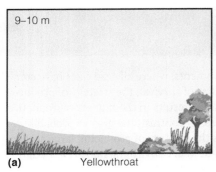  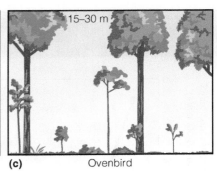

| (a) | Yellowthroat | (b) | Hooded warbler | (c) | Ovenbird |

**Figure 8.14** | The vegetation structure that characterizes the habitat of three neotropical warblers. **(a)** Yellowthroat (*Geothlypis trichas*), a bird of shrubby margins of woodland and wetlands and brushy fields. **(b)** Hooded warbler (*Wilsonia citrina*), a bird of small forest openings. **(c)** Ovenbird (*Seiurus aurocapillus*), an inhabitant of deciduous or mixed conifer–deciduous forests with open forest floor. The labels 9–10 m, 18–30 m, and 15–30 m refer to height of vegetation. (Adapted from James 1971.)

from colonizing an otherwise suitable habitat. An adequate nesting site is another requirement. Animals require sufficient shelter to protect themselves and young against enemies and adverse weather. Cavity-nesting animals require suitable dead trees or other structures in which they can access cavities. In areas where such sites are absent, populations of birds and squirrels can be increased dramatically by providing nest boxes and den boxes.

Habitat selection is a common behavioral characteristic of a wide variety of vertebrates other than birds; fish, amphibians, reptiles, and mammals furnish numerous examples. Garter snakes (*Thamnophis elegans*) living along the shores of Eagle Lake in the sagebrush—ponderosa pine country of northeastern California select rocks of intermediate thickness (20 to 30 cm) over thinner and thicker rocks as their retreat sites. Shelter under thin rocks becomes lethally hot; shelter under thicker rocks does not allow the snakes to warm to their preferred range of body temperature ($T_b$, see Chapter 7). Under the rocks of intermediate thickness, snakes are able to achieve and maintain their preferred body temperature for a long period. Insects, too, cue in on habitat features. Thomas Whitham studied habitat selection by the gall-forming aphid *Pemphigus*, which parasitizes the narrow-leaf cottonwood (*Populus angustifolia*). He found that aphids select the largest leaves to colonize and discriminate against small leaves. Beyond that, they select the best positions on the leaf. Occupying this particular habitat, which provides the best food source, produces individuals with the highest fitness.

Even though a given habitat may provide suitable cues, it still may not be selected. The presence or absence of others of the same species may influence individuals to choose or avoid a particular site. In social or colonial species like herring gulls (*Larus argentatus*), an animal will choose a site only if others of the same species are already there. On the other hand, the presence of predators

and human activity may discourage a species from occupying an otherwise suitable habitat (see Section 14.8).

Most species exhibit some flexibility in habitat selection. Otherwise, these animals would not settle in what appears to us as a less-suitable habitat or colonize new habitats. Often, individuals are forced to make this choice. Available habitats range from optimal to marginal; the optimal habitats, like good seats at a concert, fill up fast. The marginal habitats go next, and latecomers or subdominant individuals are left with the poor habitats where they may have little chance of reproducing successfully.

Do plants select habitats, and if so how? Plants can hardly get up and move about to find a suitable site. Plants, like animals, fare better in certain habitat types, characterized by such environmental factors as light, moisture, nutrients, and presence of herbivores. The only recourse plants have in habitat selection is through the evolution of dispersal strategies that influence the probability that a seed will arrive at a place suitable for germination and seedling survival. Habitat selection involves the ability of plants to disperse with the aid of wind, water, or animal agents to preferred patches of habitat, which more often than not involves an element of chance.

## 8.13 | Environmental Conditions Influence the Evolution of Life History Characteristics

The life history characteristics exhibited by a species are the product of evolution and should reflect adaptations to the prevailing environmental conditions under which natural selection occurred (see Ecological Issues: The Life History of Maize: A Story of Unnatural Selection). If this is the case, do species inhabiting similar environments exhibit similar patterns of life history characteristics? Do life history characteristics exhibit patterns related to the habitats that species occupy?

Corn is one of the major global food crops and perhaps one of the most generally recognized plant species on Earth. Current annual global production approaches 600 million metric tons, or approximately 100 kg for every person on the planet. The plant that we know as modern corn, however, has undergone an amazing transformation from its ancestral form, a transformation that has involved the alteration of life history characteristics through selective breeding—a process of human guided evolution.

Corn, or maize as it is called in most parts of the world, is a domesticated plant of the Americas. Along with many other indigenous plants like beans, squash, melons, and tobacco, European colonists in America quickly adopted maize agriculture from Native Americans, and maize as well as other crop species developed by Native Americans quickly spread to other parts of the world, changing the nature of global agriculture. The original maize plant that the early colonist encountered, however, already had a long history of transformation. Maize was developed about 7000 years ago from Teosinte, a wild grass growing in Central America (southern Mexico). Teosinte is a group of large, Central and South American grasses of the genus *Zea*. There are five recognized species of Teosinte, including *Zea mays* from which maize has been developed. The ancestral kernels of Teosinte looked very different from today's corn (see Figure 1). These kernels were small and were not fused together like the kernels on the husked ear of early maize and modern corn.

By systematically collecting and cultivating those plants best suited for human consumption, Native Americans encouraged the formation of ears or cobs on early maize plants. The first ears of maize were only a few inches long and had only eight rows of kernels. Cob length and size of early maize grew over the next several thousand years, which gradually increased the yields of each crop. This transformation involved a major shift in the pattern of resource (carbon and other nutrients) allocation. The major criterion for the selection of plants for breeding was increased allocation of resources to those parts of the plant that are used as food. In the case of corn, this translated into an increased allocation of resources to reproduction—the production of seeds. By selectively breeding those plants that allocated the greatest amount of resources to the production of seeds, humans have altered the species' life history to meet our needs for food. The increased allocation to reproduction is at the expense of allocation to the production of other structures, primarily roots. The well-developed root system characteristic of grasses allow for the uptake of water in the regions of limited rainfall where these species grow naturally. Modern varieties of maize often need to be irrigated to compensate for their reduced ability to tolerate periods of low soil moisture. To avoid the need for irrigation, varieties have been specifically developed for regions where soil moisture is depleted by midsummer. These varieties grow and mature more quickly, avoiding the drought stress associated with late summer.

The original ancestors of modern corn can still be found in Central America today, but virtually all populations of Teosinte are either threatened or endangered. The Mexican government has taken action in recent years to protect wild Teosinte populations, and there is currently a large amount of scientific interest in using wild populations in the future development of domesticated corn, including conferring beneficial Teosinte traits, such as insect resistance and perennialism, to cultivated maize lines. •

1. Can you think of another example where the life history of a plant or animal species has been actively manipulated for human purposes? Which characteristics have been manipulated?

2. Can you think of any life history characteristics of humans that have been altered by the development of technology or modern culture? Think of life history in the broadest sense to include behavioral and cultural factors that influence lifetime patterns of growth, development, and reproduction.

**Figure 1** | The domestication of the corn plant involved the selection for increased allocation to reproduction: the production of seed. The ancestral kernels of Teosinte were small and not fused together like the kernels on the husked ear of modern corn.

One way of classifying environments (or species habitats) relates to their variability in time. We can envision two contrasting types of habitats: (1) those that are variable in time or short-lived and (2) those that are relatively stable (long-lived and constant), with little random environmental fluctuations. The ecologists Robert MacArthur of the University of Pennsylvania, E. O. Wilson of Harvard University, and later E. Pianka of the University of Texas used this dichotomy to develop the concept of $r$- and $K$-selection.

The theory of $r$- and $K$-selection predicts that species adapted to these two different environments will differ in life history traits such as size, fecundity, age at first reproduction, number of reproductive events during a lifetime, and total life span. Species popularly known as **$r$-strategists** are typically short-lived. They have high reproductive rates at low population densities, rapid development, small body size, large number of offspring (but with low survival), and minimal parental care. They make use of temporary habitats. Many inhabit unstable or unpredictable environments that can cause catastrophic mortality independent of population density. For these species, environmental resources are rarely limiting. They exploit noncompetitive situations. Some $r$-strategists, such as weedy species, have means of wide dispersal, are good colonizers, and respond rapidly to disturbance.

**$K$-strategists** are competitive species with stable populations of long-lived individuals. They have a slower growth rate at low populations, but they maintain that growth rate at high densities. $K$-strategists can cope with physical and biotic pressures. They possess both delayed and repeated reproduction and have a larger body size and slower development. They produce few seeds, eggs, or young. Among animals, parents care for the young; among plants, seeds possess stored food that gives the seedlings a strong start. The mortality of $K$-strategists relates more to density than to unpredictable environmental conditions. They are specialists, efficient users of a particular environment, but their populations are at or near carrying capacity and are resource-limited. These qualities, combined with their lack of means of wide dispersal, make $K$-strategists poor colonizers of new and empty habitats.

The terms $r$ and $K$ used to characterize these two contrasting strategies relate to the parameters of the logistic model of population growth presented later in Chapter 10, where $r$ is the per capita rate of growth, and $K$ is the carrying capacity (maximum size a population can sustain). Using the classification of $r$- and $K$- strategies for comparing species across a wide range of sizes is of limited value. For example, the correlation among body size, metabolic rate, and longevity in warm-blooded organisms (see Chapter 7) results in species with small body size generally being classified as $r$ species and those with large body size as $K$ species. The concept of $r$ species

(a)

(b)

**Figure 8.15** | The **(a)** spotted (*Ambystoma maculatum*) and **(b)** redback (*Plethodon cinereus*) salamanders found in eastern North America provide an example of contrasting life history strategies. The spotted salamander lays a large number of eggs that form an egg mass, which it then abandons. In contrast the redback lays only few eggs, which it guards until they hatch.

and $K$ species is most useful in comparing organisms of the same type. The spotted (*Ambystoma maculatum*) and redback (*Plethodon cinereus*) salamanders found in eastern North America provide such an example of contrasting life history strategies (Figure 8.15).

The spotted salamander, an $r$-strategist, is found under logs and piles of damp leaves in deciduous forest habitats. During the month of February, individuals migrate to ponds and other small bodies of water to reproduce. After mating, females lay up to 250 eggs in large compact gelatinous masses that are attached to twigs just under the surface of the water. After mating, adults leave the water, providing no parental care of eggs or young. In contrast, the redback salamander, a $K$-strategist, occupies similar habitats in mixed coniferous–deciduous forests. After mating, females lay between 4 to 10 eggs, which are deposited in a cluster within the crevice of a rotting log or stump. The female then curls about the egg cluster, guarding them until the larvae hatch.

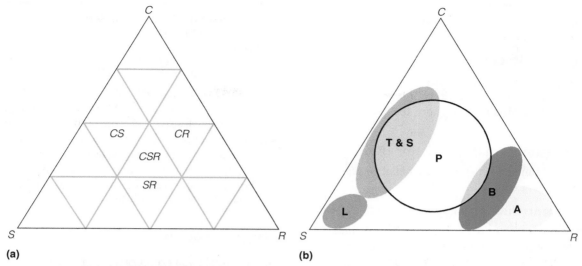

**Figure 8.16** | Grime's model of life history variation in plants based on three primary strategies: ruderals (R), competitive (C), and stress-tolerant (S). **(a)** These primary strategies define the three points of the triangle. Intermediate strategies are defined by combinations of these three (e.g., CS, CR, CSR, and SR). **(b)** Grime's assessment of life history strategies of most trees and shrubs (T & S), lichens (L), biennial herbs (B), perennial herbs (P), and annual herbs (A). (Adapted from Grime 1977.)

The plant ecologist J. Phillip Grime of Sheffield, England, used a similar framework to that of MacArthur and Wilson to develop a life history classification for plants based on three primary strategies (R, C, and S) that relate plant adaptations to different habitats (Figure 8.16). Species exhibiting the R, or ruderal, strategy rapidly colonize disturbed sites but are small in stature and short-lived. Allocation of resources is primarily to reproduction, with characteristics allowing for a wide dispersal of seeds to newly disturbed sites. Predictable habitats with abundant resources favor species that allocate resources to growth, favoring resource acquisition and competitive ability (C species). Habitats where resources are limited favor stress-tolerant species (S species) that allocate resources to maintenance. These three strategies form the end points of a triangular classification system that allows for intermediate strategies, depending on such environmental factors as resource availability and frequency of disturbance.

---

## Summary

### Asexual and Sexual Reproduction (8.1)

The ability of an organism to leave behind reproducing offspring is its fitness. Organisms that contribute the most offspring to the next generation are the fittest. Reproduction can be asexual or sexual. Asexual reproduction, or cloning, results in new individuals that are genetically the same as the parent. Sexual reproduction combines egg and sperm in a diploid cell, or zygote. Sexual reproduction produces genetic variability among offspring.

### Forms of Sexual Reproduction (8.2)

Sexual reproduction takes a variety of forms. Plants with separate males and females are called dioecious. An organism possessing both male and female sex organs is hermaphroditic. Plant hermaphrodites have bisexual flowers or, if they are monoecious, separate male and female flowers on the same individual. Some plants and animals change gender.

### Mating Systems (8.3)

Mating systems include two basic types: monogamy and polygamy. In polygyny, the male acquires more than one female; in polyandry, the female acquires more than one male. The potential for competitive mating and sexual selection is higher in polygamy than in monogamy.

### Sexual Selection (8.4)

Selection of a proper mate is essential if an organism is to contribute to the next generation. An important component of mating strategy is sexual selection. In general, males compete with males for the opportunity to mate with females, but females finally choose mates. Sexual selection favors traits that enhance mating success, even if they handicap the male by making him more vulnerable to predation. Male competition is intrasexual selection, whereas intersexual selection involves the differential attractiveness of individuals of one sex to another. By choosing the best males, females ensure their own fitness.

## Resources and Mate Selection (8.5)

Females may also choose mates based on the acquisition of resources; usually a defended territory or habitat. By choosing a male with a high-quality territory, the female may increase her fitness.

## Energy Investment in Reproduction (8.6)

The amount of time and energy parents allot to reproduction is reproductive effort.

## Timing of Reproduction (8.7)

To maximize fitness, an organism has to balance immediate reproductive efforts against future prospects. One alternative, semelparity, is to invest maximum energy in a single reproductive effort. The other alternative, iteroparity, is to allocate less energy each time to repeated reproductive efforts.

## Number and Size of Offspring (8.8)

Organisms that produce a large number of offspring have a minimal investment in each offspring. They can afford to send a large number into the world with a chance that a few will survive. By so doing, they increase parental fitness but decrease the fitness of the young. Organisms that produce few young invest considerably more in each one. Such organisms increase the fitness of the young at the expense of the fitness of the parents.

## Age and Size (8.9)

A direct relationship between size and fecundity exists among plants and ectotherms. The larger the size, the more young are produced. Among both endotherms and ectotherms, heavier females are more successful in producing a greater number of offspring.

## Food Supply (8.10)

Production of young often reflects the availability of food. In times of food scarcity, parents may fail to feed some offspring. In other situations, vigorous young kill their weaker siblings.

## Latitudinal Variation (8.11)

In general, clutch and litter sizes increase from the tropics to the poles. This gradient may reflect length of daylight, which influences foraging time, or the more stable climate in the tropics.

## Habitat Selection (8.12)

Reproductive success depends heavily on the choice of habitats. Habitat selection is genetic and partly behavioral. Most studies of habitat selection have focused on birds that defend breeding territories. Results suggest that habitat selection involves a hierarchical approach, with the initial selection based on general features of the landscape; within this area, individuals respond to specific features of the vegetation or habitat.

## Environmental Influences (8.13)

Organisms living in variable or ephemeral environments or facing heavy predation produce numerous offspring, ensuring that some will survive. A large number of young is characteristic of annual plants, short-lived mammals, insects, and semelparous species. Having few young is characteristic of long-lived species. Iteroparous species may adjust the number of young in response to environmental conditions and the availability of resources.

## Study Questions

1. Why might you expect sexual reproduction to be an advantage in a variable environment?
2. Contrast dioecious, monoecious, and hermaphroditism.
3. What are some advantages of hermaphroditism?
4. Distinguish among monogamy, polygamy, polygyny, and polyandry.
5. Why is monogamy more common in birds than it is in mammals?
6. How might female preference for a male trait (sexual selection), such as coloration or body size, drive selection in a direction counter to that of natural selection?
7. Contrast intrasexual selection and intersexual selection.
8. Discuss the trade-off in the number of offspring produced and the degree of parental care.
9. What conditions favor semelparity over iteroparity?
10. For a given allocation to reproduction, there is a trade-off between the number and size of offspring produced (see Figure 8.10). What type(s) of environment would favor plant species with a strategy of producing many small seeds rather than few large ones?
11. What is the difference between $r$-selected and $K$-selected organisms? Which strategy would you expect to be more prevalent in unpredictable environments (high stochastic variation in conditions)?

## Further Readings

Alcock, J. 2001. *Animal behavior: An evolutionary approach*. 7th ed. Sunderland, MA: Sinauer Associates.

   This text is an excellent treatment of topics covered in this chapter. It is a good reference for students that might want to pursue specific topics relating to behavioral ecology.

Andersson, M., and Y. Iwasa. 1996. Sexual selection. *Trends in Ecology and Evolution* 11:53–58.

   An excellent but technical review of sexual selection.

Buss, D. M. 1994. The strategies of human mating. *American Scientist* 82:238–249.

   This article, an application of sexual selection theory to humans, is a fun read for students. It explores the question of whether mate selection by females has influenced male characteristics in humans.

Krebs, J. R., and N. D. Davies. 1993. *An introduction to behavioral ecology.* 3rd ed. Oxford: Blackwell Scientific Publications.

This text provides a comprehensive discussion of behavioral topics that are covered in this chapter.

Policansky, D. 1982. **Sex change in plants and animals.** *Annual Review of Ecology and Systematics* 13:471–495.

A review article that explores the variety of examples, in both plants and animals, of individuals that change sex over the course of their lifetime. It explores our understanding of cues that result in the shift and mechanisms by which the shift occurs.

Stearns, S. C. 1992. *The evolution of life histories.* Oxford: Oxford Univ. Press.

This book explores the link between natural selection and life history. It does an excellent job of illustrating how both biotic and abiotic factors interact to influence the evolution of specific life history traits.

# Part Eight | Biogeographical Ecology

The 19th century witnessed the golden age of the naturalist-explorer, and the tropics were the frontier of natural science. Aspiring young naturalists such as Alfred Russel Wallace, Henry Walter Bates, Joseph Hooker, Alexander Von Humboldt, and Charles Darwin traveled the tropics, cataloging its amazing array of plants and animals. In 11 years in Brazil, Henry Bates collected some 14,712 species of animals, of which more than 8000 were previously unknown to science. To someone who had been trained in the temperate zone, the biological diversity of the tropics was awe-inspiring.

These young naturalists, however, were struck not only by the diversity of life encountered but also by the similar appearance and nature of organisms found in geographically different regions; a similarity that appeared to link form and function. For example, the flying squirrel of eastern North America (a rodent) and the Australian sugar glider (a marsupial) are unrelated species inhabiting the canopy of forests half a world apart, yet they are remarkably similar in appearance

(Figure 1). Both species have a flat, bushy tail and an extension of the skin between the foreleg and the hindleg. This body form enables them to glide through the air from one tree limb to another.

The observed link between form and function made by early naturalists was not limited to animals. One of the most striking patterns of similarity observed by these early explorers was that geographically different regions characterized by similar climates support similar types of plant communities. Consider the photos of two desert regions in southern Africa and Australia shown in Figure 2. Both regions have a similar climate with low, seasonal precipitation. Although the plant species that occupy these two shrub-desert ecosystems are quite distinct, the dwarf-shrubs and the physical structure of the plant communities are very similar in appearance and function. The early naturalists were therefore faced with two conflicting observations in need of explanation. On the one hand, a mechanism was needed to explain the amazing variation observed among plants and animals—diversity. On the other hand, an explanation was needed for the observed similarity among different, unrelated species that exhibited similar behaviors (such as the flying squirrel and sugar glider) or inhabited similar types of environments (such as the dwarf-shrubs of the shrub deserts).

Although the primary focus of Darwin's theory of natural selection presented in Chapter 2 is to explain the mechanism by which diversity (differences among species) can arise from common ancestry, it offers a second explanation for the similar characteristics observed in plants and animals found in geographically distinct regions—that of convergent evolution. Evolutionary biologists use the term **convergent evolution** to describe the independent evolution of a similar characteristic in two different species not derived from a recent, common ancestor. Recall that natural selection is essentially a two-step process: (1) the produc-

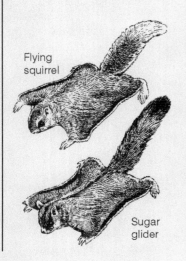

Flying squirrel

Sugar glider

**Figure 1** | Convergent evolution of unrelated species showing similar relationships between form and function. A North American rodent, the flying squirrel, and an Australian marsupial, the sugar glider, both have a flat, bushy tail and an extension of the skin between the foreleg and the hindleg that enables them to glide down from one tree limb to another.

(a)

(b)

Figure 2 | Shrub desert ecosystems: (a) Karoo Desert in southern Africa, (b) western New South Wales, Australia. All three sites are characterized by low, seasonal precipitation.

tion of variation among individuals within the population in some characteristic, (2) which results in differences among individuals in their survival and reproduction. It is the random processes of genetic mutation and recombination that give rise to variation, but it is the necessity of adaptation to the prevailing (and often changing) environmental conditions that guides the invisible hand of design.

The physical processes discussed in Chapters 3–5 give rise to the broad-scale patterns of climate and abiotic environment on Earth. These processes transcend oceans, continents, mountain ranges, and the geographic barriers that function as the mechanisms of isolation in the process of evolution. The similarity between shrub deserts in southern Africa and Australia shown in Figure 2 reflects the similar form and function of the plant species that have adapted to

these distant ecosystems—species that evolved independently but under similar constraints imposed by the physical environment.

The observed similarity in the structure of plant communities found in geographically distant yet physically similar environments led 19th-century plant geographers J. F. Schouw, A. deCandolle, and A. F. W. Schimper to correlate the distribution of vegetation to climate. First, they noted that the world could be divided into zones that represent broad categories of vegetation, categories that are defined on the basis of having a similar physical appearance (physiognomy): deserts; grasslands; and coniferous, temperate, and tropical forests. They called these categories **formations.** Second, they noted that regions of the globe occupied by a given type of vegetation formation were characterized by a similar climate. Their observations led to the development of a general understanding of the factors controlling the distribution of vegetation at a global scale.

These early studies relating the global distribution of plant life—and later animal life—with climate developed into the field of biogeography. **Biogeography** is the study of the spatial or geographical distribution of organisms, both past and present. Its goal is to describe and understand the processes responsible for the many patterns in the distribution of species and larger taxonomic groups (genus, family, etc.). Historical biogeography is concerned with the reconstruction of the origin, dispersal, and extinction of various taxonomic groups. Ecological biogeography is concerned with studying the distribution of contemporary organisms, and it is this topic that will be the focus of Part Eight. We will first explore the large-scale distribution of what the early plant geographers called formations but what we now generally refer to as *biomes* (see the introduction to Chapter 23). To frame this discussion, we can return to the dichotomy we proposed in Part Three of dividing Earth's environments into categories of terrestrial (Chapter 23) and aquatic (Chapter 24). To this we will add one additional category to include those environments that form an ecotone or transition zone between land and water (Chapter 25). These chapters reflect an ecology of place, examining how the processes and patterns that we have discussed thus far in the text are reflected in different regions of the world.

We will finish our discussion of biogeographical ecology by exploring patterns of biological diversity on Earth, both in time and space (Chapter 26).

# Chapter 23 | Terrestrial Ecosystems

Spectacular fall color is a hallmark of the eastern deciduous mixed hardwood forest (Harvey Pond, Madrid, Maine).

In 1939, the ecologists F. E. Clements and V. E. Shelford introduced an approach for combining the broad-scale distribution of both plants and associated animals into a single classification system. Clements and Shelford called these biotic units **biomes**. Biomes are classified according to the predominant plant types, and, depending on how finely biomes are classified, there are at least eight major terrestrial biome types: tropical forest, temperate forest, conifer forest (taiga or boreal forest), tropical savanna, temperate grasslands, chaparral (shrublands), tundra, and desert. These broad categories reflect the relative contribution of three general plant life forms: trees, shrubs, and grasses. A closed canopy of trees characterizes forest ecosystems. Woodland and savanna ecosystems are characterized by the codominance of grasses and trees (or shrubs). As the names imply, shrubs are the dominant plant form in shrublands and grasses in grasslands. Desert is a general category used to describe the scarcity of plant cover.

When the plant ecologist Robert Whittaker of Cornell University plotted these biome types on gradients of mean annual temperature and mean annual precipitation, he found they formed a distinctive climatic pattern, as graphed in Figure 23.1. As the graph indicates, boundaries between biomes are broad and often indistinct as they blend into each other. In addition to climate, other factors such as topography, soils, and exposure to disturbances such as fire can influence which one of the several biome types occupies an area.

If we plot the relationship between mean annual temperature and precipitation for locations on the land surface, another general pattern emerges from Whittaker's analysis of the relationship between biomes and climate. The range of observed values for mean annual precipitation declines with decreasing mean annual temperature (note that the range of biomes defined by precipitation along the *y*-axis decreases with declining temperatures along the *x*-axis). In geographic terms, this relationship indicates a decrease in the range of environmental conditions defined by moisture availability as one moves from the tropics to the temperate and arctic regions (see label on *x*-axis of Figure 23.1 and Figure 3.17). This reflects the systematic latitudinal pattern of environmental conditions discussed in Chapter 3 that are a direct result of seasonal variations in the influx of solar radiation to Earth's surface. Mean annual temperature decreases from the Equator to the poles, as does seasonal variation in temperatures (and daylength) (see Figure 3.5). The result is a decline in the growing season (period over which photosynthesis and plant growth can be maintained).

The systematic variation in climate with latitude is not limited to temperature. Average annual precipitation decreases with increasing latitude (see Figure 3.16) due to the interaction of humidity and temperature (see Section 3.6). With declining temperatures, the amount of moisture that can be held in the air declines (see Figure 3.16), reducing the overall amount of precipitation. As we shall see in the following sections, these systematic patterns of climate across the globe dictate the general distribution of terrestrial biomes on Earth's surface.

## 23.1 | Terrestrial Ecosystems Reflect Adaptations of the Dominant Plant Life Forms

Given that the broad classification of terrestrial biomes presented in Figure 23.1 (forest, woodland/savanna, shrubland, and grassland) reflects the relative contribution of three general plant life forms (trees, shrubs, and grasses), the question of what controls the distribution of biomes relative to climate becomes: Why are there consistent patterns in the distribution and abundance of these three dominant plant life forms that relate to climate and the physical environment? The answer to this question lies in the adaptations that these three very different plant life forms represent and the advantages and constraints that arise from these adaptations under different environmental conditions.

Although the broad categories of grasses, shrubs, and trees each represent a diverse range of species and characteristics, they represent fundamentally different patterns of carbon allocation and morphology (see Chapter 6). Grasses allocate less carbon to the production of supportive tissues (stems) than do woody plants (shrubs and

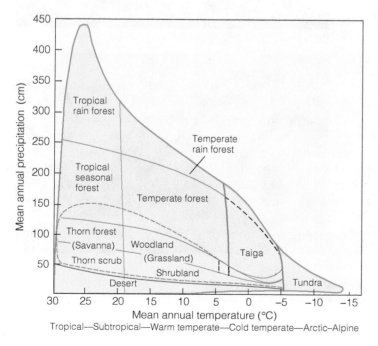

**Figure 23.1** | The pattern of terrestrial biomes in relation to temperature and moisture. Where the climate varies, soil can shift the balance between types. The dashed line encloses environments in which either grassland or one of the types dominated by woody plants may prevail. (Adapted from Whittaker 1970.)

trees), enabling them to maintain a higher proportion of their biomass in photosynthetic tissues (leaves). For woody plants, shrubs allocate a lower percentage of their resources to stems than do trees. The production of woody tissue provides the advantage of height and access to light, but it also has the associated cost of maintenance and respiration. If this cost cannot be offset by carbon gain through photosynthesis, the plant will not be able to maintain a positive carbon balance and will die (see Chapter 6, Figure 6.5). As a result, as environmental conditions become adverse for photosynthesis (dry, low nutrient concentrations, or short growing-season and cold temperatures), trees will decline in both stature and density until they are no longer able to persist as a component of the plant community.

Within the broad classes of forest and woodland ecosystems in which trees are dominant or codominant, leaf form is another plant characteristic that ecologists use to classify ecosystems. Leaves can be classified into two broad categories based on their longevity. Leaves that live for only a single year or growing season are classified as **deciduous,** whereas those that live beyond a year are called **evergreen.** The deciduous leaf is characteristic of environments with a distinct growing season. Leaves are typically shed at the end of the growing season and then regrown at the beginning of the next. Deciduous leaf type is further divided into two categories based on the period of dormancy. Winter-deciduous leaves are characteristic of the temperate regions where the period of dormancy corresponds to low (below freezing) temperatures (Figure 23.2a,b). Drought-deciduous leaves are characteristic of environments with seasonal rainfall, especially in the subtropical and tropical regions, where leaves are shed during the dry period (Figure 23.2c,d). The advantage of the deciduous habit is that the plant does not have the additional cost of maintenance and respiration during the period of the year when environmental conditions restrict photosynthesis.

Evergreen leaves can likewise be classified into two broad categories. The broadleaf-evergreen leaf type (Figure 23.3a) is characteristic of environments with no distinct growing season where photosynthesis and growth continue year-round, such as tropical rain forests. The needle-leaf evergreen form (Figure 23.3b) is charac-

(a)

(b)

(c)

(d)

**Figure 23.2** | Examples of winter and drought deciduous trees. Temperate deciduous forest in central Virginia during the **(a)** summer and **(b)** winter seasons. Semiarid savanna/woodland in Zimbabwe, Africa, during the **(c)** rainy and **(d)** dry seasons.

**(a)**

**(b)**

**Figure 23.3** | Examples of evergreen trees. **(a)** Broadleaf evergreen trees dominate the canopy of this tropical rain forest in Queensland, Australia. **(b)** Needle-leaf evergreen trees (foxtail pine) inhabit the high-altitude zone of the Sierra Nevada in western North America.

teristic of environments where the growing season is very short (northern latitudes) or nutrient availability severely constrains photosynthesis and plant growth. A simple economic model has been proposed to explain the adaptation of this leaf form (see Chapter 6). The production of a leaf has a "cost" to the plant that can be defined in terms of the carbon and other nutrients required to construct the leaf. The time required to pay back the cost of production (carbon) will be a function of the rate of net photosynthesis (carbon gain). If environmental conditions result in low rates of net photosynthesis, the period of time required to pay back the cost of production will be longer. If the rate of photosynthesis is low enough, it may not be possible to pay back the cost over the period of a single growing season. A plant adapted to such environmental conditions cannot "afford" a deciduous leaf form, which requires producing new leaves every

year. The leaves of evergreens, however, may survive for a number of years. So, under this model, we can view the needle-leaf evergreen as a plant adapted for survival in an environment with a distinct growing season, where conditions limit the ability of the plant to produce enough carbon through photosynthesis during the growing season to pay for the cost of producing the leaves.

Combining the simple classification of plant life forms and leaf type with the large-scale patterns of climate presented above, we can begin to understand the distribution of biome types relative to the axes of temperature and precipitation shown in Figure 23.1. Ecosystems characteristic of warm, wet climates with no distinct seasonality are dominated by broadleaf evergreen trees and are called tropical (and subtropical) rain forest. As conditions become drier, with a distinct dry season, the broadleaf evergreen habit gives way to drought-deciduous trees that characterize the seasonal tropical forests. As precipitation declines further, the stature and density of these trees declines, giving rise to the woodlands and savannas that are characterized by the coexistence of trees (shrubs) and grasses. As precipitation further declines, trees can no longer be supported, giving rise to the arid shrublands (thorn scrub) and desert.

The temperature axis represents the latitudinal gradient from the Equator to the poles (see geographical labels on $x$-axis of Figure 23.1). Moving from the broadleaf evergreen forests of the wet tropics into the cooler, seasonal environments of the temperate regions, the dominant trees are winter-deciduous. These are the regions of temperate deciduous forest. In areas of the temperate region where precipitation is insufficient to support trees, grasses dominate, giving rise to the prairies of North America and the steppes of Eurasia. Moving poleward, the temperate deciduous forests give way to the needle-leaf–dominated forests of the boreal region (conifer forest or taiga). As temperatures become more extreme and the growing season shorter, trees can no longer be supported, and the short-stature shrubs and grasses characteristic of the tundra dominate the landscape ecosystems of the arctic region.

In the following sections, we will examine the eight major categories of terrestrial biomes outlined in Figure 23.1, with an emphasis on their geography and unique physical and biological characteristics.

## 23.2 | Tropical Forests Characterize the Equatorial Zone

The tropical rain forests are restricted primarily to the equatorial zone between latitudes 10°N and 10°S (Figure 23.4), where the temperatures are warm throughout the year and rainfall occurs almost daily (see Quantifying Ecology 23.1: Climate Diagrams). The largest and most

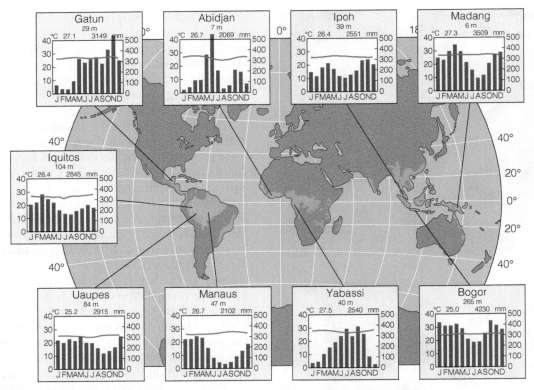

**Figure 23.4** | Geographic distribution of the tropical forest ecosystems of the world and associated climate diagrams showing the long-term patterns of monthly temperature and precipitation for selected locations. (Adapted from Archibold 1995.)

continuous region of rain forest in the world is in the Amazon basin of South America (Figure 23.5). The second largest is located in Southeast Asia. The third major region of rain forest is in West Africa around the Gulf of Guinea, in the Congo basin. Smaller rain forests occur along the northeastern coast of Australia, the windward side of the Hawaiian Islands, the South Pacific Islands, the east coast of Madagascar, northern South America, and southern Central America.

The climate of tropical rain forest regions varies geographically but is typically characterized by a mean temperature of all months exceeding 18°C and minimum monthly precipitation above 60 mm. Within the lowland forest zone, mean annual temperatures typically exceed 25°C with an annual range less than 5°C.

Tropical rain forests have a high diversity of plant and animal life. Covering only seven percent of the land surface, tropical rain forests account for more than one-half of all known plant and animal species. Tree species number in the thousands. A 10-km$^2$ area of tropical rain forest may contain 1500 species of flowering plants and up to 750 species of trees. The richest area is the lowland tropical forest of peninsular Malaysia, which contains some 7900 species.

Nearly 90 percent of all primate species live in the tropical rain forests of the world (Figure 23.6). Sixty-four species of New World primates, small with prehensile tails, live in the trees. The Indo-Malaysian forests are inhabited by a number of primates, many of which have a limited distribution within the region. The orangutan, an arboreal ape, is confined to the island of Borneo. Peninsular Malaysia has seven species of primates, including three gibbons, two langurs, and two macaques. The long-tailed macaque is common in disturbed or secondary forests, and the pig-tailed macaque is a terrestrial species, adaptable to human settlements. The tropical rain forest of Africa is home to mountain gorillas and chimpanzees. The diminished rain forest of Madagascar holds 39 species of lemurs.

Tropical rain forests may be divided into five vertical layers (Figure 23.7): emergent trees, high upper canopy, low tree stratum, shrub understory, and a ground layer of herbs and ferns. Conspicuous in the rain forest are lianas or climbing vines growing upward into the canopy, epiphytes growing on the trunks and branches, and stranglers that grow downward from the canopy to the ground. Many large trees develop plank-like outgrowths called buttresses (Figure 23.8). They function as prop roots, providing support for trees rooted in shallow soil that offers poor anchorage. The floor of a tropical rain forest is thickly laced with roots, both large and small, forming a dense mat on the ground.

(a)

(c)

Figure 23.5 | Tropical rain forests in **(a)** Amazon Basin (South America), **(b)** Malaysia (Southeast Asia), and **(c)** northeast Australia.

(b)

The continually warm, moist conditions in rain forests promote strong chemical weathering and rapid leaching of soluble materials. The characteristic soils are Oxisols, deeply weathered with no distinct horizons. Ultisols may develop in areas with more seasonal precipitation regimes and are typically associated with forested regions that exhibit seasonal soil moisture deficits. In addition, areas of volcanic activity in parts of Central and Southeast Asia, where recent ash deposits quickly weather, are characterized by Andosols (see Figure 5.12).

The warmer, wetter conditions of the tropical rain forest result in high rates of net primary productivity and subsequent high annual rates of litter input to the forest floor. Little litter accumulates, however, because decomposers consume the dead organic matter about as rapidly as it falls to the forest floor. Most of the nutrients available for uptake by plants are a result of the rapidly decomposed organic matter that is continuously falling to the surface. These nutrients, however, are rapidly absorbed by the growing plants. The average time for leaf litter to decompose is 24 weeks.

Moving from the equatorial zone to the regions of the tropics that are characterized by a greater seasonality in precipitation, the broadleaf evergreen forests are replaced by the dry tropical forests (Figure 23.9). Dry tropical forests undergo a dry season, the length of which is based on latitude. The more distant the forest is from the Equator, the longer is the dry season, in some areas up to 8 months. During the dry season, the drought-deciduous

Figure 23.6 | Chimpanzee, one of the many primate species that inhabit the tropical rain forests of Central Africa.

Figure 23.8 | Plank-like buttresses help to support tall rain forest trees.

Emergent canopy, trees widely spaced

Canopy, medium-spaced crowns

Lower canopy

Shrubs, saplings, ferns, tall herbs

Ground layer, roots

Figure 23.7 | Vertical stratification of a tropical rain forest.

trees and shrubs drop their leaves. Before the start of the rainy season, which may be much wetter than the wettest time in the rain forest, the trees begin to leaf. During the wet season, the landscape becomes uniformly green.

The largest proportion of tropical dry forest is found in Africa and South America, to the south of the zones dominated by rain forest. These regions are influenced by the seasonal migration of the Intertropical Convergence Zone (see Figure 3.17). In addition, areas of Central America, northern Australia, India, and Southeast Asia are also classified as dry tropical forest. Much of the original forest, especially in Central America and India, has been converted to agricultural and grazing land.

## 23.3 | Tropical Savannas Are Characteristic of the Semiarid Regions with Seasonal Rainfall

The term *savanna* was originally used to describe the treeless areas of South America. Now it is generally applied to a range of vegetation types in the drier tropics and subtropics characterized by a ground cover of grasses with scattered shrubs or trees. Savanna includes an array of vegetation types representing a continuum of increasing cover of woody vegetation, from open grassland to widely spaced shrubs or trees and to woodland (Figure 23.10). In South America, the more densely

wooded areas are referred to as *cerrado*. The campos and llano are characterized by a more open appearance (lower density of trees), and thorn scrub is the dominant cover of the caatinga. In Africa, the miombo, mopane, and Acacia woodlands can be distinguished from the more open and parklike bushveld. The mulga and brigalow of Australia are dominated by scattered individuals of *Acacia* and *Eucalyptus*.

**Figure 23.9** | A tropical dry forest in Costa Rica. Most of the tropical dry forests in Central America have disappeared from land-clearing for agriculture.

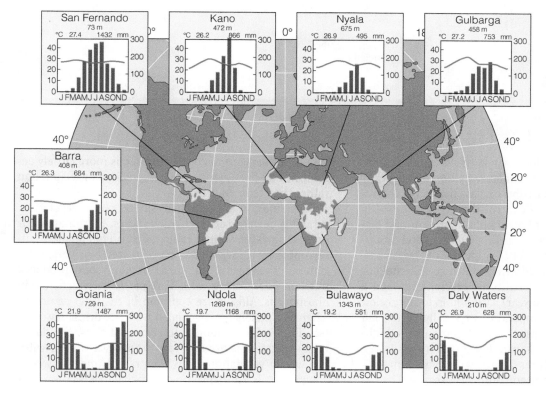

**Figure 23.10** | Geographic distribution of the tropical savanna ecosystems of the world and associated climate diagrams showing the long-term patterns of monthly temperature and precipitation for selected locations. (Adapted from Archibold 1995.)

As illustrated in Figure 23.1, the distribution of terrestrial biomes is closely related to climate. The measures of regional climate used in Whittaker's graph (Figure 23.1) are mean annual temperature and precipitation. Yet, as we will see in the discussion of the various biome types, the distribution of terrestrial ecosystems is influenced by other aspects of climate as well, namely seasonality of both temperature and precipitation. In addition, topographic features such as mountains and valleys influence the climate of a region.

To help understand the relationship between regional climate and the distribution of terrestrial ecosystems, for each biome discussed in this chapter (tropical forest, savanna, etc.) a map will be presented showing its global distribution. Accompanying the map will be a series of climate diagrams. The diagrams describe the local climate at representative locations around the world where that particular biome type is found. A representative climate diagram is presented below (Figure 1). The diagram has been labeled to help you interpret the information that it presents. As you study the diagram, take particular note of the patterns of seasonality. ●

1. In Figure 23.10, what is the distinctive feature of the climate diagrams for these tropical savanna ecosystems? How do the patterns differ between sites in the Northern and Southern Hemispheres? What feature of Earth's climate system discussed in Chapter 3 is responsible for these distinctive patterns?

2. In Figure 23.15, what feature of the climate is common to all mediterranean ecosystems?

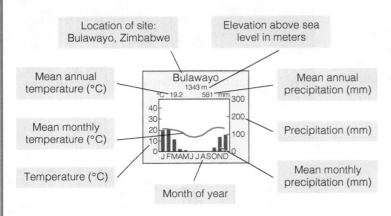

Location of site: Bulawayo, Zimbabwe

Elevation above sea level in meters

Mean annual temperature (°C)

Mean annual precipitation (mm)

Mean monthly temperature (°C)

Precipitation (mm)

Temperature (°C)

Mean monthly precipitation (mm)

Month of year

**Figure 1** | Climate diagram for Bulawayo, Zimbabwe. Being in the Southern Hemisphere, the cooler winter months occur during the period May–August. Note the distinct dry season during the winter months, with the rainy season beginning in October (spring) and lasting through the summer months.

The physiognomic diversity of the savanna vegetation reflects the different climate conditions that occur throughout this widely distributed classification of ecosystem. Moisture appears to control the density of woody vegetation, a function of both rainfall (amount and distribution) and soil—its texture, structure, and water-holding capacity (see Chapter 5) (Figure 23.11).

Savannas are associated with a warm continental climate with a distinct seasonality in precipitation and a large interannual (year to year) variation in total precipitation. Mean monthly temperatures typically do not fall below 18°C, although during the coldest months in highland areas, temperatures can be considerably lower. Seasonality in temperatures occurs, with maximum temperatures occurring at the end of the wet season. The nature of the vegetation cover, however, is more closely determined by the amount and seasonality of precipitation rather than temperature.

Savannas, in spite of their differences in vegetation, exhibit a certain set of characteristics. Savannas occur on land surfaces of little relief, often on old plateaus, interrupted by escarpments and dissected by rivers. Continuous weathering in these regions has produced nutrient-poor Oxisols, which are particularly deficient in phosphorus. Alfisols are common in the drier savannas, whereas Entisols are associated with the driest savannas (see Figure 5.12). Subject to recurrent fires, the dominant vegetation is fire-adapted. Grass cover with or without woody vegetation is always present and the woody component is short-lived, with individuals seldom sur-

**Figure 23.11** | Diagram showing the interaction between annual precipitation and soil texture in defining the transition from woodland to savanna and grassland in southern Africa. Access by plants to soil moisture is more limited on the heavy textured soils (clays) than on the coarser sands, requiring a greater annual precipitation to support the productivity of woody plants.

viving for more than several decades. Savannas are characterized by a two-layer vertical structure as a result of the ground cover of grasses and the presence of shrubs or trees.

The yearly cycle of plant activity and subsequent productivity in tropical savannas is largely controlled by the markedly seasonal precipitation and corresponding changes in available soil moisture. Most leaf litter is decomposed during the wet season, and most woody debris is consumed by termites during the dry season.

The microenvironments associated with tree canopies can influence species distribution, productivity, and soil characteristics. Stem flow and associated litter accumulation result in higher soil nutrients and moisture under tree canopies, often resulting in increased productivity, and the establishment of species adapted to the more shaded environments.

Savannas can support a large and varied assemblage of herbivores, invertebrate and vertebrate, grazing and browsing. The African savanna, visually at least, is dominated by a large and diverse ungulate fauna of at least 60 species that partition the vegetative resources among them. Some, such as the wildebeest and zebra, are migratory during the dry season.

Savanna vegetation supports an incredible number of insects: flies, grasshoppers, locusts, crickets, carabid beetles, ants, and detrital-feeding dung beetles and termites. Mound-building termites excavate and move tons of soil, mixing mineral soil with organic matter. Some species construct extensive subterranean galleries, and others accumulate organic matter.

An array of carnivores live on the ungulate fauna, including the lion, leopard, cheetah, hyena, and wild dog. Subsisting on leftover prey are scavengers, including vultures and jackals.

## 23.4 | Deserts Represent a Diverse Group of Ecosystems

The arid regions of the world occupy from 25 to 35 percent of Earth's land mass (Figure 23.12). The wide range reflects the various definitions used to define desert ecosystems based on climate conditions and vegetation types. Much of this land lies between 15° and 30° latitude, where the air that is carried aloft along the Intertropical Convergence Zone subsides to form the semipermanent high-pressure cells that dominate the climate of the

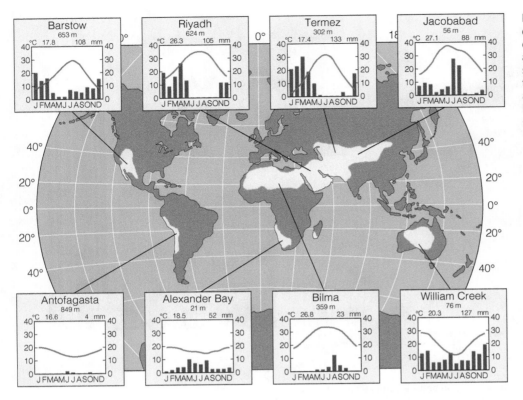

**Figure 23.12** | Geographic distribution of the desert (arid) ecosystems of the world and associated climate diagrams showing the long-term patterns of monthly temperature and precipitation for selected locations. (Adapted from Archibold 1995.)

tropical deserts (see Figure 3.17). The warming of the air as it descends, and cloudless skies, result in intense radiation heat during the summer season.

The tropical deserts grade into the savannas as precipitation increases toward the Equator.

The temperate deserts lie in the rainshadow of mountain barriers or are located far inland where moist maritime air rarely penetrates. Here, temperatures are high during the summer but can drop to below freezing during the winter months. Thus, it is the lack of precipitation rather than continually high temperatures that is the distinctive characteristic of all deserts.

The majority of arid environments are found in the Northern Hemisphere. The Sahara, the world's largest desert, covers approximately 9 million km$^2$ of North Africa. It extends the breadth of the African continent to the deserts of the Arabian Peninsula, continuing eastward to Afghanistan and Pakistan and finally terminating in the Thar Desert of northwest India. The temperate deserts of Central Asia lie to the north. The most westerly of these is the Kara Kum desert region of Turkmenistan. Eastward lie the high-elevation deserts of western China and the high plateau of the Gobi Desert.

A similar transition to temperate desert occurs in western North America. Here, it is the Sierra Nevada that effectively blocks the passage of moist air into the interior of the Southwest. Mountain ranges run parallel to the Sierras throughout the northern part of this region, and desert basins occur on the eastern side of these ranges.

Apart from the drier parts of southern Argentina, the deserts of the Southern Hemisphere all lie within the subtropical high-pressure belt that mirrors that of the Northern Hemisphere (see above discussion). Cold ocean currents also contribute to the development of arid coastal regions (see Section 3.15). Drought conditions are severe along a narrow strip of the coast that includes Chile and Peru. The drier parts of Argentina lie in the rainshadow of the Andes.

The desert regions of southern Africa include three regions. The Namib Desert occupies a narrow strip of land that runs along the west coast of Africa from southern Angola to the border of the cape region of South Africa. It continues south and east across South Africa as the Karoo, which merges with the Kalahari Desert to the north in Botswana. The most extensive region of arid land in the Southern Hemisphere is found in Australia, where more than 40 percent of the land is classified as desert.

Deserts are not the same everywhere. Differences in moisture, temperature, soil drainage, topography, alkalinity, and salinity create variations in vegetation cover, dominant plants, and groups of associated species. There are hot deserts and cold deserts, extreme deserts and semideserts, ones with sufficient moisture to verge on being grasslands or shrublands, and gradations between those extremes within continental deserts.

Cool deserts—including the Great Basin of North America, the Gobi, Takla Makan, and Turkestan deserts of Asia—and high elevations of hot deserts are domi-

(a)

(b)

Figure 23.13 | Two examples of desert scrub: **(a)** The northern desert shrubland in Wyoming is dominated by sagebrush (*Artemisia*). Although classified as cool desert, sagebrush forms one of the most important shrub types in North America. **(b)** Saltbrush shrubland in Victoria, Australia, is dominated by *Atriplex*. It is an ecological equivalent of the shrublands of the Great Basin in North America.

nated by *Artemisia* and chenopod shrubs (Figure 23.13). They may be considered shrub steppes or desert scrub. In the Great Basin of North America, the northern, cool, arid region lying west of the Rocky Mountains is the northern desert scrub. The climate is continental, with warm summers and prolonged cold winters. The vegetation falls into two main associations: one is sagebrush, dominated by *Artemisia tridentata,* which often forms pure stands; the other is shadscale, *Atriplex conifertifolia,* a $C_4$ species, and other chenopods (halophytes tolerant of saline soils).

A similar type of desert scrub exists in the semiarid inland of southwestern Australia. Numerous chenopod species, particularly the saltbushes of the genera *Atriplex* and *Maireana,* form extensive low shrublands on low riverine plains.

The hot deserts range from those lacking vegetation to ones with some combination of chenopods, dwarf-shrubs, and succulents (Figure 23.14). The deserts of southwestern North America—the Mojave, the Sonoran, and the Chihuahuan—are dominated by creosote bush (*Larrea divaricata*) and bur sage (*Franseria* spp.). Areas of favorable moisture support tall growths of *Acacia* spp., saguaro (*Cereus giganteus*), palo verde (*Cercidium* spp.), ocotillo (*Fouquieria* spp.), yucca (*Yucca* spp.), and ephemeral plants.

Both plants and animals adapt to the scarcity of water either by drought evasion or by drought resistance. Plant drought-evaders flower only when moisture is present. They persist as seeds during drought periods, ready to sprout, flower, and produce seeds when moisture and temperature are favorable. If no rains come, these ephemeral species do not grow.

Drought-evading animals, like their plant counterparts, adopt an annual cycle of activities or go into estivation or some other stage of dormancy during the dry season. For example, the spadefoot toad (*Scaphiopus*) remains underground in a gelatinous-lined underground cell, making brief reproductive appearances during periods of winter and summer rains. If extreme drought develops during the breeding season, many animals such as lizards and birds do not reproduce.

Desert plants may be deep-rooted woody shrubs, such as mesquite (*Prosopis* spp.) and *Tamarix*, whose taproots reach the water table, rendering them independent of water supplied by rainfall. Some, such as *Larrea* and *Atriplex,* are deep-rooted perennials with superficial laterals that extend as far as 15 to 30 m from the stems. Other perennials, such as the various species of cactus, have shallow roots, often extending no more than a few centimeters below the surface.

In spite of their aridity, desert ecosystems support a surprising diversity of animal life, including a wide assortment of beetles, ants, locusts, lizards, snakes, birds, and mammals. The mammals are mostly herbivorous species. Grazing herbivores of the desert tend to be generalists and opportunists in their mode of feeding. They consume a wide range of species, plant types, and parts. Desert rodents, particularly the family Heteromyidae, and ants feed largely on seeds and are important in the dynamics of desert ecosystems. Seed-eating herbivores can eat up to 90 percent of the seed production. That consumption can have a pronounced effect on plant composition and plant populations. Desert carnivores, such as foxes and coyotes, have mixed diets that include leaves and fruits; even insectivorous birds and rodents

**(a)**

**(b)**

**(c)**

Figure 23.14 | Three examples of hot deserts: **(a)** The Chihuahuan Desert in Nuevo Leon, Mexico. The substrate of this desert is sand-sized particles of gypsum. **(b)** The edge of the Great Victorian Desert in Australia. This desert and the Chihuahuan Desert are dominated by woody, brittle-stemmed shrubs. **(c)** Dunes in the Saudi Arabian desert near Riyadh. Note the extreme sparseness of vegetation.

eat some plant material. Omnivory, rather than carnivory and complex food webs, seems to be the rule in desert ecosystems.

The infrequent rainfall coupled with high rates of evaporation limit the availability of water to plants, and, consequently, primary productivity is low. Most desert soils are poorly developed Aridisols and Entisols (see Figure 5.12), and the sparse cover of arid lands limits the ability of vegetation to heavily modify the soil environment. Underneath established plants, however, "islands of fertility" can develop as a result of higher litter input and the enrichment by wastes from animals that seek shade, particularly under shrubs.

## 23.5 | Mediterranean Climates Support Temperate Shrublands

Shrublands—plant communities where the shrub growth form is either dominant or codominant—are difficult types of ecosystems to categorize, in large part because of the difficulty in characterizing the term *shrub* itself. A rough definition is that a shrub is a plant with multiple woody, persistent stems but no central trunk and a height from 4.5 to 8 m. However, under severe environmental conditions, many trees will not exceed that size. Some trees, particularly individuals that coppice (resprout from the stump) after destruction of the above-ground tissues by fire or browsing, are multistemmed, and some shrubs can have large, single stems. In addition, the shrub growth form can be a dominant component of a variety of tropical and temperate ecosystems, including the tropical savannas and scrub desert communities (see Sections 23.2 and 23.3, respectively). However, in five widely disjunct regions along the western margins of the continents, between 30° and 40° latitude, are found the mediterranean ecosystems dominated by evergreen shrubs and sclerophyllous trees that have adapted to the distinctive climate of summer drought and cool moist winters.

The five regions of mediterranean ecosystems include the semiarid regions of western North America, the regions bordering the Mediterranean Sea, central Chile, the cape region of South Africa, and southwestern and southern Australia (Figure 23.15). The mediterranean climate has hot, dry summers, with at least 1 month of protracted drought, and cool, moist winters. About 65 percent of the annual precipitation falls during the winter months. Winter temperatures typically average 10–12°C with a risk of frost. The hot, dry summer climates of the mediterranean regions arise from the seasonal change in the semipermanent high-pressure zones that are centered over the tropical deserts at about 20°N and 20°S (see discussion in Section 22.3). The persistent flow of dry air out of these regions during the summer brings several months of hot, dry weather. Fire is a frequent hazard during these periods.

All five regions support similar-looking communities of xeric broadleaf evergreen shrubs and dwarf trees known as sclerophyllous (*scleros*, "hard"; *phyll*, "leaf") vegetation with an herbaceous understory. Sclerophyllous vegetation possesses small leaves, thickened cuticles, glandular hairs, and sunken stomata, all characteristics that function to reduce water loss during the hot, dry summer period (Figure 23.16). Vegetation in each of the mediterranean systems also shares adaptations to fire and to low nutrient levels in the soil.

The largest area of mediterranean ecosystem forms a discontinuous belt around the Mediterranean Sea in southern Europe and North Africa. Much of the area is currently or was once dominated by mixed evergreen

**Figure 23.15** | Geographic distribution of the mediterranean ecosystems of the world and associated climate diagrams showing the long-term patterns of monthly temperature and precipitation for selected locations. (Adapted from Archibold 1995.)

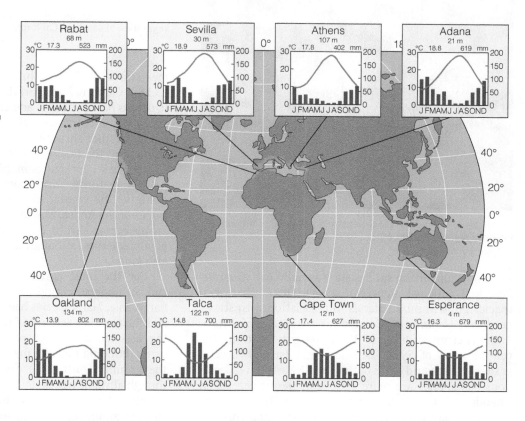

(a)       (b)       (c)

**Figure 23.16** | Sclerophyllous leaves of some tree and shrub species inhabiting mediterranean shrublands (chaparral) of California: **(a)** chamise (*Adenostone fusciculatum*), **(b)** scrub oak (*Quercus dumosa*), and **(c)** chinquapin (*Chrysolepis sempervirens*).

Figure 23.17 | Mediterranean vegetation (fynbos) of the western cape region of South Africa.

Figure 23.18 | Chaparral is the dominant mediterranean shrub vegetation of southern California.

woodland supporting species such as holm oak (*Quercus ilex*) and cork oak (*Quercus suber*). Often, these two species grow in mixed stands in association with strawberry-tree (*Arbutus unedo*) and various species of shrubs. The easternmost limit of these ecosystems is in the coastal areas of Syria, Lebanon, and Israel, where it grades into the arid lands of the Middle East. Here, deciduous oak species are more abundant. Desert vegetation extends across North Africa as far as Tunisia, with mediterranean shrub and woodland extending through the northern coastal areas of Algeria and Morocco.

The mediterranean zone in southern Africa is restricted to the mountainous region of the Cape Province where the vegetation is known as *fynbos*. The vegetation is composed primarily of broadleaf proteoid shrubs that grow to a height of 1.5–2.5 m (Figure 23.17). In southwest Australia, the mediterranean shrub community known as *mallee* is dominated by low-growing *Eucalyptus*, 5 to 8 m in height, with broad sclerophyllous leaves.

In North America, the sclerophyllous shrub community is known as chaparral, a word of Spanish origin

meaning a thicket of shrubby evergreen oaks (Figure 23.18). California chaparral, dominated by scrub oak (*Quercus berberidifolia*) and chamise (*Adenostoma fasciculatum*), is evergreen, winter-active, and summer-dormant. Another shrub type, also designated as chaparral, is found in the Rocky Mountain foothills. Dominated by Gambel oak (*Quercus gambelii*), it is winter-deciduous.

The matorral shrub communities of central Chile occur in the coastal lowlands and on the west-facing slopes of the Andes. The majority of the matorral species are evergreen shrubs 1–3 m in height with small sclerophyllous leaves, although drought-deciduous shrubs are also found.

For the most part, mediterranean-type shrublands lack an understory and ground litter and are highly inflammable. Many species have seeds that require the heat and the scarring action of fire to induce germination. In the absence of fire, chaparral grows taller and more dense, building up large fuel loads of leaves and twigs on the ground. During the dry season, the shrubs, even though alive, nearly explode when ignited.

After fire, the land returns either to lush green sprouts coming up from buried root crowns or to grass if a seed source is nearby. As the regrowth matures, the chaparral vegetation once again becomes dense, the canopy closes, the litter accumulates, and the stage is set for another fire.

Shrub communities have a complex of animal life that varies with the region. Within the mediterranean-type shrublands, similarity in habitat structure has resulted in pronounced parallel and convergent evolution (see Chapter 26) among bird species and some lizard species, especially between the Chilean mattoral and the California chaparral. In North America, chaparral and sagebrush communities support mule deer (*Odocoileus hemionus*), coyotes (*Canis latrans*), a variety of rodents, jackrabbits (*Lepus* spp.), and sage grouse (*Centrocercus urophasianus*). The Australian mallee is rich in birds, including the endemic mallee-fowl (*Leipoa ocellata*), which incubates its eggs in a large mound. Among the mammalian life are the gray kangaroo (*Macropus giganteus*) and various species of wallaby.

The diverse topography and geology of the mediterranean environments give rise to a diversity of soil conditions, but soils are typically classified as Alfisols (see Figure 5.12). The soils of the regions are generally deficient in nutrients, and litter decomposition is limited by low temperatures during the winter and low soil moisture during the summer months. These ecosystems vary in productivity depending on the annual precipitation and the severity of summer drought.

## 23.6 | Forest Ecosystems Dominate the Wetter Regions of the Temperate Zone

Climatic conditions in the humid midlatitude regions give rise to the development of forests dominated by broadleaf deciduous trees (Figure 23.19). But in the mild, moist climates of the Southern Hemisphere, temperate evergreen forests become predominant. Deciduous forest once covered large areas of Europe and China, parts of North and South America, and the highlands of Central America. The deciduous forests of Europe and Asia, however, have largely disappeared, cleared over the centuries for agriculture. In eastern North America, the deciduous forest consists of a number of forest types or associations (see Figure 23.20) including the mixed mesophytic forest of the unglaciated Appalachian plateau; the beech–maple and northern hardwood forests (with pine and hemlock) in northern regions that eventually grade into the boreal forest (see Section 23.8); the maple–basswood forests of the Great Lake states; the oak–chestnut (now oak since the die-off of the American chestnut) or central hardwood forests, which cover most of the Appalachian Mountains; the magnolia–oak forests of the Gulf Coast states; and the oak–hickory forests of the Ozarks. In North America, temperate deciduous forests reach their greatest development in the mesic forests of the central Appalachians, where the number of tree species is unsurpassed by any other temperate area in the world.

The Asiatic broadleaf forest, found in eastern China, Japan, Taiwan, and Korea, is similar to the North American deciduous forest and contains a number of plant

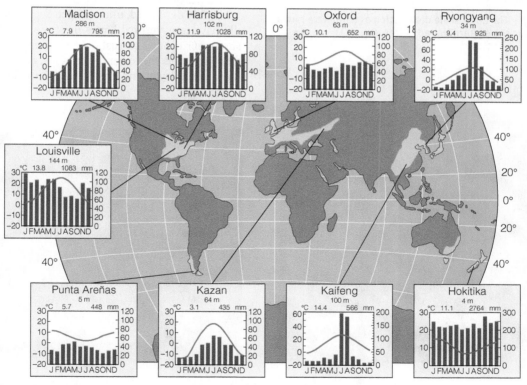

**Figure 23.19** | Geographic distribution of the temperate forest ecosystems of the world and associated climate diagrams showing the long-term patterns of monthly temperature and precipitation for selected locations. (Adapted from Archibold 1995.)

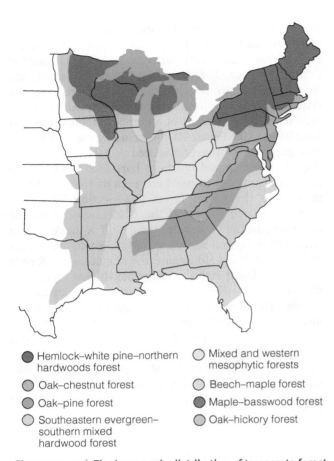

Legend:
- ● Hemlock–white pine–northern hardwoods forest
- ● Oak–chestnut forest
- ● Oak–pine forest
- ○ Southeastern evergreen–southern mixed hardwood forest
- ○ Mixed and western mesophytic forests
- ○ Beech–maple forest
- ● Maple–basswood forest
- ○ Oak–hickory forest

**Figure 23.20** | The large-scale distribution of temperate forest communities in the eastern United States. (Adapted from Braun 1950.)

species of the same genera as those found in North America and western Europe. However, broadleaf evergreen species become increasingly present in Japan, South Korea, and southern China and in the wet foothills of the Himalayas. In southern Europe, their presence reflects the transition into the mediterranean region. Evergreen oaks and pines are also widely distributed in the southeastern United States, where they are usually associated with poorly developed sandy soils or swampy soils.

In the Southern Hemisphere, temperate deciduous forests are found only in the drier parts of the southern Andes. In southern Chile, broadleaf evergreen rain forests have developed in an oceanic climate that is virtually frost-free. Evergreen forests are also found in New Zealand, Tasmania, and parts of southeastern Australia where the winter temperatures are moderated by the coastal environment. Climate regions in these areas are similar to those of the Pacific Northwest of North America, but here the predominant species are conifers.

In the broadleaf deciduous forests of the temperate region, the end of the growing season is marked by the autumn colors of foliage shortly before the trees enter into their leafless winter period (Figure 23.21). The trees resume growth in the spring in response to increasing temperatures and longer daylengths. Many herbaceous species flower at this time before the developing canopy casts a heavy shade on the forest floor.

Highly developed, uneven-aged deciduous forests usually have four vertical layers or strata (see Figure 16.5). The upper canopy consists of the dominant tree species, below which is the lower tree canopy, or understory. Next is the shrub layer, and finally the ground layer consisting

(a)

(b)

**Figure 23.21** | A temperate forest of the Appalachian region (a) during autumn and (b) the interior of the forest during the spring. The forest is dominated by oaks (*Quercus* spp.) and yellow poplar (*Liriodendron tulipifera*), with an understory of red bud (*Cercis canadensis*) in bloom.

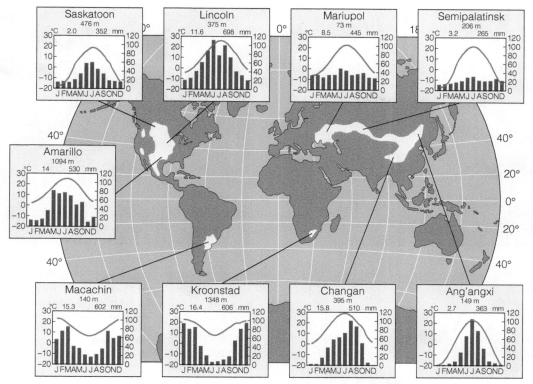

**Figure 23.22** | Geographic distribution of the temperate grassland ecosystems of the world and associated climate diagrams showing the long-term patterns of monthly temperature and precipitation for selected locations. (Adapted from Archibold 1995.)

of herbs, ferns, and mosses. The diversity of animal life is associated with this vertical stratification and the growth forms of plants (see Chapter 16). Some animals, particularly forest arthropods, spend the major part of their lives in a single stratum; others range over two or more strata. The greatest concentration and diversity of life in the forest occurs on and just below the ground layer. Many animals, the soil and litter invertebrates in particular, remain in the subterranean stratum. Others, such as mice, shrews, ground squirrels, and forest salamanders, burrow into the soil or litter for shelter and food. Larger mammals live on the ground layer and feed on herbs, shrubs, and low trees. Birds move rather freely among several strata but typically favor one layer over another (see Figure 16.6).

Differences in climate, bedrock, and drainage are reflected in the variety of soil conditions that are present. Alfisols, Inceptisols, and Ultisols (see Figure 5.12) are the dominant soil types with Alfisols typically associated with glacial materials in more northern regions. Primary productivity varies geographically and is influenced largely by temperatures and the length of the growing season (see Section 20.3). Leaf fall in deciduous forests occurs over a short period in autumn, and the availability of nutrients is related to rates of decomposition and mineralization (see Chapter 21).

## 23.7 | Grasssland Ecosystems of the Temperate Zone Vary with Climate and Geography

Natural grasslands occupy regions where rainfall is between 250 mm and 800 mm a year, but they are not exclusively climatic. Many exist through the intervention of fire and human activity. Conversions of forests into agricultural lands and the planting of hay and pasture lands extended grasslands into once-forested regions. Once covering about 42 percent of the land surface of Earth, natural grasslands have shrunk to less than 12 percent of their original size because of conversion to cropland and grazing lands.

The natural grasslands of the world occur in the midlatitudes in midcontinental regions where annual precipitation declines as air masses move inward from the coastal environments (Figure 23.22). In the Northern Hemisphere, these regions include the prairies of North America and the steppes of central Eurasia. In the Southern Hemisphere, grasslands are represented by the pampas of Argentina and the grassveld of the high plateaus of southern Africa. Smaller areas occur in southeastern Australia and the drier parts of New Zealand.

The temperate grassland climate is one of recurring drought, and much of the diversity of vegetation cover

(a)

(b)

(c)

Figure 23.23 | North American grasslands: (a) a remnant tallgrass prairie in Iowa; (b) the mixed-grass prairie has been called "daisyland" because of the diversity of its wildflowers; (c) shortgrass steppe in western Wyoming.

reflects differences in the amount and reliability of precipitation. Grasslands do the poorest where precipitation is lowest and the temperatures are high. They are tallest in stature and the most productive where mean annual precipitation is greater than 800 mm and the mean annual temperature is above 15°C. Thus, native grasslands of North America, influenced by declining precipitation from east to west, consist of three main types, distinguished by the height of the dominant species: tallgrass, mixed grass, and shortgrass prairie. **Tallgrass prairie** (Figure 23.23a) is dominated by big bluestem (*Andropogon gerardi*), growing 1 m tall with flowering stalks 1 to 3 1/2 m tall. **Mixed-grass prairie** (Figure 23.23b), typical of the Great Plains, is composed largely of needlegrass–grama grass (*Bouteloua–Stipa*). South and west of the mixed prairie and grading into the desert regions is the **shortgrass prairie** (Figure 23.23c), dominated by sod-forming blue grama (*Bouteloua gracilis*) and buffalo grass (*Buchloe*

*dactyloides*), which has remained somewhat intact, and desert grasslands. From southeastern Texas to southern Arizona and south into Mexico lies the **desert grassland,** similar in many respects to the shortgrass plains, except that three-awn grass (*Aristida* spp.) replaces buffalo grass. Confined largely to the Central Valley of California is **annual grassland.** It is associated with mediterranean-type climate (see Section 23.5), characterized by rainy winters and hot, dry summers. Growth occurs during early spring, and most plants are dormant in summer, turning the hills a dry tan color accented by the deep green foliage of scattered California oaks.

At one time, the great grasslands of the Eurasian continent extended from eastern Europe to western Siberia south to Kazakhstan. These **steppes,** treeless except for ribbons and patches of forest, are divided into four belts of latitude, from the mesic meadow steppes in the north to semiarid grasslands in the south.

In the Southern Hemisphere, the major grasslands exist in southern Africa and southern South America. Known as **pampas,** the South American grasslands extend westward in a large semicircle from Buenos Aires to cover about 15 percent of Argentina. These pampas have been modified by the introduction of European forage grasses and alfalfa (*Medicago sativa*), and the eastern tallgrass pampas have been converted to wheat and corn. In Patagonia, where annual rainfall averages about 250 mm, the pampas change to open steppe.

The **velds** of southern Africa (not to be confused with savanna) occupy the eastern part of a high plateau 1500 to 2000 m above sea level in the Transvaal and the Orange Free State.

Australia has four types of grasslands: arid tussock grassland in the northern part of the continent, where the rainfall averages between 200 and 500 mm, mostly in the summer; arid hummock grasslands in areas with less than 200 mm rainfall; coastal grasslands in the tropical summer rainfall region; and subhumid grasslands along coastal areas where annual rainfall is between 500 and 1000 mm. However, the introduction of fertilizers, non-native grasses, legumes, and sheep grazing have changed most of these grasslands.

Grasslands support a diversity of animal life dominated by herbivorous species, both invertebrate and vertebrate. Large grazing ungulates and burrowing mammals are the most conspicuous vertebrates. The North American grasslands once were dominated by huge migratory herds of millions of bison (*Bison bison*) and the forb-consuming pronghorned antelope (*Antilocarpa americana*). The most common burrowing rodent was the prairie dog (*Cynomys* spp.), which along with gophers (*Thomomys* and *Geomys*) and the mound-building harvester ants (*Pogonmyrex* spp.) appeared to be instrumental in the development and maintenance of the ecological structure of the shortgrass prairie.

The Eurasian steppes and the Argentine pampas lack herds of large ungulates. On the pampas, the two major large herbivores are the pampas deer (*Ozotoceras bezoarticus*) and, farther south, the guanaco (*Lama guanaco*), a small relative of the camel. These species, however, are greatly reduced in number compared to historical times.

The African grassveld once supported great migratory herds of wildebeest (*Connochaetes taurinus*) and zebra (*Equus* spp.) along with their associated carnivores, the lion (*Panthera leo*), leopard (*Panthera pardus*), and hyena (*Crocuta crocuta*). The great ungulate herds have been destroyed and replaced with sheep, cattle, and horses.

The Australian marsupial mammals evolved many forms that are the ecological equivalents of placental grassland mammals. The dominant grazing animals are a number of species of kangaroos, especially the red kangaroo (*Macropus rufus*) and the gray kangaroo (*Macropus giganteus*).

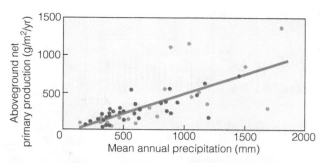

**Figure 23.24** | Relationship between aboveground primary production and mean annual precipitation for 52 grassland sites around the world. Each point represents a different grassland site. North American grasslands are indicated by dark-green dots. (Adapted from Lauenroth 1979.)

Grasslands evolved under the selective pressure of grazing. Thus, up to a point, grazing stimulates primary production (see Section 14.14). Although the most conspicuous grazers are large herbivores, the major consumers in grassland ecosystems are invertebrates. The heaviest consumption takes place below ground, where the dominant herbivores are nematodes.

The most visible feature of grassland is the tall, green, ephemeral herbaceous growth that develops in spring and dies back in autumn. One of the three strata in the grassland, it arises from the crowns, nodes, and rosettes of plants hugging the soil. The ground layer and the below-ground root layer are the other two major strata of grasslands. The highly developed root layer can make up more than half the total plant biomass and typically extends to a considerable depth into the soil.

Depending on their history of fire and degree of grazing and mowing, grasslands accumulate a layer of mulch that retains moisture and, with continuous turnover of fine roots, add organic matter to the mineral soil. Dominant soils of the grasslands are Mollisols (see Figure 5.12) with a relatively thick, dark-brown to black surface horizon that is rich in organic matter. Soils typically become thinner and paler in color in the drier regions as a result of less organic material becoming incorporated into the surface horizon.

The productivity of temperate grassland ecosystems is primarily related to annual precipitation (Figure 23.24), yet temperature can complicate this relationship. Increasing temperatures have a positive effect on photosynthesis but can actually reduce productivity by increasing the demand for water.

## 23.8 | Conifer Forests Dominate the Cool Temperate and Boreal Zones

Conifer forests, dominated by needle-leaf evergreen trees, are found primarily in a broad circumpolar belt across the Northern Hemisphere and on mountain

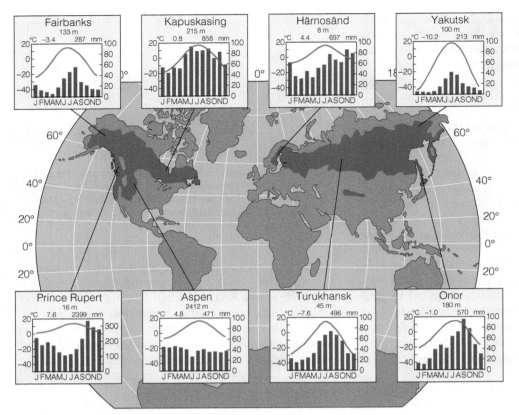

**Figure 23.25** | Geographic distribution of the conifer forest ecosystems of the world and associated climate diagrams showing the long-term patterns of monthly temperature and precipitation for selected locations. (Adapted from Archibold 1995.)

ranges where low temperatures limit the growing season to a few months each year (Figure 23.25). The variable composition and structure of these forests reflect the wide range of climatic conditions in which they grow. In central Europe, extensive coniferous forests, dominated by Norway spruce (*Picea abies*), cover the slopes up to the subalpine zone in the Carpathian Mountains and the Alps (Figure 23.26a). In North America, several coniferous forest associations blanket the Rocky, Wasatch, Sierra Nevada, and Cascade mountains. At high elevations in the Rocky Mountains grows a subalpine forest dominated by Engelmann spruce (*Picea engelmannii*) and subalpine fir (*Abies lasiocarpa*) (Figure 23.26b). Midelevations have stands of Douglas-fir, and lower elevations are dominated by open stands of ponderosa pine (*Pinus ponderosa*) (Figure 23.26c) and dense stands of the early successional conifer, lodgepole pine (*Pinus contorta*). The largest tree of all, the giant sequoia (*Sequoiadendron giganteum*), grows in scattered groves on the west slopes of the California Sierra. In addition, the mild, moist climate of the Pacific Northwest supports a highly productive coastal forest that extends along the coastal strip from Alaska to northern California.

The largest expanse of conifer forest, in fact the largest vegetation formation on Earth, is the boreal forest, or taiga (Russian for "land of little sticks"). This belt of coniferous forest encompassing the high latitudes of the Northern Hemisphere covers about 11 percent of Earth's terrestrial surface (see Figure 23.25). In North America, the boreal forest covers much of Alaska and Canada and spills into northern New England, with fingers extending down the western mountain ranges and the Appalachians. In Eurasia, the boreal forest begins in Scotland and Scandinavia and extends across the continent, covering much of Siberia, to northern Japan.

Four major vegetation zones make up the taiga: the forest–tundra ecotone with open stands of stunted spruce, lichens, and moss; the open boreal woodland with stands of lichens and black spruce; the main boreal forest (Figure 23.27) with continuous stands of spruce and pine broken by poplar and birch on disturbed areas; and the boreal–mixed forest ecotone where the boreal forest grades into the temperate forest of southern Canada and the northern United States. Occupying, for the most part, formerly glaciated land, the taiga is also a region of cold lakes, bogs, rivers, and alder thickets.

A cold continental climate with strong seasonal variation dominates the taiga. The summers are short, cool, and moist, and the winters are prolonged, harsh, and dry, with a prolonged period of snowfall. The driest winters and the most extreme seasonal fluctuations are in interior Alaska and central Siberia, which experience as much as 100°C seasonal temperature extremes (difference between minimum and maximum annual temperatures).

(a)

(b)

(c)

**Figure 23.26** | Some coniferous forest types. **(a)** A Norway spruce forest in the Carpathian Mountains of central Europe. **(b)** Rocky Mountain subalpine forest dominated by subalpine fir (*Abies lasiocarpa*), which grows with Engelmann spruce and mountain hemlock. **(c)** A montane coniferous forest in the Rocky Mountains. The dry, lower slopes support ponderosa pine; the upper slopes are cloaked with Douglas-fir.

**Figure 23.27** | Black spruce is a dominant conifer in the North American taiga.

Much of the taiga is under the controlling influence of permafrost, which impedes infiltration and maintains high soil moisture. Permafrost is the perennially frozen subsurface that may be hundreds of meters deep. It develops where the ground temperatures remain below 0°C for extended periods of time. Its upper layers may thaw in summer and refreeze in winter. Because the permafrost is impervious to water, it forces all water to remain and move above it. Thus, the ground stays soggy even though precipitation is low, enabling plants to exist in the driest parts of the Arctic.

Fires are recurring events in the taiga. During periods of drought, fires can sweep over hundreds of thousands of hectares. All of the boreal species, both broadleaf trees and conifers, are well adapted to fire. Unless too severe, fire provides a seedbed for regeneration of trees. Light surface burns favor early successional hardwood species. More severe fires eliminate hardwood competition and favor spruce and jack pine regeneration.

The boreal forest has a unique animal community. Caribou (*Rangifer tarandus*), wide-ranging and feeding on grasses, sedges, and especially lichens, inhabit open spruce–lichen woodlands. Joining the caribou is the moose (*Alces alces*), called elk in Eurasia, the largest of all deer. It is a lowland mammal feeding on aquatic and emergent vegetation as well as alder and willow. Competing with moose for browse is the cyclic snowshoe hare (*Lepus americanus*). The arboreal red squirrel (*Sciurus hudsonicus*) inhabits the conifers and feeds on young pollen-bearing cones and seeds of spruce and fir; and the quill-bearing porcupine (*Erethizon dorsatum*) feeds on leaves, twigs, and the inner bark of trees. Preying on these are an assortment of predators including the wolf, lynx (*Lynx canadensis*), pine martin (*Martes americana*), and owls. The taiga is also the nesting ground of migratory neotropical birds and the habitat of northern seed-eating birds such as crossbills (*Loxia* spp.), grosbeaks (*Coccothraustes* spp.), and siskins (*Carduelis* spp.).

Of great ecological and economic importance are major herbivorous insects such as the spruce budworm (*Choristoneura fumiferana*). Although major food items for the insectivorous summer birds, these insects experience periodic outbreaks during which they defoliate and kill large expanses of forest.

Net primary productivity of boreal forests is generally low in comparison to more temperate forests, limited by low nutrients, cooler temperatures, and the short growing season. Likewise, inputs of plant litter are low compared to the forests of the warmer temperate zone. However, rates of decomposition are slow under the cold, wet conditions, resulting in the accumulation of organic matter. Soils are primarily Spodosols (see Figure 5.12) characterized by a thick organic layer. The mineral soils beneath mature coniferous forests are comparatively infertile, and growth is often limited by the rate at which mineral nutrients are recycled through the ecosystem.

## 23.9 | Low Precipitation and Cold Temperatures Define the Arctic Tundra

Encircling the top of the Northern Hemisphere is a frozen plain, clothed in sedges, heaths, and willows, dotted with lakes, and crossed by streams (Figure 23.28). Called tundra, its name comes from the Finnish *tunturi*, meaning "a treeless plain." The arctic tundra falls into two broad types: *tundra* with up to 100 percent plant cover and wet to moist soil (Figure 23.29), and *polar desert* with less than 5 percent plant cover and dry soil.

Conditions unique to the Arctic tundra are a product of at least three interacting forces: permafrost, vegetation, and the transfer of heat. Vegetation and its accumulated organic matter protect the permafrost by shading and insulation, which reduce the warming and retard thawing of the soil in summer. In turn, permafrost chills the soil, retarding the general growth of plant parts, both aboveground and below ground, limiting the activity of soil microorganisms and diminishing the aeration and nutrient content of the soil. Alternate freezing and thawing of the upper layer of soil creates the unique, symmetrically patterned landforms typical of the tundra (Figure

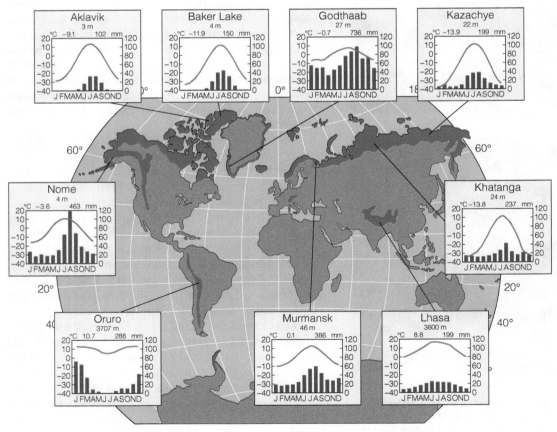

**Figure 23.28** | Geographic distribution of the tundra ecosystems of the world and associated climate diagrams showing the long-term patterns of monthly temperature and precipitation for selected locations. (Adapted from Archibold 1995.)

23.30). This action of frost pushes stones and other material upward and outward from the mass to form a patterned surface of frost hummocks, frost boils, earth stripes, and stone polygons. On sloping ground, creep, frost thrusting, and downward flow of supersaturated soil over the permafrost form *solifluction terraces,* or "flowing soil." This gradual downward creep of soils and rocks eventually rounds-off ridges and other irregularities in topography. Such molding of the landscape by frost action, called *cryoplanation,* is far more important than erosion in wearing down the Arctic landscape.

Structurally, the vegetation of the tundra is simple. The number of species tends to be few and growth is slow. Only those species able to withstand constant disturbance of the soil, buffeting by the wind, and abrasion from wind-carried particles of soil and ice can survive. Low ground is covered with a complex of cotton grasses, sedges, and *Sphagnum.* Well-drained sites support heath shrubs, dwarf willows and birches, herbs, mosses, and lichens. The driest and most exposed sites support scattered heaths and crustose and foliose lichens growing on the rock. Arctic plants propagate themselves almost entirely by vegetative means, although viable seeds many hundreds of years old exist in the soil.

Plants are photosynthetically active on the Arctic tundra about 3 months out of the year. As snow cover disappears, plants commence photosynthetic activity. They maximize use of the growing season and light by photosynthesizing during the 24-hour daylight period, even at midnight when light is one-tenth that of noon. The nearly erect leaves of some Arctic plants permit the almost complete interception of the low angle of the Arctic sun.

Much of the photosynthate goes into the production of new growth, but about 1 month before the growing season ends, plants cease to allocate photosynthate to aboveground biomass. They withdraw nutrients from the leaves and move them to roots and below-ground biomass, sequestering 10 times the amount stored by temperate grasslands.

Structurally, most of the tundra vegetation is underground. Root-to-shoot ratios of vascular plants range from 3:1 to 10:1. Roots are concentrated in the upper soil that thaws during the summer, and aboveground parts seldom grow taller than 30 cm. It is not surprising, then, that the below-ground net annual production is typically three times that of the aboveground productivity.

**Figure 23.29** | The wide expanse of the Arctic tundra in the Northwest Territories of Canada.

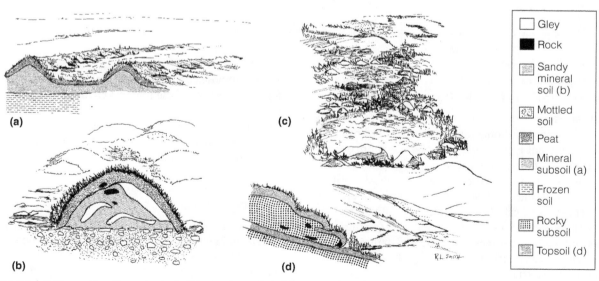

Gley
Rock
Sandy mineral soil (b)
Mottled soil
Peat
Mineral subsoil (a)
Frozen soil
Rocky subsoil
Topsoil (d)

**Figure 23.30** | Patterned landforms typical of the tundra region: **(a)** unsorted earth stripes; **(b)** frost hummocks; **(c)** sorted stone nets and polygons; and **(d)** a solifluction terrace.

The tundra hosts fascinating animal life even though the diversity of species is low. Invertebrates are concentrated near the surface, where there are abundant populations of segmented whiteworms (Enchytraeidae), collembolas, and flies (Diptera), chiefly craneflies. Summer in the Arctic tundra brings hordes of blackflies (*Simulium* spp.), deerflies (*Chrysops* spp.), and mosquitoes.

Dominant vertebrates on the Arctic tundra are herbivores, including lemmings, Arctic hare, caribou, and musk-ox (*Ovibos moschatus*). Although caribou have the greatest herbivore biomass, lemmings, which breed throughout the year, may reach densities as great as 125 to 250 per hectare, consuming three to six times as much forage as caribou. Arctic hares that feed on willows disperse over the range in winter and congregate in more restricted areas in summer. Caribou are extensive grazers, spreading out over the tundra in summer to feed on sedges. Musk-ox are more intensive grazers, restricted to more localized areas where they feed on sedges, grasses, and dwarf willow. Herbivorous birds are few, dominated by ptarmigan and migratory geese.

The major Arctic carnivore is the wolf, which preys on musk-ox, caribou, and, when they are abundant, lemmings. Medium-sized to small predators include the Arctic fox (*Alopex lagopus*), which preys on Arctic hare, and several species of weasel, which prey on lemmings. Also feeding on lemmings are snowy owls (*Nyctea scandiaca*) and the hawk-like jaegers (*Stercorarius* spp.). Sandpipers (*Tringa* spp.), plovers (*Pluvialis* spp.), longspurs (*Calcarius* spp.), and waterfowl, which nest on the wide expanse of ponds and boggy ground, feed heavily on insects.

At lower latitudes, alpine tundra occurs in the higher mountains of the world. The alpine tundra is a land of

**Figure 23.31** | Rocky Mountains alpine tundra.

rock-strewn slopes, bogs, meadows, and shrubby thickets (Figure 23.31). The environment of the alpine tundra is severe. It is a land of strong winds, snow, cold, and widely fluctuating temperatures. During summer, the temperature on the surface of the soil ranges from 40°C to 0°C. The atmosphere is thin, so light intensity, especially ultraviolet, is high on clear days. Alpine tundras have little permafrost, confined mostly to very high elevations. Lacking permafrost, soils are drier. Only in alpine wet meadows and bogs do soil moisture conditions compare with those of the Arctic. Precipitation, especially snowfall and humidity, is higher in the alpine regions than in the Arctic tundra, but steep topography induces a rapid runoff of water.

## Summary

### Ecosystem Distribution and Plant Adaptations (23.1)

Terrestrial ecosystems can be classified into broad categories called biomes. Biomes are classified according to the predominant plant types. There are at least eight major terrestrial biome types: tropical forest, temperate forest, conifer forest (taiga or boreal forest), tropical savanna, temperate grasslands, chaparral (shrublands), tundra, and desert. These broad categories reflect the relative contribution of three general plant life forms: trees, shrubs, and grasses. Interaction between moisture and temperature is the primary factor limiting the nature and geographic distribution of terrestrial ecosystems.

Terrestrial ecosystems are classified based on vegetation structure, which is typically defined on the basis of the dominant plant life forms (grasses, shrubs, and trees). Con-straints imposed on the adaptations of these major plant life forms to features of the physical environment (climate and soils) determine their patterns of dominance along gradients of temperature and moisture. The patterns of plant life form dominance along these two gradients determine the corresponding distribution of ecosystems after which they are named.

### Tropical Forests (23.2)

Seasonality of rainfall determines the types of tropical forests. Rain forests, associated with high aseasonal rainfall, are dominated by broadleaf evergreen trees. They are noted for their enormous diversity of plant and animal life. The vertical structure of the forest is divided into five general layers: emergent trees, high upper canopy, low tree stratum, shrub understory, and a ground layer of herbs and ferns.

Conspicuous in the rain forest are the lianas or climbing vines, epiphytes growing up in the trees, and stranglers growing downward from the canopy to the ground. Many large trees develop buttresses for support. Nearly 90 percent of primate species live in tropical rain forests.

Tropical rain forests support high levels of primary productivity. The high rainfall and consistently warm temperatures also result in high rates of decomposition and nutrient cycling.

Dry tropical forests undergo varying lengths of dry season, during which trees and shrubs drop their leaves (drought-deciduous). Leaves are once again grown at the onset of the rainy season. Most dry tropical forests have been lost to agriculture and grazing and other disturbances.

## Tropical Savannas (23.3)

Savannas are characterized by a codominance of grasses and woody plants. They are characteristic of regions with alternating wet and dry seasons. Savannas range from grass with occasional trees to shrubs to communities where trees form an almost continuous canopy as a function of precipitation and soil texture.

Both productivity and decomposition in savanna ecosystems are closely tied to the seasonality of precipitation.

Savannas support a large and varied assemblage of herbivores, invertebrate and vertebrate. The African savanna is dominated by a large and diverse population of ungulate fauna and associated carnivores.

## Deserts (23.4)

Deserts occupy about one-seventh of Earth's land surface and are largely confined to two worldwide belts between 15° and 30° north and south latitude. Deserts result from dry descending air masses within these regions, the rainshadows of coastal mountain ranges, and remoteness from oceanic moisture. Two broad types of deserts exist: cool deserts exemplified by the Great Basin of North America, and hot deserts, like the Sahara. Deserts are structurally simple with scattered shrubs, ephemeral plants, and open, stark topography. In this harsh environment, plants and animals have evolved ways of circumventing aridity and high temperatures by either evading or resisting drought. In spite of their aridity, deserts support a diversity of animal life, notably opportunistic herbivorous species and carnivores.

## Shrubland (23.5)

Shrubs have a densely branched woody structure and low height. Shrublands are difficult to classify because of the variety of climates in which shrubs can be a dominant or codominant component of the plant community. In five widely disjunct regions along the western margins of the continents between 30° and 40° latitude, however, are found the mediterranean ecosystems dominated by evergreen shrubs and sclerophyll trees, which have adapted to the distinctive climate of summer drought and cool, moist winters. These shrublands are fire-adapted and highly flammable.

## Temperate Forests (23.6)

Broadleaf deciduous forests are found in the wetter environments of the warm temperate region. They once covered large areas of Europe and China, but their distribution has been reduced by human activity. In North America, deciduous forests are still widespread. They include a number of types such as beech–maple and oak–hickory; the greatest development is in the mixed mesophytic forest of the unglaciated Appalachians. Well-developed deciduous forests have four strata: upper canopy, lower canopy, shrub layer, and ground layer. Vertical structure influences the diversity and distribution of life in the forest. Certain species are associated with each stratum.

## Temperate Grasslands (23.7)

Natural grasslands occupy regions where rainfall is between 250 mm and 800 mm a year. Once covering extensive areas of the globe, natural grasslands have shrunk to a fraction of their original size because of conversion to cropland and grazing lands.

Grasslands vary with climate and geography. Native grasslands of North America, influenced by declining precipitation from east to west, consist of tallgrass prairie, mixedgrass prairie, shortgrass prairie, and desert grasslands. Eurasia has steppes, South America the pampas, and southern Africa the veldt. Grassland consists of an ephemeral herbaceous layer that arises from crowns, nodes, and rosettes of plants hugging the ground. In addition, there is a ground layer and a highly developed root layer. Depending on the history of fire and degree of grazing and mowing, grasslands accumulate a layer of mulch.

Grasslands support a diversity of animal life dominated by herbivorous species, both invertebrate and vertebrate. Grasslands once supported herds of large grazing ungulates such as bison in North America, migratory herds of wildebeest in Africa, and the marsupial kangaroos in Australia. Grasslands evolved under the selective pressure of grazing. Although the most conspicuous grazers are large herbivores, the major consumers are invertebrates. The heaviest consumption takes place below ground, where the dominant herbivores are nematodes.

## Conifer Forests (23.8)

The coniferous forests of temperate regions include the montane pine forests and lower elevation pine forests of Eurasia and North America and the temperate rain forests of the Pacific Northwest.

North of the temperate coniferous forest is the circumpolar taiga, or boreal forest, the largest biome on Earth. Characterized by a cold continental climate, the taiga consists of four major zones: the forest ecotone, open boreal woodland, main boreal forest, and boreal–mixed forest ecotone.

Permafrost, the maintenance of which is influenced by tree and ground cover, has a strong influence on the pattern of vegetation, as do recurring fires. Spruces and pines dominate boreal forest with successional communities of birch and poplar. Ground cover below spruce is mostly moss; in open spruce and pine stands, the cover is mostly lichens.

Major herbivores of the boreal region include caribou, moose (called elk in Europe), and snowshoe hare. Predators include the wolf, lynx, and pine martin.

## Tundra (23.8)

The Arctic tundra extends beyond the tree line of the far north of the Northern Hemisphere. It is characterized by low temperature, low precipitation, a short growing season, a perpetually frozen subsurface (the permafrost), and a frost-molded landscape. Plant species are few, the growth forms are low, and growth rates are slow. Over much of the Arctic, the dominant vegetation is cotton grass, sedge, and dwarf heaths. They exploit the long days of summer by photosynthesizing during the 24-hour daylight period. Most plant growth occurs underground. The animal community is low in diversity but unique. Summer in the Arctic brings hordes of insects, providing a rich food source for shorebirds. Dominant vertebrates are lemming, Arctic hare, caribou, and musk-ox. Major carnivores are the wolf, Arctic fox, and snowy owl.

Alpine tundras occur in the mountains of the world. They are characterized by widely fluctuating temperatures, strong winds, snow, and a thin atmosphere.

## Study Questions

1. What are the main differences between tropical rain forest and tropical dry forest?
2. What are the major strata in the tropical rain forest?
3. How does the warm, wet environment of tropical rain forest influence rates of net primary productivity and decomposition?
4. What types of trees characterize tropical rain forest (leaf type)?
5. What distinguishes savannas from grassland ecosystems?
6. Under what climate conditions do you find tropical savanna ecosystems?
7. How does seasonality influence rates of net primary productivity and decomposition in savanna ecosystems?
8. What features of regional climate lead to the formation of desert ecosystems?
9. What climate characterizes mediterranean ecosystems?
10. What type of leaves characterize mediterranean plants?
11. What types of leaves characterize the trees of temperate forest ecosystems?
12. How does seasonality of temperature influence the structure and productivity of temperate forest ecosystems?

13. What climate is characteristic of temperate grasslands?
14. How does annual precipitation influence the structure and productivity of grassland ecosystems?
15. What type of trees characterize boreal forest?
16. What is permafrost, and how does it influence the structure and productivity of boreal forest ecosystems?
17. What physical and biological features characterize Arctic tundra?
18. How does alpine tundra differ from Arctic tundra?

## Further Readings

Archibold, O. W. 1995. *Ecology of world vegetation.* London: Chapman & Hall.

An outstanding reference for those interested in the geography and ecology of terrestrial ecosystems.

Bliss, L. C., O. H. Heal, and J. J. Moore, eds. 1981. *Tundra ecosystems: A comparative analysis.* New York: Cambridge University Press.

A major reference on the geography, structure, and function of these high-latitude ecosystems.

Bonan, G. B., and H. H. Shugart. 1989. Environmental factors and ecological processes in boreal forests. *Annual Review of Ecology and Systematics* 20:1–18.

An excellent review paper providing a good introduction to boreal forest ecosystems.

Evenardi, M., I. Noy-Meir, and D. Goodall, eds. 1986. *Hot deserts and arid shrublands of the world.* Ecosystems of the World 12A and 12B. Amsterdam: Elsevier Scientific.

A major reference work on the geography and ecology of the world deserts.

French, N., ed. 1979. *Perspectives on grassland ecology.* New York: Springer-Verlag.

This text provides a good summary of grassland ecology.

Murphy, P. G., and A. E. Lugo. 1986. Ecology of tropical dry forests. *Annual Review of Ecology and Systematics* 17:67–88.

This paper provides an overview of the distribution and ecology of tropical dry forests, one of the most endangered terrestrial ecosystems.

Reichle, D. E., ed. 1981. *Dynamic properties of forest ecosystems.* Cambridge, England: Cambridge Univ. Press.

The major reference source on the ecology and function of forest ecosystems throughout the world.

Richards, P. W. 1996. *The tropical rain forest: An ecological study,* 2nd ed. New York: Cambridge University Press.

A thoroughly revised edition of a classic book on the ecology of tropical rain forests.

Sinclair, A. R. E., and P. Arcese, eds. 1995. *Serengeti II: Dynamics, management, and conservation of an ecosystem.* Chicago: University of Chicago Press.

A masterful study of an ecosystem. A valuable reference on the ecology of tropical savanna ecosystems.

# Chapter 24 | Aquatic Ecosystems

Waves heavily influence the pattern of life on rocky shores along the California coastline.

Whereas scientists classify terrestrial ecosystems according to their dominant plant life forms, classification of aquatic ecosystems is largely based on features of the physical environment. One of the major features that influence the adaptations of organisms to the aquatic environment is water salinity (see Section 4.5). For this reason, aquatic ecosystems fall into two major categories: freshwater or saltwater (or marine). These categories are further divided into a number of ecosystem types based on substrate, depth and flow of water, and the type of dominant organisms (typically plants).

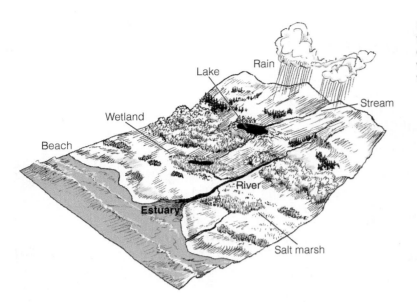

**Figure 24.1** | Idealized landscape/seascape showing the linkages among the various types of aquatic ecosystems via the water cycle. Go to **GRAPHIT!** at **www.ecologyplace.com** to learn about global fresh-water resources.

Ecologists subdivide marine ecosystems into two broad categories of coastal and open-water systems. Freshwater ecosystems are classified on the basis of depth and flow of water. Flowing water, or **lotic,** ecosystems include rivers and streams. Nonflowing water, or **lentic** ecosystems, include ponds, lakes, and inland wetlands.

All aquatic ecosystems, both freshwater and marine, are linked directly or indirectly as components of the hydrological cycle (Figure 24.1; also see Section 4.1). Water evaporated from both oceans and terrestrial environments falls as precipitation. That portion of precipitation that remains on the land surface (i.e., that does not infiltrate into the soil or evaporate) follows a path determined by gravity and topography—more specifically, geomorphology. Flowing water ecosystems begin as streams. These streams, in turn, coalesce into rivers as they follow the topography of the landscape or they collect in basins and floodplains to form nonflowing water ecosystems, such as ponds, lakes, and inland wetlands. Rivers eventually flow to the coast, forming estuaries, which represent the transition from freshwater to marine.

In this chapter, we will examine the basic characteristics of aquatic ecosystems, both freshwater and marine. Beginning first with freshwater ecosystems, we will examine lentic ecosystems (lakes and ponds) and then turn our attention to lotic ecosystems, following the path and changing characteristics of streams as they coalesce to form rivers, eventually flowing to coastal environments. After examining estuarine environments where freshwater meets the sea, we will conclude by examining the marine environments that cover over 70 percent of Earth's surface.

## 24.1 | Lakes Have Many Origins

Lakes and ponds are inland depressions containing standing water (Figure 24.2). They vary in depth from 1 m to more than 2000 m. They range in size from small ponds of less than a hectare to large lakes covering thousands of square kilometers. Ponds are small bodies of water so shallow that rooted plants can grow over much of the bottom. Some lakes are so large that they mimic marine environments. Most ponds and lakes have outlet streams, and both may be more or less temporary features on the landscape, geologically speaking.

Some lakes have formed by glacial erosion and deposition. Abrading slopes in high mountain valleys, glaciers carved basins that filled with water from rain and melting snow to form tarns. Retreating valley glaciers left behind crescent-shaped ridges of rock debris called moraines that dammed up water behind them. Numerous shallow kettle lakes and potholes were left behind by the glaciers that covered much of northern North America and northern Eurasia.

Lakes also form when silt, driftwood, and other debris deposited in beds of slow-moving streams dam up water behind them. Loops of streams that meander over flat valleys and floodplains often become cut off by sediments, forming crescent-shaped oxbow lakes.

Shifts in Earth's crust, uplifting mountains or displacing rock strata, sometimes develop water-filled depressions. Craters of some extinct volcanoes have also become lakes. Landslides may block streams and valleys to form new lakes and ponds.

Many lakes and ponds form through nongeological activity. Beavers dam streams to make shallow but often extensive ponds. Humans create huge lakes by damming

Figure 24.2 | Lakes and ponds fill basins or depressions in the land. (a) A rock basin glacial lake or tarn in the Rocky Mountains. (b) A swampy tundra in Siberia is dotted with numerous ponds and lakes. (c) A beaver dam forms a pond in this Colorado Rocky Mountain meadow. (d) An oxbow lake formed when a bend in the river was cut off from the main channel. (e) A human-constructed, old New England millpond. Note the floating vegetation.

rivers and streams for power, irrigation, or water storage and construct smaller ponds and marshes for recreation, fishing, and wildlife (see Ecological Issues: Dams: Regulating the Flow of River Ecosystems). Quarries and surface mines can also form ponds.

## 24.2 | Lakes Have Well-Defined Physical Characteristics

All lentic ecosystems share certain characteristics. Life in still-water ecosystems depends on light. The amount of light penetrating the water is influenced not only by natural attenuation but also by silt and other material carried into the lake and by the growth of phytoplankton. Temperatures vary seasonally and with depth (Figure 4.7). Oxygen can be limiting, especially in summer, because only a small proportion of the water is in direct contact with air, and respiration by decomposers on the bottom consumes large quantities (Figure 4.10). Thus, variation in oxygen, temperature, and light strongly influences the distribution and adaptations of life in lakes and ponds (see Chapter 4 for more detailed discussion).

Ponds and lakes may be divided into both vertical and horizontal strata based on penetration of light and photosynthetic activity (Figure 24.3). The horizontal zones are obvious to the eye; the vertical ones, influenced by depth of light penetration, are not. Surrounding most lakes and ponds and engulfing some ponds completely is the **littoral zone**, or shallow-water zone, in which light

reaches the bottom, stimulating the growth of rooted plants. Beyond the littoral is open water, the **limnetic zone**, which extends to the depth of light penetration. Inhabiting this zone are microscopic phytoplankton (autotrophs) and zooplankton (heterotrophs), and **nekton**, free-swimming organisms such as fish. Beyond the depth of effective light penetration is the **profundal zone**. Its beginning is marked by the compensation depth of light, the point at which respiration balances photosynthesis (see Figure 20.8). The profundal zone depends on a rain of organic material from the limnetic zone for energy. Common to both the littoral and profundal zones is the third vertical stratum, the **benthic zone**, or bottom region, which is the primary place of decomposition. Although these zones are named and often described separately, all are closely dependent on one another in the dynamics of lake ecosystems.

## 24.3 | The Nature of Life Varies in the Different Zones

Aquatic life is richest and most abundant in the shallow water about the edges and in other places within lakes and ponds where sediments have accumulated on the bottom, decreasing water depth (Figure 24.4). Dominating these areas is emergent vegetation such as cattails and sedges, plants whose roots are anchored in the bottom mud, lower stems are immersed in water, and upper stems and leaves stand above water. Beyond the emer-

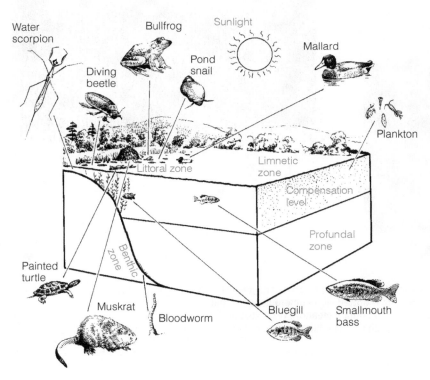

**Figure 24.3** | The major zones of a lake in midsummer: littoral, limnetic, profundal, and benthic. The compensation level is the depth at which light levels are such that gross production in photosynthesis is equal to respiration, so net production (primary) is zero. The organisms shown are typical of the various zones in a lake community.

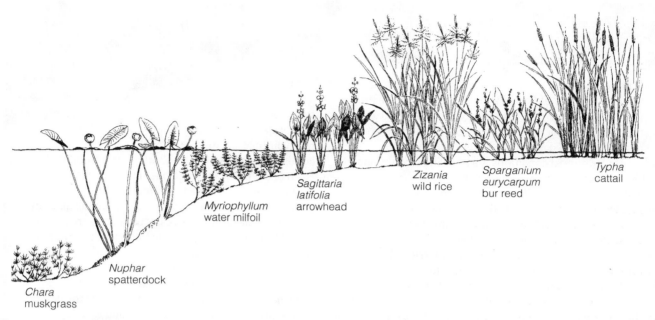

Chara
muskgrass

Nuphar
spatterdock

Myriophyllum
water milfoil

Sagittaria
latifolia
arrowhead

Zizania
wild rice

Sparganium
eurycarpum
bur reed

Typha
cattail

**Figure 24.4** | Zonation of emergent, floating, and submerged vegetation at the edge of a lake or pond. Such zonation does not necessarily reflect successional stages but rather a response to water depth (see Chapter 13, Figure 13.12).

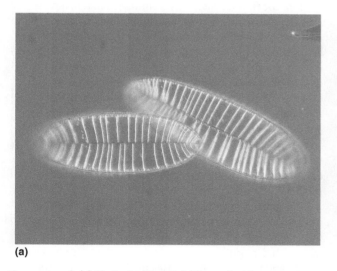

(a)

(b)

**Figure 24.5** | **(a)** Phytoplankton and **(b)** zooplankton.

gents and occupying even deeper water is a zone of floating plants such as pondweed (*Potamogeton*) and pond lily (*Nuphar* sp.). In depths too great for floating plants live submerged plants, such as species of pondweed with their finely dissected or ribbon-like leaves.

Associated with the emergents and floating plants is a rich community of organisms, among them hydras, snails, protozoans, dragonflies and diving insects, pickerel (*Esox* spp.), sunfish (*Lepomis* spp.), herons (Ardei-

dae), and blackbirds (*Agelaius* spp. and *Xanthocephalus xanthocephalus*). Many species of pond fish have compressed bodies permitting them to move with ease through the masses of aquatic plants. The littoral zone contributes heavily to the large input of organic matter into the system.

The main forms of life in the limnetic zone are phytoplankton and zooplankton (Figure 24.5). The phytoplankton, including desmids, diatoms, and filamentous

**D**ams constructed across rivers and steams interrupt and regulate the natural flow of water (Figure 1), which profoundly affects the river's hydrology and ecology. Dams change the environment in which lotic organisms live, more often than not to their detriment.

Under normal conditions, free-flowing streams and rivers experience seasonal fluctuation in flow. Snowmelt and early spring rains bring scouring high water; summer brings low water levels that expose some of the streambed and speed the decomposition of organic matter along the edges. Life has adapted to these seasonal changes. Damming a river or stream interrupts both nutrient spiraling and the river continuum.

Downstream flow is greatly reduced as a pool of water fills behind the dam, developing characteristics similar to those of a natural lake yet retaining some features of the lotic system, such as a constant inflow of water. Heavily fertilized by decaying material on the newly flooded land, the lake develops a heavy bloom of phytoplankton and, in tropical regions, dense growths of floating plants. Species of fish, often introduced exotics adapted to lake-like conditions, replace fish of flowing water.

The type of pool allowed to develop depends on the purpose of the dam and has a strong effect on downstream conditions. Single-purpose dams serve only for flood control or water storage; multipurpose dams provide hydroelectric power, irrigation water, and recreation, among other uses. A flood-control dam has a minimum pool; the dam fills only during a flood, at which time inflow exceeds outflow. Engineers release the water slowly to minimize downstream flooding. In time, the water behind the dam recedes to the original pool depth. During and after floods, the river below carries a strong flow for some time, scouring the riverbed. During normal times, flow below the dam is stabilized. If the dam is for water storage, the reservoir holds its maximum pool; but during periods of water shortage and drought, drawdown of the pool can be considerable, exposing large expanses of shoreline for a long time and stressing or killing life in the littoral zone. Only a minimal quantity of water is released downstream, usually an amount required by law, if such exists. Hydroelectric and multipurpose dams hold a variable amount of water, determined by consumer needs. During periods of power production, pulsed releases are strong enough to wipe out or dislodge benthic life downstream, which under the best of conditions has a difficult time becoming established.

Reservoirs with large pools of water become stratified, with well-developed vertical structure—epilimnion, thermocline, and hypolimnion (see Figure 4.7). If water is discharged from the upper layer of the reservoir, the effect of the flow downstream is similar to that of a natural lake. Warm, nutrient-rich, well-oxygenated water creates highly favorable conditions for some species of fish below the spillway and on downstream. If the discharge is from the cold hypolimnion, downstream receives cold, oxygen-poor water carrying an accumulation of iron and other minerals and a concentration of soluble organic materials. Such adverse conditions to stream life may persist for hundreds of kilometers downstream before the river reaches anything near normal conditions. Gated selective withdrawal structures or induced artificial circulation to increase oxygen concentration reduce such problems at some dams.

The impact of dams is compounded when a series of multipurpose dams is built on a river. The amount of water released and moving downstream becomes less with each dam until eventually all available water is consumed and the river simply dries up. This describes the situation on the Colorado River, the most regulated river in the world. The river is nearly dry by the time it reaches Mexico and disappears before it reaches the mouth of the Gulf of California. ●

1. How might the development of dams in coastal regions impact migratory fish species, such as the populations of sockeye salmon along the Pacific Northwest coast of North America discussed in the introduction to Part Four?

2. What is the source of freshwater (residential, commercial, and agricultural) for your community? Does water storage involve a reservoir? If so, what watershed (streams and rivers) are affected by the dam(s)?

**Figure 1 |** A dammed river.

algae, are the primary producers of open water and form the base on which the rest of life in open water depends. Also suspended in the water column are small grazing animals, mostly tiny crustaceans that feed on the phytoplankton. These animals form an important link in energy flow in the limnetic zone.

During the spring and fall turnovers (see Section 21.8 and Figure 21.18), plankton are carried downward, but at the same time nutrients released by decomposition on the bottom are carried upward to the impoverished surface layers. In spring when surface waters warm and stratification develops, phytoplankton have access to both nutrients and light. A spring bloom develops, followed by a rapid depletion of nutrients and a reduction in planktonic populations, especially in shallow water.

Fish make up most of the nekton in the limnetic zone. Their distribution is influenced primarily by food supply, oxygen, and temperature. During the summer, large predatory fish such as largemouth bass, pike, and muskellunge inhabit the warmer epilimnion waters, where food is abundant. In winter, they retreat to deeper water. Lake trout, on the other hand, move to greater depths as summer advances. During the spring and fall turnover, when oxygen and temperature are fairly uniform throughout, both warm-water and cold-water species occupy all levels.

Life in the profundal zone depends not only on the supply of energy and nutrients from the limnetic zone above but also on the temperature and availability of oxygen. In highly productive waters, oxygen may be limiting, because the decomposer organisms so deplete it that little aerobic life can survive. Only during spring and fall turnovers, when organisms from the upper layers enter this zone, is life abundant in profundal waters.

Easily decomposed substances drifting down through the profundal zone are partly mineralized while sinking. The remaining organic debris—dead bodies of plants and animals of the open water, and decomposing plant matter from shallow-water areas—settles on the bottom. Together with quantities of material washed in, they make up the bottom sediments, the habitat of benthic organisms.

The bottom ooze is a region of great biological activity, so great, in fact, that the oxygen curves for lakes and ponds show a sharp drop in the profundal water just above the bottom. Because the organic muck is so low in oxygen, the dominant organisms there are anaerobic bacteria. Under anaerobic conditions, however, decomposition cannot proceed to inorganic end products. When the amounts of organic matter reaching the bottom are greater than can be used by bottom fauna, they form a muck, rich in hydrogen sulfide and methane.

As the water becomes shallower, the benthos changes. The action of water, plant growth, and recent organic deposits modifies the bottom material, typically consisting of stones, rubble, gravel, marl, and clay. Increased oxygen, light, and food encourage a richness of life not found on the bottom of the profundal zone.

Closely associated with the benthic community are organisms collectively called **periphyton** or **aufwuchs.** They are attached to or move on a submerged substrate but do not penetrate it. Small aufwuchs communities colonize the leaves of submerged aquatic plants, sticks, rocks, and debris. Periphyton, mostly algae and diatoms living on plants, are fast-growing and lightly attached. Aufwuchs on stones, wood, and debris form a more crust-like growth of cyanobacteria, diatoms, water moss, and sponges.

## 24.4 | The Character of a Lake Reflects Its Surrounding Landscape

Because a close relationship exists between land and water ecosystems, lakes reflect the character of the landscape in which they occur. Water that falls on land flows over the surface or moves through the soil to enter springs, streams, and lakes. The water transports with it silt and nutrients in solution. Human activities, including road construction, logging, mining, construction, and agriculture, add another heavy load of silt and nutrients, especially nitrogen, phosphorus, and organic matter. These inputs enrich aquatic systems, a process called **eutrophication.** The term **eutrophy** (from the Greek *eutrophos,* "well nourished") means a condition of being rich in nutrients.

A typical eutrophic lake (Figure 24.6a) has a high surface-to-volume ratio; that is, the surface area is large relative to depth. Nutrient-rich deciduous forest and farmland often surround it. An abundance of nutrients, especially nitrogen and phosphorus, flowing into the lake stimulates a heavy growth of algae and other aquatic plants. Increased photosynthetic production leads to increased recycling of nutrients and organic compounds, stimulating even further growth.

Phytoplankton concentrates in the warm upper layer of the water, giving it a murky green cast. Algae, inflowing organic debris and sediment, and remains of rooted plants drift to the bottom, where bacteria feed on this dead organic matter. Their activities deplete the oxygen supply of the bottom sediments and deep water to the point at which this region of the lake cannot support aerobic life. The number of bottom species declines, although the biomass and numbers of organisms remain high.

In contrast to eutrophic lakes and ponds are bodies of water that are oligotrophic (Figure 24.6b). **Oligotrophy** is the condition of being poor in nutrients. Oligotrophic lakes have a low surface-to-volume ratio. The water is clear and appears blue to blue-green in the sunlight. The nutrient content of the water is low; and although nitrogen may be abundant, phosphorus is highly limited. A low input of nutrients from surrounding terrestrial

(a)

(b)

Figure 24.6 | **(a)** A eutrophic lake. Note the floating algal mats on the water surface. **(b)** An oligotrophic lake in Montana.

ecosystems and other external sources is mostly responsible for this condition. Low availability of nutrients causes low production of organic matter that leaves little for decomposers, so oxygen concentration remains high in the hypolimnion. The bottom sediments are largely inorganic. Although the numbers of organisms in oligotrophic lakes and ponds may be low, species diversity is often high.

Lakes that receive large amounts of organic matter from surrounding land, particularly in the form of humic materials that stain the water brown, are called **dystrophic** (from *dystrophos,* "ill-nourished"). These bodies of water occur generally on peaty substrates, or in contact with peaty substrates in bogs or heathlands that are usually highly acidic (see Section 25.6). Dystrophic lakes generally have highly productive littoral zones. This littoral vegetation dominates the metabolism of the lake, providing a source of both dissolved and particulate organic matter.

## 24.5 | Flowing-Water Ecosystems Vary in Structure and Types of Habitats

Even the largest rivers begin somewhere back in the hinterlands as springs or seepage areas that become headwater streams, or they arise as outlets of ponds or lakes. A few emerge fully formed from glaciers. As a stream drains away from its source, it flows in a direction and manner dictated by the lay of the land and the underlying rock formations. Joining the new stream are other small streams, spring seeps, and surface water.

Just below its source the stream may be small, straight, and swift, with waterfalls and rapids. Farther downstream, where the gradient is less steep, velocity decreases and the stream begins to meander, depositing its

Figure 24.7 | River delta formed by the deposition of sediments.

load of sediment as silt, sand, or mud. At flood time, a stream drops its load of sediment on surrounding level land, over which floodwaters spread to form floodplain deposits.

Where a stream flows into a lake or a river into the sea, the velocity of water is suddenly checked. The river then is forced to deposit its load of sediment in a fan-shaped area about its mouth to form a delta (Figure 24.7). Here, its course is carved into a number of channels, which are blocked or opened with subsequent deposits. As a result, the delta becomes an area of small lakes, swamps, and marshy islands. Material the river fails to deposit in the delta is carried out to open water and deposited on the bottom.

Because streams become larger on their course to rivers and are joined along the way by many others, we

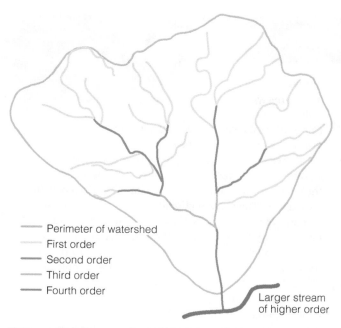

Figure 24.8 | Stream orders within a watershed.

Perimeter of watershed
First order
Second order
Third order
Fourth order

Larger stream
of higher order

(a)

(b)

Figure 24.9 | (a) A fast mountain stream. The gradient is steep and the bottom is largely bedrock. (b) A slow stream is deeper and has a lower slope gradient.

Figure 24.10 | Two different but related habitats in a stream: a riffle (background) and a pool (foreground).

can classify them according to order (Figure 24.8). A small headwater stream without any tributaries is a first-order stream. Where two streams of the same order join, the stream becomes one of higher order. If two first-order streams unite, the resulting stream becomes a second-order one; and when two second-order streams unite, the stream becomes a third-order one. The order of a stream can increase only when a stream of the same order joins it. It cannot increase with the entry of a lower order stream. In general, headwater streams are orders 1 to 3; medium-sized streams, 4 to 6; and rivers, greater than 6.

The velocity of a current molds the character and structure of a stream (Quantifying Ecology 24.1: Stream Flow). The shape and steepness of the stream channel, its width, depth, and roughness of the bottom, and the intensity of rainfall and rapidity of snowmelt all function to affect velocity. Fast streams are those whose velocity of flow is 50 cm/s or higher. At this velocity, the current will remove all particles less than 5 mm in diameter and will leave behind a stony bottom. High water increases the velocity; it moves bottom stones and rubble, scours the streambed, and cuts new banks and channels. As the gradient decreases and the width, depth, and volume of water increase, silt and decaying organic matter accumulate on the bottom. The character of the stream changes from fast water to slow (Figure 24.9), with an associated change in species composition.

Flowing-water ecosystems often alternate two different but related habitats: the turbulent riffle and the quiet pool (Figure 24.10). Processes occurring in the rapids above influence the waters of the pool, and in turn, the waters of the rapids are influenced by events in the pool.

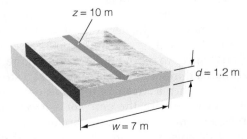

The ecology of a stream ecosystem is determined largely by its stream flow—the water discharge that occurs within the natural streambed or channel. The rate at which water flows through the stream channel influences the water temperature, oxygen content, rate of nutrient spiraling, physical structure of the benthic environment, and subsequently the types of organisms that inhabit the stream. As such, stream flow is an important parameter used by ecologists to characterize the stream environment.

Flow is defined simply as the volume of water moving past a given point in the stream per unit time. As such, it can be estimated from the cross-sectional area of the stream channel and the velocity of the flow as follows:

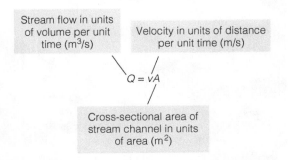

Stream flow in units of volume per unit time ($m^3/s$)

Velocity in units of distance per unit time (m/s)

$$Q = vA$$

Cross-sectional area of stream channel in units of area ($m^2$)

The cross-sectional area ($A$) can be calculated by measuring the depth ($d$) and width ($w$) of the stream and multiplying the two ($A = w \times d$) (Figure 1). Estimates of depth and width can be easily made for a point along the stream channel using a tape measure and meter stick. The velocity ($v$) can generally be thought of as distance ($z$) traveled over time ($t$) (see Figure 1). The velocity can be estimated using a "current" or "flow" meter. One flow meter commonly used in streams and rivers is an apparatus with rotating cups (Figure 2a). The flow causes the cups to rotate (Figure 2b), and the number of rotations is monitored electronically. The number of rotations (distance traveled) per unit time provides a measure of velocity.

For example, in the simple representation of a stream channel presented in Figure 1, let us assume that the stream depth ($d$) is 1.2 m and the stream width ($w$) is 7 m. The cross-sectional area ($A$) of the stream is then 8.4 $m^2$ (1.2 m $\times$ 7 m = 8.4 $m^2$). If the measured velocity ($v$) is 0.5 m/s, then the stream flow ($Q$) is 4.2 $m^3/s$ (8.4 $m^2$ $\times$ 0.5 m/s = 4.2 $m^3/s$). In reality, the profile of the stream channel is never as simple as the rectangular profile presented in Figure 1, and the water velocity varies as a function of depth and position relative to the stream bank. For this reason, it is necessary to take multiple measurements of depth and velocity across the stream profile. For example, the stream profile presented in Figure 3 is 6 m wide; however, the

**Figure 1** | Idealized representation of a stream channel (water shown in blue and land surface in yellow). The cross-sectional area ($A$) of the stream can be calculated as the stream width ($w$) times the depth ($d$). The velocity of water flow is calculated as the distance traveled ($z$) per unit time. For example, if a position on the water surface traveled downstream 10 m over a period ($t$) of 20 s, the velocity of the water is $z/t$ or 10 m/20 s = 0.5 m/s.

Riffles are the sites of primary production in the stream. Here, the periphyton or aufwuchs, organisms that are attached to or move on submerged rocks and logs, assume dominance. Periphyton, which occupy a position of the same importance as phytoplankton in lakes and ponds, consist chiefly of diatoms, cyanobacteria, and water moss.

Above and below the riffles are the pools. Here, the environment differs in chemistry, intensity of current, and depth. Just as the riffles are the sites of organic production, so the pools are the sites of decomposition. Here, the velocity of the current slows enough for organic matter to settle. Pools are the major sites of carbon dioxide production during the summer and fall, necessary for the maintenance of a constant supply of bicarbonate in solution (see Section 4.7). Without pools, photosynthesis in the riffles would deplete the bicarbonates and result in smaller and smaller quantities of available carbon dioxide downstream.

**Figure 2** | **(a)** Stream velocity can be easily measured using a cup-type flow meter. **(b)** As the water flows, the cups rotate about a fixed point on the instrument. The number of rotations per unit time provides an estimate of water velocity.

Direction of rotation

Direction of water flow

(a)

(b)

$d_1 = 0.4$    $d_3 = 1.0$    $d_5 = 0.6$
$v_1 = 0.25$    $v_3 = 0.5$    $v_5 = 0.3$

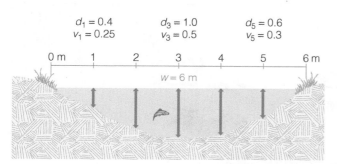

0 m   1   2   3   4   5   6 m

$w = 6$ m

**Figure 3** | Cross-sectional view of a stream channel. To estimate the cross-sectional area $(A)$, measurements of depth $(d)$ and velocity $(v)$ are taken at a number of locations along the width of the stream. By averaging these values of depth and velocity, a more accurate estimate of cross-sectional area and velocity can be obtained for calculating streamflow $(Q)$.

depth varies across the width of the stream channel. A simple approach to estimating flow for this stream would be to sample water depth and velocity at a number of locations along the width of the stream, using the average values of water depth and velocity to calculate

the value of stream flow. In most cases, however, stream ecologists will use a much more elaborate sampling scheme, estimating water depth at regular intervals along the stream profile and water velocity at a number of depths at each interval.

Both the cross-sectional area and velocity of a stream will vary through time as a function of the amount of water being discharged from the surrounding watershed. In turn, the amount of water discharged will reflect the input of water to the surrounding watershed from precipitation. As a result, an accurate picture of stream flow requires a systematic sampling of the stream morphology (width and depth) and velocity through time. •

1. In Figure 3, the water depth at 1, 3, and 5 m from the left stream bank are given as 0.4, 1.0, and 0.6 m, respectively. The estimates of velocity for the three locations are 0.25, 0.5, and 0.3 m/s, respectively. Estimate stream flow by representing depth and velocity as the simple mean of the three samples.

2. Why might the water velocity $(v)$ decrease from the center of the stream channel to the banks?

## 24.6 | Life Is Highly Adapted to Flowing Water

Living in moving water, inhabitants of streams and rivers have a major problem remaining in place and not being swept downstream. They have evolved unique adaptations for dealing with life in the current (Figure 24.11a). A streamlined form, which offers less resistance to water current, is typical of many animals of fast water.

The larval forms of many species of insects have extremely flattened bodies and broad, flat limbs that enable them to cling to the undersurfaces of stones where the current is weak. The larvae of certain species of caddisflies (Trichoptera) construct protective cases of sand or small pebbles and cement them to the bottoms of stones. Sticky undersurfaces help snails and planarians cling tightly and move about on stones and rubble in the current.

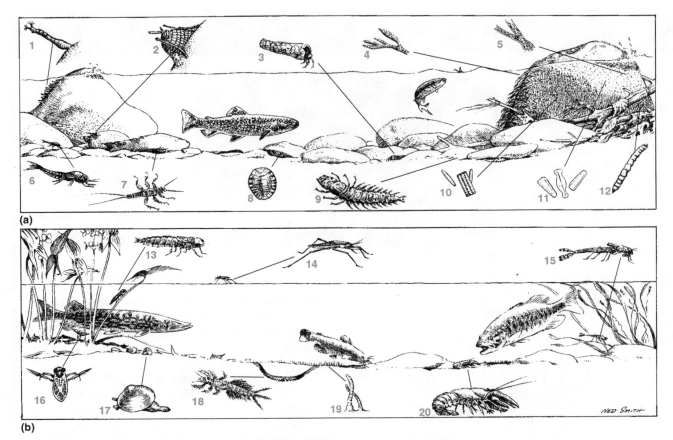

**Figure 24.11** | Life in **(a)** a fast stream and **(b)** a slow stream. Fast stream: (1) blackfly larva (Simuliidae); (2) net-spinning caddisfly (*Hydropsyche* spp.); (3) stone case of caddisfly; (4) water moss (*Fontinalis*); (5) algae (*Ulothrix*); (6) mayfly nymph (*Isonychia*); (7) stonefly nymph (*Perla* spp.); (8) water penny (*Psephenus*); (9) hellgrammite (dobsonfly larva, *Corydalis cornuta*); (10) diatoms (Diatoma); (11) diatoms (Gomphonema); (12) cranefly larva (Tipulidae). Slow stream: (13) dragonfly nymph (Odonata, *Anisoptera*); (14) water strider (*Gerris*); (15) damselfly larva (Odonata, *Zygoptera*); (16) water boatman (Corixidae); (17) fingernail clam (*Sphaerium*); (18) burrowing mayfly nymph (*Hexegenia*); (19) bloodworm (Oligochaeta, *Tubifex* spp.); (20) crayfish (*Cambarus* spp.). The fish in the fast stream is a brook trout (*Salvelinas fontinalis*). The fish in the slow stream are, from left to right: northern pike (*Esox lucius*), bullhead (*Ameiurus melas*), and smallmouth bass (*Micropterus dolommieu*).

Among the plants, water moss *(Fontinalis)* and heavily branched filamentous algae cling to rocks by strong holdfasts. Other algae grow in cushion-like colonies or form sheets covered with a slippery, gelatinous coating that lay flat against the surfaces of stones and rocks.

All animal inhabitants of fast-water streams require high, near-saturation concentrations of oxygen and moving water to keep their absorbing and respiratory surfaces in continuous contact with oxygenated water. Otherwise, a closely adhering film of liquid impoverished of oxygen forms a cloak about their bodies.

In slow-flowing streams where current is at a minimum, streamlined forms of fish give way to fish species such as smallmouth bass with compressed bodies that enable them to move through beds of aquatic vegetation. Pulmonate snails (Lymnaeacea) and burrowing mayflies (Ephemeroptera) replace rubble-dwelling insect larvae. Bottom-feeding fish, such as catfish (Akysidae), feed on life in the silty bottom, and back-swimmers and water striders inhabit sluggish stretches and still backwaters (Figure 24.11b).

Invertebrate inhabitants are classified into four major groups based on their feeding habits (Figure 24.12). **Shredders,** such as caddisflies (Trichoptera) and stoneflies (Plecoptera) make up a large group of insect larvae. They feed on coarse particulate organic matter (CPOM), mostly leaves that fall into the stream. The shredders break down the CPOM, feeding on the material not so much for the energy it contains but for the bacteria and fungi growing on it. Shredders assimilate about 40 percent of the material they ingest and pass off 60 percent as feces.

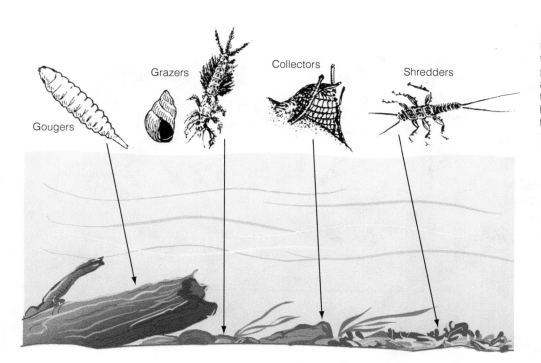

Figure 24.12 | The four major feeding groups within the stream community: gougers, grazers, collectors, and shredders. Processing the leaves and other particulate matter are bacteria and fungi.

Grazers

Gougers

Collectors

Shredders

Broken up by the shredders and partially decomposed by microbes, the leaves, along with invertebrate feces, become part of the fine particulate organic matter (FPOM). Drifting downstream and settling on the stream bottom, FPOM is picked up by another feeding group of stream invertebrates, the **filtering collectors** and **gathering collectors.** The filtering collectors include, among others, the larvae of blackflies (Simuliidae) with filtering fans and the net-spinning caddisflies. Gathering collectors, such as the larvae of midges, pick up particles from stream-bottom sediments. Collectors obtain much of their nutrition from bacteria associated with the fine detrital particles.

While shredders and collectors feed on detrital material, another group, the **grazers,** feeds on the algal coating of stones and rubble. This group includes the beetle larvae, water penny (*Psephenus* spp.), and a number of mobile caddisfly larvae. Much of the material they scrape loose enters the drift as FPOM. Another group, associated with woody debris, are the **gougers,** invertebrates that burrow into water-logged limbs and trunks of fallen trees.

Feeding on the detrital feeders and grazers are predaceous insect larvae and fish such as the sculpin (*Cottus*) and trout. Even these predators do not depend solely on aquatic insects; they also feed heavily on terrestrial invertebrates that fall or wash into the stream.

Because of the current, quantities of CPOM, FPOM, and invertebrates tend to drift downstream to form a traveling benthos. This drift is a normal process in streams, even in the absence of high water and abnormally fast currents. Drift is so characteristic of streams that a mean rate of drift can serve as an index of the production rate of a stream.

## 24.7 | The Flowing-Water Ecosystem Is a Continuum of Changing Environments

From its headwaters to its mouth, the flowing-water ecosystem is a continuum of changing environmental conditions (Figure 24.13). Headwater streams (orders 1 to 3) are usually swift, cold, and in shaded forested regions. Primary productivity is typically low, and they are heavily dependent on the input of detritus from terrestrial streamside vegetation, which contributes more than 90 percent of the organic input. Even when headwater streams are exposed to sunlight and autotrophic production exceeds inputs from adjacent terrestrial ecosystems, organic matter produced invariably enters the detrital food chain. Dominant organisms are shredders, processing large-sized litter and feeding on CPOM, and collectors, processors of FPOM. Populations of grazers are minimal, reflecting the small amount of autotrophic production, and predators are mostly small fish—sculpins, darters, and trout. Headwater streams, then, are accumulators, processors, and transporters of particulate organic matter of terrestrial origin. As a result, the ratio of gross primary production to respiration is less than 1.

As streams increase in width to medium-sized creeks and rivers (orders 4 to 6), the importance of riparian vegetation and its detrital input decreases. Exposed to the Sun, water temperature increases; and as the elevation gradient declines, the current slows. These changes bring about a

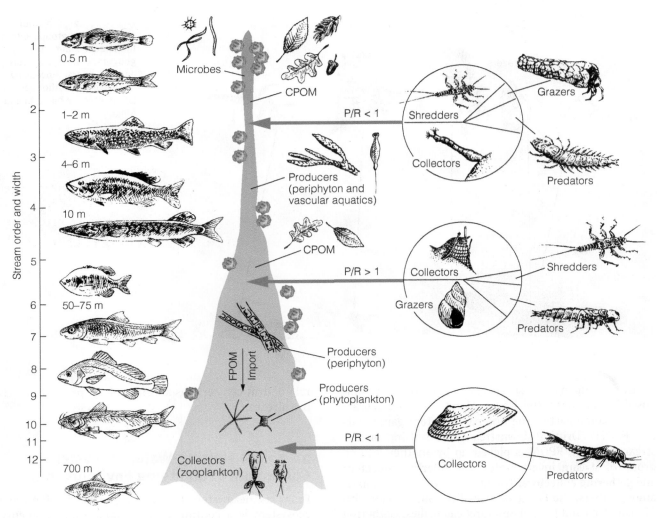

**Figure 24.13** | Changes in consumer groups along the river continuum. Stream order and width (m) are shown on the axis to the left of the figure. The headwater stream is strongly heterotrophic, dependent on terrestrial input of detritus. The dominant consumers are shredders and collectors. As stream size increases, the input of organic matter shifts to primary production by algae and rooted vascular plants. The major consumers are now collectors and grazers. As the stream grows into a river, the lotic system shifts back to heterotrophy. A phytoplankton population may develop. The consumers are mostly bottom-dwelling collectors. The fish community likewise changes as one moves downstream (from top to bottom as shown: sculpin, darter, brook trout, smallmouth bass, pickerel, sunfish, sucker, freshwater drum, catfish and shad).

shift from dependence on terrestrial input of particulate organic matter to primary production by algae and rooted aquatic plants. Gross primary production now exceeds community respiration. Because of the lack of CPOM, shredders disappear; collectors, feeding on FPOM transported downstream, and grazers, feeding on autotrophic production, become the dominant consumers. Predators show little increase in biomass but shift from cold-water species to warm-water species, including bottom-feeding fish such as suckers (Catostomidae) and catfish.

As the stream order increases from 6 through 10 and higher, riverine conditions develop. The channel is wider and deeper. The volume of flow increases, and the current becomes slower. Sediments accumulate on the bottom. Both riparian and autotrophic production decrease. A basic energy source is FPOM, used by bottom-dwelling collectors, now the dominant consumers. However, slow, deep water and DOM (dissolved organic matter) support a minimal phytoplankton and associated zooplankton population.

Throughout the downstream continuum, the community capitalizes on upstream feeding inefficiency. Downstream adjustments in production and the physical environment are reflected in changes in consumer groups.

## 24.8 | Rivers Flow into the Sea, Forming Estuaries

Waters of most streams and rivers eventually drain into the sea. The place where freshwater joins saltwater is called an estuary. Estuaries are semienclosed parts of the coastal ocean where seawater is diluted and partially mixed with freshwater coming from the land (Figure 24.14). Here, the one-way flow of freshwater streams and rivers into an estuary meets the inflowing and outflowing saltwater tides. This meeting sets up a complex of currents that varies with the structure of the estuary (size, shape, and volume), season, tidal oscillations, and winds.

Mixing waters of different salinities and temperatures creates a counterflow that works as a nutrient trap (see Figure 21.21). Inflowing river waters more often than not impoverish rather than fertilize the estuary with the possible exception of phosphorous. Instead, nutrients and oxygen are carried into the estuary by the tides. If vertical mixing takes place, these nutrients are not swept back out to sea but circulate up and down among organisms, water, and bottom sediments (see Figure 21.21).

Organisms inhabiting the estuary face two problems: maintenance of position and adjustment to changing salinity. Most estuarine organisms are benthic. They attach to the bottom, bury themselves in the mud, or occupy crevices and crannies. Mobile inhabitants are mostly crustaceans and fish, largely young of species that spawn offshore in high-salinity water. Planktonic organisms are wholly at the mercy of the currents. The seaward movements of stream flow and ebb tide transport plankton out to sea, and the rate of water movement determines the size of the plankton population.

Salinity dictates the distribution of life in the estuary. The vast majority of the organisms inhabiting an estuary are marine, able to withstand full seawater. Some estuarine inhabitants cannot withstand lowered salinities, and these species decline along a salinity gradient from the ocean to the river's mouth. Sessile and slightly motile organisms have an optimum salinity range within which they grow best. When salinities vary on either side of this range, populations decline.

Anadromous fish are those that live most of their lives in saltwater and return to freshwater to spawn. These fish are highly specialized to endure the changes in salinity. Some species of fish, such as the striped bass *(Morone saxatilis),* spawn near the interface of fresh and low-salinity water. The larvae and young fish move downstream to more saline waters as they mature. Thus, for the striped bass, an estuary serves as both a nursery and as a feeding ground for the young. Anadromous species such as the shad *(Alosa)* spawn in freshwater, but the young fish spend their first summer in an estuary, then move out to the open sea. Species such as the croaker (Sciaenidae) spawn at the mouth of the estuary, but the

Figure 24.14 | Estuary on the east coast of Australia.

Figure 24.15 | Oyster reef in estuarine environment.

larvae are transported upstream to feed in plankton-rich low-salinity areas.

The oyster bed and oyster reef are the outstanding communities of the estuary (Figure 24.15). The oyster is the dominant organism about which life revolves. Oysters may be attached to every hard object in the intertidal zone, or they may form reefs, areas where clusters of living organisms grow cemented to the almost buried shells of past generations. Oyster reefs usually lie at right angles to tidal currents, which bring planktonic food, carry away wastes, and sweep the oysters clean of sediment and debris. Closely associated with oysters are encrusting organisms such as sponges, barnacles, and bryozoans, which attach themselves to oyster shells and depend on the oyster or algae for food.

In shallow estuarine waters, rooted aquatics such as the seagrasses widgeon grass *(Ruppia maritima)* and eelgrass *(Zostera marina)* assume major importance (Figure 24.16). These aquatic plants are complex systems supporting a large number of epiphytic organisms. Such

Figure 24.16 | Seagrass meadow in the Chesapeake Bay dominated by eelgrass (*Zostera marina*).

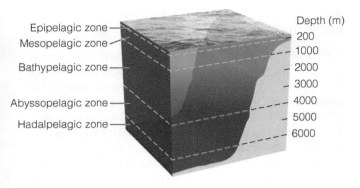

Figure 24.17 | Major regions of the ocean.

communities are important to certain vertebrate grazers, such as geese, swans, and sea turtles, and they provide a nursery ground for shrimp and bay scallops.

## 24.9 | Oceans Exhibit Zonation and Stratification

The marine environment is marked by a number of differences from the freshwater world. It is large, occupying 70 percent of Earth's surface, and it is deep, in places nearly 10 km. The surface area lighted by the sun is small compared to the total volume of water. This small volume of sunlit water and the dilute solution of nutrients limit primary production. All of the seas are interconnected by currents, influenced by wave actions and tides, and characterized by salinity (see Chapter 4).

Just as lakes exhibit stratification and zonation, so do the seas. The ocean itself has two main divisions: the **pelagic,** or whole body of water, and the **benthic zone,** or bottom region. The pelagic is further divided into two provinces: the **neritic** province, water that overlies the continental shelf, and the **oceanic** province. Because conditions change with depth, the pelagic is divided into a number of distinct vertical layers or zones (Figure 24.17). From the surface to about 200 m is the **epipelagic zone,** or **photic zone,** in which there are sharp gradients in illumination, temperature, and salinity (see Chapter 4). From 200 to 1000 m is the **mesopelagic zone,** where little light penetrates and the temperature gradient is more even and gradual, without much seasonal variation. It contains an oxygen-minimum layer and often the maximum concentration of nutrients (nitrate and phosphate). Below the mesopelagic is the **bathypelagic zone,** where darkness is virtually complete, except for bioluminescent organisms; temperature is low, and the pressure is great. The **abyssopelagic zone** (Greek meaning "no bottom") extends from about 4000 m to the sea floor. The only zone deeper than this is the **hadalpelagic zone,** which includes areas found in the deep sea trenches and canyons.

## 24.10 | Pelagic Communities Vary Among the Vertical Zones

Viewed from the deck of a ship or from an airplane, the open sea appears to be monotonously the same. Nowhere can you detect any strong pattern of life or well-defined communities, as you can over land. The reason is that pelagic ecosystems lack the supporting structures and framework of large dominant plant life. The dominant autotrophs are phytoplankton and their major herbivores are tiny zooplankton.

There is a reason for the smallness of phytoplanktons. Surrounded by a chemical medium that contains in varying quantities the nutrients necessary for life, they absorb nutrients directly from the water. The smaller the organism, the greater is the surface-to-volume ratio (see Section 7.10). More surface area is exposed for the absorption of nutrients and solar energy. Seawater is so dense that there is little need for supporting structures (see Section 4.2).

Requiring light, autotrophs are restricted to the upper surface waters where light penetration varies from tens to hundreds of meters. In shallow coastal waters, the dominant marine autotrophs are attached algae, restricted by light requirements to a maximum depth of about 120 m. The brown algae (Phaeophyceae) are the most abundant, associated with the rocky shoreline. Included in this group are the large kelps, such as *Macrocystis,* which grows to a length of 50 m and forms dense subtidal forests in the tropical and subtropical regions (see Figure 4.1). The red algae (Rhodophyceae) are the most widely distributed of the larger marine plants. They occur most abundantly in the tropical oceans where some species grow to depths of 120 m.

The dominant autotrophs of the open water are phytoplankton (see Figure 24.5a). Each ocean or region within an ocean appears to have its own dominant forms. Littoral and neritic waters and regions of upwelling are richer in plankton than the midoceans. In regions of downwelling, the dinoflagellates, a large, diverse group characterized by two whip-like flagellae, concentrate near the surface in areas of low turbulence. They attain their greatest abundance in warmer waters. In summer, they may concentrate in the surface waters in such numbers that they color it red or brown. Often toxic to vertebrates, such concentrations of dinoflagellates are responsible for "red tides." In regions of upwelling, the dominant forms of phytoplankton are diatoms. Enclosed in a silica case, diatoms are particularly abundant in Arctic waters.

Smaller than diatoms, the **nanoplankton** make up the largest biomass in temperate and tropical waters. Most abundant are the tiny cyanobacteria. The haptophytes, a group of primarily unicellular, photosynthetic algae that includes more than 500 species, are distributed in all waters except the polar seas. The most important members of this group, the coccolithophores, are a major source of primary production in the oceans. Coccolithophores have an armored appearance due to their possession of calcium carbonate platelets called coccoliths used to cover the exterior of the cell (Figure 24.18).

Conversion of primary production into animal tissue is the task of herbivorous zooplankton, the most important of which are the copepods (see Figure 24.5b). To feed on the minute phytoplankton, most of the grazing herbivores must also be small, between 0.5 and 5 mm. Most grazing herbivores in the ocean are copepods, which are probably the most abundant animals in the world. In the

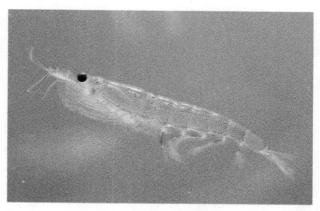

Figure 24.19 | Small euphausiid shrimps called krill are eaten by baleen whales and are essential to the marine food chain.

Antarctic, the shrimp-like euphausiids, or krill (Figure 24.19), fed on by baleen whales and penguins, are the dominant herbivores. Feeding on the herbivorous zooplankton are the carnivorous zooplankton, which include such organisms as the larval forms of comb jellies (Ctenophora) and arrowworms (Chaetognatha).

However, part of the food chain begins not with the phytoplankton, but with organisms even smaller. Bacteria and protists, both heterotrophic and photosynthetic, make up one-half of the biomass of the sea and are responsible for the largest part of energy flow in pelagic systems. Photosynthetic nanoflagellates (2–20 $\mu$m) and cyanobacteria (1–2 $\mu$m), responsible for a large part of photosynthesis in the sea, excrete a substantial fraction of their photosynthate in the form of dissolved organic material that heterotrophic bacteria use. In turn, heterotrophic nanoflagellates consume heterotrophic bacteria. This interaction introduces a feeding loop, the **microbial loop** (Figure 24.20), and adds several trophic levels to the plankton food chain.

Like phytoplankton, zooplankton live mainly at the mercy of the currents; but possessing sufficient swimming power, many forms of zooplankton exercise some control. Some species migrate vertically each day to arrive at a preferred level of light intensity. As darkness falls, zooplankton rapidly rise to the surface to feed on phytoplankton. At dawn, they move back down to preferred depths.

Feeding on zooplankton and passing energy along to higher trophic levels are the nekton, swimming organisms that can move at will in the water column. They range in size from small fish to large predatory sharks and whales, seals, and marine birds such as penguins. Some predatory fish, such as tuna, are more or less restricted to the photic zone. Others are found in deeper mesopelagic and bathypelagic zones or move between them as the sperm whale does. Although the ratio in size of predator to prey falls within limits, some of the largest

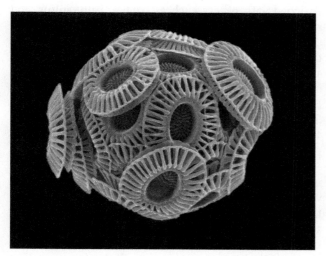

Figure 24.18 | Coccolithophores have an armored appearance due to their possession of calcium carbonate platelets called coccoliths used to cover the exterior of the cell.

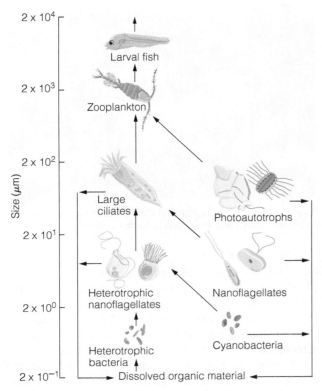

**Figure 24.20** | Diagrammatic representation of the *microbial loop* and its relationship to the plankton food web. Autotrophs are on the right side of the diagram and heterotrophs are on the left.

nekton organisms in the sea, the baleen whales, feed on disproportionately small prey, euphausiids, or krill (see Figure 24.19). By contrast, the sperm whale attacks very large prey, the giant squid.

Residents of the deep have special adaptations for securing food. Darkly pigmented and weak-bodied, many deep-sea fish depend on luminescent lures, mimicry of prey, extensible jaws, and expandable abdomens (which enable them to consume large items of food). In the mesopelagic region, bioluminescence reaches its greatest development—two-thirds of the species produce light. Fish have rows of luminous organs along their sides and lighted lures that enable them to bait prey and recognize other individuals of the same species. Bioluminescence is not restricted to fish. Squid and euphausiid shrimp possess searchlight-like structures complete with lens and iris, and some discharge luminous clouds to escape predators.

## 24.11 | Benthos Is a World of Its Own

The term *benthic* refers to the floor of the sea, and **benthos** refers to plants and animals that live there. In a world of darkness, no photosynthesis takes place, so the bottom community is strictly heterotrophic (except in vent areas), depending entirely on the rain of organic matter drifting to the bottom. Patches of dead phytoplankton, the bodies of dead whales, seals, birds, fish, and invertebrates, all provide a diversity of foods for different feeding groups and species. In spite of the darkness and depth, benthic communities support a high diversity of species. In shallow benthic regions, the number of polychaete worms may exceed 250 species and of pericarid crustaceans well over 100. But the deep-sea benthos supports a surprisingly higher diversity. The number of species collected in more than 500 samples of which the total surface area sampled was only 50 m$^2$ was 707 species of polychaetes and 426 species of pericarid crustaceans.

Important in the benthic food chain are the bacteria of the sediments. Common where large quantities of organic matter are present, bacteria may reach several tenths of a gram per square meter in the topmost layer of silt. Bacteria synthesize protein from dissolved nutrients and in turn become a source of protein, fat, and oils for other organisms.

In 1977, oceanographers first discovered high-temperature deep-sea hydrothermal vents along volcanic ridges in the ocean floor of the Pacific near the Galápagos Islands. These vents spew jets of superheated fluids that heat the surrounding water to 8°C to 16°C, considerably higher than the 2°C ambient water. Since then, oceanographers have discovered similar vents on other volcanic ridges along fast-spreading centers of the ocean floor, particularly in the mid-Atlantic and eastern Pacific.

Vents form when cold seawater flows down through fissures and cracks in the basaltic lava floor deep into the underlying crust. The waters react chemically with the hot basalt, giving up some minerals but becoming enriched with others such as copper, iron, sulfur, and zinc. Heated to a high temperature, the water reemerges through mineralized chimneys rising up to 13 m above the sea floor. Among the chimneys are white smokers and black smokers (Figure 24.21). White-smoker chimneys rich in zinc sulfides issue a milky fluid under 300°C. Black smokers, narrower chimneys rich in copper sulfides, issue jets of clear water from 300°C to more than 450°C that are soon blackened by precipitation of fine-grained sulfur-mineral particles.

Associated with these vents is a rich diversity of unique deep-sea life confined within a few meters of the vent system. The primary producers are chemosynthetic bacteria that oxidize reduced sulfur compounds such as $H_2S$ to release energy used to form organic matter from carbon dioxide. Primary consumers include giant clams, mussels, and polychaete worms that filter bacteria from water and graze on bacterial film on rocks (Figure 24.22).

**Figure 24.21** | Black smoker. Deep under the oceans, next to hydrothermal vents issuing from cracked volcanic rocks ("black smokers"), live some of the most unusual animals ever seen. The photograph shows a "black smoker" in full flow, some 2250 m down on the ocean floor west of Vancouver Island, on the Juan de Fuca Ridge. The water temperatures on the chimneys exceed 400°C. Surrounding the vents are tubeworms, a bizarre group of animals found only in conditions where high levels of hydrogen sulfide can fuel their internal symbionts—bacteria that manufacture food for them. Distribution of this fauna is related to the history of the tectonic development of the ridges, thus linking the geology and biology of this peculiar ecosystem.

**Figure 24.22** | Pictured is a colony of giant tubeworms with vent fish and crabs, all highly specialized for and found only in the extreme environment of the hydrothermal vent ecosystem. (Courtesy of Richard Lutz, Rutgers University, Stephen Low Productions, and Woods Hole Oceanographic Institution.)

## 24.12 | Coral Reefs Are Complex Ecosystems Built by Colonies of Coral Animals

Lying in the warm, shallow waters about tropical islands and continental land masses are coral reefs, which are colorful, rich oases within the nutrient-poor seas (Figure 24.23). They are a unique accumulation of dead skeletal material built up by carbonate-secreting organisms, mostly living coral (Cnidaria, Anthozoa) but also coralline red algae (Rhodophyta, Corallinaceae), green calcerous algae (*Halimeda*), foraminifera, and mollusks. Although various types of corals can be found from the water's surface to depths of 6000 m, reef-building corals are generally

**Figure 24.23** | A rich diversity of coral species, algae, and colorful fish occupy this reef in Fiji (South Pacific Ocean).

40 m deep, usually connect to the open sea by breaks in the reef, and may have small islands of patch reefs. Reefs build up to sea level.

Coral reefs are complex ecosystems that begin with the complexity of the corals themselves. Corals are modular animals, anemone-like cylindrical polyps, with prey-capturing tentacles surrounding the opening or mouth. Most corals form sessile colonies supported on the tops of dead ancestors and cease growth when they reach the surface of the water. In the tissues of the gastrodermal layer live zooxanthellae—symbiotic, photosynthetically active, endozoic dinoflagellate algae upon which coral depend for most efficient growth (see Chapter 15). On the calcareous skeletons live still other kinds of algae, both the encrusting red and green coralline species and filamentous species, including turf algae, and a large bacterial population. Also associated with coral growth are mollusks, such as giant clams *(Tridacna, Hippopus)*, echinoderms, crustaceans, polychaete worms, sponges, and a diverse array of fishes, both herbivorous and predatory.

Because the coralline community acts as a nutrient trap (see Section 21.10), offshore coral reefs are oases of productivity (1500 to 5000 g $C/m^2/yr$) within the relatively nutrient-poor, lower productivity sea (15 to 50 g $C/m^2/yr$). This productivity and the varied habitats within the reef support a high diversity of life—thousands of species of invertebrates (such as sea urchins, which feed on coral and algae). Many kinds of herbivorous fish graze on algae, including zooxanthellae within the coral tissues, and hundreds of predatory species feed upon both invertebrate and vertebrate prey. Some of these predators, such as puffers (Tetraodontidae) and filefish (Monacanthinae), are corallivores, feeding on coral polyps. Others lie in ambush for prey in coralline caverns. In addition, there is a wide array of symbionts, such as cleaning fish and crustaceans that pick parasites and detritus from larger fish and invertebrates.

found at depths of less than 45 m. Because reef-building corals have a symbiotic relationship with algal cells (zooxanthellae, see Section 15.9), their distribution is limited to depths where sufficient solar radiation (photosynthetically active radiation) is available to support photosynthesis. Precipitation of calcium from the water is necessary to form the coral skeleton. This precipitation occurs when water temperature and salinity are high and carbon dioxide concentrations are low. These requirements limit the distribution of reef-building corals to the shallow, warm tropical waters (20°C to 28°C).

Coral reefs are of three basic types: (1) *Fringing reefs* grow seaward from the rocky shores of islands and continents. (2) *Barrier reefs* parallel shorelines of continents and islands and are separated from land by shallow lagoons. (3) *Atolls* are rings of coral reefs and islands surrounding a lagoon, formed when a volcanic mountain subsides beneath the surface. Such lagoons are about

**Figure 24.24** | Map of continental shelf and upwellings. (Adapted from Archibold 1995.)

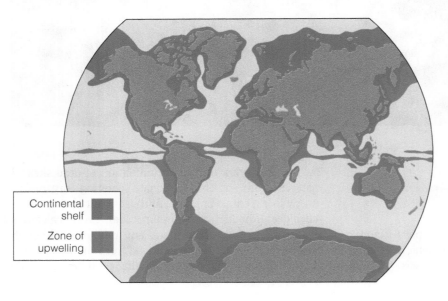

Continental shelf

Zone of upwelling

## 24.13 | Productivity of the Oceans Is Governed by Light and Nutrients

As we discussed in Chapters 19 and 20, primary productivity in marine environments is limited to regions where the availability of light and nutrients can support photosynthesis and plant growth. The vertical attenuation of light in water limits productivity to the shallower waters of the photic zone. The presence of a thermocline (see Section 21.8), however, limits the movement of nutrients from the deeper to the surface waters where light is adequate to support photosynthesis, especially in the tropics where the thermocline is permanent. The rate at which nutrients are returned to the surface, and therefore productivity, is controlled by two processes: (1) the seasonal breakdown of the thermocline and subsequent turnover (see Section 21.8) and (2) upwelling of deeper nutrient-rich waters to the surface (see Section 21.11). As a result, the highest primary productivity is found in coastal regions (see Figure 20.9), where the shallower waters of the continental shelf allow for turbulence and seasonal turnover (where it occurs) to increase vertical mixing, and coastal upwelling (see Figure 4.14) brings deeper, cold, nutrient-rich water to the surface (Figure 24.24).

In open waters, productivity is low in most tropical oceans, because the permanent nature of the thermocline slows the upward diffusion of nutrients. In these regions, the growth of phytoplankton is essentially controlled by the cycling of nutrients within the photic zone. Production rates remain more or less constant throughout the year (Figure 24.25a). The highest production in the open

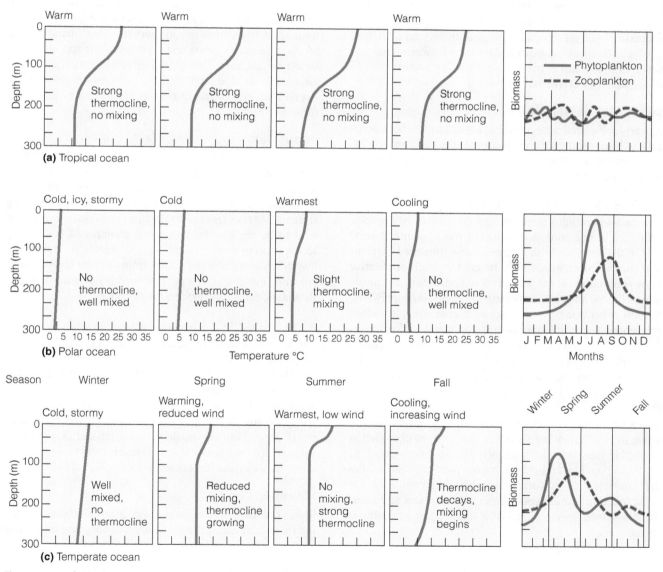

**Figure 24.25** | Thermal profiles, extent of vertical mixing, and associated patterns of productivity in **(a)** tropical, **(b)** polar, and **(c)** temperate oceans during the four seasons of the year.

waters of the tropical oceans is where nutrient-rich water is brought to the surface in the equatorial regions where upwelling occurs as surface currents diverge (see Figures 4.14 and 24.24).

Productivity is also low in the Arctic, mainly because of light limitations. A considerable amount of light energy is lost through reflection because of the low Sun angle or is absorbed by the snow-covered sea ice that covers as much as 60 percent of the Arctic Ocean during the summer.

In contrast, the waters of the Antarctic are noted for their high productivity as a result of the continuous upwelling of nutrient-rich water around the continent (Figure 24.25b). The growing season is limited by the short summer period. Primary productivity in temperate oceans (Figure 24.25c) is strongly related to seasonal variation in nutrient supply, driven by the seasonal dynamics of the thermocline (see Section 21.8).

## Summary

### Lakes Defined (24.1)

Lake and pond ecosystems are bodies of water that fill a depression in the landscape. They are formed by many processes from glacial and geological to human activities. Geologically speaking, lakes and ponds are successional features. In time, most of them fill, get smaller, and may finally be replaced by a terrestrial ecosystem.

### Lake Stratification (24.2)

A nearly self-contained ecosystem, a lake exhibits both vertical and horizontal gradients. Seasonal stratification in light, temperature, and dissolved gases influences the distribution of life in the lake.

### Zonation of Life in Lakes (24.3)

The area where light penetrates to the bottom of the lake, called the littoral zone, is occupied by rooted plants. Beyond this is the open-water or limnetic zone inhabited by plant and animal plankton and fish. Below the depth of effective light penetration is the profundal region, where the diversity of life varies with temperature and oxygen supply. The bottom or benthic zone is a place of intense biological activity, where decomposition of organic matter takes place. Anaerobic bacterica are dominant on the bottom beneath the profundal water, whereas the benthic zone of the littoral is rich in decomposer organisms and detritus feeders.

### Nutrient Input into Lakes (24.4)

Lakes are strongly influenced by the surrounding landscape in which they are situated. They may be classified as eutrophic (nutrient-rich), oligotrophic (nutrient-poor), or dystrophic (acidic and rich in humic material). Most lakes are subjected to cultural eutrophication, which is the rapid addition of nutrients—especially nitrogen and phosphorus—from sewage, industrial wastes, and agricultural runoff.

### Flowing-Water Habitat (24.5)

Currents and their dependence on detrital material from surrounding terrestrial ecosystems set flowing-water ecosystems apart from other aquatic systems. Currents shape the life in streams and rivers and carry nutrients and other materials downstream. Flowing-water ecosystems change longitudinally in flow and size from headwater streams to rivers. They may be fast or slow, characterized by a series of riffles and pools.

### Adaptations to Flowing Water (24.6)

Organisms well-adapted to living in the current inhabit fast-water streams. They may be streamlined in shape, flattened to conceal themselves in crevices and underneath rocks, or attached to rocks and other substrates. In slow-flowing streams where current is minimal, streamlined forms of fish tend to be replaced by those with compressed bodies, enabling them to move through aquatic vegetation. Burrowing invertebrates inhabit the silty bottom. Stream invertebrates fall into four major groups that feed on detrital material: shredders, collectors, grazers, and gougers.

### River Continuum (24.7)

Life in flowing water reflects a continuum of changing environmental conditions from headwater streams to the river mouth. Headwater streams depend on inputs of detrital material. As stream size increases, algae and rooted plants become important energy sources reflected in the changing species composition of fish and invertebrate life. Large rivers depend on fine particulate matter and dissolved organic matter as sources of energy and nutrients. River life is dominated by filter feeders and bottom-feeding fish.

### Estuaries (24.8)

Rivers eventually reach the sea. The place where the inflowing freshwater meets the incoming and outgoing tidal water is an estuary. The intermingling of freshwater and tides creates a nutrient trap exploited by estuarine life. The nature and distribution of estuarine life determined by salinity. As salinity declines from the estuary up through the river, so do marine species. An estuary serves as a nursery for many marine organisms, particularly a number of commercially important finfish and shellfish, for here the young are protected from predators and competing species unable to tolerate lower salinity.

## Open Ocean (24.9)

The marine environment is characterized by salinity, waves, tides, depth, and vastness. Like lakes, oceans experience both stratification of temperature (and other physical parameters), and stratification of the organisms that inhabit the differing vertical strata. The open sea can be divided into several vertical zones. The hadalpelagic zone includes areas found in the deep-sea trenches and canyons. The abyssopelagic zone extends from the sea floor to a depth of about 4000 m. Above is the bathypelagic, void of sunlight and inhabited by darkly pigmented animals possessing bioluminescence. Above that lies the dimly lit mesopelagic zone, inhabited by characteristic species, such as certain sharks and squid. Both the bathypelagic and mesopelagic depend on a rain of detrital material from the upper lighted zone, the epipelagic zone, for their energy.

## Ocean Life (24.10)

Phytoplankton dominate the surface waters. The littoral and neritic zones are richer in plankton than the open ocean. Tiny nanoplankton, which make up the largest biomass in temperate and tropical waters, are the major source of primary production. Feeding on phytoplankton are herbivorous zooplankters, especially copepods. They are preyed upon by carnivorous zooplankton. The greatest diversity of zooplankton, including larval forms of fish, occurs in the water over coastal shelves and upwellings; the least diversity occurs in the open ocean. Making up the larger life forms are free-swimming nekton, ranging from small fish to sharks and whales. Benthic organisms (those that live on the floor of the deep ocean) vary with depth and substrate. They are strictly heterotrophic and depend on organic matter that drifts to the bottom. They include filter feeders, collectors, deposit feeders, and predators.

## Hydrothermal Vents (24.11)

Along volcanic ridges are hydrothermal vents inhabited by unique and newly-discovered forms of life, including crabs, clams, and worms. Chemosynthetic bacteria that use sulfates as an energy source account for primary production in these hydrothermal vent communities.

## Coral Reefs (24.12)

Coral reefs are nutrient-rich oases in nutrient-poor tropical waters. They are complex ecosystems based on anthozoan coral and coralline algae. Their productive and varied habitats support a high diversity of invertebrate and vertebrate life.

## Ocean Productivity (24.13)

Primary productivity in marine environments is limited to regions where the availability of light and nutrients can support photosynthesis and plant growth. The areas of highest productivity are coastal regions and areas of upwelling. In open oceans, especially in tropical areas, productivity is low because the permanent nature of the thermocline slows the upward diffusion of nutrients. Primary productivity in temperate oceans is strongly related to seasonal variation in nutrient supply, driven by the seasonal dynamics of the thermocline.

## Study Questions

1. What distinguishes the littoral zone from the limnetic zone in a lake? What distinguishes the limnetic zone from the profundal zone?

2. What conditions distinguish the benthic zone from the other strata in lake ecosystems? What is the dominant role of the benthic zone?

3. Distinguish between oligotrophy, euthrophy, and dystrophy.

4. What physical characteristics are unique to flowing-water ecosystems? Contrast these conditions in a fast- and slow-flowing stream.

5. How do environmental conditions change along a river continuum?

6. What is an estuary?

7. Characterize the major life zones of the ocean, both vertical and horizontal.

8. How does temperature stratification in tropical seas differ from that of temperate regions of the ocean? How do these differences influence patterns of primary productivity?

9. What are hydrothermal vents, and what makes life around them unique?

10. What are coral reefs and how do they form?

## Further Readings

Allan, J. D. 1995. *Stream ecology: Structure and functioning of running waters.* Dordrect: Kluwer Academic Press. An extensive reference on the ecology of stream ecosystems.

Grassle, J. F. 1991. Deep-sea benthic diversity. *Bioscience* 41:464–469.

   An excellent and well-written introduction for those interested in the strange and wonderful world of the deep ocean.

Gross, M. G., and E. Gross. 1995. *Oceanography: A view of Earth,* 7th ed. Englewood Cliffs, NJ: Prentice-Hall.

   An excellent reference on the physical aspects of the sea.

Jackson, J. B. C. 1991. Adaptation and diversity of reef corals. *Bioscience* 41:475–482.

   This excellent review paper relates patterns of species distribution to life history and disturbance.

Nybakken, J. W. 2004. *Marine biology: An ecological approach,* 6th ed. Menlo Park, CA: Benjamin/Cummings.

   An excellent reference on marine life and ecosystems. Well written and illustrated.

Wetzel, R. G. 2001. *Limnology: Lake and river ecosystems,* 3rd ed. San Diego: Academic Press.

   An outstanding reference that provides an introduction to the ecology of freshwater ecosystems.

# Part Nine | Human Ecology

# Part Nine | Human Ecology

All organisms modify their environment, but perhaps no other organism has had as great an effect on Earth's environment as the human species. As the human population has grown and the power of our technology has expanded, the nature and scope of our modification of Earth's environment have changed dramatically. The story of our species is one of continuously redefining our relationship with the environment—a relationship based on energy.

With the melting of the polar ice cap from 40,000 to 10,000 years BP (before present) (see Section 18.9), the human species spread over the world's continents, with the Americas and Australia being the last to be inhabited some 25,000 to 10,000 years BP. At this time, the global population was approaching 5 million. Up until this point in human history, dependence on plants and animals for energy was the major constraint on human population growth. Hunter-gatherer societies consisted of small, autonomous bands of a few hundred individuals that were dependent on the productivity and abundance of plants and animals that make up natural ecosystems and the ability of the societies to extract and use those natural resources. They were nomadic people, tracking their resource in space and time, vulnerable to environmental change. Yet by 10,000 years BP, a change was to take place that would begin an era redefining the relationship between humans and their environment—the establishment of agriculture.

The Neolithic Period (8000–5000 BC) saw the development of agriculture—the cultivation of plants and the domestication of animals. Although the shift from hunter-gatherer to agriculture did not change the dependence of humans on primary productivity as the dominant source of energy, it shifted the dependency from the productivity of natural ecosystems to that of managed agricultural systems. The result was an increase in the quantity and predictability of food resources and with this the development of permanent villages, division of labor, and the rise of a new social structure.

Although the transition from hunter-gatherer to agricultural society greatly eased the constraints imposed by the environment on the human carrying capacity, the continued dependence on plants and animals as the sole source of energy still set an upper limit on the productivity of human activities. In a burst of effort, the human body can muster 100 watts of power (1 Joule per second = 1 watt). The most that any society could devote to a given task with humans or animals as the primary source of energy was a few hundred thousand watts. Expanding territory could increase the energy supply, but it could not raise the total that could be applied to a single task. It is impossible to concentrate more than a few thousand bodies on a given project, be it construction or battle. But by the 18th century, the mechanical energy of animals and human labor upon which the human population relied was to be replaced by a much more concentrated form of energy: coal.

The Industrial Revolution that began in the mid-18th century was a time that saw the development of the steam engine, and with it a shift in labor from humans and draft animals to machines. First developed in the late 17th century, the steam engine transformed the heat energy of steam into mechanical energy. At first, steam engines were inefficient, losing more than 99 percent of their energy. By 1800, however, their efficiency rose to about 5 percent with the capacity of 20 kilowatts of power in a single engine (the equivalent of 200 persons). By 1900, engines were capable of handling high-pressure steam, and engines became 30 times more powerful than those of 1800 (the equivalent of 6000 persons). As important as the power they provided was the fact that steam engines could be put anywhere (ships and trains), allowing for the large-scale transport of coal and establishing a positive feedback—industrialization.

With mechanization, manufacturing that was once carried out in individual homes and small workshops became centralized in factories. By the latter part of the 19th century, mechanization was changing the nature of agriculture as well. The size of fields increased, and there was a dramatic reduction in the amount of land dedicated to farm animals. Machines more efficiently accomplished work that had been done by the labor of humans and draft animals. A single large farm tractor (150–200 hp) can accomplish the work of more than 1000 workers or 200 draft animals. As a result of mechanization, by 1980, each American farmer fed about 80 people.

The mechanization of farming shifted the labor force, reducing the need for farm labor, and providing the work force needed for industrialization. In 1920, half the U.S. population was involved in the farm labor force; by 1990, the proportion had declined to 2–3 percent. In the 20th century, a transition had occurred from a rural agricultural-based to an urban industrial-based economy and with it a major shift in the distribution of the human population. At the beginning of the 20th century, just over 35 percent of the human population lived in urban areas, but as we entered the 21st century, that number had risen to almost 80 percent and continues to grow. Growing urbanization requires an ever-increasing infrastructure of transportation and trade and with it an increasing demand for energy. By the 1990s, the average global citizen deployed about 20 "human equivalents" in energy, primarily in the form of fossil

fuels, working 24 hours a day, 365 days a year—making economic and population growth possible.

This transformation of energy use has allowed industrial labor efficiency to increase about 200-fold between 1750 and 1990, so that modern workers produce as much in a week as their 18th century counterparts did in 4 years. In the 20th century alone, global industrial output grew 40-fold.

During the past 10,000 years, the human race has managed to multiply by a factor of 1000 and at the same time dramatically increase the per capita use of resources. The human population now approaches 6.5 billion, and our collective "ecological footprint" on the planet continues to grow. Nearly 40 percent of the potential terrestrial net primary productivity of the planet is used directly, coopted or foregone because of human activity (see Ecological Issues: Human Appropriation of Net Primary Productivity, p. 442). We use more than 50 percent of all freshwater resources, of which 70 percent goes to assist in agricultural production. In all, our activities have transformed between 40 and 50 percent of the terrestrial surface to produce food, fuel, and fiber, and our transformations of the natural environment have led to the extinction of thousands of species.

Although profound, the changes that humans have brought about in our environment are not the product of thoughtless, malicious behavior on our part. They are in large part the result of meeting the needs of a growing human population. Until recent decades, little was understood about the extent of the impact of human activities on our environment. As recent as the 1970s, the mantra was "the solution to pollution is dilution." We had little appreciation of the long-term consequences of our collective actions.

Times have changed, and we are beginning to understand the consequences of our past and current activities. Human ecology is a new field within the broader discipline of ecology that focuses specifically on the interaction between humans and the environment. Like ecology itself, it is an interdisciplinary field that draws upon many disciplines within the sciences, as well as anthropology, sociology, and history. In Part Nine, we will explore three general topics that form the backbone of current environmental issues regarding human impacts on the environment: resource use and environmental sustainability (Chapter 27), the declining biological diversity of our planet (Chapter 28), and the potential for human activity to significantly change Earth's climate (Chapter 29).

# Chapter 27 | Population Growth, Resource Use, and Sustainability

The human population entered the 20th century with 1.6 billion people and left the century with 6.1 billion. Demographers estimate that this number could rise to more than 9 billion in the next 50 years.

In 1890, the superintendent of the U.S. Bureau of Census announced that the frontier was closed. No longer was there a vast expanse of unsettled land waiting to be tamed. Up until that time, if you drew a map of where people were and were not living in the United States there was a very clear demarcation between the two. But by 1890, there was no longer a visible frontier line on the demographic maps that the Census was producing. From 1790 on, that line had been moving steadily westward. Thomas Jefferson had speculated that to fill the vast open spaces of America it would take a hundred generations. It took approximately 80 years.

The bland factual statement that "the frontier was closed" carried immense symbolic meaning, for it suggested to a generation of Americans that the process of exploiting inexhaustible resources had come to an end. In 1890, the year that the Census Bureau declared the frontier closed, the population of the United States was approximately 63 million. Since that time, the U.S. population has increased almost fivefold to 300 million, and the demand for resources has grown disproportionately with advancements in technology and economic growth. The frontier may have closed, but the exploitation of natural resources continued at a quickening pace.

Over that same period, the global population has increased sixfold, with our current population approaching 6.5 billion and with it the need to exploit natural resources to meet the basic human needs of food, water, and shelter. The consumption of resources is driven by two factors: the total number of individuals (population size) and the per capita rate of consumption. Both of these have continued to increase steadily over the past half century (Figure 27.1).

The growing human population and the desire for expanded economic growth within the world community have brought the issue of sustainability to the forefront of current economic, political, and environmental discussions. Although the term *environmental sustainability* is broad, covering a range of topics and activities including population growth, energy use, and economic development, most discussions of environmental sustainability focus on the use of *natural capital*. **Natural capital** is the range of natural resources provided by ecosystems, such as the air, water, soil, nutrients, forests, grasslands, and so forth, that are drawn on by humans as essential resources. By its very definition, environmental sustainability relates to the exploitation of natural ecosystems by human populations. It is the ability to sustain the exploitation of natural capital to meet the growing human needs.

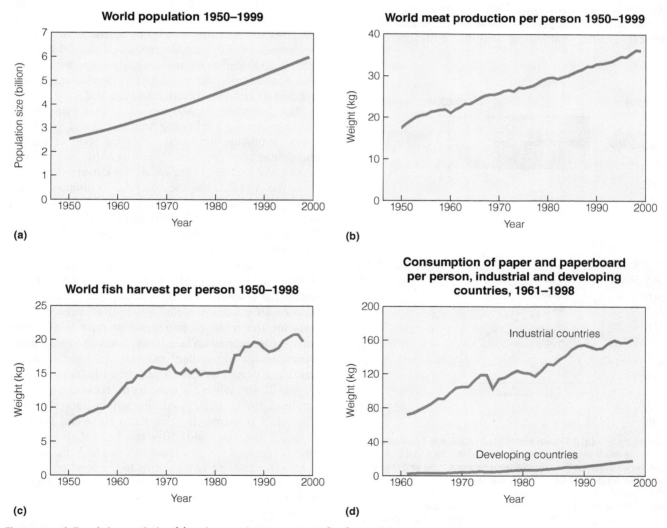

**Figure 27.1** | Trends in population **(a)** and per capita resource use **(b–d)** over the past 50 years. (Source: Census Bureau and FAO.)

In this chapter, we will examine the concept of environmental sustainability as it relates to the human activities of agriculture, forestry, and fisheries. All three of these activities involve the exploitation of populations, plant and animal, to provide the most essential of human resources: food and shelter. We will examine the basic environmental issues related to these activities of resource management and extraction and how these issues relate to the ecological processes and patterns we have discussed thus far.

## 27.1 | Sustainable Resource Use Is a Balance Between Supply and Demand

Sustainability is an idea that is fraught with ambiguity. It is widely used as a concept but rarely is a quantitative definition provided. The origins of the concept of environmental sustainability appear to lie in the concept of sustainable yield that appeared in German forestry during the late 18th and early 19th centuries. The concept is one of matching periodic harvests to the rate of biological growth; harvesting without diminishing the

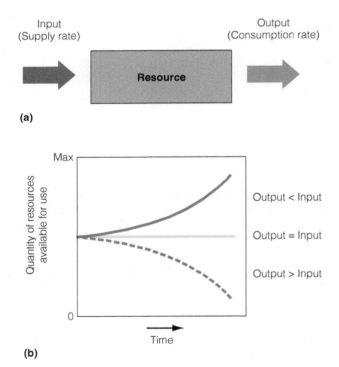

**(a)**

**(b)**

**Figure 27.2** | **(a)** A simple model of resource use. The amount of resource available at any time (green box) will be a function of the difference between the rate of supply (green arrow) and the rate of consumption (red arrow). **(b)** If the rate of consumption is less than the rate of supply, the amount of resource will increase. If the rate of consumption exceeds the rate of supply, the amount of resources available will decline. Sustainable resource use depends on the rate of consumption not exceeding the rate of supply.

forests themselves or undermining their long-term ability to regenerate.

In its simplest form, the constraint on sustainable resource use is one of supply and demand. In the graphic presented in Figure 27.2, the box represents the quantity of a resource that is being exploited; for example, water, trees, or fish. The arrow leading into the box represents the rate at which the resource is being supplied—the rate of recharge of a lake or reservoir, the rate of tree growth in a forest or plantation, or the rate of population growth of the target fish species. The arrow going out of the box represents the rate at which the resource is being harvested—the rate of water use, the harvest rate of trees, or the rate at which fish are being caught. Simply put, for the exploitation of the resource to be sustainable, the rate at which the resource is being used (consumption or harvest rate) must not exceed the rate at which the resource is being supplied (replacement or regeneration rate). Otherwise, the quantity of resources declines through time.

The graphic presented in Figure 27.3 illustrates this simple principle as it applies to the sustainable use of water resources of the Aral Sea in central Asia. In 1963, the surface of the Aral Sea measured 66,100 km². By 1987, 27,000 km² of former sea bottom had become dry land. About 60 percent of the Aral Sea's volume had been lost, and its salt concentration had doubled.

The demise of the Aral Sea was caused primarily by the diversion of the inflowing Amu Dar'ya and Syr Dar'ya rivers to provide irrigation water for local croplands. These diversions dramatically reduced the river inflows, causing the Aral Sea to shrink. At the current rate of decline, the Aral Sea has the potential to disappear completely by 2020. Using the simple model presented in Figure 27.2, the rate of harvest exceeded the rate of supply, and the consequence is a continuous decline in the resource—an example of nonsustainable resource use.

Unlike the example of the Aral Sea, where there is a continuous harvest of the water resources for irrigation, other resources can only be harvested periodically because an extended period is required between harvests for the resource to regenerate to a level where harvest can once again take place. Trees in a forest plantation provide an excellent example. After seedlings are planted, a period of time is required for trees to grow (Figure 27.4a). When the biomass of trees reaches a certain level, the forest or plantation will be harvested. The amount of resource (tree biomass) harvested per unit time is called the **yield.** After the harvest, a period of time is required for new trees to grow and the amount of resource to once again return to the level of the previous harvest. This period of time is called the **rotation period** (or **harvest interval**). If the objective is to ensure a similar yield at each harvest, termed **sustained yield,** then a sufficient amount of time must be allowed be-

Figure 27.3 | **(a)** The Aral Sea in central Asia provides an example of unsustainable resource use. **(b)** The graphic shows changes in the extent of the Aral Sea from 1960 to 2002. Because of waters diverted for irrigation, the Aral Sea decreased in volume by 60 percent between 1963 and 1987. At the current rate of decline, it has the potential to disappear completely by 2020.

**(a)**

North
Aral
Sea

Aral Sea

South
Aral
Sea

1960          1999          2002

**(b)**

tween harvests (the rotation period) for the resource to recover to preharvest levels. If the rotation period is not sufficient to allow the forest stand to recover to preharvest levels, then the yield will diminish in successive harvests (Figure 27.4b). As we will see in our discussion of agriculture, forestry, and fisheries in the following sections, maintaining a sustainable yield is where many of the conflicts in the long-term sustainable use of resources occur.

An assumption of this simple model of sustainable resource use is that the resource is renewable—it is able to resupply or regenerate. If the resource is nonrenewable, then by definition its use is not sustainable, and the rate of resource decline is a function of the rate at which the

resource is being harvested and used. Mineral resources (such as aluminum, zinc, copper, etc.) are an example of nonrenewable resources. Often, however, resources are classified as nonrenewable even though they are being resupplied, because the rate at which they are being resupplied is virtually nonexistent compared to the rate at which they are being consumed. Fossil fuels are a good example. Coal, oil, and natural gas are referred to as nonrenewable energy sources because their formation occurs on a timescale of millions of years (see Chapter 29), making their rate of resupply effectively zero on the timescale of human consumption.

Unlike fossil fuel energy, many nonrenewable resources can be recycled, reducing the rate at which the

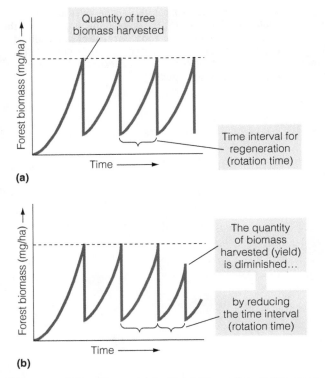

**Figure 27.4** | To achieve sustainable yield, a sufficient time must be allowed between harvests (rotation time) for biomass to return to preharvest levels. Rotation time will depend on the growth rate of the species and site conditions that influence forest productivity. (b) If the rotation time is reduced, sufficient time is not allowed for the forest stand to recover (grow) to preharvest levels, and the subsequent yield will decline. The result is that the rate of harvest exceeds the rate of resource regeneration (as shown in Figure 27.2), and the quantity of resource declines through time.

initial resource is harvested. The effect of recycling is to extend the effective lifetime of the resource.

## 27.2 | Sustainability Can Be Indirectly Limited by Adverse Consequences of Resource Use

**Ecosystem services** are the processes by which the environment produces resources (natural capital) such as clean air, water, timber, or fish. Although the rate at which ecosystems supply these essential resources functions as a fundamental constraint on sustainable use, sustainable use can also be constrained indirectly as a consequence of negative impacts on ecosystem services that arise from resource management, extraction, or use. A prime example is waste (unused or unwanted materials). Domestic, industrial, and agricultural waste is a growing environmental issue with implication to both

ecosystem and human health. Wastes and by-products of production often contaminate the environment (air, water, and soil) with harmful substances—pollution (see Chapter 21), which can function to limit or disrupt the ability of ecosystems to provide essential resources and services.

Return to the example of the Aral Sea (see Figure 27.3). Today, about 200,000 metric tons of salt and sand are carried by the wind from the Aral Sea region every day and dumped within a 300-km radius. The salt pollution is decreasing the area available for agriculture, destroying pastures, and creating a shortage of forage for domestic animals. Fishing in the Aral Sea has ceased completely, shipping and other water-related activities have declined, and the associated economic changes have taken a heavy toll on agricultural production. The quality of drinking water has continued to decline due to increasing salinity, bacteriological contamination, and the presence of pesticides and heavy metals. Diseases like anemia, cancer, and tuberculosis and the presence of allergies are on the rise. The incidence of typhoid fever, viral hepatitis, tuberculosis, and throat cancer is three times the national average in some areas.

In our discussion of sustainable resource use in the following sections, we will focus on both the ability to sustain current and future levels of resource yield (the topic of sustainable yield), as well as the negative impacts that arise from the management, extraction, and use of resources, impacts that may affect the ability of the ecosystem to continue to provide those natural resources (ecosystem services). In evaluating questions of sustainability, we must focus on not only the ability to sustain current and future rates of resource consumption but also the consequences of managing and consuming those resources for both environmental and human well-being.

## 27.3 | Sustainability Is a Concept Learned from Natural Ecosystems

When we attempt to manage and harvest natural resources in a sustainable fashion, in many ways we are attempting to mimic the function of natural ecosystems. Natural ecosystems function as sustainable units. This should be clear from our discussion of ecosystems in Chapters 20 and 21. Take as an example the link between primary productivity and decomposition. The uptake of nutrients such as nitrogen by plants is constrained by the rate at which they become available in the soil (see Figure 6.25). In effect, the rate of nutrient harvest by plants, and the subsequent rate of primary productivity within an ecosystem, are constrained by and cannot exceed the rate at which nutrients are being supplied to the soil (see Section 20.3). In turn, nutrients tied-up in organic matter are recycled through the processes of microbial decomposition and mineralization (see Section 21.5). As nutrients are mineralized and returned to the soil they are quickly taken up by plants, minimizing their loss through ground and surface waters (see Section 21.7).

To put the functioning of natural ecosystems into the context of the simple graphical model presented in Figure 27.2, the rate of resource use is limited by the resource supply rate. In the case of mineral nutrients such as nitrogen, the rate at which the resource is used is equivalent to the rate at which it is supplied (regenerated), so the size of the box representing the pool of available resources is effectively zero.

When the supply rate of a resource varies through time, the rate of resource use must likewise change. During years of drought, net primary productivity of an ecosystem will decline. If sufficient water is not available to replace water lost through transpiration, stomata will close, leaves will wilt, and potentially the plants could die. Although water stored in the soil may postpone the effects of drought, plant growth and productivity are generally tied closely to annual rates of precipitation (water availability). As we will see in the following discussions of agriculture and forestry, variations in the supply rate of resources necessary to maintain primary productivity are a major constraint on maintaining sustainable yield, and overcoming these constraints is the major source of problems related to sustainable agriculture and forestry.

## 27.4 | Agricultural Practices Vary in the Level of Energy Input

Although the exploitation and management of natural populations provides more than 80 percent of fish and shellfish harvested globally on an annual basis, the vast majority of human food resources are derived from agriculture—the production of crops and the grazing of livestock. Even though botanists estimate that, worldwide, there are as many as 30,000 native plant species with parts (seeds, roots, leaves, fruits, etc.) that can be consumed by humans, only 15 plant and 8 animal species produce 90 percent of our food supply. The seeds of only three annual grasses—wheat, rice, and corn (maize)—constitute more than 80 percent of the cereal crops consumed by the world population. Although initially derived from native plant species, the varieties of the cereal crops that are cultivated today are the products of intensive selective breeding and genetic modification by plant and agricultural scientists around the world. The same is true for domestic animals used for food production.

Approximately 11 percent of Earth's ice-free land area is under cultivation. Another 25 percent is used as pasture land for grazing livestock (primarily cattle and sheep). No matter what the crop planted or method of cultivation used, agriculture involves replacing diverse natural ecosystems—grassland, forest, shrublands—with a community consisting of a single crop species (**monoculture**) or a mixture of crops (**polyculture**). Although a wide range of agricultural practices are carried out throughout the world, agricultural production can be classified into one of two broad categories: industrialized and traditional.

Industrialized (also termed *mechanized* or *high-input*) agriculture is dependent on large inputs of energy in the form of fossil fuels (mechanization), chemical fertilizers, irrigation systems, and pesticides. Although energy demanding, this form of agriculture produces large quantities of crops and livestock per unit of land area. Industrialized agriculture is practiced on about 25 percent of all cropland, primarily in developed countries; however, these practices have spread to developing regions in recent decades.

Traditional agriculture is dominated by subsistence agriculture in which primarily human labor and draft animals are used to produce only enough crops or livestock for a family to survive. Examples of this low-input approach to agriculture are shifting cultivation in tropical forests and nomadic livestock herding.

In reality, these two forms of agricultural production, industrialized and traditional, define two points on a continuum of agricultural methods that are practiced throughout the world. However, we will use these two end points for the purpose of comparison in our discussion of sustainability of agricultural practices.

## 27.5 | Swidden Agriculture Represents a Dominant Form of Agriculture in the Wet Tropics

A method of subsistence farming that is practiced primarily in the tropical forested regions is shifting cultivation, or **swidden agriculture.** This method of traditional agriculture involves a rotating cultivation technique in which trees are first cut down and burned in order to clear land for planting (Figure 27.5). The burning of felled trees and brush serves two purposes. First, it removes debris, thus clearing the land for planting and ensuring that the plot is relatively free of weeds. Second, the resulting ash is high in mineral nutrients (see Researcher Profile: Deborah Lawrence), promoting plant growth (Figure 27.6). The plot is then cultivated and crops are harvested. A characteristic of this type of agriculture is a decline in productivity with each successive

Figure 27.5 | In swidden agriculture, a plot of forest is cleared and burned to allow for crops to be planted. The ashes provide an important source of nutrients. Fertilizers are typically not used.

crop (Figure 27.7). The reason for this decline is that each time crops are harvested, nutrients in the form of plant tissues are being removed from the plot. Because even organic fertilizers are rarely used in this form of agriculture, soil nutrients decline, and eventually the site is abandoned.

After abandonment, secondary succession occurs, and if left undisturbed for a sufficient period of time, the nutrient status of the site will recover to precultivation levels (Figure 27.8). At this point, the site can once again be cleared and planted. In the meantime, other areas have been cleared, burnt, and planted. So in effect, this type of agriculture represents a shifting patchwork of plots in various stages of cultivation and recovery (Figure 27.9).

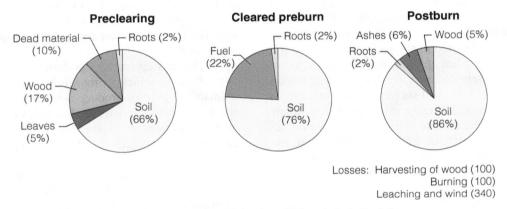

Figure 27.6 | Dynamics of total nitrogen during the burning and clearing of a forest site in Turrialba, Costa Rica (values in kg N/ha). (Adapted from Ewel et al. 1981.)

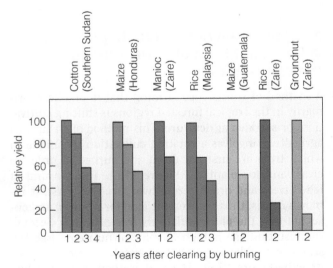

Figure 27.7 | Patterns of declining productivity in successive years in swidden agricultural systems for a variety of crops in different regions of the tropics.

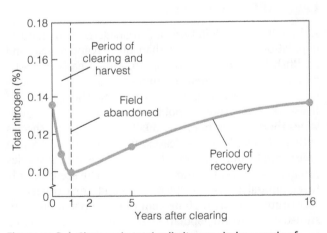

Figure 27.8 | Changes in total soil nitrogen during a cycle of clearing, harvest, abandonment, and recovery for a swidden agricultural system in Costa Rica (Central America). Note that nitrogen levels decline until the plot is abandoned after the first year. Soil nitrogen recovers to original levels by year 16. (Adapted from Ewel et al. 1981.)

**Figure 27.9** | Sequence of areas used for swidden agriculture in the Yucatan region of Mexico. The area in the foreground has recently been cleared for planting. The area directly behind it has been abandoned for a year (one year fallow), and the forest in the background has been in the stage of regeneration for several years.

Although the swidden cultivation system represents a sustainable form of agriculture when time is permitted for regrowth of natural vegetation and the recovery of soil nutrients, it requires a sufficient area of land to allow for the appropriate period of rotation. The problem currently being faced in many parts of the tropics is that growing populations are placing an ever-increasing demand on the land, and sufficient periods of recovery are not always possible. In this case, the land is quickly degraded, and yield progressively declines.

## 27.6 | Industrialized Agriculture Dominates the Temperate Zone

Industrialized agriculture is widely practiced in North America, much of Europe, Russia, sections of South America, Australia, and other areas of the world where money and land are available to support this form of agriculture. Machines and fossil fuel energy replace the energy supplied by humans and draft animals in traditional agricultural systems (Figure 27.10). Mechanization requires large expanses of land for machines to operate effectively and economically. Because different

crops (wheat, corn, cotton, etc.) require specialized equipment for planting and harvest, farmers typically plant one (monoculture) or few crop varieties season after season (continuous rotation).

With crops such as wheat and corn, most (or all) parts of the plants are removed, so little or no organic matter remains after harvest. As a consequence, at each harvest large quantities of nutrients are removed from the site in the plant materials (Table 27.1). In addition, tilling the soil to prepare for planting exposes the soil to wind and water erosion, and conventional tilling practices result in annual soil losses upward of 44 tons per hectare (Figure 27.11).

As a result of the removal of organic matter, there is effectively no nutrient cycle in these agricultural ecosystems. Instead, large quantities of chemical fertilizers must be added to maintain productivity. Nutrients are added to the soil in an inorganic (mineral) form that is readily available for uptake by plants; however, the nutrients are also readily leached to surface and groundwater (Table 27.2).

Because the same crop varieties are being planted over large, contiguous regions, pests and plant diseases spread readily. Pests are typically controlled by chemical

**(a)**

**(b)**

Figure 27.10 | Examples of traditional **(a)** and mechanized (industrial) **(b)** agriculture. In industrial agriculture, machines have replaced humans and draft animals as the source of labor (energy).

| Table 27.1 | Approximate Amounts of Nutrient Elements Contained in Various Crops (Values in kg/ha) | | | | | |
|---|---|---|---|---|---|---|
| Crop | Yield | N | P | K | Ca | Mg |
| Corn | | | | | | |
| Grain | 9416 | 151 | 26 | 37 | 18 | 22 |
| Stover | 10,080 | 112 | 18 | 135 | 31 | 19 |
| Rice | | | | | | |
| Grain | 5380 | 56 | 10 | 9 | 3 | 4 |
| Straw | 5610 | 34 | 6 | 65 | 10 | 6 |
| Wheat | | | | | | |
| Grain | 2690 | 56 | 12 | 15 | 1 | 7 |
| Straw | 3360 | 22 | 3 | 33 | 7 | 3 |
| Loblolly pine (22 yr) | 84,000 | 135 | 11 | 64 | 85 | 23 |
| Loblolly pine (60 yr) | 234,000 | 344 | 31 | 231 | 513 | 80 |

means to avoid reduction in productivity (see Ecological Issues: Insect Wars). Different chemical pesticides target different pests: insecticides (insects), herbicides (weedy herbaceous plants), fungicides (fungi), and rodenticides (rodents). These chemicals bring with them a range of environmental problems.

Figure 27.11 | A field that has recently been tilled. Note the lack of any ground cover. Fields such as this have a high rate of erosion from water and wind.

## 27.7 | Different Agricultural Methods Represent a Trade-off Between Sustainability and Productivity

The two very different agricultural systems discussed above—traditional (swidden) and industrialized—represent a trade-off between energy input in production and energy harvest in food resources. Table 27.3 presents a summary of energy inputs and yields for corn production in Mexico using traditional swidden agriculture and in the United States using large-scale, industrial-farming techniques. Energy inputs in the traditional agricultural system are dominated by labor (approximately 92% of

total energy input), with small inputs in the form of tools and seed. Total crop yield is just over 1900 kg/ha. In contrast, labor is only a minor proportion of total energy input in the industrialized agricultural system (approximately 0.05%). The major inputs are in the form of farm machinery (3.2%), fossil fuels (4%), irrigation (7.1%), chemical fertilizers (13.6%), and pesticides (3.5%). Total crop yield in this agricultural system is 7000 kg/ha, more than 3.5 times that produced by the traditional agricultural methods used in Mexico. However, the real story

| Table 27.2 | Nutrient Inputs in Precipitation and Fertilizers for a Corn Field in the Central United States (Values in kg/ha/yr) | | | |
|---|---|---|---|---|
| | In Precipitation | Fertilizer | Harvest | Runoff to Streams |
| Nitrogen | 11.0 | 160.0 | 60.0 | 35.0 |
| Calcium | 3.2 | 190.0 | 1.0 | 47.0 |
| Phosphorus | 0.03 | 30.0 | 12.0 | 3.0 |
| Potassium | 0.2 | 75.0 | 13.0 | 15.0 |

Soil loss due to erosion: 44 t/ha/yr

| Table 27.3 | Comparison of Energy Inputs in Production and Energy Yields in Corn Harvested for Traditional Agricultural System in Mexico and Industrial Agricultural Production System in the United States | |
|---|---|---|
| Item | Mexico (kcal/ha) | USA (kcal/ha) |
| *Inputs* | | |
| Labor | 589,160 | 5250 |
| Axe and hoe | 16,570 | |
| Machinery | | 1,018,000 |
| Gasoline | | 400,000 |
| Diesel | | 855,000 |
| Irrigation | | 2,250,000 |
| Electricity | | 100,000 |
| Nitrogen | | 3,192,000 |
| Phosphorus | | 730,000 |
| Potassium | | 240,000 |
| Lime | | 134,000 |
| Seeds | 36,608 | 520,000 |
| Insecticides | | 300,000 |
| Herbicides | | 800,000 |
| Drying | | 660,000 |
| Transportation | | 89,000 |
| Total | 642,338 | 11,036,650 |
| *Outputs* | | |
| Total Corn Yield | 1944 kg | 7000 kg |
| | 8,748,000 kcal | 31,500,000 kcal |
| kcal output/kcal input | 13.62 | 2.85 |

emerges when we look at the ratio of energy input in production to energy produced in harvested food. The ratio of kcal output (food) to kcal energy input (energy involved in production) is 13.6 for the traditional agriculture while only 2.8 for the industrialized system of production. Although industrialized agriculture produces 3.5 times the yield of corn per unit of land area under cultivation, it does so at the cost of more than 17 times the energy input for production. In addition, this large input of energy is in the form of materials and services that carry with them a large environmental cost.

The loss of chemical fertilizers such as nitrates and phosphates from agricultural fields to adjacent streams, lakes, and coastal waters (estuaries and wetlands) has led to nutrient enrichment. This accelerated enrichment causes chemical and environmental changes that result in major shifts in plant and animal life, a process termed **cultural eutrophication** (see Section 24.4).

In addition to the impacts on adjacent natural ecosystems, the widespread use of chemical fertilizers has impacts on human health. Groundwater provides drinking water for more than one-half of the U.S. population and is the sole source of drinking water for many rural communities. Nitrate (from chemical fertilizers) is one of the most common groundwater contaminants in rural areas. Recent U.S. Environmental Protection Agency (EPA) surveys indicate that 1.2 percent of community water systems and 2.4 percent of rural domestic wells nationwide contain concentrations of nitrate that exceed public health standards. Although this value may seem low, contamination of groundwater is concentrated in agricultural areas, such as the Midwest, where the percentage of wells contaminated is much higher (Figure 27.12). High concentrations of nitrate in drinking water may cause birth defects, cancer, nervous system impairments, and "blue baby syndrome," a condition in which the oxygen content in the infant's blood falls to dangerously low levels. In addition, high concentration of nitrate can indicate the possible presence of other more serious residential or agricultural contaminants, such as bacteria or pesticides.

In addition to the environmental problems caused by the widespread use of chemical fertilizers and pesticides, the large inputs of fossil fuels used for mechanization, irrigation, and the production of chemical fertilizers add to the growing input of carbon dioxide and other greenhouse gases to the atmosphere (see Chapter 29).

Upon first inspection, it may appear that the solution to sustainable agriculture is the adoption of more traditional agricultural practices, such as those used in swidden agriculture. However, agricultural production must be viewed in the context of the growing human population. Increasing agricultural production to meet the growing human demand can be accomplished in two ways: increasing the land under cultivation or increasing the production of food per unit land area. Historically, the total land under cultivation worldwide has risen exponentially, keeping pace with the growing human population. However, in the last half of the 20th century, this trend has begun to slow (Figure 27.13a), and the per

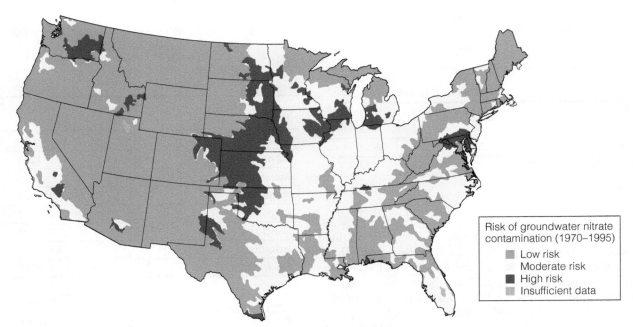

**Figure 27.12** | A national risk map designed to present patterns of risk for nitrate contamination at large regional or national scales. It was produced using an overlay analysis in a geographic information system. Knowing where and what type of risks to groundwater exist can alert water-resource managers and private users of the need to protect water supplies. By targeting regions with the highest risk of nitrate contamination, resources can be directed to areas most likely to benefit from pollution-prevention programs and long-term monitoring.

capita land area under production has declined (Figure 27.13b). This decline is due in part to the development of more productive varieties of crops and an expansion of the use of irrigation, but by far the largest factor responsible for the increased productivity per unit land is the growing use of chemical fertilizers, particularly nitrogen (Figure 27.13c). Synthetic nitrogen fertilizer now supplies about half of the nitrogen used annually by the world's crops. At least one-third of the protein in the current global food supply is derived from the synthesis of ammonia ($NH_3$) from hydrogen and nitrogen using the Haber–Bosch process, named after the two engineers, Fritz Haber and Carl Bosch, who would later win the Nobel Prize for developing this process of synthesizing ammonia for use in chemical fertilizers (see Ecological Issues: Nitrogen Fertilizers, Chapter 21, p. 464).

So the reality of our situation is that we are dependent on industrialized agriculture to feed the world's growing population. In addition, by slowing the amount of land being cleared for agricultural production, we are reducing the single greatest cause of Earth's declining biological diversity—habitat loss primarily due to the conversion of lands for agriculture (see Chapter 28). The task has now become one of developing methods of large-scale mechanized agriculture that minimize environmental impacts.

## 27.8 | Sustainable Agriculture Depends on a Variety of Methods

As with the broader concept of environmental sustainability, the term **sustainable agriculture** refers more to a notion of maintaining agriculture production while minimizing environmental impacts rather than to a quantitative set of criteria. As it pertains to agriculture, *sustainable* describes farming systems that are capable of maintaining their productivity and usefulness to society while at the same time conserving resources and minimizing the negative impacts that we have discussed above.

Today, sustainable farming techniques commonly include a variety of practices designed to reduce soil erosion, reduce the use of chemical fertilizers and pesticides, and conserve and protect the quality of water resources. The following are examples of these practices:

*Soil conservation methods*: Methods such as contour and strip cropping (Figure 27.14a) and reduced tillage or "no-till" farming (Figure 27.14b) help prevent loss of soil due to wind and water erosion. Likewise, planting shrubs and trees as fencerows provides wind barriers, thus reducing soil erosion.

**World grain area harvested 1950–1996**

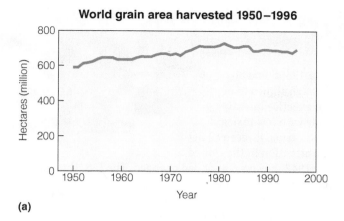

**(a)**

**World grain area harvested per capita 1950–1996**

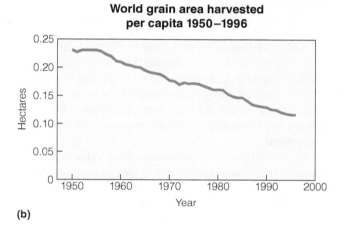

**(b)**

**Nitrogen fertilizer use**

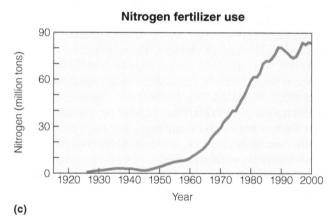

**(c)**

**Figure 27.13** | The global total of land in crop production **(a)** has begun to stabilize in recent decades, while the per capita area harvested **(b)** has actually declined. This decline is due to an increase in productivity per hectare, largely as a function of increasing use of chemical fertilizers (primarily nitrogen) over the same period **(c)**. (Source: FAO.)

*Reduction in the use of pesticides*: Crop rotations (such as planting wheat one season and hay the next) and strip cropping with multiple crops or varieties reduce the spread of pests and disease.

**(a)**

**(b)**

**Figure 27.14** | Among the methods being adopted as part of an effort to promote sustainable agricultural practices are **(a)** contour and **(b)** no-till farming. Go to ɢʀᴀᴘʜɪᴛ! at **www.ecologyplace.com** to graph food production efficiency.

*Alternative sources of soil nutrients*: Increased use of on-farm nutrient sources, such as manure and leguminous cover crops (see Section 15.10), provide alternatives to chemical fertilizers.

*Water conservation and protection*: Water conservation has become an important part of agricultural stewardship. Many practices have been developed to improve the quality of drinking and surface water, as well as to protect wetlands. Wetlands play a key role in filtering nutrients and pesticides, in addition to providing wildlife habitat (see Chapter 25).

To most of us, picking up a can of insect spray to zap a pesky mosquito or fly does not conjure up images of war, but, in his recent book, *War and Nature*, environmental historian Edmund Russell of the University of Virginia does just that. In the book, Russell investigates the interwoven history of the U.S. Army's Chemical Warfare Service and pest control efforts during the first half of the 20th century.

When we think of the casualties of war, we naturally think of weapons of destruction—guns and bombs. Yet by creating troop concentrations, food shortages, exhaustion, and poor sanitation, war throughout history has resulted in the outbreak of disease epidemics, creating both public health and military problems. World War I saw some of its worst casualties from typhus. Typhus broke out in Siberia in November 1914 and spread through both troops and refugees. The epidemic killed more than 150,000 people in less than 6 months. During World War II, louse-borne typhus was a serious problem for American troops on both the European and Pacific Fronts, and in the early years of World War II in the Pacific, malaria caused 8 to 10 times more American casualties than did enemy soldiers.

As part of a program to combat the spread of typhus, the military used both aerosol bombs (compressed insecticide in a metal container) and louse powder to combat lice; however, both used pyrethrum as the active ingredient. Ground from the petals of several species of chrysanthemum, pyrethrum achieved prominence as "insect powder" before 1800. First produced in Persia (Iran), then Dallmatia (part of Austria-Hungary at the time), its major importer was France in the 18th and 19th centuries. Because flowers were picked by hand, the production of pyrethrum was concentrated in areas where labor was cheap. During World War II, naval warfare had virtually halted the export of pyrethrum, and the need for a substitute was urgent.

A Swiss chemist, Paul Muller, first developed DDT [1,1,1-trichloro-2, 2-bis-(p-chlorophenyl)ethane] in the late 1930s, and although shown to be an effective insecticide with low toxicity to humans, it received little attention in the United States.

By 1942, however, a lot had changed. The U.S. Bureau of Entomology was given some reports from the Swiss company for which Muller worked, and tests of DDT were undertaken by various government agencies. DDT powder was found to kill lice for four times longer than pyrethrum powder, and when sprayed on walls of buildings, DDT killed adult mosquitoes for months. As a synthetic, DDT could be manufactured in the United States. DDT provided the solution that the military needed, and large-scale production of DDT was begun. The army was able to start spraying DDT around the world as soon as the chemical arrived in combat theaters, using the already deployed chemical warfare equipment.

Organizationally, war stimulated the creation, growth, and linkage of military and civilian institutions devoted to pest control and chemical warfare, accelerating development in both spheres. Scientifically and technologically, pest control and chemical warfare each created knowledge and tools that the other used to meet its goals. During the mid-1930s, for example, the German chemist I. G. Farben developed a new class of insecticides called organophosphates. Although extremely effective, several of these compounds were lethal to humans as well as insects. Undesirable as an insecticide, this attribute was valuable as a potential chemical weapon. One of these compounds, later named tabun, was the first organophosphate nerve gas. So in creating a new class of insecticides, Farben had also created a new class of chemical weapons.

At home, DDT spraying inspired military and civilian researchers to link chemical warfare and pest control in new ways. By the mid–20th century the American chem-

## 27.9 | The Goal of Sustainable Forestry Is to Achieve a Balance Between Net Growth and Harvest

Forest ecosystems cover approximately 35 percent of Earth's surface (see Chapter 23) and provide a wealth of resources, including fuel, building materials, and food (Figure 27.15). Although plantations provide a growing percentage of forest resources, more than 90 percent of global forest resources are still harvested from native forests.

Globally, about half of the forest that was present under modern (post-Pleistocene) climatic conditions (see Section 18.9, Figure 18.20), and before the spread of human influence, has disappeared (see Figure 28.2), largely through the impact of human activities. The spread of agriculture and animal husbandry, the harvesting of forests for timber and fuel, and the expansion of

ical industry grew in size, expertise, profitability, and status. American scientists developed new chemicals to kill insect pests. Farmers applied more kinds of insecticides, in greater quantities, than ever before. Using surplus military planes piloted by veterans, crop dusting delivered DDT to farm fields.

Research on the application of classes of chemical compounds once used for war as insecticides moved the battlefield to the farm, and the enemy was the insect pest—redefining chemical warfare as pest control. Chemical companies capitalized on the expertise that had been developed and the capital that had been put in place as part of the war effort. At first, the rhetoric of World War II pervaded this transfer of military technology to civilian pest control (Figure 1), taking advantage of the role of insecticides (specifically DDT) as a "war hero."

Although an effective means of pest control, by the early 1960s the use of chemical pesticides such as DDT began to raise concerns when they were detected in the tissues of animals in regions far removed from any applied source of the insecticides. DDT sprayed on forests and croplands enters streams and lakes, where it is subject to further distribution and dilution as it moves downstream, eventually reaching the oceans. The major movement of pesticide residues takes place in the atmosphere. Not only does the atmosphere receive the bulk of the pesticide spray, but it also picks up the fractions volatized from soil, water, and vegetation.

The high solubility of DDT in lipids leads to its concentration through the food chain. Most of the DDT contained in ingested food is retained in the fatty tissue of consumers. Because it breaks down slowly, DDT accumulates to high and even toxic levels.

As the 20th century progressed, our perception of chemical warfare, both on the battlefield and farm, changed. In 1972, the U.S. government banned the domestic use of DDT, although production and distribution to other countries continue. International discussions to

**PENICK INSECTICIDAL BASES...**
*Super Ammunition for the Continued Battle of the Home Front*

Figure 1

ban the use of chemical weapons began that same year. It would take another 25 years (1997), however, before the Chemical Weapons Convention banning the development and use of chemical weapons was to take effect. ●

1. Based on the discussion of sustainability in Section 27.2, would you consider the use of chemical pesticides consistent with sustainable agriculture?

2. What alternatives to chemical pesticides exist for the control of plant and insect pests in agricultural systems (see Ecological Issues: Providing a Competitive Edge: Weed Control in Agriculture, p. 278)?

populated areas have all taken their toll on forests. The causes and timing of forest loss differ between regions and forest types, as do the current trends in change in forest cover. In the face of increasing demand and declining forest cover, the goal of sustained yield in forestry is to achieve a balance between net growth and harvest. To achieve this end, foresters have an array of silvicultural and harvesting techniques from clear-cutting to selection cutting.

**Clear-cutting** involves removal of the forest and reversion to an early stage of succession (Figure 27.16a). The area harvested can range from thousands of hectares to small patch cuts of a few hectares designed to create habitat for wildlife species that require an opening within the forest (see Sections 19.2 and 19.3). Postharvest management varies widely for areas that are clear-cut. When natural forest stands are clear-cut, there is generally no follow-up management. Stands are left to

**Figure 27.15** | A variety of products derived from forests.

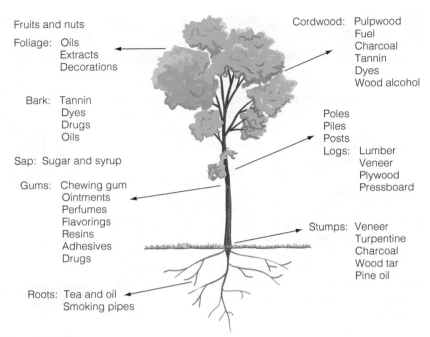

Fruits and nuts

Foliage: Oils
　　　　Extracts
　　　　Decorations

Bark: Tannin
　　　Dyes
　　　Drugs
　　　Oils

Sap: Sugar and syrup

Gums: Chewing gum
　　　Ointments
　　　Perfumes
　　　Flavorings
　　　Resins
　　　Adhesives
　　　Drugs

Roots: Tea and oil
　　　Smoking pipes

Cordwood: Pulpwood
　　　　　Fuel
　　　　　Charcoal
　　　　　Tannin
　　　　　Dyes
　　　　　Wood alcohol

Poles
Piles
Posts

Logs: Lumber
　　　Veneer
　　　Plywood
　　　Pressboard

Stumps: Veneer
　　　　Turpentine
　　　　Charcoal
　　　　Wood tar
　　　　Pine oil

(a)

(b)

**Figure 27.16** | Examples of (a) clear-cut and (b) shelterwood (seed-tree) forest harvest.

regenerate naturally from existing seed and sprouts on the site and the input of seeds from adjacent forest stands. With no follow-up management, clear-cut areas can be badly disturbed by erosion, affecting the subsequent recovery of the site as well as adjacent aquatic communities.

Harvest by clear-cutting is the typical practice on forest plantations, but here, intensive site management follows clearing. Plant materials that are not harvested (branches, leaves, and needles) are typically burnt to clear the site for planting. After clearing, seedlings are planted and fertilizer applied to encourage plant growth. Herbicides are often used to discourage the growth of weedy plants that would compete with the seedlings for resources.

The **seed-tree,** or **shelterwood,** system is a method of regenerating a new stand by removing all trees from an area except for a small number of seed-bearing trees (Figure 27.16b). The uncut trees are intended to be the main source of seed for establishment of natural regeneration after harvest. Seed trees can be uniformly scattered or left in small clumps and may or may not be harvested at a later date.

In many ways, the shelterwood system is similar to a clear-cut, as there are generally not enough trees left standing to affect the microclimate of the harvested area. The advantage of this approach to harvesting is that the seed source for natural regeneration is not limited to adjacent stands. This can result in improved distribution (or stocking) of seedlings, as well as a more desirable mix of species.

Like any silviculture system, shelterwood harvesting requires careful planning to be effective. Trees left on the site must be strong enough to withstand winds and capable of producing adequate seed; seed bed conditions must be conducive to seedling establishment (this may require a preparatory treatment during or after harvest); and follow-up management may be required to fully establish the regeneration.

In **selection cutting**, mature single trees or groups of trees scattered through the forest are removed. Selection cutting produces only small openings or gaps in the forest canopy. Although this form of timber harvest can minimize the scale of disturbance within the forest from the direct removal of trees, the network of trails and roads necessary to provide access can be a major source of disturbance (to both plants and soils). In addition, selective cutting can result in changes in species composition and diversity, as only certain species are selectively removed.

Regardless of the differences in approach, a number of general principles can be stated regarding sustainable forestry. Forest trees function in the manner discussed for competition in plant populations in Chapter 11 (Section 11.3). Whether planted as seedlings or by natural regeneration, the establishment of a forest begins with a population of small individuals (seedlings) that grow and compete for the essential resources of light, water, and nutrients. As biomass in the forest increases, the density of trees decreases, while the average tree size increases as a result of self-thinning (Figure 27.17; also see Section 11.4 and Figure 11.8). For a stand to be considered economically available for harvest (referred to as in an *operative state*), minimum thresholds for the harvestable volume of timer per hectare and average tree size must be satisfied (see Figure 27.17), which will vary as a function of the species. In plantation forestry, for a given set of thresholds (timber volume and average tree size), the initial stand density (planting density) can be controlled to influence the timing of the stand's availability for harvest (Figure 27.18).

When trees are harvested, a sufficient time must pass for the forest to once again repeat this process. For sustained yield, the period of time between harvests must be sufficient for the forest to regain the level of biomass at the time of the previous harvest (see Figure 27.4). The rotation time is dependent on a variety of factors related to the tree species, site conditions, type of management, and the intended use of the trees that are being harvested. Wood for paper products (pulp wood), fence posts, and poles are harvested from fast-growing species, allowing a short rotation period (15–40 years). These species are often grown in highly managed plantations where trees can be spaced to reduce competition and fertilized to maximize growth rates. Trees harvested for timber (saw logs) require a much longer rotation period.

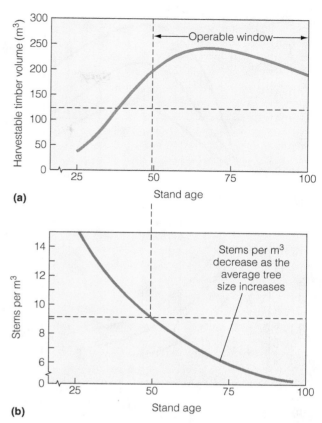

**(a)**

**(b)**

**Figure 27.17** | Determination of when a stand of trees is suitable for harvest (referred to as the *operable window*) is based on two criteria: (1) salable volume of wood per hectare (m³/ha) and (2) the average tree size as measured by the stems per cubic meter (the number of trees required to make a cubic meter of wood volume). In the example above, the dashed horizontal lines represent constraints of **(a)** minimum salable wood volume of 100 m³/ha and **(b)** minimum average tree size of 9 stems/m³. Dashed vertical lines indicate the earliest stage at which both constraints are satisfied. (Adapted from Orizens et al. 1986.)

Hardwood species used for furniture and cabinetry are typically slower growing and may have a rotation time of 80 to 120 years. Sustained forestry of these species works best on extensive areas where blocks of land can be maintained in different age classes.

As with agricultural crops, a significant amount of nutrients are lost from the forest when trees are harvested and removed (see Table 27.1). The loss of nutrients in plant biomass is often compounded by further losses from soil erosion and various postharvest management practices—particularly the use of fire (see Researcher Profile: Deborah Lawrence). The reduction of nutrients will reduce plant growth, requiring a longer rotation period for subsequent harvests or causing a reduction in forest yield if the rotation period is maintained. Forest managers often counter the loss of nutrients by using chemical fertilizers, creating other

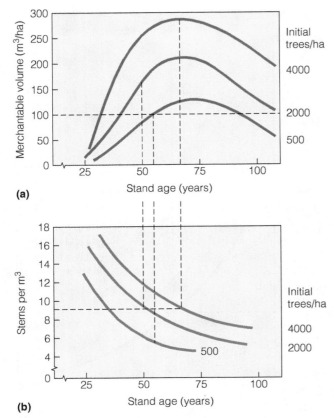

**(a)**

**(b)**

**Figure 27.18** | Effects of initial stand density on timing of stand availability for harvest (operable window). As in Figure 27.17, the dashed horizontal lines represent constraints of **(a)** minimum marketable wood volume of $100 \ m^3/ha$ and **(b)** a minimum average tree size of $9 \ stems/m^3$. Dashed vertical lines indicate the earliest stage at which both constraints are satisfied. Note that the intermediate planting density of 2000 trees per hectare has the earliest operable window. (Adapted from Orizens et al. 1983.)

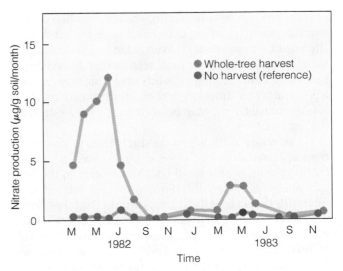

**Figure 27.19** | Comparison of nitrate $(NO_3^-)$ production after logging for a loblolly pine (*Pinus taeda*) plantation in the southeastern United States. Data for the reference stand (no harvest) are compared with those of a whole-tree harvest clear-cut. (Adapted from Vitousek 1992.)

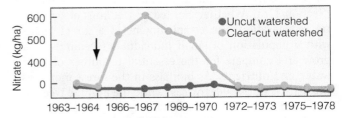

**Figure 27.20** | Temporal changes in the nitrate concentration of stream water for two forested watersheds in Hubbard Brook, New Hampshire. The forest on one watershed was clear-cut, whereas the other forest remained undisturbed. Note the large increase in concentrations of nitrate in the stream on the clear-cut watershed. This increase is due to increased decomposition and nitrogen mineralization after the removal of trees. The nitrogen was then leached into the surface water and groundwater. (Adapted from Likens and Borman 1995.)

environmental problems for adjacent aquatic ecosystems (see Sections 23.4 and 27.7).

In addition to the nutrients removed directly through biomass removal, logging can also result in the transport of nutrients from the ecosystem by altering processes involved in internal cycling. The removal of trees in clear-cutting and other forest management practices increases the amount of radiation (including direct sunlight) reaching the soil surface. The resulting increase in soil temperatures promotes decomposition of remaining soil organic matter (see Section 21.4) and results in an increase in net mineralization rates (see Section 21.5) (Figure 27.19). This increase in nutrient availability in the soil occurs at the same time that demand for nutrients is low because plants have been removed and net primary productivity is low. As a result, there is a dramatic increase in the leaching of nutrients from the soil into ground and surface waters (Figure 27.20). This export of nutrients from the ecosystem re-

sults from decoupling the two processes of nutrient release in decomposition and nutrient uptake in net primary productivity.

Sustained yield is a key concept in forestry and is practiced to some degree by large timber companies and federal and state forestry agencies. But, all too often, industrial forestry's approach to sustained yield is to grow trees as a crop rather than maintaining a forest ecosystem. Their management approach is a form of agriculture in which trees are grown as crops: clear-cut, spray herbicides, plant or seed the site to one species, clear-cut, and plant again. Clear-cutting practices in some national forests, especially in the Pacific Northwest and the Tongass National Forest in Alaska, hardly qualify as

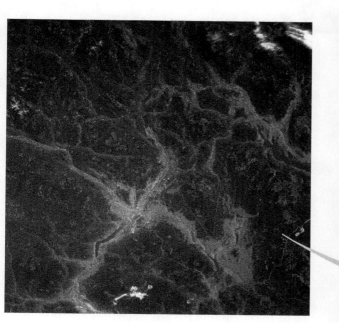

Figure 27.21 | **(a)** Photograph of large-scale forest clearing in British Columbia taken from the space shuttle and **(b)** a more localized view from aerial photography. Go to **GRAPHit!** at **www.ecologyplace.com** to graph rates of deforestation.

sustained-yield management when below-cost timber sales are mandated by the government to meet politically determined harvesting quotas. Even more extensive clear-cutting of forests is taking place in the northern forests of Canada, especially British Columbia (Figure 27.21), and in large areas of Siberia. As the timber supply dwindles in the Pacific Northwest, the timber industry that moved west after the depletion of eastern hardwoods and pine forests of the lake states is moving east again to exploit the regrowth of eastern hardwood forests, especially the rich and diverse central hardwood forest. From Virginia and eastern Tennessee to Arkansas and Alabama, timber companies have built more than 140 highly automated chip mills that cut up trees of all sizes into chips for paper pulp and particle board. Feeding the mills requires clear-cutting 500,000 ha annually. The growing demand for timber has boosted timber prices, stimulating more clear-cutting. The rate of harvest is wholly unsustainable. In face of growing timber demands, sustained-yield management has hardly filtered down to smaller parcels of private land.

The problem of sustained-yield forestry is its economic focus on the resource with little concern for the forest as a biological community. A carefully managed stand of trees, often reduced to one or two species, is not a forest in an ecological sense. Rarely will a naturally regenerated forest, and certainly not a planted one, ever support the diversity of life found in old-growth forests (see Section 17.6 and Figure 17.14). By the time the trees reach economic or financial maturity—based on the type of rotation—they are cut again.

## 27.10 | Exploitation of Fisheries Has Led to the Need for Management

Although the advent of agriculture some 10,000 years ago has functioned to reduce the dependence of humans on natural populations, more than 80 percent of the world commercial catch of fish and shellfish is from the harvest of naturally occurring populations in the oceans (71%) and inland freshwaters (10%).

For hundreds of years, the villagers of Kembera in West Kalimantan, Indonesia have been practicing the same form of shifting cultivation. An area of rain forest approximately 1 ha in size is cleared of all vegetation (Figure 1). After drying for several weeks, the debris is burned. With the onset of heavy rains, the field is planted with rice and a few vegetable crops. This type of upland agriculture involves no tillage or mounding, no irrigation, and no chemical inputs. The rice crop is then weeded by hand from one to three times during the 5- or 6-month growing period. One rice crop is grown per year, and although plots are sometimes used for a second year, fields are typically abandoned after a single harvest. After abandonment, the plot will naturally regenerate to secondary forest. After a period of recovery (fallow), which on average lasts 20 years, the area is once again ready to be cleared and planted.

Are these land-use practices sustainable, and what impact are they having on the biological diversity of the region? These are the questions being addressed by ecologist Deborah Lawrence of the Department of Environmental Sciences, University of Virginia.

The area surrounding the Dayak village of Kembera in West Kalimantan has been the location of Lawrence's work which has focused on the impacts of traditional agriculture on soil resources. The availability of phosphorus (P) is often a major limitation on agricultural production in the tropics. Its availability is controlled by the weathering of phosphorus containing rocks and minerals, and rapid sorption (absorption and adsorption) of P on abundant iron and aluminum minerals in tropical soils (see Section 5.10) precludes its free movement through the soil solution to plant roots. In addition,

high rainfall results in heavy leaching of nutrients such as P from the surface soil. To understand the limitations of P on the long-term sustainability of agriculture in this region, it was necessary for Lawrence to quantify the influence of the process of shifting cultivation on the dynamics of soil P.

Fire transfers nutrients from the vegetation and surface organic matter to the soil. Where temperatures rise to high levels, **pyromineralization** occurs, resulting in the transformation of organic forms of P into inorganic (mineral) forms available for uptake by plants. Depending on the intensity of the fire, Lawrence found that up to 55 percent of total P stocks is lost to the atmosphere as smoke, although much of this may be redistributed across the landscape rather than being lost entirely from the forest. In addition, upward of 50 percent of mineral P that is deposited during the fire may be lost from the site through erosion by water and wind or through leaching. Despite these losses of P from the soil during the preparation of the site for planting, burning results in a large immediate increase in available inorganic P, promoting growth of the rice plants. The harvesting of rice, however, represents a further loss of P, depleting soil stocks. These losses of soil P during the preparation of fields and the harvesting of crops are large relative to the input of P to the soil through the process of weathering. Given these facts, one would hypothesize a decline in total P with each subsequent cultivation cycle, influencing not only the long-term potential for agricultural productivity but also the process of secondary forest growth (forest regeneration).

To examine this hypothesis, Lawrence undertook a study to examine patches of land around the village of Kembera that had been used exclusively for shifting cultivation for up to 200 years. To determine long-term changes in soil P, she sampled the top 30 cm of soil at 24 sites representing a gradient of cultivation history, from zero (primary forest) to 10 or more previous swidden–fallow cultivation cycles. At each site, 30 soil cores were collected, and each core was divided by depth (0–2.5 cm, 2.5–15 cm, and 15–30 cm).

Results of the analyses were surprising. Rather than declining, total soil P actually increased with each suc-

Figure 1 | Aerial view of plot cleared for planting.

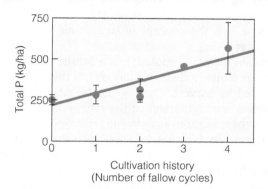

**Figure 2** | Changes in phosphorus stocks in the top 30 cm of soil during the first four cycles of cultivation. Values shown are mean ±1 standard deviation for 6 sites on sandy soil.

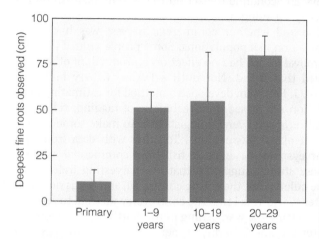

**Figure 3** | Maximum depth of fine roots observed as a function of forest age. Deepest roots are defined as the midpoint of soil horizons in which the roots were found. Data are from 2 sites newly cleared from primary forest and 17 sites in secondary forest fallows 1–28 years after clearing.

cessive cultivation cycle over the first four cycles (approximately 80 years) (Figure 2), remaining relatively constant thereafter. How could this be, given the large losses associated with clearing and harvest? To understand how P was increasing in the top 30 cm of soil through time, Lawrence turned to examining the fallow process between periods of cultivation, during which secondary forest growth occurs.

Following abandonment, nutrients accumulate in the secondary forest biomass before soil stocks begin to increase. Soil P taken up by the trees is then returned to the soil surface through litterfall and subsequent decomposition and mineralization. Upon examining the vertical distribution of roots on the study plots, a possible explanation began to emerge for the observed increase in P in the surface soil through time. Tree species that colonize the secondary forest have more fine roots deeper in the soil profile than species that dominate the primary (uncleared) forest (Figure 3). It is these fine roots that are responsible for the majority of nutrient uptake from the soil. The maximum observed depth of fine roots in the secondary forest is 50 cm, as compared to 20 cm in the primary forest. This suggests that the increase in total P after cultivation and fallow is a result of "nutrient pumping." As fine roots located deeper in the soil profile take up P, it is incorporated into the plant tissues as the secondary forest grows during the fallow period. Organic P in the form of senescent plant tissues is then deposited on the soil surface, where it is eventually released as inorganic P. Therefore, profuse deep rooting and the periodic death (with each fire) are likely to encourage the transfer of inorganic P to the surface and organic P (in the form of fine roots) to the deeper horizons.

Despite the increase in total P in the top 30 cm of soil observed during the first four cycles of cultivation, potential P losses through the erosion and harvest dictate that the future rice production will depend on continued acquisition of P from deeper in the soil profile, hence maintaining the critical periods of fallow necessary for regeneration of nutrient stocks in the surface soils. In many parts of Indonesia, however, shifting cultivators are having to reduce the length of the fallow period due to the pressures of population growth, potentially jeopardizing this sustainable form of agricultural production that has supported the populations of this region for so long. ●

### Bibliography

Lawrence, D., and W. H. Schlesinger. 2001. Changes in soil phosphorus during 200 years of shifting cultivation in Indonesia. *Ecology* 82:2769–2780.

Lawrence, D., D. R. Peart, and M. Leighton. 1998. The impact of shifting cultivation on a rainforest landscape in West Kalimantan: Spatial and temporal dynamics. *Landscape Ecology* 13:135–148.

1. What possible impacts other than altering soil nutrient availability might these agricultural practices have on the tropical forest ecosystems of this region?

2. How does the practice of burning the site to prepare for planting influence the availability of P in the soil; both organic and mineral forms?

There are numerous historical accounts of overexploitation and population declines, yet not until the later 1800s was there any effort to manage fisheries resources to ensure their continuance. At that time, wide fluctuations in the catch of fishes in the North Sea began to have an economic impact on the commercial fishing industry. Ensuing debates raged over the cause of the decline and whether commercial harvest was having an impact on fish populations. Some people argued that the removal of fish had no effect on reproduction; others argued that it did. Not until a Danish fishery biologist, C. D. J. Petersen, developed a method for estimating population size based on a technique of tagging, releasing, and recapture were biologists able to make some assessment of fish populations. Together with data from egg surveys and the aging of fish from commercial catches, these studies suggested that overharvesting indeed was the culprit. But the debate continued, and it was not until after World War I that the controversy was laid to rest.

During the war, fishing in the North Sea had stopped. After the war, fishermen experienced sizable increases in their catches. Fishery biologists suggested that the renewed fishing would once again reduce population sizes and catches would stabilize and eventually decline with overexploitation. Their predictions were correct, and with time, attention turned to the question of sustainable harvest.

The goal of long-term sustainable harvest has been a mainstay of fisheries science for the past half century. A central concept of sustainable harvest is the logistic model of population growth presented in Chapter 10 (Section 10.10). Under conditions of the logistic model, growth rate (overall numbers of new organisms produced per year) is low when the population is small (Figure 27.22). It is also low when a population nears its carrying capacity ($K$) because of density-dependent processes such as food availability. Intermediate-sized populations have the greatest growth capacity and ability

to produce the most harvestable fish per year. The key realization of this model is that fisheries could optimize harvest of a particular species by keeping the population at an intermediate level and harvesting the species at a rate equal to the annual growth rate. This strategy was called the **maximum sustainable yield** (see Quantifying Ecology 27.1: Maximum Sustainable Yield).

In effect, the concept of sustainable yield is an attempt at being a "smart predator." The objective is to maintain the prey population at a density where the production of new individuals just offsets the mortality represented by harvest. The higher the rate of population increase, the higher will be the rate of harvest that produces the maximum sustainable yield. Species characterized by a very high rate of population growth often lose much of their production to a high density-independent mortality, influenced by variation in the physical environment such as temperature (see Section 11.12). The management objective for these species is to reduce "waste" by taking all individuals that otherwise would be lost to natural mortality. Such a population is difficult to manage. The stock can be depleted if annual patterns of reproduction are interrupted due to environmental conditions. An example is the Pacific sardine (*Sardinops sagax*). Exploitation of the Pacific sardine population in the 1940s and 1950s shifted the age structure of the population to younger age classes. Before exploitation, reproduction was distributed among the first five age classes (years). In the exploited population, this pattern of reproduction shifted, and close to 80 percent of reproduction was associated with the first two age classes. Two consecutive years of environmentally induced reproductive failure (a result of natural climate variations associated with ENSO; see Section 3.9) caused a collapse of the population from which the species never recovered (Figure 27.23).

Sustainable yield requires a detailed understanding of the population dynamics of the fish species. Recall from

**Figure 27.22** | Assuming that the growth rate of the fish population follows the logistic model presented in Chapter 10 [$dN/dt = rN(1 - N/K)$], **(a)** in the absence of fishing, the population will grow to carrying capacity, $K$. **(b)** The relationship between the rate of population growth, $dN/dt$, and population size, $N$, takes the form of a parabola, reaching a maximum value at a population size of $N = K/2$.

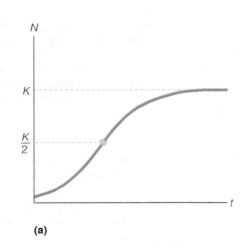

(a)

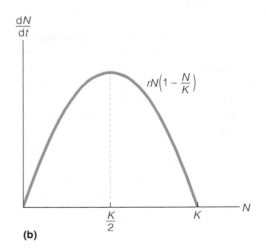

(b)

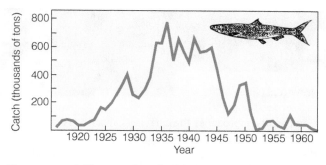

**Figure 27.23** | The annual catch of the Pacific sardine along the Pacific Coast of North America. Overfishing, environmental changes, and an increase in the population of a competing fish species, the anchovy, resulted in a collapse of the population. (Adapted from Murphy 1966.)

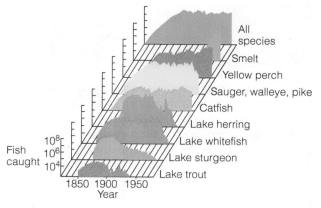

**Figure 27.24** | Annual catches of selected species of fish, and all species combined, by the Lake Erie commercial fishery since 1820. The vertical scale is logarithmic. (Adapted from Regier and Hartman 1973.) Go to GRAPHit! at **www.ecologyplace.com** to explore global data on overfishing.

Chapter 10 that the intrinsic rate of population growth, *r,* is a function of the age-specific birth and mortality rates. Unfortunately, the usual approach to maximum sustained yield fails to consider adequately size and age classes, differential rates of growth among them, sex ratio, survival, reproduction, and environmental uncertainties—all data difficult to obtain. Adding to the problem is the common-property nature of the resource: Because it belongs to no one, it belongs to everyone to use as each sees fit.

Perhaps the greatest problem with models of sustainable harvest is that they fail to incorporate the most important component of population exploitation: economics (see Section 27.12). Once commercial exploitation begins, the pressure is on to increase it to maintain the underlying economic infrastructure. Attempts to reduce the rate of exploitation meet strong opposition. People argue that reduction will mean unemployment and industrial bankruptcy—that, in fact, the harvest effort should increase. This argument is short-sighted. An overused resource will fail, and the livelihoods it supports will collapse, because in the long run the resource will be depleted. That fact is written in abandoned fish processing plants and rusting fishing fleets. With conservative exploitation, the resource could be maintained.

## 27.11 | Fisheries Management Requires an Ecosystem Approach

Another problem with the concept of sustainable harvest is that traditional population management, especially by fisheries, considers stocks of individual species as single biological units rather than components of a larger ecological system. Each stock is managed to bring in a maximum economic return, overlooking the need to leave behind a certain portion to continue its ecological role within the larger community, be it predator or prey. This attitude encourages a tremendous discard problem, eu-

phemistically called *bycatch.* Employing large drift nets that encompass square kilometers of ocean, fishermen haul in not only commercial species they seek but also a range of other marine life as well, including sea turtles, dolphins, and scores of other species of fish. Fishermen discard this unwanted catch by dumping it back into the sea. Discarded fish alone make up one-fourth of the annual marine catch. In 1995 in the Pacific Northwest, of the 27 metric tons of fish taken, 9 metric tons was bycatch. The ecological effects of bycatch can be enormous. Because much of the bycatch consists of juvenile and undersized fish of commercial species, the practice can seriously affect the future of those fisheries. The removal or reduction of other species can alter the nature of interactions within the community (see Section 17.3). Such disturbances can alter food webs of ocean ecosystems and upset the functioning of the pelagic ecosystem.

The history of the fishery in Lake Erie illustrates this point (Figure 27.24). Before the War of 1812, the lake, whose shores were lightly settled, held an abundance of whitefish (*Coregonus clupeaformis*), lake trout (*Salvelinus namaycush*), blue pike (*Stizostedion vitreum glaucum*), sauger (*Stizostedion canadense*), and lake herring (*Coregonus artedii*). After the war, settlement increased rapidly and so did the exploitation of the fishery resource. A subsistence fishery grew into a thriving industry by 1820. For the next 70 years, rapid improvement in transportation, fishing boats, gear, and techniques and an expanding market increased the average rate of the catch by 20 percent a year. By 1890, this rapid growth in catch slowed, as stocks became depleted. However, increased intensity of fishing, further improvement of equipment, and heavy capital input maintained the size of the catch until the late 1950s.

Early to go was the lake sturgeon (*Acipenser fulvescens*), at first netted and burned on the shore because

When harvesting renewable resources, the goal is a balancing act of maximizing economic gains while at the same time allowing for the regeneration of the resource base into the future—sustainability. The concept of sustainable yield requires only that the rate of harvest does not exceed the rate at which the resource can regenerate (recover to preharvest levels). However, what the resource manager often wants to identify is the maximum sustainable yield: the largest average catch or yield that can continuously be taken from a stock (population) under existing environmental conditions.

Consider a population of fish that is growing in a manner described by the logistic model of population growth presented in Chapter 10 (Section 10.10) that is being harvested. We can incorporate the effect of fishing on the population ($N$) in a manner similar to that used in modeling the influence of predation on prey populations (see Section 14.2).

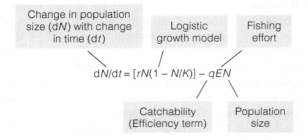

$$dN/dt = [rN(1 - N/K)] - qEN$$

Change in population size ($dN$) with change in time ($dt$) — Logistic growth model — Fishing effort — Catchability (Efficiency term) — Population size

As with predation, the harvest rate is the product of three terms: prey density ($N$, fish population), a constant $q$ that represents the efficiency of the predator (catchability), and a term representing the fishing effort, $E$. Fishing effort ($E$) functions as a substitute for predator density and takes into consideration a variety of factors such as the size of the fishing fleet and the length of the season. The product of catchability and effort, $qE$, is the fishing mortality rate; it has the same dimension as $r$ and will play an important role in what follows.

In the absence of fishing, the population will grow to carrying capacity ($K$) (Figure 27.22a). The relationship between the rate of population growth ($dN/dt$: the change in $N$ over the time interval $t$) and population size takes the form of a parabola (Figure 27.22b). At a population density of zero, the rate of growth is likewise zero. As population density increases, the rate of population growth increases, reaching its maximum at a population density of half the carrying capacity ($K/2$), referred to as the *inflection point*. As the density continues to rise above this point, the rate of population growth declines, reaching zero as the population density approaches the carrying capacity ($N = K$).

To maintain a sustainable harvest, the growth rate of the fish population must be equal to the rate of harvest:

$$rN(1 - N/K) = qEN$$

Solving this equation algebraically, we see that there are two solutions:

$$N^* = K(1 - qE/r)$$
$$N^* = 0$$

The second solution corresponds to the extinction of the fish population.

The values of $N^*$ for a fish population with constant values of $r$ and $K$ will vary depending on the fishing effort ($qE$). Using the two values of $N^*$ that correspond to a given fishing effort (value of $qE$), we can draw a line that represents the harvest rate ($qEN$ as a function of $N$) on the graph shown in Figure 27.22b (Figure 1a). For values of $N$ above $N^*$, the rate of harvest ($qEN$) is greater than the rate of population growth [$rN(1 - N/K)$] and the population declines. If the rate of harvest is less than the rate of population growth, the population increases (Figure 1b). In both instances, the population returns to a density of $N^*$. If we continue to further increase the fishing effort (mortality), we eventually reach a point where the harvest rate exceeds the growth rate for all densities ($N$) and the population is driven to extinction (Figure 1c). The relationship between $N^*$ and fishing effort ($qE$) is shown in Figure 2. When fishing effort is zero, the population will be at carrying capacity ($K$). The upper limit to fishing effort will be when the per capita rate of mortality due to fishing effort ($qE$) is equal to the maximum per capita growth rate of the population ($r$). Each point along the line shown in Figure 2 is the value of $N^*$ for a corresponding fishing effort ($qE$) at which growth rate of the fish population is equal to the rate of harvest—the condition for sustainable yield.

The sustainable yield, $Y$, at each point is therefore:

$$Y = qEN^*$$

Using this equation, the relationship between yield and effort is plotted in Figure 3. The yield initially rises with effort, reaching a **maximum sustainable yield** (MSY). Further increase in fishing effort will lower the yield as population becomes overexploited and depleted. At the maximum sustainable yield, harvest takes the population down to a level at which the remaining stock can replace the amount removed before the next harvest period. •

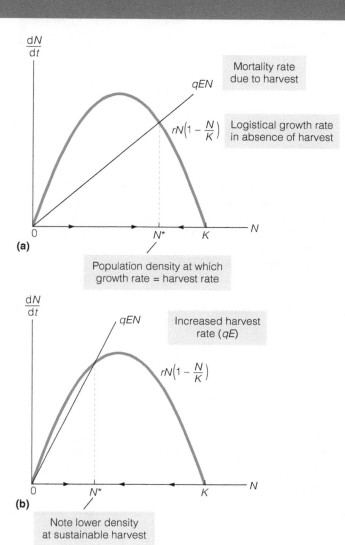

Mortality rate due to harvest

$qEN$

$rN\left(1 - \dfrac{N}{K}\right)$ Logistical growth rate in absence of harvest

**(a)**

Population density at which growth rate = harvest rate

$qEN$ Increased harvest rate ($qE$)

$rN\left(1 - \dfrac{N}{K}\right)$

**(b)**

Note lower density at sustainable harvest

**Figure 1** | **(a)** The relationship between the rate of population growth, dN/dt, and population density for the two components of the fish population model with harvest: logistic population growth [$rN(1 - N/K)$] and mortality due to harvest ($qEN$). Line describing harvest assumes a given value for fishing effort ($qE$). The population density at which growth rate is equal to harvest rate (sustainable harvest) is labelled as $N*$ on the x-axis. For population densities above $N*$, harvest exceeds the growth rate and the population declines. For densities below $N*$, the population growth rate exceeds the rate of harvest and the density increases. **(b)** As the fishing effort (value of $qE$) increases, the corresponding population density decreases.

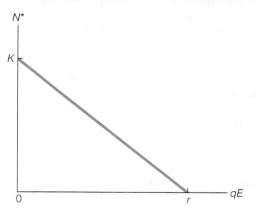

**Figure 2** | The relationship between fishing effort and the corresponding population density at sustainable yield, $N*$. When fishing effort ($qE$) is very low or zero (no fishing), the population will approach carrying capacity ($K$). The population density at sustainable yield declines as fishing effort increases. For sustainable yield to occur, the rate of harvest cannot exceed the maximum (intrinsic) rate of population growth defined by $r$.

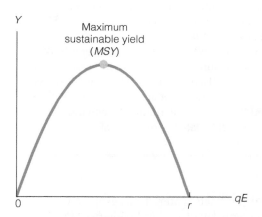

**Figure 3** | Relationship between fishing effort ($qE$) and yield ($Y$) under conditions of sustainable yield ($Y = qEN*$). The relationship takes the form of a parabola. An increase in effort increases sustainable yield up to a point. Further increases in effort lower the yield as the stock ($N*$) becomes increasingly overexploited and reduced. The maximum value of $Y$ (and corresponding value of effort) is the maximum sustainable yield (MSY).

1. Based on the discussion (and equations) presented above, how would a reduction in the carrying capacity ($K$) of the fish population influence the value for maximum sustainable yield (assume that values of $r$ remain constant)?

2. Assuming the carrying capacity ($K$) remains constant, how would an increase in $r$ (instrinsic rate of growth) influence the value of fishing effort ($qE$) at maximum sustainable yield?

**M**ost of us are familiar with the concept of interest rates. If we invest money as savings or in stocks, we expect some future return on that investment. The rate of return is called the investment rate, $i$. We can calculate the future value or benefit ($B$) of our investment using the following simple approach.

Suppose we invest $100 at an interest rate of 10 percent (expressed as 0.1). We can calculate our expected benefit 1 year later, $B_1$ (the future value of our $100 investment), using the following equation:

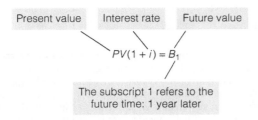

Present value    Interest rate    Future value

$$PV(1 + i) = B_1$$

The subscript 1 refers to the future time: 1 year later

The value of our initial investment after 1 year is $110.

This same approach can be used in reverse to calculate the present value of some benefit expected in the future. Say for example that you expect to be paid $100 a year from now. What is the present value of that benefit ($100) you will receive in the future? We refer to this procedure as discounting, and the interest rate is now referred to as the discount rate, $r$. (As we will discuss later, the discount rate is not always the same as the interest rate.) We can now rearrange the equation presented above to calculate the present value:

$r$ is the discount rate

$$PV = B_1/(1 + r)$$
$$90.91 = 100/(1 + 0.1)$$

In other words, the $100 you will receive next year is only worth approximately $91 today (current value). Why is this so? Because as we calculated above, $100 invested today will be worth $110 1 year from now. You would have to receive a benefit of $110 next year for it to have a current value of $100.

The process of calculating the present value of some future benefit can be done for any period of time in the future by generalizing the equation presented above:

$t$ is the number of years in the future

$$PV = B_1/(1 + r)^t$$

Now we can use the approach of discounting to calculate the present value of expected benefits over a series of years. Suppose we expect to receive a benefit of $100 for each of the next 3 years.

---

it destroyed fishing nets. Later, it was exploited as a market fish along with lake trout and whitefish. Fishing intensity grew with incentives to increase production during World War I and the introduction of a gill net that was extremely wasteful in its catch. In 1950, the development of the nylon gill net, which could be left in the water much longer, made fishing more intense than ever. Now walleye (*Stizostedion vitreum vitreum*), blue pike, and yellow perch (*Perca flavescens*) joined the ranks of overexploited species. By 1960, the stocks of walleye and blue pike had been commercially depleted. The fishery is now dominated by yellow perch.

Adding to the stress was pollution in the lake. Industrial, agricultural, and urban wastes, toxic pollutants and biocides, and runoff from shore developments wiped out phytoplankton that supported fish life. An invasion of

rainbow smelt (*Osmerus mordax*), an anadromous fish of the North Atlantic and Pacific that was first introduced to Lake Michigan in 1912, dealt the final blow. Young smelt feed on plankton and crustaceans and the older smelt on small fish. In turn, the smelt is valuable prey for adult lake trout, blue pike, walleyes, and sauger. With the decimation of those species, smelt increased rapidly and became the predators of young remnant stocks. Had the invasion of rainbow smelt been halted, and had fishing been regulated, the preferred commercial species would still be in harvestable numbers.

The history of this Great Lakes fishery is a microcosm of the history of marine fisheries. Certain stocks of fish, such as the Pacific sardine, Atlantic halibut (*Hippoglossus hippoglossus*), Atlantic cod (*Gadus morhua*), and Peruvian anchovy (*Engraulis ringens*), have been

| Year 1 | Year 2 | Year 3 |
|--------|--------|--------|

$$PV = B_1/(1+r)^1 + B_2/(1+r)^2 + B_3/(1+r)^3$$

$$248.68 = 90.91 + 82.64 + 75.13$$

The procedure of discounting is an important tool in making economic decisions where benefits are gained over an extended future period. For example, we can compare three alternative projects that provide the same total benefits over a 5-year period ($150) but that differ in the timing of when the benefits are realized. In Project A, the benefits are front-loaded, declining into future years. In Project B, the benefits are spread evenly over the 5 years. In Project C, the benefits are back-loaded, increasing as the project progresses. Using a discount rate of 0.1 and the formula presented above, we can calculate the present value (PV) of each of these projects.

Net Benefit ($) in Year $t$

| $t =$ | 1 | 2 | 3 | 4 | 5 | Combined Present Value |
|-------|---|---|---|---|---|------------------------|
| Project A | 50 | 40 | 30 | 20 | 10 | 120.93 |
| Project B | 30 | 30 | 30 | 30 | 30 | 113.72 |
| Project C | 10 | 20 | 30 | 40 | 50 | 106.52 |

Two important points emerge from this example. First, the alternative that provides most of the benefits early in the project is economically superior to the alternative (Project B) that provides a sustained benefit over the lifetime of the project. Unfortunately, this is often the case when analyzing the economics of harvesting renewable resources. Deriving benefits early by overharvesting is often the most economically attractive alternative when profits can be invested to provide a future source of revenue.

The second important point from this example is that the alternative that defers benefits until later in the project (Project C) is the least economically attractive choice. In this way, the practice of discounting has major implications for future generations. In the appraisal of alternative projects, decision-makers are often less willing to consider those that accrue benefits to future generations when compared to those that benefit the present.

The practice of discounting is an important and critical economic tool in evaluating investment options, however, methods must be developed to include benefits that are not always easily quantifiable and to explicitly consider the costs and benefits of current activities on future generations. ●

1. What is the effect of increasing the discount rate on the present value of an expected (future) benefit?

2. How would a reduction in the discount rate from 10 percent (0.1) to 5 percent (0.05) change the analyses presented for the three projects in the table presented opposite (complete the calculations using the equations for PV presented earlier)?

exploited to commercial extinction, causing ecological and economic damage. The sad plight of the whales is another example of decreased catches followed by increased hunting intensity, made possible by greater capital input and technological advances such as factory ships and fleets of hunters. Despite warnings of overharvesting, the marketplace and short-term profits dictated the take.

## 27.12 | Economics Are a Key Factor Governing Resource Management

Although a large portion of the human population produces its own food and forest products (such as fuel wood) through subsistence farming, fishing, and wood gathering, these essential human resources are now part of the global marketplace—produced for sale and profit. As such, economic considerations are central to the production and management of natural resources.

A critical tool of economics that is used in making decisions regarding the production and management of natural resources is benefit–cost analysis. A **benefit–cost analysis** involves measuring, adding up, and comparing all the benefits and all the costs of a particular project or activity. For example, if it costs a farmer $100 per hectare to produce corn this year, and the expected value of that corn is $200 per hectare, the benefits ($200) outweigh the costs ($100) and the decision will most likely be to plant the corn. If the corn produced per hectare was only worth $80, however, the costs outweigh the benefits, and the farmer is unlikely to plant the fields with corn and incur a loss. In this example, the dollar value of costs and benefits can be compared directly because both costs (expenses) and benefits (revenue) occur during the same time period—the year the corn crop is planted and harvested. When costs and benefits are extended over a much longer period of time, it is necessary to use a procedure called discounting.

**Discounting** is a technique employed to add and compare costs and benefits that occur at different points in time. It is a major driving force in the economics of natural resource management and unfortunately often runs counter to the objectives of sustainable resource management. The problem arises because in farming, forestry, and fisheries, there are substantial initial costs in the acquisition of land, equipment, permits, and so forth. These costs must then be weighed against expected future earnings from the production and harvesting of natural resources (crops, trees, or fish). As we all know, a dollar earned in the future does not have the same value as a dollar in hand today. Inflation depreciates the value of future earnings. In addition, a dollar invested today is worth more in the future as a result of compounding interest. Therefore, in comparing present-day costs with expected benefits (revenue) in the future, those benefits must be discounted (see Quantifying Ecology 27.2: Discounting the Future) to reflect the reduced value of future dollars. When this is done for activities such as harvesting forests or fisheries, the result of this comparison often leads to the conclusion that it is economically more advantageous to "overexploit" the resource now and invest the resulting profits rather than to harvest the resource in a sustainable fashion over a much longer period of time.

In 1973, the economist Colin W. Clark made this point persuasively in the case of the blue whale, *Balaenopterus musculus*. More than 100 feet long and weighing upward of 150 tons at full maturity, the blue whale is the largest animal on either land or sea. It is also among the easiest to hunt and kill. More than 300,000 blue whales were harvested during the 20th century, with a peak harvest of more than 29,000 in the 1930–1931 season. By the early 1970s, the population had plummeted to several hundred individuals. Although international negotiations were held to address the problem of overharvest and discuss potential regulatory policies, there were a number of countries that were especially eager to continue the hunt even at the risk of total extinction. So Clark asked what practice would yield the whalers the most money: cease hunting and let the blue whales recover in numbers and then harvest them sustainably into the future, or kill the rest off as quickly as possible and invest the profits in the stock market? The troubling answer was that if the whalers could achieve an annual rate of return on their investments of 20 percent or more, it would be economically advantageous to harvest all of the blue whales at that time and invest their profits.

The problem with this purely economic approach to evaluation of natural resources is that the value of a blue whale was based only on the measures relevant to the existing market; that is, on the going price per unit weight of whale oil and meat. It does not consider other services provided by the blue whale, such as ecotourism (whale watching), nor does it consider the value of blue whales to future generations. But perhaps most importantly, it views blue whales, trees, and even whole ecosystems as having no inherent value beyond those calculated in economic terms.

A second important economic concept that is essential to understanding the sustainable use of natural resources is that of externalities. **Externalities** occur when the actions of one individual (or group of individuals) affect another individual's well-being, but the relevant costs (or benefits) are not reflected in market prices. For example, if a timber company clear-cuts an area of forest, it may well have adverse environmental consequences on adjacent areas. Erosion may transport silt to adjacent streams and rivers. Fertilizers and pesticides used as part of site preparation may likewise find their way to surface water and groundwater. The result may be reduced water quality, affecting drinking water, recreational value of the waterways, and aquatic plants and animals. Although the economic costs of these impacts can often be quantified, these costs are typically not borne by the timber company. These are externalities, or costs that are not reflected in the market prices. The timber company reaps the monetary benefit of the trees that have been harvested, but the environmental costs resulting from the harvest of those trees are passed on to the public. If these external costs were included in the analysis of costs associated with the timber harvest, the benefits (profits) may no longer outweigh the costs and the clear-cut would not take place. Another option is to pass on these costs to the consumer to reflect the actual costs of the goods and services.

Recent decades have seen the emergence of a new discipline within the field of economics: **environmental economics.** The objective of environmental economics is to study environmental problems with the perspective and analytic tools of economics, such as those presented above. The incorporation of economic principles into the environmental decision-making process is critical. Until the true value of natural resources and the costs of their extraction and use are understood and incorporated into economic decisions, the sustainable management and use of natural resources seems unlikely.

# Summary

## Sustainable Resource Use (27.1)

In its simplest form, the constraint on sustainable resource use is one of supply and demand. For the exploitation of the resource to be sustainable, the rate at which the resource is being used (consumption rate) must not exceed the rate at which the resource is being supplied (regeneration rate). Otherwise, the quantity of resources declines through time. If the resource is nonrenewable, then by definition its use is not sustainable, and the rate of resource decline is a function of the rate at which the resource is being harvested and used.

## Negative Impacts of Resource Extraction and Use (27.2)

Sustainable resource use can also be constrained indirectly as a consequence of negative impacts that arise from resource management, extraction, or use. Domestic, industrial, and agricultural waste is a growing environmental issue with implication to both ecosystem and human health. Wastes and by-products of production often contaminate the environment (air, water, and soil) with harmful substances—pollution.

## Natural Ecosystems (27.3)

When we attempt to manage and harvest natural resources in a sustainable fashion, in many ways we are attempting to mimic the function of natural ecosystems. Natural ecosystems function as sustainable units.

## Agriculture and Energy (27.4)

No matter what the crop planted or method of cultivation used, agriculture involves replacing diverse natural ecosystems with a community consisting of a single crop species or a mixture of crops. Although a wide range of agricultural practices are carried out throughout the world, agricultural production can be classified into one of two broad categories: industrialized and traditional.

Industrialized agriculture is dependent on large inputs of energy in the form of fossil fuels, chemical fertilizers, irrigation systems, and pesticides. Although energy demanding, this form of agriculture produces large quantities of crops and livestock per unit of land area. Traditional agriculture is dominated by subsistence agriculture in which primarily human labor and draft animals are used to produce only enough crops or livestock for a family to survive.

## Swidden Agriculture (27.5)

This traditional method of production in the wet tropics is swidden agriculture, a rotating cultivation technique in which trees are first cut down and burned in order to clear land for planting. Crops are planted, but production declines with each succeeding harvest. The plot is then abandoned, and the forest is allowed to reestablish. Eventually, the nutrient status of the site recovers, and it can once again be used for crops.

## Industrialized Agriculture (27.6)

In industrial agriculture, machines and fossil fuel energy replace the energy supplied by humans and draft animals in traditional agricultural systems. Mechanization requires large expanses of land for machines to operate effectively, and because different crops require specialized equipment for planting and harvest, farmers typically plant one or few crop varieties, season after season. Tilling and removal of organic matter at the time of harvest has the effects of reducing the nutrient status of the soil and encouraging soil erosion. Large quantities of chemical fertilizers and pesticides must be used to maintain productivity.

## Trade-offs in Agricultural Production (27.7)

The two very different agricultural systems—traditional (swidden) and industrialized—represent a trade-off between energy input in production and energy harvest in food resources. Industrial agriculture produces high yields per hectare at the expense of large inputs of energy in the form of fossil fuels, fertilizers, and pesticides. Each of these inputs produces serious environmental impacts. In contrast, yields are lower in traditional agricultural systems, but they are more energy efficient, yielding a greater amount of energy in crops per unit energy input in crop production.

## Sustainable Agriculture (27.8)

The term *sustainable agriculture* refers more to a notion of maintaining agriculture production while minimizing environmental impacts rather than to a quantitative set of criteria. It involves the use of farming methods that conserve soil and water resources, reduce the use of pesticides, and use alternative (on-site) sources of fertilizers.

## Forestry (27.9)

The goal of sustained yield in forestry is to achieve a balance between net growth and harvest. To achieve this end, foresters have an array of silvicultural and harvesting techniques from clear-cutting to selection cutting. For a stand to be considered economically available for harvest, minimum thresholds for the harvestable volume of timber per hectare and average tree size must be satisfied. When trees are harvested, a sufficient time must pass for the forest to once again repeat this process. For sustained yield, the period of time between harvests must be sufficient for the forest to regain the level of biomass at the time of the previous harvest.

The harvesting of trees, and the alterations to the site after harvesting, result in loss of nutrients from the site. To maintain productivity, it is often necessary to fertilize the site, which can lead to further nutrient loss from the site to adjacent aquatic ecosystems.

## Fisheries (27.10)

The goal of long-term sustainable harvest has been a mainstay of fisheries science for the past half century. A central concept of sustainable harvest is the logistic model of population growth in which the population growth rate is highest at intermediate population densities. The key realization of this model is that fisheries could optimize harvest of a particular species by keeping the population at an intermediate level and harvesting the species at a rate equal to the annual growth rate. This strategy was called the maximum sustainable yield. In practice, the concept of maximum sustainable yield is difficult to achieve, requiring a detailed understanding of the population structure and dynamics of the species being harvested.

## Ecosystem Approach (27.11)

A problem with the concept of sustainable harvest is that traditional population management, especially by fisheries, considers stocks of individual species as single biological units rather than components of a larger ecological system. Each stock is managed to bring in a maximum economic return, overlooking the need to leave behind a certain portion to continue its ecological role within the larger community.

## Environmental Economics (27.12)

A critical tool of economics that is used in making decisions regarding the production and management of natural resources is benefit–cost analysis. A benefit–cost analysis involves measuring, adding up, and comparing all the benefits and all the costs of a particular project or activity. When costs and benefits are extended over a much longer period of time, it is necessary to use a procedure called discounting. In this procedure, those benefits derived in the future must be discounted to reflect the reduced value of future dollars. Discounting often leads to economic choices that run counter to sustainable yield.

Externalities occur when the actions of one individual (or group of individuals) affect another individual's well-being but the relevant costs (or benefits) are not reflected in market prices. Externalities are important in evaluating methods of sustainable resource extraction because the actual costs of production (pollution, habitat degradation, and negative impacts on human health) are typically not built into the price structure, so the true cost of the activity or resource is not being considered.

## Study Questions

1. What relationship between supply rate and consumption rate must exist for the consumption of a resource to be sustainable?

2. Contrast renewable and nonrenewable resources in the context of sustainable resource use.

3. How might the sustainable use of resources be limited indirectly by adverse consequences from the management, extraction, and consumption of resources? Provide examples.

4. Contrast traditional and industrialized agricultural methods. What are the major inputs of energy (for production) in each?

5. Which agricultural method (industrial or traditional) produces the greatest yield of crops per unit area? Which produces the most crops per unit of energy input for production?

6. Name some methods/practices that can function to increase the sustainability of current industrialized agricultural production.

7. What is sustained yield? What is maximum sustainable yield? How do these two concepts differ?

8. Identify and discuss two sources of nutrient loss during forest harvest and management.

9. Why is it important to take a community approach to fisheries management rather than approaching the management and harvest of each species as a separate issue?

10. Why do economists discount future benefits? What is the consequence of disounting on sustainable management of resources?

11. Why is air pollution caused by coal-fired power plants an externality?

## Further Readings

Daily, G., ed. 1997. *Nature's services: Societal dependence on natural ecosystems*. Washington, D.C.: Island Press.
> In this excellent book, a group of eminent scientists explain in simple terms the critical role of natural ecosystems in meeting basic human needs.

Gliessman, S. R., ed. 1990. *Agroecology: Researching the ecological basis for sustainable agriculture*. Ecological Studies Series no. 78. New York: Springer-Verlag.
> This book provides examples of agricultural systems employed in different parts of the world, both tropical and temperate zones, and the ecological issues associated with agricultural production.

Jenkins, M. B., ed. 1998. *The business of sustainable forestry: Case studies*. Chicago: J.D. and K.T. MacArthur Foundation.
> This excellent volume integrates and analyzes a series of 21 case studies that provide a composite snapshot of the business of sustainable forestry; presents management practices, techniques, and technologies.

Orians, G., ed. 1986. *Ecological knowledge and environmental problem solving*. Washington, D.C.: National Academy Press.
> An excellent introduction to the application of the science of ecology to addressing environmental problems; excellent case studies dealing with sustainable forestry and fisheries.

Pesek, J., ed. 1989. *Alternative agriculture*. Washington, D.C.: National Academy Press.
> This volume includes 11 case studies that describe in detail the practices and performance of alternative farming systems in the United States.

Taken from

# Environment: The Science Behind the Stories
## Second Edition

### by Jay Withgott and Scott Brennan

# PART TWO

# Environmental Issues and the Search for Solutions

Canal Street, New Orleans, after Hurricane Katrina

# 8 Human Population

Hong Kong, China

## Upon successfully completing this chapter, you will be able to:

▶ Assess the scope of human population growth

▶ Evaluate how human population, affluence, and technology affect the environment

▶ Explain and apply the fundamentals of demography

▶ Outline and assess the concept of demographic transition

▶ Describe how wealth and poverty, the status of women, and family planning programs affect population growth

▶ Characterize the dimensions of the HIV/AIDS epidemic

Billboard in Chengdu, China, promoting One-Child Policy

# Central Case:
# China's One-Child Policy

"Population growth is analogous to a plague of locusts. What we have on this earth today is a plague of people."
—TED TURNER,
MEDIA MAGNATE AND SUPPORTER OF THE UNITED NATIONS POPULATION FUND

"There is no population problem."
—SHELDON RICHMAN,
SENIOR EDITOR,
CATO INSTITUTE

The People's Republic of China is the world's most populous nation, home to one-fifth of the 6.5 billion people living on Earth at the start of 2006. When Mao Zedong founded the country's current regime 57 years earlier, roughly 540 million people lived in a mostly rural, war-torn, impoverished nation. Mao believed population growth was desirable, and under his leadership China grew and changed. By 1970, improvements in food production, food distribution, and public health allowed China's population to swell to approximately 790 million people. At that time, the average Chinese woman gave birth to 5.8 children in her lifetime.

Unfortunately, the country's burgeoning population and its industrial and agricultural development were eroding the nation's soils, depleting its water, leveling its forests, and polluting its air. Chinese leaders realized that the nation might not be able to feed its people if their numbers grew much larger. They saw that continued population growth could exhaust resources and threaten the stability and economic progress of Chinese society. The government decided to institute a population-control program that precluded large numbers of Chinese couples from having more than one child.

The program began with education and outreach efforts encouraging people to marry later and have fewer children. Along with these efforts, the Chinese government increased the accessibility of contraceptives and abortion. By 1975, China's annual population growth rate had dropped from 2.8% to 1.8%. To further decrease birthrates, in 1979 the government took the more drastic step of instituting a system of rewards and punishments to enforce a one-child limit. One-child families received better access to schools, medical care, housing, and government jobs, and mothers with only one child were given longer maternity leaves. Families with more than one child, meanwhile, were subjected to social scorn and ridicule, employment discrimination, and monetary fines. In some cases, the fines exceeded half the offending couple's annual income.

In enforcing these policies, China has, in effect, been conducting one of the largest and most controversial social experiments in history. In purely quantitative terms, the experiment has been a major success; the nation's growth rate is now down to 0.6%, making it easier for the country to deal with its many social, economic, and environmental challenges. However, China's population control policies have also produced unintended consequences, such as widespread killing of female infants, an unbalanced sex ratio, and a black-market trade in teen-aged girls. Moreover, the policies have elicited intense criticism from those who oppose government intrusion into personal reproductive choices.

China embarked on its policy because its leaders felt it necessary. As other nations become more and more crowded, might their governments also feel forced to turn to drastic policies that restrict individual freedoms? In this chapter, we examine human population dynamics worldwide, consider their causes, and assess their consequences for the environment and our society.

# Human Population Growth: Baby 6 Billion and Beyond

While China was working to slow its population growth and speed its economic growth, on the other side of the Eurasian continent, a milestone was reached in 1999. On the morning of October 12 of that year, the first cries of a newborn baby in Sarajevo, Bosnia-Herzegovina, marked the arrival of the six-billionth human being on our planet (Figure 8.1). At least that was how the milestone was symbolically marked by the United Nations, which monitors human population growth, among other global trends.

Just how much is 6 billion? We often have trouble conceptualizing the scale of huge numbers like a billion. Keep in mind that a billion is 1,000 times greater than a million. If you were to count once each second without ever sleeping, it would take over 30 years to reach a billion. In order to put a billion miles on your car, you would need to drive from New York to Los Angeles more than 350,000 times.

**FIGURE 8.1**  U.N. Secretary-General Kofi Annan recognized the newborn son of Fatima Nevic and her husband, Jasminko, as our six-billionth neighbor. Although it is impossible to know the precise moment—or day, week, or even month—the world's population reached 6 billion, U.N. population experts pinpointed October 12, 1999, as the best approximation to make the symbolic declaration. Many observers interpreted the selection of a child born in war-ravaged Sarajevo as a harbinger of the hard times that could face future generations as population grows and competition for scarce resources increases.

## The human population is growing nearly as fast as ever

As we saw in Chapter 1 (▶pp. 4–5), the human population has been growing at a tremendous rate. Our population has doubled just since 1964 and is growing by roughly 78 million people annually (nearly 2.5 people every *second*). This is the equivalent of adding all the people of California, Texas, and New York to the world each year. It took until after 1800, virtually all of human history, for our population to reach 1 billion. Yet we reached 2 billion by 1930, and 3 billion in just 30 more years, in 1960. Our population added its next billion in just 15 years (1975), its next billion in a mere 12 years (1987), and its most recent billion in another 12 years (Figure 8.2). Think about when you were born and how many people have been added to the planet just since that time. This unprecedented growth means that today's generations are in circumstances that previous generations never experienced. Our grandparents never had to deal with the number of people that crowd our planet today.

How and why has our growth accelerated? We saw in Chapter 5 (▶ p. 136) how exponential growth—the increase in a quantity by a *fixed percentage* per unit time—accelerates the absolute increase of population size over time, just as compound interest accrues in a savings

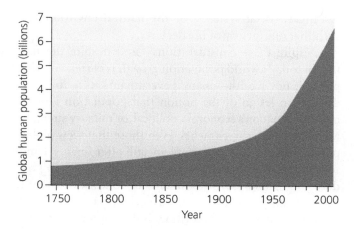

**FIGURE 8.2** The global human population has grown exponentially, rising from less than 1 billion in 1800 to over 6.5 billion today. Data from U.S. Bureau of the Census.

account. The reason, you will recall, is that a given percentage of a large number is a greater quantity than the same percentage of a small number. Thus, even if the growth rate remains steady, population size will increase by greater increments with each successive generation.

In fact, our growth rate has not remained steady. Instead, for much of the 20th century, the growth rate of the human population actually rose from year to year. It peaked at 2.1% during the 1960s and has declined to 1.2% since then. Although 1.2% may sound small, exponential growth endows small numbers with large consequences. For instance, a hypothetical population starting with 1 man and 1 woman that grows at 1.2% gives rise to a population of 2,939 after 40 generations and 112,695 after 60 generations. In today's world, rates of annual growth vary greatly from region to region. Figure 8.3 maps this variation.

At a 2.1% annual growth rate, a population doubles in size in only 33 years. For low rates of increase, we can estimate doubling times with a handy rule-of-thumb. Just take the number 70, and divide it by the annual percentage growth rate: 70 ÷ 2.1 = 33.3. Had China not instituted its one-child policy—that is, had its growth rate remained unchecked at 2.8%—it would have taken only 25 years to double in size. Had population growth continued at this rate, China's population would have surpassed 2 billion people in 2004.

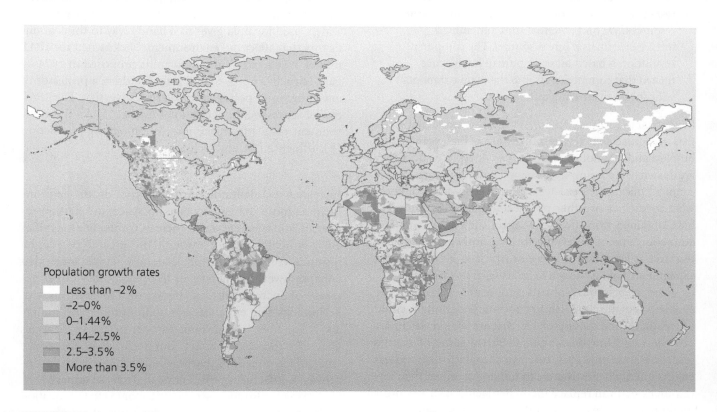

Population growth rates
- Less than –2%
- –2–0%
- 0–1.44%
- 1.44–2.5%
- 2.5–3.5%
- More than 3.5%

**FIGURE 8.3** A map of population growth rates from the period 1990–1995 shows great variation from place to place. Population is growing fastest in tropical regions and in some desert and rainforest areas that have historically been sparsely populated. Data from Center for International Earth Science Information Network (CIESIN), Columbia University; and Harrison, P., and F. Pearce. 2000. *AAAS atlas of population and environment.* Berkeley, CA: University of California Press.

## Is population growth really a "problem"?

Our ongoing population growth has resulted largely from technological innovations, improved sanitation, better medical care, increased agricultural output, and other factors that have led to a decline in death rates, particularly a drop in rates of infant mortality. Birth rates have not declined as much, so births have outpaced deaths for many years now. Thus, the so-called population problem actually arises from a very good thing—our ability to keep more of our fellow humans alive longer.

Indeed, just as the mainstream view in the day of Thomas Malthus (▸ pp. 4–5) held that population increase was a good thing, there are many people today who argue that population growth poses no problems. Under the Cornucopian view that many economists hold, resource depletion due to population increases is not a problem if new resources can be found to replace depleted resources (▸ p. 43). Libertarian writer Sheldon Richman expressed this view at the time the six-billionth baby was born:

> The idea of carrying capacity doesn't apply to the human world because humans aren't passive with respect to their environment. Human beings create resources. We find potential stuff and human intelligence turns it into resources. The computer revolution is based on sand; human intelligence turned that common stuff into the main component [silicon] of an amazing technology.

In contrast to Richman's point of view, environmental scientists recognize that few resources are actually created by humans and that not all resources can be replaced once they are depleted. For example, once species have gone extinct, we cannot replicate their exact function in ecosystems, or know what medicines or other practical applications we might have obtained from them, or regain the educational and aesthetic value of observing them. Another irreplaceable resource is land, that is, space in which to live; we cannot expand Earth like a balloon to increase its surface area.

Even if resource substitution could hypothetically enable population growth to continue indefinitely, could we maintain the *quality* of life that we would desire for ourselves and our descendants? Surely some of today's resources are bound to be easier or cheaper to use, and less environmentally destructive to harvest or mine, than any resources that can replace them. Replacing such resources might make our lives more difficult or less pleasant. In any case, unless resource availability keeps pace with population growth, the average person in the future will have less space in which to live, less food to eat, and less material wealth than the average person does today. Thus population increases are indeed a problem if they create stress on resources, social systems, or the natural environment, such that our quality of life declines.

Despite these considerations—and despite the fact that in today's world population growth is correlated with poverty, not wealth—many governments have found it difficult to let go of the notion that population growth increases a nation's economic, political, or military strength. Many national governments, even those that view global population increase as a problem, still offer financial and social incentives that encourage their own citizens to produce more children. Governments of countries currently experiencing population declines (such as many in Europe) feel especially uneasy. According to the Population Reference Bureau, more than 3 of every 5 European national governments now take the view that their birth rates are too low, and none state that theirs is too high. However, outside Europe, 56% of national governments feel their birth rates are too high, and only 8% feel they are too low.

## Population is one of several factors that affect the environment

The extent to which population increase can be considered a problem involves more than just numbers of people. One widely used formula gives us a handy way to think about factors that affect the environment. Nicknamed the **IPAT model,** it is a variation of a formula proposed in 1974 by Paul Ehrlich (▸ pp. 5–6) and John Holdren, a professor of environmental policy at Harvard University. The IPAT model represents how our total impact (I) on the environment results from the interaction among population (P), affluence (A), and technology (T):

$$I = P \times A \times T$$

Increased population intensifies impact on the environment as more individuals take up space, use natural resources, and generate waste. Increased affluence magnifies environmental impact through the greater per capita resource consumption that generally has accompanied enhanced wealth. Changes in technology may either decrease or increase human impact on the environment. Technology that enhances our abilities to exploit minerals, fossil fuels, old-growth forests, or ocean fisheries generally increases impact, but technology to reduce smokestack emissions, harness renewable energy, or improve manufacturing efficiency can decrease impact.

We might also add a sensitivity factor (S) to the equation to denote how sensitive a given environment is to human pressures:

$$I = P \times A \times T \times S$$

For instance, the arid lands of western China are more sensitive to human disturbance than the moist regions of southeastern China. Plants grow more slowly in the arid west, making deforestation and soil degradation more likely. Thus, adding an additional person to western China should have more environmental impact than adding one to southeastern China.

We could refine the IPAT equation further by adding terms for the effects of social institutions, such as education, laws and their enforcement, stable and cohesive societies, and ethical standards that promote environmental well-being. Factors like these all affect how population, affluence, and technology translate into environmental impact.

Impact can be thought of in various ways, but it can generally be boiled down to either pollution or resource consumption. Pollution became a problem in the modern world once our population grew large enough that we produced great quantities. The depletion of resources by larger and hungrier populations has been a focus of scientists and philosophers since Malthus's time. Recall how on Easter Island (▶ pp. 8–9), islanders brought down their own civilization by depleting their most important limited resource, trees. History offers other cases in which resource depletion helped end civilizations, from the

Mayans to the Mesopotamians. Some environmental scientists have predicted similar problems for our global society in the near future if we do not manage to embark on a path toward sustainability (Figure 8.4).

However, as we noted in Chapter 1, Malthus and his "neo-Malthusian" followers have not yet seen their direst predictions come true. The reason is that we have developed technology—the T in the IPAT equation—time and again to alleviate our strain on resources and allow us to further expand our population. For instance, we have employed technological advances to increase global agricultural production faster than our population has risen (▶ pp. 278–279).

Modern-day China shows how all elements of the IPAT formula can combine to cause tremendous environmental impact in very little time. The world's fastest-growing economy over the past two decades, China is "demonstrating what happens when large numbers of poor people rapidly become more affluent," in the words of Earth Policy Institute president Lester Brown. While millions of Chinese are increasing their material wealth and their consumption of resources, the country is battling unprecedented environmental challenges brought

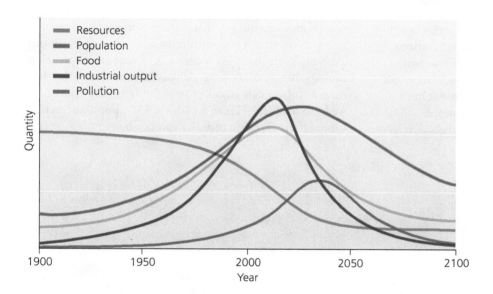

**FIGURE 8.4** Environmental scientists Donella Meadows, Jorgen Randers, and Dennis Meadows used computer simulations to generate a series of projections of trends in human population, resource availability, food production, industrial output, and pollution. Their projections for trends over the coming century are based on data from the past century and current scientific understanding of the environment's biophysical limits. Shown here is their projection for a world in which "society proceeds in a traditional manner without any major deviation from the policies pursued during most of the twentieth century." In this projection, population and production increase until declining nonrenewable resources make further growth impossible, causing population and production to decline rather suddenly. The researchers also ran their simulations with different parameters to examine possible alternative futures. Under a scenario with policies aimed at sustainability, population leveled off at 8 billion, production and resource availability leveled off at medium-high levels, and pollution declined to low levels. Data from Meadows, D., et al. 2004. *Limits to growth: The 30-year update.* White River Junction, VT: Chelsea Green Publishing.

about by its pell-mell economic development. Intensive agriculture has expanded westward out of the country's historic moist rice-growing areas, causing farmland to erode and literally blow away, much like the Dust Bowl tragedy that befell the U.S. agricultural heartland in the 1930s (▸ p. 260). China has overpumped many of its aquifers and has drawn so much water for irrigation from the Yellow River that the once-mighty waterway now dries up in many stretches. Although China has been reducing its air pollution from industry and charcoal-burning homes, the country faces new urban pollution and congestion threats from rapidly increasing numbers of automobiles. As the world's developing countries try to attain the level of material prosperity that industrialized nations enjoy, China is a window on what much of the rest of the world could soon become.

**Weighing** the **Issues:**
### Population Growth and Reproductive Freedom

It is often suggested that if human population growth remains unchecked, everyone will eventually suffer a poorer quality of life. Would you be willing to make this sacrifice if it meant that people in other countries (such as China) could avoid government-imposed limitations on their reproductive freedom? If your own government ever implemented a strict reproductive policy, how would you feel? Would you rather have the government limit your reproductive freedom or your consumption?

# Demography

As we have seen, it is a fallacy to think of people as being somehow outside nature. Humans exist within their environment as one species out of many. As such, all the principles of population ecology we outlined in Chapter 5 that apply to toads, frogs, and passenger pigeons apply to humans as well. Environmental factors set limits on our population growth, and the environment has a carrying capacity (▸ pp. 136–137) for our species, just as it does for every other.

We happen to be a particularly successful organism, however—one that has repeatedly raised its carrying capacity by developing technology to overcome the natural limits on its growth. We did so with the agricultural and the industrial revolutions (▸ p. 4) and likely before that with our invention of tools (Figure 8.5).

Environmental scientists who have tried to pin a number to the human carrying capacity have come up with wildly differing estimates. The most rigorous estimates range from 1–2 billion people living prosperously in a healthy environment to 33 billion living in extreme poverty in a degraded world of intensive cultivation without natural areas. As our population climbs toward 7 billion and beyond, we may yet continue to find ways to raise our carrying capacity. Given our knowledge of population ecology, however, we have no reason to presume that human numbers can go on growing indefinitely. Indeed, as we have seen (see Figure 5.17d, ▸ p. 138), populations that exceed their carrying capacity can crash.

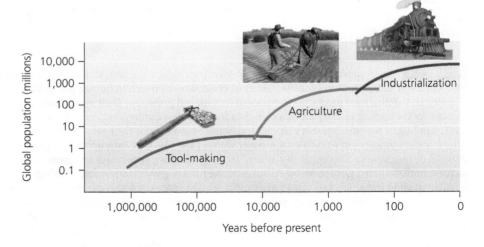

**FIGURE 8.5** Tool making, the advent of agriculture, and industrialization each allowed our species to raise its global carrying capacity. The logarithmic scale of the axes makes it easier to visualize this pattern. Data from Goudie, A. 2000. *The human impact.* Cambridge, MA: MIT Press.

# Demography is the study of human population

The application of population ecology principles to the study of statistical change in human populations is the focus of the social science of **demography.** The field of demography developed along with and partly preceding population ecology, and the disciplines have influenced and borrowed from one another. Data gathered by demographers help us understand how differences in population characteristics and related phenomena (for instance, decisions about reproduction) affect human communities and their environments. Demographers study population size, density, distribution, age structure, sex ratio, and rates of birth, death, immigration, and emigration of humans, just as population ecologists study these characteristics in other organisms. Each of these characteristics is useful for predicting population dynamics and potential environmental impacts.

**Population size** The global human population of more than 6.5 billion consists of well over 200 nations with populations ranging from China's 1.3 billion, India's 1.1 billion, and the 300 million of the United States down to a number of island nations with populations below 100,000 (Figure 8.6). The size that our global population will eventually reach remains to be seen (Figure 8.7). However, population size alone—the absolute number of individuals—doesn't tell the whole story. Rather, a population's environmental impact depends on its density, distribution, and composition (as well as on affluence, technology, and other factors outlined earlier).

**Population density and distribution** People are distributed very unevenly over the globe. In ecological terms, our distribution is clumped (▸ pp. 133–134) at all spatial scales. At the largest scales (Figure 8.8), population density is high in regions with temperate, subtropical, and tropical climates, such as China, Europe, Mexico, southern Africa, and India. Population density is low in regions with extreme-climate biomes, such as desert, deep rainforest, and tundra. Dense along seacoasts and rivers, human population is less dense at locations far from water. At intermediate scales, we cluster together in cities and suburbs and are spread more sparsely across rural areas. At small scales, we cluster in certain neighborhoods and in individual households.

This uneven distribution means that certain areas bear far more environmental impact than others. Just as the Yellow River has experienced intense pressure from millions of Chinese farmers, the world's other major rivers, from the Nile to the Danube to the Ganges to the

**FIGURE 8.6** The world's nations range in human population from several thousand (on some South Pacific islands) up to China's 1.3 billion. Shown here are the 2005 populations for the world's most populous 15 countries, followed by a selection of other countries. Data from Population Reference Bureau. 2005. *2005 world population data sheet.*

Mississippi, have all received more than their share of human impact. The urban way of life entails the packaging and transport of goods, intensive fossil fuel consumption, and hotspots of pollution. However, people's concentration in cities relieves pressure on ecosystems in less-populated areas by releasing some of them from direct human development (▸ p. 395).

At the same time, areas with low population density are often vulnerable to environmental impacts, because the reason they have low populations in the first place is that they are sensitive and cannot support many people (a high S value in our revised IPAT model). Deserts, for instance, are easily affected by development that commandeers a substantial share of available water. Grasslands can be turned to deserts if they are farmed too intensively, as has happened across vast stretches of the Sahel region

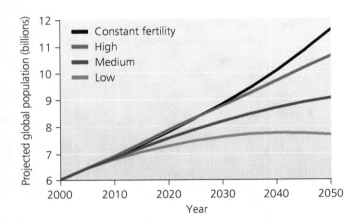

The United Nations predicts trajectories of world population growth, presenting its estimates in several scenarios based on different assumptions of fertility rates. In this 2004 projection, population is estimated to reach 11.7 billion in the year 2050 if fertility rates remain constant at 2004 levels (top line in graph). However, U.N. demographers expect fertility rates to continue falling, so they arrived at a best guess (*medium* scenario) of 9.1 billion for the human population in 2050. In the *high* scenario, if women on average have 0.5 child more than in the medium scenario, population will reach 10.6 billion in 2050. In the *low* scenario, if women have 0.5 child less than in the medium scenario, the world will contain 7.7 billion people in 2050. Data from United Nations Population Division. 2004. *World population prospects: The 2004 revision.*

bordering Africa's Sahara Desert, in the Middle East, and in parts of China and the United States.

**Age structure** Data on the age structure or age distribution of human populations are especially valuable to demographers trying to predict future dynamics of populations. As we saw in Chapter 5 (▶ p. 134), large proportions of individuals in young age groups portend a great deal of reproduction and, thus, rapid population growth. Examine age pyramids for the nations of Canada and Madagascar (Figure 8.9). Not surprisingly, it is Madagascar that has the greater population growth rate. In fact, its annual growth rate, 2.7%, is 9 times that of Canada's 0.3%.

By causing dramatic reductions in the number of children born since 1970, China virtually guaranteed that its population age structure would change. Indeed, in 1995 the median age in China was 27; by 2030 it will be 39. In 1997 there were 125 children under age 5 for every 100 people 65 or older in China, but by 2030 there will be only 32. The number of people older than 65 will rise from 100 million in 2005 to 236 million in 2030 (Figure 8.10). This dramatic shift in age structure will challenge China's economy, health care systems, families, and military forces because fewer working-age people will be available to support social programs that assist the increasing number of older people. However, the shift in age structure also reduces the proportion of dependent children. The reduced

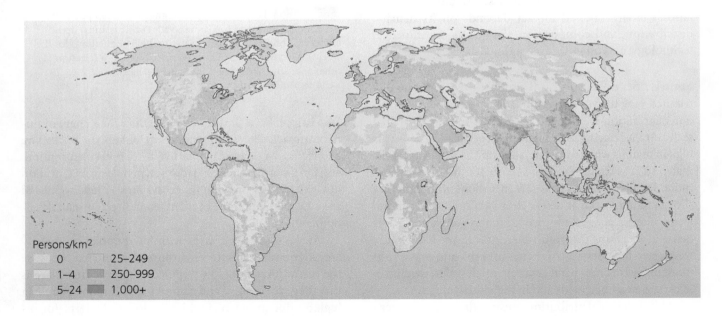

Human population density varies tremendously from one region to another. Arctic and desert regions have the lowest population densities, whereas areas of India, Bangladesh, and eastern China have the densest populations. Data are for 2000, from Center for International Earth Science Information Network (CIESIN), Columbia University; and Centro Internacional de Agricultura Tropical (CIAT), 2004.

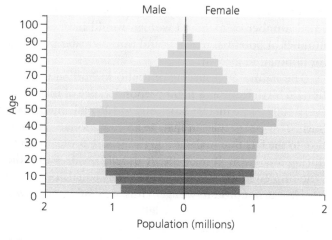

**(a) Age pyramid of Canada in 2005**

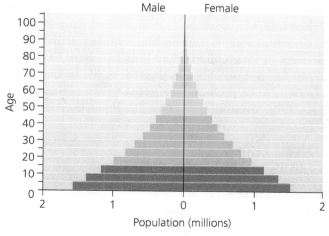

**(b) Age pyramid of Madagascar in 2005**

**FIGURE 8.9** Canada (**a**) shows a balanced age structure, with relatively even numbers of individuals in various age classes. Madagascar (**b**) shows an age distribution heavily weighted toward young people. Madagascar's population growth rate is 9 times that of Canada's. Go to **GRAPHIt!** at www.aw-bc.com/withgott or on the student CD-ROM. Data from U.N. Population Division.

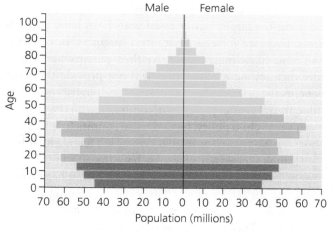

**(a) Age pyramid of China in 2005**

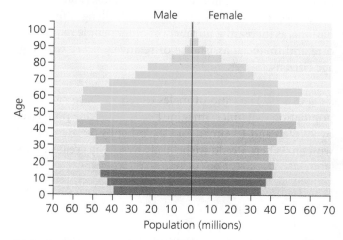

**(b) Projected age pyramid of China in 2030**

**FIGURE 8.10** As China's population ages, older people will outnumber the young. Age pyramids show the predicted graying of the Chinese population between 2005 (**a**) and 2030 (**b**). Today's children may, as working-age adults (**c**), face pressures to support greater numbers of older citizens than has any previous generation. Data from U.N. Population Division.

**(c) Young female factory workers in Hong Kong**

number of young adults may mean a decrease in the crime rate. Moreover, older people are often productive members of society, contributing volunteer activities and services to their children and grandchildren. Clearly, in terms of both benefits and drawbacks, life in China will continue to be profoundly affected by the particular approach its government has taken to population control.

**Weighing the Issues:**
## China's Reproductive Policy

Consider the benefits as well as the problems associated with a reproductive policy such as China's. Do you think a government should be able to enforce strict penalties for citizens who fail to abide by such a policy? If you disagree with China's policy, what alternatives can you suggest for dealing with the resource demands of a quickly growing population?

This pattern of aging in the population is occurring in many countries, including the United States (Figure 8.11). Older populations will present new challenges for many nations, as increasing numbers of older people require the care and financial assistance of relatively fewer working-age citizens.

**Sex ratios** The ratio of males to females also can affect population dynamics. Imagine two islands, one populated by 99 men and 1 woman and the other by 50 men and 50 women. Where would we be likely to see the greatest population increase over time? Of course, the island with an equal number of men and women would have a greater number of potential mothers and thus a greater potential for population growth.

The naturally occurring sex ratio in human populations at birth features a slight preponderance of males; for every 100 female infants born, 105 to 106 male infants are born. This phenomenon may be an evolutionary adaptation to the fact that males are slightly more prone to death during any given year of life. It usually ensures that the ratio of men to women is approximately equal at the time people reach reproductive age. Thus, a slightly uneven sex ratio at birth may be beneficial. However, a greatly distorted ratio can lead to problems.

In recent years, demographers have witnessed an unsettling trend in China: The ratio of newborn boys to girls has become strongly skewed. In the 2000 census, 120 boys were reported born for every 100 girls. Some provinces reported sex ratios as high as 138 boys for every 100 girls. A leading hypothesis for these unusual sex ratios is that many parents, having learned the sex of their fetuses by ultrasound, are selectively aborting female fetuses. Traditionally, Chinese culture has valued sons because they can carry on the family name, assist with farm labor in rural areas, and care for aging parents. Daughters, in contrast, will most likely marry and leave their parents, as the culture dictates. As a result, they will not provide the same benefits to their parents as will sons. Sociologists hold that this cultural gender preference, combined with the government's one-child policy, has led some couples to selectively abort female fetuses or to abandon or kill female infants.

China's skewed sex ratio may have the effect of further lowering population growth rates. However, it has proved tragic for the "missing girls." It is also beginning to have the undesirable social consequence of leaving many Chinese men single. This, in turn, has resulted in a grim new phenomenon. In parts of rural China, teen-aged girls are being kidnapped and sold to families in other parts of the country as brides for single men.

## Population growth depends on rates of birth, death, immigration, and emigration

Just as they do for other organisms, rates of birth, death, immigration, and emigration help determine whether a human population grows, shrinks, or remains stable. The formula for measuring population growth that we used in Chapter 5 (▶ p. 135) also pertains to humans: birth and immigration add individuals to a population, whereas death and emigration remove individuals. Technological advances have led to a dramatic decline in

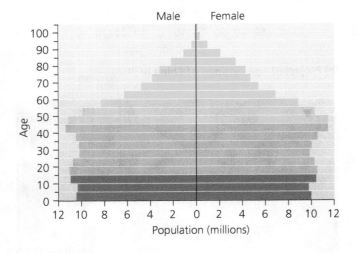

**FIGURE 8.11** The "baby boom" is visible in the 2005 age pyramid for the United States, in the age brackets between 40 and 50. In future years the nation will experience an aging population as baby-boomers grow older. Data from U.N. Population Division.

human death rates, widening the gap between birth rates and death rates and resulting in the global human population expansion.

In today's ever-more-crowded world, immigration and emigration are playing increasingly large roles. Refugees, people forced to flee their home country or region, have become more numerous in recent decades as a result of war, civil strife, and environmental degradation. The United Nations puts the number of refugees who flee to escape poor environmental conditions at 25 million per year and possibly many more. Often the movement of refugees causes environmental problems in the receiving region as these desperate victims try to eke out an existence with no livelihood and with no cultural or economic attachment to the land or incentive to conserve its resources. The millions who fled Rwanda following the genocide there in the mid-1990s, for example, inadvertently destroyed large areas of forest while trying to obtain fuelwood, food, and shelter to stay alive once they reached the Democratic Republic of Congo (Figure 8.12).

For most of the past 2,000 years, China's population has been relatively stable. The first significant increases resulted from enhanced agricultural production and a powerful government during the Qing, or Manchu, Dynasty in the 1800s. Population growth began to outstrip food supplies by the mid-1850s, and quality of life for the average Chinese peasant began to decline. From the mid-1800s, an era of increased European intervention in China, until 1949, China's population grew very slowly, at about 0.3% per year. This slow population growth was due, in part, to food shortages and political instability. As we have seen, population growth rates rose again follow-

| Table 8.1 | Trends in China's Population Growth | | | |
|---|---|---|---|---|
| Measure | 1950 | 1970 | 1990 | 2005 |
| Total fertility rate | 5.8 | 5.8 | 2.2 | 1.6 |
| Rate of natural population increase (% per year) | 1.9 | 2.6 | 1.4 | 0.6 |
| Doubling time (years) | 37 | 27 | 49 | 117 |

Data from China Population Information and Research Center, 2005; and Population Reference Bureau. 2005. *2005 World population data sheet.*

ing Mao's establishment of the People's Republic, and they have declined since the establishment of the one-child policy (Table 8.1).

Since 1970, growth rates in many countries have been declining, even without population control policies, and the global growth rate has declined (Figure 8.13). This decline has come about, in part, from a steep drop in birth rates.

## A population's total fertility rate influences population growth

One key statistic demographers calculate to examine a population's potential for growth is the **total fertility rate (TFR)**, or the average number of children born per female member of a population during her lifetime. **Replacement fertility** is the TFR that keeps the size of a population stable. For humans, replacement fertility is equal to a TFR of 2.1. When the TFR drops below 2.1, population size, in the absence of immigration, will shrink.

**FIGURE 8.12** The flight of refugees from Rwanda into the Democratic Republic of Congo in 1994 following the Rwandan genocide caused tremendous hardship for the refugees and tremendous stress on the environment into which they moved.

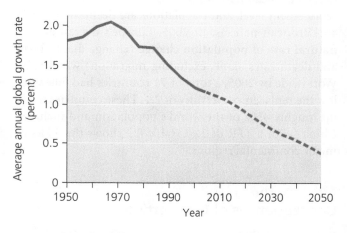

**FIGURE 8.13** The annual growth rate of the global human population peaked in the 1960s and has been declining since then. The dashed line indicates projected future trends. Data from United Nations Population Division. 2004. *World population prospects: The 2004 revision.*

| Table 8.2 | Total Fertility Rates for Major Continental Regions |
|-----------|------------------------------------------------------|

| Region | Total fertility rate (TFR) |
|--------|---------------------------|
| Africa | 5.1 |
| Latin America and the Caribbean | 2.6 |
| Asia | 2.5 |
| Oceania | 2.1 |
| North America | 2.0 |
| Europe | 1.4 |

Data from Population Reference Bureau. 2005. *2005 World population data sheet.*

Various factors influence TFR and have acted to drive it downward in many countries in recent years. Historically, people tended to conceive many children, which helped ensure that at least some would survive, but lower infant mortality rates have made this less necessary. Increasing urbanization has also driven TFR down; whereas rural families need children to contribute to farm labor, in urban areas children are usually excluded from the labor market, are required to go to school, and impose economic costs on their families. If a government provides some form of social security, as most do these days, parents need fewer children to support them in their old age when they can no longer work. Finally, with greater education and changing roles in society, women tend to shift into the labor force, putting less emphasis on child rearing.

All these factors have come together in Europe, where TFR has dropped from 2.6 to 1.4 in the past half-century. Every European nation now has a fertility rate below the replacement level, and populations are declining in 18 of 43 European nations. In 2005, Europe's overall annual **natural rate of population change** (change due to birth and death rates alone, excluding migration) was −0.1%. Worldwide by 2005, a total of 71 countries had fallen below the replacement fertility of 2.1. These countries made up roughly 45% of the world's population and included China (with a TFR of 1.6). Table 8.2 shows the TFRs of major continental regions.

**Weighing the Issues:**

## Consequences of Low Fertility?

In the United States, Canada, and every European nation, the total fertility rate has now dipped below the replacement fertility rate. What economic or social consequences do you think might result from below-replacement fertility rates?

## Some nations have experienced a change called the demographic transition

Many nations that have lowered their birth rates and TFRs have been going through a similar set of interrelated changes. In countries with good sanitation, good health care, and reliable food supplies, more people than ever before are living long lives. As a result, over the past 50 years the life expectancy for the average person has increased from 46 to 67 years as the global crude death rate has dropped from 20 deaths per 1,000 people to 9 deaths per 1,000 people. Strictly speaking, **life expectancy** is the average number of years that an individual in a particular age group is likely to continue to live, but often people use this term to refer to the average number of years a person can expect to live from birth. Much of the increase in life expectancy is due to reduced rates of infant mortality. Societies going through these changes are mostly the ones that have undergone urbanization and industrialization and have been able to generate personal wealth for their citizens.

To make sense of these trends, demographers developed a concept called the **demographic transition.** This is a model of economic and cultural change proposed in the 1940s and 1950s by demographer Frank Notestein and elaborated on by others to explain the declining death rates and birth rates that have occurred in Western nations as they became industrialized. Notestein believed nations moved from a stable pre-industrial state of high birth and death rates to a stable post-industrial state of low birth and death rates. Industrialization, he proposed, caused these rates to fall naturally by first decreasing mortality and then lessening the need for large families. Parents would thereafter choose to invest in quality of life rather than quantity of children. Because death rates fall before birth rates fall, a period of net population growth results. Thus, under the demographic transition model, population growth is seen as a temporary phenomenon that occurs as societies move from one condition to another.

**The pre-industrial stage** Notestein's demographic model describing the population impacts of industrialization proceeds in several stages (Figure 8.14). The first is the **pre-industrial stage,** characterized by conditions that have defined most of human history. In pre-industrial societies, both death rates and birth rates are high. Death rates are high because disease is widespread, medical care rudimentary, and food supplies unreliable and difficult to obtain. Birth rates are high because people must compensate for high mortality rates in infants and young children by having several children. In this stage, children are

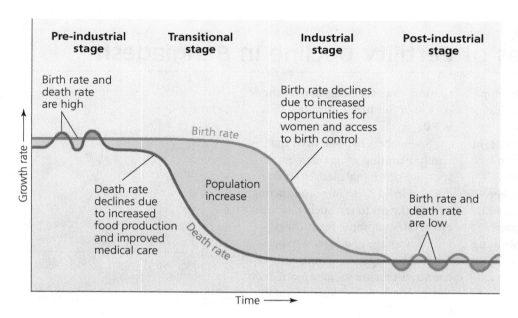

**FIGURE 8.14** The demographic transition is an idealized process that has taken some populations from a pre-industrial state of high birth rates and high death rates to a post-industrial state of low birth rates and low death rates. In this diagram, the wide green area between the two curves illustrates the gap between birth and death rates that causes rapid population growth during the middle portion of this process. Data from Kent, M. M. and K. A. Crews. 1990. *World population: Fundamentals of growth*. Population Reference Bureau.

valuable as additional workers who can help meet a family's basic needs. Populations within the pre-industrial stage are not likely to experience much growth, which is why the human population was relatively stable from Neolithic times until the industrial revolution.

**Industrialization and falling death rates** Industrialization initiates the second stage of the demographic transition, known as the **transitional stage.** This transition from the pre-industrial stage to the industrial stage is generally characterized by declining death rates due to increased food production and improved medical care. Birth rates in the transitional stage remain high, however, because people have not yet grown used to the new economic and social conditions. As a result, population growth surges.

**The industrial stage and falling birth rates** The third stage in the demographic transition is the **industrial stage.** Industrialization increases opportunities for employment outside the home, particularly for women. Children become less valuable, in economic terms, because they do not help meet family food needs as they did in the pre-industrial stage. If couples are aware of this, and if they have access to birth control, they may choose to have fewer children. Birth rates fall, closing the gap with death rates and reducing the rate of population growth.

**The post-industrial stage** In the final stage, the **post-industrial stage,** both birth and death rates have fallen to low and stable levels. Population sizes stabilize or decline slightly. The society enjoys the fruits of industrialization without the threat of runaway population growth.

## Is the demographic transition a universal process?

The demographic transition has occurred in many European countries, the United States, Canada, Japan, and several other developed nations over the past 200 to 300 years. Nonetheless, it is a model that may not apply to all developing nations as they industrialize now and in the future. Some social scientists doubt that it will apply; they point out that population dynamics may be different for developing nations that adopt the Western world's industrial model rather than devising their own. Some demographers assert that the transition will fail in cultures that place greater value on childbirth or grant women fewer freedoms.

Moreover, natural scientists warn that there are not enough resources in the world to enable all countries to attain the standard of living that developed countries now enjoy. It has been estimated that for all nations to enjoy the quality of life that United States citizens enjoy, we would need the natural resources of two more planet Earths. Whether developing nations, which include the vast majority of the planet's people, pass through the demographic transition as developed nations have is one of the most important and far-reaching questions for the future of our civilization and Earth's environment.

## Population and Society

Demographic transition theory links the statistical study of human populations with various societal factors that influence, and are influenced by, population dynamics. Let's now examine a few of these major societal factors more closely.

## Causes of Fertility Decline in Bangladesh

**The Science behind the Story**

Research in developing countries indicates that poverty and overpopulation can create a vicious cycle, in which poverty encourages high fertility and high fertility obstructs economic development. Are there policy steps that such countries can take to bring down fertility rates? Scientific analysis of family-planning programs in the South Asian nation of Bangladesh suggests that the answer is yes.

Bangladesh is one of the poorest, most densely populated countries on the planet. Its 145 million people live in an area about the size of Wisconsin, and 45% of them live below the poverty line. With few natural resources and 1,000 people per km$^2$ (over 2,500/mi$^2$—more than twice the population density of New Jersey), limiting population growth is critically important. As Bangladeshi president Ziaur Rahman declared in 1976, "If we cannot do something about population, nothing else that we accomplish will matter much."

Fortunately, Bangladesh has made striking progress in controlling population growth in the past three decades. Despite stagnant economic development, low literacy rates, poor health care, and limited rights for women, the nation's total fertility rate (TFR) has dropped markedly. In the 1970s, the average woman in Bangladesh gave birth to more than six children over the course of her life. Today, the TFR is 3.0.

Researchers hypothesized that family-planning programs were responsible for Bangladesh's rapid reduction in TFR. Because conducting an experiment to test such a hypothesis is difficult, some researchers took advantage of a natural experiment. By comparing Bangladesh to countries that are socioeconomically similar but have had less success in lowering TFR, such as Pakistan, researchers concluded that Bangladesh succeeded because of aggressive, well-funded outreach efforts that were sensitive to the values of its traditional society.

However, because no two countries are identical, it is difficult to draw firm conclusions from such broad-scale studies. This is why the Matlab Family Planning and Health Services Project, in the isolated rural area of Matlab, Bangladesh, has become one of the best-known experiments in family planning in developing countries. The Matlab Project was an intensive outreach program run collaboratively by the Bangladeshi government and international aid organizations. Each household in the project area received biweekly visits from local women offering counseling, education, and free contraceptives. Compared to a similar government-run program in a nearby area, the Matlab

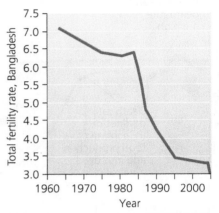

Total fertility rate has declined markedly in Bangladesh in the past 40 years, in part because of the enhanced availability of contraceptives. However, TFR has leveled off in recent years, suggesting that other societal changes are needed to lower it further. Data from Bangladesh Bureau of Statistics; Bangladesh Fertility Survey; The Global Reproductive Health Forum at Harvard; International Centre for Diarrhoeal Disease Research, Bangladesh; National Family Planning and Fertility Survey; United States Agency for International Development.

Project featured more training, more services, and more frequent visits. In both areas, a highly organized health surveillance system gave researchers detailed information about births, deaths, and health-related behaviors such as contraceptive use. The result was an experiment comparing the Matlab Project with the government-run area.

When Matlab Project director James Phillips and his colleagues

### Women's empowerment greatly affects population growth rates

Many demographers had long believed that fertility rates were influenced largely by degrees of wealth or poverty.

However, affluence alone cannot determine TFR, because a number of developing countries now have fertility rates lower than that of the United States. Instead, recent research is highlighting factors pertaining to the social empowerment of women. Drops in TFR have

reviewed a decade's worth of data in 1988, they found that fertility rates had declined in both areas. The decline appeared to be due almost entirely to a rise in contraceptive use, because other factors—such as the average age of marriage—remained the same. Phillips and his colleagues also found that the declines had been significantly greater in the Matlab area than in the government-run area. These findings suggested that high-intensity outreach efforts can affect fertility rates even in the absence of significant improvements in women's status, education, or economic development.

But why exactly was the outreach program successful? One hypothesis was that visits from health care workers had helped convince local women that small families are desirable. However, in 1999, Mary Arends-Kuenning, a graduate student in economics at the University of Michigan, and her colleagues reported that there was no relationship between women's perception of the ideal family size and the number of visits made by outreach workers, either in Matlab or nearby comparison areas. Ideal family size declined equally in all areas. Instead of creating new demand for birth control, the Matlab Project appears to have helped women convert an already-existing desire for fewer children into behaviors, such as

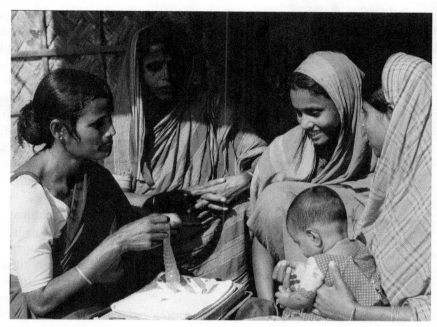

In the Matlab Project, Bangladeshi households received visits from local women offering counseling, education, and free contraceptives.

contraceptive use, that reduce fertility.

Bangladesh's ability to rein in fertility rates despite unfavorable social and economic conditions bodes well for impoverished nations facing explosive population growth. However, significant challenges remain. Since the 1990s, Bangladesh's TFR has appeared to level off at slightly more than 3 children per woman. If rates fail to decline further, the country's population could double to 290 million—nearly the size of today's U.S. population—

within 30 years. Scientific research has helped illuminate the impact of family-planning programs on fertility, but further reductions may require fundamental social, political, and economic changes that are difficult to implement in traditional, resource-strapped countries such as Bangladesh. Nonetheless, the scientific evidence collected at Matlab since the 1970s has played an important role in informing population control efforts in Bangladesh and elsewhere.

been most noticeable in countries where women have gained improved access to contraceptives and education, particularly family-planning education (see "The Science behind the Story," above; also see Figure 8.15 and Figure 8.16).

In 2005, 53% of married women worldwide (ages 15–49) reported using some modern method of contraception to plan or prevent pregnancy. China, at 86%, had the highest rate of contraceptive use of any nation. Six western European nations showed rates of contraceptive

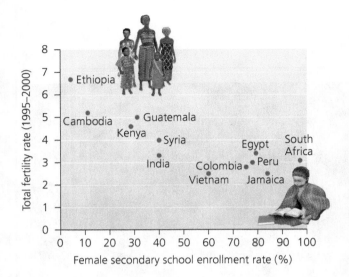

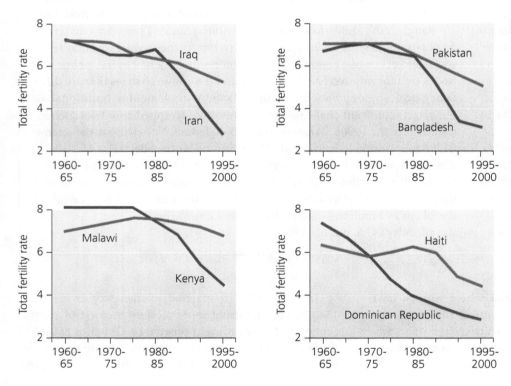

**FIGURE 8.15** Increasing female literacy is strongly associated with reduced birth rates in many nations. Data from McDonald, M., and D. Nierenberg. 2003. Linking population, women, and biodiversity. *State of the World 2003*. Washington, D.C.: Worldwatch Institute.

use above 70%, as did Costa Rica, Cuba, New Zealand, Canada, Brazil, and Thailand (the U.S. rate was 68%). At the other end of the spectrum, 23 African nations had rates below 10%. These low rates of contraceptive use contribute to high fertility rates in sub-Saharan Africa, where the region's TFR is 5.6 children per woman. By comparison, in Asia, where the TFR in 1950 was 5.9, today it is 2.5—in part a legacy of the population control policies of China and some other Asian countries.

These data clearly indicate that in societies where women have little power, substantial numbers of pregnancies are unintended. Unfortunately, many women still lack the information and personal freedom of choice to allow them to make their own decisions about when to have children and how many to have. Today, many social scientists and policymakers recognize that for population growth to slow and stabilize, women need to achieve equal power with men in societies worldwide. Studies show that in societies in which women are freer to decide whether and when to have children, fertility rates have fallen, and the resulting children are better cared for, healthier, and better educated.

Unfortunately, we are still a long way from achieving gender equality. Over two-thirds of the world's people who cannot read, and 60% of those living in poverty, are women. Violence against women remains shockingly common. In many societies, by tradition men restrict women's decision-making abilities, including decisions as to how many children they will bear. The gap between the power held by men and the power held by women is just as obvious at the highest levels of government. Worldwide, only 13% of elected government officials in national legislatures are women (Figure 8.17). The United States

**FIGURE 8.16** Data from four pairs of neighboring countries demonstrate the effectiveness of family planning in reducing fertility rates. In each case, the nation that invested in family planning and (in some cases) made other reproductive rights, education, and health care more available to women (blue lines) reduced its total fertility rate (TFR) far more dramatically than its neighbor (red lines). Data from U.N. Population Division; and Harrison, P., and F. Pearce. 2000. *AAAS atlas of population and environment* Berkeley, CA: University of California Press.

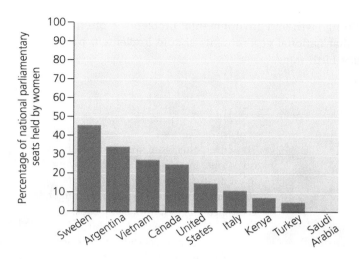

**FIGURE 8.17** Although women make up more than half of the world's population, they are vastly underrepresented in positions of political power. Measured by the percentages of seats held by women in national legislatures, women in some regions fare better than those in others. Note that the United States may not rank quite as highly as you might guess. Data from Inter-Parliamentary Union, Women in national parliaments. (Aug. 2005).

lags behind not only Europe but also many developing nations in the proportion of women in positions of power in its government. As more women win positions of power, perhaps gender equality will become a more tangible reality. Such equality would have environmental consequences, for when women have economic and political power and access to education, they gain the option, and often the motivation, to limit the number of children they bear.

## Population policies and family-planning programs are working around the globe

Data show that funding and policies that encourage family planning have been effective in lowering population growth rates in all types of nations, even those that are least industrialized. No nation has pursued a population control program as extreme as China's, but other rapidly growing nations have implemented less-restrictive programs.

The government of Thailand has relied on an education-based approach to family planning that has reduced birth rates and slowed population growth. In the 1960s, Thailand's growth rate was 2.3%, but by 2005 it had declined to 0.7%. This decline was achieved without a one-child policy. It has resulted, in large part, from government-sponsored programs devoted to family-planning education and increased availability of contraceptives.

India has had long-standing policies, but many observers think they are too weak. Unless it strengthens its efforts to slow population growth, India seems set to overtake China in population soon, and its population is projected to exceed China's by 200 million people in the year 2050. Brazil, Mexico, Iran, Cuba, and many other developing countries have instituted active programs to reduce their population growth. These programs entail setting targets and providing incentives, education, contraception, and reproductive health care.

Many of these programs are working. The data shown in Figure 8.16 are not the only cases in which family-planning programs have helped lower fertility rates. One study in 2000 examined four different pairs of nations located in the same parts of the world, with one country in each pair having a stronger program: Thailand and the Philippines, Pakistan and Bangladesh, Tunisia and Algeria, and Zimbabwe and Zambia. The demographers concluded that in all four cases, the country with the stronger program (Thailand, Bangladesh, Tunisia, and Zimbabwe) initiated or accelerated a decline in fertility with its policies. In the case of Thailand and the Philippines, the researchers also concluded that the Catholic Church's strong presence in the Philippines held back the success of family planning there.

In 1994, the United Nations hosted a milestone conference on population and development in Cairo, Egypt, at which 179 nations endorsed a platform calling on all governments to offer universal access to reproductive health care within 20 years. The conference marked a turn away from older notions of command-and-control population policy geared toward pushing contraception and lowering population to preset targets. Instead, it urged governments to offer better education and health care and to address social needs that bear indirectly on population (such as alleviating poverty, disease, and sexism).

Despite the successes of family planning internationally, the United States has often declined to fund family-planning efforts by the United Nations. Canceling this funding, for example, was one of George W. Bush's first acts on becoming U.S. president in 2001.

---

**Weighing the issues:**
## U.S. Involvement in International Family Planning

From 1998 to 2001, the U.S. government provided $46.5 million to the United Nations Population Fund (UNFPA), whose programs provide education in family planning, HIV/AIDS prevention, and teen pregnancy prevention in many nations, including China. Since then,

Debate over human population growth and environmental problems is often contentious. **Do you believe that national governments should implement policies, subsidies, or other programs to reduce birth rates?**

### Implement ICPD Program of Action

Access to reproductive health care, including family planning, is a basic human right. To exercise this right, men and women need to be informed about family planning. They also need to have access to safe, effective, affordable, and acceptable methods of family planning of their choice.

All national governments should adopt policies, subsidies, and other programs to help implement the Program of Action, which the United Nations agreed to at the International Conference on Population and Development (ICPD), held in Cairo in 1994.

The ICPD is based on principles virtually every country in the world agreed to, one of which is as follows:

... States should take all appropriate measures to ensure, on a basis of equality of men and women, universal access to health-care services, including those related to reproductive health care, which includes family planning and sexual health. Reproductive health-care programs should provide the widest range of services without any form of coercion. All couples and individuals have the basic right to decide freely and responsibly the number and spacing of their children and to have the information, education and means to do so.

In the same way that democratic nations are obligated to assist emerging democracies in holding fair and free elections, developed nations ought to assist developing nations in implementing the ICPD Program of Action. In every society where the principles of the ICPD have been implemented, birth rates have gone down, infant survival rates have gone up, maternal mortality has declined, and the quality of life has improved.

**Timothy Cline** is director of communication at Population Connection, where he has held a variety of positions, including publications manager. He has also served as chief of advocacy and policy research at the Johns Hopkins University Center for Communication Programs. Before joining Population Connection, Cline served as operations manager for the Washington Regional Alliance and was a senior editor at Ecomedia.

### Population Control: A Bad Idea for Governments

To address this issue, we must ask three questions. First, is population growing at an unsustainable rate? Second, are the world's problems—poverty, hunger, ecological degradation, etc.—caused by population growth? And third, do governments possess rightful authority to engage in population control?

1. The world is experiencing historically unprecedented fertility decline. In about half the countries on Earth—including rich and poor, developed and developing—fertility is at or below replacement rate, meaning that in many countries women are not having enough babies to maintain current population levels. Some demographers now worry that entire economies and social welfare systems may face profound difficulties because of this decline.

2. The population growth that has occurred over the past century (from roughly 2 billion to 6 billion) is not the direct cause of severe development problems. For instance, according to the U.N. Population Division, "Even for those environmental problems that are concentrated in countries with rapid population growth, it is not necessarily the case that population increase is the main cause, nor that slowing population growth would make an important contribution to resolving the problem." Persistent development problems are more likely linked to types of economic and political organization (nondemocratic countries tend to have worse environmental records, for instance) and should be addressed through political reform.

3. The quest for government control over such an intimate matter as family size seems prone to abuse, which has occurred in such diverse nations as India, Peru, and China. In China, where the "one child policy" has often been touted as history's most successful population control program, over 100 million women have been forced to abort unborn babies or to be sterilized.

For these practical and ethical reasons, the world's limited development funds could be better spent than in encouraging further fertility decline.

**Douglas A. Sylva** is senior fellow of the Catholic Family and Human Rights Institute, a think tank and lobbying group that consults governments on international social policy. He is also a regular columnist for thefactis.org, focusing on international affairs and development. He received a Ph.D. in political science from Columbia University.

Explore this issue further by accessing **Viewpoints** at www.aw-bc.com/withgott.

Table 8.3  Per Capita Wealth, with Rates of Fertility, Population Growth, and Contraceptive Use, for Selected Nations

| Nation | Per Capita GNI PPP (U.S. $)* | Population increase (% per year) | Children born per woman (TFR) | Population density (per mi$^2$) | Infant mortality (per 1,000) | Percentage of couples using birth control |
|---|---|---|---|---|---|---|
| Ethiopia | 810 | 2.5 | 5.9 | 182 | 100 | 6 |
| Niger | 830 | 3.4 | 8.0 | 29 | 153 | 4 |
| Haiti | 1,680 | 1.9 | 4.7 | 774 | 80 | 22 |
| Cameroon | 2,090 | 2.3 | 5.0 | 89 | 74 | 13 |
| Pakistan | 2,160 | 2.4 | 4.8 | 528 | 85 | 20 |
| India | 3,100 | 1.7 | 3.0 | 869 | 60 | 43 |
| Nicaragua | 3,300 | 2.7 | 3.8 | 115 | 36 | 66 |
| Syria | 3,550 | 2.7 | 3.7 | 257 | 22 | 35 |
| China | 5,530 | 0.6 | 1.6 | 353 | 27 | 86 |
| Brazil | 8,020 | 1.4 | 2.4 | 56 | 27 | 70 |
| Mexico | 9,590 | 1.9 | 2.6 | 142 | 25 | 59 |
| Czech Republic | 18,400 | −0.1 | 1.2 | 335 | 4 | 58 |
| Spain | 25,070 | 0.1 | 1.3 | 223 | 4 | 53 |
| United Kingdom | 31,460 | 0.2 | 1.7 | 635 | 5 | 79 |
| Japan | 30,040 | 0.1 | 1.3 | 876 | 3 | 48 |
| Canada | 30,660 | 0.3 | 1.5 | 8 | 5 | 73 |
| United States | 39,710 | 0.6 | 2.0 | 80 | 7 | 68 |

*GNI PPP is "gross national income in purchasing power parity," a measure that standardizes income and makes it comparable among nations, by converting income to "international" dollars using a conversion factor. International dollars indicate the amount of goods and services one could buy in the United States with a given amount of money. Data from Population Reference Bureau. 2005. *2005 World population data sheet.*

the Bush administration has withheld funds, pointing out that U.S. law prohibits funding any organization that "supports or participates in the management of a program of coercive abortion or involuntary sterilization," and claiming that the Chinese government has been implicated in both these activities. Many nations and organizations criticized the U.S. decision, and the European Union offered additional funding to UNFPA to offset the loss of U.S. contributions. What do you think of the U.S. decision? Should the United States fund family planning efforts in other nations? What conditions, if any, should it place on the use of such funds?

---------------------------------------------------------------

## Poverty is strongly correlated with population growth

The alleviation of poverty, one target of the Cairo conference, has been linked to population because poorer societies tend to show higher population growth rates than do wealthier societies. This pattern is consistent with demographic transition theory. Note in Table 8.3 how poorer nations tend to have higher fertility and growth rates, along with higher birth and infant mortality rates and lower rates of contraceptive use.

Trends such as these have affected the distribution of people on the planet. In 1960, 70% of all people lived in developing nations. By 2005, 81% of the world's population was living in these countries. Moreover, fully 98% of the next billion people to be added to the global population will be born in these poor, less developed regions (Figure 8.18). This is unfortunate from a social standpoint, because these people will be added to the countries that are least able to provide for them. It is also unfortunate from an environmental standpoint, because poverty often results in environmental degradation. People dependent on agriculture in an area of poor farmland, for instance, may need to try to farm even if doing so degrades the soil and is not sustainable. This is largely why Africa's once-productive Sahel region, like many regions of western China, is turning to desert (Figure 8.19). Poverty also drives the hunting of many large mammals in Africa's forests, including the great apes that are now disappearing as local settlers and miners kill them for their "bush meat."

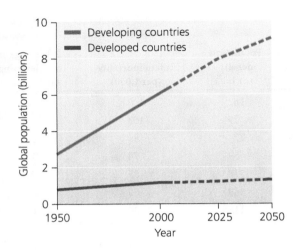

**FIGURE 8.18** Nearly 98% of the next 1 billion people added to Earth's human population will reside in the less developed, poorer parts of the world. The dashed line indicates projected future trends. Data from U.N. Population Division; and Harrison, P., and F. Pearce. 2000. *AAAS atlas of population and environment.* 2000. Berkeley, CA: University of California Press.

## Consumption from affluence creates environmental impact

Poverty can lead people into environmentally destructive behavior, but wealth can produce even more severe and far-reaching environmental impacts. The affluence that characterizes a society such as the United States, Japan, or the Netherlands is built on massive and unprecedented levels of resource consumption. Much of this chapter has dealt with numbers of people rather than on the amount of resources each member of the population consumes or the amount of waste each member produces. The environmental impact of human activities, however, depends not only on the number of people involved but also on the way those people live. Recall the A for affluence in the IPAT equation. Patterns of affluence and consumption are spread unevenly across the world, and affluent societies generally consume resources from other societies as well as from their own.

In Chapter 1 (▶ pp. 6–7, 19, and 25), we introduced the concept of the *ecological footprint,* the cumulative amount of Earth's surface area required to provide the raw materials a person or population consumes and to dispose of or recycle the waste that they produce. Individuals from affluent societies leave a considerably larger per capita ecological footprint (see Figure 1.13, ▶ p. 19). This fact should remind us that the "population problem" does not lie entirely with the developing world. Just as population is rising, so is consumption, and environmental scientists have calculated that we are already living beyond the planet's means to support us sustainably. One recent

**FIGURE 8.19** In the semi-arid Sahel region of Africa, where population is increasing beyond the land's ability to handle it, dependence on grazing agriculture has led to environmental degradation.

analysis concluded that humanity's global ecological footprint surpassed Earth's capacity to support us in 1987 and that our species is now living more than 20% beyond its means (Figure 8.20).

## The wealth gap and population growth contribute to violent conflict

The stark contrast between affluent and poor societies in today's world is, of course, the cause of social as well as

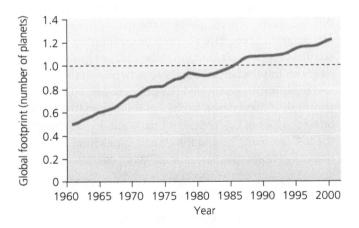

**FIGURE 8.20** The global ecological footprint of the human population is 2.5 times larger than it was in 1961 and now exceeds what Earth can bear in the long run, scientists have calculated. The estimate shown here indicates that we have already overshot our carrying capacity by at least 20%; that is, we are using renewable natural resources 20% faster then they are being replenished. Data from WWF-World Wide Fund for Nature, 2004. *Living planet report.* Gland, Switzerland: WWF.

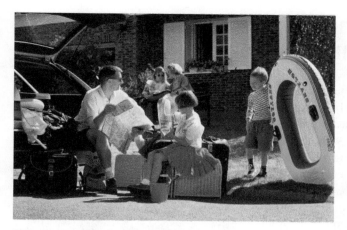

**(a) A family living in the United States**

**(b) A family living in Egypt**

**FIGURE 8.21** A typical U.S. family (**a**) may own a large house, keep numerous material possessions, and have enough money to afford luxuries such as vacation travel. A typical family in a developing nation such as Egypt (**b**) may live in a small, sparsely furnished dwelling with few material possessions and little money or time for luxuries. The ubiquity of television sets, even among poor families of the developing world, means that the world's poor see representations (both real and exaggerated) of wealth in the United States as depicted on American TV shows. Many sociologists hold that this has increased the poor's awareness of the global wealth gap and has spurred aspirations for consumption among the poor of developing nations.

environmental stress. Over half the world's people live below the internationally defined poverty line of U.S. $2 per day. The richest one-fifth of the world's people possesses over 80 times the income of the poorest one-fifth (Figure 8.21). The richest one-fifth also uses 86% of the world's resources. That leaves only 14% of global resources—energy, food, water, and other essentials—for the remaining four-fifths of the world's population to share. As the gap between rich and poor grows wider

as the sheer numbers of those living in poverty continue to increase, it seems reasonable to predict increasing tensions between the "haves" and the "have-nots." This is why the inequitable distribution of wealth is one of the key factors the U.S. Departments of Defense and State take into account when assessing the potential for armed conflict around the world, whether it be conventional warfare or terrorism.

## HIV/AIDS is a major influence on populations in parts of the world

The rising material wealth and falling fertility rates of many industrialized nations today is slowing population growth in accordance with the demographic transition model. Some other nations, however, are not following Notestein's script. Instead, in these countries mortality is beginning to increase, presenting a scenario more akin to Malthus's fears. This is especially the case in countries where the HIV/AIDS epidemic has taken hold (Figure 8.22). African nations are being hit hardest. Of the 38 million people around the world infected with HIV/AIDS as of 2004, 25 million live in the nations of sub-Saharan Africa. The low rate of use of contraceptives, which contributes to this region's high fertility rate, also fuels the expansion of AIDS. One in every 13 people aged 15 to 49 in sub-Saharan Africa is infected with HIV, and for southern African nations, the figure is more than one in five.

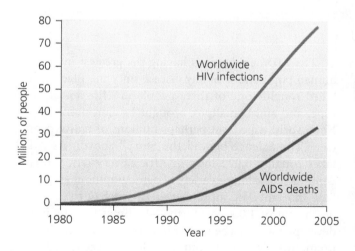

**FIGURE 8.22** AIDS cases are increasing rapidly in much of the world. As of 2004, total cumulative HIV infections since 1980 were estimated at nearly 78 million, and 34 million people are estimated to have died from the disease so far. Data from UNAIDS; and *Vital signs 2005.* Washington, D.C.: Worldwatch Institute.

# AIDS Resistance Genes and the Black Death: An Unexpected Connection?

**The Science behind the Story**

When HIV was first identified as the cause of AIDS in the early 1980s, some scientists predicted that a cure for the disease would be found within a few years. In the two decades that followed, however, progress toward a cure or vaccine remained slow, even as the number infected grew to more that 60 million. Thus, the discovery in 1996 of a genetic mutation that appeared to confer resistance to AIDS was an important breakthrough. Still more surprising was a possible connection between AIDS and the Black Death, a disease that decimated Europe in the mid-14th century.

Beginning in 1984, geneticists Stephen J. O'Brien, Michael Dean, and colleagues at the National Cancer Institute (NCI) began searching for individuals who were naturally resistant to HIV. They gathered genetic samples from people with and without the virus,

trying to identify mutations unique to people who had been exposed to HIV but remained uninfected.

Until the mid-1990s, the search was largely unsuccessful. Then in 1995, NCI researchers identified molecules called chemokines that carry signals from one part of the immune system to another. Other researchers discovered that HIV uses the immune system's own chemokine receptors to penetrate the cell membrane. Together, these advances revealed how HIV gains entry into human hosts. They also gave O'Brien, Dean, and other researchers a promising place to look for resistance genes.

The search quickly produced exciting results. In 1996, three separate groups reported the discovery of a mutation conferring resistance to HIV. The mutation—a deletion of 32 base-pairs of DNA—affected the chemokine receptor CCR5, which is expressed on the surface of macrophages, the first cells HIV

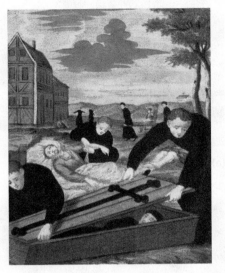

The Black Death killed one of every three Europeans in the 14th century but may have conferred on the descendants of its survivors some resistance to AIDS.

attacks when it enters a new host. People with two copies of the mutation appeared to be immune to HIV. People with one copy developed AIDS, but slowly.

---

The AIDS epidemic is having the greatest impact on human populations of any disease since the Black Death killed roughly one of three people in 14th-century Europe, and since smallpox brought by Europeans to the New World wiped out perhaps millions of native people (see "The Science behind the Story," above). As AIDS takes roughly 6,000 lives in Africa every day, the epidemic is unleashing a variety of demographic changes. Infant mortality in sub-Saharan Africa has risen to 96 deaths out of 1,000 live births—14 times the rate in the developed world. The high numbers of infant deaths and premature deaths of young adults has caused life expectancy in parts of southern Africa to fall from a high of close to 59 years in the early 1990s back down to less than 40 years, where it stood in the early 1950s. AIDS is also leaving behind millions of orphans. As of 2002, 14 million

children under the age of 15 worldwide had lost one or both parents to the disease.

----------------------------------------------------

**Weighing the Issues:**
### HIV/AIDS and Population

What sorts of problems would you predict might occur in the surviving population after a major disease such as AIDS kills a high percentage of the population?

----------------------------------------------------

## Severe demographic changes have social, political, and economic repercussions

Beyond its demographic effects, AIDS is having immediate social, economic, and political consequences. Everywhere in sub-Saharan Africa, AIDS is undermining the

Surprisingly, the mutation was unevenly distributed across human populations. One research team, led by Belgian scientists Michael Samson and Marc Parmentier, found that about 9% of the Caucasians they tested had at least one copy of the mutation, but none of the Japanese or Africans they tested had the mutation. Other groups found similar results, and it soon became clear that the mutation was present only in Europeans and their descendants.

A key step toward answering why the mutation was unique to Europeans occurred when O'Brien and Dean determined when the mutation had first arisen. To do so, they analyzed the mutation's association with distinctive genetic variants, or alleles, on the chromosome. In each generation, the association, or linkage, between the mutation and its neighbors is weakened by recombination, the chromosomal reshuffling that takes place during reproduction. Scientists can thus use the strength of the linkage to identify the mutation's approximate age. When O'Brien and Dean used this technique, they found that the CCR5 mutation was about 700 years old.

That put the mutation's origin at about the time when the Black Death, which most scientists have identified as bubonic plague, was ravaging Europe. Like the AIDS virus, the bacterium responsible for bubonic plague *(Yersinia pestis)* initially attacks macrophages, using them as a refuge before spreading to the rest of the body. Thus a mutation in CCR5 could potentially have conferred resistance to bubonic plague, just as it now confers resistance to AIDS. Under the strong selection pressure of the Black Death, which killed a third of Europe's population, the prevalence of the mutation could have risen greatly. Thus, the researchers suggested, the plague had one positive legacy: it offered the descendants of Europeans who survived it some degree of immunity to AIDS.

As with any exciting hypothesis, other researchers set out to confirm or refute it by testing the idea in different ways. This time, two labs taking different approaches cast doubt on the idea. Joan Mecsas and colleagues at Stanford University experimented with lab mice and found that mice with the CCR5 mutation were *not* protected against bubonic plague.

Shortly before the Mecsas team published its results in February 2004, two researchers from University of California–Berkeley conducted a modeling study that considered the population dynamics of diseases, and found that plague was not the most likely candidate for causing natural selection for the CCR5 mutation. Instead, they suggested that smallpox—another disease that killed millions in the Middle Ages—played this role.

ability of developing countries to make the transition to modern technologies because it is removing many of the youngest and most productive members of society. For example, in 1999 Zambia lost 600 teachers to AIDS, and only 300 new teachers graduated to replace them. In Rwanda, more than one in three college-educated residents of the city of Kigali are infected with the virus. South Africa loses an estimated $7 billion per year to declines in its labor force as AIDS patients fill the nation's hospitals (Figure 8.23). The loss of productive household members to AIDS causes families and communities to break down as income and food production decline while medical expenses and debt skyrocket.

These problems are hitting many countries at a time when their governments are already experiencing what has been called *demographic fatigue.* Demographically

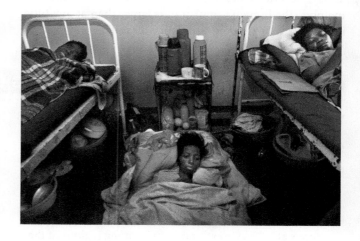

**FIGURE 8.23** AIDS patients occupy 60% of South Africa's hospital beds. By 2010, AIDS in Africa may orphan an estimated 40 million children.

fatigued governments face overwhelming challenges related to population growth, including educating and finding jobs for their swelling ranks of young people. With the added stress of HIV/AIDS, these governments face so many demands that they are stretched beyond their capabilities to address problems. As a result, the problems grow worse, and citizens lose faith in their governments' abilities to help them.

If nations in sub-Saharan Africa—and other regions where the disease is spreading fast, such as India and southeast Asia—do not take aggressive steps soon, and if the rest of the world does not step in to help, these countries could fail to advance through the demographic transition. Instead, their rising death rates could push birth rates back up, potentially causing these countries to fall back to the pre-industrial stage of the demographic transition model. Such an outcome would lead to greater population growth while economic and social conditions worsen. It would be a profoundly negative outcome, both for human welfare and for the well-being of the environment.

If one of humanity's goals is to generate a high standard of living and quality of life for all the world's people, then developing nations must find ways to reduce their population growth. However, those of us living in the industrialized world must also be willing to reduce our consumption. Earth does not hold enough resources to sustain all 6.5 billion of us at the current North American standard of living, nor can we go out and find extra planets; so, we must make the best of the one place that supports us all.

# Conclusion

Today, several years after welcoming its six-billionth member, the human population is larger than at any time in the past. Our growing population, as well as our growing consumption, affects the environment and our ability to meet the needs of all the world's people. Approximately 90% of children born today are likely to live their lives in conditions far less healthy and prosperous than most of us in the industrialized world are accustomed to.

However, there are at least two major reasons to be encouraged. First, although global population is still rising, the *rate* of growth has decreased nearly everywhere, and some countries are even seeing population declines. Most developed nations have passed through the demographic transition, showing that it is possible to lower death rates while stabilizing population and creating more prosperous societies. A second reason to feel encouraged is the progress in expanding rights for women worldwide. Although there is still a long way to go, women are slowly being treated more fairly, receiving better education, obtaining more economic independence, and gaining more ability to control their reproductive decisions. Aside from the clear ethical progress these developments entail, they are helping slow population growth.

Human population cannot continue to rise forever. The question is how it will stop rising: through the gentle and benign process of the demographic transition, through restrictive governmental intervention such as China's one-child policy, or through the miserable Malthusian checks of disease and social conflict caused by overcrowding and competition for scarce resources. Moreover, sustainability demands a further challenge—that we stabilize our population size in time to avoid destroying the natural systems that support our economies and societies. We are indeed a special species. We are the only one to come to such dominance as to change fundamentally so much of Earth's landscape, and even its climate system. We are also the only species with the intelligence needed to turn around an increase in our own numbers before we destroy the very systems on which we depend.

## REVIEWING OBJECTIVES

**You should now be able to:**

**Assess the scope of human population growth**

▶ Our global population of 6.5 billion people adds about 78 million people per year (2.5 people every second). (p. 218)

▶ Our growth rate peaked at 2.1% in the 1960s and now stands at 1.2%. Growth rates vary among regions of the world. (p. 219)

▶ Rising population is a problem to the extent that it depletes resources, intensifies pollution, stresses social systems, or degrades ecosystems, such that the natural environment or our quality of life decline. (p. 220)

**Evaluate how human population, affluence, and technology affect the environment**

▶ The IPAT model summarizes how environmental impact (I) results from interactions among population size (P), affluence (A), and technology (T). (pp. 220–221)

▶ Rising population and rising affluence (leading to greater consumption) each increase environmental impact. Technological advances have frequently exacerbated environmental degradation, but they can also help mitigate our impact. (pp. 220–222)

## Explain and apply the fundamentals of demography

▶ Demography applies principles of population ecology to the statistical study of human populations. (p. 223)
▶ Demographers study size, density, distribution, age structure, and sex ratios of populations, as well as rates of birth, death, immigration, and emigration. (pp. 223–227)
▶ Total fertility rate (TFR) contributes greatly to change in a population's size. (pp. 227–228)

## Outline and assess the concept of demographic transition

▶ The demographic transition model explains why population growth has slowed in industrialized nations. Industrialization and urbanization have reduced the economic need for children, while education and the empowerment of women have decreased unwanted pregnancies. Parents in developed nations choose to invest in quality of life rather than quantity of children. (pp. 228–229)
▶ The demographic transition may or may not proceed to completion in all of today's developing nations. Whether it does is of immense importance for the quest for sustainability. (p. 229)

## Describe how wealth and poverty, the status of women, and family planning programs affect population growth

▶ When women are empowered and achieve equality with men, fertility rates fall, and children tend to be better cared for, healthier, and better educated. (pp. 230–233)
▶ Family-planning programs and reproductive education have successfully reduced population growth in many nations. (pp. 230–233)
▶ Poorer societies tend to have higher population growth rates than do wealthier societies. (p. 235)
▶ The high consumption rates of affluent societies may make their ecological impact greater than that of poorer nations with larger populations. (pp. 236–237)

## Characterize the dimensions of the HIV/AIDS epidemic

▶ About 38 million people worldwide are infected with HIV/AIDS, of which 25 million live in sub-Saharan Africa. (pp. 237–238)
▶ Epidemics that claim large numbers of young and productive members of society influence population dynamics and can have severe social and political ramifications. (pp. 238–240)

## TESTING YOUR COMPREHENSION

1. What is the approximate current human global population? How many people are being added to the population each day?
2. Why has the human population continued to grow in spite of environmental limitations?
3. Contrast the views of environmental scientists with those of the libertarian writer Sheldon Richman and similar-thinking economists over whether population growth is a problem. Why does Richman think the concept of carrying capacity does not apply to human populations?
4. Explain the IPAT model. How can technology either increase or decrease environmental impact? Provide at least two examples.
5. What characteristics and measures do demographers use to study human populations? Which of these help determine the impact of human population on the environment?
6. What is the total fertility rate (TFR)? Can you explain why the replacement fertility for humans is approximately 2.1? How is Europe's TFR affecting its natural rate of population change?
7. Why have fertility rates fallen in many countries?
8. In the demographic transition model, why is the pre-industrial stage characterized by high birth and death rates, and the industrial stage by falling birth and death rates?
9. How does the demographic transition model explain the increase in population growth rates in recent centuries? How does it explain the decrease in population growth rates in recent decades?
10. Why do poorer societies have higher population growth rates than wealthier societies? How does poverty affect the environment? How does affluence affect the environment?

## SEEKING SOLUTIONS

1. China's reduction in birth rates is leading to significant change in the nation's age structure. Review Figure 8.10, which portrays the projected change. You can see that the population is growing older, based on the top-heavy age pyramid for the year 2030. What sorts of effects might this ultimately have on Chinese society? Explain your answer.

2. The World Bank estimates that half the world's people survive on less than the equivalent of two dollars per day. What effect would you expect this situation to have on the political stability of the world? Explain your answer.

3. Apply the IPAT model to the example of China provided in the chapter. How do population, affluence, technology, and ecological sensitivity affect China's environment? Now consider your own country, or your own state. How do population, affluence, technology, and ecological sensitivity affect your environment? How can we regulate the relationship between population and its effects on the environment?

4. Do you think that all of today's developing nations will complete the demographic transition and come to enjoy a permanent state of low birth and death rates? Why or why not? What steps might we as a global society take to help ensure that they do? Now think about developed nations like the United States and Canada. Do you think these nations will continue to lower and stabilize their birth and death rates in a state of prosperity? What factors might affect whether they do so?

5. Imagine that India's prime minister puts you in charge of that nation's population policy. India has a population growth rate of 1.7% per year, a TFR of 3.0, a 43% rate of contraceptive use, and a population that is 72% rural. What policy steps would you recommend, and why?

6. Now imagine that you have been tapped to design population policy for Germany. Germany is losing population at an annual rate of 0.1%, has a TFR of 1.3, a 72% rate of contraceptive use, and a population that is 88% urban. What policy steps would you recommend, and why?

## INTERPRETING GRAPHS AND DATA

Below are graphed data representing the economic condition of the world's population. The y axis indicates the per capita income for each country or region expressed as purchasing power in U.S. dollars (termed *gross national income*

*in purchasing power parity*, or *GNI PPP*; see Table 8.3). The x axis indicates the cumulative percentage of the world population whose per capita GNI PPP is equal to or greater than that country's or region's per capita GNI PPP. The horizontal dotted line indicates the global average per capita GNI PPP.

Percent of world population at various income levels. Data source: Population Reference Bureau. 2005. *World population data sheet 2005.*

1. What percentage of the world population lives at or below the global average per capita GNI PPP? What percentage lives at or below one half of the global average per capita GNI PPP? What percentage lives at or above twice the global average per capita GNI PPP?

2. Given a global average per capita GNI PPP of $8,540 and a world population of 6,477,000,000 people (as of mid-2005), what is the total global GNI PPP? What would the global GNI PPP be if everyone lived at the level of affluence of the United States?

3. How do you personally resolve the ethical conflict between the desirable goal of raising the standard of living of the billions of desperately poor people in the world and the likelihood that increasing their affluence (A in the equation I = PAT) will have a negative impact on the environment?

# CALCULATING ECOLOGICAL FOOTPRINTS

The equation I = PAT (Impact = Population × Affluence × Technology) suggests that a population's size and affluence are not the only determinants of its ecological impact; its technological choices also have an effect. Technologies can be either efficient or wasteful. One way of gauging the relative value of T is to calculate a per capita value of I/A (equivalent to I divided by A divided by P). The table presents per capita values of I (estimated ecological footprints) and A (income). Calculate the relative values of T by completing the blank column.

| Country | Impact (ecological footprint, in acres per capita) | Affluence (per capita income, in GNI PPP) | Technology (I/A) (footprint per $1,000 income) |
|---|---|---|---|
| Bangladesh | 1.2 | $1,980 | 0.61 |
| Colombia | 4.9 | $6,820 | |
| Mexico | 6.4 | $9,590 | |
| Sweden | 14.6 | $29,770 | |
| Thailand | 6.9 | $8,020 | |
| United States | 25.4 | $39,710 | |
| World average | 6.9 | $8,540 | |

*Data sources:* Population Reference Bureau. 2005. *World population data sheet 2005*; and Wackernagel, M., et al. 1999. National natural capital accounting with the ecological footprint concept. *Ecological Economics* 29: 375–390.

1. If the world average value of T were decreased (improved) to that of the United States, what per capita GNI PPP could be supported at the current average per capita ecological footprint of 6.9 acres?
2. What value of T would enable the world's population to live at its current affluence within the 4.9 acres per capita that Wackernagel et al. estimate are available? Do you think this is achievable?
3. Which country's technological choices would you choose to study if you were interested in learning how to maximize your standard of living while minimizing your ecological impact? Using the value of T for this country and the mid-2005 world population of 6,477,000,000, calculate the following:
   (a) The number of people the world could support at the current per capita impact of 6.9 acres and affluence of $8,540
   (b) The number of people the world could support sustainably on the available 4.9 acres per capita and at an affluence of $8,540
   (c) The per capita GNI PPP that the world's current population could achieve on 6.9 acres per capita
   (d) The per capita GNI PPP that the world's current population could achieve on 4.9 acres per capita

## Take It Further

Go to www.aw-bc.com/withgott or the student CD-ROM where you'll find:

▶ Suggested answers to end-of-chapter questions
▶ Quizzes, animations, and flashcards to help you study
▶ *Research Navigator™* database of credible and reliable sources to assist you with your research projects

▶ **GRAPHit!** tutorials to help you master how to interpret graphs
▶ **INVESTIGATEit!** current news articles that link the topics that you study to case studies from your region to around the world

# 9 Soil and Agriculture

Wheat fields in Paraná, Brazil

## Upon successfully completing this chapter, you will be able to:

▶ Explain the importance of soils to agriculture, and describe the impacts of agriculture on soils

▶ Outline major historical developments in agriculture

▶ Delineate the fundamentals of soil science, including soil formation and the properties of soil

▶ State the causes and predict the consequences of soil erosion and soil degradation

▶ Recite the history and explain the principles of soil conservation

No-till farm in
Ceara, Brazil

# Central Case: No-Till Agriculture in Southern Brazil

**"The nation that destroys its soil destroys itself."**
— U.S. PRESIDENT FRANKLIN D. ROOSEVELT

**"There are two spiritual dangers in not owning a farm. One is the danger of supposing that breakfast comes from the grocery, and the other that heat comes from the furnace."**
— CONSERVATIONIST AND PHILOSOPHER ALDO LEOPOLD

In southernmost Brazil, hundreds of thousands of people make their living farming. The warm climate and rich soils of this region's rolling highlands and coastal plains have historically made for bountiful harvests. However, repeated cycles of plowing and planting over many decades diminished the productivity of the soil. More and more topsoil—the valuable surface layer of soil richest in organic matter and nutrients—was being eroded away by water and wind. Meanwhile, the synthetic fertilizers used to restore nutrients were polluting area waterways. Yields were falling, and by 1990 farmers were looking for help.

As a result, many of southern Brazil's farmers abandoned the conventional practice of tilling the soil after harvests. In its place, they turned to *no-tillage* farming, otherwise known as *zero-tillage, no-till,* or in Brazil, *plantio direto.* Turning the earth by tilling (plowing, disking, harrowing, or chiseling) aerates the soil and works weeds and old crop residue into the soil to nourish it. Tilling, however, also leaves the surface bare of vegetation for a period of time, during which erosion by wind and water can remove precious topsoil. Although tilling historically boosted the productivity of agriculture in Europe, many experts now think it is less appropriate for soils in subtropical regions such as southern Brazil. The reason is that the heavy rainfall of tropical and subtropical regions results in greater rates of erosion, causing tilled soils to lose organic matter and nutrients.

Working with agricultural scientists and government extension agents, southern Brazil's farmers began leaving crop residues on their fields after harvesting, and planting "cover crops" to keep soil protected during periods when they weren't raising a commercial crop.

When they went to plant the next crop, they merely cut a thin, shallow groove into the soil surface, dropped in seeds, and covered them. They did not invert the soil as they had when tilling, and the soil stayed covered with plants or their residues at all times, reducing erosion by 90%.

With less soil eroding away, and more organic material being added to it, the soil held more water and was better able to support crops. The improved soil quality meant better plant growth and greater crop production. In the state of Santa Catarina, maize yields per hectare increased by 47% between 1991 and 1999, wheat yields rose by 82%, and soybean yields by 83%, according to local farmers, extension agents, and international scientists. In the states of Paraná and Rio Grande do Sul, maize yields were up 67% over 10 years, and soybean yields were up 68%.

Besides boosting yields, no-till farming methods reduced farmers' costs, because farmers now used less labor and less fuel. No-till agriculture spread quickly in the region as farmers saw their neighbors' successes and traded information through "Friends of the Land" clubs organized on local, municipal, regional, and statewide levels. In Paraná and Rio Grande do Sul, the area being farmed with no-till methods shot up from 700,000 ha (1.7 million acres) in 1990 to 10.5 million ha (25.9 million acres) in 1999, when it involved 200,000 farmers. In Santa Catarina, where farms are generally smaller, over 100,000 farmers now apply no-till methods to 880,000 ha (2.2 million acres) of farmland. No-till farming is now spreading northward into Brazil's tropical regions and to other parts of Latin America.

By enhancing soil conditions and reducing erosion, no-till techniques have benefited southern Brazil's society and environment as well; its air, waterways, and ecosystems are less polluted. Similar effects are being felt in parts of the United States and elsewhere in the world where no-till and reduced-tillage methods are increasingly being applied.

Reduced tillage is certainly not a panacea for all areas of the world. In general, tropical areas benefit more than temperate regions, because erosion is greater in the tropics and hot weather can overheat tilled soil. The benefits and drawbacks of different tillage approaches vary with location, soil characteristics, and type of crop. In regions suitable for reduced tillage, proponents say these approaches can help make agriculture sustainable. We will need sustainable agriculture if we are to feed the world's human population while protecting the natural environment, including the soils that vitally support our production of food.

# Soil: The Foundation for Feeding a Growing Population

As the human population has increased, so have the amounts of land and resources we devote to agriculture, which currently covers 38% of Earth's land surface. We can define **agriculture** as the practice of raising crops and livestock for human use and consumption. We obtain most of our food and fiber from **cropland,** land used to raise plants for human use, and **rangeland** or pasture, land used for grazing livestock.

Healthy soil is vital for agriculture, for forestry (Chapter 12), and for the functioning of Earth's natural systems. **Soil** is not merely lifeless dirt; it is a complex plant-supporting system consisting of disintegrated rock, organic matter, water, gases, nutrients, and microorganisms. Each of these components can be altered by the way we treat soil. Productive soil is a renewable resource, but if we abuse it through careless or uninformed practices, we can greatly reduce its productivity.

## As population and consumption increase, soils are being degraded

If we are to feed the world's rising human population, we will need to change our diet patterns or increase agricultural production—and do so sustainably, without degrading the environment and reducing its ability to support agriculture. However, we cannot simply keep expanding agriculture into new areas, because land suitable and available for farming is running out. Instead, we must find ways to improve the efficiency of food production in areas that are already in agricultural use.

Today many lands unsuitable for farming are being farmed, causing considerable environmental damage. Mismanaged agriculture has turned grasslands into deserts and has removed ecologically precious forests. It has extracted nutrients from soils and added them to water bodies, harming both systems. It has diminished biodiversity; encouraged invasive species; and polluted soil, air, and water with toxic chemicals. Poor agricultural practices have allowed countless tons of fertile soil to be blown and washed away.

As our planet gains over 70 million people each year, we lose 5–7 million ha (12–17 million acres) of productive cropland annually. Throughout the world, especially in drier regions, it has gotten more difficult to raise crops and graze livestock as soils have become eroded and

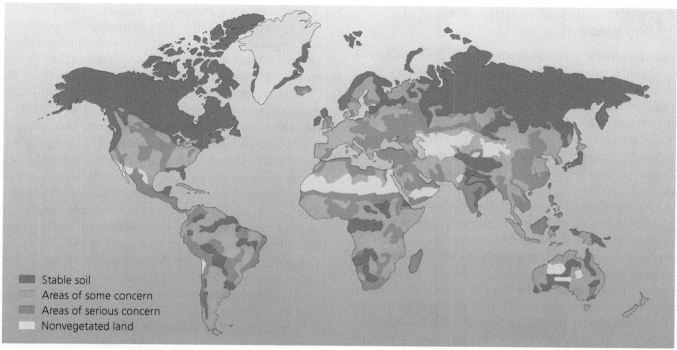

Stable soil
Areas of some concern
Areas of serious concern
Nonvegetated land

**(a) World soil conditions**

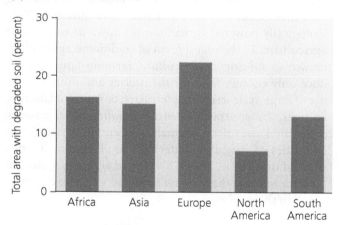

**(b) Soil degradation by continent**

**FIGURE 9.1** Soils are becoming degraded in many areas worldwide (**a**). Europe currently has a higher proportion of degraded land than other continents (**b**) because of its long history of intensive agriculture, but degradation is rising quickly in developing countries in Africa and Asia. Go to **GRAPHit!** at www.aw-bc.com/withgott or on the student CD–ROM. Data from International Soil Reference and Information Centre (ISRIC) and United Nations Environment Programme (UNEP), 1996. *Human–induced soil degradation.* Rome: ISRIC, UNEP, and U.N. Food and Agriculture Organization (FAO) (a); UNEP 2002. *Global environmental outlook 3.* London: UNEP and Earthscan Publ. (b).

degraded (Figure 9.1). Soil degradation around the globe has resulted from roughly equal parts forest removal, cropland agriculture, and overgrazing of livestock (Figure 9.2).

Soil degradation has direct impacts on agricultural production. It is estimated that degradation over the past 50 years has reduced potential rates of global grain production by 13% on cropland and 4% on rangeland. By the middle of the 21st century, there will likely be 3 billion more mouths to feed. For these reasons, it is imperative that we learn to farm in sustainable ways that are gentler on the land and that maintain the integrity of soil.

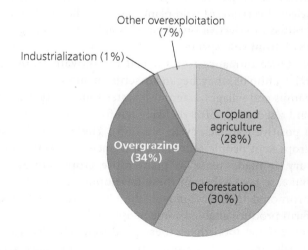

**FIGURE 9.2** The great majority of the world's soil degradation results from cropland agriculture, overgrazing by livestock, and deforestation. Data from Wali, M. K. et al., 1999. Assessing terrestrial ecosystem sustainability: Usefulness of regional carbon and nitrogen models. *Nature and Resources* 35: 21–33.

## Agriculture began to appear around 10,000 years ago

Agriculture is a relatively new approach for meeting our nutritional needs; on the scale of human history, there was no such thing as a farm until very recently. During most of our species' 160,000-year existence, we were hunter-gatherers, depending on wild plants and animals. Then about 10,000 years ago, as the climate warmed following a period of glaciation, people in some cultures began to raise plants from seed and to domesticate animals.

How and why did agriculture begin? The most plausible hypothesis is that it began as hunter-gatherers brought back to their encampments wild fruits, grains, and nuts. Some of these foods fell to the ground, were thrown away, or were eaten and survived passage through the digestive system. The plants that grew from these seeds near human encampments likely produced fruits that were on average larger and tastier than those in the wild, because they sprang from seeds of fruits selected by people because they were especially large and delicious. As these plants bred with others nearby that shared their characteristics, they gave rise to subsequent generations of plants with large and flavorful fruits. Eventually, people realized that they could guide this selective process through conscious effort, and our ancestors began intentionally planting seeds from the plants whose produce was most desirable. This is, of course, artificial selection at work (▸pp. 120–122). This practice of selective breeding continues to the present day and has produced the many hundreds of crops we enjoy, all of which are artificially selected versions of wild plants. People followed the same process of selective breeding with animals, creating livestock from wild species.

Once our ancestors learned to cultivate crops and raise animals, they began to settle in more permanent camps and villages, often near water sources. Agriculture and a sedentary lifestyle likely reinforced one another in a positive feedback cycle (▸p. 185). The need to harvest crops kept people sedentary, and once they were sedentary, it made sense to plant more crops. Population increase resulted from these developments and further promoted them. Moreover, the ability to grow excess farm produce enabled some people to leave farming and live off the food that others produced. This led to the development of professional specialties, commerce, technology, densely populated urban centers, social stratification, and politically powerful elites. For better or worse, the advent of agriculture eventually brought us the civilization we have today.

Archaeological and paleoecological evidence suggests that agriculture was invented independently by different cultures in at least five areas of the world and possibly 10 or more (Figure 9.3). The earliest widely accepted archaeological evidence for plant domestication is from the "Fertile Crescent" region of the Middle East about 10,500 years ago, and the earliest evidence for animal domestication also is from that region, just 500 years later. Crop remains have been dated using radiocarbon dating (▸p. 94) and similar methods. Wheat and barley originated in the Fertile Crescent, as did rye, peas, lentils, onions, garlic, carrots, grapes, and other food plants familiar to us today. The people of this region also domesticated goats and sheep. Meanwhile, in China, domestication began as early as 9,500 years ago, leading eventually to the rice, millet, and pigs we know today. Agriculture in Africa (coffee, yams, sorghum, and more) and the Americas (corn, beans, squash, potatoes, llamas, and more) developed later in several areas, 4,500–7,000 years ago.

For most of these thousands of years, the work of cultivating, harvesting, storing, and distributing crops was performed by human and animal muscle power, along with hand tools and simple machines (Figure 9.4). This biologically powered agriculture is known as **traditional agriculture.** In the oldest form of traditional agriculture, known as *subsistence agriculture,* farming families produce only enough food for themselves and do not make use of large-scale irrigation, fertilizer, or teams of laboring animals. In contrast, *intensive traditional agriculture* sometimes uses draft animals and employs significant quantities of irrigation water and fertilizer, but it stops short of using fossil fuels. This type of agriculture aims to produce food for the farming family, as well as excess food to sell in the market.

## Industrialized agriculture is newer still

The industrial revolution introduced large-scale mechanization and fossil fuel combustion to agriculture just as it did to industry, enabling farmers to replace horses and oxen with faster and more powerful means of cultivating, harvesting, transporting, and processing crops. Other advances facilitated irrigation and fertilizing, while the invention of chemical pesticides reduced competition from weeds and herbivory by insects and other crop pests. To be efficient, however, **industrialized agriculture** demands that vast fields be planted with single types of crops. The uniform planting of a single crop, termed **monoculture,** is distinct from the *polyculture* approach of much traditional agriculture, such as Native American

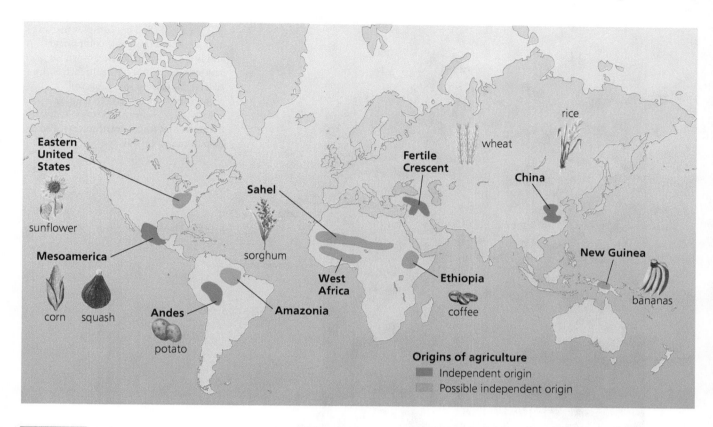

**FIGURE 9.3** Agriculture appears to have originated independently in multiple locations throughout the world, as different cultures domesticated certain plants and animals from wild species living in their environments. This depiction summarizes conclusions from diverse sources of research on evidence for early agriculture. Areas where people are thought to have independently invented agriculture are colored green. (China may represent two independent origins.) Areas colored blue represent regions where people either invented agriculture independently or obtained the idea from cultures of other regions. A few of the many crop plants domesticated in each region are shown. Data from syntheses in Diamond, J., 1997. *Guns, germs, and steel.* New York: W.W. Norton; and Goudie, A. 2000. *The human impact,* 5th ed. Cambridge, MA: MIT Press.

**FIGURE 9.4** Hunting and gathering was the predominant human lifestyle until the onset of agriculture and sedentary living, which centered around farms, villages, and cities, beginning nearly 10,000 years ago. Over the millennia, societies practicing traditional agriculture gradually replaced hunter-gatherer cultures. Only within the past century has industrialized agriculture spread, replacing much traditional agriculture.

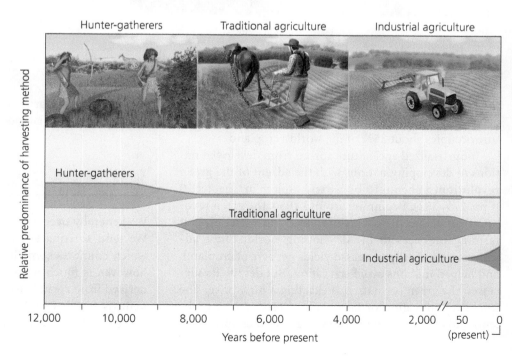

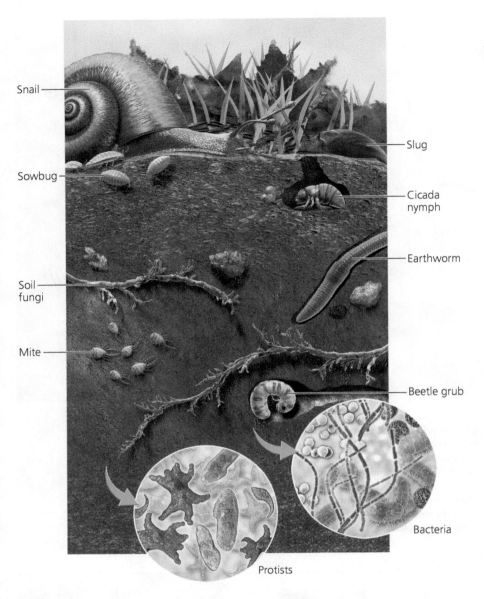

Snail

Sowbug

Soil
fungi

Mite

Slug

Cicada
nymph

Earthworm

Beetle grub

Bacteria

Protists

**FIGURE 9.5**  Soil is a complex mixture of organic and inorganic components and is full of living organisms whose actions help keep it fertile. In fact, entire ecosystems exist in soil. Most soil organisms, from bacteria to fungi to insects to earthworms, decompose organic matter. Many, such as earthworms, also help to aerate the soil.

farming systems that mixed maize, beans, squash, and peppers in the same fields. Today, industrialized agriculture occupies about 25% of the world's cropland.

Industrialized agriculture spread from developed nations to developing nations with the advent of the **green revolution,** a phenomenon we will explore in Chapter 10 (▸pp. 279–282). Beginning around 1950, the green revolution introduced new technology, crop varieties, and farming practices to the developing world. These advances dramatically increased yields per acre of cropland, and helped millions avoid starvation. But despite its successes, the green revolution is exacting a high price. The intensive cultivation of farmland is creating new problems and exacerbating old ones. Many of these problems pertain to the integrity of soil, which is the very foundation of our terrestrial food supply.

## Soil as a System

We generally overlook the startling complexity of soils. We tend to equate the word *soil* with the word *dirt,* which connotes something useless or undesirable. Soil, however, is much more. It is not merely loose material derived from rock; it also contains a large biotic component, is molded by life, and is capable of supporting plant growth (Figure 9.5).

By volume, soil consists very roughly of half mineral matter and up to 5% organic matter. The rest consists of pore space taken up by air or water. The organic matter in soil includes living and dead microorganisms as well as decaying material derived from plants and animals. Most of us tend to think of soil as inert and lifeless, but a single teaspoon of soil can contain 100 million bacteria, 500,000 fungi, 100,000 algae, and 50,000 protists. Soil also provides habitat for earthworms, insects, mites, millipedes, centipedes, nematodes, sow bugs, and other invertebrates, as well as burrowing mammals, amphibians, and reptiles. The composition and quality of a region's soil can have as much influence on the region's ecosystems as do the climate, latitude, and elevation. In fact, because soil is composed of living and nonliving components that interact in complex ways, soil itself meets the definition of an ecosystem (▶pp. 189–191).

## Soil formation is slow and complex

The formation of soil plays a key role in terrestrial primary succession (▶p. 163), which begins when the lithosphere's parent material is exposed to the effects of the atmosphere, hydrosphere, and biosphere. **Parent material** is the base geological material in a particular location. It can include lava or volcanic ash; rock or sediment deposited by glaciers; wind-blown dunes; sediments deposited by rivers, in lakes, or in the ocean; or **bedrock,** the continuous mass of solid rock that makes up Earth's crust.

The processes most responsible for soil formation are weathering, erosion, and the deposition and decomposition of organic matter. **Weathering** describes the physical, chemical, and biological processes that break down rocks and minerals, turning large particles into smaller particles (Figure 9.6).

*Physical* or *mechanical weathering* breaks rocks down without triggering a chemical change in the parent material. Wind and rain are two main forces of physical weathering. Daily and seasonal temperature variation aids their action by causing the thermal expansion and contraction of parent material. Areas with extreme temperature fluctuations experience rapid rates of physical weathering. Water freezing and expanding in cracks in rock also causes physical weathering.

*Chemical weathering* results when water or other substances chemically interact with parent material. Warm, wet conditions usually accelerate chemical weathering.

*Biological weathering* occurs when living things break down parent material by physical or chemical means. For instance, lichens initiate primary terrestrial succession by producing acid, which chemically weathers rock. A tree

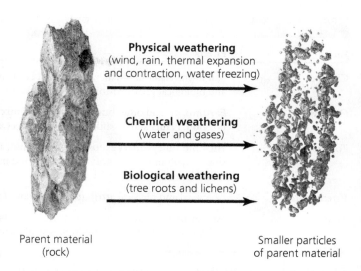

Physical weathering
(wind, rain, thermal expansion
and contraction, water freezing)

Chemical weathering
(water and gases)

Biological weathering
(tree roots and lichens)

Parent material
(rock)

Smaller particles
of parent material

**FIGURE 9.6** The weathering of parent material is the first step in soil formation. Rock is broken down into finer particles by physical, chemical, or biological means.

may accelerate weathering through the physical action of its roots as they grow and rub against rock. It may also accelerate weathering chemically through the decomposition of its leaves and branches or with chemicals it releases from its roots.

Weathering produces fine particles, and is the first step in soil formation. Another process often involved is **erosion,** the movement of soil from one area to another. Erosion may sometimes help form soil in one locality by depositing material it has depleted from another. Erosion is particularly prevalent when soil is denuded of vegetation, leaving the surface exposed to water and wind that may wash or blow it away. Although erosion can sometimes help build new soil in the long term, on the timescale of human lifetimes and for the natural systems on which we depend, erosion is generally perceived as a destructive process that reduces the amount of life that a given area of land can support.

Biological activity contributes to soil formation through the deposition, decomposition, and accumulation of organic matter. As plants, animals, and microbes die or deposit waste, this material is incorporated into the substrate, mixing with minerals. The deciduous trees of temperate forests, for example, drop their leaves each fall, making leaf litter available to the detritivores and decomposers (▶pp. 157–158) that break it down and incorporate its nutrients into the soil. In decomposition, complex organic molecules are broken down into simpler ones, including those that plants can take up through their roots. Partial decomposition of organic matter creates *humus,* a

| Table 9.1 | Five Factors That Influence Soil Formation |
|---|---|
| **Factor** | **Effects** |
| Climate | Soil forms faster in warm, wet climates. Heat speeds chemical reactions and accelerates weathering, decomposition, and biological growth. Moisture is required for many biological processes and can speed weathering. |
| Organisms | Earthworms and other burrowing animals mix and aerate soil, add organic matter, and facilitate microbial decomposition. Plants add organic matter and affect a soil's composition and structure. |
| Topographical relief | Hills and valleys affect exposure to sun, wind, and water, and they influence where and how soil moves. Steeper slopes result in more runoff and erosion and in less leaching, accumulation of organic matter, and differentiation of soil layers. |
| Parent material | Chemical and physical attributes of the parent material influence properties of the resulting soil. |
| Time | Soil formation takes decades, centuries, or millennia. The four factors above change over time, so the soil we see today may be the result of multiple sets of factors. |

*Adapted from:* Jenny, H. 1941. *Factors of soil formation: A system of quantitative pedology.* New York: McGraw-Hill, Inc. Reprinted 1994 by Dover Publications, Mineola, New York.

dark, spongy, crumbly mass of material made up of complex organic compounds. Soils with high humus content hold moisture well and are productive for plant life.

Weathering, erosion, the accumulation and transformation of organic matter, and other processes that contribute to soil formation are all influenced by outside factors. Soil scientists cite five primary factors that influence the formation of soil (Table 9.1).

---

**Weighing the Issues:**
## Earth's Soil Resources

It can take 500 to 1,000 years to produce 1 inch of natural topsoil. Is soil a renewable resource? How do you think soil's long renewal time should influence its management? What types of practices encourage the formation of new topsoil?

---

## A soil profile consists of distinct layers known as horizons

Once weathering has produced an abundance of small particles between the parent material and the atmosphere, then wind, water, and organisms begin to move and sort them. Eventually, distinct layers develop. Each layer of soil is known as a **horizon,** and the cross-section as a whole, from surface to bedrock, is known as a **soil profile.**

The simplest way to categorize soil horizons is to recognize A, B, and C horizons corresponding to topsoil, subsoil, and parent material. However, soil scientists often

find it useful to subdivide the layers more finely, by their characteristics and the processes that take place within them. For our purposes we will discuss six major horizons, known as the O, A, E, B, C, and R horizons (Figure 9.7). Soils from different locations vary, and few soil profiles contain all six of these horizons, but any given soil contains at least some of them. Generally, the degree of weathering and the concentration of organic matter decrease as one moves downward in the soil profile.

Many soil profiles include an uppermost layer consisting mostly of organic matter, such as decomposing branches, leaves, and animal waste. This thin layer is designated the **O horizon** (O for *organic*) or litter layer. Just below the O horizon lies the **A horizon,** consisting of inorganic mineral components such as weathered substrate, with organic matter and humus from above mixed in. The A horizon is often referred to as **topsoil,** that portion of the soil that is most nutritive for plants and therefore most vital to ecosystems and agriculture. Topsoil takes its loose texture and dark coloration from its humus content. The O and A horizons are home to most of the countless organisms that give life to soil.

Beneath the A horizon in some soils lies the **E horizon.** E refers to *eluviation,* meaning loss, and the E horizon is characterized by the loss of some minerals and organic matter through leaching. **Leaching** is the process whereby solid particles suspended or dissolved in liquid are transported to another location. Generally in soils, the solvent is water, and leaching carries minerals downward. Soil that undergoes leaching is a bit like coffee grounds in a drip filter. When it rains, water infiltrates the soil (just as it infiltrates coffee grounds), dissolves

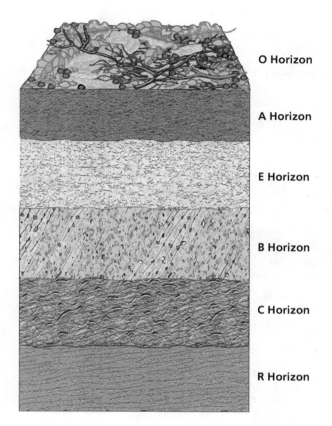

**FIGURE 9.7** Mature soil consists of layers, or horizons, that have different compositions and characteristics. The number and depth of horizons vary from place to place and from soil type to soil type, producing different soil profiles. In general, organic matter and the degree of weathering decrease as one moves downward in a soil profile. The O horizon consists mostly of organic matter deposited by organisms. The A horizon, or topsoil, consists of some organic material mixed with mineral components. Minerals tend to leach out of the E horizon down into the B horizon. The C horizon consists largely of weathered parent material, which may overlie an R horizon of pure parent material.

some of its components, and carries them downward into the deeper horizons. Minerals commonly leached from the E horizon include iron, aluminum, and silicate clay. In some soils, minerals may be leached so rapidly that plants are deprived of nutrients. Minerals that leach rapidly from soils may be carried into groundwater and can pose human health threats when the water is extracted.

Minerals leaching from the A and E horizons move into the layer beneath them, the **B horizon,** or subsoil. This horizon collects and accumulates minerals from above. Often called the *illuviation horizon, zone of accumulation,* or *zone of deposition,* the B horizon contains a greater concentration of minerals and organic acids leached from above than does the E horizon.

The **C horizon,** if present, is located below the B horizon and consists of parent material unaltered or only slightly altered by the processes of soil formation. It therefore contains rock particles that are larger and less weathered than the layers above. The C horizon sits directly above the **R horizon,** or parent material.

## Soil can be characterized by color, texture, structure, and pH

The six horizons presented above depict an idealized, "typical" soil, but soils display great variety. U.S. soil scientists classify soils into 12 major groups, based largely on the processes thought to form them. Within these 12 "orders," there are dozens of "suborders," hundreds of "great groups," and thousands of soils belonging to lower categories, all arranged in a hierarchical system. Scientists classify soils using properties such as color, texture, structure, and pH.

**Soil color** The color of soil (Figure 9.8) can indicate soil composition and sometimes soil fertility. Black or dark brown soils are usually rich in organic matter, whereas a

**FIGURE 9.8** The color of soil may vary drastically from one location to another. A soil's composition affects its color. For instance, soils high in organic matter tend to be dark brown or black.

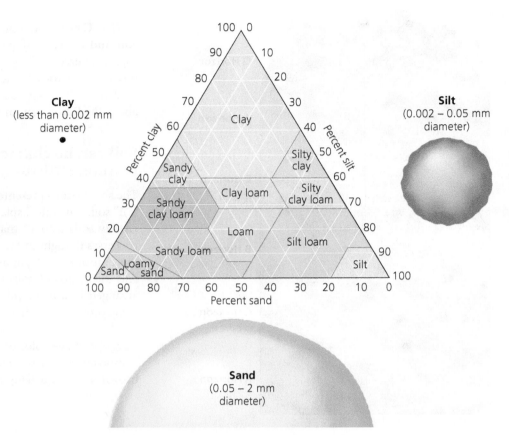

**FIGURE 9.9** The texture of soil depends on its mix of particle sizes. Using the triangular diagram shown, scientists classify soil texture according to the relative proportions of sand, silt, and clay. After measuring the percentage of each type of particle size in a soil sample, a scientist can trace the appropriate white lines extending inward from each side of the triangle to determine what type of soil texture that particular combination of values creates. Loam is generally the best for plant growth, although some types of plants grow better in other textures of soil.

pale gray to white color often indicates leaching or low organic content. This color variation occurs among soil horizons in any given location and also among soils from different geographic locations. Long before modern analytical tests of soil content were developed, the color of topsoil provided farmers and ranchers with information about a region's potential to support crops and provide forage for livestock.

**Soil texture** Soil texture is determined by the size of particles and is the basis on which the United States Department of Agriculture (USDA) assigns soils to one of three general categories (Figure 9.9). **Clay** consists of particles less than 0.002 mm in diameter, **silt** of particles 0.002–0.05 mm, and **sand** of particles 0.05–2 mm. Sand grains, as any beachgoer knows, are large enough to see individually and do not adhere to one another. Clay particles, in contrast, readily adhere to one another and give clay a sticky feeling when moist. Soil with a relatively even mixture of the three particle sizes is known as **loam.**

For the farmer, soil texture influences a soil's "workability," its relative ease or difficulty of cultivation. Soil texture also influences *soil porosity,* a measure of the size of spaces between particles. In general, the finer the particles, the smaller the spaces between them. The smaller the spaces, the harder it is for water and air to travel through the soil, slowing infiltration and reducing the amount of oxygen available to soil biota. Conversely, soils with large particles allow water to pass through (and beyond the reach of plants' roots) too quickly. Thus, crops planted in sandy soils require frequent irrigation. For this reason, silty soils with medium-sized pores, or loamy soils with mixtures of pore sizes, are generally best for plant growth and crop agriculture.

**Soil structure** Soil structure is a measure of the "clumpiness" of soil. Some degree of structure encourages soil productivity, and biological activity helps promote this structure. However, soil clumps that are too large can discourage plant roots from establishing if soil particles are compacted too tightly together. Repeated tilling can compact soil and make it less able to absorb water. When farmers repeatedly till the same field at the same depth, they may end up forming *plowpan,* a hard layer that resists the infiltration of water and the penetration of roots.

**Soil pH** The degree of acidity or alkalinity (▶p. 98) influences a soil's ability to support plant growth. Plants can die in soils that are too acidic or alkaline, but moderate variation can influence the availability of nutrients for

**FIGURE 9.10** In tropical forested areas, the traditional form of farming is *swidden* agriculture, as seen here in Surinam. In this practice, forest is cut, the plot is farmed for one to a few years, and the farmer then moves on to clear another plot, leaving the first to regrow into forest. This frequent movement is necessary because tropical soils are nutrient-poor, with nearly all nutrients held in the vegetation. Burning the cut vegetation adds nutrients to the soil, which is why this practice is often called "slash-and-burn" agriculture. At low population densities, this form of farming had little large-scale impact on forests, but at today's high population densities, it is a leading cause of deforestation.

plants' roots. During leaching, for instance, acids from organic matter may remove some nutrients from the sites of exchange between plant roots and soil particles, and water carries these nutrients deeper.

## Regional differences in soil traits can affect agriculture

The characteristics of soil and soil profiles can vary from place to place. One example that bears on agriculture is the difference between soils of tropical rainforests and those of temperate grasslands. Although rainforest ecosystems have high primary productivity (▸ pp. 192–193), most of their nutrients are tied up in plant tissues and not in the soil. The soil of Amazonian rainforest in northern Brazil is in fact much less productive than the soil of grassland in Kansas.

To understand how this can be, consider the main differences between the two regions: temperature and rainfall. The enormous amount of rain that falls in the Amazon readily leaches minerals and nutrients out of the topsoil and E horizon. Those not captured by plants are taken quickly down to the water table, out of reach of most plants' roots. High temperatures speed the decomposition of leaf litter and the uptake of nutrients by plants, so amounts of humus remain small, and the topsoil layer remains thin.

Thus when forest is cleared for farming, cultivation quickly depletes the soil's fertility. This is why the traditional form of agriculture in tropical forested areas is *swidden* agriculture, in which the farmer cultivates a plot for one to

a few years and then moves on to clear another plot, leaving the first to grow back to forest (Figure 9.10). This method may work well at low population densities, but with today's high human populations, soils may not be allowed enough time to regenerate. As a result, intensive agriculture has ruined the soils and forests of many tropical areas.

In temperate grassland areas such as the Kansas prairie, in contrast, rainfall is low enough that leaching is reduced and nutrients remain high in the soil profile, within reach of plants' roots. Plants take up nutrients and then return them to the topsoil when they die; this cycle maintains the soil's fertility. The thick, rich topsoil of temperate grasslands can be farmed repeatedly with minimal loss of fertility if proper farming techniques are used. However, growing and harvesting crops without returning adequate organic matter to the soil gradually depletes organic material, and leaving soil exposed to the elements increases erosion of topsoil. It is such consequences that farmers in southern Brazil, the U.S. Midwest, and other locations have sought to forestall through the use of reduced tillage.

# Soil Degradation: Problems and Solutions

Scientists' studies of soil and the practical experience of farmers have shown that the most desirable soil for agriculture is a loamy mixture with a pH close to neutral that is workable and capable of holding nutrients. Many soils

# Measuring Erosion

Can a hedge of grass help stop soil erosion? Grass hedges are widely used, especially in the tropics, to trap eroding soil by slowing runoff from rain. But Jerry Ritchie, a researcher with the U.S. Department of Agriculture, wanted to measure how well they actually work. Going beyond the visible signs of soil loss, he used techniques ranging from simple measuring pins to complex radiation detectors to document erosion and calculate just how much soil has moved.

In the 1990s, Ritchie and his team of researchers began by measuring erosion around hedges planted near a set of gullies in Maryland. They relied on cheap, simple tools known as erosion pins (see the figure), which were developed in the 1960s and 1970s by scientists working for the U.N. Food and Agriculture Organization. Erosion pins are spikes that can be made from almost anything, includ-

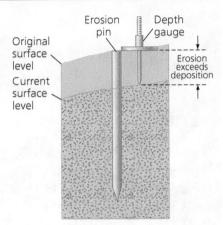

As soil erodes around an erosion pin, more of the pin is exposed, enabling the soil scientist to measure the amount of soil loss.

ing bamboo stakes or pieces of plastic pipe. The pins, each cut to a uniform length, are driven into the soil until their tops are level with the ground's surface. Over time, if soil in the area is eroding, the soil surface will recede, and the erosion pins will be increasingly exposed.

By using many pins over a wide area and averaging their readings, scientists can determine an overall erosion rate for the area.

Researchers often dig expansive holes, called catchpits, nearby. These pits are lined with plastic and serve as collection sites for eroding soil. Researchers measure the volume of soil that accumulates in the catchpits and compare that data with the extent of exposure on erosion pins. In the Maryland experiment, Ritchie used such techniques and found that 1–2 cm (0.4–0.8 in.) of soil was accumulating upslope from the hedges per year, indicating that the grass was trapping soil as it moved.

Erosion pins and catchpits work well in one spot but are impractical over a large region. To get the best evidence of erosion on a wide scale, scientists have turned to measuring a modern-day leftover rarely considered an environmental benefit— nuclear fallout from atomic

---

deviate from this ideal and prevent land from being arable or limit the productivity of arable land. Increasingly, limits to productivity are being set by human impact that has degraded many once-excellent soils. Common problems affecting soil productivity include erosion, desertification, salinization, waterlogging, nutrient depletion, structural breakdown, and pollution.

## Erosion can degrade ecosystems and agriculture

Erosion, as we have noted, is the removal of material from one place and its transport toward another by the action of wind or water. *Deposition* is the arrival of eroded material at its new location. Erosion and deposition are natural processes that in the long run can help create soil. Flowing water can deposit eroded sediment in river valleys and deltas,

producing rich and productive soils. This is why floodplains are excellent for farming and why flood-control measures can decrease the productivity of agriculture in the long run.

However, erosion often becomes a problem locally for ecosystems and agriculture because it nearly always takes place much more quickly than soil is formed. Furthermore, erosion tends to remove topsoil, the most valuable soil layer for living things. People have increased the vulnerability of fertile lands to erosion through three widespread practices:

1. Overcultivating fields through poor planning or excessive plowing, disking, or harrowing
2. Overgrazing rangelands with more livestock than the land can support
3. Clearing forested areas on steep slopes or with large clear-cuts (▶pp. 355–357)

weapons testing. In 1945, the United States exploded the world's first nuclear bomb, and since then more than 2,000 nuclear devices have been tested by the United States, the former Soviet Union, and other nations. Nuclear weapons testing has spread radioactive material through the atmosphere worldwide, and fallout from the atmosphere has covered Earth's surface with minuscule but measurable amounts of nuclear debris.

Fallout includes cesium-137, a radioactive isotope of the element cesium. As discussed in Chapter 4 (▸pp. 94–95), isotopes of chemical elements are often tracked and measured by environmental scientists. Cesium-137, a product of nuclear fuel and weapons reactions, has a half-life of 30 years—a duration that enables soil scientists to use the isotope as a universal environmental tracer for erosion and sediment deposits. Soil tends to absorb cesium-137 quickly and

evenly, so if soil in an area hasn't moved or been heavily disturbed, testing will show fairly uniform levels of the isotope. But if such measurements are not uniform—with some areas showing lower concentrations of cesium-137 and others showing higher concentrations—then erosion may be at work. Ritchie decided to use cesium-137 tests on the area around the hedges and compare the results against his physical soil measurements.

In studies involving cesium-137, soil samples are tested using a gamma spectrometer. This device measures gamma rays, which serve as unique signatures of energy emitted by chemical elements in soil or rock. As they are emitted, gamma rays show up as sharp emission lines on a spectrum. The energy represented in these emissions reflects which elements are present, and the intensity of the lines reveals the concentration of the element. Thus it is possible to calculate the

amount of an isotope such as cesium-137 in a test sample. In erosion tests, each sample from the study area is measured for cesium-137, and those levels are compared to baseline levels for the region. By pinpointing places in the study area with lower or higher levels of accumulated cesium, scientists can detect where soil has moved and how much has shifted.

In Maryland, the radioactive testing helped Ritchie determine that hedges may offer only partial help against erosion. Although his team's physical measurements of soil accumulation showed soil being deposited near the hedges, the cesium-137 tests revealed that the area around the hedges had nonetheless undergone a net loss of soil over a period of four decades. Grass hedges can help, Ritchie wrote when releasing his findings for the Federal Agricultural Research Service in 2000, but they "should not be seen as a panacea."

Erosion can be gradual and hard to detect. For example, an erosion rate of 12 tons/ha (5 tons/acre) removes only a penny's thickness of soil. In many parts of the world, scientists, farmers, and extension agents are measuring erosion rates in hopes of identifying areas in danger of serious degradation before they become too badly damaged (see "The Science behind the Story," above).

## Soil erodes by several mechanisms

Grasslands, forests, and other plant communities protect soil from wind and water erosion. Vegetation breaks the wind and slows water flow, while plant roots hold soil in place and take up water. Removing plant cover will nearly always accelerate erosion. Several types of erosion can occur, including wind erosion and four principal kinds of water erosion (Figure 9.11).

*Splash erosion* (Figure 9.11a) occurs when rain striking the soil surface breaks aggregates into smaller sizes. Soil particles are released and fill in gaps between the remaining clumps, decreasing a soil's ability to absorb water. In *sheet erosion*, or overland flow (Figure 9.11b), surface water flows downhill, washing topsoil away in relatively uniform layers. *Rill erosion* (Figure 9.11c) takes place when water runs along small furrows on the surface of the topsoil, gradually deepening and widening the furrows into rills, or small channels. Rills can merge to form larger and larger channels and eventually gullies. *Gully erosion* (Figure 9.11d) is least common but causes the most dramatic and visible changes in the landscape.

Research indicates that rill erosion has the greatest potential to move topsoil, followed by sheet erosion and splash erosion, respectively. All types of water erosion—particularly gully erosion—are more likely to occur where

**(a) Splash erosion**

**(b) Sheet erosion**

**(c) Rill erosion**

**(d) Gully erosion**

**FIGURE 9.11** The erosion of soil by water can be classified into at least four categories. Splash erosion (**a**) occurs as raindrops strike the ground with enough force to dislodge small amounts of soil. Sheet erosion (**b**) results when thin layers of water traverse broad expanses of sloping land. Rill erosion (**c**) leaves small pathways along the surface where water has carried topsoil away. Gully erosion (**d**) cuts deep into soil, leaving large gullies that can expand as erosion proceeds.

slopes are steeper. In general, steeper slopes, greater precipitation intensities, and sparser vegetative cover all lead to greater water erosion.

One study conducted in the early 1990s determined that at erosion rates typical for the United States, U.S. croplands lose about 2.5 cm (1 in.) of topsoil every 15–30 years, reducing corn yields by 4.7–8.7% and wheat yields by 2.2–9.5%. According to U.S. government figures, erosion rates in the United States declined from 9.1 tons/ha (3.7 tons/acre) in 1982 to 5.9 tons/ha (2.4 tons/acre) in 2001, thanks to soil conservation measures discussed below. Yet in spite of these measures, U.S. farmlands still lose 6 tons of soil for every ton of grain harvested.

## Soil erosion is a global problem

Erosion has become a major problem in many areas of the world, including Australia, sub-Saharan Africa, central Asia, India, the Middle East, and parts of South America, Central America, Europe, and the United States. In total, more than 19 billion ha (47 billion acres) of the world's croplands suffer from erosion and other forms of soil degradation resulting from human activities. Between 1957 and 1990, China lost as much arable farmland as exists in Denmark, France, Germany, and the Netherlands combined. In Kazakhstan, central Asia's largest nation, industrial cropland agriculture imposed on land better suited for grazing caused tens of millions of hectares to be degraded by wind erosion. For Africa, projections indicate that soil degradation over the next 40 years could reduce crop yields by half. Couple these declines in soil quality and crop yields with the rapid population growth occurring in many of these areas, and we begin to see why some observers describe the future of agriculture as a crisis situation.

In today's world, humans are the primary cause of erosion, and we have accelerated it to unnaturally high rates. A 2004 study by geologist Bruce Wilkinson analyzed prehistoric erosion rates from the geologic record and compared these with modern rates. Wilkinson concluded that humans are over 10 times more influential at moving soil than are all other natural processes on the surface of the planet combined.

## Arid land may lose productivity by desertification

Much of the world's population lives and farms in arid environments, where **desertification** is a concern. This term describes a loss of more than 10% productivity due to erosion, soil compaction, forest removal, overgrazing, drought, salinization, climate change, depletion of water sources, and other factors. Severe desertification can result in the expansion of desert areas or creation of new ones in areas that once supported fertile land. This process has occurred in many areas of the Middle East that have been inhabited, farmed, and grazed for long periods of time. To appreciate the cumulative impact of centuries of traditional agriculture, we need only look at the present desertified state of that portion of the Middle East where agriculture originated, nicknamed the "Fertile Crescent." These arid lands—in present-day Iraq, Syria, Turkey, Lebanon, and Israel—are not so fertile anymore.

Arid and semiarid lands are prone to desertification because their precipitation is too meager to meet the demand for water from growing human populations. According to

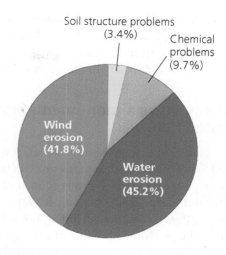

**FIGURE 9.12** Soil degradation on drylands is due primarily to erosion by wind and water. Data from United Nations Environment Programme. 2002. *Tackling land degradation and desertification.* Washington and Rome: Global Environment Facility and International Fund for Agricultural Development.

the United Nations Environment Programme (UNEP), 40% of Earth's land surface can be classified as drylands, arid areas that are particularly subject to degradation. Declines of soil quality in these areas have endangered the food supply or well-being of more than 1 billion people around the world. Of the affected lands, most degradation results from wind and water erosion (Figure 9.12).

It has been estimated that desertification affects fully one-third of the planet's land area, impinging on people in 110 countries. Desertification cost the world's people at least $300–600 billion in income just in the period 1978–1991, UNEP estimates. China alone loses $6.5 billion annually from desertification. In its western reaches, desert areas are expanding and joining one another because of overgrazing from over 400 million goats, sheep, and cattle. In the Sistan Basin along the border of Iran and Afghanistan, an oasis that supported a million livestock recently turned barren in just 5 years, and windblown sand buried over 100 villages. In Africa, the continent's most populous nation, Nigeria, loses an amount of land equal to half the state of Delaware each year to the expanding Sahara Desert. In Kenya, overgrazing and deforestation fueled by rapid population growth has left 80% of its land vulnerable to desertification. In a positive feedback cycle, the soil degradation forces ranchers to crowd onto more marginal land and farmers to reduce fallow periods, both of which further exacerbate soil degradation.

As a result of desertification, in recent years gigantic dust storms from denuded land in China have blown across the Pacific Ocean to North America, and dust storms from Africa's Sahara Desert have blown across the

Atlantic Ocean to the Caribbean Sea. Such massive dust storms occurred in the United States during the Dust Bowl days of the early 20th century, when desertification shook American agriculture and society to their very roots.

## The Dust Bowl was a monumental event in the United States

Prior to large-scale cultivation of the southern Great Plains of the United States, native prairie grasses of this temperate grassland region held erosion-prone soils in place. In the late 19th and early 20th centuries, however, many homesteading settlers arrived in Oklahoma, Texas, Kansas, New Mexico, and Colorado with hopes of making a living there as farmers. Between 1879 and 1929, cultivated area in the region soared from around 5 million ha (12 million acres) to 40 million ha (100 million acres). Farmers grew abundant wheat, and ranchers grazed many thousands of cattle, sometimes expanding onto unsuitable land. Both types of agriculture contributed to erosion by removing native grasses and breaking down soil structure.

During the early 1930s, a drought in the region exacerbated the ongoing human impacts on the soil. The region's strong winds began to carry away millions of tons of topsoil. Dust storms traveled up to 2,000 km (1,250 mi), blackening rain and snow as far away as New York and Vermont. Some areas in the affected states lost as much as 10 cm (4 in.) of topsoil in a few short years (Figure 9.13). The affected region in the Great Plains became known as the **Dust Bowl,** a term now also used for the historical event itself. The "black blizzards" of the Dust Bowl destroyed livelihoods and caused many people to suffer a type of chronic lung irritation and degradation known as dust pneumonia,

similar to the silicosis that afflicts coal miners exposed to high concentrations of coal dust. Large numbers of farmers were forced off their land, and many who remained had to rely on government assistance programs to survive.

## The Soil Conservation Service pioneered measures to slow soil degradation

In response to the devastation in the Dust Bowl, the U.S. government, along with state and local governments, increased its support of research into soil conservation measures. The U.S. Congress also passed the Soil Conservation Act of 1935. This act described soil erosion as a threat to the nation's well-being and established the Soil Conservation Service (SCS) to address the problem. The new agency worked closely with farmers to develop conservation plans for individual farms, following several aims and principles:

▶ Assess the land's resources, its problems, and opportunities for conservation.
▶ Draw on science to prepare an integrated plan for the property.
▶ Work closely with land users to ensure that conservation plans harmonize with the users' objectives.
▶ Implement conservation measures on individual properties to contribute to the overall quality of life in the watershed or region.

The early teams that the SCS formed to combat erosion typically included soil scientists, forestry experts, engineers, economists, and biologists. These teams were among the earliest examples of interdisciplinary approaches to environmental problem solving. The first director of the SCS, Hugh Hammond Bennett, was an innovator and

**FIGURE 9.13** Drought combined with poor agricultural practices brought devastation and despair to millions of U.S. farmers in the 1930s, especially in the Dust Bowl region of the southern Great Plains. The tragedy spurred the development of soil conservation practices that have since been put into place in the United States and around the world.

evangelist for soil conservation. Under his leadership, the agency promoted soil-conservation practices through county-based **conservation districts.** These districts operate with federal direction, authorization, and funding, but they are organized by state law. The districts implement soil conservation programs locally and aim to empower local residents to plan and set priorities in their home areas. In 1994 the SCS was renamed the *Natural Resources Conservation Service,* and its responsibilities were expanded to include water quality protection and pollution control.

The SCS served as a model for similar efforts elsewhere in the world (Figure 9.14). Southern Brazil's no-till movement came about through local grass-roots organization by farmers, with the help of agronomists and government extension agents who provided them information and resources. In this model of collaboration between local farmers and trained experts, 8,000 Friends of the Land clubs now exist in Paraná and Rio Grande do Sul, and 7,700 in Santa Catarina. Many of these groups are delineated by the boundaries of the more than 3,000 small-scale watersheds *(microbacias)* in which they farm.

No-till agriculture as practiced in southern Brazil is one of many approaches to soil conservation. Hugh Hammond Bennett advocated a complex approach, combining techniques such as crop rotation, contour farming, strip-cropping, terracing, grazing management, and reforestation, as well as wildlife management. Such measures have been widely applied in many places around the world.

## Farmers can protect soil against degradation in various ways

Several farming techniques can reduce the impacts of conventional cultivation on soils (Figure 9.15). Some of these have been promoted by the SCS since the Dust Bowl. Some, like no-till farming in Brazil, are finding popularity more recently. Others have been practiced by certain cultures for centuries.

**Crop rotation** The practice of alternating the kind of crop grown in a particular field from one season or year to the next is **crop rotation** (Figure 9.15a). Rotating crops can return nutrients to the soil, break cycles of disease associated with continuous cropping, and minimize the erosion that can come from letting fields lie fallow. Many U.S. farmers rotate their fields between wheat or corn and soybeans from one year to the next. Soybeans are legumes, plants that have specialized bacteria on their roots that can fix nitrogen (▸ pp. 198–200). Soybeans revitalize soil that the previous crop had partially depleted of nutrients. Crop rotation also reduces insect pests; if an insect is adapted to feed and lay eggs on one particular

**FIGURE 9.14** Government agricultural extension agents assist farmers by providing information on the newest research and techniques that can help them farm productively while minimizing damage to the land. Such specialists have helped U.S. farmers since the Dust Bowl and now assist farmers worldwide. Here, an extension agent from Colombia's Instituto Colombiano Agropecuario inspects yuca plants grown by farmer Pedro Gomez on a farm in Valle del Cauca.

crop, planting a different crop will leave its offspring with nothing to eat.

In a practice similar to crop rotation, southern Brazil's farmers plant "cover crops" designed to prevent erosion and forestall nitrogen loss from leaching during times of the year when the main crops are not growing. Santa Catarina's extension agents have worked with farmers to test over 60 species as cover crops, including both legumes and other plants, such as oats and turnips.

**Contour farming** Water running down a hillside can easily carry soil away, particularly if there is too little vegetative cover to hold the soil in place. Thus, sloped agricultural land is especially vulnerable to erosion. Several methods have been developed for farming on slopes. **Contour farming**

**(a) Crop rotation**

**(b) Contour farming**

**(c) Intercropping**

**(d) Terracing**

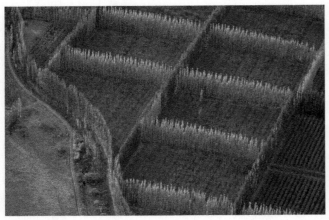

**(e) Shelterbelts**

**(f) No-till farming cover crop**

**FIGURE 9.15** The world's farmers have adopted various strategies to conserve soil. Rotating crops such as soybeans and corn (**a**) helps restore soil nutrients and reduce impacts of crop pests. Contour farming (**b**) reduces erosion on hillsides. Intercropping (**c**) can reduce soil loss while maintaining soil fertility. Terracing (**d**) minimizes erosion in steep mountainous areas. Shelterbelts (**e**) protect against wind erosion. In (**f**), corn grows up from amid the remnants of a "cover crop" used in no-till agriculture.

(Figure 9.15b) consists of plowing furrows sideways across a hillside, perpendicular to its slope, to help prevent formation of rills and gullies. The technique is so named because the furrows follow the natural contours of the land. In contour farming, the downhill side of each furrow acts as a small dam that slows runoff and catches soil before it is carried away. Contour farming is most effective on gradually sloping land with crops that grow well in rows. Extension agents from Santa Catarina in Brazil have helped those farmers who still plow to switch to contour plowing and to plant barriers of grass along their contours.

**Intercropping** Farmers may also gain protection against erosion by **intercropping,** planting different types of crops in alternating bands or other spatially mixed arrangements (Figure 9.15c). Intercropping helps slow erosion by providing more complete ground cover than does a single crop. Like crop rotation, intercropping offers the additional benefits of reducing vulnerability to insect and disease incidence, and, when a nitrogen-fixing legume is one of the crops, of replenishing the soil. Some southern Brazilian farmers intercrop food crops with cover crops. The cover crops are physically mixed with primary crops, which include maize, soybeans, wheat, onions, cassava, grapes, tomatoes, tobacco, and orchard fruit.

**Terracing** On extremely steep terrain, terracing (Figure 9.15d) is the most effective method for preventing erosion. Terraces are level platforms, sometimes with raised edges, that are cut into steep hillsides to contain water from irrigation and precipitation. **Terracing** transforms slopes into series of steps like a staircase, enabling farmers to cultivate hilly land without losing huge amounts of soil to water erosion. Terracing is common in ruggedly mountainous regions, such as the foothills of the Himalayas and the Andes, and has been used for centuries by farming communities in such areas. Terracing is labor-intensive to establish but in the long term is likely the only sustainable way to farm in mountainous terrain.

**Shelterbelts** A widespread technique to reduce erosion from wind is to establish **shelterbelts** or *windbreaks* (Figure 9.15e). These are rows of trees or other tall, perennial plants that are planted along the edges of fields to slow the wind. Shelterbelts have been widely planted across the U.S. Great Plains, where fast-growing species such as poplars are often used. Shelterbelts have also been combined with intercropping in a practice known as *agroforestry,* or *alley cropping.* In this approach, fields planted in rows of mixed crops are surrounded by or interspersed with rows of trees that provide fruit, wood,

| Table 9.2   No-Till Farming in Brazil |
| --- |
| **Benefits of no-till farming** |
| ▶ Conserves biodiversity in soil and in terrestrial and aquatic ecosystems |
| ▶ Produces sustainable, high crop yields |
| ▶ Heightens environmental awareness among farmers |
| ▶ Provides shelter and winter food for animals |
| ▶ Reduces irrigation demands by 10–20% |
| ▶ Crop residues act as a sink for carbon (1 metric ton/ha) |
| ▶ Reduces fossil fuel use by 40–70% |
| ▶ Enhances food security by increasing drought resistance |
| ▶ Reduces erosion by 90% |
| **Other benefits arising from the reduction in erosion** |
| ▶ Reduces silt deposition in reservoirs |
| ▶ Reduces water pollution from chemicals |
| ▶ Increases groundwater recharge and lessens flooding |
| ▶ Increases sustained crop yields and lowers food prices |
| ▶ Lowers costs of treating drinking water |
| ▶ Reduces costs of maintaining dirt roads |
| ▶ Eliminates dust storms in towns and cities |
| ▶ Increases efficiency in use of fertilizer and machinery |

Modified from Shaxson, T. F. 1999. The roots of sustainability: Concepts and practice: Zero tillage in Brazil, *ABLH Newsletter ENABLE; World Association for Soil and Water Conservation (WASWC) Newsletter.*

or protection from wind. Such methods have been used in India, Africa, and in Brazil, where coffee growers near a national conservation area have established farming systems combining farming and forestry.

**Reduced tillage** To plant using the zero-tillage method (Figure 9.15f), a tractor pulls a "no-till drill" that cuts long furrows through the O horizon of dead weeds and crop residue and the upper levels of the A horizon. The device drops seeds into the furrow and closes the furrow over the seeds. Often a localized dose of fertilizer is added to the soil along with the seed. Reduced-tillage agriculture disturbs the soil surface more than no-tillage does, but less than conventional cultivation does. By increasing organic matter and soil biota while reducing erosion, no-till and reduced tillage farming can build soil up, restore it, and improve it. Based on the Brazilian experience, proponents of no-till farming have claimed that the practice offers a number of benefits (Table 9.2).

No-till and reduced tillage methods were pioneered in the United States and United Kingdom, where no-till is still rare but where reduced tillage has been slowly spreading for decades. Today nearly half of U.S. acreage is farmed with reduced-tillage methods. As the appeal of no-till farming spread in Brazil, it also spread in neighboring Argentina and Paraguay. In Argentina, the area under no-till farming exploded from 100,000 ha (247,000 acres) in 1990 to 7.3 million ha (18.0 million acres) in 1999, covering 30% of all arable land in the country. The results there parallel those in Brazil: increased crop yields, reduced erosion, enhanced soils, and a healthier environment. Maize yields grew by 37% and soybean yields by 11%, while costs to farmers fell by 40–57%. Erosion, pesticide use, and water pollution declined. As in Brazil, the techniques spread largely because of the actions of farmers themselves and their national no-till farmers' organization.

Critics of no-till and reduced-tillage farming in the United States have noted that these techniques often require substantial use of chemical herbicides (because weeds are not physically removed from fields) and synthetic fertilizer (because other plants take up a significant portion of the soil's nutrients). In many industrialized countries, this has indeed been the case. Proponents of the Brazilian program, however, assert that it does not always need to be so. Southern Brazil's farmers have departed somewhat from the industrialized model by relying more heavily on *green manures* (dead plants as fertilizer) and by rotating fields with cover crops, including nitrogen-fixing legumes. The manures and legumes nourish the soil, and cover crops also reduce weeds by taking up space the weeds might occupy. Critics maintain, however, that green manures are generally not practical for large-scale intensive agriculture. Certainly, reduced tillage methods work well in some areas but not in others, and they work better with some crops than with others. Farmers will do best by educating themselves on the options and doing what is best for their particular crops on their own land.

The methods we have described to combat soil degradation can be used in combination. When they have been, the results have sometimes been dramatic. One town in the Guatemalan highlands that established shelterbelts, crop rotation, and cover crops with the help of a U.S.-based nonprofit organization improved its corn production from 0.4 tons/ha (1.0 tons/acre) in 1972 to 2.5 tons/ha (6.2 tons/acre) in 1979. It went on to improve production to 4.5 tons/ha (11.1 tons/acre) by 1994.

**Weighing the issues:**
## How Would You Farm?

You are a farmer owning land on both sides of a steep ridge. You want to plant a sun-loving crop on the sunny, but very windy, south slope of the ridge and a crop that needs a great deal of irrigation on the north slope. What

**FIGURE 9.16** Vast swathes of countryside in western China have been planted with fast-growing poplar trees. These "reforestation" efforts do not create ecologically functional forests—the plantations are too biologically simple—but they do greatly slow soil erosion.

type of farming techniques might maximize conservation of your soil? What other factors might you want to know about before you decide to commit to one or more methods?

## Erosion-control practices protect and restore plant cover

Farming methods to control erosion make use of the general principle that maximizing vegetative cover will protect soils, and this principle has been applied widely beyond farming. It is common throughout the developed world to stabilize eroding banks along creeks and roadsides by planting plants to anchor the soil. In areas with severe and widespread erosion, some nations have planted vast plantations of fast-growing trees. China has embarked on the world's largest tree-planting program to slow its soil loss (Figure 9.16). Although such "reforestation" efforts do help slow erosion, they do not at the same time produce ecologically functioning forests, because tree species are selected only for their fast growth and are planted in monocultures.

## Irrigation has boosted productivity but has also caused long-term soil problems

Erosion is not the only threat to the health and integrity of soils. Soil degradation can result from other factors as well, such as impacts caused by our application of water to crops. The artificial provision of water to support agriculture is known as **irrigation.** Some crops, such as rice and cotton, require large amounts of water, whereas others, such as beans and wheat, require relatively little. Other factors influencing the amount of water required for growth include the rate of evaporation, as determined by climate, and the soil's ability to hold water and make it available to plant roots. If the climate is too dry or too much water evaporates or runs off before it can be absorbed into the soil, crops may require irrigation. By irrigating crops, people have managed to turn previously dry and unproductive regions into fertile farmland. Seventy percent of all freshwater withdrawn by people is used for irrigation. Irrigated acreage has increased dramatically around the world, reaching 276 million ha (683 million acres) in 2002, greater than the entire area of Mexico and Central America. We will examine irrigation further in Chapter 15 (▶pp. 440–441).

If some water is good for plants and soil, it might seem that more must be better. But this is not necessarily the case; there is indeed such a thing as too much water. Overirrigation in poorly drained areas can cause or exacerbate certain soil problems. Soils too saturated with water may become waterlogged. When **waterlogging** occurs, the water table is raised to the point that water bathes plant roots, depriving them of access to gases and essentially suffocating them. If it lasts long enough, waterlogging can damage or kill plants.

An even more frequent problem is **salinization,** the buildup of salts in surface soil layers. In dryland areas where precipitation is minimal and evaporation rates are high, water evaporating from the soil's A horizon may pull water from lower horizons upward by capillary action. As this water rises through the soil, it carries dissolved salts, and when it evaporates at the surface, those salts precipitate and are left at the surface. Irrigation in arid areas generally hastens salinization, because it provides repeated doses of moderate amounts of water, which dissolve salts in the soil and gradually raise them to the surface. Moreover, because irrigation water often contains some dissolved salt in the first place, irrigation introduces new sources of salt to the soil. Overirrigation and waterlogging can worsen salinization problems, and in many areas of farmland, soil is turning whitish with encrusted salt. Salinization now inhibits agricultural production on one-fifth of all irrigated cropland globally, costing more than $11 billion annually.

## Salinization is easier to prevent than to correct

The remedies for mitigating salinization once it has occurred are more expensive and difficult to implement than the techniques for preventing it in the first place. The best way to prevent salinization is to avoid planting crops that require a great deal of water in areas that are prone to

the problem. A second way is to irrigate with water that is as low as possible in salt content. A third way is to irrigate efficiently, supplying no more water than the crop requires, thus minimizing the amount of water that evaporates and hence the amount of salt that accumulates in the topsoil. Currently, irrigation efficiency worldwide is low; only 43% of the water applied actually gets used by plants. Drip irrigation systems (Figure 9.17) that target water directly to plants are one solution to the problem. These systems allow more control over where water is aimed and waste far less water. Once considered expensive to install, they are becoming cheaper, such that more farmers in developing countries will be able to afford them.

**(a) Conventional irrigation**

**(b) Drip irrigation**

**FIGURE 9.17** Currently, less than half the water we apply in irrigation actually gets taken up by plants. Conventional methods that lose a great deal of water to evaporation (**a**) are now being replaced by more efficient ones in which water is more precisely targeted to plants. In drip irrigation systems, such as this one watering grape vines in California (**b**), hoses are arranged so that water drips from holes in the hoses directly onto the plants that need the water.

If salinization has occurred, one potential way to mitigate it would be to stop irrigating and wait for rain to flush salts from the soil. However, this solution is unrealistic because salinization generally becomes a problem in dryland areas where precipitation is never adequate to flush soils. A better option may be to plant salt-tolerant plants, such as barley, that can be used as food or pasture. A third option is to bring in large quantities of less-saline water with which to flush the soil. However, using too much water may cause waterlogging. As is the case with many environmental problems, preventing salinization is easier than correcting it after the fact.

## Measuring and Regulating Soil Quality

The U.S. EPA has adopted measures of air quality and water quality and has set legal standards for allowable levels of various pollutants in air and water. Could such standards be developed for soil quality? If so, what properties should be measured to inform such standards? Should such standards be developed? Why or why not?

## Agricultural fertilizers boost crop yields but can be over-applied

Salinization is not the only source of chemical damage to soil. Overapplying fertilizers can also chemically damage soils. Plants grow through photosynthesis, requiring sunlight, water, and carbon dioxide, but they also require nitrogen, phosphorus, and potassium, as well as smaller amounts of over a dozen other nutrients. Plants remove these nutrients from soil as they grow, and leaching likewise removes nutrients. If agricultural soils come to contain too few nutrients, crop yields decline. Therefore, a great deal of effort has aimed to enhance nutrient-limited soils by adding **fertilizer,** any of various substances that contain essential nutrients (Figure 9.18).

There are two main types of fertilizers. **Inorganic fertilizers** are mined or synthetically manufactured mineral supplements. **Organic fertilizers** consist of natural materials (largely the remains or wastes of organisms) and include animal manure; crop residues; fresh vegetation, known as *green manure*; and *compost,* a mixture produced when decomposers break down organic matter, including food and crop waste, in a controlled environment. Organic fertilizers can provide some benefits that inorganic fertilizers cannot. The proper use of compost improves soil structure, nutrient retention, and water-retaining capacity, helping to prevent erosion. As a form of recycling, composting reduces the amount of waste consigned to landfills

**FIGURE 9.18** Farmers often add nutrients to soils with fertilizers. Organic fertilizers such as manure and vegetation may be used, or synthetically manufactured chemicals may be applied to supply nitrogen, phosphorus, and other nutrients, as this North Dakota farmer is doing.

and incinerators (▶p. 658). However, organic fertilizers are no panacea. For instance, manure, when applied in amounts needed to supply sufficient nitrogen for a crop, may introduce excess phosphorus that can run off into waterways. Inorganic fertilizers are generally more susceptible than are organic fertilizers to leaching and runoff, and they are somewhat more likely to cause unintended off-site impacts. Inorganic and organic fertilizer use is growing globally (Figure 9.19). Unfortunately, its mismanagement is causing increasingly severe pollution problems.

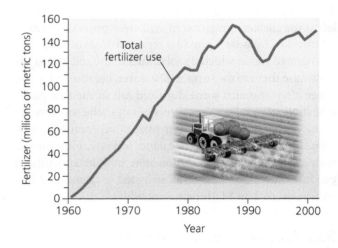

**FIGURE 9.19** Use of synthetic fertilizers has risen sharply over the past half-century and now stands at over 140 million metric tons. (The temporary drop during the early 1990s was due to economic decline in countries of the former Soviet Union following that nation's dissolution.) Data from Food and Agriculture Organization of the United Nations (FAO); and Worldwatch Institute, 2001. *Vital signs 2001.*

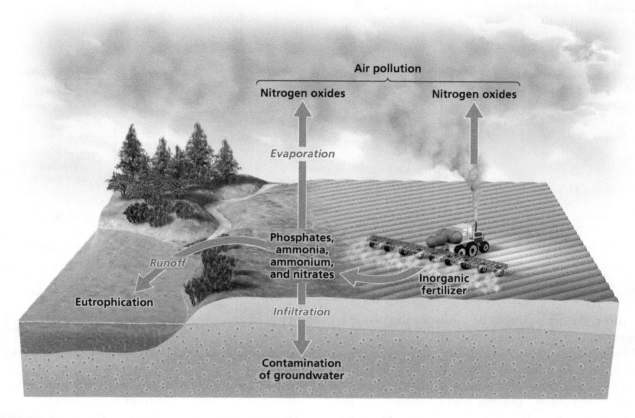

**FIGURE 9.20** The overapplication of inorganic (or organic) fertilizers can have effects beyond the farm field, because nutrients that are not taken up by plants may end up in other places. Nitrates can leach into groundwater, where they can pose a threat to human health in drinking water. Phosphates and some nitrogen compounds can run off into surface waterways and alter the ecology of streams, rivers, ponds, and lakes through eutrophication. Some compounds like nitrogen oxides can even enter and pollute the air. Anthropogenic inputs of nitrogen have greatly modified the nitrogen cycle (▸pp. 197–199), and now account for one-half the total nitrogen flux on Earth.

Applying substantial amounts of fertilizer to croplands has impacts far beyond the boundaries of the fields (Figure 9.20). We saw in Chapter 7 one impact of excess fertilizer use. Nitrogen and phosphorus runoff from farms and other sources in the Mississippi River basin each year spurs phytoplankton blooms in the Gulf of Mexico and creates an oxygen-depleted "dead zone" that kills fish and shrimp. Such eutrophication occurs at many river mouths, lakes, and ponds throughout the world. Moreover, nitrates readily leach through soil and contaminate groundwater, and components of some nitrogen fertilizers can even volatilize (evaporate) into the air. Through these processes, unnatural amounts of nitrates and phosphates spread through ecosystems and pose human health risks, including cancer and methemoglobinemia, or blue-baby disease, which can asphyxiate and kill infants. The U.S. Environmental Protection Agency (EPA) has determined that nitrate concentrations in excess of

10 mg/L for adults and 5 mg/L for infants in drinking water are unsafe, yet many sources around the world exceed even the looser standard of 50 mg/L set by the World Health Organization.

## Grazing practices and policies can contribute to soil degradation

We have focused in this chapter largely on the cultivation of crops as a source of impacts on soils and ecosystems, but raising livestock also has such impacts. When sheep, goats, cattle, or other livestock graze on the open range, they feed primarily on grasses. As long as livestock populations do not exceed a range's carrying capacity (▸pp. 136–137) and do not consume grasses faster than grasses can be replaced, grazing may be sustainable. However, when too many animals eat too much of the plant cover, impeding plant regrowth and

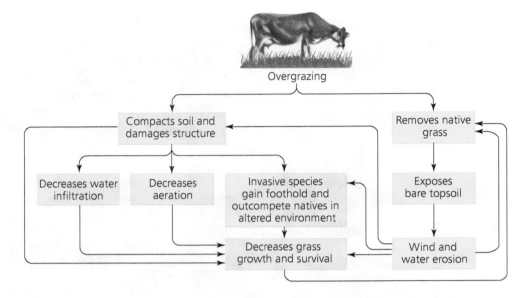

**FIGURE 9.21** When grazing by livestock exceeds the carrying capacity of rangelands and their soil, overgrazing can set in motion a series of consequences and positive feedback loops that degrade soils and grassland ecosystems.

preventing the replacement of biomass, the result is **overgrazing.**

Rangeland scientists have shown that overgrazing causes a number of impacts, some of which give rise to positive feedback cycles that exacerbate damage to soils, natural communities, and the land's productivity for grazing (Figure 9.21). When livestock remove too much of an area's plant cover, more soil surface is exposed and made vulnerable to erosion. Soil erosion makes it difficult for vegetation to regrow, perpetuating the lack of cover and giving rise to more erosion. Moreover, non-native weedy plants may invade denuded soils (Figure 9.22). These invasive plants are usually less palatable to livestock and can outcompete native vegetation in the new, modified environment, further decreasing native plant cover.

In addition, overgrazing can compact soils and alter their structure. Soil compaction makes it harder for water to infiltrate, harder for soils to be aerated, harder for plants' roots to expand, and harder for roots to conduct cellular respiration (▸ p. 107). All of these effects further decrease the growth and survival of native plants.

Overgrazing is a serious problem worldwide. As a cause of soil degradation, it is equal to cropland agriculture, and it is a greater cause of desertification. Humans keep a total of 3.3 billion cattle, sheep, and goats. Rangeland classified as degraded now adds up to 680 million ha (1.7 billion acres), five times the area of U.S. cropland, although some estimates put the number as high as 2.4 billion ha (5.9 billion acres), fully 70% of the world's rangeland area. Rangeland degradation is estimated to cost $23.3 billion per year. Grazing exceeds the sustainable

supply of grass in India by 30% and in parts of China by up to 50%. To relieve pressure on rangelands, both nations are now beginning to feed crop residues to livestock.

Range managers in the United States do their best to assess the carrying capacity of rangelands and inform livestock owners of these limits, so that herds are rotated from site to site as needed to conserve grass cover and soil integrity. Managers also can establish and enforce limits on grazing on publicly owned land when necessary. U.S.

**FIGURE 9.22** The effects of overgrazing can be striking, as shown in this photo along a fence line separating a grazed plot (right) from an ungrazed plot (left) in the Konza Prairie Reserve in Kansas. The overgrazed plot has lost much of its native grass and has been invaded by weedy plants that compete more effectively in conditions of degraded soil.

**VIEWPOINTS**

## Soil Conservation

Productive farming depends on fertile soil, but our farming practices have all too often eroded and degraded soil. **How much erosion constitutes a problem? How can we best protect the condition of soil while we farm?**

### Land Policy Is Necessary for Soil Conservation

Claiming that soil erosion is a major problem in the more-developed parts of the world is environmental nonsense. Pierre Crosson of Resources for the Future, Washington, D.C., has looked carefully at the U.S. data over many years and concluded that soil erosion does *not* constitute a significant problem for contemporary agriculture and its sustainability.

There are surely many cases of local erosive effects, but these usually amount to small quantities of soil shifting around the agricultural landscape. Erosion can be beneficial in some cases, such as in the creation of new farmland in Bangladesh, which formed when materials washed down from Nepal and other parts of the Himalayas.

Soil conservation is a problem that must be approached from all sides. The most important factor will be to secure legally protected property rights for resource users. Farmers must have the right to own their own land resource. Ethiopia is usually regarded as one of the most eroded countries in the world. The state owns all farmland and has a history of moving people against their will to different areas. If a farmer thinks he will not be able to continue managing his farm for the next several years, he will not invest his scarce resources in erosion-reducing practices such as terracing, stone building, maintaining vegetative contour strips, and reducing grazing pressure. For resource custody, and hence the treatment of soil, land policy really matters.

Land policy also affects public investment in infrastructure such as rural roads, which reduce the cost of farmers' transactions. Farmers must haul supplies such as fertilizer to their farms and must transport their product to market. Inadequate access to markets can significantly influence the incentives to employ resource-consuming soil conservation practices. Thus, social science has key roles to play along with physical and biological sciences in addressing soil management.

**Jock R. Anderson** joined the World Bank in its Agriculture and Natural Resources Department, where he served variously as adviser of agricultural technology policy and, more recently, as adviser of strategy and policy for agriculture and rural development. He is a fellow of the Australian Institute of Agricultural Science and of the American Agricultural Economics Association.

### Sustainable Soil Productivity Requires Good Land Stewards

How much soil erosion is tolerable? The standard answer to this question ranges from 1 to 5 tons of soil per acre annually, depending on soil depth and other characteristics that affect sustainability. However, this answer is admittedly subjective and debatable.

Some say these values are too low. They argue that land has been used for centuries with higher rates of erosion, and it is difficult or impossible to reduce erosion on some land without drastic reductions in high-value crops. Others say the standard tolerable erosion values are too high. They argue that the average annual rate of soil formation is less than 1 ton per acre, so a greater erosion rate will inevitably make the soil shallower and less productive. Most agree that excessive erosion is undesirable and a major cause of land abandonment.

Tillage was fundamental to the development of civilization, but it also exposed the soil to erosion—a problem that became more serious as population increased. Tillage can now be reduced or even eliminated by using modern no-till equipment that can cut through crop residues and plant seeds in a narrow slot. Weeds, insects, and plant diseases are controlled by integrated pest management using crop rotations, biological methods, and chemicals. We can now grow crops with much less erosion and still produce good yields.

Conserving water and planting drought-tolerant crops in semi-arid climates is another important advance in areas where erosion due to summer fallow has been common. These practices are effective ways to conserve soil.

The most important requirement for sustainable productivity is a fervent desire to be good land stewards—people who use the best soil conservation practices and are alert for detecting problem spots.

**Frederick R. Troeh** grew up in Idaho, surveyed soils for the Soil Conservation Service, earned his Ph.D. from Cornell University, and taught soil science and researched for Iowa State University. He has worked internationally in Uruguay, Argentina, and Morocco, and he is lead author of the textbooks *Soils and Soil Fertility* and *Soil and Water Conservation*.

 Explore this issue further by accessing **Viewpoints** at www.aw-bc.com/withgott

## Overgrazing and Fire Suppression in the Malpai Borderlands

**The Science behind the Story**

In the high desert of southern Arizona and New Mexico, scientists trying to heal the scars left by decades of cattle ranching and overgrazing found they had to contend with a creature even more damaging than a hungry steer: Smokey the Bear.

Wildfires might seem a natural enemy of grasslands, but in the Malpai Borderlands, researchers realized that people's efforts to suppress fire had done far more harm. Before large numbers of Anglo settlers and ranchers arrived more than a century ago, this rocky stretch of arid Western landscape thrived under an ecological cycle common to many grasslands. Scrubby trees such as mesquite grew near creeks. Hardy grasses such as black grama covered the drier plains. Periodic wildfires, usually sparked by lightning, burned back shrubs and trees and kept grasslands open. Native grazing animals, such as deer, rabbits, and bighorn sheep, ate the grasses, but rarely ate enough to deplete the range. Fed by seasonal rains, new grasses sprouted without being overeaten or crowded out by larger plants.

To restore native grasslands, the Malpai Borderlands Group reinstated fire as a natural landscape process, conducting controlled burns on over 100,000 ha since 1994. Monitoring indicates that restoring fire has improved ecological conditions in the region.

By the early 1990s, however, those grasslands were increasingly scarce. Ranchers had brought large cattle herds to the area in the late 1800s. The cows chewed through vast expanses of grass, trampled soil, and scattered mesquite seed into areas where grasses had dominated. Ranchers fought wildfires to keep their herds safe, and the federal government joined in the firefighting efforts. Gradually, the Malpai's ranching families found themselves struggling to feed their cattle and make a living from the land. Decades of photos taken by ranchers showed how the area's soil had eroded, and how trees and brush had overgrown the grass. The ranchers knew their cattle were part of the problem, but they also suspected that firefighting efforts might be to blame.

In 1993, a group of ranchers launched an innovative plan. They formed the Malpai Borderlands

ranchers have traditionally had little incentive to conserve rangelands because most grazing has taken place on public lands leased from the government, not on lands privately owned by ranchers. In addition, the U.S. government has heavily subsidized grazing. As a result, overgrazing has been extensive and has caused many environmental problems in the American West. Today increasing numbers of ranchers are working cooperatively with government agencies, environmental scientists, and even environmental advocates to find ways to ranch more sustainably and safeguard the health of the land (see "The Science behind the Story," above).

### Forestry, too, has impacts on soil

Farming and grazing are agricultural practices that help feed human populations, that depend on healthy soils, and that affect the conditions of those soils. Forestry, the

Group, designating about 325,000 ha (800,000 acres) of land as an area for protection and study. Through study of the region, ranchers joined government agencies, environmentalists, and scientists to bring back grasses, restore native animal species, and return periodic fires to the landscape (see the figure).

The group's research efforts have centered on the Gray Ranch, a 121,000-ha (300,000-acre) parcel in the heart of the borderlands. Scientists led by researcher Charles Curtin created study sites by dividing pastureland on the ranch into four study areas of about 890 ha (2,200 acres) each. Each area is further divided into four different "treatments," or areas with varying land management techniques:

► In Treatment 1, fire is not suppressed, and grazing by cattle and native animals is permitted.

► In Treatment 2, fire is not suppressed, and grazing is not allowed.

► In Treatment 3, animals can graze, but fire is suppressed.

► In Treatment 4, fire is suppressed, and grazing is not permitted.

Treatments 1 and 3, which allow grazing, also feature small fenced-off areas that prevent animals from eating grass. These exclosures allow scientists to make precise side-by-side comparisons of how grazing affects grasses. Scientists measure rainfall in each area and monitor soils for degradation and erosion. Teams of wildlife and vegetation specialists monitor each treatment for the distribution and abundance of birds, insects, animals, and vegetation.

By comparing areas where fire is suppressed to those where fire can burn, researchers have documented how the suppression of fire leads to more brush and trees and less grass. When fire burns an area, woody plants such as mesquite are damaged and their seed production disrupted, and the flames are often followed by a return of grass. Such benefits follow both natural fires and carefully monitored, deliberately set controlled burns.

Cattle don't do heavy damage to grass if they are managed carefully, the researchers have found. The scientists have helped ranchers develop a cycle of grassbanking, in

which herds are allowed to graze on shared plots of land while other areas recover. And ranchers must work with the weather. Scientists have found that controlled burns or grassbanking should track with cycles of rain and drought to bring back grass.

Because of such research, controlled burns are now a regular part of the Malpai landscape. More than 100,000 ha (250,000 acres) have been burned since 1994. Natural fires are often allowed to run their course with little or no intervention. Damaged areas have been reseeded with native grasses. Scientists increasingly believe that ranching, if managed properly, can help bring damaged grazing areas back to life. "We cannot assume rangelands will recover on their own," Curtin wrote in a recent study on the Malpai Borderlands. "Conservation of grazed lands requires restoring and sustaining natural processes."

---

cultivation of trees, is a similar practice that we will discuss in Chapter 12. Forestry practices can have substantial impacts on soils, just as farming and ranching can. As with farming and ranching techniques, forestry practices have been modified over the years to try to minimize damage to soils. Some practices, such as clear-cutting—the removal of all trees from an area at once—can lead to severe erosion. This is particularly the case on steep slopes (Figure 9.23). Alternative timbering methods that remove

fewer trees over longer periods of time are more successful in minimizing erosion.

## A number of U.S. and international programs promote soil conservation

In recent years, the U.S. Congress has enacted a number of laws promoting soil conservation. The Food Security Act of 1985 required farmers to adopt soil conservation

**FIGURE 9.23** Deforestation, discussed further in Chapter 12, can be a major cause of erosion, particularly when trees are clear-cut for timber on steep slopes.

influence over many farm products. It also created the Environmental Quality Incentive Program and the Natural Resources Conservation Foundation to promote and pay for the adoption of conservation practices in agriculture. In 1998, the USDA initiated the Low-Input Sustainable Agriculture Program to provide funding for individual farmers to develop and practice sustainable agriculture.

Internationally, the United Nations promotes soil conservation and sustainable agriculture through a variety of programs of its Food and Agriculture Organization (FAO). The FAO's Farmer-Centered Agricultural Resource Management Program (FAR) is a project undertaken in partnership by China, Thailand, Vietnam, Indonesia, Sri Lanka, Nepal, the Philippines, and India to support innovative approaches to resource management and sustainable agriculture. This program studies agricultural success stories and tries to help other farmers duplicate the successful efforts. Rather than following a top-down, government-controlled approach, the FAR program calls on the creativity of local communities to educate and encourage farmers throughout Asia to conserve soils and secure their food supply.

## Conclusion

Many of the policies enacted and the practices developed to combat soil degradation in the United States and worldwide have been quite successful, particularly in reducing the erosion of topsoil. Despite these successes, however, soil is still being degraded at a rate that calls into question the sustainability of industrial agriculture.

Our species has enjoyed a 10,000-year history with agriculture, yet despite all we have learned about soil degradation and conservation, many challenges remain. It is clear that even the best-conceived soil conservation programs require research, education, funding, and commitment from both farmers and governments if they are to fulfill their potential. In light of continued population growth, we will likely need better technology and wider adoption of soil conservation techniques to avoid an eventual food crisis. Increasingly, it seems relevant to consider whether the universal adoption of Aldo Leopold's land ethic (▸ pp. 35–36) will also be required if we are to feed the 9 billion people expected to crowd our planet in mid-century.

plans and practices as a prerequisite for receiving price supports and other government benefits. The Conservation Reserve Program, also enacted in 1985, pays farmers to stop cultivating highly erodible cropland and instead place it in conservation reserves planted with grasses and trees. The USDA estimates that for an annual cost of $1 billion, this program saves 700 million metric tons (771 million tons) of topsoil each year. Besides reducing erosion, the Conservation Reserve Program has generated income for farmers and has provided habitat for native wildlife. In 1996, Congress extended the program by passing the Federal Agricultural Improvement and Reform Act. Also known as the "Freedom to Farm Act," this law aimed to reduce subsidies and government

## REVIEWING OBJECTIVES

You should now be able to:

### Explain the importance of soils to agriculture, and describe the impacts of agriculture on soils

▶ Successful agriculture requires healthy soil. (p. 246)

▶ As the human population grows and consumption increases, pressures from agriculture are degrading Earth's soil, and we are losing 5–7 million ha (12–17 million acres) of productive cropland annually. (pp. 246–247)

### Outline major historical developments in agriculture

▶ Beginning about 10,000 years ago, people began breeding crop plants and domesticating animals. (p. 248)

▶ Domestication took place through the process of selective breeding, or artificial selection. (p. 248)

▶ Agriculture is thought to have originated multiple times independently in different cultures across the world. (pp. 248–249)

▶ Industrial agriculture is gradually replacing traditional agriculture, which largely replaced hunting and gathering. (pp. 248–250)

### Delineate the fundamentals of soil science, including soil formation and the properties of soil

▶ Soil includes diverse biotic communities that decompose organic matter. (pp. 250–251)

▶ Climate, organisms, relief, parent material, and time are factors influencing soil formation. (pp. 251–252)

▶ Soil profiles consist of distinct horizons with characteristic properties. (pp. 252–253)

▶ Soil can be characterized by color, texture, structure, and pH. (pp. 253–255)

▶ Soil properties affect the potential for plant growth and agriculture in any given location. (p. 255)

### State the causes and predict the consequences of soil erosion and soil degradation

▶ Some agricultural practices have resulted in high rates of erosion across the world, lowering crop yields. (pp. 256–258)

▶ Desertification affects a large portion of the world's soils, especially those in arid regions. (pp. 259–260)

▶ Overirrigation can cause salinization and waterlogging, which lower crop yields and are difficult to mitigate. (pp. 264–266)

▶ Overapplying fertilizers can cause pollution problems that affect ecosystems and human health. (pp. 266–267)

▶ Overgrazing can cause soil degradation on grasslands, as well as diverse impacts to native ecosystems. (pp. 267–270)

▶ Careless forestry practices, such as deforesting steep slopes, are a major cause of erosion. (pp. 270–271)

### Recite the history and explain the principles of soil conservation

▶ The Dust Bowl in the United States and similar events elsewhere have encouraged scientists and farmers to develop ways of better protecting and conserving topsoil. (pp. 260–261)

▶ Farming techniques such as crop rotation, contour farming, intercropping, terracing, shelterbelts, and reduced tillage enable farmers to reduce soil erosion and boost crop yields. (pp. 261–264)

▶ In the United States and across the world, governments are devising innovative policies and programs to deal with the problems of soil degradation. (pp. 271–272)

## TESTING YOUR COMPREHENSION

1. How did the practices of selective breeding and human agriculture begin roughly 10,000 years ago? Summarize the influence of agriculture on the development and organization of human communities.

2. Describe the methods used in traditional agriculture, and contrast subsistence agriculture with intensive traditional agriculture. What makes industrialized agriculture different from traditional agriculture?

3. What processes are most responsible for the formation of soil? Describe the three types of weathering that may contribute to the process of soil formation.

4. Name the five primary factors thought to influence soil formation, and describe one effect of each.

5. How are soil horizons created? What is the general pattern of distribution of organic matter in a typical soil profile?

6. Why is erosion generally considered a destructive process? Name three human activities that can promote

soil erosion. Describe four kinds of soil erosion by water. What factors affect the intensity of water erosion?

7. List innovations in soil conservation introduced by Hugh Hammond Bennett, first director of the SCS. What other farming techniques can help reduce the risk of erosion due to conventional cultivation methods?

8. How does terracing effectively turn very steep and mountainous areas into arable land? Explain the

method of no-till farming. Why does this method reduce soil erosion?

9. How do fertilizers boost crop growth? How can large amounts of fertilizer added to soil also end up in water supplies and the atmosphere?

10. What policies can be linked to the practice of overgrazing? Describe the effects of overgrazing on soil. What conditions characterize sustainable grazing practices?

## SEEKING SOLUTIONS

1. How do you think a farmer can best help to conserve soil? How do you think a scientist can best help to conserve soil? How do you think a national government can best help to conserve soil?

2. How and why might actual soils differ from the idealized six-horizon soil profile presented in the chapter? How might departures from the idealized profile indicate the impact of human activities? Provide at least three examples.

3. What method of farming would you choose to employ on a gradual slope with the threat of natural erosion? What kinds of plants might you use to prevent erosion, and why?

4. Discuss how the methods of no-till or reduced tillage farming, as described in this chapter, can enhance soil quality. What drawbacks or negative effects might no-till or reduced-tillage practices have on soil quality, and how might these be prevented?

5. Discuss how methods of locally based sustainable agriculture described in this chapter are promoting the science of soil conservation. In reference to Aldo Leopold's land ethic (▶ pp. 35–36), how are humans and the soil members of the same community?

6. Imagine that you are the head of an international granting agency that assists farmers with soil conservation and sustainable agriculture. You have $10 million to disburse. Your agency's staff has decided that the funding should go to (1) farmers in an arid area of Africa prone to salinization, (2) farmers in a fast-growing area of Indonesia where swidden agriculture is practiced, (3) farmers in southern Brazil practicing no-till agriculture, and (4) farmers in a dryland area of Mongolia undergoing desertification. What types of projects would you recommend funding in each of these areas, how would you apportion your funding among them, and why?

## INTERPRETING GRAPHS AND DATA

Kishor Atreya and his colleagues at Kathmandu University in Nepal conducted a field experiment to test the effects of reduced tillage versus conventional tillage on erosion and nutrient loss in the Himalayan Mountains in central Nepal. The region in which they worked has extremely steep terrain (with an average slope of 18%), and receives over 138 cm (55 in.) of rain per year, with 90% of it coming during the monsoon season from May to September. Atreya's team measured the amounts of soil, organic carbon, and nitrogen lost from the research plots (which were unterraced) over the course of a year. Some of their results are presented in the graph.

1. Under the conditions of the study reported above, how much soil, organic carbon, and nitrogen would be saved annually in fields with reduced tillage relative to fields with conventional tillage? Express your answers both in absolute units and as percentages.

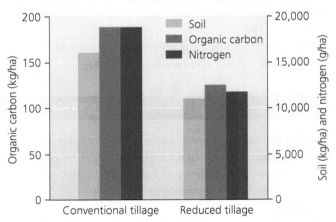

Annual soil and nutrient losses in plots under conventional and reduced tillage systems. All reduced tillage values are significantly different than their conventional tillage counterparts. Data from Atreya, K., et al. 2005. Applications of reduced tillage in hills of central Nepal. *Soil & Tillage Research*, in press.

2. Given that annual crop yields in the study plots were approximately 4 metric tons/ha, what is the ratio of soil lost to crop yield under conventional tillage? Under reduced tillage?

3. Is reduced tillage a sustainable management practice for Nepalese farmers? If so, what data from the study above would you cite in support of your answer? If not, or if you cannot say, then what concerns raised by the data above would still need to be addressed, or what additional data would be needed, to answer the question?

## CALCULATING ECOLOGICAL FOOTPRINTS

As you learned in this chapter, rates of soil loss due to erosion can be high. Even in the United States, approximately 6 pounds of topsoil are lost for every 1 pound of grain harvested. Erosion rates vary greatly with soil type, topography, tillage method, and crop type. For simplicity let us assume that the 6:1 ratio applies to all plant crops and that a typical diet includes 1 pound of plant material or its derived products (sugar, for example) per day. In the first two columns of the table, calculate the annual topsoil losses associated with growing this food for you and for other groups, assuming the same diet.

| | Plant products consumed (lb) | Soil loss at 6:1 ratio (lb) | Soil loss at 4:1 ratio (lb) | Reduced soil loss at 4:1 relative to 6:1 ratio (lb) |
|---|---|---|---|---|
| You | 365 | 2,190 | 1,460 | 730 |
| Your class | | | | |
| Your state | | | | |
| United States | | | | |

1. Improved soil conservation measures reduced erosion by approximately one-third from 1982 to 1997. If additional measures were again able to reduce the current rate of soil loss by a third, the ratio of soil lost to grain harvested would fall from 6:1 to 4:1. Calculate the soil losses associated with food production at a 4:1 ratio, and record your answers in the third column of the table.

2. Calculate the amount of topsoil hypothetically saved by the additional conservation measures in Question 1, and record your answers in the fourth column of the table.

3. Define a "sustainable" rate of soil loss. Describe how you might determine if a given farm was practicing sustainable use of soil.

## Take It Further

Go to www.aw-bc.com/withgott or the student CD-ROM where you'll find:

▶ Suggested answers to end-of-chapter questions
▶ Quizzes, animations, and flashcards to help you study
▶ *Research Navigator™* database of credible and reliable sources to assist you with your research projects

▶ **GRAPHit!** tutorials to help you master how to interpret graphs
▶ **INVESTIGATEit!** current news articles that link the topics that you study to case studies from your region to around the world

# 11 Biodiversity and Conservation Biology

The Sikhote-Alin Mountains meet the Pacific Ocean

## Upon successfully completing this chapter, you will be able to:

▶ Characterize the scope of biodiversity on Earth

▶ Describe ways to measure biodiversity

▶ Contrast background extinction rates and periods of mass extinction

▶ Evaluate the primary causes of biodiversity loss

▶ Specify the benefits of biodiversity

▶ Assess conservation biology and its practice

▶ Explain island biogeography theory and its application to conservation biology

▶ Compare and contrast traditional and more innovative biodiversity conservation efforts

# Central Case: Saving the Siberian Tiger

"Future generations would be truly saddened that this century had so little foresight, so little compassion, such lack of generosity of spirit for the future that it would eliminate one of the most dramatic and beautiful animals this world has ever seen."

—GEORGE SCHALLER, WILDLIFE BIOLOGIST, ON THE TIGER

"Except in pockets of ignorance and malice, there is no longer an ideological war between conservationists and developers. Both share the perception that health and prosperity decline in a deteriorating environment. They also understand that useful products cannot be harvested from extinct species."

—EDWARD O. WILSON, HARVARD UNIVERSITY BIODIVERSITY EXPERT

Historically, tigers roamed widely across Asia from Turkey to northeast Russia to Indonesia. Within the past 200 years, however, people have driven the majestic striped cats from most of their historic range. Today, tigers are exceedingly rare and are creeping toward extinction.

Of the tigers that still survive, those of the subspecies known as the Siberian tiger are the largest cats in the world. Males reach 3.66 m (12 ft) in length and weigh up to 363 kg (800 lb). Also named Amur tigers for the watershed they occupied along the Amur River, which divides Siberian Russia from Manchurian China, these cats now find their last refuge in the forests of the remote Sikhote-Alin Mountains of the Russian Far East.

For thousands of years the Siberian tiger coexisted with the region's native people and held a prominent place in native language and lore. These people referred to the tiger as "Old Man" or "Grandfather" and equated it with royalty or viewed it as a guardian of the mountains and forests. Indigenous people of the region rarely killed a tiger unless it had preyed on a person.

The Russians who moved into the region and exerted control in the early 20th century had no such cultural traditions. They hunted tigers for sport and hides, and some Russians reported killing as many as 10 tigers in a single hunt. In addition, poachers began killing tigers to sell their body parts to China and other Asian countries, where they are used in traditional medicine and as aphrodisiacs. Meanwhile, road building, logging, and agriculture began to fragment tiger habitat and provide easy access for well-armed hunters. The tiger population dipped to perhaps 20–30 animals.

International conservation groups began to get involved, working with Russian biologists to try to save the dwindling tiger population. One such group was the Hornocker Wildlife Institute, now part of the Wildlife Conservation Society. In 1991 the group helped launch the Siberian Tiger Project, devoted to studying the tiger and its habitat. The team put together a plan to protect the tiger, began educating people regarding the tiger's importance and value, and worked closely with those who live in proximity to the big cats.

Thanks to such efforts by conservation biologists, today Siberian tigers in the wild number roughly 330–370, and about 600 more survive in zoos and captive breeding programs around the world. The outlook for the species' survival still looks challenging, but many people are trying to save these endangered animals. It is one of many efforts around the world today to stem the loss of our planet's priceless biological diversity.

# Our Planet of Life

Growing human population and resource consumption are putting ever-greater pressure on the flora and fauna of the planet, from tigers to tiger beetles. We are diminishing Earth's diversity of life, the very quality that makes our planet so special. In Chapter 5 we introduced the concept of **biological diversity,** or **biodiversity,** as the sum total of all organisms in an area, taking into account the diversity of species, their genes, their populations, and their communities. In this chapter we will refine this definition and examine current biodiversity trends and their relevance to our lives. We will then explore science-based solutions to biodiversity loss.

## Biodiversity encompasses several levels

Biodiversity is a concept as multifaceted as life itself, and definitions of the term are plentiful. As sociologist of science David Takacs explains in his 1996 book, *The Idea of Biodiversity,* different biologists employ different working definitions according to their own aims, interests, and values. Nonetheless, there is broad agreement that the concept applies across several major levels in the organization of life (Figure 11.1). The level that is easiest to visualize and most commonly used is species diversity.

**Ecosystem diversity**

**Species diversity**

**Genetic diversity**

**FIGURE 11.1** The concept of biodiversity encompasses several levels in the hierarchy of life. Species diversity (middle frame of figure) refers to the number or variety of species. Genetic diversity (bottom frame) refers to variation in DNA composition among individuals within a species. Ecosystem diversity (top frame) and related concepts refer to variety at levels above the species level, such as ecosystems, communities, habitats, or landscapes.

**Species diversity** As you recall from Chapter 5 (▸p. 122), a *species* is a distinct type of organism, a set of individuals that uniquely share certain characteristics and can breed with one another and produce fertile offspring. Biologists may use somewhat differing criteria to delineate species boundaries; some emphasize characteristics shared because of common ancestry, whereas others emphasize ability to interbreed. In practice, however, scientists broadly agree on species identities. We can express **species diversity** in terms of the number or variety of species in the world or in a particular region. One component of species diversity is *species richness,* the number of species. Another is *evenness* or *relative abundance,* the extent to which numbers of individuals of different species are equal or skewed.

As we saw in Chapter 5 (▸pp. 122–126), speciation generates new species, adding to species richness, whereas extinction decreases species richness. Although immigration, emigration, and local extinction may increase or decrease species richness locally, only speciation and extinction change it globally.

*Taxonomists,* the scientists who classify species, use an organism's physical appearance and genetic makeup to determine its species. Taxonomists also group species by their similarity into a hierarchy of categories meant to reflect evolutionary relationships. Related species are grouped together into *genera* (singular, *genus*), related genera are grouped into families, and so on (Figure 11.2). Every species is given a two-part Latin or Latinized scientific name denoting its genus and species. The tiger, *Panthera tigris,* differs from the world's other species of large cats such as the jaguar *(Panthera onca),* the leopard *(Panthera pardus),* and the African lion *(Panthera leo).* These four species are closely related in evolutionary terms, as indicated by the genus name they share, *Panthera.* They are more distantly related to cats in other genera such as the cheetah *(Acinonyx jubatus)* and the bobcat *(Felis rufus),* although all cats are classified together in the family Felidae.

Biodiversity exists below the species level in the form of *subspecies,* populations of a species that occur in different geographic areas and differ from one another in some characteristics. Subspecies are formed by the same processes that drive speciation, but result when divergence does not proceed far enough to create separate species. Scientists denote subspecies with a third part of the scientific name. The Siberian tiger, *Panthera tigris altaica,* is one of five subspecies of tiger still surviving (Figure 11.3). Tiger subspecies differ in color, coat thickness, stripe patterns, and size. For example, *Panthera tigris altaica* is 5–10 cm (2–4 in.) taller at the shoulder than the Bengal tiger *(Panthera tigris tigris)* of India and Nepal, and it has a thicker coat and larger paws.

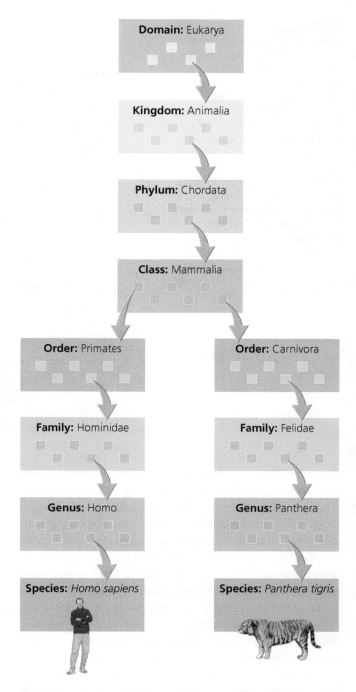

**FIGURE 11.2** Taxonomists classify organisms using a hierarchical system meant to reflect evolutionary relationships. Species that are similar in their appearance, behavior, and genetics (because of recent common ancestry) are placed in the same genus. Organisms of similar genera are placed within the same family. Families are placed within orders, orders within classes, classes within phyla, phyla within kingdoms, and kingdoms within domains. For instance, humans (*Homo sapiens,* a species in the genus *Homo*) and tigers (*Panthera tigris,* a species in the genus *Panthera*) are both within the class Mammalia. However, the differences between our two species, which have evolved over millions of years, are great enough that we are placed in different orders and families.

**FIGURE 11.3** Three of the eight subspecies of tiger became extinct during the 20th century. The Bali, Javan, and Caspian tigers are extinct. Today only the Siberian (Amur), Bengal, Indochina, Sumatran, and South China tigers persist, and the Chinese government estimates that less than 30 individuals of the South China tiger remain. Deforestation, hunting, and other pressures from people have caused tigers of all subspecies to disappear from most of the geographic range they historically occupied. This map contrasts the ranges of the eight subspecies in the years 1800 (orange) and 2000 (red). Data from the Tiger Information Center.

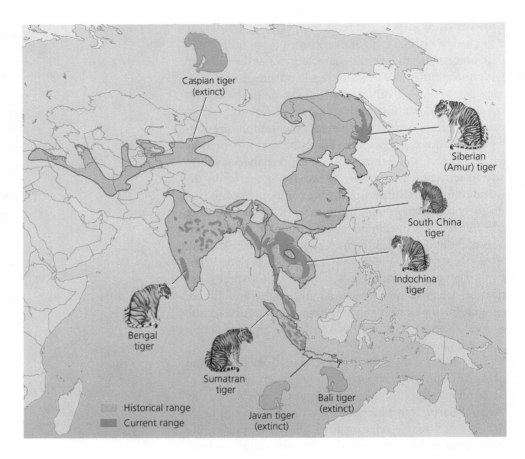

**Genetic diversity** Scientists designate subspecies when they recognize substantial genetically based differences among individuals from different populations of a species. However, all species consist of individuals that vary genetically from one another to some degree, and this genetic diversity is an important component of biodiversity. **Genetic diversity** encompasses the differences in DNA composition among individuals within species and populations.

Genetic diversity provides the raw material for adaptation to local conditions. A diversity of genes for coat thickness in tigers allowed natural selection to favor genes for thin coats of fur in Bengal tigers living in warm regions, and genes for thick coats of fur for Siberian tigers living in cold regions. In the long term, populations with more genetic diversity may stand better chances of persisting, because their variation better enables them to cope with environmental change. Populations with little genetic diversity are vulnerable to environmental change for which they are not genetically prepared. Populations with depressed genetic diversity may also be more vulnerable to disease and may suffer *inbreeding depression*, which occurs when genetically similar parents mate and produce weak or defective offspring. Scientists have sounded warnings over low genetic diversity in species

that have dropped to low population sizes in the past, including cheetahs, bison, and elephant seals, but the full consequences of reduced diversity in these species remain to be seen. Diminishing genetic diversity in our crop plants also is a prime concern to humanity, as we saw in Chapter 10 (▶pp. 295–296).

**Ecosystem diversity** Biodiversity also encompasses levels above the species level. *Ecosystem diversity* refers to the number and variety of ecosystems, but biologists may also refer to the diversity of biotic community types or habitats within some specified area. If the area is large, scientists may also consider the geographic arrangement of habitats, communities, or ecosystems at the landscape level, including the sizes, shapes, and interconnectedness of patches of these entities. Under any of these concepts, a seashore of rocky and sandy beaches, forested cliffs, offshore coral reefs, and ocean waters would hold far more biodiversity than the same acreage of a monocultural cornfield. A mountain slope whose vegetation changes from desert to hardwood forest to coniferous forest to alpine meadow would hold more biodiversity than an area the same size consisting of only desert, forest, or meadow.

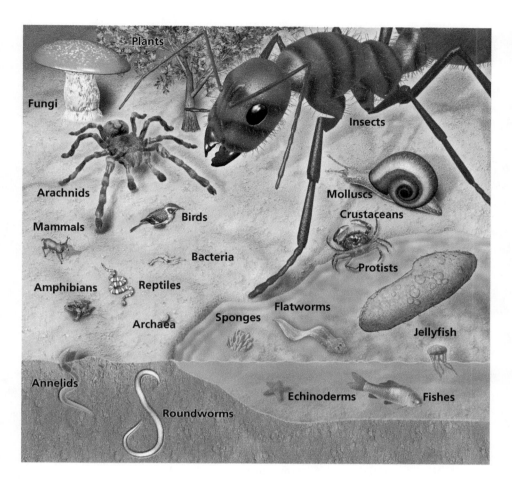

Plants
Fungi
Insects
Arachnids
Molluscs
Birds
Crustaceans
Mammals
Bacteria
Protists
Amphibians
Reptiles
Flatworms
Archaea
Sponges
Jellyfish
Annelids
Echinoderms
Fishes
Roundworms

**FIGURE 11.4** This illustration shows organisms scaled in size to the number of species known so far from each major taxonomic group, giving a visual sense of the disparity in species richness among groups. However, because most species are not yet discovered or described, some groups (such as bacteria, archaea, insects, nematodes, protists, fungi, and others) may contain far more species than we now know of. Data from Groombridge, B., and M. D. Jenkins. 2002. *Global biodiversity: Earth's living resources in the 21st century.* UNEP-World Conservation Monitoring Centre. Cambridge, U.K.: Hoechst Foundation.

## Measuring biodiversity is not easy

Coming up with precise quantitative measurements to express a region's biodiversity is difficult. This is partly why scientists often express biodiversity in terms of its most easily measured component, species diversity, and in particular, species richness. Species richness is a good gauge for overall biodiversity, but we still are profoundly ignorant of the number of species that exist worldwide. So far, scientists have identified and described 1.7–2.0 million species of plants, animals, and microorganisms. However, estimates for the total number that actually exist range from 3 million to 100 million, with our best educated guesses ranging from 5 million to 30 million.

Species are not evenly distributed among taxonomic groups. In terms of number of species, insects show a staggering predominance over all other forms of life (Figures 11.4 and 11.5). Within insects, about 40% are beetles. Beetles outnumber all noninsect animals and all plants. No wonder the 20th-century British biologist J. B. S. Haldane famously quipped that God must have had "an inordinate fondness for beetles."

Our knowledge of species numbers is incomplete for several reasons. First, some areas of Earth remain little

explored. We have barely sampled the ocean depths, hydrothermal vents (▸pp. 107–108), or the tree canopies and soils of tropical forests. Second, many species are tiny and easily overlooked. These inconspicuous organisms include bacteria, nematodes (roundworms), fungi, protists, and soil-dwelling arthropods. Third, many organisms are so difficult to identify that ones thought to be identical sometimes turn out, once biologists look more closely, to be multiple species. This is frequently the case with microbes, fungi, and small insects, but also sometimes with organisms as large as birds, trees, and whales.

Smithsonian Institution entomologist Terry Erwin pioneered one method of estimating species numbers. In 1982, Erwin's crews fogged rainforest trees in Central America with clouds of insecticide and then collected insects, spiders, and other arthropods as they died and fell from the treetops. Erwin concluded that 163 beetle species specialized on the tree species *Luehea seemannii.* If this were typical, he figured, then the world's 50,000 tropical tree species would hold 8,150,000 beetle species and— since beetles represent 40% of all arthropods—20 million arthropod species. If canopies hold two-thirds of all arthropods, then arthropod species in tropical forests alone would number 30 million. Many assumptions were

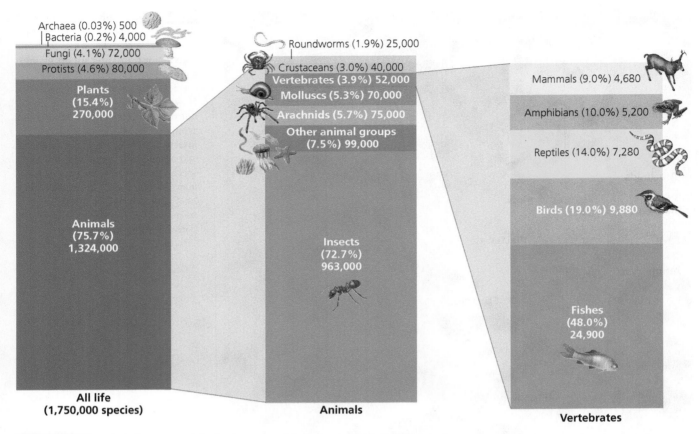

**FIGURE 11.5** In the left portion of the figure, we see that three-quarters of known species are animals. The central portion subdivides animals, revealing that nearly three-quarters of animals are insects and that vertebrates comprise only 3.9% of animals. Among vertebrates (right portion of figure), nearly half are fishes, and mammals comprise only 9%. As noted, most species are not yet discovered or described, so some groups may contain far more species than we now know of. Data from Groombridge, B., and M.D. Jenkins. 2002. *Global biodiversity: Earth's living resources in the 21st century.* UNEP-World Conservation Monitoring Centre. Cambridge, U.K.: Hoechst Foundation.

involved in this calculation, and several follow-up studies have revised Erwin's estimate downward.

## Biodiversity is unevenly distributed

Numbers of species tell only part of the story of Earth's biodiversity. Living things are distributed across our planet unevenly, and scientists have long sought to explain the distributional patterns they see. For example, as we have noted, some groups of organisms include only one or a few species, whereas other groups contain many. Some groups have given rise to many species in a relatively short period of time through the process of adaptive radiation (see Figure 5.3, ▶p. 121). Species diversity also varies according to biome. Tropical dry forests and rainforests tend to support more species than tundra and boreal forests, for instance. The variation in diversity by biome is related to one of the planet's most striking patterns of

species diversity: the fact that species richness generally increases as one approaches the equator (Figure 11.6). This pattern of variation with latitude, called the *latitudinal gradient,* has been one of the most obvious patterns in ecology, but it also has been one of the most difficult ones for scientists to explain.

Hypotheses abound for the cause of the latitudinal gradient in species richness, but it seems likely that plant productivity and climate stability play key roles in the phenomenon (Figure 11.7). Greater amounts of solar energy, heat, and humidity at tropical latitudes lead to more plant growth, making areas nearer the equator more productive and able to support larger numbers of animals. In addition, the relatively stable climates of equatorial regions—their similar temperatures and rainfall from day to day and season to season—help ensure that single species won't dominate ecosystems, but that instead numerous species can coexist. Whereas varying environmental

**FIGURE 11.6** For many types of organisms, number of species per unit area tends to increase as one moves toward the equator. This trend, the latitudinal gradient in species richness, is one of the most readily apparent—yet least understood—patterns in ecology. One example is bird species in North and Central America: In any one spot in arctic Canada and Alaska, 30 to 100 species can be counted; in areas of Costa Rica and Panama, the number rises to over 600. Adapted from Cook, R. E. 1969. Variation in species density in North American birds. *Systematic Zoology* 18: 63–84.

**FIGURE 11.7** Ecologists have offered many hypotheses for the latitudinal gradient in species richness, and one set of ideas is summarized here. The variable climates (across days, seasons, and years) of polar and temperate latitudes favor organisms that can survive a wide range of conditions. Such generalist species have expansive niches; they can do many things well enough to survive, and they spread over large areas. In tropical latitudes, the abundant solar energy, heat, and humidity induce greater plant growth, which supports more organisms. The stable climates of equatorial regions favor specialist species, which have restricted niches but do certain things very well. Together these factors are thought to promote greater species richness in the tropics.

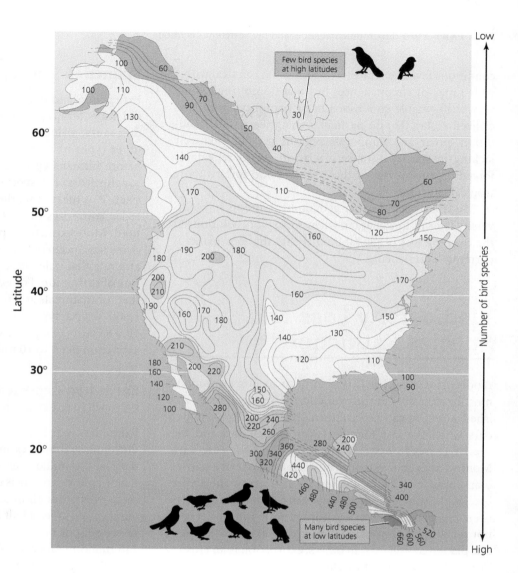

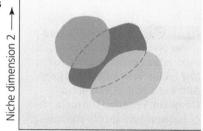

**Temperate and polar latitudes**
- Variable climate favors fewer species, and species that are widespread generalists.

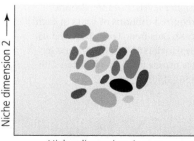

**Tropical latitudes**
- Greater solar energy, heat, and humidity promote more plant growth to support more organisms. Stable climate favors specialist species. Together these encourage greater diversity of species.

conditions favor generalists—species that can deal with a wide range of circumstances but that do no single thing very well—stable conditions favor organisms with specialized niches that do particular things very well. In addition, polar and temperate regions may be relatively lacking in species because glaciation events repeatedly forced organisms out of these regions and toward more tropical latitudes.

We will discuss further geographic patterns in biodiversity later in this chapter, when we explore solutions to the ongoing loss of global biodiversity that our planet is currently experiencing.

# Biodiversity Loss and Species Extinction

Biodiversity at all levels is being lost to human impact, most irretrievably in the extinction of species. Once vanished, a species can never return. *Extinction* (▸ p. 126) occurs when the last member of a species dies and the species ceases to exist, as apparently was the case with Monteverde's golden toad. The disappearance of a particular population from a given area, but not the entire species globally, is referred to as **extirpation.** The tiger has been extirpated from most of its historic range, but it is not yet extinct. Although a species that is extirpated from one place may still exist in others, extirpation is an erosive process that can, over time, lead to extinction.

## Extinction is a natural process

Extirpation and extinction occur naturally. If organisms did not naturally go extinct, we would be up to our ears in dinosaurs, trilobites, ammonites, and the millions of other types of creatures that vanished from Earth long before humans appeared. Paleontologists estimate that roughly 99% of all species that have ever lived are now extinct. This means that the wealth of species on our planet today comprises only about 1% of all species that ever lived. Most extinctions preceding the appearance of humans have occurred one by one for independent reasons, at a rate that paleontologists refer to as the **background rate of extinction.** For example, the fossil record indicates that for mammals and marine animals, one species out of 1,000 would typically become extinct every 1,000 to 10,000 years. This translates to an annual rate of one extinction per 1 to 10 million species.

## Earth has experienced five previous mass extinction episodes

Extinction rates have risen far above this background rate during several mass extinction events in Earth's history. In the past 440 million years, our planet has experienced five major episodes of **mass extinction** (Figure 11.8). Each of these events has eliminated more than one-fifth of life's families and at least half its species (Table 11.1). The most severe episode occurred at the end of the Permian period, 248 million years ago, when close to 54% of all families, 90% of all species, and 95% of marine species went extinct.

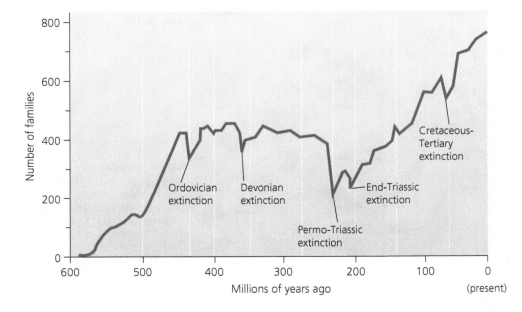

**FIGURE 11.8** The fossil record shows evidence of five episodes of mass extinction during the past half-billion years of Earth history. At the end of the Ordovician, Devonian, Permian, Triassic, and Cretaceous periods, 50–95% of the world's species appear to have gone extinct. Each time, biodiversity later rebounded to equal or higher levels, but the rebound required millions of years in each case. Data from Raup, D. M., and J. J. Sepkoski. 1982. Mass extinctions in the marine fossil record. *Science* 215: 1501–1503.

| Table 11.1 Mass Extinctions | | | | |
|---|---|---|---|---|
| Event | Date (millions of years ago) | Cause | Types of life most affected | Percentage of life depleted |
| Ordovician | 440 mya | Unknown | Marine organisms; terrestrial record is unknown | >20% of families |
| Devonian | 370 mya | Unknown | Marine organisms; terrestrial record is unknown | >20% of families |
| Permo-Triassic | 250 mya | Possibly volcanism | Marine organisms; terrestrial record is less known | >50% of families; 80–95% of species |
| End-Triassic | 202 mya | Unknown | Marine organisms; terrestrial record is less known | 20% of families; 50% of genera |
| Cretaceous-Tertiary | 65 mya | Asteroid impact | Marine and terrestrial organisms, including dinosaurs | 15% of families; >50% of species |
| Current | Beginning 0.01 mya | Human impact, through habitat destruction and other means | Large animals, specialized organisms, island organisms, and organisms hunted or harvested by humans | Ongoing |

The best-known episode occurred at the end of the Cretaceous period, 65 million years ago, when an apparent asteroid impact brought an end to the dinosaurs and many other groups (▶ pp. 128–129). In addition, there is evidence for further mass extinctions in the Cambrian period and earlier, more than half a billion years ago.

If current trends continue, the modern era, known as the Quaternary period, may see the extinction of more than half of all species. Although similar in scale to previous mass extinctions, today's ongoing mass extinction is different in two primary respects. First, humans are causing it. Second, humans will suffer as a result of it.

## Humans set the sixth mass extinction in motion years ago

We have recorded many instances of human-induced species extinction over the past few hundred years. Sailors documented the extinction of the dodo on the Indian Ocean island of Mauritius in the 17th century, and we still have a few of the dodo's body parts in museums. Among North American birds in the past two centuries, we have driven into extinction the Carolina parakeet, great auk, Labrador duck, and passenger pigeon (▶ p. 132), and probably the Bachman's warbler and Eskimo curlew. Several more species, including the whooping crane, California condor, Kirtland's warbler, and the ivory-billed woodpecker, recently rediscovered in the wooded swamps of Arkansas, teeter on the brink of extinction.

However, species extinctions caused by humans precede written history. Indeed, people may have been hunting species to extinction for thousands of years. Archaeological evidence shows that in case after case, a wave of extinctions followed close on the heels of human arrival on islands and continents (Figure 11.9). After Polynesians reached Hawaii, half its birds went extinct. Birds, mammals, and reptiles vanished following human arrival on many other oceanic islands, including large island masses such as New Zealand and Madagascar. The pattern appears to hold for at least two continents, as well. Dozens of species of large vertebrates died off in Australia after Aborigines arrived roughly 50,000 years ago, and North America lost 33 genera of large mammals after people arrived on the continent at least 10,000 years ago.

## Current extinction rates are much higher than normal

Today, species loss is accelerating as our population growth and resource consumption put increasing strain on habitats and wildlife. A decade ago, 1,500 of the world's leading scientists reported to the United Nations in their Global Biodiversity Assessment that in the preceding 400 years, 484 animal and 654 plant species were known to have become extinct, and that more than 30,000 plant and animal species currently faced extinction. In 2005, scientists with the Millennium Ecosystem Assessment (▶ p. 20) calculated that the current global extinction rate is 100 to 1,000 times greater than the background rate. Moreover, they projected that the rate would increase tenfold or more in future decades.

To keep track of the current status of endangered species, the World Conservation Union maintains the

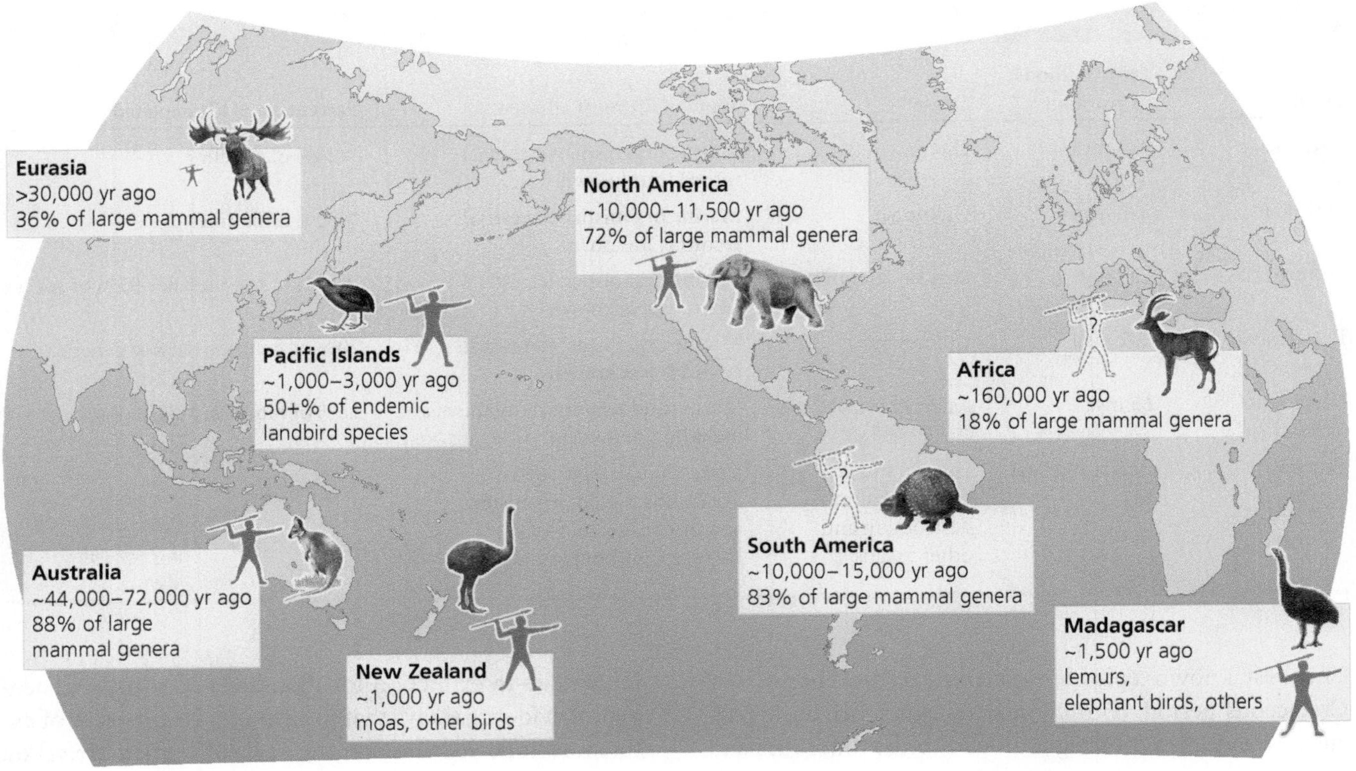

**FIGURE 11.9** This map shows for each region the time of human arrival and the extent of the recent extinction wave. Illustrated are representative extinct megafauna from each region. The human hunter icons are sized according to the degree of evidence that human hunting was a cause of extinctions; larger icons indicate more certainty that humans (as opposed to climate change or other forces) were the cause. Data for South America and Africa are so far too sparse to be conclusive, and future archaeological and paleontological research could well alter these interpretations. Adapted from Barnosky, A. D., et al. 2004. Assessing the causes of late Pleistocene extinctions on the continents. *Science* 306: 70–75; and Wilson, E. O. 1992. *The diversity of life.* Cambridge, MA: Belknap Press.

**Red List,** an updated list of species facing high risks of extinction. The 2004 Red List reported that 23% (1,101) of mammal species and 12% (1,213) of bird species are threatened with extinction. Among other major groups (for which assessments are not fully complete), estimates of the percentage of species threatened ranged from 31% to 86%. Since 1996, the total number of vertebrate animals listed as threatened climbed by more than 6%. Since 1970, at least 58 fish species, 9 bird species, and 1 mammal species have become extinct, and in the United States alone over the past 500 years, 236 animals and 17 plants are confirmed to have gone extinct. For all of these figures, the *actual* numbers of species extinct and threatened, like the actual number of total species in the world, are doubtless greater than the *known* numbers.

Among the 1,101 mammals facing possible extinction on the Red List is the tiger, which despite—or perhaps because of—its tremendous size and reputation as a fierce predator, is one of the most endangered large animals on the planet. In 1950, eight tiger subspecies existed (see Figure 11.3). Today, three are extinct. The Bali tiger, *Panthera tigris balica,* went extinct in the 1940s; the Caspian tiger, *Panthera tigris virgata,* during the 1970s; and the Javan tiger, *Panthera tigris sondaica,* during the 1980s.

## Biodiversity loss involves more than extinction

Statistics on extinction tell only part of the story of biodiversity loss. The larger part of the story is the decline in population sizes of many organisms. Declines in numbers are accompanied by shrinkage of species' geographic ranges. Thus, many species today are less numerous and occupy less area than they once did. These patterns mean that genetic diversity and ecosystem diversity, as well as species diversity, are being lost. To measure and quantify

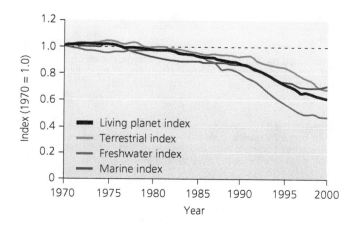

**FIGURE 11.10** The Living Planet Index serves as an indicator of the state of global biodiversity. Index values summarize population trends for 1,145 species. Between 1970 and 2000, the Living Planet Index fell by roughly 40%. The indices for terrestrial and marine species fell 30%, and the index for freshwater species fell 50%. Data from World Wide Fund for Nature and U.N. Environment Programme. 2004. *The Living Planet Report, 2004.* Gland, Switzerland: WWF.

this degradation, scientists at the World Wildlife Fund and the United Nations Environment Programme (UNEP) developed a metric called the *Living Planet Index.* This index summarizes trends in the populations of 555 terrestrial species, 323 freshwater species, and 267 marine species that are well enough monitored to provide reliable data. Between 1970 and 2000, the Living Planet Index fell by roughly 40% (Figure 11.10).

## There are several major causes of biodiversity loss

Reasons for the decline of any given species are often multifaceted and complex, so they can be difficult to determine. The current precipitous decline in populations of amphibians throughout the world provides an example. Frogs, toads, and salamanders worldwide are decreasing drastically in abundance. Several have already gone extinct, and scientists are struggling to explain why. Recent studies have implicated a wide array of factors, and most scientists now suspect that such factors may be interacting synergistically (see "The Science behind the Story," ▶ pp. 322–323).

Nonetheless, overall, scientists have identified four primary causes of population decline and species extinction: habitat alteration, invasive species, pollution, and overharvesting. Global climate change (Chapter 18) now threatens to become the fifth. Each of these factors is exacerbated by human population growth and by our increase in per capita consumption of resources.

**Habitat alteration** Nearly every human activity can alter the habitat of the organisms around us. Farming replaces diverse natural communities with simplified ones of only one or a few plant species. Grazing modifies the structure and species composition of grasslands. Either type of agriculture can lead to desertification. Clearing forests removes the food, shelter, and other resources that forest-dwelling organisms need to survive. Hydroelectric dams turn rivers into reservoirs upstream and thereby affect water conditions and floodplain communities downstream. Urbanization and suburban sprawl supplant diverse natural communities with simplified human-made ones, driving many species from their homes.

Such changes in habitat generally have negative effects. Organisms are already adapted to the habitats in which they live, so any change is likely to render the habitat less suitable for them. Of course, human-induced habitat change may benefit some species. Animals such as starlings, house sparrows, pigeons, and gray squirrels do very well in urban and suburban environments and benefit from our modification of natural habitats. However, the species that benefit are relatively few; for every species that gains, more lose. Furthermore, the species that do well in our midst tend to be weedy, cosmopolitan generalists that are in little danger of disappearing any time soon.

Habitat alteration is by far the greatest cause of biodiversity loss today. It is the primary source of population declines for 83% of threatened mammals and 85% of threatened birds, according to UNEP data. As just one example of thousands, the prairies native to North America's Great Plains have been almost entirely converted to agriculture. The area of prairie habitat has been reduced by more than 99%. As a result, grassland bird populations have declined by an estimated 82–99%. Many grassland species have been extirpated from large areas, and the two species of prairie chickens still persisting in pockets of the Great Plains could soon go extinct. Habitat destruction has occurred widely in nearly every biome. Estimates by UNEP in 2002 reported that 45% of Earth's forests, 50% of its mangrove ecosystems, and 10% of its coral reefs had been destroyed by recent human activity.

**Invasive species** Human introduction of non-native species to new environments, where some may become invasive (Figure 11.11), has also pushed native species toward extinction. Some introductions have been accidental. Examples include aquatic organisms (such as zebra mussels; Chapter 6) transported among continents in the ballast water of ships, animals that have escaped from the pet trade, and the weed seeds that cling to our socks as we travel from place to place. Other introductions have been

| Invasive Species | | | |
|---|---|---|---|
| **Species** | **Native to...** | **Invasive in...** | **Effects** |
| Mosquito fish (*Gambusia affinis*)  | North America | Africa, Asia, Europe, and Australia | Introduced to control mosquito populations, the mosquito fish outcompetes native fish, eats their eggs, and does no better than native species in controlling mosquitoes. |
| Zebra mussels (*Dreissenna polymorpha*)  | Caspian Sea | Freshwater ecosystems including the Great Lakes of Canada and the United States | Zebra mussels (Chapter 6) most likely made their way from their home by traveling in ballast water taken on by cargo ships. They compete with native species and clog water treatment facilities and power plant cooling systems. |
| Kudzu (*Pueraria montana*)  | Japan | Southeastern United States | A vine that can grow 30 m (100 ft) in a single season. The U.S. Soil Conservation Service introduced kudzu in the 1930s to help control erosion. Adaptable and extraordinarily fast-growing, kudzu has taken over thousands of hectares of forests, fields, and roadsides in the southeastern United States. |
| Asian long-horned beetles (*Anoplophora glabripennis*)  | Asia | United States | Having first arrived in the United States in imported lumber in the 1990s, these beetles burrow into hardwood trees and interfere with the trees' ability to absorb and process water and nutrients. They may wipe out the majority of hardwood trees in an area. Several U.S. cities, including Chicago in 1999 and Seattle in 2002, have cleared thousands of trees after detecting these invaders. |
| Rosy wolfsnail (*Euglandina rosea*) 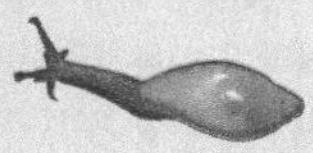 | Southeastern United States and Latin America | Hawaii | In the 1950s, well-meaning scientists introduced the rosy wolfsnail to Hawaii to prey upon and reduce the population of another invasive species, the giant African land snail (*Achatina fulica*), which had been introduced early in the 20th century as an ornamental garden animal. Within a few decades, however, the carnivorous rosy wolfsnail had instead driven more than half of Hawaii's native species of banded tree snails to extinction. |
| Cane toad (*Bufo marinus*)  | Southern United States to tropical South America | Northern Australia and other locations | Since being introduced 70 years ago to control insects in sugarcane fields, the cane toad has wreaked havoc across northern Australia (and other locations). The skin of this tropical American toad can kill its predators, and the cane toad outcompetes native amphibians. |
| Bullfrog (*Rana catesbiana*)  | Eastern North America | Western North America | The bullfrog is contributing to amphibian and reptile declines in western North America. Bullfrog tadpoles grow large and can outcompete and prey on other tadpoles, but need to grow a long time in permanent water to do so. Historically most water bodies in the arid West dried up part of the year, making it impossible for bullfrogs to live there, but artificial impoundments—dams, farm ponds, canals—gave the bullfrogs bases from which they could spread. |

**FIGURE 11.11**   Invasive species are species that thrive in areas where they are introduced, outcompeting, preying on, or otherwise harming native species. Of the many thousands of invasive species, this chart shows a few of the best known.

intentional. People have brought with them food crops, domesticated animals, and other organisms as they colonized new places, generally unaware of the ecological consequences that could result. Species native to islands are especially vulnerable to disruption from introduced species because the native species have been in isolation for so long with relatively few parasites, predators, and competitors. As a result, they have not evolved the

| Invasive Species | | | |
|---|---|---|---|
| **Species** | **Native to...** | **Invasive in...** | **Effects** |
| Gypsy moth (*Lymantria dispar*) | Eurasia | Northeastern United States | In the 1860s, a scientist introduced the gypsy moth to Massachusetts in the mistaken belief that it might be bred with others to produce a commercial-quality silk. The gypsy moth failed to start a silk industry, and instead spread through the northeastern United States and beyond, where its outbreaks defoliate trees over large regions every few years. |
| European starling (*Sturnus vulgaris*) | Europe | North America | The bird was first introduced to New York City in the late 19th century by Shakespeare devotees intent on bringing every bird mentioned in Shakespeare's plays to the new continent. It only took 75 years for the birds to spread to the Pacific coast, Alaska, and Mexico, becoming one of the most abundant birds on the continent. Starlings are thought to outcompete native birds for nest sites. |
| Indian mongoose (*Herpestes auropunctatus*) | Southeast Asia | Hawaii | Rats that had invaded the Hawaiian islands from ships in the 17th century were damaging sugarcane fields, so in 1883 the Indian mongoose was introduced to control rat populations. Unfortunately, the rats were active at night and the mongooses fed during the day, so the plan didn't work. Instead mongooses began preying on native species like ground-nesting seabirds and the now-endangered Nene or Hawaiian goose (*Branta sandvicensis*). |
| A green alga (*Caulerpa taxifolia*) | Tropical oceans and seas | Mediterranean Sea | Dubbed the "killer algae," *Caulerpa taxifolia* has spread along the coasts of several Mediterranean countries since it apparently escaped from Monaco's aquarium in 1984. Creeping underwater over the sand and mud like a green shag carpet, it crowds out other plants, is inedible to most animals, and tangles boat propellers. It has been the focus of intense eradication efforts since arriving recently in Australia and California. |
| Cheatgrass (*Bromus tectorum*) | Eurasia | Western United States | In just 30 years after its introduction to Washington state in the 1890s, cheatgrass has spread across much of the western United States. Its secret: fire. Its thick patches that choke out other plants and use up the soil's nitrogen burn readily. Fire kills many of the native plants, but not cheatgrass, which grows back even stronger amid the lack of competition. |
| Brown tree snake (*Boiga irregularis*) | Southeast Asia | Guam | Nearly all native forest bird species on the South Pacific island of Guam have disappeared. The culprit is the brown tree snake. The snakes were likely brought to the island inadvertantly as stowaways in cargo bays of military planes in World War II. Guam's birds had not evolved with tree snakes, and so had no defenses against the snake's nighttime predation. The snakes also cause numerous power outages each year on Guam and have spread to other islands where they are repeating their ecological devastation. The arrival of this snake is the greatest fear of conservation biologists in Hawaii. |

defenses necessary to resist invaders that are better adapted to these pressures.

Most organisms introduced to new areas perish, but the few types that survive may do very well, especially if they find themselves without the predators and parasites that attacked them back home or without the competitors that had limited their access to resources. Once released from the limiting factors of predation, parasitism, and

# Amphibian Diversity and Amphibian Declines

Amphibians illustrate the two most salient aspects of Earth's biodiversity today. Scientists are discovering more and more species while more and more populations and species are vanishing.

New species of most classes of vertebrates are discovered at a rate of only one or a few per year, but the number of known amphibian species (which include frogs, salamanders, and others)—about 5,800 as of 2005—has jumped nearly 42% just since 1985.

At the same time, however, over 200 species are in steep decline. Researchers feel that they may be naming some species just before they go extinct and losing others before they are even discovered. At least 32 species of frogs, toads, and salamanders studied just years or decades ago, including the golden toad (Chapter 5), are now altogether gone.

These losses are especially worrying because amphibians are widely regarded as "biological indicators" that indicate whether an ecosystem is in good shape or is degraded. Amphibians rely on both

The odd-looking purplish frog *Nasikabatrachus sahyadrensis*, of India, is one of many new amphibian species recently discovered.

aquatic and terrestrial environments and may breathe and absorb water through their skin, so they are sensitive to pollution and other environmental stresses. The link between amphibians and environmental quality suggests that studying the reasons for their declines can tell us much about the state of our environment.

In Sri Lanka and other countries, scientific scrutiny and improved technology have revealed amphibian "hot spots." In the 1990s, an international team of scientists

set out to determine whether Sri Lanka, a large tropical island off the coast of India, held more than the 40 frog species that were already known. Researcher Madhava Meegaskumbura and his team combed through trees, rivers, ponds, and leaf litter for 8 years, collecting more than 1,400 frogs at 300 study sites. The scientists analyzed the frogs' physical appearance, habitat use, and vocalizations. They also examined the frogs' genes by obtaining sequences of nucleotides in several regions of their DNA. They then compared these genetic, physical, and behavioral characteristics to those of known species of frogs.

The team found that the DNA from many of their frogs didn't match that of known species. And they found that many of their frogs looked different, sounded different, or behaved differently from known species. Clearly, they had discovered new species of frogs unknown to science. Some of these novel species live on rocks and sport leg fringes and markings that help disguise them as clumps of moss. Others are tree frogs that lay their eggs in baskets they construct. In all, more

competition, an introduced species may increase rapidly, spread, and displace native species. Moreover, invasive species cause billions of dollars in economic damage each year.

**Pollution**  Pollution can negatively affect organisms in many ways. Air pollution (Chapter 17) can degrade forest ecosystems. Water pollution (Chapter 15) can adversely affect fish and amphibians. Agricultural runoff (including

fertilizers, pesticides, and sediments; Chapters 7, 9, and 10) can harm many terrestrial and aquatic species. Heavy metals, PCBs, endocrine-disrupting compounds, and various other toxic chemicals can poison people and wildlife (Chapter 14), and the effects of oil and chemical spills on wildlife are dramatic and well known. However, although pollution is a substantial threat, it tends to be less significant than public perception holds it to be. The damage to wildlife and ecosystems caused by pollution can be severe,

than 100 new species of amphibians were discovered—all on an island only slightly larger than the state of West Virginia! When reported in the journal *Science* in 2002, the study caught the attention of conservation biologists worldwide.

Such promising discoveries, however, come against a backdrop of distressing declines. Observed numbers of amphibians are down around the globe. Scientists are racing to pin down the causes, and have found evidence for causes as varied as habitat destruction, chemical pollution, disease, invasive species, and climate change. Most worrisome is that many populations are vanishing even when no direct damage, such as habitat loss, is apparent. In some cases, researchers surmise that a combination of factors may be at work.

In one study, researchers Rick Relyea and Nathan Mills presented young frogs with two common dangers—pesticides and predators—to see how the mix affected their survival. The team collected 10 pairs of tree frogs from a wildlife area in Missouri and placed their eggs in clean water. When tad-

poles emerged from the eggs, groups of 10 were each put in different tubs of water. Some tubs contained pure water, others contained varying levels of the pesticide carbaryl, and others contained the harmless solvent acetone as a control. To some of each of these three types of tubs, the researchers added a hungry predator—a young salamander. The salamander was caged and couldn't reach the tadpoles, but the tadpoles were aware of its presence. In a series of experiments, over up to 16 days, researchers watched to see how many tadpoles survived the different combinations of stress factors.

Their results, published in the *Proceedings of the National Academy of Sciences* in 2001, revealed that tadpoles that withstood one type of stress might not survive two. As expected, all tadpoles in clean water with no predators survived, and all tadpoles exposed to high concentrations of carbaryl died within several days, regardless of predator presence. But when carbaryl levels were lower, the presence of the salamander made a noticeable difference. In one trial, about 75% of tadpoles survived the pesticide if no predator

was present, but in the presence of the salamander, survival rates dropped to about 25%. Thus, when both stresses were present (a condition likely in the tadpoles' natural habitat), death rates increased by two to four times.

One year later, a study published in the same journal by herpetologist Joseph Kiesecker found similar results with pathogens and pesticides. His field and lab experiments revealed that wood frogs were more vulnerable to parasitic infections that cause limb deformities when they were exposed to water containing pesticides.

As scientists learn more about how such factors combine to threaten amphibians, they are gaining a clearer picture of how the fate of these creatures may foreshadow the future for other organisms. "Amphibians have been around for 300 million years. They're tough, and yet they're checking out all around us," says David Wake, a biologist at the University of California at Berkeley, who was among the first to note the creatures' decline. "We really do see amphibians as biodiversity bellwethers."

but it tends to be less than the damage caused by habitat alteration or invasive species.

**Overharvesting** For most species, a high intensity of hunting or harvesting by humans will not *in itself* pose a threat of extinction, but for some species it can. The Siberian tiger is one such species. Large in size, few in number, long-lived, and raising few young in its lifetime—a classic K-selected species (▶ p. 139)—the Siberian tiger is

just the type of animal to be vulnerable to population reduction by hunting. The advent of Russian hunting nearly drove the animal extinct, whereas decreased hunting during and after World War II contributed to a population increase. By the mid-1980s, the Siberian tiger population was likely up to 250 individuals. The political freedom that came with the Soviet Union's breakup in 1989, however, brought with it a freedom to harvest Siberia's natural resources, the tiger included, without

**FIGURE 11.12** Body parts from tigers have long been used as medicines or aphrodisiacs in some traditional Asian cultures. Hunters and poachers have illegally killed countless tigers through the years to satisfy market demand for these items. Here a street vendor in northern China displays tiger penises and other body parts for sale.

regulations or rules. This coincided with an economic expansion in many Asian countries, where tiger penises are traditionally used to try to boost human sexual performance and where tiger bones, claws, whiskers, and other body parts are used to treat a wide variety of maladies (Figure 11.12). Thus, the early 1990s brought a boom in poaching (poachers killed at least 180 Siberian tigers between 1991 and 1996), as well as a dramatic increase in logging of the Korean pine forests on which the tigers and their prey depend.

Over the past century, hunting has led to steep declines in the populations of many other K-selected animals. The Atlantic gray whale has gone extinct, and several other whales remain threatened or endangered. Gorillas and other primates that are killed for their meat may be facing extinction soon. Thousands of sharks are killed each year simply for their fins, which are used in soup. Today the oceans contain only 10% of the large animals they once did (▶ p. 483).

**Climate change** The preceding four types of human impacts affect biodiversity in discrete places and times. In contrast, our manipulation of Earth's climate system (Chapter 18) is beginning to have global impacts on biodiversity. As we will explore in Chapter 18, our emissions of carbon dioxide and other "greenhouse gases" that trap heat in the atmosphere are causing average temperatures to warm worldwide, modifying global weather patterns and increasing the frequency of extreme weather events. Scientists foresee that these effects, together termed *global climate change,* will accelerate and become more severe in the years ahead until we find ways to reduce our emissions from fossil fuels.

Climate change is beginning to exert effects on plants and animals. Extreme weather events such as droughts put increased stress on populations, and warming temperatures are forcing species to move toward the poles and higher in altitude. Some species will be able to adapt, but others will not. Consider the cloud-forest fauna from Monteverde that we examined in Chapter 5. Mountaintop organisms cannot move further upslope to escape warming temperatures, so they will likely perish. Trees may not be able to move poleward fast enough. Animals and plants may find themselves among different communities of prey, predators, and parasites to which they are not adapted. The impacts of climate change will likely play a large role in shaping the future world that we and our children will inhabit.

All five of these avenues are influenced by human population growth and rising per capita consumption. More people and more consumption mean more habitat alteration, more invasive species, more pollution, more overharvesting, and more climate change. Growth in population and growth in consumption are the ultimate reasons behind the proximate threats to biodiversity.

# Benefits of Biodiversity

Scientists worldwide are presenting us with data that confirm what any naturalist who has watched the habitat change in his or her hometown already knows: From amphibians to tigers, biodiversity is being lost rapidly and visibly within our lifetimes. This suggests the question, "Does it matter?" There are many ways to answer this question, but we can begin by considering the ways that biodiversity benefits people. Scientists have offered a number of tangible, pragmatic reasons for preserving biodiversity, showing how biodiversity directly or indirectly supports human society. In addition, many people feel that organisms have an intrinsic right to exist and that ethical and aesthetic dimensions to biodiversity preservation cannot be ignored.

## Biodiversity provides ecosystem services free of charge

Contrary to popular opinion, some things in life can indeed be free, as long as we choose to protect the living systems that provide them. Intact forests provide clean air and buffer hydrologic systems against flooding and drought. Native crop varieties provide insurance against disease and drought. Abundant wildlife can attract tourists and boost the economies of developing nations. Intact ecosystems provide these and other valuable processes, known as *ecosystem services* (▸pp. 39–41, 48–51), for all of us, free of charge.

Maintaining these ecosystem services is one clear benefit of protecting biodiversity. According to UNEP, biodiversity:

▸ Provides food, fuel, and fiber
▸ Provides shelter and building materials
▸ Purifies air and water
▸ Detoxifies and decomposes wastes
▸ Stabilizes and moderates Earth's climate
▸ Moderates floods, droughts, wind, and temperature extremes
▸ Generates and renews soil fertility and cycles nutrients
▸ Pollinates plants, including many crops
▸ Controls pests and diseases
▸ Maintains genetic resources as inputs to crop varieties, livestock breeds, and medicines
▸ Provides cultural and aesthetic benefits
▸ Gives us the means to adapt to change

Organisms and ecosystems support a vast number of vital processes that humans could not replicate or would need to pay for if nature did not provide them. As we saw in Chapter 2, the annual value of just 17 of these ecosystem services may be in the neighborhood of $16–54 trillion per year.

## Biodiversity helps maintain ecosystem function

Even if functioning ecosystems are important, however, does biodiversity really help them maintain their function? Ecologists have found that the answer appears to be

yes. Research has demonstrated that high levels of biodiversity tend to increase the *stability* of communities and ecosystems. Research has also found that high biodiversity tends to increase the *resilience* of ecological systems—their ability to weather disturbance, bounce back from stresses, or adapt to change. Most of this research has dealt with species diversity, but new work is finding similar effects for genetic diversity. Thus, a decrease in biodiversity could diminish a natural system's ability to function and to provide services to our society.

What about the extinction of selected species, however? Skeptics have asked whether the loss of a few endangered species will really make much difference in an ecosystem's ability to function. Ecological research suggests that the answer to this question depends on which species are removed. Removing a species that can be functionally replaced by others may make little difference. Recall, however, from Chapter 6 our discussion of keystone species (▸pp. 159–162). Like the keystone that holds together an arch, a keystone species is one whose removal results in significant changes in an ecological system. If a keystone species is extirpated or driven extinct, other species may disappear or experience significant population changes as a result.

Often top predators, such as tigers, are considered keystone species. A single top predator may prey on many other carnivores, each of which may prey on many herbivores, each of which may consume many plants. Thus the removal of a single individual at the top of a food chain can have impacts that multiply as they cascade down the food chain. Moreover, top predators such as tigers, wolves, and grizzly bears are among the species most vulnerable to human impact. Large animals are frequently hunted, and also need large areas of habitat, making them susceptible to habitat loss and fragmentation. In addition, top predators are vulnerable to the buildup of toxic pollutants in their tissues through the process of biomagnification (▸p. 416).

Top predators are not the only species that exert far-reaching influence over their ecosystems. The influence of other species, including "ecosystem engineers" such as ants and earthworms, can be equally significant. Ecosystems are complex, and it is difficult to predict which particular species may be important. Thus, many people prefer to apply the precautionary principle in the spirit of Aldo Leopold (▸pp. 35–36), who advised, "To keep every cog and wheel is the first precaution of intelligent tinkering."

## Biodiversity enhances food security

Biodiversity benefits our agriculture, as well. As our discussion of native landraces of corn in Oaxaca, Mexico, in Chapter 10 showed, genetic diversity within crop species and their ancestors is enormously valuable. In 1995, Turkey's wheat crops received at least $50 billion worth of disease resistance from wild wheat strains. California's barley crops annually receive $160 million in disease resistance benefits from Ethiopian strains of barley. During the 1970s a researcher discovered a maize species in Mexico known as *Zea diploperennis*. This maize is highly resistant to disease, and it is a perennial, meaning it will grow back year after year without being replanted. At the time of its discovery, its entire range was limited to a 10-ha (25-acre) plot of land in the mountains of the Mexican state of Jalisco.

Other potentially important food crops await utilization (Figure 11.13). The babassu palm (*Orbignya phalerata*) of the Amazon produces more vegetable oil than any other plant. The serendipity berry (*Dioscoreophyllum cumminsii*) produces a sweetener that is 3,000 times sweeter than table sugar. Several species of salt-tolerant grasses and trees are so hardy that farmers can irrigate them with saltwater. These same plants also produce animal feed, a substitute for conventional vegetable oil, and other economically important products. Such species could be immeasurably beneficial to areas undergoing soil salinization due to poorly managed irrigation (▸pp. 265–266).

## Biodiversity provides drugs and medicines

People have made medicines from plants for centuries, and many of today's widely used drugs were discovered by studying chemical compounds present in wild plants, animals, and microbes (Figure 11.14). Each year pharmaceutical products owing their origin to wild species generate up to $150 billion in sales.

It can truly be argued that every species that goes extinct represents one lost opportunity to find a cure for cancer or AIDS. The rosy periwinkle (*Catharanthus roseus*) produces compounds that treat Hodgkin's disease and a particularly deadly form of leukemia. Had this native plant of Madagascar become extinct prior to its discovery by medical researchers, two deadly diseases would have claimed far more victims than they have to date. In Australia, where the government has placed high priority on research into products from rare and endangered species, a rare species of cork, *Duboisia leichhardtii*, now provides hyoscine, a compound that physicians use to treat cancer, stomach disorders, and motion sickness. Another Australian plant, *Tylophora*, provides a drug that treats lymphoid leukemia. Researchers are now exploring the potential of the compound prostaglandin E2

| Food Security and Biodiversity: Potential new food sources | | |
|---|---|---|
| **Species** | **Native to...** | **Potential uses and benefits** |
| Amaranths (three species of *Amaranthus*)  | Tropical and Andean America | Grain and leafy vegetable; livestock feed; rapid growth, drought resistant |
| Buriti palm (*Mauritia flexuosa*)  | Amazon lowlands | "Tree of life" to Amerindians; vitamin-rich fruit; pith as source for bread; palm heart from shoots |
| Maca (*Lepidium meyenii*)  | Andes Mountains | Cold-resistant root vegetable resembling radish, with distinctive flavor; near extinction |
| Tree tomato (*Cyphomandra betacea*)  | South America | Elongated fruit with sweet taste |
| Babirusa (*Babyrousa babyrussa*)  | Indonesia: Moluccas and Sulawesi | A deep-forest pig; thrives on vegetation high in cellulose and hence less dependent on grain |
| Capybara (*Hydrochoeris hydrochoeris*)  | South America | World's largest rodent; meat esteemed; easily ranched in open habitats near water |
| Vicuna (*Lama vicugna*)  | Central Andes | Threatened species related to llama; valuable source of meat, fur, and hides; can be profitably ranched |
| Chachalacas (*Ortalis*, many species)  | South and Central America | Birds, potentially tropical chickens; thrive in dense populations; adaptable to human habitations; fast-growing |
| Sand grouse (*Pterocles*, many species)  | Deserts of Africa and Asia | Pigeon-like birds adapted to harshest deserts; domestication a possibility |

**FIGURE 11.13** By protecting biodiversity, we can enhance food security. The wild species shown here are a tiny fraction of the many plants and animals that could someday supplement our food supply. Adapted from Wilson, E. O. 1992. *The diversity of life.* Cambridge, MA: Belknap Press.

| Medicines and Biodiversity: Natural sources of pharmaceuticals | | |
|---|---|---|
| **Plant** | **Drug** | **Medical application** |
| Pineapple (*Ananas comosus*)  | Bromelain | Controls tissue inflammation |
| Autumn crocus (*Colchicum autumnale*)  | Colchicine | Anticancer agent |
| Yellow cinchona (*Cinchona ledgeriana*)  | Quinine | Antimalarial |
| Common thyme (*Thymus vulgaris*)  | Thymol | Cures fungal infection |
| Pacific yew (*Taxus brevifolia*)  | Taxol | Anticancer (especially ovarian cancer) |
| Velvet bean (*Mucuna deeringiana*)  | L-Dopa | Parkinson's disease suppressant |
| Common foxglove (*Digitalis purpurea*)  | Digitoxin | Cardiac stimulant |

**FIGURE 11.14** By protecting biodiversity, we can enhance our ability to treat illness. Shown here are just a few of the plants that have so far been found to provide chemical compounds of medical benefit. Adapted from Wilson, E. O. 1992. *The diversity of life.* Cambridge, MA: Belknap Press.

in treating gastric ulcers. This compound was first discovered in two frog species unique to the rainforest of Queensland, Australia. Scientists believe that both species are now extinct.

## Weighing the Issues:
### Bioprospecting in Costa Rica

Bioprospectors search for organisms that can provide new drugs, foods, or other valuable products. Scientists working for pharmaceutical companies, for instance, scour biodiversity-rich countries for potential drugs and medicines. Many have been criticized for harvesting indigenous species to create commercial products that do not benefit the country of origin. To make sure it would not lose the benefits of its own biodiversity, Costa Rica reached an agreement with the Merck pharmaceutical company in 1991. The nonprofit National Biodiversity Institute of Costa Rica (INBio) allowed Merck to evaluate a limited number of Costa Rica's species for their commercial potential in return for $1 million, plus equipment and training for Costa Rican scientists.

Do you think that both sides win in this agreement? What if Merck discovers a compound that could be turned into a billion-dollar drug? Does this provide a good model for other countries? For other companies?

## Biodiversity provides economic benefits through tourism and recreation

Besides providing for our food and health, biodiversity can represent a direct source of income through tourism, particularly for developing countries in the tropics that have impressive species diversity. As we saw in Chapter 5 with Costa Rica, many people like to travel to experience protected natural areas, and in so doing they create economic opportunity for residents living near those natural areas. Visitors spend money at local businesses, hire local people as guides, and support the parks that employ local residents. Ecotourism thus can bring jobs and income to areas that otherwise might be poverty-stricken.

Ecotourism has become a vital source of income for nations such as Costa Rica, with its rainforests; Australia, with its Great Barrier Reef; Belize, with its reefs, caves, and rainforests; and Kenya and Tanzania, with their savanna wildlife. The United States, too, benefits from ecotourism; its national parks draw millions of visitors domestically and from around the world. Ecotourism serves as a powerful financial incentive for nations, states, and local communities to preserve natural areas and reduce impacts on the landscape and on native species.

As ecotourism increases in popularity, however, critics have warned that too many visitors to natural areas can degrade the outdoor experience and disturb wildlife. Anyone who has been to Yosemite, the Grand Canyon, or the Great Smokies on a crowded summer weekend can attest to this. Ecotourism's effects on species living in parks and reserves are much debated, and likely they vary enormously from one case to the next. As ecotourism continues to increase, so will debate over its costs and benefits for local communities and for biodiversity.

## People value and seek out connections with nature

Not all of the benefits of biodiversity to humans can be expressed in the hard numbers of economics or the day-to-day practicalities of food and medicine. Some scientists and philosophers argue that there is a deeper

**FIGURE 11.15** Edward O. Wilson is the world's most recognized authority on biodiversity and its conservation and has inspired many people who study our planet's life. A Harvard professor and world-renowned expert on ants, Wilson has written over 20 books and has won two Pulitzer prizes. His books *The Diversity of Life* and *The Future of Life* address the value of biodiversity and its outlook for the future.

importance to biodiversity. E. O. Wilson (Figure 11.15) has described a phenomenon he calls **biophilia,** "the connections that human beings subconsciously seek with the rest of life." Wilson and others have cited as evidence of biophilia our affinity for parks and wildlife, our keeping of pets, the high value of real estate with a view of natural landscapes, and our interest—despite being far removed from a hunter-gatherer lifestyle—in hiking, bird-watching, fishing, hunting, backpacking, and similar outdoor pursuits.

In a 2005 book, writer Richard Louv adds that as today's children are increasingly deprived of outdoor experiences and direct contact with wild organisms, they suffer what he calls "nature-deficit disorder." Although it is not a medical condition, this alienation from biodiversity and the natural environment, Louv argues, may damage childhood development and lie behind many of the emotional and physical problems young people in developed nations face today.

**Weighing the Issues:**
## Biophilia and Nature-Deficit Disorder

What do you think of the concepts of biophilia and "nature-deficit disorder"? Have you ever felt a connection to other living things that you couldn't explain in scientific or economic terms? Do you think that an affinity for other living things is innately human? How could you determine whether or not most people in your community feel this way?

## Do we have ethical obligations toward other species?

If Wilson, Louv, and others are right, then biophilia not only may affect ecotourism and real estate prices, but also may influence our ethics. When Maurice Hornocker and his associates first established the Siberian Tiger Project, he wrote: "Saving the most magnificent of all the cat species and one of the most endangered should be a global responsibility. . . . If they aren't worthy of saving, then what are we all about? What is worth saving?"

On one hand, we humans are part of nature, and like any other animal we need to use resources and consume other organisms to survive. In that sense, there is nothing immoral about our doing so. On the other hand, we have conscious reasoning ability and are able to control our actions and make conscious decisions. Our ethical sense has developed from this intelligence and ability to choose. As our society's sphere of ethical consideration has widened over time, and as more of us take up biocentric or ecocentric worldviews (▸ pp. 32–33), more people have come to feel that other organisms have intrinsic value and an inherent right to exist.

Despite our ethical convictions, however, and despite biodiversity's many benefits—from the pragmatic and economic to the philosophical and spiritual—the future of biodiversity is far from secure. Even our protected areas and national parks are not big enough or protected well enough to ensure that biodiversity is fully safeguarded within their borders. The search for solutions to today's biodiversity crisis is an exciting and active one, and scientists are playing a leading role in developing innovative approaches to maintaining the diversity of life on Earth.

# Conservation Biology: The Search for Solutions

Today, more and more scientists and citizens perceive a need to do something to stem the loss of biodiversity. In his 1994 autobiography, *Naturalist*, E. O. Wilson wrote:

> When the [20th] century began, people still thought of the planet as infinite in its bounty. The highest mountains were still unclimbed, the ocean depths never visited, and vast wildernesses stretched across the equatorial continents. . . . In one lifetime exploding human populations have reduced wildernesses to threatened nature reserves. Ecosystems and species are vanishing at the fastest rate in 65 million years. Troubled by what we have wrought, we have begun to turn in our role from local conqueror to global steward.

## Conservation biology arose in response to biodiversity loss

The urge to act as responsible stewards of natural systems, and to use science as a tool in that endeavor, helped spark the rise of conservation biology. **Conservation biology** is a scientific discipline devoted to understanding the factors, forces, and processes that influence the loss, protection, and restoration of biological diversity. It arose as biologists became increasingly alarmed at the degradation of the natural systems they had spent their lives studying.

Conservation biologists choose questions and pursue research with the aim of developing solutions to such problems as habitat degradation and species loss. Conservation biology is thus an applied and goal-oriented science, with implicit values and ethical standards. This perceived element of advocacy sparked some criticism of conservation biology in its early years. However, as scientists have come to recognize the scope of human impact on the planet, more of them have directed their work to address environmental problems. Today conservation biology is a thriving pursuit that is central to environmental science and to achieving a sustainable society.

## Conservation biologists work at multiple levels

Conservation biologists integrate an understanding of evolution and extinction with ecology and the dynamic nature of environmental systems. They use field data, lab data, theory, and experiments to study the impacts of humans on other organisms. They also attempt to design, test, and implement ways to mitigate human impact.

These researchers address the challenges facing biological diversity at all levels, from genetic diversity to species diversity to ecosystem diversity. At the genetic level, *conservation geneticists* study genetic attributes of organisms, generally to infer the status of their populations. If two populations of a species are found to be genetically distinct enough to be considered subspecies, they may have different ecological needs and may require different types of management. In addition, as a population dwindles, genetic variation is lost from the gene pool. Conservation geneticists ask how small a population can become and how much genetic variation it can lose before running into problems such as inbreeding depression. By determining a *minimum viable population size* for a given population, conservation geneticists and population biologists provide wildlife managers with an indication of how vital it may be to increase the population.

Problems for populations and subspecies spell problems for species, because declines and local extirpation generally precede range-wide endangerment and extinction. As we will soon see, it is at the species level that much of the funding and resources for conservation biology exist. However, many efforts also revolve around habitats, communities, and ecosystems.

## Island biogeography theory is a key component of conservation biology

Safeguarding habitat for species and conserving communities and ecosystems requires thinking and working at the landscape level. One key conceptual tool for doing so is the **equilibrium theory of island biogeography.** This theory, introduced by E. O. Wilson and ecologist Robert MacArthur in 1963, explains how species come to be distributed among oceanic islands. Since then, researchers have also applied it to "habitat islands"—patches of one habitat type isolated within "seas" of others. The Sikhote-Alin Mountains, last refuge of the Siberian tiger, are a habitat island, isolated from other mountains by deforested regions, a seacoast, and populated lowlands.

Island biogeography theory predicts the number of species on an island based on the island's size and its distance from the nearest mainland. The number of species on an island results from a balance between the number added by immigration and the number lost through extinction (or more precisely, extirpation from the particular island). Immigration and extinction are ongoing

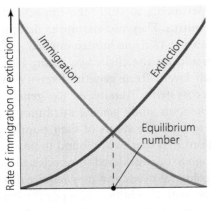

**(a) Immigration and extinction rates**

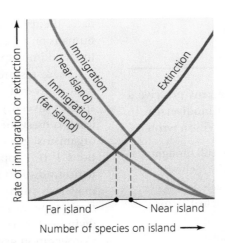

**(b) Effect of distance from mainland**

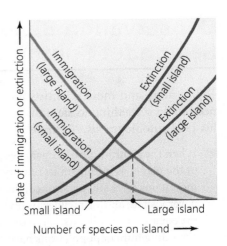

**(c) Effect of island size**

**FIGURE 11.16** Island biogeography theory explains species richness on islands as a function of immigration and extinction rates interacting with island size and distance from the mainland. In **(a)**, immigration rates are highest for islands with few species (because each new immigrant species represents a high proportion of the island's total species). Extinction rates are greatest on islands with many species (because interspecific competition for resources keeps population sizes small). These two trends set the stage for examining the effects of island size and distance. In **(b)**, islands closer to a mainland tend to hold more species, because immigration rates are higher, whereas extinction rates are not affected by distance. In **(c)**, immigration is greater on large islands because large islands are easier for dispersing organisms to discover, while extinction rates are lower on large islands, because more area allows populations to grow larger. Together these trends give large islands a higher number of species at equilibrium.

dynamic processes, so the balance between them represents an equilibrium state (Figure 11.16a).

The farther an island is located from a continent, the fewer species tend to find and colonize it. Thus, remote islands host fewer species because of lower immigration rates (Figure 11.16b). Large islands have higher immigration rates because they present fatter targets for wandering or dispersing organisms to encounter. Large islands have lower extinction rates because more space allows for larger populations, which are less vulnerable to dropping to zero by chance. Together, these trends give large islands more species at equilibrium than small islands (Figure 11.16c). Very roughly, the number of species on an island is expected to double as island size increases tenfold. This effect can be illustrated with *species-area curves* (Figure 11.17). Large islands also tend to contain more species because they generally possess more habitats than smaller islands, providing suitable environments for a wider variety of arriving species.

These theoretical patterns have been widely supported by empirical data from the study of species on islands (see "The Science behind the Story," ▶pp. 332–333). The patterns hold up for terrestrial habitat islands, such as forests

fragmented by logging and road building (Figure 11.18). Small islands of forest lose their diversity fastest, starting with large species that were few in number to begin with. In a landscape of fragmented habitat, species requiring the habitat will gradually disappear, winking out from one fragment after another over time. Fragmentation of forests and other habitats constitutes one of the prime threats to biodiversity. In response to habitat fragmentation, conservation biologists have designed landscape-level strategies to try to optimize the arrangement of areas to be preserved. We will examine a few of these strategies in our discussion of parks and preserves in Chapter 12 (▶pp. 364–369).

**Weighing the Issues:**
## Fragmentation and Biodiversity

Suppose a critic of conservation tells you that human development increases biodiversity, pointing out that when a forest is fragmented, new habitats, such as grassy lots and gardens, may be introduced to an area and allow additional species to live there. How would you respond?

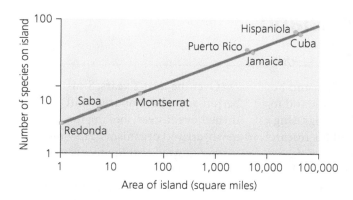

**FIGURE 11.17** The larger the island, the greater the number of species—a prediction borne out by data from around the world. By plotting the number of amphibians and reptile species on Caribbean islands as a function of the areas of these islands, the species-area curve shows that species richness increases with area. The increase is not linear, but logarithmic; note the scales of the axes. Go to **GRAPHit!** at www.aw-bc.com/withgott or on the student CD-ROM. Data from MacArthur, R. H., and E. O. Wilson. 1967. *The theory of island biogeography.* Princeton University Press.

## Should endangered species be the focus of conservation efforts?

The primary legislation for protecting biodiversity in the United States is the **Endangered Species Act (ESA).** Passed in 1973, the ESA forbids the government and private citizens from taking actions (such as developing land) that destroy endangered species or their habitats. The ESA also forbids trade in products made from endangered species. The aim is to prevent extinctions, stabilize declining populations, and enable populations to recover. As of 2005, there were 1,264 species in the United States listed as "endangered" or as "threatened," the latter status considered one notch less severe than endangered.

The ESA has had a number of notable successes. Following the ban on the pesticide DDT and years of intensive effort by wildlife managers, the peregrine falcon, brown pelican, bald eagle, and other birds have recovered and have been removed from the endangered list (▶p. 416). Intensive management programs with other species, such as the red-cockaded woodpecker, have held formerly declining populations steady in the face of continued pressure on habitat. In fact, roughly 40% of declining populations have been held stable.

This success comes despite the fact that the U.S. Fish and Wildlife Service and the National Marine Fisheries Service, the agencies responsible for upholding the ESA, have been perennially underfunded for the job. These agencies have faced repeated budgetary shortfalls for en-

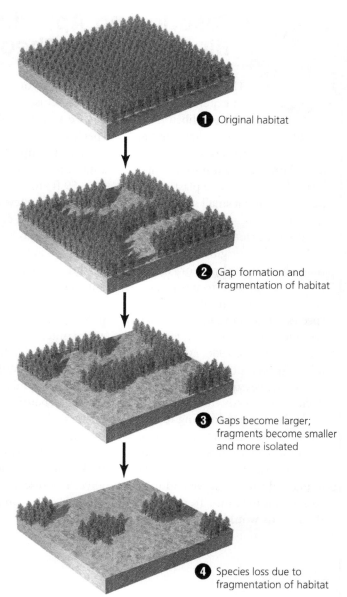

**FIGURE 11.18** Forest clearing, farming, road building, and other types of human land use and development can fragment natural habitats. Habitat fragmentation usually begins when gaps are created within a natural habitat. As development proceeds, these gaps expand, join together, and eventually dominate the landscape, stranding islands of habitat in their midst. As habitat becomes fragmented, fewer populations can persist, and numbers of species in the fragments decrease with time.

dangered species protection. Moreover, efforts to reauthorize the ESA have faced stiff opposition in the U.S. Congress since the 1990s. As this book went to press, Republican Congressman Richard Pombo was leading efforts to weaken the ESA, including stripping it of its ability to safeguard habitat.

# Testing and Applying Island Biogeography Theory

**The Science behind the Story**

The researchers who first experimentally tested the equilibrium theory of island biogeography and applied it to conservation biology leaned on their own resourcefulness, along with some plastic, some pesticides, and a small station wagon.

Robert MacArthur and Edward O. Wilson had originally developed island biogeography theory by using observational data from oceanic islands, correlating numbers of species found on islands with island size and distance between landmasses. Yet as of 1966, no one had tested its precepts in the field with a manipulative experiment. Wilson decided to remedy that.

Wilson began looking for islands in the United States where he could run an experimental test: to remove all animal life from islands and then observe and measure recolonization. To be suitable, the islands would need to be small,

contain few forms of life, and be situated close to the mainland to ensure an influx of immigrating species. Wilson found his research sites off the tip of Florida: six small mangrove islands 11–18 m (36–59 ft) in diameter, home only to trees and a few dozen species of insects, spiders, centipedes, and other arthropods.

Daniel Simberloff, Wilson's graduate student at the time, painstakingly counted each island's arthropods, breaking up bark and poking under branches to find every mite, midge, and millipede. Then with the help of professional exterminators, Wilson and Simberloff wrapped each island in a plastic tarpaulin and gassed the interior with the pesticide methyl bromide. After removing the tarpaulins, Simberloff checked to make sure no creatures were left alive. The researchers then waited to see how life on the islands would return.

Over the next 2 years, Simberloff scrambled up trees and turned over leaves, looking for newly arrived organisms. His monitoring showed that life recovered on most islands within a year, regaining about the same number of species and total number of arthropods the islands had sheltered originally. Larger islands once again became home to a greater number of species than smaller islands. Outlying islands recovered more slowly and reached lower species diversities than did islands near the mainland. These results provided the first evidence from a manipulative experiment for the predictions of island biogeography theory.

Published in the journal *Ecology* in 1969 and 1970, Simberloff and Wilson's research gave new empirical rigor to a set of ideas that was increasingly helping scientists understand geographic patterns of biodiversity. Their research also fueled a question of

Daniel Simberloff and E. O. Wilson used mangrove islands in the Florida Keys to test island biogeography theory.

pressing concern for conservation biology: Could island biogeography theory also be applied to isolated "islands" of habitat on continents? At the University of Michigan, biology graduate student William Newmark set out to address this question.

Newmark had learned that many North American national parks kept records that documented sightings of wildlife over the course of the parks' existence. He surmised that by examining these historical records, he could infer which species had vanished from parks, which were new arrivals, and roughly when these changes occurred. The parks, increasingly surrounded by development, were islands of natural habitat isolated by farms, roads, towns, and cities, so Newmark hypothesized that island biogeography theory would apply.

In 1983, Newmark drove his Toyota station wagon to 24 parks in the western United States and Canada. At each park, he studied the wildlife sighting records, focusing on larger mammals such as bear, lynx, and river otter (but not species, such as wolves, that had been deliberately eradicated by hunting). Newmark found a few species missing from many parks, and they added up to a troubling total. Forty-two species had disappeared in all, and not as a result of direct human action. The red fox and river otter had vanished from Sequoia and Kings Canyon National Parks, for example, and the white-tailed jackrabbit and spotted skunk

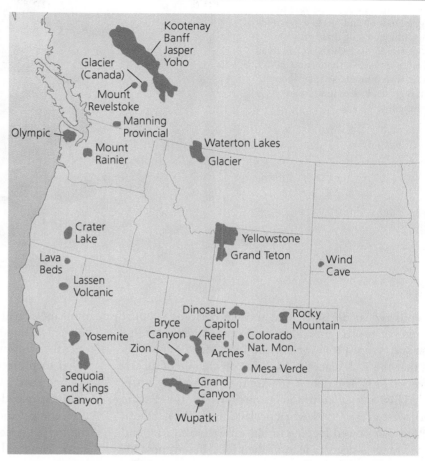

William Newmark visualized national parks of western North America as islands of natural habitat in a sea of development. His data showed that mammal species were disappearing from these recently created terrestrial "islands," in accordance with island biogeography theory. Adapted from Quammen, D. 1997. *The song of the dodo.* New York: Simon & Schuster.

no longer lived in Bryce Canyon National Park. As theory predicted, the smallest parks showed the greatest number of losses, and the largest parks retained a greater number of species.

These species disappeared because the parks, Newmark concluded, were too small to sustain their populations in the long term.

Moreover, the parks had become island habitats too isolated to be recolonized by new arrivals. Newmark's findings, published in the journal *Nature* in 1987, placed island biogeography theory squarely on the mainland. Today, this theory helps inform national park policy and biodiversity conservation plans around the world.

**FIGURE 11.19** In efforts to save the California condor *(Gymnogyps californianus)* from extinction, biologists have raised hundreds of chicks in captivity with the help of hand puppets designed to look and feel like the heads of adult condors. Using these puppets, biologists feed the growing chicks in an enclosure and shield them from all contact with humans, so that when the chick is grown it does not feel an attachment to people.

Polls repeatedly show that most Americans support the idea of protecting endangered species. Yet some oppose and resent provisions of the ESA. Many opponents feel that the ESA places more value on the life of an endangered organism than it does on the livelihood of a person. This was a common perception in the Pacific Northwest in the 1990s, when protection for the northern spotted owl slowed logging in old-growth rainforest and caused many loggers to fear for their jobs. Resentment toward the ESA also comes from landowners worried that federal officials will restrict the use of private land if threatened or endangered species are found on it. This has led in many cases to a practice described as "Shoot, shovel, and shut up," among landowners who want to conceal the presence of such species on their land.

ESA supporters maintain that such fears are overblown, pointing out that the ESA has stopped few development projects. Moreover, a number of provisions of the ESA and its amendments promote cooperation with landowners. *Habitat conservation plans* and *safe harbor agreements* allow landowners to harm species in some ways if they voluntarily improve habitat for the species in others.

Debate over the U.S. law has influenced other nations' approaches to species protection. When Canada enacted its long-awaited endangered species law in 2002, the *Species at Risk Act (SARA)*, the Canadian government was careful to stress cooperation with landowners and provincial governments, rather than presenting the law as a decree from the national government. Canada's environment minister, David Anderson, wanted none of the hostility the U.S. act had unleashed. Environmentalists and many scientists, however, protested that SARA was too weak and failed to protect habitat adequately. Today a number of nations have laws protecting species. In Russia, the government issued Decree 795 in 1995, creating a Siberian tiger conservation program and declaring the tiger one of the nation's most important natural and national treasures. Time will tell how effective this decree will be.

## Captive breeding, reintroduction, and cloning are single-species approaches

In the effort to save threatened and endangered species, biologists are going to impressive lengths. Zoos and botanical gardens have become centers for the **captive breeding** of these species, so that individuals can be raised and reintroduced into the wild. One example is the program to save the California condor, North America's largest bird (Figure 11.19). Condors were persecuted in the early 20th century, collided with electrical wires, and succumbed to lead poisoning from scavenging carcasses of animals killed with lead shot. By 1982, only 22 condors remained, and biologists decided to take all the birds into captivity, in hopes of boosting their numbers and then releasing them. The ongoing program is succeeding. So far, over 100 of the 250 birds raised in captivity have been released into the wild at sites in California and Arizona, where a few pairs have begun nesting.

Other reintroduction programs have been more controversial. Reintroducing wolves to Yellowstone National Park has proven popular with the public, but reintroducing them to sites in Arizona and New Mexico has met stiff resistance from ranchers who fear the wolves will attack their livestock. The program is making slow headway; several of the wolves have been shot.

The newest idea for saving species from extinction is to create more individuals by cloning them. In this technique, DNA from an endangered species is inserted into a cultured egg without a nucleus, and the egg is implanted into a closely related species that can act as a surrogate mother. So far two Eurasian mammals have been cloned in this way. With future genetic technology, some scientists even talk of recreating extinct species from DNA recovered from preserved body parts. However, even if cloning can succeed from a technical standpoint, most biologists agree that such efforts are not an adequate response to biodiversity loss. Without ample habitat and protection in the wild, having cloned animals in a zoo does little good.

## Some species act as "umbrellas" for protecting habitat and communities

Protecting habitat and conserving communities, ecosystems, and landscapes are the goals of many conservation biologists. Often, particular species are essentially used as tools to conserve communities and ecosystems. This is because the ESA provides legal justification and resources for species conservation, but no such law exists for communities or ecosystems. Large species that roam great distances, such as the Siberian tiger, require large areas of habitat. Meeting the habitat needs of these so-called *umbrella species* automatically helps meet those of thousands of less charismatic animals, plants, and fungi that would never elicit as much public interest.

Environmental advocacy organizations have found that using large and charismatic vertebrates as spearheads for biodiversity conservation has been an effective strategy. This approach of promoting particular *flagship species* is evident in the longtime symbol of the World Wide Fund for Nature (World Wildlife Fund in North America), the panda. The panda is a large endangered animal requiring sizeable stands of undisturbed bamboo forest. Its lovable appearance has made it a favorite with the public—and an effective tool for soliciting funding for conservation efforts that protect far more than just the panda. At the same time, many conservation organizations today are moving beyond the single-species approach. The Nature Conservancy, for instance, has in recent years focused more on whole communities and

landscapes. The most ambitious effort may be the Wildlands Project, a group proposing to restore huge amounts of North America's land to its presettlement state.

### Weighing the Issues:
## Single-Species Conservation?

What would you say are some advantages of focusing on conserving single species, versus trying to conserve broader communities, ecosystems, or landscapes? What might be some of the disadvantages? Which do you think is the better approach, or should we use both?

## International conservation efforts include widely signed treaties

At the international level, biodiversity protection has been pursued in a variety of ways. Most effective so far have been several treaties facilitated by the United Nations. The 1973 **Convention on International Trade in Endangered Species of Wild Fauna and Flora** (**CITES**) protects endangered species by banning the international transport of their body parts. When nations enforce it, CITES can protect the tiger and other rare species whose body parts are traded internationally.

In 1992, leaders of many nations agreed to the **Convention on Biological Diversity.** This treaty embodies three goals: to conserve biodiversity, to use biodiversity in a sustainable manner, and to ensure the fair distribution of biodiversity's benefits. The Convention addresses a number of topics, including the following:

▶ Providing incentives for biodiversity conservation
▶ Managing access to and use of genetic resources
▶ Transferring technology, including biotechnology
▶ Promoting scientific cooperation
▶ Assessing the effects of human actions on biodiversity
▶ Promoting biodiversity education and awareness
▶ Providing funding for critical activities
▶ Encouraging every nation to report regularly on their biodiversity conservation efforts

Since the treaty was proposed, UNEP has identified a number of accomplishments, such as ensuring that Ugandan people share in the economic benefits of wildlife preserves, increasing global markets for "shade-grown" coffee and other crops grown without removing forests, and replacing pesticide-intensive farming practices with sustainable ones in some rice-producing Asian nations. As of 2005, 188 nations had become parties to the

**FIGURE 11.20** The golden lion tamarin *(Leontopithecus rosalia),* a species endemic to Brazil's Atlantic rainforest, is one of the world's most endangered primates. Captive breeding programs have produced roughly 500 individuals in zoos, but the tamarin's habitat is fast disappearing.

Convention on Biological Diversity. Those choosing *not* to do so include Iraq, Somalia, the Vatican, and the United States. This decision is just one example of why the U.S. government is no longer widely regarded as a leader in biodiversity conservation efforts.

## Biodiversity hotspots pinpoint areas of high diversity

One international approach oriented around geographic regions, rather than single species, has been the effort to map **biodiversity hotspots.** The concept of biodiversity hotspots was introduced in 1988 by British ecologist Norman Myers (▸p. 338) as a way to prioritize regions that are most important globally for biodiversity conservation. A hotspot is an area that supports an especially great number of species that are **endemic** to the area, that is, found nowhere else in the world (Figure 11.20). To qualify as a hotspot, a location must harbor at least 1,500 endemic plant species, or 0.5% of the world total. In addition, a

hotspot must have already lost 70% of its habitat as a result of human impact and be in danger of losing more.

The nonprofit group Conservation International maintains a list of 34 biodiversity hotspots (Figure 11.21). The ecosystems of these areas together once covered 15.7% of the planet's land surface, but today, because of habitat loss, cover only 2.3%. This small amount of land is the exclusive home for 50% of the world's plant species and 42% of all terrestrial vertebrate species. The hotspot concept gives incentive to focus on these areas of endemism, where the greatest number of unique species can be protected with the least amount of effort.

## Community-based conservation is increasingly popular

Taking a global perspective and prioritizing optimal locations to set aside as parks and reserves makes good sense. However, setting aside land for preservation affects the people that live in and near these areas. In past decades, many conservationists from developed nations, in their zeal to preserve ecosystems in other nations, too often neglected the needs of people in the areas they wanted to protect. Many developing nations came to view this international environmentalism as a kind of neocolonialism.

Today this has largely changed, and many conservation biologists actively engage local people in efforts to protect land and wildlife in their own backyards, in an approach sometimes called **community-based conservation.** Setting aside land for preservation deprives local people of access to natural resources, but it can also guarantee that these resources will not be used up or sold to foreign corporations and can instead be sustainably managed. Moreover, parks and reserves draw ecotourism (▸p. 143), which can support local economies.

In the small Central American country of Belize, conservation biologist Robert Horwich and his Wisconsin-based group Community Conservation, Inc., have helped start a number of community-based conservation projects. The Community Baboon Sanctuary consists of tracts of riparian forest that farmers have agreed to leave intact, to serve as homes and traveling corridors for the black howler monkey, a centerpiece of ecotourism. The fact that the reserve uses the local nickname for the monkey signals respect for residents, and today a local women's cooperative is running the project. A museum was built, and residents receive income for guiding and housing visiting researchers and tourists. Some other projects have not turned out as well, however. Nearby on the Belizean coast, efforts to create a locally run reserve for the manatee have

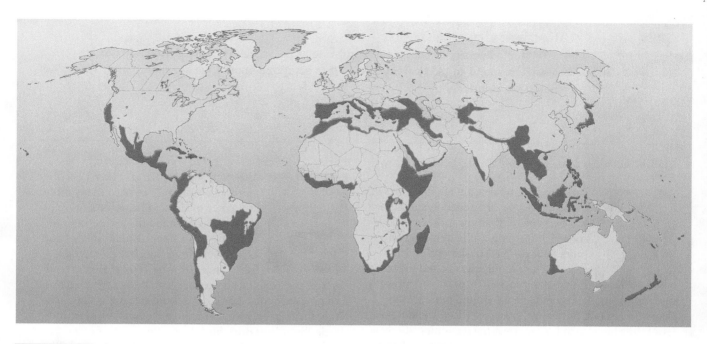

**FIGURE 11.21** Some areas of the world possess exceptionally high numbers of species found nowhere else. Some conservation biologists have suggested prioritizing habitat preservation in these areas, dubbed *biodiversity hotspots*. Shown in red are the 34 biodiversity hotspots mapped by Conservation International in 2005. Data from Conservation International, 2005.

struggled because of shortfalls in funding. Community-based conservation has not always been successful, but in a world of increasing human population, locally based management that meets people's needs sustainably will likely be essential.

## Innovative economic strategies are being employed

As conservation moves from single-species approaches to the hotspot approach to community-based conservation, innovative economic strategies are also being attempted. One strategy is the *debt-for-nature swap*. In such a swap, a conservation organization raises money and offers to pay off a portion of a developing country's international debt in exchange for a promise by the country to set aside reserves, fund environmental education, and better manage protected areas.

A newer strategy that Conservation International has pioneered is the *conservation concession*. Nations often sell concessions to foreign multinational corporations, allowing them to extract resources from the nation's land. A nation can, for instance, earn money by selling to an international logging company the right to log its forests. Conservation International has stepped in and paid nations for

concessions for conservation rather than resource extraction. The nation gets the money *and* keeps its natural resources intact. The South American country of Surinam, which still has extensive areas of pristine rainforest, entered into such an agreement and has virtually halted logging while pulling in $15 million. It remains to be seen how large a role such strategies will play in the future protection of biodiversity.

## Conclusion

The erosion of biological diversity on our planet threatens to result in a mass extinction event equivalent to the mass extinctions of the geological past. Human-induced habitat alteration, invasive species, pollution, and overharvesting of biotic resources are the primary causes of biodiversity loss. This loss matters, because human society could not function without biodiversity's pragmatic benefits. As a result, conservation biologists are rising to the challenge of conducting science aimed at saving endangered species, preserving their habitats, restoring populations, and keeping natural ecosystems intact. The innovative strategies of these scientists hold promise to slow the erosion of biodiversity that threatens life on Earth.

## Biodiversity

Biodiversity is being lost worldwide at an accelerating pace. **How should we respond to biodiversity loss? What solutions should we seek, and what strategies should we prioritize?**

### Mainstreaming Conservation through Ecosystem Services

Parks and nature reserves are the jewels of conservation, but they are not, and never will be, enough. Even the most ambitious conservation plans aspire to having no more than 20–30% of the world's lands protected as nature reserves, and the reality is that closer to 5–10% of land is currently under protection. If we put a fence around our parks to keep humans out, our nature preserves will still end up deteriorating because of how we treat the remaining 70–90% of Earth. Nature cannot be sequestered in some small portion of the globe while the bulk of land and water are left at the mercy of humans. Conservation will never be attainable unless humans learn to live in, work in, exploit, and harvest nature in a manner that does not ravage biodiversity.

An additional 3 billion people are expected in the next 50 years, bringing the total population to 9 billion. Many of the most impoverished people in the world depend on nature for their livelihood. All of us depend on nature for flood control, protection against storm damage, and other regulating services. To protect biodiversity and meet human needs, we must align biodiversity protection with these ecosystem services. As we make clear the links between ecosystem services and biodiversity protection, institutions and business should increasingly be willing to pay for nature's protection.

The disastrous tsunami of 2004 did minimal damage in coastal areas sheltered by natural mangrove forests. If only more of the Asia-Pacific region had been willing to invest in the insurance provided by mangroves, we would have saved human lives and biodiversity. The solution to biodiversity loss lies in clearly recognizing and valuing ecosystem services and in setting priorities that focus simultaneously on biodiversity and ecosystem services.

**Peter Kareiva** is lead scientist for The Nature Conservancy and an adjunct professor at the University of California at Santa Barbara and at Santa Clara University. Dr. Kareiva has also served as director of the Division for Conservation Biology at NOAA Fisheries, at the Northwest Fisheries Science Center, Seattle. His research has concerned organisms as diverse as whales, owls, Antarctic seabirds, ladybug beetles, butterflies, wildebeest, and genetically engineered microbes and crops.

### Parks: The Best Way to Protect Biodiversity?

Although protected areas cover 12% of Earth's land surface, we need many more of them. Consider 34 "biodiversity hotspots" containing the last habitats of 50% of Earth's vascular plant species and 42% of vertebrate species (excluding fish). Once covering 16% of Earth's land surface, their habitats have since lost 86% of their expanse and now cover just 2.3%. If we could safeguard these relatively small areas, we could reduce the number of extinct species by at least one-third. Protection of the hotspots (parks, reserves, and so on) would cost roughly $1.5 billion per year for 5 years—just one-seventh of all conservation funding worldwide. What a massive need and massive opportunity for protected areas!

In the tropics, however, where most biodiversity is found and where it is most threatened, no island is an island, so to speak. The Kruger Park in South Africa is drying out because rivers arising outside the park are losing their waters to ranches and other development works. The park is also being overtaken by acid rain from South Africa's main industrial region upwind.

Moreover, global warming will shift temperature bands, and consequently vegetation communities, away from the equator and toward the poles. Many plants and animals in Hawaii will have little place to go but into the sea, as will those in the southern tip of Africa, northern Philippines, and dozens of other unfortunate locales. Even if they were to be turned into giant parks and perfectly protected on the ground, they would still be vulnerable to global warming—half of which is caused by carbon dioxide emissions from fossil fuels.

Biodiversity enthusiasts, here's a key question for you: Which country has less than one-twentieth of the world's population but causes one-quarter of the world's carbon dioxide emissions?

**Norman Myers** is a Fellow of Oxford University and a member of the U.S. National Academy of Sciences. He works as an independent scientist, advising the United Nations, the World Bank, the World Conservation Union, the World Wildlife Fund, and dozens of other conservation bodies around the world.

 Explore this issue further by accessing **Viewpoints** at www.aw-bc.com/withgott.

## REVIEWING OBJECTIVES

**You should now be able to:**

### Characterize the scope of biodiversity on Earth

▶ Biodiversity can be thought of at three levels, commonly called species diversity, genetic diversity, and ecosystem diversity. (pp. 310–312)

▶ Roughly 1.7–2.0 million species have been described so far, but scientists agree that the world holds millions more. (pp. 313–314)

▶ Some taxonomic groups (such as insects) hold far more diversity than others. (pp. 313–314)

▶ Diversity is unevenly spread across different habitats and areas of the world. (pp. 314–316)

### Describe ways to measure biodiversity

▶ Global estimates of biodiversity are based on extrapolations from scientific assessments in local areas and certain taxonomic groups. (pp. 313–314)

### Contrast background extinction rates and periods of mass extinction

▶ Species have gone extinct at a background rate of roughly one species per 1 to 10 million species each year. Most species that have ever lived are now extinct. (p. 316)

▶ Earth's life has experienced five mass extinction events in the past 440 million years. (pp. 316–317)

▶ Human impact is presently causing the beginnings of a sixth mass extinction. (pp. 317–319)

### Evaluate the primary causes of biodiversity loss

▶ Habitat alteration is the main cause of current biodiversity loss. Invasive species, pollution, and overharvesting are also important causes. Climate change threatens to become a major cause very soon. (pp. 319–324)

### Specify the benefits of biodiversity

▶ Biodiversity is vital for functioning ecosystems and the services they provide us. (p. 325)

▶ Wild species are sources of food, medicine, and economic development. (pp. 325–327)

▶ Many people feel humans have a psychological need to connect with the natural world. (pp. 327–328)

### Assess conservation biology and its practice

▶ Conservation biology is an applied science that studies biodiversity loss and seeks ways to protect and restore biodiversity at all its levels. (p. 329)

### Explain island biogeography theory and its application to conservation biology

▶ Island biogeography theory explains how size and distance influence the number of species occurring on islands. (pp. 329–330)

▶ The theory applies to terrestrial islands of habitat in fragmented landscapes. (pp. 330–331)

### Compare and contrast traditional and more innovative biodiversity conservation efforts

▶ Most conservation efforts and laws so far have focused on threatened and endangered species. Efforts include captive breeding and reintroduction programs. (pp. 331, 334–335)

▶ Species that are charismatic and well known are often used as tools to conserve habitats and ecosystems. Increasingly, landscape-level conservation is being pursued in its own right. (p. 335)

▶ International conservation approaches include treaties, biodiversity hotspots, community-based conservation, debt-for-nature swaps, and conservation concessions. (pp. 335–337)

## TESTING YOUR COMPREHENSION

1. What is biodiversity? List and describe three levels of biodiversity.
2. What are the five primary causes of biodiversity loss? Can you give a specific example of each?
3. List and describe five invasive species and the adverse effects they have had.
4. Define the term *ecosystem services*. Give five examples of ecosystem services that humans would have a hard time replacing if their natural sources were eliminated.
5. What is the relationship between biodiversity and food security? Between biodiversity and pharmaceuticals? Give three examples of potential benefits of biodiversity conservation for food security and medicine.
6. Describe four reasons why people suggest biodiversity conservation is important.
7. What is the difference between an umbrella species and a keystone species? Could one species be both an umbrella species and a keystone species?
8. Explain the theory of island biogeography. Use the example of the Siberian tiger to describe how this theory can be applied to fragmented terrestrial landscapes.

**9.** Name two successful accomplishments of the U.S. Endangered Species Act. Now name two reasons some people have criticized it.

**10.** What is a biodiversity hotspot? Describe community-based conservation.

## SEEKING SOLUTIONS

**1.** In one of the quotes that open this chapter, biologist E. O. Wilson argues that "except in pockets of ignorance and malice, there is no longer an ideological war between conservationists and developers. Both share the perception that health and prosperity decline in a deteriorating environment." Do you agree or disagree? How do people in your community view biodiversity?

**2.** Many arguments have been advanced for the importance of preserving biodiversity. Which argument do you think is most compelling, and why? Which argument do you think is least compelling, and why?

**3.** Some people argue that we shouldn't worry about endangered species because extinction has always occurred. How would you respond to this view?

**4.** Imagine that you are an influential legislator in a country that has no endangered species act and that you want to introduce legislation to protect your country's vanishing biodiversity. Consider the U.S. Endangered Species Act and the Canadian Species At Risk Act, as well as international efforts such as CITES and the Convention on Biological Diversity. What strategies would you write into your legislation? How would your law be similar to and different from the U.S., Canadian, and international efforts?

**5.** Environmental advocates from developed nations who want to preserve biodiversity globally have long argued for setting aside land in biodiversity-rich regions of developing nations. Many leaders of developing nations have responded by accusing the advocates of neocolonialism. "Your nations attained their prosperity and power by overexploiting their environments decades or centuries ago," these leaders asked, "so why should we now sacrifice our own development by setting aside our land and resources?" What would you say to these leaders of developing countries? What would you say to the environmental advocates? Do you see ways that both preservation and development goals might be reached?

**6.** Compare the biodiversity hotspot approach to the approach of community-based conservation. What are the advantages and disadvantages of each? Can we—and should we—follow both approaches?

## INTERPRETING GRAPHS AND DATA

Habitat alteration is the primary cause of present-day biodiversity loss. Of all human activities, the one that has resulted in the most habitat alteration is agriculture. Between 1850 and 2000, 95% of the native grasslands of the Midwestern United States were converted to agricultural use. As a result, conventional farming practices replaced diverse natural communities with greatly simplified ones. The vast monocultures of industrialized agriculture produce bountiful harvests, but at substantial costs in lost ecosystem services.

Data from a recent study reviewing the scientific literature on the effects of organic farming versus conventional farming practices on biodiversity are shown in the graph.

**1.** How many studies showed a positive effect of organic farming on biodiversity, relative to conventional farming? How many studies reported a negative effect? How many studies reported no effect?

**2.** For which group or groups of organisms is evidence of positive effects the strongest? Reference the numbers to support your choice(s).

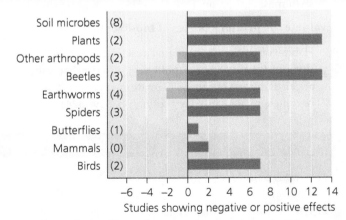

Numbers of scientific studies reporting negative or positive effects on biodiversity of organic agriculture versus conventional farming practices. In parentheses are numbers of studies reporting no effect. Data from Hole, D., et al. 2005. Does organic farming benefit biodiversity? *Biological Conservation* 122: 113–130.

**3.** Recall the ecosystem services provided by biodiversity (▶ p. 325). What services do the groups you chose in Question 2 provide?

## CALCULATING ECOLOGICAL FOOTPRINTS

Of the five major causes of biodiversity loss discussed in this chapter, habitat alteration arguably has the greatest impact. In their 1996 book introducing the ecological footprint concept, authors Mathis Wackernagel and William Rees present a consumption/land-use matrix for an average North American. Each cell in the matrix lists the number of hectares of land of that type required to provide for the different categories of a person's consumption (food, housing, transportation, consumer goods, and services). Of the 4.27 hectares required to support this average person, 0.59 hectares are forest, with most (0.40 hectares) being used to meet the housing demand. Using this information, calculate the missing values in the table.

1. Approximately two-thirds of the forests' productivity is consumed for housing. To what use(s) would you speculate that most of the other third is put?
2. If the harvesting of forest products exceeds the sustainable harvest rate, what will be the likely consequence for the forest?
3. What will be the impact of deforestation, or of the loss of old-growth forests and their replacement with plantations of young trees, on the species diversity of the forest community? In your answer, discuss the possibilities of both extirpation and extinction.

|  | Hectares of forest used for housing | Total forest hectares used |
|---|---|---|
| **You** | 0.40 | 0.59 |
| **Your class** |  |  |
| **Your state** |  |  |
| **United States** |  |  |

Data from Wackernagel, M., and W. Rees. 1996. *Our ecological footprint: reducing human impact on the earth.* British Columbia, Canada: New Society Publishers.

## Take It Further

Go to www.aw-bc.com/withgott or the student CD-ROM where you'll find:

▶ Suggested answers to end-of-chapter questions
▶ Quizzes, animations, and flashcards to help you study
▶ *Research Navigator*™ database of credible and reliable sources to assist you with your research projects

▶ **GRAPHit!** tutorials to help you master how to interpret graphs
▶ **INVESTIGATEit!** current news articles that link the topics that you study to case studies from your region to around the world

# 12 Resource Management, Forestry, Land Use, and Protected Areas

Clearcuts on timber industry land adjacent to Gifford Pinchot National Forest, Washington

## Upon successfully completing this chapter, you will be able to:

▶ Identify the principles, goals, and approaches of resource management

▶ Summarize the ecological roles and economic contributions of forests, and outline the history and scale of forest loss.

▶ Explain the fundamentals of forest management, and describe the major methods of harvesting timber

▶ Analyze the scale and impacts of agricultural land use

▶ Identify major federal land management agencies and the lands they manage

▶ Recognize types of parks and reserves, and evaluate issues involved in their design

Anti-logging protest at Clayoquot Sound

# Central Case: Battling Over the Last Big Trees at Clayoquot Sound

"What we have is nothing less than an ecological Holocaust occurring right now in British Columbia."
—MARK WAREING, WESTERN CANADA WILDERNESS COMMITTEE, 1990

"Clear-cutting . . . may be either desirable or undesirable, acceptable or unacceptable, according to the type of forest and the management objectives for the forest."
—DR. HAMISH KIMMINS, UNIVERSITY OF BRITISH COLUMBIA, 1992

It was the largest act of civil disobedience in Canadian history, and it played out along a seacoast of stunning majestic beauty, at the foot of some of the world's biggest trees. Protestors blocked logging trucks, preventing them from entering stands of ancient temperate rainforest, the forest that had once carpeted most of Vancouver Island, British Columbia.

The activists were opposing **clear-cutting,** the logging practice that removes all trees from an area. Most of Canada's old-growth temperate rainforest had already been cut, and the forests of Clayoquot Sound on the western coast of Vancouver Island were among the largest undisturbed stands of temperate rainforest left on the planet.

The protestors chanted slogans, sang songs, and chained themselves to trees. The loggers complained that the protestors were keeping them from doing their jobs and making a living. In the end, 850 of the 12,000 protestors were arrested in full view of the global media, and this remote, mist-enshrouded land of cedars and hemlocks became ground zero in the global debate over how we manage forests.

That was in 1993. Timber from old-growth forests had powered British Columbia's economy since the province's early days. Historically, one in five jobs in British Columbia depended on its $13 billion timber industry, and many small towns would have gone under without it. By 1993, however, the timber industry was cutting thousands of jobs a year because of mechanization, and the looming depletion of old growth threatened to slow the industry.

Meanwhile, half a world away in Great Britain, the environmental group Greenpeace was busy trying to convince British companies and customers to boycott forest products made from British Columbia trees that had been clear-cut by multinational timber company MacMillan Bloedel. Soon two British corporations cancelled contracts worth several million dollars with the beleaguered company, and British Columbia's premier found himself touring European nations trying to persuade them not to boycott his province's main export.

Then in 1995, the provincial government called for an end to clear-cutting at Clayoquot Sound, after its appointed scientific panel of experts submitted a new forestry plan for the region. The plan recommended reducing harvests, retaining 15–70% of old-growth trees in each stand, decreasing the logging road network, designating forest reserve areas, and managing riparian zones. Two years later the provincial government reversed many of these regulations on logging and a new premier pronounced forest activists "enemies of British Columbia," but the progressive management objectives for Clayoquot Sound have largely survived to the present day.

The antagonists called a truce and struck a deal; wilderness advocates and MacMillan Bloedel agreed to logging of old growth in limited areas, using more environmentally friendly practices. In 1998, Native people of the region formed a timber company, Iisaak, in agreement with MacMillan Bloedel's successor, Weyerhaeuser, and began logging in a more environmentally sensitive manner.

Meanwhile, leaving most of the trees standing had accomplished just what forest advocates had predicted: People from all over the world—1 million each year—were now visiting Clayoquot Sound for its natural beauty, and kayaking and whale-watching in its waters. Ecotourism (along with fishing and aquaculture) surpassed logging as the driver of local economies. The United Nations designated the site as an international biosphere reserve, encouraging land protection and sustainable development. The trees appeared to be worth more left standing than cut down.

Tensions continue today, however. Another timber company, Interfor, is harvesting areas near park and biosphere reserve boundaries. Local forest advocates worry that the provincial government's new Working Forest Policy will increase logging in the region. The town of Tofino has petitioned the province to exempt Clayoquot Sound's forests from the new policy so that pristine valleys can be preserved and the town's ecotourism economy can be maintained. As long as our demand for lumber, paper, and forest products keeps increasing, pressures will keep building on the remaining forests on Vancouver Island and around the world.

# Resource Management

Debates over forest resources epitomize the broader questions of how to manage natural resources in general. We need to manage the resources we take from the natural world because many of them are limited. In Chapter 1, we saw how some resources, such as fossil fuels, are nonrenewable on human time scales, whereas other resources, such as the sun's energy, are perpetually renewable. Between these extremes lie resources such as timber, which are renewable if they are not exploited too rapidly or carelessly. **Resource management** is the practice of harvesting potentially renewable resources in ways that do not deplete them. Resource managers are guided in their decision making by available research in the natural sciences, as well as by political, economic, and social factors.

A key question in managing resources is whether to focus narrowly on the resource of interest or to look more broadly at the environmental system of which the resource is a part. Taking a broader view can often help avoid damaging the system and can thereby help sustain the availability of the resource in the long term.

## Several natural resources are vital to us

Besides timber, several other types of natural resources are vital to our civilization. These include soils, freshwater, wildlife and fisheries, rangeland, and minerals (Figure 12.1). All natural resources also serve functions in the ecosystems of which they are a part.

**Soils** Soil resources, particularly topsoil, are of direct importance to us because they support the plants we grow for food and fiber and thus play a central role in agriculture. As we saw in Chapter 9 (▶ pp. 261–264), certain farm practices, such as terracing and use of windbreaks, can help guard against loss of topsoil to erosion, and other farm practices, such as planting nitrogen-fixing crops, can help maintain soil quality. Healthy soils also support forests and other natural communities, serving as a site for decomposition and a reservoir for nutrients.

**Freshwater** Each of us depends directly on freshwater, so ensuring a dependable supply of drinking water is a life-or-death issue. Freshwater also is necessary for agriculture; indeed, we use most freshwater not for drinking but for irrigating crops. In addition, waterways and wetlands are crucial for wildlife and properly functioning ecosystems, so those who manage water resources try to maintain supplies for all these reasons. Water managers also try to protect the

**FIGURE 12.1** Our civilization depends on a number of natural resources, including timber, soils, freshwater, wildlife and fisheries, rangeland, and minerals. Minerals are a nonrenewable resource that is mined, but the others can be kept renewable through responsible resource management.

quality of these supplies by guarding against pollution. We will examine freshwater resources in depth in Chapter 15.

**Wildlife and fisheries** Humans have long hunted animals for food. Managers regulate the hunting of game animals, such as deer and quail, for food and sport in an effort to maintain populations of these animals at desired levels. As populations of many other terrestrial species decline from habitat loss and other causes (▸ pp. 319–324), management for nongame species is becoming increasingly important. Marine animals are also harvested, and despite extensive management of fisheries, many stocks of fish and shellfish have declined throughout the world's oceans from overharvesting, as we will see in Chapter 16. Besides their use as food, living organisms provide humans with many other benefits, from materials to medicines to aesthetic appreciation (▸ pp. 325–328). Organisms are also, of course, vital components of the ecosystems that sustain our world.

**Rangeland** Most of our food from animals today comes not from wild animals but from domesticated ones that are farmed. Most cattle in North America are raised in crowded feedlots, but they have traditionally been raised by grazing on open grassland. As we saw in Chapter 9 (▸ pp. 267–268, 270), grazing can be sustainable, but overgrazing results in damage to soils, waterways, and vegetative communities. Range managers are responsible for regulating ranching on public lands, and they advise ranchers on sustainable grazing practices on private lands.

**Minerals** Our civilization depends on numerous minerals, and until we achieve a closed-loop economy (▸ pp. 664–665), we will rely on the mining of minerals. Iron is mined and processed to make steel. Copper is used in pipes, electrical wires, and a variety of other applications. Aluminum is extracted via bauxite ore and used in packaging and other end products. Lead is used in batteries, to shield medical patients from radiation, and in many other ways. Zinc, tungsten, phosphate, uranium, gold, silver—the list goes on and on.

Although we rely on these mineral resources, we do not manage their extraction as we do with the aforementioned resources. Like fossil fuels, minerals are nonrenewable resources that are mined rather than harvested. Therefore, the mining industry has no built-in incentive to conserve. Instead, it benefits by extracting as much as it can as fast as it can and then, once extraction has become too inefficient to be profitable, moving on to new sites.

The process of mining also has historically degraded surrounding environments, sometimes on massive scales. Mining may directly remove vegetation from large areas, cause erosion, and produce acidic runoff that poisons area waterways. In addition, the smelting of metals following mining can create severe air pollution. We touch on some of the environmental and social costs of coal mining in Chapter 19 (▸ pp. 576–577), but these issues exist with all types of mining. Improved technology and more environmentally sensitive extraction procedures can help minimize environmental impacts. Such advances come as a result of public pressure, government legislation, or economic savings. Industries extracting potentially renewable resources, in contrast, have an added incentive to reduce ecological impacts: doing so may help sustain their ability to harvest resources—and this is where resource management comes in.

## Managers have tried to achieve maximum sustainable yield

One guiding principle in resource management has been **maximum sustainable yield.** The aim is to achieve the maximum amount of resource extraction possible, without depleting the resource from one harvest to the next. At first this goal may sound ideal, but in reality it may sometimes harm the ecosystems from which the resource is derived. If those ecosystems cease to function effectively as a result, then in time this may decrease the availability of the resource.

For instance, recall the logistic growth curve (Figure 5.16, ▸ p. 137), which shows that a population grows most quickly when it is at an intermediate size. A fisheries manager aiming for maximum sustainable yield will therefore prefer to keep fish populations at intermediate levels so that they rebound quickly after each harvest. Doing so should

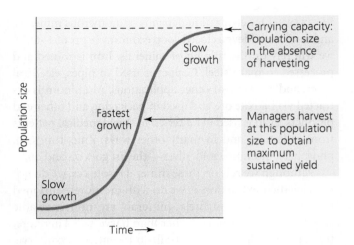

**FIGURE 12.2** Using the concept of maximum sustainable yield, resource managers attempt to maximize the amount of resource harvested, as long as the harvest is sustainable in perpetuity. In the case of a wildlife population or fisheries stock that grows according to a logistic growth curve, managers aim to keep the population at an intermediate level, well below the carrying capacity, because populations grow fastest at intermediate sizes.

result in the greatest amount of fish harvested over time, while the population sustains itself (Figure 12.2). However, this management approach keeps the fish population at only about half its carrying capacity (▸ p. 136)—well below the level it would attain in the absence of fishing. Reducing one population in this way will likely have effects on other species and on the food web dynamics of the community. From an ecological point of view, management for maximum sustainable yield may thereby set in motion complex and significant ecological changes.

In forest management, maximum sustainable yield argues for cutting trees shortly after they have gone through their fastest stage of growth, and trees often grow most quickly at intermediate ages. Thus, trees may be cut long before they have grown as large as they would in the absence of harvesting. Although this practice may maximize timber production over time, it can cause drastic changes in the ecology of a forest by eliminating habitat for species that depend on mature trees.

### Today many managers pursue ecosystem-based management

Because of these dilemmas, increasing numbers of managers today espouse ecosystem-based management. **Ecosystem-based management** attempts to manage the harvesting of resources in ways that minimize impact on the ecosystems and ecological processes that provide the resource. The plan proposed in 1995 by the Scientific Panel for Sustainable Forest Practices on Clayoquot Sound and approved

by British Columbia's government was essentially a plan for ecosystem-based management. By carefully managing ecologically important areas such as riparian corridors, by considering patterns at the landscape level, and by affording protection to some forested areas, the plan aimed to allow continued timber harvesting at reduced levels while preserving the functional integrity of the ecosystem.

Although ecosystem-based management has gained a great deal of support in recent years, it is challenging for managers to determine how best to implement this type of management. Ecosystems are complex, and our understanding of how they operate is limited. Thus, ecosystem-based management has often come to mean different things to different people.

### Adaptive management evolves and improves

Some management actions will succeed, and some will fail. A wise manager will try new approaches if old ones are not effective. In recent years, many resource managers have taken this a step further by implementing adaptive management. **Adaptive management** involves systematically testing different management approaches with the aim of improving methods as time goes on. It calls for changing practices midstream if necessary, as managers learn which work best. This approach represents a true fusion of science and management, because hypotheses about how best to manage resources are explicitly tested.

Adaptive management can be time-consuming and complicated. It entails monitoring the results of one's practices and continually adjusting them as needed, based on what is learned. It has posed a challenge for many managers, because those who adopt new approaches must often overcome inertia and resistance to change from proponents of established practices. Adaptive management is beginning to be used in forestry (see "The Science behind the Story," ▸ pp. 348–349). The management of timber and other forest resources is a clear and representative example of resource management.

## Forest Management

Forests cover much of Earth's land surface, provide habitat for countless organisms, and play key roles in our planet's biogeochemical cycles (▸ pp. 195–206). Forests have also long provided humanity with wood for fuel, construction, paper production, and more. Foresters, those professionals who manage forests through the practice of **forestry**, today must balance the central importance

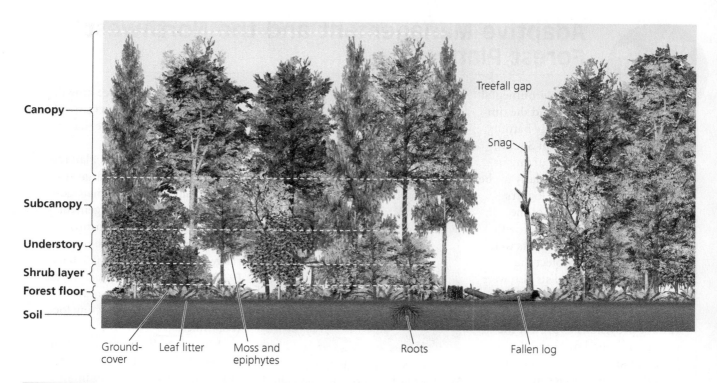

Canopy

Subcanopy

Understory

Shrub layer

Forest floor

Soil

Treefall gap

Snag

Ground-cover    Leaf litter    Moss and epiphytes    Roots    Fallen log

**FIGURE 12.3** Mature forests are complex ecosystems. In this cross-section of a generalized mature forest, the crowns of the largest trees form the canopy, and smaller trees beneath them form the shaded subcanopy and understory. Shrubs and groundcover grow just above the forest floor, which may be covered in leaf litter rich with invertebrate animals. Vines, mosses, lichens, and epiphytes cover portions of trees and the forest floor. Snags (standing dead trees), whose wood can be easily hollowed out, provide food and nesting and roosting sites for woodpeckers and other animals. Fallen logs nourish the soil and young plants and provide habitat for countless invertebrates as the logs decompose. Treefall gaps caused by fallen trees let light through the canopy and create small openings in the forest, allowing early successional plants to grow in patches within the mature forest.

of forests as ecosystems with civilization's demand for wood products.

## Forests are ecologically valuable

Most of the world's forests occur as boreal forest, the biome (▶ pp. 170, 176–177) that stretches across much of Canada, Russia, and Scandinavia, or as tropical rainforest, the biome that occurs in South and Central America, equatorial Africa, and Indonesia and southeast Asia. Temperate forests cover less area globally, in part because so many have already been cleared by people.

Because of their structural complexity and their ability to provide many niches for organisms, forests comprise some of the richest ecosystems for biodiversity (Figure 12.3). Trees furnish food and shelter for an immense diversity of vertebrate and invertebrate animals. Countless insects, birds, mammals, and other organisms subsist on the leaves, fruits, and seeds that trees produce.

Some animals are adapted for living in dense treetop canopies. Here beetles, caterpillars, and other leaf-eating insects abound, providing food for birds such as tanagers and warblers, while arboreal mammals from squirrels to sloths to monkeys consume fruit and leaves. Other animals specialize on the subcanopies of trees, and still others utilize the bark, branches, and trunks. Cavities in trunks provide nest and shelter sites for a wide variety of vertebrates. Dead and dying trees are valuable for many species; these snags are decayed by insects that are eaten by woodpeckers and other animals.

Understory shrubs and groundcover plants give a forest structural complexity and provide habitat for still more organisms. Moreover, the leaves, stems, and roots of forest plants are colonized by an extensive array of fungi and microbes, in both parasitic and mutualistic relationships (▶ pp. 153–155). And much of a forest's diversity resides in the forest floor, where the soil is generally nourished by leaf litter. As we saw in Chapter 11, myriad

# Adaptive Management and the Northwest Forest Plan

**The Science behind the Story**

While environmental advocates and the timber industry were battling one another at Clayoquot Sound, similar debates were occurring in the United States, particularly in the Pacific Northwest. Here loggers were closing in on some of the nation's last stands of old-growth conifers, and preservationists were staging protests to protect the stands. Environmentalists also were winning lawsuits to force the U.S. Forest Service and other agencies to enforce provisions to protect the northern spotted owl (and thus its habitat, old-growth forest) under the Endangered Species Act (▶ pp. 331–333). As a result, logging was being significantly restricted.

In 1993, the Clinton administration waded into the impasse and helped direct the development of a new plan to manage the forests of western Washington, Oregon, and northwestern California so that consensus could be reached and logging could continue with adequate protections for species and ecosystems. The resulting **Northwest Forest Plan**, approved in February 1994, used

Interstate 90 at Snoqualmie Pass, Washington, is a barrier to many animal species traveling through the forested areas on either side of it.

science extensively to guide management.

Research conducted over the past decade since the plan's inception has fallen into several categories: (1) wildlife conservation and population viability, (2) aquatic conservation, (3) socioeconomic research, (4) ecological processes and function, (5) spatial and

landscape studies, (6) tree growth studies, (7) adaptive management concepts, and (8) adaptive management areas.

The Northwest Forest Plan represented one of the first large-scale applications of adaptive management. Ten adaptive management areas (AMAs) were established throughout the region. These areas ranged from 37,000 to 200,000 ha (92,000 to 500,000 acres), and were located in regions where reduced timber harvests were affecting local economies.

Several studies were carried out at one AMA, Snoqualmie Pass in Washington's Cascade Mountains (see figure). Some of this research found that understanding plant associations at the landscape scale could help predict disturbance from fire, insects, and disease. Another study addressed habitat fragmentation and its effects on wildlife. Land ownership at Snoqualmie Pass in 1994 was like a checkerboard, with alternating blocks of land owned by various government agencies, timber companies, and individuals. Landscape ecologists thought the area might

soil organisms help decompose plant material and cycle nutrients.

In general, forests with a greater diversity of plants host a greater diversity of organisms overall. And, in general, fully mature forests, such as the undisturbed old-growth forests remaining at Clayoquot Sound, contain more biodiversity than younger forests, because older forests contain more structural diversity and thus more microhabitats and resources for more species.

The complex systems we call forests provide all manner of vital ecosystem services (▶ pp. 39–41). Forest vegetation acts to stabilize soil and prevent erosion. Forest plants also

help regulate the hydrologic cycle, slowing runoff, lessening flooding, and purifying water as they take it in from the soil and release it to the atmosphere. Forest plants also store carbon, release oxygen, and moderate climate. By performing such ecological functions, forests are indispensable for our survival and help make our planet's environment what it is.

## Forest products are economically valued

Forests also provide people with economically valuable wood products. For millennia, wood from forests has fueled our fires, keeping people warm and well fed. It has

serve as a vital north–south corridor for wildlife to travel, so land was transacted to try to consolidate ownership to form corridors of publicly managed land. But an outstanding question was whether wildlife would be able to cross Interstate 90, which runs east–west over the pass.

Forest Service researchers led by Peter Singleton and John Lehmkuhl spent 2 years studying the movements of wildlife in relation to a 48-km (30-mi) stretch of I-90 to find out how much of a barrier the highway represented.

First, they used GIS methods (see the next "Science behind the Story" on ▶pp. 352–353) to predict how accessible areas were to animal species with different dispersal abilities and habitat preferences.

They also set up cameras that took pictures of animals that passed in front of heat and motion detectors. From data at 115 stations, they found no difference between sites near and far from the interstate. However, they did find that some animals, for example, bobcats, skunks, hares, and bears, appeared near certain portions of the highway more than other portions.

Third, the researchers mapped all road-killed animals discovered along 86 km (54 mi) of the interstate by Washington Department of Transportation employees. They found that the 450 deer and elk killed in the 2-year period were concentrated along four particular stretches of interstate.

Fourth, they surveyed the interstate in winter for tracks left in snow by animals crossing the highway. Twenty-three of 37 crossings by coyotes, bobcats, and raccoons took place in a single 2-mile stretch of road.

Fifth, they monitored underpasses and overpasses, as well as drainage culverts crossing beneath the interstate, to determine how animals were using these structures. Using cameras and plates of soot or sand that recorded footprints, the researchers detected 15 mammal species using culverts to cross the interstate, with deer mice the most frequent crossers. Different species used different types of culverts, but dry ones 0.4–1.1 m in diameter were regularly used.

With these data, Singleton and Lehmkuhl could pinpoint locations preferred by wildlife and could recommend that opportunities for safely crossing the interstate be provided at those locations. In particular, they wrote, providing dry drainage culverts near areas of mature forest could help promote the ecological functions that small mammals provide, such as dispersing plant seeds and fungal spores. They also urged that habitat be restored and maintained on the landscape level in patterns that facilitated animal movement.

Key for adaptive management is that data continue to be collected, to assess whether actions that are taken succeed or fail. In this respect, the AMAs under the Northwest Forest Plan have not yet lived up to their potential. Doing adaptive management right requires time, money, and a rare combination of flexibility and commitment. However, science and management under the Northwest Forest Plan is ongoing, and the Plan's proponents are committed to making it work.

---

housed people, keeping us sheltered. It built the ships that carried people and cultures from one continent to another. It allowed us to produce paper, the medium of the first information revolution.

In recent decades, industrial harvesting has allowed the extraction of more timber than ever before, supplying all these needs of a rapidly growing human population and its expanding economy. The exploitation of forest resources has been instrumental in helping our society achieve the standard of living we enjoy today. Indeed, without industrial timber harvesting, you would not be reading this book.

Most commercial logging today takes place in Canada, Russia, and other nations that hold large expanses of boreal forest, and in tropical countries with large amounts of rainforest, such as Brazil. In the United States, most logging takes place on land both private and public, primarily in the conifer forests of the West and the pine plantations of the South.

## Demand for wood has led to deforestation

We all depend in some way on wood, from the subsistence herder in Nepal cutting trees for firewood to the

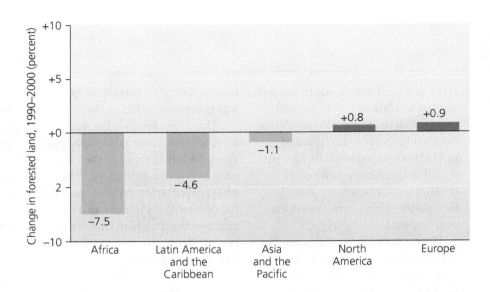

**FIGURE 12.4** Nations in Africa and in Latin America are experiencing rapid deforestation as they attempt to develop, extract resources, and provide new agricultural land for their growing populations. In parts of Europe and North America, meanwhile, forested area is slowly increasing as some former farmed areas are abandoned and allowed to grow back into forest. Go to **GRAPHit!** at www.aw-bc.com/withgott or on the student CD-ROM. Data from United Nations Environmental Programme. 2002. *Global environmental outlook 3.* London: Earthscan Publications.

American student consuming reams upon reams of paper in the course of getting a degree. For such reasons, people have cleared forests for millennia to exploit timber resources. Still more forest has been cleared to make way for agriculture.

**Deforestation,** the clearing and loss of forests, has altered the landscapes and ecosystems of much of the planet. It has caused soil degradation, population declines, and species extinctions, and, as we saw with Easter Island (▶ pp. 8–9), has in some cases helped bring whole civilizations to ruin. Continued deforestation threatens dire ecological and economic consequences. Impacts are greatest in tropical areas, because of the potentially massive loss of biodiversity, and in arid regions, because of the vulnerability to desertification (▶ pp. 259–260). In addition, deforestation adds carbon dioxide ($CO_2$) to the atmosphere: $CO_2$ is released when plant matter is burned or decomposed, and thereafter less vegetation remains to soak up $CO_2$. Deforestation is thereby one contributor to global climate change (▶ p. 530).

All continents have experienced deforestation, but forests are being felled at the fastest rates today in the tropical rainforests of Latin America and Africa (Figure 12.4). Developing countries in these regions are striving to expand areas of settlement for their burgeoning populations and to boost their economies by extracting natural resources and selling them abroad. Meanwhile, areas of Europe and eastern North America are slowly gaining forest cover as they recover from severe deforestation of past decades and centuries. In total, depending on one's definition, one-fifth to one-third of Earth's land area is currently covered by forest (see "The Science behind the Story," ▶ pp. 352–353).

## The growth of the United States and Canada was fed by deforestation

Deforestation for timber and farmland propelled the growth of the United States and Canada throughout their phenomenal expansion westward across the North American continent over the past 400 years. The vast deciduous forests of the East were virtually stripped of their trees by the mid-19th century, making way for countless small farms. Timber from these forests built the cities of the Atlantic seaboard. Later, cities such as Chicago were constructed with timber felled in the vast pine and hardwood forests of Wisconsin and Michigan. As a farming economy shifted to an industrial one, wood was used to stoke the furnaces of industry. Logging operations moved south to the Ozarks of Missouri and Arkansas, while the pine woodlands of the South were logged and converted to pine plantations. Once most mature trees were removed from these areas, timber companies moved west, cutting the continent's biggest trees in the Rocky Mountains, the Sierra Nevada, the Cascade Mountains, and the Pacific Coast ranges (Figure 12.5).

By the early 20th century, very little virgin timber was left in the lower 48 U.S. states (Figure 12.6). Today, the largest oaks and maples found in eastern North America, and even most redwoods of the California coast, are merely **second-growth** trees, trees that have sprouted and grown to partial maturity after old-growth timber has been cut. The size of the gargantuan trees they replaced can be seen in the enormous stumps that remain in the more recently logged areas of the Pacific coast. The scarcity of old-growth trees on the North American continent

**FIGURE 12.5** A mule team drags logs of Douglas fir from a clear-cut in Mason County, Washington, in 1901. Early timber harvesting practices in North America caused significant environmental impacts and removed virtually all the virgin timber from one region after another.

**(a) Areas of natural forest, 1620**

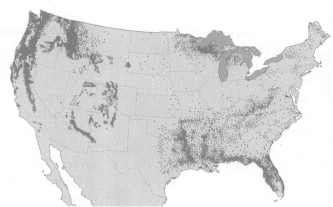

**(b) Areas of natural forest, 1920**

**FIGURE 12.6** When Europeans first were colonizing North America, the entire eastern half of the continent and substantial portions of the western half were covered in forest (**a**). By the early 20th century, the vast majority of this forest had been cut, replaced mostly by agriculture and other human land uses (**b**). Since that time, most of the remaining original forest has been cut, but much of the landscape has also become reforested with second-growth forest. *Source:* Williams, M. 1989. *Americans and their forests.* Cambridge: Cambridge University Press. As adapted by Goudie, A., 2000. *The human impact.* Cambridge, MA: MIT Press.

today explains the passion with which environmental advocates have fought for the preservation of ancient forests in areas such as Clayoquot Sound.

The fortunes of loggers have risen and fallen with the availability of big trees. As each region was denuded of timber, the industry declined there and the timber com-

panies moved on, while local loggers lost their jobs. If the remaining ancient trees of North America—most in British Columbia and Alaska—are cut, many U.S. and Canadian loggers will likely be out of jobs once again. Meanwhile, their employers will move on to nations of the developing world, as many already have.

# Using Geographic Information Systems to Survey Earth's Forests

*The Science behind the Story*

One map is washed in splashes of green, showing broad stretches of largely undisturbed forest. Another outlines political boundaries. A third map marks human population centers, denoting their density with different colors. A fourth lays out parks, reserves, and other land protected from development. On its own, each map shows only one physical characteristic of Earth. But layered together through the use of a powerful technology, these maps reveal something entirely different: the condition of the world's last intact forests.

Used in a groundbreaking study published by the United Nations Environment Programme (UNEP) in 2001, these maps, in conjunction with a *geographic information system (GIS),* have become an essential tool for environmental planners and resource managers around the world.

A GIS consists of software that builds layered maps, using different sets of data to compile various views of landscapes (see figure). Environmental researchers most often use data on the status and uses of natural resources. In the case of the

UNEP study, researchers wanted a comprehensive look at global forests—where they are, which countries govern them, which forests face the most pressure from encroaching human settlements, and which are most protected. The researchers especially wanted to know the status of "closed" forests: forests whose canopies cover more than 40% of their area. Conducting such a survey on the ground, going from forest to forest and country to country, would have been neither practical nor accurate. Synthesizing the findings from such research into a comprehensive paper map would have been almost impossible. With a GIS, however, researchers pull data such as satellite imagery and computerized maps into an all-inclusive view of the area they are studying.

Some of the researchers' most critical data are gathered via a sensor, an advanced very high resolution radiometer (AVHRR), orbiting the Earth by satellite. The rotating mirror, telescope, and internal electronics of the AVHRR measure wavelengths of energy rising from Earth's surface. Different types of substrate release different

wavelengths, which the AVHRR translates into color images. Different colors in the satellite imagery thus denote whether an area is covered by water, rock, houses, or vegetation.

For more than a decade, scientists have taken advantage of AVHHR to produce the Normalized Difference Vegetation Index (NDVI). NDVI researchers survey forests and plants and gauge changes to vegetation. Using the NDVI's catalog of worldwide vegetation images, UNEP researchers loaded forest data into their GIS. They then added three other sets of electronic data into the GIS: the distribution of the world's population, global political boundaries, and land protected against development.

Once compiled, the data layers offered UNEP researchers an unprecedented global view of forests. About 20% of Earth's surface remains covered by closed forest, the study indicated. Moreover, the study confirmed previous findings that forests in densely populated countries, such as India and Indonesia, are under pressure from expanding human settlement. Such

## Deforestation is proceeding rapidly in many developing nations

Uncut tropical forests still remain in many developing countries, and these nations are in the position the United States and Canada faced a century or two ago: having a vast frontier that they can develop for human use. Today's advanced technology, however, has allowed these countries to exploit their resources and push back their frontiers even faster than occurred in North America. As a result, deforestation is rapid in places such as Brazil and Indonesia.

Developing nations are often desperate enough for economic development that they impose few or no restrictions on logging. Often their timber is extracted by foreign multinational corporations, which have paid fees to the developing nation's government for a *concession,* or right to extract the resource. In such cases, the foreign corporation has little or no incentive to manage forest resources sustainably. Many of the short-term economic benefits are reaped not by local residents but by the corporations that log the timber and export it elsewhere.

countries require stronger and immediate conservation efforts, researchers determined. The team also found that more than 80% of the world's intact forests were concentrated in just 15 countries and that 88% of those forests were sparsely inhabited by people. These findings could prove critical in starting conservation efforts in regions at risk, to help prevent further forest degradation.

GIS is not foolproof; GIS maps are only as good as the data that go into them. Some of the UNEP data—those on population size and protected areas—may not be reliable, researchers warn, because the countries providing the information may not always keep accurate records. Some satellite images used in the UNEP study were ambiguous, as was the case with the maps indicating forest cover; the team couldn't be sure every tree farm or plantation had been removed from that set of data before loading into the GIS.

However, the UNEP scientists stressed that without GIS such a major forest assessment would never have been possible. With it, forest planners can focus conservation priorities on areas with the best prospects for continued existence.

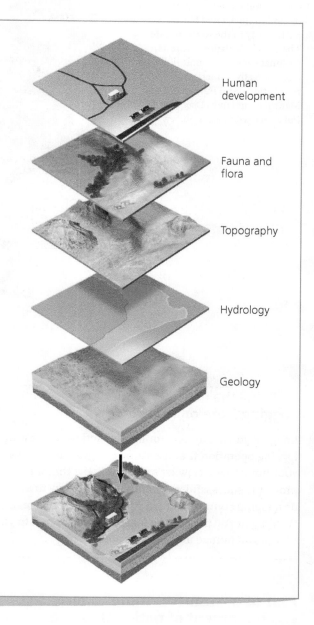

Human development

Fauna and flora

Topography

Hydrology

Geology

Geographic information systems (GIS) allow the layering of different types of data on natural landscape features and human land uses so as to produce maps integrating this information. GIS can then be used to explore informative correlations between these data sets.

Local people may or may not receive temporary employment from the corporation, but once the timber is harvested they no longer have the forest and the ecosystem services it once provided.

In Sarawak, the Malaysian portion of the island of Borneo, foreign corporations that were granted logging concessions have deforested several million hectares of tropical rainforest since 1963. The clearing of this forest—one of the world's richest, hosting such organisms as orangutans and the world's largest flower, *Rafflesia arnoldii*—has had direct impacts on the 22 tribes of people who live as hunter-gatherers in Sarawak's rainforest. The Malaysian government did not consult the tribes about the logging, which decreased the wild game on which these people depended. Oil palm agriculture was established afterward, leading to pesticide and fertilizer runoff that killed fish in local streams. The tribes protested peacefully and finally began blockading logging roads. The government, which at first jailed them, now is negotiating, but it insists on converting the tribes to a farming way of life.

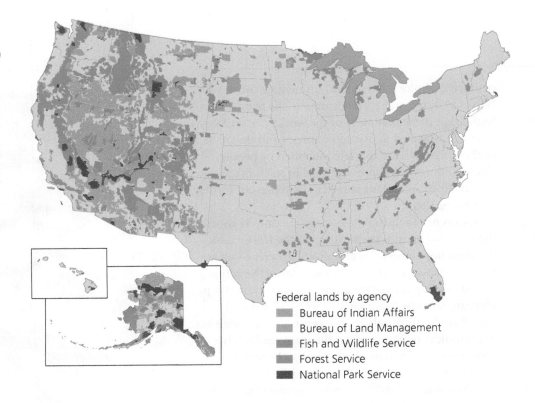

**FIGURE 12.7** Federal agencies own and manage well over 250 million ha (600 million acres) of land in the United States, particularly in the western states. These include national forests, national parks, national wildlife refuges, Native American reservations, and Bureau of Land Management lands. Data from United States Geological Survey.

Federal lands by agency
- Bureau of Indian Affairs
- Bureau of Land Management
- Fish and Wildlife Service
- Forest Service
- National Park Service

## Weighing the Issues:
### Logging Here or There

Imagine you are an environmental activist protesting a logging operation that is cutting old-growth trees near your hometown. Now let's say you know that if the protest is successful, the company will move to a developing country and cut its virgin timber instead. Would you still protest the logging in your hometown? Would you pursue any other approaches?

## Fear of a "timber famine" spurred establishment of national forests

In the United States, the depletion of the eastern forests and widespread fear of a "timber famine" spurred the formation of a system of forest reserves: public lands set aside to grow trees, produce timber, protect watersheds, and serve as insurance against future scarcities of lumber. Today the U.S. **national forest** system consists of 77 million ha (191 million acres) spread across all but a few states (Figure 12.7). The system, managed by the U.S. Forest Service, covers over 8% of the nation's land area.

The U.S. Forest Service was established in 1905 under the leadership of Gifford Pinchot (▶ pp. 34–35). Pinchot

and others developed the concepts of resource management and conservation during the Progressive Era, a time of social reform when people urged that science and education be applied to public policy to improve society. In line with Pinchot's conservation ethic, the Forest Service aimed to manage the forests for "the greatest good of the greatest number in the long run." Pinchot believed the nation should extract and use resources from its public lands, so timber harvesting was, from the start, a goal behind establishing the national forests. But conservation meant planting trees as well as harvesting them, and the Forest Service intended to pursue wise management of timber resources.

Management goals are similar for the Canadian Forest Service and the provincial forestry ministries. Of Canada's 310 million ha (765 million acres) of forested land, 77% belongs to the provinces, and only 16% is federally owned and 7% privately owned. About one-third of the nation's forests are in British Columbia, and 38% are in Quebec and Ontario.

## Timber is extracted from public and private lands

Timber is extracted from publicly held forests in the United States and Canada not by the governments of these nations, but by private timber companies. In the United States, Forest Service employees plan and manage timber sales and build roads to provide access for logging companies, which sell the timber they harvest for profit.

However, most timber harvesting in the United States these days takes place on private land, including land owned by timber companies. In 2001, the most recent year for which good data are available, timber companies extracted 31.7 million m³ (340 million ft³) of live timber from national forests. Although this is a large amount, it is considerably less than the amount cut from private lands and other public forests (Figure 12.8). Timber harvesting declined on national forests during the 1980s and 1990s, and in 2001 tree regrowth outpaced tree removal on these lands by nearly 12 to 1. Overall, timber production in the United States and other developed countries has remained roughly stable for the past 40 years. Meanwhile, it has more than doubled in developing countries.

The equivalent rates of growth and removal on private lands in Figure 12.8 reflect attempts by timber companies to manage their resources in accordance with the maximum sustainable yield approach, so that they can obtain maximal profits over many years for their owners and investors. On public lands, rates of growth and removal reflect not only economic forces but social and political ones as well, and these have changed over time. From the U.S. national forests, private timber extraction began to increase in the 1950s as the country experienced a postwar economic boom, consumption of paper products rose, and the population expanded into newly built suburban homes. In more recent decades, harvests from national forests decreased as economic trends shifted, public concern over clear-cutting grew, and forest management philosophy evolved.

## Plantation forestry has grown

Today the North American timber industry focuses most on maximizing production from tree plantations in the Northwest and the South. These plantations feature stands of fast-growing tree species, and are single-species monocultures (▶ pp. 281–282). Because all trees in a given stand are planted at the same time, the stands are **even-aged,** with all trees the same age (Figure 12.9). Stands are cut after a certain number of years (called the *rotation time*), and the land is replanted with seedlings. Most ecologists and foresters view these plantations more as crop agriculture than as ecologically functional forests. Because there are few tree species and little variation in tree age, plantations do not offer many forest organisms the habitat they need. However, some harvesting methods aim to maintain **uneven-aged** stands, where a mix of ages (and often a mix of tree species) makes the stand more similar to a natural forest.

## Timber is harvested by several methods

When they harvest trees, timber companies use any of several methods. From the 1950s through the 1970s, many timber harvests were conducted using the clear-cutting method, in which all trees in an area are cut, leaving only stumps. Clear-cutting is generally the most cost-efficient method in the short term, but it has the greatest impacts

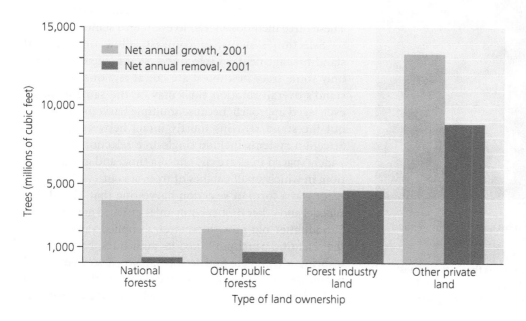

**FIGURE 12.8** Forest Service data indicate that in the United States, trees (measured in cubic feet of wood biomass) are growing at a faster rate than they are being removed. The exception is on land privately owned by the timber industry, where extraction is narrowly outpacing growth. Go to **GRAPHit!** at www. aw-bc.com/withgott or on the student CD-ROM. Data are for 2001, from United States Forest Service, 2001.

**FIGURE 12.9** Even-aged management is practiced on tree plantations where all trees are of equal age, as seen in the stand in the foreground that is regrowing after clear-cutting. In uneven-aged management, harvests are designed so as to maintain a mix of tree ages, as seen in the more mature forest in the background. The increased structural diversity of uneven-aged stands provides superior habitat for most wild species and makes these stands more akin to ecologically functional forests.

on forest ecosystems (Figure 12.10). In the best-case scenario, clear-cutting may mimic natural disturbance events such as fires, tornadoes, or windstorms that knock down trees across large areas. In the worst-case scenario, entire communities of organisms are destroyed or displaced, soil erodes, and the penetration of sunlight to ground level changes microclimatic conditions such that new types of plants replace those that dominated the native forest. Essentially, an artificially driven process of succession (▸ p. 163) is set in motion, in which the resulting

**FIGURE 12.10** Clear-cutting is the most cost-efficient method for timber companies, but it can have severe ecological consequences, including soil erosion and species turnover. Although certain species do use clear-cuts as they regrow, most people find these areas aesthetically unappealing, and public reaction to clear-cutting has driven changes in forestry methods.

climax community may turn out to be quite different from the original climax community.

Widespread clear-cutting occurred across North America at a time when public awareness of environmental problems was blossoming. The combination produced public outrage toward the timber industry and public forest managers. Eventually the industry integrated other harvesting methods (Figure 12.11). Clear-cutting (Figure 12.11a) is still widely practiced, but other methods involve cutting some trees and leaving some standing. In the *seed-tree* approach (Figure 12.11b), small numbers of mature and vigorous seed-producing trees are left standing so that they can reseed the logged area. In the *shelterwood* approach (also Figure 12.11b), small numbers of mature trees are left in place to provide shelter for seedlings as they grow. These three methods all lead to even-aged stands of trees.

Selection systems, in contrast, allow uneven-aged stand management. In selection systems (Figure 12.11c), only some trees in a forest are cut at any one time. The stand's overall rotation time may be the same as in an even-aged approach, because multiple harvests are made, but the stand remains mostly intact between harvests. Selection systems include single-tree selection, in which widely spaced trees are cut one at a time, and group selection, in which small patches of trees are cut.

It was a form of selection harvesting that MacMillan Bloedel and other timber companies pursued at Clayoquot Sound, after old-growth advocates applied pressure and the scientific panel published its guidelines. Not wanting to bring a complete end to logging when so many local people depended on the industry for work, these activists and scientists instead promoted what they considered a

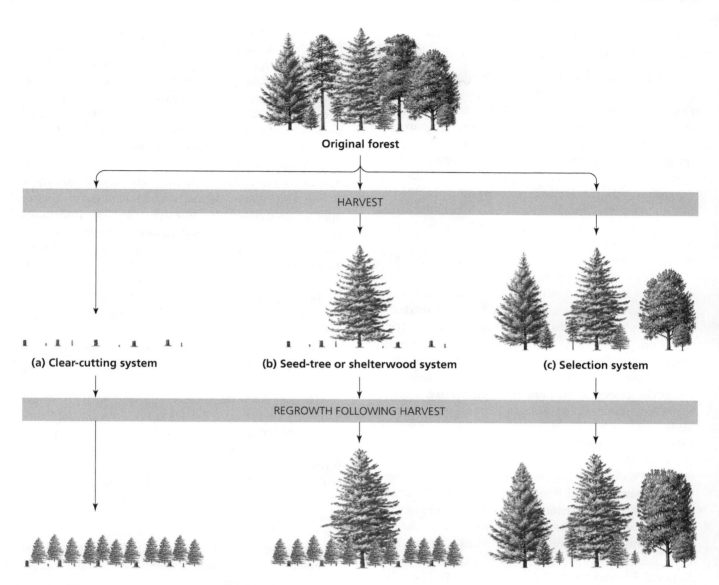

**Original forest**

HARVEST

**(a) Clear-cutting system**

**(b) Seed-tree or shelterwood system**

**(c) Selection system**

REGROWTH FOLLOWING HARVEST

**FIGURE 12.11** Foresters and timber companies have devised various methods of harvesting timber from forests. In clear-cutting (**a**), all trees in an area are cut, extracting a great deal of timber inexpensively but leaving a vastly altered landscape. In seed-tree systems and shelterwood systems (**b**), small numbers of large trees are left in clearcuts, to help re-seed the area or provide shelter for growing seedlings. In selection systems (**c**), a minority of trees is removed at any one time, while most are left standing. These latter methods involve less environmental impact than clear-cutting, but all methods can cause significant changes to the structure and function of natural forest communities.

more environmentally friendly method of timber removal. However, selection systems are by no means ecologically harmless. Moving trucks and machinery over an extensive network of roads and trails to access individual trees compacts the soil and disturbs much of the forest floor. Selection methods are also unpopular with timber companies because they are expensive, and loggers dislike them because they are more dangerous than clear-cutting.

All methods of logging result in habitat disturbance, which invariably affects the plants and animals inhabiting an area. All methods change forest structure and composition. Most methods increase soil erosion, leading to siltation of waterways, which can degrade habitat and affect drinking water quality. Most methods also speed runoff, sometimes causing flooding. In extreme cases, as when steep hillsides are clear-cut, landslides can result.

## Public forests may be managed for recreation and ecosystems

In recent decades, increased awareness of these problems has prompted many citizens to protest the way public forests are managed in the United States and Canada. These citizens have urged that the national, state, and provincial forests be managed for recreation, wildlife, and ecosystem integrity, rather than for timber. They want forests managed as ecologically functional entities, not as cropland for trees.

Critics of the U.S. Forest Service have also protested the fact that taxpayers' money is used to subsidize the extraction of publicly held resources by private corporations. Scientists who have analyzed government subsidies have concluded that the U.S. Forest Service loses at least $100 million of taxpayers' money each year by selling timber well below its costs for marketing and administering the harvest and for building access roads. Subsidies also inflate harvest levels beyond what would occur in a free market.

In one sense, the U.S. Forest Service has long had a policy of attending to interests beside timber production. For the past half century, forest management has nominally been guided by the policy of **multiple use,** meaning that the national forests were to be managed for recreation, wildlife habitat, mineral extraction, and various other uses. In reality, however, timber production was most often the primary use.

In 1976 the U.S. Congress passed the **National Forest Management Act,** which mandated that plans for renewable resource management be drawn up for every national forest. These plans were to be explicitly based on the concepts of multiple use and sustained yield, and they were to be subject to broad public participation under the National Environmental Policy Act (▸ p. 68). Guidelines specified that these plans:

▸ Consider both economic and environmental factors.
▸ Provide for diversity of plant and animal communities and preserve the regional diversity of tree species.
▸ Ensure research and monitoring of management practices.
▸ Permit increases in harvest levels only if sustainable.
▸ Ensure that timber is harvested only where soils and wetlands will not be irreversibly damaged, lands can be restocked quickly, and economic return alone does not guide the choice of harvest method.
▸ Ensure that logging is conducted only where impacts have been assessed; cuts are shaped to the terrain; maximum size limits are established; and "cuts are carried out in a manner consistent with the protection of soil, watershed, fish, wildlife, recreation, and aesthetic resources, and the regeneration of the timber resource."

Over the years following passage of the National Forest Management Act, the U.S. Forest Service began responding to the increasing public demand that national forests be managed for uses other than timber. It developed new programs to manage wildlife, nongame animals, and endangered species. It pushed for ecosystem-based management and even ran extensive programs of ecological restoration, attempting to recover whole plant and animal communities that had been lost or degraded. Moreover, timber harvesting methods were brought more in line with ecosystem-based management goals. A set of approaches dubbed **new forestry** called for timber cuts that came closer to mimicking natural disturbances. For instance, "sloppy clear-cuts" that leave a variety of trees standing were intended to mimic the changes a forest might experience if hit by a severe windstorm.

In late 2004, however, the George W. Bush administration issued new regulations that bucked these trends. These new rules freed local forest managers from requirements imposed by the National Forest Management Act, granting them more flexibility in managing forests, but loosening environmental protections and restricting public oversight.

Then in 2005, the Bush administration repealed the Clinton administration's roadless rule, by which 23.7 million ha (58.5 million acres)—31% of national forest land and 2% of total U.S. land—were in 2001 put off limits to further road construction or maintenance. Although the roadless rule had been supported by a record 4.2 million public comments, the Bush administration overturned it and required state governors to petition the federal government if they want to keep areas in their states roadless. The states of California, Oregon, and New Mexico responded by suing the federal government, asking that the roadless rule be reinstated.

## Fire policy has also stirred controversy

Some ecosystem management efforts, ironically, run counter to the U.S. Forest Service's best-known symbol, Smokey the Bear. The cartoon bear wearing a ranger's hat who advises us to fight forest fires is widely recognized, but unfortunately Smokey's message is badly outdated, and many scientists assert that it has done great harm to American forests.

For over a century, the Forest Service and other land management agencies suppressed fire whenever and wherever it broke out. Yet ecological research now clearly shows that many ecosystems depend on fire. Certain plants have seeds that germinate only in response to fire, and researchers studying tree rings have documented that many ecosystems historically experienced frequent fire. Burn marks in a tree's rings reveal past fires, giving scientists

## Managing Forests

The U.S. Forest Service attempts to manage the national forests for multiple uses, including timber production, wildlife habitat, and recreation. **How well is the agency doing in balancing its multiple goals? What changes, if any, do you think are needed in the way the national forests are managed?**

### Restoring America's National Forests

The U.S. Forest Service completed the 20th century with a celebrated and criticized record. Its challenge is that laws direct the Forest Service to provide society with often conflicting values from the national forests, including wood, water, wildlife, fish, forage, and recreation.

The Forest Service also must "preserve and protect" forests as required in the Organic Act of 1897. Therefore, conservation guides management because it integrates the need to use and protect national forests.

For much of the last century, the Forest Service protected forests by putting out fires, without realizing that frequent, gentle fires kept forests thinned and healthy. Then they stopped timber harvests and active management on many national forests, so forests grew even thicker and less healthy.

Today's forests are 10 to 20 times denser than historic forests. Consequently, between the years 2000 and 2003, unnatural wildfires destroyed 9.7 million ha (24 million acres) of forest, many human lives, and thousands of homes. Insects devoured millions more hectares of unhealthy forest.

Restoration should guide the Forest Service in the 21st century. Restoration means using active management to restore ecologically and economically sustainable forests that represent natural historic landscapes. Restored forests provide diverse public values, from scenery and recreation to lumber and safety.

However, we don't have the billions of tax dollars needed to manage our forests. That means we must form a partnership with the private sector to make restoration economically feasible.

We have a choice. Adopt a "hands-off" policy and let the harsh indifference of unnatural wildfires and mindless insects determine the fate of national forests, or shape their destiny through restoration forestry.

**Thomas M. Bonnicksen** is a historian of North American forests and originator of the concept of restoration forestry. He is professor emeritus of forest science at Texas A&M University, visiting professor at the University of California at Davis, and the author of *America's Ancient Forests* (John Wiley, 2000.)

### Protect Our Forests from Logging

Most Americans are shocked when they learn that over the past century the Forest Service's management has largely emphasized logging, road building, and other forms of resource extraction.

Unfortunately, because the Forest Service's budgets are still tied to logging and resource extraction—not to forest protection and restoration—the public's clean water, wildlife habitat, wildlands, and recreational opportunities continue to be sacrificed. Just consider these facts:

▶ There are 716,500 km (445,000 mi) of roads on national forests—enough to circle Earth 18 times.
▶ An estimated 50% of riparian areas on national forests require restoration because of impacts from logging, road building, grazing, mining, and offroad vehicles.
▶ Taxpayers spend over $1 billion annually subsidizing private logging companies to cut down national forests—all to supply less than 2% of our nation's wood products.
▶ Although less than 5% of America's ancient, old-growth forests remain, these heritage forests continue to be logged, with over 160 km² (100 mi²) of the public's ancient forests currently on the chopping block in the Northwest alone.

Fully protecting and restoring our national forests will take a heroic effort. The first step in the restoration process is to prevent further ecological degradation by protecting our national forests from logging and other forms of resource extraction. Next, we need to redirect taxpayer subsidies toward ecologically based restoration projects—such as road removal and watershed restoration—with the goal of restoring natural processes and reestablishing fully functioning ecosystems.

Only once this happens will we see the Forest Service's management of national forests in step with the desires of an American public that wants to see our forests protected and restored.

**Matthew Koehler** is executive director of the Native Forest Network and a co-founder of the National Forest Protection Alliance, a national network of 130 grassroots forest protection organizations working to protect and restore national forests.

Explore this issue further by accessing **Viewpoints** at www.aw-bc.com/withgott.

**FIGURE 12.12** Forest fires are natural phenomena to which many plants are well adapted and which maintain many ecosystems. The suppression of fires by humans over the past century has led to a buildup of leaf litter and young trees, which serve as fuel to increase the severity of fires when they do occur. As a result, catastrophic forest fires (such as this one in Yellowstone National Park in 1988) have become more common in recent years. These unnaturally severe fires can do great damage to ecosystems and human communities. The best solution, most fire ecologists agree, is to forego suppressing natural fires as much as possible and to institute controlled burning to reduce fuel loads and restore forest ecosystems.

an accurate history of fire events extending back hundreds or even thousands of years. Researchers have found that North America's grasslands and open pine woodlands burned regularly. Ecosystems dependent on fire are adversely affected by its suppression; pine woodlands become cluttered with hardwood understory that ordinarily would be cleared away by fire, for instance, and animal diversity and abundance decline in such cluttered habitats.

In the long term, fire suppression can lead to catastrophic fires that truly do damage forests, destroy human property, and threaten human lives. Fire suppression allows limbs, logs, sticks, and leaf litter to accumulate on the forest floor over the years, effectively producing kindling for a catastrophic fire. Such fuel buildup helped cause the 1988 fires in Yellowstone National Park (Figure 12.12), the 2003 fires in southern California, the 2003 fires in British Columbia, and thousands of other fires across the continent. Fire suppression and fuel buildup have made catastrophic fires significantly greater problems than they were in the past. At the same time, increasing residential development on the edges of forested land is placing more homes in fire-prone situations.

To reduce fuel load and improve the health and safety of forests, the Forest Service and other land management agencies have in recent years been burning areas of forest under carefully controlled conditions. These **prescribed burns** or **controlled burns** have worked effectively, but have been implemented on only a relatively small amount of land. And every once in a while, a prescribed burn may

get out of control, as happened in 2000 when homes and government labs were destroyed at Los Alamos, New Mexico. All too often, these worthy efforts have been impeded by public misunderstanding and by interference from politicians who have not taken time to understand the science behind the approach.

In the wake of the 2003 California fires, the U.S. Congress, intending to make forests less fire-prone, passed the Bush administration's Healthy Forests Restoration Act. Although this legislation encourages some prescribed burning, it primarily promotes the physical removal of small trees, underbrush, and dead trees by timber companies. The removal of dead trees, or snags, following a natural disturbance is called **salvage logging.** From an economic standpoint, salvage logging may seem to make good sense. However, ecologically, snags have immense value; the insects that decay them provide food for wildlife, and many birds, mammals, and reptiles depend on holes in snags for nesting and roosting sites. Conducting timber removal operations on recently burned land can also cause severe erosion and soil damage. Many scientists and environmental advocates have criticized the Healthy Forests Restoration Act, saying it increases commercial logging in national forests while doing little to reduce catastrophic fires near populated areas. By streamlining procedures for timber removal on public lands, the law also decreases oversight and public participation in enforcing environmental regulations, critics contend.

## How to Handle Fire?

A century of fire suppression has left millions of hectares of forested lands in North America in danger of catastrophic wildfires. Yet we will probably never have adequate resources to conduct careful prescribed burning over all these lands. Can you suggest any possible solutions that might help protect people's homes near forests while improving the ecological condition of some forested lands?

## Sustainable forestry is gaining ground

Any company can claim that its timber harvesting practices are sustainable, but how is the purchaser of wood products to know whether they really are? In the last several years, a consumer movement has grown that is making informed consumer choice possible. Several organizations now examine the practices of timber companies and offer **sustainable forestry certification** to products produced using methods they consider sustainable (Figure 12.13).

Organizations such as the International Organization for Standardization (ISO), the Sustainable Forestry Initiative (SFI) program, and the Forest Stewardship Council (FSC) have varying standards for certification. Consumers can look for the logos of these organizations on forest products they purchase. The FSC is widely perceived to have the strictest certification standards. In 2001, Iisaak, the Native-run timber company at Clayoquot Sound, became the first tree farm license holder in British Columbia to receive FSC certification.

Consumer demand for sustainable wood has been great enough that several major retail businesses have announced that they will sell only sustainable wood. Home Depot in 2002 began selling only FSC-certified lumber, and the company says it is doing its best to keep prices as low as possible. B&Q, a major British retailer similar to Home Depot, also switched to sustainable wood, and the company's head said he was "taken aback" by the favorable public response. The decisions of such retailers are influencing the logging practices of many timber companies. In British Columbia, 70% of the province's annual harvest now is certified or meets ISO requirements.

Sustainable forestry is more costly for the timber industry, but if certification standards can be kept adequately strong, then consumer choice in the marketplace can be a powerful driver for good forestry practices for the future.

**FIGURE 12.13** A Brazilian woodcutter taking inventory marks timber harvested from a forest certified for sustainable management in Amazonian Brazil. A consumer movement centered on independent certification of sustainable wood products is allowing consumer choice to promote sustainable forestry practices.

# Agricultural Land Use

Having replaced many forests, agriculture now covers more of the planet's surface than does forest. Thirty-eight percent of Earth's terrestrial surface is devoted to agriculture—more than the area of North America and Africa combined. Of this land, 26% supports pasture, and 12% consists of crops and arable land. Agriculture is the most widespread type of human land use, and causes tremendous impacts on land and ecosystems. Although agricultural methods such as organic farming and no-till farming can be sustainable, the majority of the world's cropland hosts intensive traditional agriculture and monocultural industrial agriculture, involving heavy use of fertilizers, pesticides, and irrigation, and often producing soil erosion, salinization, and desertification (Chapters 9 and 10).

In theory, the marketplace should discourage people from farming with intensive methods that degrade land they own if such practices are not profitable. But agriculture in many countries is supported by massive subsidies. Governments of 30 developed nations handed out $311 billion in farm subsidies in 2001, averaging $12,000 per farmer. Roughly one-fifth of the income of the average U.S. or Canadian farmer comes from subsidies. Proponents of such subsidies stress that the vagaries of weather make profits and losses from farming unpredictable from year to year. To persist in the long term,

**FIGURE 12.14** Cropland agriculture exerts dramatic effects over a large portion of Earth's landscape. The huge green circles visible during any airplane trip over the Great Plains are created by center-pivot irrigation. Immense sprinklers pivot around a central point, watering a circular area. Shown are fields in eastern Oregon.

these proponents say, an agricultural system needs some way to compensate farmers for bad years. Opponents of subsidies argue that farmers can buy insurance to protect themselves against crop failures and that subsidizing environmentally destructive agricultural practices is unsustainable (Figure 12.14).

## Wetlands have been drained for farming

Many of today's crops grow on the sites of former wetlands (▶ pp. 435–436)—swamps, marshes, bogs, and river floodplains—that were drained and filled in (Figure 12.15). Throughout recent history, governments have encouraged laborious efforts to drain wetlands. To promote settlement and farming, the United States passed a series of laws known as the Swamp Lands Acts in 1849, 1850, and 1860, which encouraged draining wetlands for agriculture. The government transferred over 24 million ha (60 million acres) of wetlands to state ownership (and eventually to private hands) to stimulate drainage, conversion, and flood control.

In the Mississippi River valley, the Midwest, and a handful of states from Florida to Oregon, these transfers eradicated malaria (because mosquito vectors breed in wetlands) and created over 10 million ha (25 million acres) of new farmland. A U.S. Department of Agriculture (USDA) program in 1940 provided monetary aid and technical assistance to farmers draining wetlands on their property, resulting in the conversion of almost 23 million ha (57 million acres).

Today, less than half the original wetlands in the lower 48 U.S. states and southern Canada remain. However, many people now have a new view of wetlands. Rather than viewing them as worthless swamps, science has made clear that they are valuable ecosystems. This scientific knowledge, along with a preservation ethic, has induced policymakers to develop regulations to safeguard remaining wetlands. However, because of loopholes, differing state laws, development pressures—and even debate over the legal definition of wetlands—many of these valuable ecosystems are still being lost.

Financial incentives are also being used as a tool to influence agricultural land use in the United States. The Conservation Reserve Program begun in 1985 was a landmark initiative that provided farmers with a different kind of subsidy—it paid them to take highly erodible lands out of production and instead encouraged them to make the areas more habitable for wildlife. Now, under the Wetland Reserve Program, the U.S. government is offering subsidies to landowners who refrain from developing wetland areas.

----

**Weighing the Issues:**
## Subsidies, Soil, and Wetlands

Do you think that subsidy programs such as the Conservation Reserve Program and the Wetland Reserve Program are a good use of taxpayers' money? Are financial incentives such as these better tools than government regulation for promoting certain land use goals?

----

**FIGURE 12.15** Most of North America's wetlands have been drained and filled, and the land converted to agricultural use. The northern Great Plains region of Canada and the United States was pockmarked with thousands of "prairie potholes," water-filled depressions that served as nesting sites for most of the continent's waterfowl. Today many of these wetlands have been lost; shown are farmlands encroaching on prairie potholes in North Dakota.

## Livestock graze one-fourth of Earth's land

Cropland agriculture uses less than half the land taken up by livestock grazing, which covers a quarter of the world's land surface. Human use of rangeland, however, does not necessarily exclude its use by wildlife or its continued functioning as a grassland ecosystem. Grazing can be sustainable if done carefully and at low intensity. In the American West, ranching proponents claim that cattle are merely taking the place of the vast herds of bison that once roamed the plains. Indeed, most of the world's grasslands have historically been home to large herds of grass-eating mammals, and grasses have adapted to herbivory. Nonetheless, poorly managed grazing, as we saw in Chapter 9, can have adverse impacts on soil and grassland ecosystems.

Most U.S. rangelands are federally owned and managed by the **Bureau of Land Management (BLM)**. The BLM is the nation's single largest landowner; its 106 million ha (261 million acres) are spread across 12 western states (see Figure 12.7). Ranchers are allowed to graze cattle on BLM lands for inexpensive fees, a practice that many public lands advocates say encourages overgrazing. Thus ranchers and environmentalists have traditionally been at loggerheads. In the past several years, however, ranchers and environmentalists have been finding common ground, teaming up to preserve ranchland against what each of them views in common as a threat—the encroaching housing developments of suburban sprawl

(▶ pp. 378–379). Although developers often pay high prices for ranchland, many ranchers do not want to see the loss of the wide open spaces and the ranching lifestyle that they cherish.

## Land use in the American West might have been better managed

Land uses such as grazing, farming, and timber harvesting need not have strongly adverse impacts. It is not these activities per se that cause environmental problems, but rather the overexploitation of resources beyond what ecosystems can handle. In the American West, a great deal of damage was done to the land by poor farming practices, overgrazing, and attempts to farm arid lands that were more suitable for grazing or preservation.

Most land to the west of the 100th meridian, the longitudinal line slicing through the Great Plains from Manitoba south through Texas, receives less than 50 cm (20 in.) of rain per year, making it too arid for unirrigated agriculture. One man in U.S. history recognized this fact and attempted to reorient policy so the West could be settled in a way that allowed farmers to succeed. John Wesley Powell, an extraordinary individual who explored the raging Colorado River by boat despite having lost an arm in the Civil War, undertook vast surveys of the Western lands for the U.S. government in the late 19th century (Figure 12.16). A pioneer in calling for government

**FIGURE 12.16** John Wesley Powell, Civil War hero and 19th-century Western explorer, tried to shift U.S. land use policy to take account of the aridity of Western lands.

agencies to base their policies on science, Powell maintained that lands beyond the 100th meridian were too dry to support farming on the 65-ha (160-acre) plots the government parceled out through the Homestead Act (▸ p. 66). Plots in the West, he said, would have to be 16 times as large and would require irrigation. Moreover, to prevent individuals or corporations from monopolizing scarce water resources, he urged the government to organize farmers into cooperative irrigation districts, with each district encompassing a watershed.

Powell's ideas, based on science and close study of the land, were too revolutionary for the entrenched political interests and prevailing misconceptions of his time, which held that the West was a utopia for frontier settlement. The ideas in Powell's 1878 *Report on the Lands of the Arid Region of the United States* were, for the most part, never implemented. Instead, existing land use policies contributed to failures such as the Dust Bowl of the 1930s (▸ p. 260).

For agriculture and forestry alike, debates continue today over how best to use land and manage resources. Resource extraction from public lands in the United States and Canada has helped propel the economies of these countries. But as resources dwindle, as forests and soils are degraded, and as the landscape fills with more people, the arguments for conservation of resources—for their sustainable use—have grown stronger. Also growing stronger is the argument for preservation of land—setting aside tracts of relatively undisturbed land intended to remain forever undeveloped.

# Parks and Reserves

Preservation has been part of the American psyche ever since John Muir rallied support for saving scenic lands in the Sierras (▸ p. 34). For ethical reasons as well as pragmatic ecological and economic ones, U.S. citizens and many other people worldwide have chosen to set aside tracts of land in perpetuity to be preserved and protected from development.

## Why have we created parks and reserves?

What specifically in this mix of ethics, ecology, and economics has driven so many cultures to refrain voluntarily from exploiting land for material resources? The historian Alfred Runte has cited four traditional reasons that parks and protected areas have been established:

1. Enormous, beautiful, or unusual features such as the Grand Canyon, Mount Rainier, or Yosemite Valley inspire people to protect them—an impulse termed *monumentalism* (Figure 12.17).
2. Protected areas offer recreational value to tourists, hikers, fishers, hunters, and others.
3. Protected areas offer utilitarian benefits. For example, undeveloped watersheds provide cities with clean drinking water and a buffer against floods.
4. Parks make use of sites lacking economically valuable material resources; land that holds little monetary value is easy to set aside because no one wants to buy it.

To these four traditional reasons, a fifth has been added in recent years: the preservation of biodiversity. As we saw in Chapter 11, human impact alters habitats and has led to countless population declines and species extinctions. A park or reserve is widely viewed as a kind of Noah's Ark, an island of habitat that can, scientists hope, maintain species that might otherwise disappear.

## Federal parks and reserves began in the United States

The striking scenery of the American West impelled the U.S. government to create the world's first **national parks,** publicly held lands protected from resource extraction and development but open to nature appreciation and various forms of recreation. In 1872, Yellowstone National Park was established as "a public park or pleasuring-ground for the benefit and enjoyment of the people." Yosemite, General Grant, Sequoia, and Mount Rainier National Parks followed after 1890. The Antiquities Act of 1906 gave the president authority to declare selected

**FIGURE 12.17** The awe-inspiring beauty of some regions of the western United States was one reason for the establishment of national parks. Images of scenic vistas such as this one of Bridal Veil Falls in Yosemite National Park, portrayed by the landscape painter Albert Bierstadt, have inspired millions of people from North America and abroad to visit these parks.

public lands as national monuments, which can be an interim step to national park status. Presidents from Theodore Roosevelt to Bill Clinton have used this authority to expand the nation's system of protected lands.

The National Park Service (NPS) was created in 1916 to administer the growing system of parks and monuments, which today numbers 388 sites totaling 32 million ha (79 million acres) and includes national historic sites, national recreation areas, national wild and scenic rivers, and other types of areas (see Figure 12.7). This most widely used park system in the world received 277 million reported recreation visits in 2004—about as many visits as there are U.S. residents. The high visitation rates signal the success of the park system, but they also create overcrowded conditions at some parks. Many observers have therefore suggested that the parks' popularity indicates a pressing need to expand the system.

Many other nations now have national park systems. Canada's system covers 26.5 million ha (65.5 million acres) and receives 16 million visits yearly. At Clayoquot Sound, Pacific Rim National Park Reserve is a protected area designated for future national park status. The Clayoquot Sound region also encompasses several provincial parks. Provincial parks in Canada cover more area than national parks. In the United States, state parks are numerous and tend to be more oriented toward recreation than are national parks.

Another type of federal protected area in the United States is the **national wildlife refuge.** The system of national wildlife refuges, begun in 1903 by President Theodore Roosevelt, now totals 37 million ha (91 million acres) spread over 541 sites (see Figure 12.7). The U.S. Fish and Wildlife Service administers the refuges with management ranging "from preservation to active manipulation of habitats and populations." Indeed, these refuges not only serve as havens for wildlife, but also in many cases encourage hunting, fishing, wildlife observation, photography, environmental education, and other public uses. Some wildlife advocates find it ironic that hunting is allowed at many refuges, but hunters have long been in the forefront of the conservation movement and have traditionally supplied the bulk of funding for land acquisition and habitat management for the refuges. Many refuges are managed for waterfowl, but the FWS increasingly considers nongame species as well as game species. The FWS manages at the habitat and ecosystem levels, engaging in ecological restoration of marshes and grasslands, for example.

## Wilderness areas have been established on various federal lands

In response to the public's desire for undeveloped areas of land, in 1964 the U.S. Congress passed the Wilderness Act, which allowed areas of existing federal lands to be designated as **wilderness areas.** These areas are off-limits to development of any kind, but they are open to public recreation such as hiking, nature study, and other activities that have minimal impact on the land. Congress declared that wilderness areas were necessary "to assure that an increasing population, accompanied by expanding settlement and growing mechanization, does not occupy and modify all areas within the United States and its possessions, leaving no lands designated for preservation and protection in their natural condition." Wilderness areas have been established within portions of national forests, national parks, national wildlife refuges, and BLM land, and they are overseen by the agencies that

**FIGURE 12.18** Wilderness areas were designated on various federally managed lands in the United States following the 1964 Wilderness Act. These include areas little disturbed by human activities, such as the Selway-Bitterroot Wilderness in Idaho, shown here.

administer those areas (Figure 12.18). Some preexisting extractive land uses, such as grazing and mining, were "grandfathered in," or allowed to continue, within wilderness areas as a political compromise so the act could be passed.

## Not everyone supports land set-asides

The restriction of activities in wilderness areas has helped generate opposition to U.S. land protection policies. Sources of such opposition include the governments of some western states, where large portions of land are federally owned. When those states came into existence, the federal government retained ownership of much of the acreage inside their borders. Idaho, Oregon, and Utah own less than 50% of the land within their borders, and in Nevada 80% of the land is federally owned. Western state governments have traditionally sought to obtain land from the federal government and encourage resource extraction and development on it.

The drive to extract more resources, secure local control of lands, and expand recreational access to public lands is epitomized by the **wise-use movement,** a loose confederation of individuals and groups that coalesced in the 1980s and 1990s in response to the increasing success of environmental advocacy. Wise-use advocates are dedicated to protecting private property rights; opposing government regulation; transferring federal lands to state,

local, or private hands; and promoting more motorized recreation on public lands. Wise-use advocates include farmers, ranchers, trappers, and mineral prospectors at the grassroots level who live off the land, as well as groups representing the large corporations of industries that extract timber, mineral, and fossil fuel resources.

Debate between mainstream environmental groups and wise-use spokespeople has been vitriolic. Each side claims to represent the will of the people and paints the other as the oppressive establishment. Wise-use advocates have played key roles in ongoing debates over national park policy, such as whether recreational activities that disturb wildlife, such as snowmobiles and jet-skis, should be allowed. Under the Bush administration, wilderness protection policies have been weakened, and federal agencies have generally shifted policies and enforcement away from preservation and conservation, and toward recreation and extractive uses.

## Nonfederal entities also protect land

Efforts to set aside land—and the debates over such efforts—at the federal level are paralleled at regional and local levels. Each U.S. state and Canadian province has agencies that manage resources on state or provincial lands, as do many counties and municipalities. As just one example, New York State in the 19th century created Adirondack State Park in a mountainous area whose streams converge to form the headwaters of the Hudson River, which flows south past Albany to New York City. Seeing the need for river water to power industries, keep canals filled, and provide drinking water, the state set the land aside, a farsighted decision that has paid dividends through the years.

Private nonprofit groups also preserve land. **Land trusts** are local or regional organizations that preserve lands valued by their members. In most cases, land trusts purchase land outright with the aim of preserving it in its natural condition. The Nature Conservancy can be considered the world's largest land trust, but smaller ones are springing up throughout North America. By one estimate, there are 900 local and regional land trusts in the United States that together own 177,000 ha (437,000 acres) and have helped preserve an additional 930,000 ha (2.3 million acres), including well-known scenic areas such as Big Sur on the California coast, Jackson Hole in Wyoming, and Maine's Mount Desert Island.

## Parks and reserves are increasing internationally

Many nations have established national park systems and are benefiting from ecotourism as a result—from Costa Rica (Chapter 5) to Ecuador to Thailand to Tanzania. The total worldwide area in protected parks and reserves increased more than fourfold from 1970 to 2000, and in 2003 the world's 38,536 protected areas covered 1.3 billion ha (3.2 billion acres), or 9.6% of the planet's land area. However, parks in developing countries do not always receive the funding they need to manage resources, provide for recreation, and protect wildlife from poaching and timber from logging. Thus many of the world's protected areas are merely *paper parks*—protected on paper but not in reality.

Some types of protected areas fall under national sovereignty but are designated or partly managed internationally by the United Nations. *World heritage sites* are an example; currently over 560 sites across 125 countries are listed for their cultural value and nearly 150 for their natural value. One such site is Australia's Kakadu National Park, discussed in Chapter 2. Another is the mountain gorilla reserve shared by three African countries. The gorilla reserve, which integrates national parklands of Rwanda, Uganda, and the Democratic Republic of Congo, is also an example of a *transboundary park*, an area of protected land overlapping national borders. Transboundary parks can be quite large, and they account for 10% of protected areas worldwide, involving 113 countries. A North American example is Waterton-Glacier National Parks on the

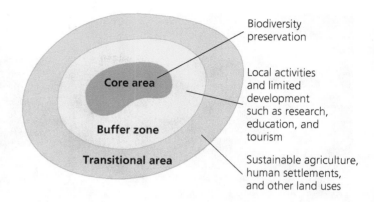

**FIGURE 12.19** Biosphere reserves are international efforts that couple preservation with sustainable development to benefit local residents. Each reserve includes a core area that preserves biodiversity, a buffer zone that allows limited development, and a transition zone that permits various uses.

Canadian–U.S. border. Some transboundary reserves function as *peace parks,* helping ease tensions by acting as buffers between nations that have quarreled over boundary disputes. This is the case with Peru and Ecuador as well as Costa Rica and Panama, and many people hope that peace parks can also help resolve conflicts between Israel and its neighbors.

**Biosphere reserves** are tracts of land with exceptional biodiversity that couple preservation with sustainable development to benefit local people. They are designated by UNESCO (the United Nations Educational, Scientific, and Cultural Organization) following application by local stakeholders. Each biosphere reserve consists of (1) a core area that preserves biodiversity, (2) a buffer zone that allows local activities and limited development that do not hinder the core area's function, and (3) an outer transition zone in which agriculture, human settlement, and other land uses can be pursued in a sustainable way (Figure 12.19).

Clayoquot Sound was designated as Canada's 12th biosphere reserve in 2000, in an attempt to help build cooperation among environmentalists, timber companies, Native peoples, and local residents and businesses. The core area consists of provincial parks and Pacific Rim National Park Reserve. Environmentalists hoped the designation would help promote stronger land preservation efforts. Local residents supported it because outside money was being offered for local development efforts. The timber industry did not stand in the way once it was clear that harvesting operations would not be affected. The designation has brought Clayoquot Sound more international attention, but it has not created new protected areas and has not altered land use policies.

**(a) Mount Hood National Forest, Oregon**

**(b) Wood thrush**

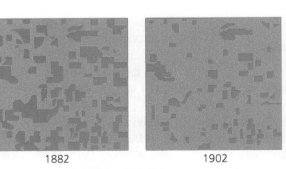

| 1831 | 1882 | 1902 | 1950 |

**(c) Fragmentation of wooded area (green) in Cadiz Township, Wisconsin**

**FIGURE 12.20** As human populations have grown and human impacts have increased, most large expanses of natural habitat have become fragmented into smaller disconnected areas. Forest fragmentation from timber harvesting, for example, is evident on the Mount Hood National Forest, Oregon (**a**). Fragmentation has significant impacts on forest-dwelling species such as the wood thrush, *Hylocichla mustelina* (**b**), a migrant songbird of eastern North America. In forest fragments, wood thrush nests are parasitized by cowbirds that thrive in open country and edge habitats. Forest fragmentation has been extreme in the eastern and midwestern United States; shown in (**c**) are historical changes in forested area in Cadiz Township, Wisconsin, between 1831 and 1950. *Source for (c):* Curtis, J. T. 1956. The modification of mid-latitude grasslands and forests by man. In Thomas, W. L. Jr., ed., *Man's role in changing the face of the earth*. Chicago: Univ. of Chicago Press.

## The design of parks and reserves has consequences for biodiversity

Often it is not outright destruction of habitat that threatens species, but rather the fragmentation of habitat (▶ pp. 330–331). Expanding agriculture, spreading cities, highways, logging, and many other impacts have chopped up large contiguous expanses of habitat into small disconnected ones (Figure 12.20a and 12.20c). When this happens, many species suffer. Bears, mountain lions, and other animals that need large ranges in which to roam may disappear. Bird species that thrive in the interior of forests may fail to reproduce when forced near the edge of a fragment (Figure 12.20b). Their nests often are attacked by predators and parasites that favor open habitats surrounding the fragment or that travel along habitat edges. Avian ecologists judge forest fragmentation to be a main reason why populations of many songbirds of eastern North America are declining.

Because habitat fragmentation is such a central issue in biodiversity conservation, and because there are limits on how much land can be set aside, conservation biologists have argued heatedly about whether it is better to make reserves large in size and few in number, or many in number but small in size. Nicknamed the **SLOSS dilemma,** for "single large or several small," this debate is ongoing and complex, but it seems clear that large species that roam great distances, such as the Siberian tiger (Chapter 11), benefit more from the "single large" approach to reserve design. In contrast, creatures such as insects that live as larvae in small areas may do just fine in a number of small isolated reserves, if they can disperse as adults by flying from one reserve to another.

A related issue is whether **corridors** of protected land are important for allowing animals to travel between islands of protected habitat. In theory, connections between fragments provide animals access to more habitat and help enable gene flow to maintain populations in the long term. Many land management agencies and environmental groups try, when possible, to join new reserves to existing reserves for these reasons. It is clear that we will need to think on the landscape level if we are to preserve a great deal of our natural heritage.

# Conclusion

Managing natural resources is necessary for resources such as timber, which can be either responsibly and sustainably managed or carelessly exploited and overharvested. The United States, Canada, and other nations have established various federal and regional agencies to oversee and manage publicly held land and the natural resources that are extracted from public land.

Forest management in North America reflects trends in land and resource management in general. Early emphasis on resource extraction evolved into policies on sustained yield and multiple use, a shift that occurred as land and resource availability declined and as the public became more aware of environmental degradation. Public forests today are managed not only for timber production, but also for recreation, wildlife habitat, and ecosystem integrity.

Meanwhile, public support for preservation of natural lands has resulted in parks, wilderness areas, and other reserves, both in North America and abroad. These trends are positive ones, because the preservation and conservation of land and resources is essential if we wish our society to be sustainable and to thrive in the future.

## REVIEWING OBJECTIVES

**You should now be able to:**

**Identify the principles, goals, and approaches of resource management**

▶ Resource management enables us to sustain natural resources that are renewable if we are careful not to deplete them. (pp. 344–345)

▶ Resource managers have increasingly focused not only on extraction, but also on sustaining the ecological systems that make resources available. (pp. 344–346)

▶ Resource managers have long managed for maximum sustainable yield and are beginning to implement ecosystem-based management and adaptive management. (pp. 345–346)

**Summarize the ecological roles and economic contributions of forests, and outline the history and scale of forest loss**

▶ Forests provide us economically important timber, but also support biodiversity and contribute ecosystem services. (pp. 347–349)

▶ Developed nations deforested much of their land as settlement, farming, and industrialization proceeded. To-

day deforestation is taking place most rapidly in developing nations. (pp. 350–354)

**Explain the fundamentals of forest management, and describe the major methods of harvesting timber**

▶ The U.S. national forests were established to conserve timber for the nation and allow for its sustainable extraction. (p. 354)

▶ Harvesting methods include clear-cutting and other even-aged techniques, as well as selection strategies that maintain uneven-aged stands that more closely resemble natural forest. (pp. 355–357)

▶ Foresters have responded to public demand by beginning to manage for recreation, wildlife habitat, and ecosystem integrity, as well as timber production. (p. 358)

▶ Fire policy has been politically controversial, but scientists agree that we need to take steps to reverse the impacts of a century of fire suppression. (pp. 358, 360)

▶ Certification of sustainable forest products is allowing consumer choice in the marketplace to influence forestry techniques. (p. 361)

**Analyze the scale and impacts of agricultural land use**

▶ Agriculture has contributed greatly to deforestation, and has had enormous impacts on landscapes and ecosystems worldwide. (pp. 361–364)

**Identify major federal land management agencies and the lands they manage**

▶ The U.S. Forest Service, National Park Service, Fish and Wildlife Service, and Bureau of Land Management manage U.S. national forests, national parks, national wildlife refuges, and BLM land. (pp. 354, 364–366)

**Recognize types of parks and reserves, and evaluate issues involved in their design**

▶ Public demand for preservation and recreation has led to the creation of parks, reserves, and wilderness areas in North America and across the world. (pp. 364, 367)

▶ Biosphere reserves are one of several types of internationally managed protected lands. (p. 367)

▶ Because habitat fragmentation threatens wildlife, and landscape patterns matter, conservation biologists are working on how best to design parks and reserves. (pp. 368–369)

## TESTING YOUR COMPREHENSION

1. How do minerals differ from timber when it comes to resource management?
2. Compare and contrast maximum sustainable yield, adaptive management, and ecosystem management. Why may pursuing maximum sustainable yield sometimes conflict with what is ecologically desirable?
3. Name several major causes of deforestation. Where is deforestation most severe today?
4. Describe the major methods of timber harvesting.
5. What are some ecological effects of logging? What has been the U.S. Forest Service's response to public concern over the ecological effects of logging?
6. Are forest fires a bad thing? Explain your answer.

7. Approximately what percentage of Earth's land is used for agriculture? What policies have caused conversion of wetlands for agriculture in the United States?
8. Name five reasons that parks and reserves have been created. Why did the U.S. Congress determine in 1964 that wilderness areas were necessary? How do these areas differ from national parks and national wildlife refuges?
9. Why do some people in the United States oppose federal land protection?
10. Roughly what percentage of Earth's land is protected? What types of protected areas have been established in countries outside the United States?

## SEEKING SOLUTIONS

1. Do you think maximum sustained yield represents an appropriate policy for resource managers to follow?
2. Consider the economic importance of timber and the ecological roles that forests play. How would you manage the public forests of your country, if you were in charge?
3. People in developed countries are fond of warning people in developing countries to stop destroying rainforest. People of developing countries often respond that this is hypocritical, because the developed nations became wealthy by deforesting their land and exploiting its resources in the past. What would you say to the president of a developing nation, such as Brazil, that is seeking to clear much of its forest?
4. Can you think of a land use conflict that has occurred in your region? How was it resolved, or is it unresolved?

5. What are some ecological effects of agricultural subsidies? Propose arguments for and against subsidies from an ecological point of view.
6. Imagine you have just been elected mayor of a town on Clayoquot Sound. A timber company that employs 20% of your town's residents wants to log a hillside above the town, and the provincial government is supportive of the harvest. But owners of ecotourism businesses that run whale-watching excursions and rent kayaks to out-of-town visitors are complaining that the logging would destroy the area's aesthetic appeal and devastate their businesses—and these businesses provide 40% of the tax base for your town. Greenpeace is organizing a demonstration in your town soon, and news reporters are beginning to call your office, asking what you will do. How will you proceed?

## INTERPRETING GRAPHS AND DATA

The invention of the moveable-type printing press by Johannes Gutenberg in 1450 stimulated a demand for paper that has only increased as the world population has grown. The 20th-century invention of the xerographic printing process used in photocopiers and laser printers has accelerated our demand for paper, with most of the raw fiber for paper production coming from wood pulp from forest trees.

1. Approximately how many millions of tons of paper and paperboard were consumed worldwide in 1970? 1980? 1990? 2000?

2. By what percentage did worldwide consumption of paper and paperboard increase from 1970 to 1980? From 1980 to 1990? From 1990 to 2000?

3. If consumption continues to increase at current rates, what do you predict the worldwide consumption of paper and paperboard will be in 2010?

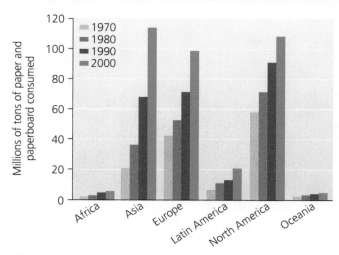

Global consumption of paper and paperboard, 1970–2000. Data from the Food and Agriculture Organization of the United Nations.

## CALCULATING ECOLOGICAL FOOTPRINTS

|  | Population (millions)* | Total paper consumed in 2000 (millions of tons) | Per capita paper consumed in 2000 (pounds) |
|---|---|---|---|
| **Africa** | 840 | 6 | 14 |
| **Asia** | 3,766 |  |  |
| **Europe** | 728 |  |  |
| **Latin America** | 531 |  |  |
| **North America** | 319 |  |  |
| **Oceania** | 32 |  |  |
| **World** | 6,216 |  | ~114 |

*Data source:* Population Reference Bureau.

How much paper do you think you use? You may be surprised to learn that the average North American uses over 300 kg (660 lb) of paper and paperboard per year. Using the estimates of paper and paperboard consumption for each region of the world for the year 2000—as shown in the table in the "Interpreting Graphs and Data" section—calculate the per capita consumption of paper and paperboard for each region of the world using the population data in the table.

1. How much paper would North Americans save each year if we consumed paper at the rate of Europeans?

2. How much paper would be consumed if everyone in the world used as much paper as the average European? As the average North American?

3. Why do you think people in other regions consume less paper, per capita, than North Americans? Name three things you could do to reduce your paper consumption.

## Take It Further

Go to www.aw-bc.com/withgott or the student CD-ROM where you'll find:

▶ Suggested answers to end-of-chapter questions
▶ Quizzes, animations, and flashcards to help you study
▶ *Research Navigator*™ database of credible and reliable sources to assist you with your research projects

▶ **GRAPHIt!** tutorials to help you master how to interpret graphs
▶ **INVESTIGATEIt!** current news articles that link the topics that you study to case studies from your region to around the world

# The Oceans: Natural Systems, Human Use, and Marine Conservation

Portion of the
Florida Keys

## Upon successfully completing this chapter you will be able to:

▶ Identify physical, geographical, chemical, and biological aspects of the marine environment

▶ Describe major types of marine ecosystems

▶ Outline historic and current human uses of marine resources

▶ Assess human impacts on marine environments

▶ Review the current state of ocean fisheries and reasons for their decline

▶ Evaluate marine protected areas and reserves as innovative solutions

Coral reef in the Florida Keys National Marine Sanctuary

# Central Case: Seeding the Seas with Marine Reserves

> "I saw the fisheries spiral down. There's less fish and they're smaller. It's not anything like it was 15 years ago."
> —DON DEMARIA, COMMERCIAL FISHERMAN, FLORIDA KEYS

> "We have no water-quality problems. We have no problems with our reef. The sanctuary was shoved down our throats."
> —BETTYE CHAPLIN, FLORIDA KEYS REALTOR AND CO-FOUNDER OF THE CONCH COALITION

Stretching southwest from the southern tip of Florida for 320 km (200 mi), the string of islands known as the Florida Keys hosts some of North America's richest marine and coastal ecosystems. These islands boast the world's third-largest barrier coral reef, as well as sea grass meadows, coastal mangrove forests, and estuaries. As more people have come to enjoy this remarkable natural environment, tourism in the Keys has grown to 3 million visitors each year.

As tourism was increasing, however, so was human impact. Overfishing, trash and sewage dumping, boat groundings, and careless anchoring were damaging the region's ecosystems while its waters received inputs of pesticides, oil, and heavy metals from roads, residential areas, and farms on the islands. Runoff rich in sediments, fertilizer, and nutrients from leaky septic systems were damaging sea grass beds and causing plankton blooms and eutrophication in Florida Bay, between the Keys and the mainland. All these impacts were harming the coral, living animals whose skeletons give structure to coral reefs, which are home to so much biodiversity. From 1966 to 2000, biologists documented declines in the diversity of living coral and the area covered by coral at two-thirds of the sites they monitored.

These impacts on water quality, sea grass, and coral reefs combined with overfishing to depress fish stocks. Since the 1970s, scientists and fishers alike had reported that the Keys' fish and lobster populations were declining and that the remaining fish and lobsters were smaller. Scientists monitoring the Keys' fish populations concluded that reef fish were severely overexploited by commercial and recreational fishing; a report held that

13 of 16 grouper populations, 7 of 13 snapper populations, and 2 of 5 grunt populations had been overfished.

To protect the area's natural and cultural resources, Congress in 1989 established the Florida Keys National Marine Sanctuary (Figure 16.1). This sanctuary incorporates several previously established protected areas and today safeguards 9,800 km² (3,800 mi²) of marine habitat, including 530 km² (205 mi²) of coral reef, and over 6,000 plant, fish, and invertebrate species. Oil exploration, mining, dumping, and large ships are banned. Fishing is allowed throughout most of the sanctuary, but 24 smaller areas recently zoned as reserves protect 65% of the sanctuary's shallow reef habitat and prohibit all harvesting of natural resources.

Although these 24 reserves amount to only 6% of the sanctuary's area, they have been a magnet for controversy. After the sanctuary was established, a group of Keys residents formed the Conch Coalition to protest the sanctuary and the proposal for no-fishing reserves within it. (A conch is a large marine snail that is a popular food item in the Keys.) The Conch Coalition, which eventually claimed 3,000 supporters, fought the proposal in public meetings and brought a lawsuit. Some Conch Coalition supporters hanged and burned in effigy

the sanctuary superintendent and another sanctuary proponent during a protest. Today, however, as fish populations have begun to increase both inside and outside the reserves, most Keys residents have come to support the sanctuary and its no-fishing reserves.

Sanctuaries and reserves are types of *marine protected areas,* portions of ocean that are protected from some human activities. Whereas national parks and other types of protected areas (▶ pp. 364–369) have existed on land for over a century, the oceanic equivalent is quite new. "Most people think it's common sense on land to have areas where we don't hunt," James Bohnsack, a Florida-based National Marine Fisheries Service researcher, explained. "We're now trying to create natural water areas—to see the buffalo roam, so to speak. It's a major change of thinking that protects the ecosystem and biodiversity, but it also protects the fishery."

# Oceanography

The oceans cover the vast majority of our planet's surface, and understanding them is crucial for understanding how our planet's systems work. The oceans influence global climate, teem with biodiversity, facilitate transportation

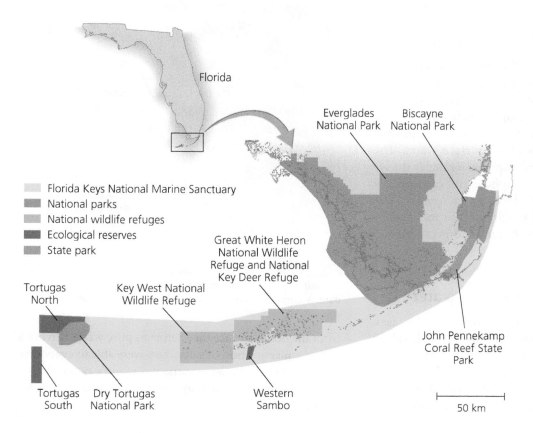

**FIGURE 16.1** The Florida Keys National Marine Sanctuary includes over 9,800 km² (3,800 mi²) of mangrove islands, coral reefs, and shallow waters, from the southeastern tip of Florida westward to the distant keys called the Tortugas. The sanctuary is adjacent to or encompasses three national parks, one state park, two national wildlife refuges, and three marine ecological reserves.

Florida

Everglades National Park

Biscayne National Park

Florida Keys National Marine Sanctuary
National parks
National wildlife refuges
Ecological reserves
State park

Great White Heron National Wildlife Refuge and National Key Deer Refuge

Tortugas North

Key West National Wildlife Refuge

John Pennekamp Coral Reef State Park

Tortugas South    Dry Tortugas National Park

Western Sambo

50 km

**FIGURE 16.2** The world's oceans are connected in a single vast body of water but are given different names for convenience. The Pacific Ocean is the largest and, like the Atlantic and Indian Oceans, includes both tropical and temperate waters. The smaller Arctic and Antarctic Oceans include the waters in the north and south polar regions, respectively. Many smaller bodies of water are named as seas or gulfs; a selected few are shown here.

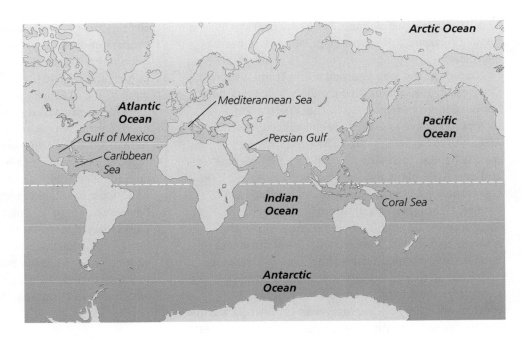

and commerce, and provide us many resources. Even landlocked areas far from salt water are affected by the oceans and the ways we interact with them. The oceans provide fish for people to eat in Iowa, supply oil to power cars in Ontario, and influence the weather in Nebraska. The study of the physics, chemistry, biology, and geography of the oceans is called **oceanography.**

## Oceans cover most of Earth's surface

Although we generally speak of the world's oceans (Figure 16.2) in the plural, giving each major basin a name—Pacific, Atlantic, Indian, Arctic, and Antarctic—all these oceans are connected, comprising a single vast body of water. This one "world ocean" covers 71% of our planet's surface and contains 97.2% of its surface water. The oceans take up most of the hydrosphere, influence the atmosphere, interact with the lithosphere, and encompass a large portion of the biosphere, including at least 250,000 species. The world's oceans touch and are touched by virtually every environmental system and every human endeavor.

## The oceans contain more than water

Ocean water contains approximately 96.5% $H_2O$ by mass; most of the remainder consists of ions from dissolved salts (Figure 16.3). Ocean water is salty primarily because ocean basins are the final repositories for water that runs off the land. Rivers carry sediment and dissolved salts from the continents into the ocean, as do winds. Evaporation

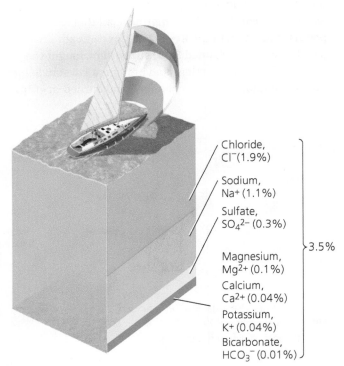

Chloride, $Cl^-$ (1.9%)

Sodium, $Na^+$ (1.1%)

Sulfate, $SO_4^{2-}$ (0.3%)

Magnesium, $Mg^{2+}$ (0.1%)

Calcium, $Ca^{2+}$ (0.04%)

Potassium, $K^+$ (0.04%)

Bicarbonate, $HCO_3^-$ (0.01%)

3.5%

**FIGURE 16.3** Ocean water consists of 3.5% salt, by mass. Most of this salt is NaCl in solution, so sodium and chloride ions are abundant. A number of other ions and trace elements are also present.

from the ocean surface then removes pure water, leaving a higher concentration of salts. If we were able to evaporate all the water from the oceans, the world's ocean basins would be covered with a layer of dried salt 63 m (207 ft) thick.

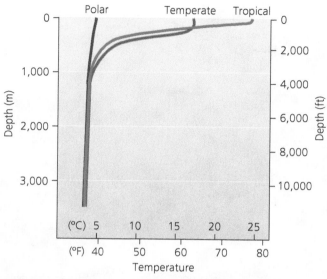

**(a) Temperature profiles at polar, temperate, and tropical latitudes**

**FIGURE 16.4** Ocean water varies in temperature and density with depth. Water temperatures (**a**) near the surface are warmer because of daily heating by the sun, and become rapidly colder with depth over the top 1,000 m (3,300 ft). This temperature differential is greatest in the tropics because of intense solar heating and is least in the polar regions. Deep water at all latitudes is equivalent in temperature. Density decreases unevenly with depth, giving rise to several distinct zones (**b**). Waters of the surface zone are well mixed and roughly equivalent in density, whereas density decreases rapidly with depth in the pycnocline. Waters of the deep zone resist mixing and are largely unaffected by sunlight, winds, and storms.

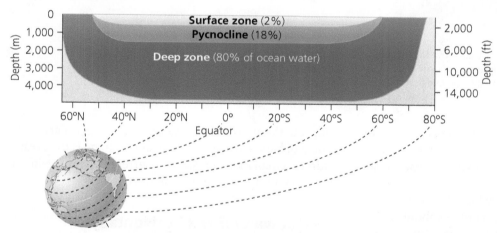

**(b) Variation in the average depth of density zones with latitude**

The salinity of ocean water generally ranges from 33 to 37 parts per thousand (ppt), varying from place to place because of differences in evaporation, precipitation, and freshwater runoff from land and glaciers. Salinity near the equator is low because this region has a great deal of precipitation, which is relatively salt-free. In contrast, at latitudes roughly 30–35 degrees north and south, evaporation exceeds precipitation, making the surface salinity of the oceans higher than average.

Besides the dissolved salts shown in Figure 16.3, nutrients such as nitrogen and phosphorus occur in seawater in trace amounts (well under 1 part per million) and play essential roles in nutrient cycling in marine ecosystems. Another aspect of ocean chemistry is dissolved gas content, particularly the dissolved oxygen on which many marine animals depend. Oxygen concentrations are high-est in the upper layer of the ocean, reaching 13 ml/L of water. Roughly 36% of the gas dissolved in seawater is oxygen, which is produced by photosynthetic plants, bacteria, and phytoplankton, and by diffusion from the atmosphere.

## Ocean water is vertically structured

Surface waters in tropical regions receive more solar radiation and therefore are warmer than surface waters in temperate or polar regions. In all regions, however, temperature declines with depth (Figure 16.4a). Water density by definition increases as salinity rises and as temperature falls. These relationships give rise to different layers of water; heavier (colder and saltier) water sinks, and lighter (warmer and less salty) water remains nearer the surface

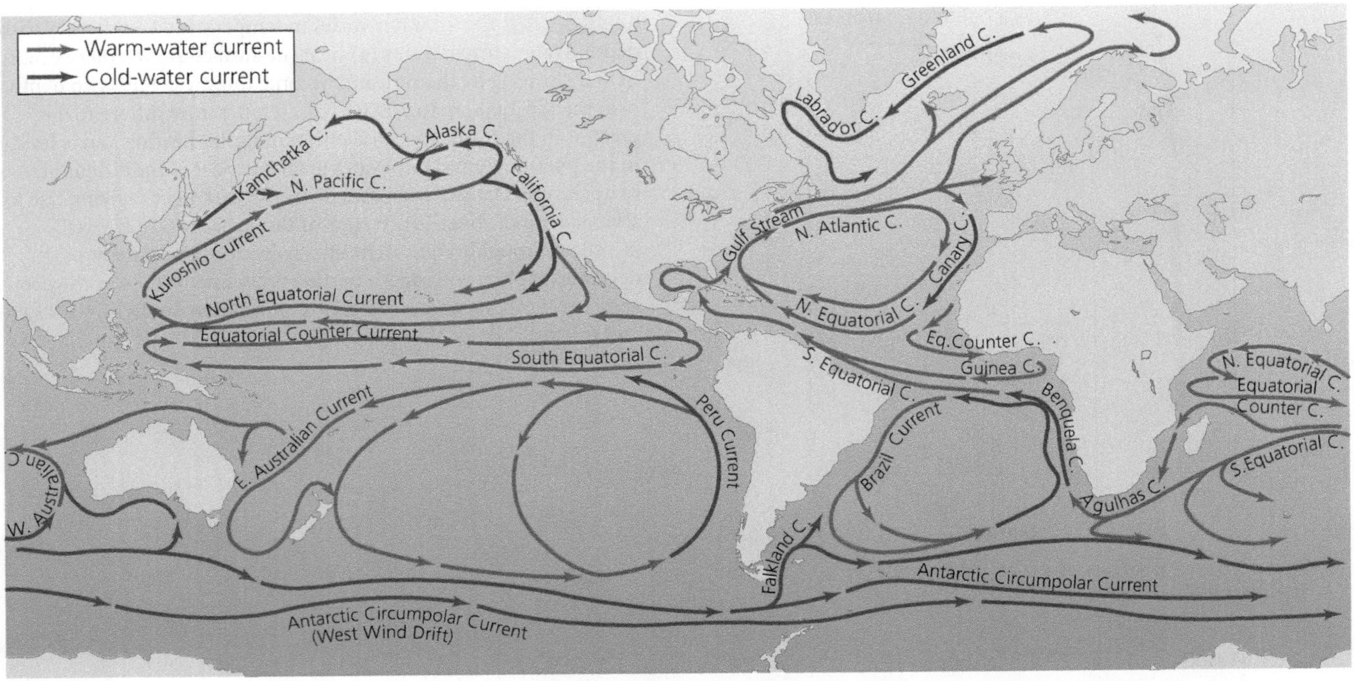

**FIGURE 16.5** The upper waters of the oceans move in currents, which are long-lasting and predictable global patterns of water movement. Warm- and cold-water currents interact with the planet's climate system and have been used by people to navigate the oceans for centuries. *Source:* Garrison, T. S. 1999. *Oceanography,* 3rd ed. Belmont, CA: Wadsworth.

(Figure 16.4b). Waters of the surface zone are heated by sunlight each day and are stirred by wind such that they are of similar density throughout, down to a depth of approximately 150 m (490 ft). Below the zone of surface water lies the *pycnocline,* a region in which density increases rapidly with depth. The pycnocline contains about 18% of ocean water by volume, compared to the surface zone's 2%. The remaining 80% resides in the deep zone beneath the pycnocline. The dense water in this zone is sluggish and not affected by winds and storms, sunlight, and daily temperature fluctuations.

Despite the daily heating and cooling of surface waters, ocean temperatures are much more stable than temperatures on land. Midlatitude oceans experience yearly temperature variation of only around 10 °C (18 °F), and tropical and polar oceans are still more stable. The reason for this stability is that water has a very high *heat capacity,* a measure of the heat required to increase temperature by a given amount. It takes much more heat energy to increase the temperature of water than it does to increase the temperature of air by the same amount. High heat capacity enables the oceans to absorb a tremendous amount of heat from the atmosphere. In fact, the heat content of the entire atmosphere is equal to that of just the top 2.6 m (8.5 ft) of the oceans. By absorbing heat and later releas-

ing it to the atmosphere, the oceans help shape Earth's climate (Chapter 18). Also influencing climate is the ocean's surface circulation, a system of currents that move in the pycnocline and the surface zone.

## Ocean water flows horizontally in currents

Far from being a static pool of water, Earth's ocean is composed of vast riverlike flows (Figure 16.5) driven by density differences, heating and cooling, gravity, and wind. These surface **currents** move in the upper 400 m (1,300 ft) of water, horizontally and for great distances. These long-lasting patterns influence global climate and play key roles in the phenomena known as El Niño and La Niña (▸ pp. 534, 536–537). They also have been crucial in navigation and human history; currents helped carry Polynesians to Easter Island, Darwin to the Galapagos, and Europeans to the New World. Currents transport heat, nutrients, pollution, and the larvae of many marine species.

Some currents are very slow. Others, like the Gulf Stream, are rapid and powerful. From the Gulf of Mexico, the Gulf Stream moves eastward along the southern edge of the Florida Keys, then northward past Miami at a rate of 160 km per day (nearly 2 m/sec, or over 4.1 mi/hr). An

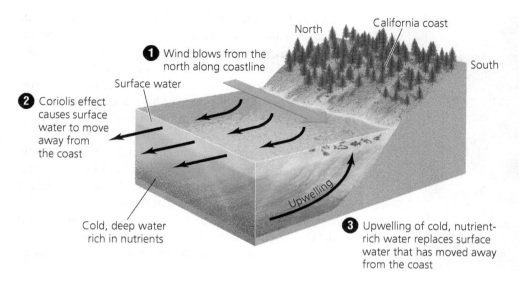

**①** Wind blows from the north along coastline

**②** Coriolis effect causes surface water to move away from the coast

Surface water

North

California coast

South

Cold, deep water rich in nutrients

Upwelling

**③** Upwelling of cold, nutrient-rich water replaces surface water that has moved away from the coast

**FIGURE 16.6** Upwelling is the movement of bottom waters upward. This type of vertical current often brings nutrients up to the surface, creating rich areas for marine life. For example, north winds blow along the California coastline, while the Coriolis effect draws wind and water away from the coast. Water is then drawn up from the bottom to replace the water that moves away from shore.

average width of 70 km (43 mi) across, the Gulf Stream continues across the North Atlantic, bringing warm water to Europe and moderating that continent's climate, which otherwise would be much colder.

## Vertical movement of water affects marine ecosystems

Surface winds and heating also create vertical currents in seawater. **Upwelling,** the vertical flow of cold, deep water toward the surface, occurs in areas where horizontal currents diverge, or flow away from one another. Because upwelled water is rich in nutrients from the bottom, upwellings are often sites of high primary productivity (▶ pp. 192–193) and lucrative fisheries. Upwellings also occur where strong winds blow away from or parallel to coastlines (Figure 16.6). An example is the California coast, where north winds and the Coriolis effect (▶ pp. 504–505) move surface waters away from shore, raising nutrient-rich water from below and creating a biologically rich region. The cold water also chills the air along the coast, giving San Francisco its famous fog and cool summers.

In areas where surface currents converge, or come together, surface water sinks, a process called **downwelling.** Downwelling transports warm water rich in dissolved gases, providing an influx of oxygen for deep-water life. Vertical currents also occur in the deep zone, where differences in water density can lead to rising and falling convection currents, such as those seen in molten rock (▶ pp. 208–209) and in air (▶ pp. 501–502). The North Atlantic Deep Water (▶ p. 534) is an example of such circulation that has far-reaching effects on global climate.

**Weighing the Issues:**
## Why Understand Ocean Currents?

Mapping ocean currents is crucial to understanding where and how the larvae of many fish and marine invertebrates become distributed from place to place. Currents help determine where larvae will settle and mature into adults. Why do you think this information might be important for people to know? What else can be carried by currents? Describe another reason that an understanding of ocean currents can be helpful and important.

## Seafloor topography can be rugged and complex

Although oceans are depicted on most maps and globes as smooth, blue swaths, parts of the ocean floor are just as complex as the terrestrial portion of the lithosphere. Underwater volcanoes shoot forth enough magma to build islands above sea level, such as the Hawaiian Islands. Steep canyons similar in scale to Arizona's Grand Canyon lie just offshore of some continents. The deepest spot in the oceans—the Mariana Trench, located in the South Pacific near Guam—is deeper than Mount Everest is high, by over 2.1 km (1.3 mi). Our planet's longest mountain range is under water—the Mid-Atlantic Ridge runs the length of the Atlantic Ocean (Figure 16.7).

We can gain an understanding of the major types of underwater geographic features by examining a stylized map that reflects *bathymetry* (the study of ocean depths)

**FIGURE 16.7** The seafloor can be every bit as rugged as continental topography. The spreading margin between tectonic plates at the Mid-Atlantic Ridge gives rise to a vast underwater volcanic mountain chain, cross-hatched by immense perpendicular breaks in the oceanic crust.

and topography (physical geography, or the shape and arrangement of landforms) (Figure 16.8). In bathymetric profile, gently sloping **continental shelves** underlie the shallow waters bordering the continents. Continental shelves vary in width from 100 m (330 ft) to 1,300 km (800 mi), averaging 70 km (43 mi) wide, with an average slope of 1.9 m/km (10 ft/mi). These shelves drop off with relative suddenness at the *shelf-slope break.* The *continental slope* angles somewhat steeply downward, connecting the continental shelf to the deep ocean basin below.

Most of the seafloor is flat, but volcanic peaks that rise above the ocean floor provide physical structure for marine animals and are frequently the site of productive fishing grounds. Some island chains, such as the Florida Keys, are formed by reef development and lie atop the continental shelf. Others, such as the Aleutian Islands curving across the North Pacific from Alaska toward Russia, are volcanic in origin, with peaks that rise above sea level. The Aleutians are also the site of a deep trench that, like the Mariana Trench, formed at a convergent tectonic plate boundary, where one slab of crust dives under another in the process of subduction (▶ p. 209).

Oceanic zones differ greatly, and some support more life than others. The uppermost 10 m (33 ft) of ocean water absorbs 80% of the solar energy that reaches its surface. For this reason, nearly all of the oceans' primary productivity occurs in the well-lit top layer, or *photic zone.* Generally, the warm, shallow waters of continental shelves are most biologically productive and support the greatest species diversity. Biological oceanographers, or marine biologists, tend to classify marine habitats and ecosystems into two types. Those occurring between the ocean's surface and floor are **pelagic,** whereas those that occur on the ocean floor are **benthic.** Each of these major areas contains several vertical zones (Figure 16.9).

**FIGURE 16.8** A stylized bathymetric profile shows key geologic features of the submarine environment. Shallow regions of water exist around the edges of continents over the continental shelf, which drops off at the shelf-slope break. The relatively steep dropoff called the continental slope gives way to the more gradual continental rise, all of which are underlain by sediments from the continents. Vast areas of seafloor are flat abyssal plain. Seafloor spreading occurs at oceanic ridges, and oceanic crust is subducted in trenches. Volcanic activity along trenches often gives rise to island chains such as the Aleutian Islands. Features on the left side of this diagram are more characteristic of the Atlantic Ocean, and features on the right side of the diagram are more characteristic of the Pacific Ocean. Adapted from Thurman, H. V. 1990. *Essentials of oceanography,* 4th ed. New York: Macmillan.

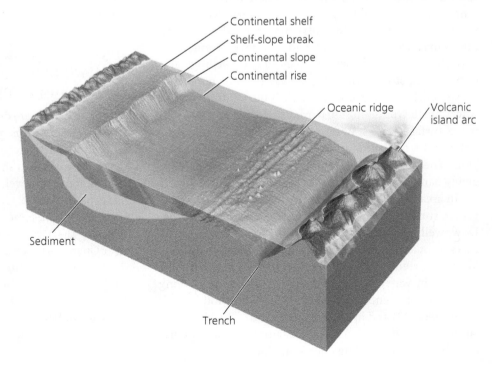

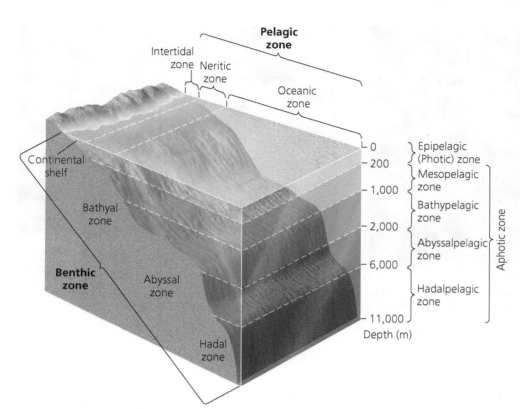

**FIGURE 16.9** Oceanographers classify marine habitats into benthic (seafloor) and pelagic (open-water) categories and subdivide these major categories into zones based on depth. Pelagic waters extend from the epipelagic zone at and near the surface down to the hadalpelagic zone at depths below 6,000 m (19,700 ft). Near-surface waters that receive adequate light for photosynthesis are also often termed the *photic zone*, and waters above the continental shelves are also said to be in the *neritic zone*. Benthic zones range from the intertidal zone where the ocean meets the land, to the continental shelves, and down to the bathyal, abyssal, and hadal zones.

# Marine Ecosystems

With their variation in topography, temperature, salinity, nutrients, and sunlight, marine environments feature a variety of ecosystems. Most marine ecosystems are powered by solar energy, with sunlight driving photosynthesis by phytoplankton in the photic zone. Yet even the darkest ocean depths host life.

## Open-ocean ecosystems vary in their biological diversity

Biological diversity in pelagic areas of the open ocean is highly variable in its distribution. Plant productivity and animal life near the surface are concentrated in regions of nutrient-rich upwelling. Microscopic phytoplankton constitute the base of the marine food chain in the pelagic zone. These photosynthetic algae, protists, and cyanobacteria feed zooplankton, which in turn become food for fish, jellyfish, whales, and other free-swimming animals (Figure 16.10). Predators at higher trophic levels include larger fish, sea turtles, and sharks. In addition, many bird species feed at the surface of the open ocean, returning periodically to nesting sites on islands and coastlines.

In recent years biologists have been learning more about animals of the deep ocean, although tantalizing questions remain and many organisms are not yet discovered. In deep-water ecosystems, animals have adapted to

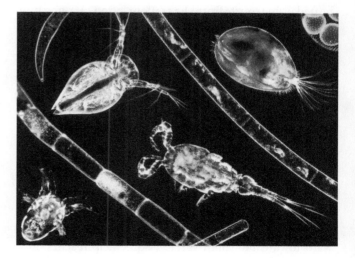

**FIGURE 16.10** The uppermost reaches of ocean water contain billions upon billions of phytoplankton—tiny photosynthetic algae, protists, and bacteria that form the base of the marine food chain—as well as zooplankton, tiny animals and protists that dine on phytoplankton and comprise the next trophic level.

**FIGURE 16.11** Life is scarce in the dark depths of the deep ocean, but the creatures that do live there often appear bizarre to us. The anglerfish lures prey toward its mouth with a bioluminescent (glowing) organ that protrudes from the front of its head.

**FIGURE 16.12** Tall brown algae known as *kelp* grow from the floor of the continental shelf and provide structure with kelp forests, a key marine ecosystem. Numerous fish and other creatures eat kelp or find refuge among its fronds.

deal with extreme water pressures and to live in the dark without food from plants. Some of these often bizarre-looking creatures scavenge carcasses or detritus (organic particles) that fall from above. Others are predators, and still others attain food from symbiotic mutualistic (▸ pp. 155–156) bacteria. Some species carry bacteria that produce light chemically by bioluminescence (Figure 16.11).

Finally, as we explored in Chapter 4 (▸ pp. 106–107), some ecosystems form around hydrothermal vents, where heated water spurts from the seafloor, often carrying minerals that precipitate to form large rocky structures. Tube-worms, shrimp, and other creatures in these recently discovered systems use symbiotic bacteria to derive their energy ultimately from chemicals in the heated water rather than from sunlight. They manage to thrive within the amazingly narrow zones between scalding-hot and icy cold water.

## Kelp forests harbor many organisms in temperate waters

Large brown algae, or **kelp** (often nicknamed *seaweed*), grow from the floor of continental shelves, reaching upward toward the sunlit surface. Some kelp reaches 60 m (200 ft) in height and can grow 45 cm (18 in.) in a single day. Dense stands of kelp form underwater forests on the continental shelves in many temperate waters (Figure 16.12). Kelp forests, with their complex structure, supply shelter and food for invertebrates and fish, which in

turn provide food for higher-trophic-level predators, such as seals and sharks. Indeed, kelp forests were the setting for our discussion of keystone species in Chapter 6 (▸ pp. 159–165). Recall that sea otters control sea urchin populations, and when otters disappear, urchins overgraze the kelp, destroying the forests and creating "urchin barrens" in their place. Kelp forests also absorb wave energy and protect shorelines from erosion. People in Asian cultures eat some types of kelp, and kelp provides compounds known as alginates, which serve as thickeners in a wide range of consumer products, from cosmetics to paints to paper to soaps.

## Coral reefs are treasure troves of biodiversity

In subtropical and tropical waters, kelp forests give way to coral reefs. A reef is an outcrop of rock, sand, or other material that rises near the surface of a relatively shallow body of salt water. A **coral reef** is a mass of calcium carbonate composed of the skeletons of tiny colonial marine organisms known as *corals*. A coral reef may occur as an extension of a shoreline, along a *barrier island* paralleling a shoreline, or as an *atoll*, a ring around a sunken island.

Corals are tiny invertebrate animals related to sea anemones and jellyfish. Some corals have hard external skeletons encompassing a soft hollow body, whereas others have flexible internal skeletons. Corals are sessile (stationary), attached to rock or existing reef and capturing

**(a) Elkhorn coral**

**(c) Partially bleached staghorn coral**

**(b) Moray eel hiding behind seafan**

**FIGURE 16.13** Different species of reef-dwelling corals give rise to a variety of distinct structures on reefs in the Florida Keys and elsewhere. One example is elkhorn coral (**a**). Fish take refuge among corals, but reef crevices also hide predators, such as moray eels (**b**), that ambush them. Coral reefs face multiple environmental stresses from natural and human impacts, and many corals have died as a result of coral bleaching, in which corals lose their zooxanthellae. Such bleaching is evident in the whitened portions of this antler-shaped staghorn coral (**c**).

passing food with stinging tentacles. They also derive nourishment from symbiotic algae, known as *zooxanthellae,* that inhabit their bodies and produce food through photosynthesis. Most corals are colonial, and the colorful surface of a coral reef is made up of thousands or millions of densely packed individuals. As corals die, their skeletons remain part of the reef while new corals grow atop them, increasing the size of the reef.

The reefs of the Florida Keys National Marine Sanctuary host many types of coral (Figure 16.13a). Coral reefs absorb wave energy and protect the shore from damage. They also provide essential habitat for many of the Keys' 6,000 species of marine organisms. Globally, coral reefs host as much biodiversity as any other type of ecosystem. The likely reason is that coral reefs provide complex physical structure (and thus many habitats) in shallow nearshore waters, which are regions of high primary productivity. Besides the staggering diversity of anemones, sponges, hydroids, tube-worms, and other sessile invertebrates, innumerable molluscs, flatworms, starfish, and urchins patrol the reefs, and

thousands of fish species find food and shelter in reef nooks and crannies. Larger predators, such as grouper and moray eels (Figure 16.13b), feed on the smaller fish.

Coral reefs are experiencing worldwide declines, however. Many reefs have undergone "coral bleaching," a process that occurs when zooxanthellae leave the coral, depriving it of nutrition (Figure 16.13c). Corals lacking zooxanthellae lose color and frequently die, leaving behind ghostly white patches in the reef. Coral bleaching is thought to result from increased sea surface temperatures associated with global climate change, from the influx of pollutants, from unknown natural causes, or from some combination of these factors. Nutrient pollution in coastal waters also promotes the growth of algae, which are blanketing reefs in the Florida Keys and many other regions. Coral reefs also sustain damage when divers stun fish with cyanide to capture them for food or for the pet trade, a common practice in waters of Indonesia and the Philippines. It is estimated that for each fish caught in this way, cyanide poisoning destroys one square meter of reef.

**(a) Tidal zones**

Supratidal zone (splash zone)

Level of high tide

Intertidal zone

Level of low tide

Subtidal zone

**(b) Tidepools at low tide**

**FIGURE 16.14** The rocky intertidal zone is the region along a rocky shoreline between the lowest and highest reaches of the tides **(a)**. This is an ecosystem rich in biodiversity, typically containing large invertebrates such as seastars (starfish), barnacles, crabs, sea anemones, corals, bryozoans, snails, limpets, chitons, mussels, nudibranchs (sea slugs), and sea urchins. Fish swim in tidal pools **(b)**, and many types of algae cover the rocks. Areas higher on the shoreline are exposed to the air more frequently and for longer periods, so those organisms that can tolerate exposure best specialize in the upper intertidal zone. The lower intertidal zone is less frequently exposed and for shorter periods, so organisms less able to tolerate exposure thrive here.

**Weighing the Issues:**
**The Coral Crisis**

Some scientists are exploring new technologies to enhance coral growth and the abundance of reef-inhabiting organisms, including chemical cues to attract larvae and special wavelengths of light to attract fish. Do you think such technology could offer adequate solutions to the global decline of coral reefs? Why or why not? What other solutions can you suggest to address the problems facing coral reefs? What challenges might each of these solutions encounter?

A few coral species thrive in waters outside the tropics and build reefs on the ocean floor at depths of 200–500 m (650–1,650 ft). These little-known reefs, which occur in cold-water areas off the coasts of Norway, Spain, the British Isles, and elsewhere, are only now beginning to be studied by scientists. Already, however, many have been badly damaged by trawling, the fishing practice in which heavy nets are dragged over the seafloor (▶ p. 485). Norway and other countries are now beginning to protect some of these deep-water reefs.

## Intertidal zones undergo constant change

Where the ocean meets the land, **intertidal,** or **littoral,** ecosystems (Figure 16.14) lie along shorelines between the farthest reach of the highest tide and the lowest reach of the lowest tide. **Tides** are the periodic rising and falling of the ocean's height at a given location, caused by the gravitational pull of the moon and sun. High and low tides occur roughly 6 hours apart, although three overlapping tidal cycles make the timing and height of tides complex. Intertidal organisms spend part of each day submerged in water, part of the day dry and exposed to the air and sun, and part of the day being lashed and beaten by waves. Subject to tremendous extremes in temperature, moisture, sun exposure, and salinity, these creatures must also protect themselves from marine predators at high tide and terrestrial predators at low tide.

The intertidal environment is a tough place to make a living, but it is home to a remarkable diversity of organisms. Rocky shorelines can be full of life among the crevices, which provide shelter and pools of water (tide pools) during low tides. Sessile animals such as anemones, mussels, and barnacles live attached to rocks, filter-feeding on plankton in the water that washes over them. Urchins, sea slugs, chitons, and limpets eat intertidal algae or scrape food from the rocks. Starfish creep slowly along, preying on the filter-feeders and herbivores at high tide. Crabs clamber around the rocks, scavenging detritus. At low tide, birds, raccoons, and other land animals come by and dine on exposed animals.

The rocky intertidal zone is so diverse because environmental conditions, including temperature, salinity, and the presence or absence of water, change dramatically from the highest to the lowest reaches. This environmental variation gives rise to conspicuous bands formed by dominant organisms as they array themselves according to their habitat needs. Sandy intertidal areas, such as those of the Florida Keys, host less biodiversity, yet plenty of organisms burrow into the sand at low tide to await the return of high tide, when they emerge to feed.

## Salt marshes cover large areas of coastline in temperate areas

Along many of the world's coastlines at temperate latitudes, **salt marshes** occur where the tides wash over gently sloping sandy or silty substrates. Rising and falling tides flow into and out of channels called *tidal creeks* and at highest tide spill over onto elevated marsh flats (Figure 16.15). Marsh flats grow thick with grasses, rushes, shrubs, and other herbaceous plants. Grasses such as those in the genera *Spartina* and *Distichlis* comprise the dominant vegetation in most salt marshes. Salt marshes boast very high primary productivity and provide critical habitat for shorebirds, waterfowl, and the adults and young of many commercially important fish and shellfish species. In many parts of the world, people have altered salt marshes

**FIGURE 16.15** Salt marshes occur in temperate intertidal zones where the substrate is muddy, allowing salt-adapted grasses to grow. Tidal waters generally flow through marshes in channels called *tidal creeks,* amid flat areas called *benches,* sometimes partially submerging the grasses. In this salt marsh in Delaware, people have cut linear ditches to drain shallow areas to control mosquito populations.

to make way for coastal shipping, industrial facilities, farming, and other development.

## Mangrove forests line coastlines in the tropics and subtropics

In tropical and subtropical latitudes, mangrove forests replace salt marshes along gently sloping sandy and silty coasts. **Mangroves** are trees with unique types of roots, some of which curve upward like snorkels to attain oxygen lacking in the mud, and some of which curve downward, serving as stilts to support the tree in changing water levels (Figure 16.16). Fish, shellfish, crabs, snakes, worms, and other organisms thrive among the root networks, and birds find habitat for feeding and nesting in the dense foliage of these coastal forests. Mangroves also provide materials that people use for food, medicine, tools, and construction. Mangroves just reach the southern edge of the United States, and the Florida Keys National Marine Sanctuary contains tens of thousands of acres forested by three species of mangrove, each adapted to specialize in a different tidal zone.

In south Florida and elsewhere, mangrove forests have been destroyed as people have converted coastal areas for residential, recreational, and commercial uses. It is estimated that people have eliminated half the world's mangrove forests and that mangrove forest area continues to decline by 2–8% per year. When mangroves are

**FIGURE 16.16** Mangrove forests are important ecosystems along tropical and subtropical coastlines throughout the world. Mangrove trees, such as these at Lizard Island, Australia, show specialized adaptations for growing in salt water and provide habitat for many types of fish, birds, crabs, and other animals.

removed, coastal areas lose the ability to slow runoff, filter pollutants, and retain soil. As a result, offshore systems such as eelgrass beds and coral reefs are more readily degraded. Only about 1% of the world's remaining mangroves benefit from some sort of protection against development.

### Freshwater meets salt water in estuaries

Many salt marshes and mangrove forests occur in or near **estuaries,** water bodies where rivers flow into the ocean, mixing freshwater with salt water. Biologically productive ecosystems, estuaries experience significant fluctuations in salinity as tidal currents and freshwater runoff vary daily and seasonally. For shorebirds and for many commercially important shellfish species, estuaries provide critical habitat. For anadromous fishes (those, like salmon, that spawn in freshwater and mature in salt water), estuaries provide a transitional zone where young fish make the passage from freshwater to salt water.

Estuaries around the world have been affected by urban and coastal development, water pollution, habitat alteration, and overfishing. The estuary of Florida Bay, where freshwater from the Everglades system mixes with salt water, has suffered pollution and a reduction in freshwater input due to irrigation and fertilizer use by sugarcane farmers, housing development, septic tank leakage, and other human impacts. Coastal ecosystems have borne the brunt of human impact because two-thirds of Earth's people choose to live within 160 km (100 mi) of the ocean.

# Human Use and Impact

Our species has a long history of interacting with the oceans. We have long traveled across their waters, clustered our settlements along coastlines, and been fascinated by the beauty, power, and vastness of the seas. We have also left our mark upon them by exploiting oceans for their resources and polluting them with our waste.

## Oceans provide transportation routes

The oceans have provided transportation routes for thousands of years and continue to provide affordable means of moving people and products over vast distances. Ocean shipping has accelerated the global reach of some cultures and has promoted interaction among long-isolated peoples. It has had substantial impacts on the environment as well. The thousands of ships plying the world's oceans today carry everything from cod to cargo containers to crude oil. Ships transport ballast water as well, which, when discharged at ports of destination, may transplant aquatic organisms picked up at ports of departure. Some of these species—such as the zebra mussel (Chapter 6)—establish and become invasive in their new homes.

## We extract energy and minerals

We use the oceans as sources of commercially valuable energy. By the 1980s about 25% of our production of crude oil and natural gas came from exploitation of deposits

**FIGURE 16.17** Crude oil and natural gas from beneath the seafloor are some of the economically valuable resources that we take from the oceans. Offshore petroleum drilling at platforms such as these off Santa Barbara, California, creates some of the many human impacts on the marine environment.

beneath the seafloor (Figure 16.17). According to recent estimates, offshore areas may contain as much as 2 trillion barrels of oil, roughly half the amount known to exist underground on land. The exploitation of oil and gas deposits in the Gulf of Mexico has triggered debate in recent years. The risk of an oil spill in the Florida Keys National Marine Sanctuary concerns many sanctuary supporters.

Ocean sediments also contain a novel potential source of fossil fuel energy. **Methane hydrate** is an ice-like solid consisting of molecules of methane ($CH_4$, the main component of natural gas) embedded in a crystal lattice of water molecules. Methane hydrates are stable at temperature and pressure conditions found in many sediments on the Arctic seafloor and the continental shelves. The U.S. Geological Survey estimates that the world's deposits of methane hydrates may hold twice as much carbon as all known deposits of oil, coal, and natural gas combined. Some people hope that methane hydrates can be developed as an energy source to power our civilization through the 21st century and beyond. However, a great deal of research remains before scientists and engineers can be sure of how to extract these energy sources safely. Destabilizing a methane hydrate deposit could lead to a catastrophic release of gas, which could cause a massive landslide and tsunami (tidal wave). This would also release huge amounts of methane, a potent greenhouse gas, into the atmosphere, exacerbating global climate change.

The oceans also hold potential for providing renewable energy sources that do not emit greenhouse gases. Engineers have developed ways of harnessing energy from waves, tides, and the heat of ocean water (▶ pp. 635–637).

These promising energy sources are awaiting further research, development, and investment.

We extract minerals from the ocean floor, as well. By using large vacuum-cleaner-like hydraulic dredges, miners collect sand and gravel from beneath the sea. Also extracted are sulfur from salt deposits in the Gulf of Mexico and phosphorite from offshore areas near the California coast and elsewhere. Other valuable minerals found on or beneath the seafloor include calcium carbonate (used in making cement), silica (used as fire-resistant insulation and in manufacturing glass), and rich deposits of copper, zinc, silver, and gold ore. Many minerals are found concentrated in manganese nodules, small ball-shaped accretions that are scattered across parts of the ocean floor. It is estimated that over 1.5 trillion tons of manganese nodules exist in the Pacific Ocean alone and that their reserves of metal exceed all terrestrial reserves. The logistical difficulty of mining them, however, has kept their extraction uneconomical so far.

## Marine pollution threatens resources

People have long made the oceans a sink for waste and pollution. Even into the mid-20th century, it was common for coastal cities in the United States to dump trash and untreated sewage along their shores. Fort Bragg, a bustling town on the northern California coast, boasts of its Glass Beach, an area where beachcombers can collect sea glass, the colorful surf-polished glass sometimes found on beaches after storms. Glass Beach is in fact the site of the former town dump, and besides well-polished glass, the perceptive visitor may also spot old batteries, rusting car frames, and all other manner of trash protruding from the bluffs above the beach.

Oil, plastic, industrial chemicals, and excess nutrients all eventually make their way from land into the oceans. Raw sewage and trash from cruise ships and abandoned fishing gear from fishing boats add to the input. The scope of trash in the sea can be gauged by the amount picked up each September by volunteers who trek beaches in the Ocean Conservancy's annual International Coastal Cleanup. In this nonprofit organization's 2004 cleanup, 300,000 people from 88 nations picked up 3.5 million kg (7.7 million lb) of trash from 17,700 km (11,000 mi) of shoreline.

## Nets and plastic debris endanger marine life

Plastic bags and bottles, fishing nets, gloves, fishing line, buckets, floats, abandoned cargo, and much else that people transport on the sea or deposit into it can harm marine organisms. Because most plastic is not biodegradable, it can drift for decades before washing up on beaches. Marine mammals, seabirds, fish, and sea turtles may mistake floating plastic debris for food and can die as a result of ingesting material they cannot digest or expel. Fishing nets that are lost or intentionally discarded can continue snaring animals for decades.

Of 115 marine mammal species, 49 are known to have eaten or become entangled in marine debris, and 111 of 312 species of seabirds are known to ingest plastic. Sea turtles of five species in the Gulf of Mexico have died from consuming or contacting marine debris. Marine debris harms people, as well. A survey of fishers off the Oregon coast indicated that more than half had encountered equipment damage or other problems from plastic debris, and debris has caused over $50 million dollars in insurance payments.

## Oil pollution comes not only from massive spills

Major oil spills, such as the *Exxon Valdez* spill in Prince William Sound, Alaska (Chapter 4), make headlines and cause serious environmental problems. Yet it is important to put such accidents into perspective. The majority of oil pollution in the oceans comes not from large spills in a few particular locations, but from the accumulation of innumerable widely spread small sources, including leakage from small boats and runoff from human activities on land. In addition, the amount of petroleum spilled into the oceans in recent years is equaled by the amount that seeps into the water from naturally occurring seafloor deposits (Figure 16.18a).

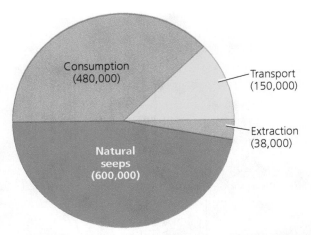

**(a) Sources of petroleum input into oceans (metric tons)**

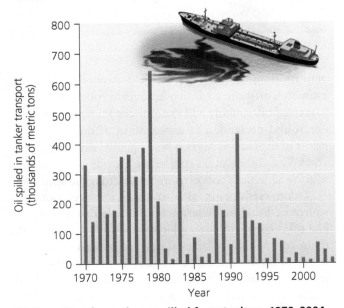

**(b) Quantity of petroleum spilled from tankers, 1970–2004**

**FIGURE 16.18** Of the 1.3 million metric tons of petroleum spilled into the world's oceans each year, nearly half is from natural seeps **(a)**. Petroleum consumption by people accounts for 38% of total input, and this includes numerous diffuse non-point sources, especially runoff from rivers and coastal communities and leakage from two-stroke engines. Spills during petroleum transport account for 12%, and leakage during petroleum extraction accounts for 3%. Less oil is being spilled into ocean waters today in large tanker spills, thanks in part to regulations on the oil shipping industry and improved spill response techniques **(b)**. The figure shows cumulative quantities of oil spilled worldwide from nonmilitary spills over 7 metric tons. Data from: (a) National Research Council. 2003. *Oil in the sea III. Inputs, fates, and effects.* Washington, DC: National Academies Press. (b) International Tanker Owners Pollution Federation Ltd. 2005. *Oil tanker spill statistics: 2004.* London: ITOPF.

Nonetheless, minimizing the amount of oil we release into coastal waters is important, because petroleum pollution is detrimental to the marine environment and the human economies that draw sustenance from that environment. Petroleum can physically coat and kill marine organisms, and ingested chemical components in petroleum can poison marine life. In response to headline-grabbing oil spills, governments around the world have begun to implement more stringent safety standards for tankers, such as requiring industry to pay for tugboat escorts in sensitive and hazardous coastal waters, and to develop prevention and response plans for major oil spills.

The U.S. Oil Pollution Act of 1990 created a $1 billion prevention and cleanup fund and required that by 2015 all oil tankers in U.S. waters be equipped with double hulls as a precaution against puncture. The oil industry has resisted many such safeguards, and today the ship that oiled Prince William Sound is still plying the world's oceans, renamed the *Sea River Mediterranean,* and still featuring only a single hull. However, over the past three decades, the amount of oil spilled in U.S. and global waters has decreased (Figure 16.18b), in part because of an increased emphasis on spill prevention and response.

## Excess nutrients cause algal blooms

Pollution from fertilizer runoff or other nutrient inputs can have dire effects on marine ecosystems, as we saw with the Gulf of Mexico's dead zone in Chapter 7. The release of excess nutrients into surface waters can spur unusually high growth rates and population densities of phytoplankton, causing eutrophication in freshwater and saltwater systems. Such problems have occurred in the Florida Keys, leading the U.S. Environmental Protection Agency (EPA) in 2001 to prohibit the discharge of sewage and other waste from boats into the waters of the Florida Keys National Marine Sanctuary.

Excessive nutrient concentrations sometimes give rise to population explosions among several species of marine algae that produce powerful toxins that attack the nervous systems of vertebrates. Blooms of these algae are known as **harmful algal blooms.** Some algal species produce reddish pigments that discolor surface waters, and blooms of these species are nicknamed **red tides** (Figure 16.19). Harmful algal blooms can cause illness and death among zooplankton, birds, fish, marine mammals, and humans as their toxins are passed up the food chain. They also cause economic loss for communities dependent on fishing or beach tourism. Reducing nutrient runoff into coastal waters can lessen the risk of these outbreaks, and health impacts can be minimized by monitoring to prevent human consumption of affected organisms.

As severe as the impacts of marine pollution can be, however, most marine scientists concur that the more worrisome dilemma is overharvesting. Unfortunately, the old cliché that "there are always more fish in the sea" appears not to be true; the oceans today have been overfished, and many fishing stocks have been largely depleted.

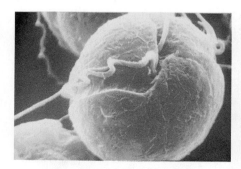

(a) Dinoflagellate (*Gymnodinium*)

**FIGURE 16.19** In a harmful algal bloom, certain types of algae multiply to great densities in surface waters, producing toxins that can bioaccumulate and harm organisms. Red tides are a type of harmful algal bloom in which the algae, such as dinoflagellates of the genus *Gymnodinium* (a), produce pigment that turns the water red (b).

(b) Red tide, Gulf of Carpentaria, Australia

# Emptying the Oceans

The oceans and their biological resources have provided for human needs for thousands of years, but today we are placing unprecedented pressure on marine resources. Half the world's marine fish populations are fully exploited, meaning that we cannot harvest them more intensively without depleting them, according to a 2004 U.N. Food and Agriculture Organization (FAO) report. An additional 25% of marine fish populations are overexploited and already being driven toward extinction, the FAO reported. Thus only one-quarter of the world's marine fish populations can yield more than they are already yielding without being driven into decline. Total global fisheries catch, after decades of increases, leveled off after about 1988 (Figure 16.20).

As our population grows, we will become even more dependent on the oceans' bounty. Existing fishing practices are not sustainable given present consumption rates, many scientists and fisheries managers have concluded. This makes it vital, they say, that we take immediate steps to modify our priorities and improve our use of science in fisheries management.

## Overfishing is nothing new

People have harvested fish, shellfish, turtles, seals, and other animals from the oceans for millennia. Archaeological evidence from ancient coastal communities reveals shellfish-rich diets, and many sites around the world include vast middens, or piles, of discarded oyster and clam shells. Although much of this harvesting may have been sustainable, paleoecologists are learning that the depletion of marine animals by humans did not begin with to-day's industrialized fishing fleets. Rather, overfishing took a toll on a variety of marine species beginning centuries or millennia ago. It then accelerated during the colonial period of European expansion and intensified further in the 20th century.

A recent synthesis of historical evidence by marine biologist Jeremy Jackson and others revealed that ancient overharvesting likely affected ecosystems in astounding ways we only partially understand today. Several large animals, including the Caribbean monk seal, Steller's sea cow, and Atlantic gray whale, were hunted to extinction long enough ago that scientists never studied them or the ecological roles they played. Overharvesting of the vast oyster beds of Chesapeake Bay led to the collapse of its oyster fishery in the late 19th century. Eutrophication and hypoxia similar to that of the Gulf of Mexico (Chapter 7) have resulted, because there are no longer oysters to filter algae and bacteria from the water.

Florida Bay, according to Jackson and his colleagues, suffers today from the results of overhunting of green sea turtles in past centuries. The once-abundant turtles ate sea grass (often called turtle grass) and likely kept it cropped low, like a lawn. But with today's turtle population a tiny fraction of what it once was, sea grass grows thickly, dies, and rots, giving rise to disease like sea grass wasting disease, which ravaged Florida Bay in the 1980s.

A better-known case of historical overharvesting is the near-extinction of many species of whales. This resulted from commercial whaling that began centuries ago and was curtailed only in 1986. Although overfishing has a long history, the industrialized methods, new technology, and global reach of today's commercial fleets are making our impacts much more rapid and far-reaching than in past centuries.

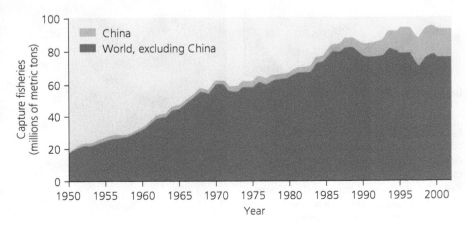

**FIGURE 16.20** The total global fisheries catch has increased over the past half-century, but in recent years growth has stalled, and many fear that a global catch decline is imminent if conservation measures are not taken soon. The figure shows trends with and without China's data (see "The Science behind the Story," ▶ pp. 486–487). With China's data, global catch has leveled off since the mid-1990s. Without China's data, catch has decreased slightly since 1988. Go to **GRAPHit!** at www.aw-bc.com/withgott or on the student CD-ROM. Data from U.N. Food and Agricultural Organization (FAO). 2004. *World review of fisheries and aquaculture.* Rome: FAO.

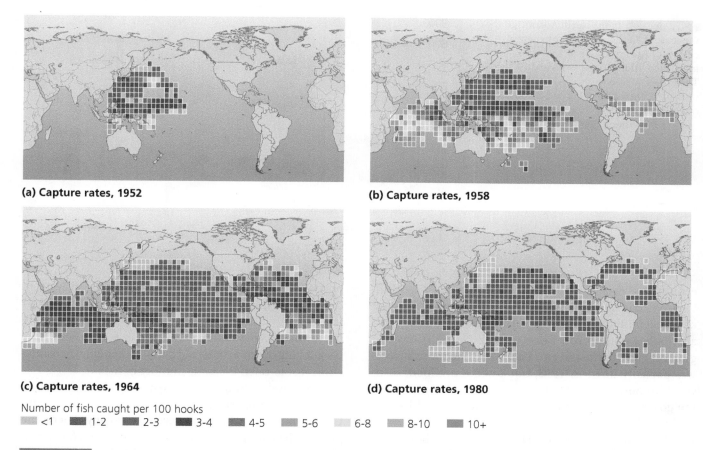

**(a) Capture rates, 1952**

**(b) Capture rates, 1958**

**(c) Capture rates, 1964**

**(d) Capture rates, 1980**

Number of fish caught per 100 hooks

<1   1-2   2-3   3-4   4-5   5-6   6-8   8-10   10+

**FIGURE 16.21** As industrial fishing fleets reached each new region of the world's oceans, capture rates of large predatory fishes were initially high and then within a decade declined markedly. In the figure, reds and oranges signify high capture rates, and maroons and purples signify low capture rates. High capture rates in the southwestern Pacific in 1952 (**a**) gave way to low ones in later years. Excellent fishing success in the tropical Atlantic and Indian Oceans in 1958 (**b**) had turned mediocre by 1964 (**c**) and poor by 1980 (**d**). High capture rates in the north and south Atlantic in 1964 (**c**) gave way to low capture rates there in 1980 (**d**).

## Modern fishing fleets deplete marine life rapidly

Today's industrialized fishing fleets can deplete marine populations quickly. In a 2003 study, fisheries biologists Ransom Myers and Boris Worm analyzed fisheries data from FAO archives, looking for changes in the catch rate of fish in various regions of ocean since they were first exploited by industrialized fishing. For one region after another, they found the same pattern: Catch rates dropped precipitously, with 90% of large-bodied fish and sharks eliminated within only a decade (Figure 16.21). Following that, populations stabilized at 10% of their former levels. This means, Myers and Worm concluded, that the oceans today contain only one-tenth of the large-bodied animals they once did. It also means that declines happened so fast in most regions of the world that scientists never knew the original abundance of these animals.

## Many fisheries are collapsing today

The proportion of marine fish stocks that are overfished increased tenfold between 1950 and 1990. Many fisheries have collapsed, and others are in danger of collapsing. These collapses are ecologically devastating and also take a severe economic toll on human communities that depend on fishing.

A prime example of fishery collapse took place in the 1990s, affecting groundfish in the North Atlantic off the Canadian and U.S. coasts. The term *groundfish* refers to various species that live in benthic habitats, such as Atlantic cod, haddock, halibut, and flounder. These fish are major food sources that powered fishing economies in Newfoundland, Labrador, the Maritime Provinces, and the New England states for close to 400 years. Yet fishing pressure became so intense that most stocks collapsed in recent years, bringing fishing

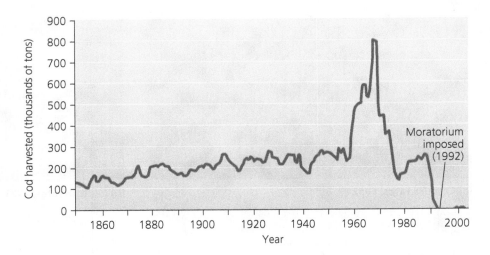

**FIGURE 16.22** In the North Atlantic off the coast of Newfoundland, commercial catches of Atlantic cod increased with intensified fishing in the 1960s and 1970s. The fishery subsequently crashed, and moratoria imposed in 1992 and 2003 have not brought it back. Data from Millennium Ecosystem Assessment, 2005.

economies down with them (Figure 16.22). With Canada's cod stocks down by 99% and showing no sign of recovery, the Canadian government in 1992 ordered a complete ban on cod fishing in the Grand Banks region off Newfoundland and Labrador. The moratorium was partially lifted in 1998, but catches declined, so it was reimposed in 2003. To soften the economic blow, the government offered $50 million to affected fishers of the region.

The experience on the U.S. side of the border is showing that such bans can sometimes help restore depleted fisheries. When the groundfish fisheries of Georges Bank in the Gulf of Maine collapsed in the mid-1990s, three areas totaling 17,000 km² (6,600 mi²) were closed to fishing. The closures worked; five years later, haddock, flounder, and yellowtail were recovering, and scallops rebounded strongly, attaining sizes 9–14 times as large as before the closures. Fishers began having better luck, especially just outside the closed regions. Unfortunately, cod have not recovered. Because adult cod eat fish that prey on young cod, some ecologists hypothesize that once the adult cod were depleted, intensified predation on young cod prevented the population from recovering.

## Fisheries declines are masked by several factors

Although industrialized fishing has depleted fish stocks in region after region, the overall global catch has remained roughly stable for two decades (see Figure 16.20). You might wonder how this could be. The seeming stability of the total global catch can be explained by several factors that mask population declines. One is that fishing fleets have been traveling longer distances to reach less-fished

portions of the ocean. They also have been fishing in deeper waters; average depth of catches was 150 m (495 ft) in 1970 and 250 m (820 ft) in 2000. Moreover, fishing fleets have been spending more time fishing and have been setting out more nets and lines—expending increasing effort just to catch the same number of fish.

Improved technology also helps explain high catches despite declining stocks. Today's Japanese, European, Canadian, and U.S. fleets can reach almost any spot on the globe with boats that can attain speeds of 80 kph (50 mph). They have access to an array of technologies that militaries have developed for spying and for chasing enemy submarines, including advanced sonar mapping equipment, satellite navigation, and thermal sensing systems. Some fleets rely on aerial spotters to find schools of commercially valuable fish, such as bluefin tuna.

Finally, another cause of misleading stability in global catch numbers is that not all data supplied to international monitoring agencies may be accurate (see "The Science behind the Story," ▸ pp. 486–487).

## We are "fishing down the food chain"

Overall figures on total global catch tell only part of the story, because they do not include information on the species, age, and size of fish harvested. Careful analyses of fisheries data have revealed in case after case that as fishing increases, the size and age of fish caught decline. In addition, as particular species become too rare to fish profitably, fleets begin targeting other species that are in greater abundance. Generally this means shifting from large, desirable species to smaller, less desirable ones. Fleets have time and again depleted popular food fish such as cod and snapper and shifted their emphasis to species that were previously of lower value. Because this often entails catching species at lower trophic levels, this phenomenon has been termed "fishing down the food chain."

## Some fishing practices kill nontarget animals and damage ecosystems

Some fishing practices catch more than just the species they target. **By-catch** refers to the capture of animals not meant to be caught, and it accounts for the deaths of many thousands of fish, sharks, marine mammals, and birds each year.

Boats that drag huge *driftnets* through the water (Figure 16.23a) capture substantial numbers of dolphins, seals, and sea turtles, as well as countless nontarget fish. Most of these end up drowning (mammals and turtles need to surface to breathe) or dying from air exposure on deck (fish breathe through gills in the water). Many nations have banned or restricted driftnetting because of excessive by-catch. The widespread death of dolphins in driftnets also motivated consumer efforts to label tuna as "dolphin-safe" if its capture uses methods designed to avoid dolphin by-catch. Such measures helped reduce dolphin deaths from an estimated 133,000 per year in 1986 to less than 2,000 per year since 1998.

Similar by-catch problems exist with *longline fishing* (Figure 16.23b), which involves dragging extremely long lines with baited hooks spaced along their lengths. Longline fishing kills turtles, sharks, and many albatrosses, magnificent seabirds with wingspans up to 3.6 m (12 ft). It is estimated that 300,000 seabirds of various species die each year from longline fishing.

Other fishing practices can directly damage entire ecosystems. *Bottom-trawling* (Figure 16.23c) involves dragging weighted nets over the floor of the continental shelf to catch such benthic organisms as scallops and groundfish. Trawling crushes many organisms in its path and leaves long swaths of damaged sea bottom. It is especially destructive to structurally complex areas, such as reefs, that provide shelter and habitat for many animals. Only in recent years has underwater photography begun to reveal the extent of structural and ecological disturbance done by trawling.

## Consumer choice can influence fishing practices

To most of us, marine fishing practices may seem a distant phenomenon over which we have no control. Yet by exercising careful choice when we buy seafood, consumers can influence the ways fisheries function. Purchasing ecolabeled seafood products such as dolphin-safe tuna is one

**(a) Driftnetting**

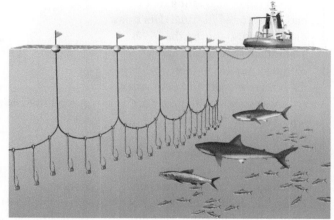

**(b) Longlining**

**(c) Bottom-trawling**

**FIGURE 16.23** Commercial fishing fleets use several methods of capture. In driftnetting (**a**), huge nets are dragged through the open water to capture schools of fish. In longlining (**b**), lines with numerous baited hooks are pulled through the open water. In bottom-trawling (**c**), weighted nets are dragged along the floor of the continental shelf. All methods result in large amounts of by-catch, or capture of nontarget animals. Bottom-trawling can also result in severe structural damage to reefs and benthic habitats.

## The Science behind the Story

# China's Fisheries Data

China is responsible for a larger share of the world's fisheries catch than any other nation, according to the United Nations Food and Agriculture Organization (FAO). Thus, China's catch data has a major impact on the FAO's attempts to assess the health of global fisheries. In 2001, two fisheries scientists published a paper suggesting that China had exaggerated its catch data by as much as 100% during the 1990s. The inflated catch data had led to complacency among the world's fisheries managers and policymakers, these scientists argued, because it led the FAO to overestimate the true amount of fish left in the ocean.

The authors of the paper, University of British Columbia researchers Reg Watson and Daniel Pauly, had become suspicious of China's data for several reasons. First, China's coastal fisheries had been overexploited for decades, yet reported catches continued to increase. Second, China's "catch per unit effort" remained unchanged from 1980 to 1995, even though the abundance of fish had decreased. Finally, China's catch statistics suggested that its coastal waters were far more productive than ecologi-

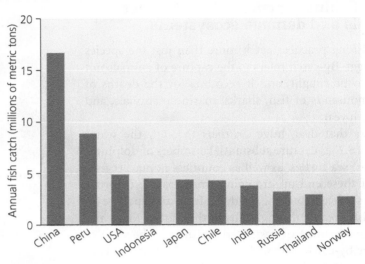

China's reported fish catches in recent years have dwarfed those of other nations, but a recent study asserted that Chinese fisheries managers had been falsely inflating their catches. Data from U.N. Food and Agriculture Organization, 2004.

cally similar areas fished by other nations.

In the November 29, 2001, issue of the journal *Nature,* Watson and Pauly reported the results of their study testing the hypothesis that China's apparent productivity was unrealistically high. Using a number of different databases, including FAO catch data collected since the 1950s, they built a statistical model to predict global fisheries catch. They divided the world's oceans into approximately 180,000 "cells," each

spanning half a degree longitudinally and latitudinally. The cells were then characterized by factors that affect catch size, such as depth, primary productivity, fishing rights, and species distribution. The researchers then used these factors to predict total annual catch for each cell.

For most cells, the catch predicted by the model was similar to the catch reported by fleets that fished those waters. In large swaths of China's coastal waters, however, predicted catches were far smaller than

way to exercise choice, but in most cases consumers have no readily available information about how their seafood was caught. Thus, several nonprofit organizations have recently devised concise guides to help consumers make choices. These guides differentiate fish and shellfish that are overfished or whose capture is ecologically damaging from those that are harvested more sustainably. For instance, the Monterey Bay Aquarium provides a wealth of this information on its Web site.

## Marine Conservation Biology

Because we bear responsibility and stand to lose a great deal if valuable ecological systems collapse, marine scientists have been working to develop solutions to the problems that threaten the oceans. Many have begun by taking a hard look at the strategies used traditionally in fisheries management.

reported catches. For instance, the model predicted that in 1999 China's total catch would be 5.5 million metric tons, whereas the figure reported by Chinese fisheries authorities was 10.1 million metric tons.

When Watson and Pauly proceeded to analyze global fisheries trends using the model's predictions rather than China's official numbers, they found that the total annual global catch had decreased by 360,000 metric tons since 1988, instead of increasing by 330,000 metric tons, as reported by the FAO. Their finding suggested that the global catch, rather than remaining stable through the 1990s, actually had begun to decline in the 1980s.

Fisheries managers and policymakers depend on the FAO for information about the state of the world's fisheries. By using China's apparently inflated numbers, Watson later wrote, the FAO had encouraged a global "mopping-up operation" in which the last of the world's fish were being decimated.

The Chinese government and the FAO both criticized the study. China's reported catch was "basically correct," said Yang Jian, director-general of the Chinese Bureau of Fisheries. Watson and

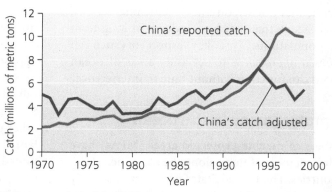

Fisheries biologists used models to estimate China's fish harvests, and found estimated amounts to be much lower than reported amounts. Data from Watson, R., and D. Pauly. 2001. Systematic distortions in world fisheries catch trends. *Nature* 414: 536–538.

Pauly's model, he suggested, failed to take into account unique aspects of China's fisheries, such as its large catch of crabs and jellyfish. Yang also noted that China had already begun to address the problems of overfishing and overreporting that did exist. In 1998, for instance, the Chinese government had promoted a "zero-growth policy" that capped China's total catch at 1998 levels.

For its part, the FAO noted that it was already treating China's statistics with caution. In its recent publications, global fisheries catches were being reported with and without China's data (see Figure 16.20). The FAO had also held several meetings

with Chinese officials to discuss ways of reducing overreporting. Moreover, the FAO suggested, nothing in its reports had encouraged complacency. Although it had indeed reported that the global catch remained stable through the 1990s, it also noted that many individual fisheries had declined or collapsed and that others were being aggressively overfished.

Assigning blame for the state of the world's fisheries is not the most productive response to Watson and Pauly's findings, says fisheries scientist Andy Rosenberg of the University of New Hampshire. "This is a global problem, not a case of a few bad actors."

## Fisheries management has been based on maximum sustainable yield

For decades, fisheries management has sought to use scientific assessments to ensure sustainable harvests. Historically, fisheries managers have studied fish population biology and used that knowledge to regulate the timing of harvests, the techniques used to catch fish, and the scale of harvests. The goal was to allow for maximal harvests of

particular populations while keeping fish available for the future—the concept of *maximum sustainable yield* (▸ pp. 345–346). If data indicated that current yields were unsustainable, managers might limit the number or total mass of that fish species that could be harvested or restrict the type of gear fishers could use.

Despite such efforts, a number of fish stocks have plummeted, and many marine scientists and managers now feel it is time to rethink fisheries management. One key change these reformers suggest is to shift the focus away from the individual fish species and toward viewing marine resources as elements of larger ecological systems. This means considering the effects of fishing practices on habitat quality, on interspecific interactions, and on other factors that may have indirect or long-term effects on populations. One key aspect of such an *ecosystem-based approach* is to set aside areas of ocean where systems can function without human interference.

## We can protect areas in the ocean

Large numbers of **marine protected areas (MPAs)** have been established, most of them along the coastlines of developed countries. The United States now contains nearly 300 federally managed MPAs. However, despite the name, marine protected areas do not necessarily protect their natural resources, because nearly all MPAs allow fishing or other extractive activities. As a recent report from an environmental advocacy group put it, even national marine sanctuaries "are dredged, trawled, mowed for kelp, crisscrossed with oil pipelines and fiber-optic cables, and swept through with fishing nets."

Because of the lack of true refuges from fishing pressure, many scientists—and some fishers—now want to establish areas where no fishing is allowed. Such "no-take" areas have come to be called **marine reserves.** Designed to preserve entire ecosystems intact without human interference, marine reserves are also intended to improve fisheries. Scientists have argued that marine reserves can act as production factories for fish for surrounding areas, because fish larvae produced inside reserves will disperse outside and stock other parts of the ocean. By serving both purposes, proponents argue, marine reserves are a win-win proposition for environmentalists and fishers alike.

------------------------------------------------------------
**Weighing** the **Issues:**
## Preservation on Land and at Sea

Almost 4% of U.S. land area is designated as wilderness, yet far less than 1% of coastal waters are protected in reserves. Why do you think it is taking so long for the preservation ethic to make the leap to the oceans?
------------------------------------------------------------

## Marine reserves have met forceful opposition

Many fishers don't like the idea of no-take reserves, however. Nearly every marine reserve proposed has met with pockets of intense opposition from people and businesses who use the area for fishing or recreation. Opposition comes from industrial fishing fleets that fish commercially as well as from individuals who fish recreationally. Both types of fishers are concerned that marine reserves will simply put more areas off-limits to fishing.

In the Florida Keys, property rights advocates who had opposed the sanctuary protested the 1998 establishment of reserve zones where fishing was to be prohibited. They rallied citizen opposition in local newspapers and filed a $27 million lawsuit against the federal government. In other parts of the world, such protests have become violent. Fishermen in the Galapagos Islands have rioted, looted, and destroyed the administration building at Galapagos National Park to protest fishing restrictions.

However, people in the Florida Keys have come to see that the reserves have not greatly threatened their access to areas. They have also witnessed improvements in the marine life around them. Surveys just 3 years after establishment of the no-take zones showed increases in the size and number of spiny lobsters and in the populations of three of four major reef fish. Keys fishers are catching more fish, and fishing revenues are up. As a result, many opponents of the reserve system have become supporters. Reserve workers estimated in 2000 that 70% of Keys residents supported the no-take reserves and that over 50% would support establishing more of them.

## Reserves can work for both fish and fishers

In the past decade, data synthesized from marine reserves around the world have been indicating that reserves *do* work as win-win solutions that benefit ecosystems, fish populations, and fishing economies. In 2001, 161 prominent marine scientists signed a "consensus statement" summarizing the effects of marine reserves. Besides boosting fish biomass, total catch, and record-sized fish, the report stated, marine reserves yield several benefits. Within reserve boundaries, they

▶ Produce rapid and long-term increases in abundance, diversity, and productivity of marine organisms.
▶ Decrease mortality and habitat destruction.
▶ Lessen the likelihood of extirpation of species.

Outside reserve boundaries, marine reserves

▶ Can create a "spillover effect" when individuals of protected species spread outside reserves.
▶ Allow larvae of species protected within reserves to "seed the seas" outside reserves.

## Marine Reserves

Can marine reserves or other forms of "no-fishing" zones help us solve problems facing the oceans today? Why or why not?

### "No-Fishing" Zones Do Not Prevent Overfishing

If you close off part of the ocean from all forms of "take," there will obviously be more fish in the protected area. That is just common sense. However, a major problem with our oceans is severe overfishing. Fish are being killed faster than they can replenish themselves. There is a simple way to improve this situation—stop killing so many fish.

"No-fishing" zones don't accomplish this. What they do is to shift the fishing pressure to another area. Anything short of reducing the number of fish being killed, such as marine reserves, not only won't solve the problem, but also may give a false impression that something is being done, thus delaying action to actually solve the problem.

There are many traditional fishery management tools that can be used to prevent overfishing. These tools include bag limits, size limits, slot limits, closed seasons, protected species, and catch-and-release-only species. For commercial fishermen there are quotas, gear restrictions, trip limits, and limited entry, plus all the management tools listed above for recreational anglers.

A major problem for fishery managers has been politics. Commercial fishing interests have very effective lobbyists who have been instrumental in preventing or delaying needed management restrictions. If lobbying fails, they often challenge regulations through the court system. The result is management regulations that are not restrictive enough. Marine reserves will not solve this problem.

In cases where remote, pristine areas are meant to be preserved, perhaps marine reserves allowing only catch and release could be effective. Examples of this are the remote reefs in northern Hawaii and some snapper spawning areas far west of Key West, Florida. However, "no-fishing" zones by themselves will not rebuild fisheries.

**Michael Leech** joined the International Game Fish Association (IGFA) in 1983 and became president of IGFA in 1992. Under his leadership, the IGFA recently constructed their permanent world headquarters in Dania Beach, Florida. The IGFA Fishing Hall of Fame and Museum not only is a tourist attraction but also serves as the world center for most fishing-related information.

### Marine Reserves Restore Ecosytems

Marine reserves are a powerful tool for protecting and restoring marine ecosystems. They are successful because they protect not only species but also habitats. In the past, there were innumerable naturally recurring marine reserves around the oceans—places that were too far from land, too deep, or too rocky to fish. Modern technology systematically eliminated those reserves, and today we protect far less than 1% of the oceans in established reserves.

Recent scientific studies have demonstrated that reserves provide a clear benefit to conservation of marine organisms: Biomass, density, individual size, and diversity all increase inside reserves. It is especially important to protect large marine organisms, which produce disproportionately more offspring than smaller ones. A 37-cm (14.6-in.) vermilion rockfish produces 150,000 young, whereas a 60-cm (23.6-in.) one produces 1.7 million young! Allowing individuals to get big and fat is very valuable.

Modeling results indicate that reserves substantially benefit fisheries, from both spillover (fish spilling from the reserve) and export (larvae produced inside the reserve and transported away by currents). However, not all species will recover immediately when a reserve is established. Species that grow slowly and reproduce late will need longer to colonize and recover.

Networks of marine reserves, connected by the movement of organisms, are likely to provide the best combination of conservation and fishery benefit. A network provides protection for a large total area and a long perimeter over which organisms can escape to reseed adjacent areas. Networks of reserves are not a panacea—they need to be coupled with good fishery management and pollution control—but marine reserves are one of the most promising tools available for solving the problems plaguing ocean environments today.

**Jane Lubchenco** is a professor of marine biology and zoology at Oregon State University. She works with policymakers, business leaders, private foundations, religious leaders, other scientists, governmental and nongovernmental organizations, and students to help figure out how to make a transition to sustainability. She is president of the International Council for Science and co-founded the Aldo Leopold Leadership Program, PISCO (Partnership for Interdisciplinary Studies of Coastal Oceans), and COMPASS (Communication Partnership for Science and the Sea).

 Explore this issue further by accessing **Viewpoints** at www.aw-bc.com/withgott.

# The Science behind the Story

# Do Marine Reserves Work?

In November 2001, a team of fisheries scientists published a paper in the journal *Science*, providing some of the first clear evidence that marine reserves can benefit nearby fisheries. The team, led by York University researcher Callum Roberts, focused on reserves off the coasts of Florida and the Caribbean island of St. Lucia.

Following the establishment in 1995 of the Soufrière Marine Management Area (SMMA), a network of reserves intended to help restore St. Lucia's severely depleted coral reef fishery, Roberts and his colleague, Julie Hawkins, conducted annual visual surveys of fish abundance in the reserves and nearby areas. Within 3 years, they found that the biomass of five commercially important families of fish—surgeonfishes, parrot fishes, groupers, grunts, and snappers—had tripled inside the reserves and doubled outside them. Roberts and Hawkins also interviewed local

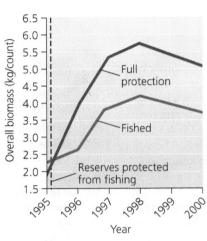

Established in 1995, the Soufrière Marine Management Area (SMMA), along the coast of St. Lucia, had a rapid impact. By 1998, fish biomass within the five reserves tripled and in adjacent, fished areas, it doubled. Data from Roberts, C., et al. 2001. Effects of marine reserves on adjacent fisheries. *Science* 294: 1920–1923.

fishers and found that those with large traps were catching 46% more fish per trip in 2000–2001 than they had in 1995–1996 and that fishers with small traps were catching 90%

more. Roberts and his colleagues concluded that "in 5 years, reserves have led to improvement in the SMMA fishery, despite the 35% decrease in area of fishing grounds."

Roberts and his coworkers also studied the oldest fully protected marine reserve in the United States, the Merritt Island National Wildlife Refuge (MINWR), established in 1962 as a buffer around what is today the Kennedy Space Center on Cape Canaveral, Florida. In a previous study, Darlene Johnson and James Bohnsack of the National Oceanic and Atmospheric Administration and Nicholas Funicelli of the United States Geological Service had found that the reserve contained more and larger fish than did nearby unprotected areas. This team also found that some of the reserve's fish appeared to be migrating to nearby fishing areas.

Bohnsack, Roberts, and their colleagues corroborated the evidence for migration by analyzing trophy records from the International

---

The consensus statement was backed up by research into reserves in the Caribbean and Florida (see "The Science behind the Story," above) and others worldwide. At Apo Island in the Philippines, biomass of large predators increased eightfold inside a marine reserve, and outside the reserve fishing improved. At two coral reef sites in Kenya, commercially fished and keystone species were up to 10 times more abundant in the protected area as in the fished area. At Leigh Marine Reserve in New Zealand, snapper increased 40-fold, and spiny lobsters were increasing by 5–11% yearly. Spillover from this reserve improved fishing and ecotourism, and—as in

Florida— local residents who once opposed the reserve now support it.

The review of data from existing marine reserves as of 2001 revealed that just 1–2 years after their establishment, marine reserves

▶ Increased densities of organisms on average by 91%.
▶ Increased biomass of organisms on average by 192%.
▶ Increased average size of organisms by 31%.
▶ Increased species diversity by 23%.

From data like these and considerations of socioeconomic factors, the scientific consensus statement concluded that

Game Fish Association. They found that the proportion of Florida's record-sized fish caught near Merritt Island increased significantly after 1962. Nine years after the refuge was established, for instance, the number of spotted sea trout records from the Merritt Island area jumped dramatically. Bohnsack, Roberts, and their colleagues hypothesized that the reserve was providing a protected zone in which fish could grow to trophy size before migrating to nearby areas, where they were caught by recreational fishers.

Not everyone saw the St. Lucia and Merritt Island cases as proof that marine reserves could rescue depleted fisheries. In February 2002, several alternative interpretations were published as letters in *Science*. Mark Tupper, a fisheries scientist at the University of Guam, suggested that the St. Lucia results were relevant only to coral reef fisheries in developing nations, whereas Florida's boost in fish populations

was due primarily to limits on recreational fishing. Karl Wickstrom, editor-in-chief of *Florida Sportsman* magazine, suggested that the increase in trophy fish near MINWR was caused by commercial fishing regulations and changes in how trophies were recorded and promoted. And Ray Hilborn, a fisheries scientist at the University of Washington, challenged the study's scientific methods. In the St. Lucia case, he pointed out, there had been no control condition.

In response, Roberts and his colleagues reaffirmed the validity of their results while acknowledging some limitations. They agreed with Tupper that marine reserves are not always effective and often need to be complemented by other management tools, such as size limits. "We agree that inadequately protected reserves are useless," they wrote, "but our study shows that well-enforced reserves can be extremely effective and can play a critical role in achieving sustainable fisheries."

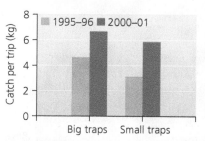

**(a) Catch per trip**

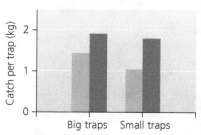

**(b) Catch per trap**

Roberts and his colleagues studied biomass of fish caught at the SMMA over two 5-month periods in 1995–1996 and 2000–2001. For fishers with big traps, catch increased by 46%, and for those with small traps, it increased by 90%. Per trap, catch increased by 36% for big traps and by 80% for small traps. Data from Roberts, C., et al. 2001. Effects of marine reserves on adjacent fisheries. *Science* 294: 1920–1923.

existing scientific information justifies the immediate application of fully protected marine reserves as a central management tool.

## How should reserves be designed?

If marine reserves work in principle, the question becomes how best to design reserves and arrange them into networks. Scientists today are asking how large reserves need to be, how many there need to be, and where they need to be placed. Involving fishers directly in the planning process is crucial for coming up with answers to such

questions. Of the 40 studies that have estimated how much area of the ocean should be protected in no-take reserves, estimates range from 10% to 65%, with most falling between 20% and 50%. Other studies are modeling how to optimize the size and spacing of individual reserves so that ecosystems are protected, fisheries are sustained, and people are not overly excluded from marine areas (Figure 16.24). If marine reserves are designed strategically to take advantage of ocean currents, many scientists say, then they may well seed the seas and help lead us toward solutions to one of our most pressing environmental problems.

| Effects of Different–Sized Marine Reserves | Consequences for conservation | Consequences for small fisheries | Consequences for commercial fisheries | Overall consequences |
|---|---|---|---|---|
| 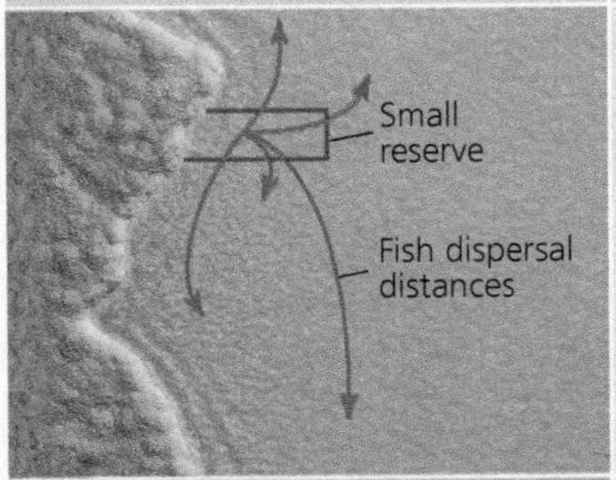 Small reserve / Fish dispersal distances | Reserve is not self-sustaining; most species are lost. | High periphery-to-area ratio makes many fish available to fishers outside reserve. This is unsustainable, however, because small reserves offer too little protection for fish populations. | Provides little or no boost to fish populations outside reserve, but does not appreciably decrease area of fishing grounds. | Too many fish wander out of reserve, yet fisheries experience little gain. Many populations are not sustained. Reserve fails to meet any stakeholder goals. |
| 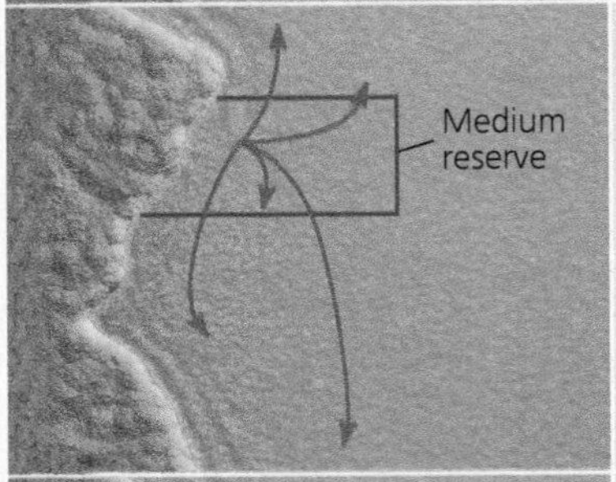 Medium reserve | Reserve is moderately self-sustaining; some species are lost. | Intermediate periphery-to-area ratio makes some fish available to fishers outside reserve, while offering a large enough area of refuge to protect other fish, thus sustaining many populations. | Provides a significant boost to fish populations outside reserve, with only a moderate decrease in area of fishing grounds. | Conservation is effective inside reserve, and fisheries gain fish while not losing too much fishing area. Good balance of benefits for all stakeholders. |
| 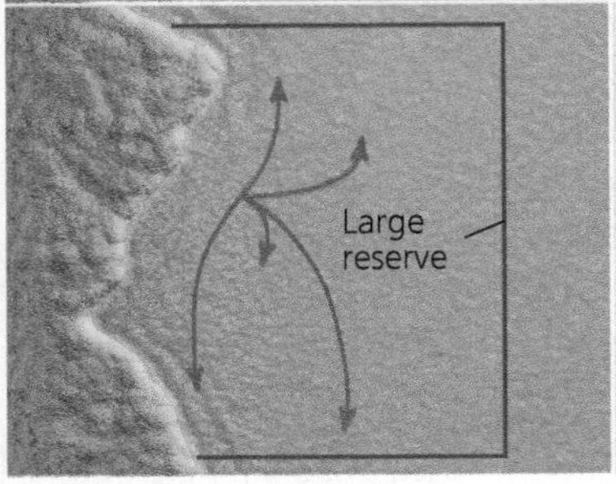 Large reserve | Reserve is completely self-sustaining; all species are retained. | Low periphery-to-area ratio makes relatively few fish available to fishers outside reserve; the "spillover" for fisheries is small in relation to the area protected in the reserve. | Provides relatively little boost to fish populations in regions around reserve, and severely decreases area of fishing grounds. | Preservation is effective inside reserve, but too few fish spill over into fishing grounds that have been much reduced in area. Outcome not acceptable to fisheries stakeholders. |

**FIGURE 16.24** Marine reserves of different sizes may have varying effects on ecological communities and fisheries. Young and adult fish and shellfish of different species can disperse different distances, as indicated by the red arrows in the figure. A small reserve may fail to protect animals because too many disperse out of the reserve. A large reserve may protect fish and shellfish very well but will provide relatively less "spillover" into areas where people can legally fish. Thus medium-sized reserves may offer the best hope of preserving species and ecological communities while also providing adequate fish to fishermen and human communities. Determining the actual size of such reserves requires a great deal of data on dispersal distances, water currents, community composition, animal behavior, and human economies. *Source:* Halpern, B. S., and R. R. Warner. 2003. Matching marine reserve design to reserve objectives. *Proceedings of the Royal Society of London B: Biological sciences* 270: 1871–1878.

# Conclusion

Oceans cover most of our planet and contain diverse topography and ecosystems, some of which we are only now beginning to explore and understand. We are learning more about the oceans and coastal environments while we are intensifying our use of their resources. In so doing, we are coming to understand better how to use these resources without depleting them or causing undue ecological harm. In the Florida Keys and hundreds of other areas, scientists are demonstrating that setting aside protected areas of the ocean can serve to maintain natural systems and also to enhance fisheries. As historical studies reveal more information on how much biodiversity our oceans formerly contained and have now lost, we may increasingly look beyond simply making fisheries stable and instead consider restoring the ecological systems that used to flourish in our waters.

## REVIEWING OBJECTIVES

You should now be able to:

### Identify physical, geographical, chemical, and biological aspects of the marine environment

▶ Oceans cover 71% of Earth's surface and contain over 97% of its surface water. (p. 468)

▶ Ocean water contains 96.5% $H_2O$ by mass and various dissolved salts. (p. 468–469)

▶ Colder, saltier water is denser and sinks. Water temperatures vary with latitude, and temperature variation is greater in surface layers. (pp. 469–470)

▶ Persistent currents move horizontally through the oceans, driven by density differences, sunlight, and wind. (pp. 470–471)

▶ Vertical water movement includes upwelling and downwelling, which affect the distribution of nutrients and life. (p. 471)

▶ Seafloor topography can be complex and rugged. (pp. 471–472)

### Describe major types of marine ecosystems

▶ Major types of marine and coastal ecosystems include pelagic and deep-water open ocean systems, kelp forest, coral reefs, intertidal zones, salt marshes, mangrove forests, and estuaries. (pp. 473–478)

▶ Many of these systems are highly productive and rich in biodiversity. Many also suffer heavy impacts from human influence. (pp. 473–478)

### Outline historic and current human uses of marine resources

▶ For millennia, people have drawn resources from the oceans and used ocean waters for transportation. (p. 478)

▶ Today we extract energy and minerals from the oceans, as well as using them for transportation. (pp. 478–479)

### Assess human impacts on marine environments

▶ People pollute ocean waters with trash, untreated sewage, petroleum spills, plastic that harms marine life, and nutrient pollution that leads to harmful algal blooms. (pp. 479–481)

▶ Overharvesting is perhaps the major human impact on marine systems. (p. 482)

### Review the current state of ocean fisheries and reasons for their decline

▶ Half the world's marine fish populations are fully exploited, 25% are already overexploited, and 25% can yield more without declining. (p. 482)

▶ People began depleting marine resources long ago, but impacts have intensified in recent decades. (p. 483)

▶ Global fish catches have stopped growing since the late 1980s, despite increased fishing effort and improved technologies. (p. 482, 484)

▶ Today's oceans hold only one-tenth the number of large animals that they did before the advent of industrialized commercial fishing. (pp. 483–484)

▶ As fishing intensity increases, the fish available become smaller. (pp. 484–485)

▶ Fishing practices such as driftnetting, longline fishing, and trawling capture nontarget organisms, called bycatch. (p. 485)

▶ Traditional fisheries management has not stopped declines, so many scientists feel that ecosystem-based management is needed. (pp. 487–488)

### Evaluate marine protected areas and reserves as innovative solutions

▶ We have established fewer protected areas in the oceans than we have on land and most marine protected areas allow many extractive activities. (p. 488)

▶ No-take marine reserves can protect ecosystems while also boosting fish populations and making fisheries sustainable. (pp. 488–491)

## TESTING YOUR COMPREHENSION

**1.** What proportion of Earth's surface do oceans cover? About how much salt does ocean water contain? How are water density, salinity, and temperature related in each layer of ocean water?

**2.** What factors drive the system of ocean currents? In what directions do ocean currents move, and how do such movements affect conditions for life in the oceans?

3. Where in the oceans are productive areas of biological activity likely to be found?

4. Describe three kinds of ecosystems found near coastal areas and the kinds of life they support.

5. Why are coral reefs biologically valuable? What are some possible ways in which they are being degraded by human impact? What is causing the disappearance of mangrove forests and salt marshes?

6. Describe three major forms of pollution in the oceans and the consequences of each.

7. Provide an example of how overfishing can lead to ecological damage and fishery collapse.

8. Explain the conclusion of the Myers and Worm study of 2003 (see Figure 16.21).

9. Name three industrial fishing practices that create by-catch and harm marine life, and explain how they do so.

10. How does a marine protected area differ from a marine reserve? Why do many fishers oppose marine reserves? Explain why many scientists say no-take reserves will be good for fishers.

## SEEKING SOLUTIONS

1. What benefits do you derive from the oceans? How does your behavior affect the oceans? Give specific examples.

2. We have been able to reduce the amount of oil we spill into the oceans, but petroleum-based products such as plastic continue to litter our oceans and shorelines. Discuss some ways that we can reduce this threat to the marine environment.

3. What factors account for the trends in global fish capture over the past 20 years?

4. Consider what you know about biological productivity in the oceans, about the scientific data on marine reserves, and about the social and political issues surrounding the establishment of marine reserves. What ocean regions do you think it would be particularly appropriate to establish as marine reserves? Why?

5. Why does the 2001 scientific consensus statement argue for networks of reserves to be established? What role

should science and scientists play in this kind of decision making? Discuss how you would engage a group of fishers, environmentalists, and scientists in a reserve-planning process.

6. You are mayor of a coastal town where some residents are employed as commercial fishers and others make a living serving ecotourists who come to snorkel and scuba-dive at the nearby coral reef. In recent years, several fish stocks have crashed, and ecotourism is dropping off as fish disappear from the increasingly degraded reef. Scientists are urging you to help establish a marine reserve around portions of the reef, but most commercial and recreational fishers are opposed to this idea. What steps would you take to restore your community's economy and environment?

## INTERPRETING GRAPHS AND DATA

The accompanying graph presents trends in the status of ocean fisheries. Fully exploited fisheries (green line) are ones currently producing their maximum sustainable yield. Moderately exploited and underexploited fisheries (blue line) are ones that could be more heavily fished than they are and could produce larger, yet sustainable, yields. Over-exploited, depleted, and recovering fisheries (red line) are ones that have been overfished.

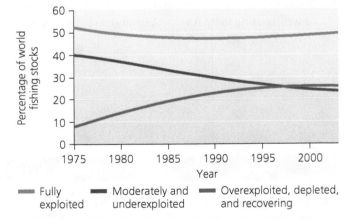

Global trends in the state of ocean fishing stocks from 1975 to 2003. Data from U.N. Food and Agriculture Organization (FAO), Fisheries Department. 2004. *The state of world fisheries and aquaculture: 2004.*

1. What is the sum of the percentages for any given year in the figure above? Explain why this is so.
2. Describe the trend from 1975 to 2003 in the percentage of fisheries categorized as overexploited, depleted, or recovering. Describe the trend from 1975 to 2003 in the percentage of fisheries categorized as moderately exploited or underexploited.
3. Based on the data in the graph, predict the likely trend in overall ocean fisheries production over the next 25 years. Explain your answer.

## CALCULATING ECOLOGICAL FOOTPRINTS

The relationship between the ecological goods and services used by individuals and the amount of *land* area needed to provide those goods and services is relatively well developed. People also use goods and services from Earth's oceans, where the concept of *area* is less useful. It is clear, however, that our removal of fish from the oceans has an impact, or an ecological footprint, on remaining fish populations.

The table shows data on the mean annual per capita consumption from ocean fisheries for North America, China, and the world as a whole. Using the data provided, calculate the amount of fish each consumer group would consume at the annual per capita consumption rates for each of these three regions, and record your results in the table.

|  | Annual per capita consumption rate | | |
|---|---|---|---|
| Consumer group | North America 21.6 kg | China 27.7 kg | World 16.2 kg |
| You | | | |
| Your class | | | |
| Your state | | | |
| United States | $6.48 \times 10^9$ kg | $8.31 \times 10^9$ kg | $4.86 \times 10^9$ kg |
| World | | | |

Data from U.N. Food and Agriculture Organization (FAO), Fisheries Department. 2004. *The state of world fisheries and aquaculture: 2004.* Data are for 2002, the most recent year for which comparative data are available.

1. Calculate the ratio of North America's per capita fish consumption rate to that of the world. Compare this ratio to the ratio of the per capita ecological footprints for the United States, Canada, and Mexico (see Figure 1.13, ▶ p. 19) versus the world average footprint of 2.2 ha/person/year. Can you account for similarities and differences between these ratios?
2. The population of China has grown at an annual rate of 1.1% since 1987, while over the same period fish consumption in China has grown at an annual rate of 8.9%. Speculate on the reasons behind China's rapidly increasing consumption of fish.
3. What ecological concerns do the combined trends of human population growth and increasing per capita fish consumption raise for you? What role might you play in contributing to these concerns or to their solutions?

## Take It Further

Go to www.aw-bc.com/withgott or the student CD-ROM where you'll find:

▶ Suggested answers to end-of-chapter questions
▶ Quizzes, animations, and flashcards to help you study
▶ *Research Navigator*™ database of credible and reliable sources to assist you with your research projects

▶ **GRAPHit!** tutorials to help you master how to interpret graphs
▶ **INVESTIGATEit!** current news articles that link the topics that you study to case studies from your region to around the world

# 17 Atmospheric Science and Air Pollution

View of Earth's atmosphere from space

## Upon successfully completing this chapter, you will be able to:

▶ Describe the composition, structure, and function of Earth's atmosphere

▶ Outline the scope of outdoor air pollution and assess potential solutions

▶ Explain stratospheric ozone depletion and identify steps taken to address it

▶ Define acidic deposition and illustrate its consequences

▶ Characterize the scope of indoor air pollution and assess potential solutions

London — Europe
Atlantic Ocean
Africa

# Central Case: The 1952 "Killer Smog" of London

"You had this swirling, like somebody had set a load of car tires on fire."
—STAN CRIBB, EYEWITNESS TO THE DECEMBER 1952 "GREAT SMOKE" OF LONDON

"The modern field of environmental health owes much to the tragedy that befell Greater London some 50 years ago."
—DEVRA L. DAVIS, MICHELLE L. BELL, AND TONY FLETCHER, IN AN EDITORIAL FOR THE JOURNAL ENVIRONMENTAL HEALTH PERSPECTIVES

December 5, 1952, was a particularly cold Friday in London, and many residents stoked their coal stoves to keep the chill away. Few people took notice when thick, foul-smelling smog, a fog polluted with smoke and chemical fumes, first settled over the city. After all, London had been famous for its "pea souper" fogs for well over a century.

But the smog that December weekend was particularly thick; the city's air quality was ten times worse than usual for that year. Visibility was so poor that pedestrians could not see across the street.

Transportation came to a standstill, and roads became clogged with abandoned cars. Schools closed, cattle asphyxiated, and an opera was halted because the audience could not see the stage.

A wind finally relieved Londoners of the miserable smog on Tuesday, December 9. By that time, however, authorities estimated that over 4,000 people had died, mostly from lung ailments such as bronchitis that were induced or aggravated by the pollution. A 2002 study by American researchers estimated that the actual death toll, including delayed cases that appeared over the next 2 months and were considered unrelated at the time, may have been as high as 12,000.

The "killer smog" of 1952 was remarkable, but hardly unique. Similar, although less severe, phenomena had occurred in London as early as 1813 and again in 1873, 1880, 1891, and 1948. Other such events have taken lives in Pennsylvania, New York, Mexico, and Malaysia. London's killer smog, together with other severe smog events, helped change the way the public viewed air pollution. Before the 1950s, most people considered urban smog a necessary burden. Today, we recognize the importance of clean air and view air pollution as an environmental challenge that can be overcome.

We have overcome much already; declines in air pollution represent some of the biggest successes of environmental policy. These declines have been due largely to limits on emissions brought about through legislation, such as the British Clean Air Acts of 1956 and 1968 and the U.S. Clean Air Acts of 1970 and 1990. Today, the air in many U.S. cities is cleaner, and the concentration of airborne particles around London averages one-tenth that of the 1950s.

However, much remains to be done. In 2002, a London governmental body estimated that vehicle emissions contribute to the premature deaths of 380 city residents each year. Furthermore, many cities in developing nations that have increasing populations, older technologies, and lax legislation and enforcement face conditions similar to those of 1950s London. For example, in 1995 air pollution in Delhi, India, was measured at 1.3 times London's average for the year 1952, and air pollution in Lanzhou, China, was measured at 2.7 times London's 1952 level. To understand what caused London's killer smog and how we can prevent recurrences of such events, we must examine both natural atmospheric conditions and human-made pollutants.

# Atmospheric Science

Every breath we take reaffirms our connection to the **atmosphere,** the thin layer of gases that surrounds Earth. We live at the bottom of this layer, which provides us oxygen, absorbs hazardous solar radiation, burns up incoming meteors, transports and recycles water and nutrients, and moderates climate.

The atmosphere consists of roughly 78% nitrogen gas ($N_2$) and 21% oxygen gas ($O_2$). The remaining 1% is composed of argon gas (Ar) and minute concentrations of several other *permanent gases* that remain at stable concentrations. The atmosphere also contains a number of *variable gases* that vary in concentration from time to time or place to place, as a result of natural processes or human activities on Earth's surface (Figure 17.1).

Over Earth's long history, the atmosphere's chemical composition has changed. Oxygen gas began to build up in an atmosphere dominated by carbon dioxide ($CO_2$), nitrogen, carbon monoxide (CO), and hydrogen ($H_2$) about 2.7 billion years ago, with the emergence of

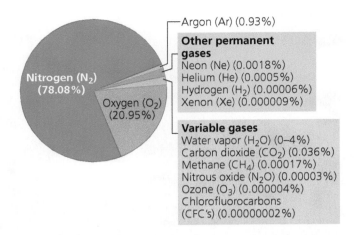

**FIGURE 17.1** Earth's atmosphere consists mostly of nitrogen, secondarily of oxygen, and lastly of a mix of gases at dilute concentrations. Permanent gases are fixed in concentration. Variable gases vary in concentration as a result of either natural processes or human activities. Data from Ahrens, D.C. 1998. *Essentials of meteorology,* 2nd ed. New York: Wadsworth.

autotrophic microbes that emitted oxygen as a by-product of photosynthesis (▶ p. 108). Just as these early organisms had a substantial impact on the Earth's atmosphere long ago, human activity is altering the quantities of some atmospheric gases today, such as carbon dioxide, methane ($CH_4$), and ozone ($O_3$). In this chapter and in Chapter 18, we will explore the atmospheric changes brought about by artificial pollutants, but we must first begin with an overview of Earth's atmosphere.

## The atmosphere consists of several layers

The atmosphere that stretches so high above us and seems so vast is actually just a thin coating about 1/100th of Earth's diameter, like the fuzzy skin of a peach. This coating consists of four layers whose boundaries are not visible to the human eye, but which atmospheric scientists recognize by measuring differences in temperature, density, and composition (Figure 17.2).

The bottommost layer, the **troposphere,** blankets Earth's surface and provides organisms the air they need to live. The movement of air within the troposphere is also largely responsible for the planet's weather. Although it is thin (averaging 11 km [7 mi] high) relative to the atmosphere's other layers, the troposphere contains three-quarters of the atmosphere's mass, because air is denser near Earth's surface. On average, tropospheric air temperature declines by about 6 °C for each

**FIGURE 17.2** Some aspects of the atmosphere change with altitude across its four layers. Temperature drops with altitude in the troposphere, rises with altitude in the stratosphere, drops in the mesosphere, then rises again in the thermosphere. The tropopause separates the troposphere from the stratosphere. Ozone reaches a peak in a portion of the stratosphere, giving rise to the term *ozone layer.* Adapted from Jacobson, M. Z. 2002. *Atmospheric pollution: History, science, and regulation.* Cambridge: Cambridge University Press; Parson, E. A. 2003. *Protecting the ozone layer: Science and strategy.* Oxford: Oxford University Press.

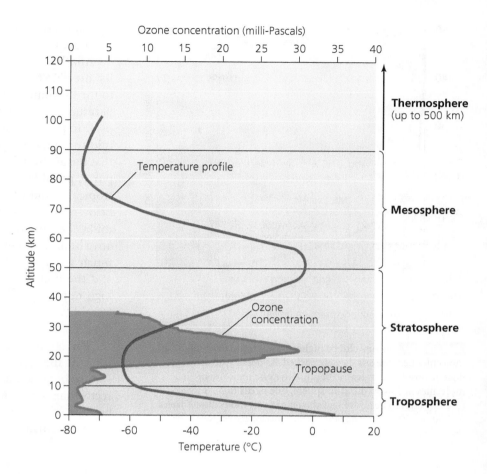

kilometer in altitude (or 3.5 °F per 1,000 ft), dropping to roughly −52 °C (−62 °F) at its highest point. At the top of the troposphere, however, temperatures cease to decline with altitude, marking a boundary called the *tropopause.* The tropopause acts like a cap, limiting mixing between the troposphere and the atmospheric layer above it, the stratosphere.

The **stratosphere** extends 11–50 km (7–31 mi) above sea level. Similar in composition to the troposphere, the stratosphere is 1,000 times drier and less dense. Its gases experience little vertical mixing, so once substances (including pollutants) enter it, they tend to remain for a long time. The stratosphere attains a maximum temperature of −3 °C (27 °F) at its highest altitude and becomes cooler in its lower reaches. The reason is that ozone and oxygen absorb and scatter the sun's ultraviolet (UV) radiation (▶p. 106), so that much of the UV radiation penetrating the upper stratosphere fails to reach the lower stratosphere. Most of the atmosphere's minute amount of ozone is concentrated in a portion of the stratosphere roughly

17–30 km (10–19 mi) above sea level, a region that has come to be called Earth's **ozone layer.** The ozone layer greatly reduces the amount of UV radiation that reaches Earth's surface. Because UV light can damage living tissue and induce DNA mutations, the ozone layer's protective effects are vital for life on Earth.

Above the stratosphere lies the *mesosphere,* which extends 50–90 km (31–56 mi) above sea level. Air pressure is extremely low here, and temperatures decrease with altitude, reaching their lowest point (−90 °C, or −130 °F) at the top of the mesosphere. From here, the *thermosphere* extends upward to an altitude of 500 km (300 mi). In the thermosphere, molecules are so few and far between that they collide only rarely. As a result, heavier molecules (such as nitrogen and oxygen) sink, and light ones (such as hydrogen and helium) end up near the top of the thermosphere. This stands in contrast to the atmosphere's lower three layers, where frequent collisions among molecules keep the chemical composition (see Figure 17.1) relatively constant throughout.

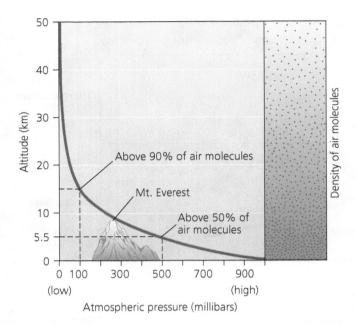

**FIGURE 17.3** As one climbs higher through the atmosphere, gas molecules become less densely packed. As density decreases, so does atmospheric pressure. Because the vast majority of air molecules lie low in the atmosphere, one needs to be only 5.5 km (3.4 mi) high to be above half the planet's air molecules. Adapted from Ahrens, D. C. 1998. *Essentials of meteorology*, 2nd ed. New York: Wadsworth.

## Atmospheric properties include temperature, pressure, and humidity

Although the lower atmosphere is stable in its composition, it is dynamic in its movement; air moves within it as a result of differences in the physical properties of air masses. Among these properties are pressure and density, relative humidity, and temperature. Gravity pulls gas molecules toward Earth's surface, causing air to be most dense near the surface and less so as altitude increases. **Atmospheric pressure,** which measures the force per unit area produced by a column of air, also decreases with altitude, because at higher altitudes fewer molecules are pulled down by gravity (Figure 17.3). At sea level, atmospheric pressure is 14.7 lb/in.$^2$ or 1,013 millibar (mb). Mountain climbers trekking to Mount Everest, the world's highest mountain, can look up and view their destination from Kala Patthar, a nearby peak, at roughly 5.5 km (18,000 ft). At this altitude, pressure is 500 mb, and half the atmosphere's air molecules are above the climber and half are below. A climber who reaches Everest's peak (8.85 km [29,035 ft]), where the "thin air" is just over 300 mb, stands above two-thirds of the molecules in the atmosphere. When we fly on a commercial jet

airline, at a typical cruising altitude of 11 km (36,000 ft), we are above roughly 80% of the atmosphere's molecules.

Another important property of air is **relative humidity,** the ratio of water vapor a given volume of air contains to the maximum amount it *could* contain at a given temperature. Relative humidity varies considerably from place to place and time to time. Average daily relative humidity in June in Phoenix, Arizona, is only 31% (meaning that the air contains just less than a third of the water vapor it possibly can at its temperature), whereas on the tropical island of Guam, relative humidity rarely drops below 88%. People are sensitive to changes in relative humidity because we perspire to cool our bodies. When relative humidity is high, the air is already holding nearly as much water vapor as it can, so sweat evaporates slowly and the body cannot cool itself efficiently. This is why high humidity makes it feel hotter than it really is. Low humidity speeds evaporation and makes it feel cooler than it really is.

The temperature of air also varies with location and time. At the global scale, temperature varies over Earth's surface because the sun's rays strike some areas more directly than others. At more local scales, temperature varies because of topography, plant cover, proximity of land to water, and many other factors.

## Solar energy heats the atmosphere, helps create seasons, and causes air to circulate

Energy from the sun influences temperatures by heating air in the atmosphere. Solar energy also drives the atmosphere's air movement, helps create seasons, and influences both weather and climate. An enormous amount of solar energy continuously bombards the upper atmosphere—over 1,000 watts/m$^2$, many thousands of times greater than the total output of electricity generated by human society. Of that solar energy, about 70% is absorbed by the atmosphere and planetary surface, while the rest is reflected back into space (see Figure 18.1, ▶p. 531).

The spatial relationship between Earth and the sun determines the amount of solar radiation that strikes each point of Earth's surface. Sunlight is most intense when it shines directly overhead and meets the planet's surface at a perpendicular angle. At this angle, sunlight passes through a minimum of energy-absorbing atmosphere, and Earth's surface receives a maximum of solar energy per unit surface area. Conversely, solar energy that approaches Earth's surface at an oblique angle loses intensity as it traverses a longer distance through the atmosphere, and it is less concentrated when it reaches the surface.

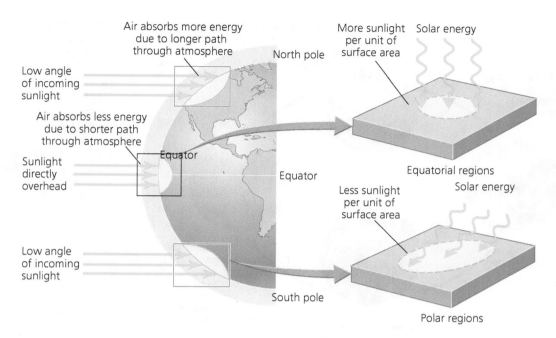

**FIGURE 17.4** Because of Earth's curvature, polar regions receive on average less solar energy than equatorial regions. One reason is that sunlight gets spread over a larger area when striking the surface at an angle, a phenomenon that increases with distance from the equator. Another reason is that as sunlight approaches at a lower angle near the poles, it must traverse a longer distance through the atmosphere before reaching the surface, during which more energy is absorbed or reflected. These patterns represent year-round averages; the latitude at which radiation approaches the surface perpendicularly varies with the seasons (see Figure 17.5).

This is why, on average, solar radiation intensity is highest near the equator and weakest near the poles (Figure 17.4).

Because Earth is tilted on its axis (an imaginary line connecting the poles, running perpendicular to the equator) by about 23.5 degrees, the Northern and Southern Hemispheres each tilt toward the sun for half the year, resulting in the change in seasons (Figure 17.5). Regions near the equator are largely unaffected by this tilt; they experience about 12 hours each of sunlight and darkness every day throughout the year. Near the poles, however, the effect is strong, and seasonality is pronounced.

Land and surface water absorb solar energy, radiating some heat and causing some water to evaporate. Air near Earth's surface therefore tends to be warmer and moister than air at higher altitudes. These differences set into motion a process of **convective circulation** (Figure 17.6). Warm air, being less dense, rises and creates vertical currents. As air rises into regions of lower atmospheric pressure, it expands and cools. Once the air cools, it descends and becomes denser, replacing warm air that is rising. The air picks up heat and moisture near ground level and prepares to rise again, continuing the process. Similar convective circulation patterns occur within ocean

waters (▸p. 471), in columns of magma beneath Earth's surface (▸p. 208), and even in a simmering pot of soup. Convective circulation influences both weather and climate.

## The atmosphere drives weather and climate

In everyday speech, we often use the terms *weather* and **climate** interchangeably. However, these words have very distinct meanings. Both concepts involve the physical properties of the troposphere, such as temperature, pressure, humidity, cloudiness, and wind. However, **weather** specifies atmospheric conditions over short time periods, typically hours or days, and within relatively small geographic areas. **Climate,** in contrast, describes the pattern of atmospheric conditions found across large geographic regions over long periods of time, typically seasons, years, or millennia. Mark Twain once noted the distinction between climate and weather by saying, "Climate is what we expect, weather is what we get." For example, even very dry climates (such as that of the desert around Phoenix) occasionally have wet weather.

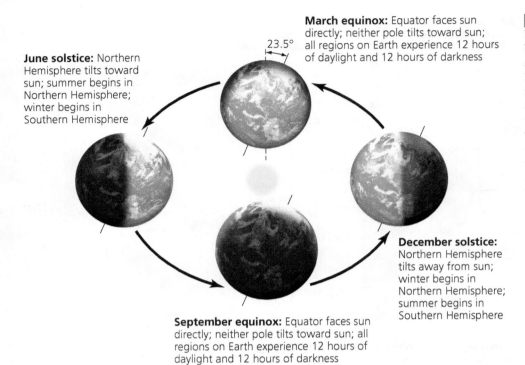

**June solstice:** Northern Hemisphere tilts toward sun; summer begins in Northern Hemisphere; winter begins in Southern Hemisphere

**March equinox:** Equator faces sun directly; neither pole tilts toward sun; all regions on Earth experience 12 hours of daylight and 12 hours of darkness

23.5°

**December solstice:** Northern Hemisphere tilts away from sun; winter begins in Northern Hemisphere; summer begins in Southern Hemisphere

**September equinox:** Equator faces sun directly; neither pole tilts toward sun; all regions on Earth experience 12 hours of daylight and 12 hours of darkness

**FIGURE 17.5** The seasons occur because Earth is tilted on its axis by 23.5 degrees. As Earth revolves around the sun, the Northern Hemisphere tilts toward the sun for one half of the year, and the Southern Hemisphere tilts toward the sun for the other half of the year. In each hemisphere, summer occurs during the period in which the hemisphere receives the most solar energy because of its tilt toward the sun.

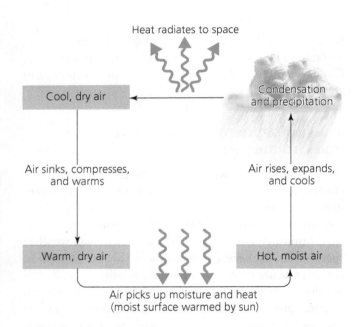

Heat radiates to space

Cool, dry air

Condensation and precipitation

Air sinks, compresses, and warms

Air rises, expands, and cools

Warm, dry air

Hot, moist air

Air picks up moisture and heat (moist surface warmed by sun)

**FIGURE 17.6** Weather is driven in part by the convective circulation of air in the atmosphere. Air being heated near Earth's surface picks up moisture and rises. Once aloft, this air cools, and moisture condenses, forming clouds and precipitation. Cool, drying air begins to descend, compressing and warming in the process. Warm dry air near the surface begins the cycle anew.

## Weather is produced by interacting air masses

Many changes in weather occur when air masses with different physical properties meet. The boundary between air masses that differ in temperature and moisture (and therefore density) is called a *front*. The boundary along which a mass of warmer, moister air replaces a mass of colder, drier air is termed a **warm front.** Some of the warm, moist air behind a warm front rises over the cold air mass and then cools and condenses to form clouds that may produce light rain. A **cold front** is the boundary along which a colder, drier air mass displaces a warmer, moister air mass. The colder air, being denser, tends to wedge beneath the warmer air. The warmer air rises, then cools and expands to form clouds that can produce thunderstorms. Once a cold front passes through, the sky usually clears, and the temperature and humidity drop (Figure 17.7).

Adjacent air masses may also differ in atmospheric pressure. An air mass with relatively high atmospheric pressure, or a **high-pressure system,** contains air that moves outward away from the center of high pressure as it descends. High-pressure systems typically bring fair weather. In a **low-pressure system,** air moves toward the low atmospheric pressure at the center of the system and spirals upward. The air expands and cools, and clouds and precipitation often result.

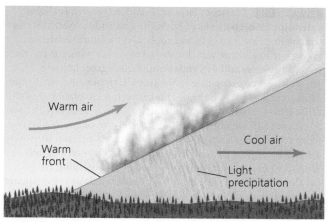

**(a) Warm front**

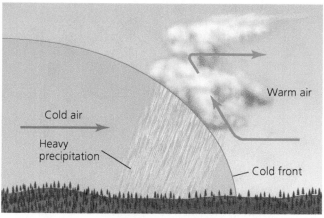

**(b) Cold front**

**FIGURE 17.7** When a warm front approaches, warmer air rises over cooler air, causing light to moderate precipitation as moisture in the warmer air condenses (**a**). When a cold front approaches, colder air pushes beneath warmer air, and the warmer air rises, causing condensation and resulting in heavy precipitation (**b**).

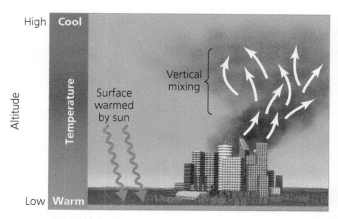

**(a) Normal conditions**

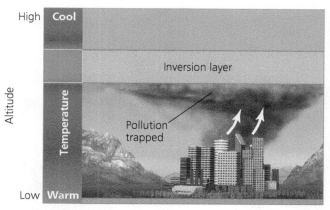

**(b) Thermal inversion**

**FIGURE 17.8** A thermal inversion is a natural atmospheric occurrence that can exacerbate air pollution locally. Under normal conditions (**a**), tropospheric temperature decreases with altitude, and air of different altitudes mixes somewhat freely, dispersing most pollutants upward and outward from their sources. During a thermal inversion (**b**), cool air remains near the ground underneath an "inversion layer" of warmer air. No mixing occurs, and pollutants are trapped within the cool layer near the surface.

Under most conditions, air in the troposphere decreases in temperature as altitude increases. Because warm air rises, this causes vertical mixing. Occasionally, however, a layer of relatively cool air occurs beneath a layer of warmer air. This departure from the normal temperature profile is known as a **temperature inversion**, or **thermal inversion** (Figure 17.8). The band of air in which temperature rises with altitude is called an **inversion layer** (because the normal direction of temperature change is inverted). The cooler air at the bottom of the inversion layer is denser than the warmer air at the top of the inversion layer, so it resists vertical mixing and remains stable. Thermal inversions can occur in different ways, sometimes involving cool air at ground level and sometimes producing an inversion layer higher above the

ground. One common type of inversion occurs in mountain valleys where slopes block morning sunlight, keeping ground-level air within the valley shaded and cool.

Whereas vertical mixing normally allows ground-level air pollution to be diluted upward, thermal inversions trap pollutants near the ground. It was a thermal inversion that sparked London's killer smog. A high-pressure system settled over the city, acting like a cap on the air pollution and keeping it in place. Although London's 1952 smog event was the worst single such event recorded, inversions regularly cause smog buildup in many areas worldwide. This is a problem particularly in large metropolitan areas in hilly terrain, such as Los Angeles; Mexico City; Seoul, Korea; and Rio de Janeiro and São Paulo, Brazil.

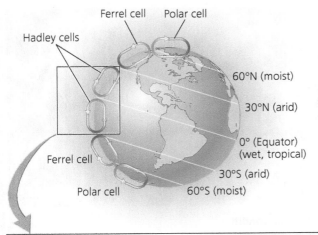

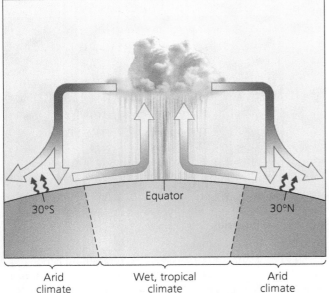

**(a) Convection currents**

**FIGURE 17.9** A series of large-scale convective cells (**a**) helps determine global patterns of humidity and aridity. Warm air near the equator rises, expands, and cools, and moisture condenses, giving rise to a warm, wet climate in tropical regions. Air travels toward the poles and descends around 30 degrees latitude. This air, which lost its moisture in the tropics, causes regions around 30 degrees latitude to be arid. This convective circulation, a Hadley cell, occurs on both sides of the equator. Between roughly 30 and 60 degrees latitude north and south, Ferrel cells occur; and between 60 and 90 degrees latitude, polar cells occur. As a result, air rises around 60 degrees latitude, creating a moist climate, and falls around 90 degrees, creating a dry climate. Global wind currents (**b**) show latitudinal patterns as well. Trade winds near the equator blow westward, while westerlies between 30 and 60 degrees latitude blow eastward.

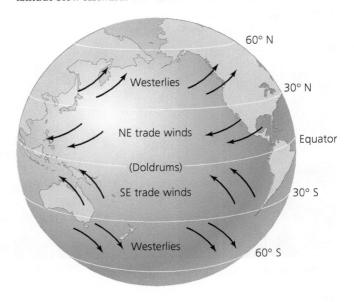

**(b) Global wind patterns**

## Global climate patterns result from large-scale circulation systems

At larger geographic scales, convective air currents contribute to climatic patterns that are maintained over long periods of time (Figure 17.9a). Near the equator, solar radiation sets in motion a pair of convective cells known as **Hadley cells.** Here, where sunlight is most intense, surface air warms, rises, and expands. As it does so, it releases moisture, producing the heavy rainfall that gives rise to tropical rainforests near the equator. After releasing much of its moisture, this air diverges and moves in currents heading northward and southward. The air in these currents cools and descends back to Earth at about 30 degrees latitude north and south. Because the descending air has low relative humidity, the regions around 30 degrees lati-

tude are quite arid, giving rise to deserts. Two pairs of similar but less intense convective cells, called **Ferrel cells** and **polar cells,** lift air and create precipitation around 60 degrees latitude north and south and cause air to descend at around 30 degrees latitude and in the polar regions.

These three pairs of cells account for the latitudinal distribution of moisture across Earth's surface: wet, tropical climates near the equator; arid climates near 30 degrees latitude; somewhat moist regions near 60 degrees latitude; and dry, arctic conditions near the poles. These patterns, combined with temperature variation, help explain why biomes tend to be arrayed in latitudinal bands (Figure 6.16, ►p. 170).

The Hadley, Ferrel, and polar cells interact with Earth's rotation to produce the global wind patterns shown in Figure 17.9b. As Earth rotates on its axis, locations on the equator spin faster than locations near the poles. As a result, the north-south air currents of the convective cells appear to be deflected from a straight path, as some portions of the globe move beneath them more quickly than others. This apparent deflection is called the **Coriolis effect**, and it results in the curving global wind patterns evident in Figure 17.9b. Near the equator lies a region with few latitudinal winds known as the *doldrums*. Between the equator and 30 degrees latitude lie the *trade winds*, which blow from east to west. From 30 to 60 degrees latitude are the *westerlies*, which originate from the west and blow east.

People used these global circulation patterns for centuries to facilitate ocean travel by wind-powered sailing ships. Moreover, the atmosphere interacts with the oceans to affect weather, climate, and the distribution of biomes. For instance, winds and convective circulation in ocean water together maintain ocean currents (▶ pp. 470–471), and trade winds weaken periodically, leading to El Niño conditions (▶ pp. 534, 536–537). The atmosphere's interactions with other systems of the planet can be complex, but even a basic understanding of how the atmosphere functions can help us comprehend how our pollution of the atmo-sphere can affect ecological systems, economies, and human health.

# Outdoor Air Pollution

Throughout human history, we have made the atmosphere a dumping ground for our airborne wastes. Whether from primitive wood fires or modern coal-burning power plants, people have generated significant quantities of **air pollutants**, gases and particulate material added to the atmosphere that can affect climate or harm people or other organisms. **Air pollution** refers to the release of air pollutants. In recent decades, government policy and improved technologies have helped us diminish *outdoor air pollution* (often called *ambient air pollution*) substantially in countries of the developed world. However, outdoor air pollution remains a problem, particularly in developing nations and in urban areas worldwide.

## Natural sources can pollute

When we think of outdoor air pollution, we tend to envision smokestacks belching black smoke from industrial plants. However, natural processes produce a great deal of the world's air pollution. Some of these natural impacts can be exacerbated by human activity and land-use policies.

Winds sweeping over arid terrain can send huge amounts of dust aloft. In 2001, strong westerlies lifted soil from deserts in Mongolia and China. The dust blanketed Chinese towns, spread to Japan and Korea, traveled eastward across the Pacific Ocean to the United States, then crossed the Atlantic and left evidence atop the French Alps. Every year, hundreds of millions of tons of dust are blown westward by trade winds across the Atlantic Ocean from northern Africa to the Americas (Figure 17.10a). Fungal and bacterial spores carried along with the dust have been linked to die-offs in Caribbean coral reef systems. Although dust storms are natural, the immense scale of these events results from nonsustainable farming and grazing practices that strip vegetation from the soil and promote wind erosion. Continental-scale dust storms took place in the United States in the 1930s, when soil from the drought-stricken Dust Bowl states blew eastward to the Atlantic (▶ p. 260).

Volcanic eruptions release large quantities of particulate matter, as well as sulfur dioxide and other gases, into the troposphere. Major eruptions may blow matter into the stratosphere, where it can remain for months or years. The 1980 eruption of Mount Saint Helens in Washington produced 1.1 billion m$^3$ (1.4 billion yd$^3$) of dust that circled the planet in 15 days (Figure 17.10b). The massive 1883 eruption on the Indonesian island of Krakatau blew enough dust into the atmosphere to cause a 1°C drop in global temperature (and produce gorgeous sunsets throughout the world).

The burning of vegetation also pollutes the atmosphere with soot and gases. Over 60 million ha (150 million acres) of forest and grassland burn in a typical year (Figure 17.10c). Fires occur naturally, but many today result from "slash-and-burn" forest clearing for farming and grazing in the tropics (▶ p. 255). In 1997, a severe drought brought on by the 20th century's strongest El Niño event caused fires in Indonesia to rage out of control. Their smoke sickened 20 million Indonesians, caused cargo ships to collide, and brought about a plane crash in Sumatra. More than 170 million metric tons of carbon monoxide were released from these fires. These, along with tens of thousands of fires in drought-plagued Mexico, Central America, and Africa, released more carbon monoxide into the atmosphere during 1997–1998 than did the worldwide burning of fossil fuels.

## Human activities create various types of outdoor air pollution

Human activity can exacerbate the severity of natural air pollution and can also introduce new sources of air pollution.

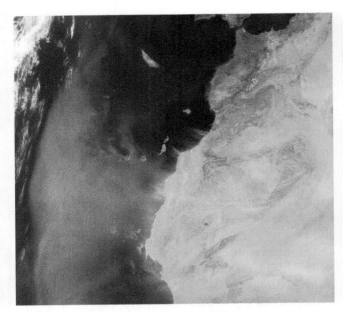

**(a) Dust storm from Africa to the Americas**

**(b) Mount Saint Helens eruption, 1980**

**(c) Natural fire in California**

**FIGURE 17.10** Massive dust storms, such as this one blowing across the Atlantic Ocean from Africa to the Americas (**a**), are one type of natural air pollution. Volcanoes are another, as shown by Mount Saint Helens (**b**), which erupted in Washington State in 1980. A third cause is natural fires in forests and grasslands (**c**).

may be stationary or may emit pollutants while in motion, as do automobiles, aircraft, ships, locomotives, construction equipment, and lawn mowers.

Once pollutants are in the atmosphere at sufficient concentrations, they may do harm directly or they may induce chemical reactions that produce harmful compounds. **Primary pollutants,** such as soot and carbon monoxide, are pollutants emitted into the troposphere in a form that can be directly harmful or that can react to form harmful substances. **Secondary pollutants** are harmful substances produced when primary pollutants interact or react with constituents of the atmosphere.

Arguably the greatest human-induced air pollution problem today is our emission of greenhouse gases that contribute to global climate change. We will address this issue separately in Chapter 18.

## Clean Air Act legislation has addressed pollution in the United States

To address air pollution in the United States, Congress has passed a series of laws, beginning with the Air Pollution Control Act of 1955. The Clean Air Act of 1963 funded research into pollution control and encouraged emissions standards for automobiles and stationary point sources, such as industrial plants. Subsequent amendments

As with water pollution, air pollution can emanate from *point sources* or *non-point sources* (▶ p. 452). A point source describes a specific spot—such as a factory's smokestacks—where large quantities of pollutants are discharged. In contrast, *non-point sources* are more diffuse, often consisting of many small sources (such as millions of automobiles). In 1952 London, coal-burning power plants acted as point sources contributing to the killer smog, while millions of home fireplaces together comprised a potent non-point source. Pollution sources

expanded the legislation's scope and established a nation-wide air quality monitoring system.

In 1970, Congress thoroughly revised the law in what came to be known as the **Clean Air Act of 1970.** This legislation set stricter standards for air quality, imposed limits on emissions from new stationary and mobile sources, provided new funds for pollution-control research, and enabled citizens to sue parties violating the standards. Once some of these goals came to be viewed as too ambitious, amendments in 1977 altered some standards and extended some deadlines for compliance.

The **Clean Air Act of 1990** sought to strengthen regulations pertaining to air quality standards, auto emissions, toxic air pollution, acidic deposition, and stratospheric ozone depletion. It also introduced an emissions trading program (▶ p. 73) for sulfur dioxide. Beginning in 1995, businesses and utilities were allocated permits for emitting this pollutant, and could then buy, sell, or trade these allowances with one another. Each year the overall amount of allowed pollution was decreased. This market-based incentive program has proven successful, and has spawned similar programs at state and regional levels and for other pollutants.

As a result of Clean Air Act legislation, the U.S. Environmental Protection Agency (EPA) sets nationwide standards for emissions of pollutants and concentrations of pollutants in ambient air throughout the nation. However, it is largely up to the states to monitor air quality and develop, implement, and enforce regulations within their boundaries. States submit implementation plans to the EPA for approval, and if a state's plans are not adequate, the EPA can take over enforcement in that state.

## The EPA sets standards for "criteria pollutants"

The EPA and the states focus on six **criteria pollutants,** pollutants judged to pose especially great threats to human health—carbon monoxide (CO), sulfur dioxide ($SO_2$), nitrogen dioxide ($NO_2$), tropospheric ozone ($O_3$), particulate matter, and lead (Pb). For these, the EPA has established *national ambient air quality standards (NAAQS),* which are maximum allowable concentrations of these pollutants in ambient outdoor air. Through risk assessment procedures (▶ pp. 422–423), these six pollutants were selected on the basis of criteria relating to human health.

**Carbon monoxide** Carbon monoxide is a colorless, odorless gas produced primarily by the incomplete combustion of fuels. In the United States in 2004, 87.2 mil-lion tons of CO were released, making it the most abundant air pollutant by mass. Vehicles account for about 62% of these emissions, but other sources include lawn and garden equipment (10%), forest fires (6%), open burning of industrial waste (3%), and residential wood burning (2%). Carbon monoxide poses risk to humans and other animals, even in small concentrations. It can bind irreversibly to hemoglobin in red blood cells, preventing the hemoglobin from binding with oxygen. U.S. emissions of CO have decreased in recent decades largely because of cleaner-burning motor vehicle engines.

**Sulfur dioxide** Like CO, sulfur dioxide is a colorless gas. Of the 15.2 million metric tons of $SO_2$ released in the United States in 2004, about 70% resulted from the combustion of coal for electricity generation and industry. During combustion, elemental sulfur (S) in coal reacts with oxygen gas ($O_2$) to form $SO_2$. Once in the atmosphere, $SO_2$ may react to form sulfur trioxide ($SO_3$) and sulfuric acid ($H_2SO_4$), which may then fall back to Earth in the form of acid precipitation.

**Nitrogen dioxide** Nitrogen dioxide is a highly reactive, foul-smelling reddish brown gas that contributes to smog and acid precipitation. Along with nitric oxide (NO), $NO_2$ belongs to a family of compounds called nitrogen oxides ($NO_x$). Nitrogen oxides result when atmospheric nitrogen and oxygen react at the high temperatures created by combustion engines. Of the 18.8 million tons of nitrogen oxides released in the United States in 2004, over half resulted from combustion in vehicle engines. Electrical utility and industrial combustion accounted for most of the rest.

**Tropospheric ozone** Although ozone in the stratosphere shields organisms from the dangers of UV radiation, $O_3$ from human activity forms and accumulates low in the troposphere and acts as a pollutant. In the troposphere, this colorless gas results from the interaction of sunlight, heat, nitrogen oxides, and volatile carbon-containing chemicals. Ozone is therefore categorized as a secondary pollutant. A major component of smog, $O_3$ can pose health risks as a result of its instability as a molecule; this triplet of oxygen atoms will readily release one of its threesome, leaving a molecule of oxygen gas and a free oxygen atom. The free oxygen atom may then participate in reactions that can injure living tissues and cause respiratory problems. Although concentrations fell by 11–18% (depending on how they were measured) in the United States from 1982 to 2001, tropospheric $O_3$ is the pollutant that most frequently exceeds the EPA standard.

**Particulate matter** Particulate matter is composed of solid or liquid particles small enough to be suspended in the atmosphere. Particulate matter includes primary pollutants such as dust and soot, as well as secondary pollutants such as sulfates and nitrates. Particulate matter can damage respiratory tissues when inhaled. Most particulate matter in the atmosphere is wind-blown dust (60%), but 2.5 million tons of particulate matter was released by human activities in the United States in 2004. Along with sulfur dioxide, it was largely the emission of particulate matter from industrial and residential coal-burning sources that produced London's 1952 killer smog and the deaths resulting from that episode.

**Lead** Lead is a heavy metal that enters the atmosphere as a particulate pollutant. The lead-containing compounds tetraethyl lead and tetramethyl lead, when added to gasoline, improve engine performance. However, the exhaust from leaded gasoline emits lead into the atmosphere, from which it can be inhaled or can be deposited on land and water. Lead can enter the food chain, accumulate within body tissues, and cause central nervous system malfunction, mental retardation among children, and a variety of other ailments. Once people recognized the dangers of lead, leaded gasoline was phased out in the United States and other industrialized nations, and U.S. lead emissions plummeted 93% from 1980 to 1990. Since then, lead emissions have remained steady and low. Today most lead emitted in the United States comes from industrial metal smelting. However, many developing nations continue to add lead to gasoline and experience significant lead pollution.

## Agencies monitor pollutants that affect air quality

State and local agencies also monitor, calculate, and report to the EPA emissions of major pollutants that affect ambient concentrations of the six criteria pollutants. These include the four criteria pollutants that are primary pollutants (carbon monoxide, sulfur dioxide, particulate matter, and lead), as well as all nitrogen oxides (because NO reacts readily in the atmosphere to form $NO_2$, which is both a primary and secondary pollutant). Tropospheric ozone is a secondary pollutant only, so there are no emissions to monitor. Instead the EPA monitors emissions of volatile organic compounds, which can react to produce ozone and other secondary pollutants.

**Volatile organic compounds (VOCs)** are carbon-containing chemicals used in industrial processes such as dry-cleaning and manufacturing. One group of VOCs consists of hydrocarbons (▶ pp. 98–99) such as methane ($CH_4$, the primary component of natural gas), propane

($C_3H_8$, used as a portable fuel), butane ($C_4H_{10}$, found in cigarette lighters), and octane ($C_8H_{18}$, a component of gasoline). Human activity accounts for about half the VOC emissions in the United States, and the remainder comes from natural sources. For example, plants produce isoprene ($C_5H_8$) and terpene ($C_{10}H_{15}$), and animals produce methane. The largest sources of anthropogenic VOC emissions include industrial use of solvents (28%) and vehicle emissions (27%).

## Air pollution has decreased markedly since 1970

Since the Clean Air Act of 1970, emissions of each of the six monitored pollutants have decreased, and total emissions of the six together have declined by 54% (Figure 17.11a).

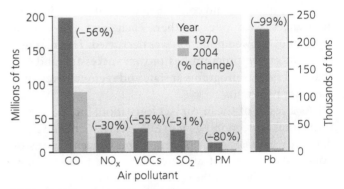

**(a) Declines in six major pollutants**

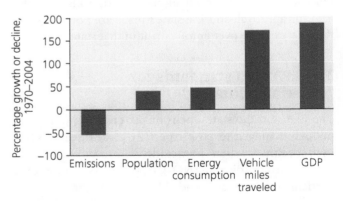

**(b) Trends in major indicators**

**FIGURE 17.11** The EPA tracks emissions of several major pollutants into ambient air. Shown are emissions of four of the six "criteria pollutants," along with nitrogen oxides and volatile organic compounds. Each of these pollutants has shown substantial declines since 1970, and emissions from all six together have declined by 54% **(a)**. This decrease in emissions has occurred despite increases in U.S. population, energy consumption, vehicle miles traveled, and gross domestic product **(b)**. Go to **GRAPHit!** at www.aw-bc.com/withgott or on the student CD-ROM. Data from U.S. EPA, 2004.

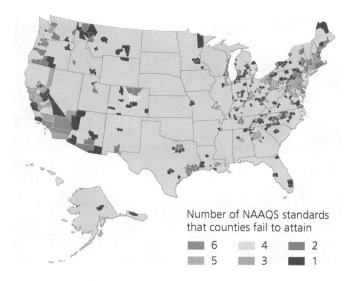

Number of NAAQS standards
that counties fail to attain

6    4    2
5    3    1

**FIGURE 17.12** Nearly half of all Americans live in counties that periodically fail to meet the EPA's national ambient air quality standards (NAAQS) for at least one criteria pollutant. This map shows counties that failed to attain the standards for one (blue) through six (red) of the six criteria pollutants. Data are for April 2005, from U.S. EPA.

This has occurred despite substantial increases in the nation's population, energy consumption, miles traveled by vehicle, and gross domestic product (Figure 17.11b). Because of the success in reducing emissions, air quality in the United States has improved markedly. As just one indicator, EPA data show that the percentage of days U.S. citizens were exposed to unhealthy air dropped from 10% in 1988 to 3% in 2001.

The reduction of outdoor air pollutant levels since 1970 represents one of the greatest accomplishments in safeguarding human health and environmental quality in the United States. However, the nation still has plenty of room to improve. Outdoor air pollution remains a problem, and in recent years, EPA monitoring has found that nearly half of all Americans live in counties where at least one of the six criteria pollutants periodically reaches unhealthy levels (Figure 17.12).

**Weighing the Issues:**
**Your County's Air Quality**

Locate where you live on the map in Figure 17.12. What is the status of your county's air quality, and how does your county compare to the rest of the nation? What factors do you think account for the quality of its air? Can you propose any solutions for reducing air pollution in your county?

## Toxic substances are also major pollutants

Other chemicals known to cause serious health or environmental problems are classified as **toxic air pollutants.** These include substances known to cause cancer, reproductive defects, or neurological, developmental, immune system, or respiratory problems. Also included are substances that cause substantial ecological harm by affecting the health of nonhuman animals and plants. Some toxic air pollutants are produced naturally. For example, hydrogen sulfide gas ($H_2S$) gives the mud of swamps and bogs the odor of rotten eggs. However, most toxic air pollutants are produced by human activities, such as metal smelting, sewage treatment, and industrial processes. The 1990 Clean Air Act identifies 188 different toxic air pollutants, ranging from the heavy metal mercury (from coal-burning power plant emissions and other sources) to VOCs such as benzene (a component of gasoline) and methylene chloride (found in paint stripper). Among the 188 pollutants are 21 from mobile sources (such as diesel exhaust) and 33 "urban hazardous" pollutants judged to pose the greatest health risks in urban areas.

State and federal agencies do not monitor toxic air pollutants as extensively as they do the six criteria pollutants, but so far 300 monitoring sites are operating, and coverage is improving. The EPA estimates that because of Clean Air Act regulations, from 1990 to 1999 emissions of toxic air pollutants decreased by 30%.

## Burning fossil fuels produces industrial smog

In response to the increasing incidence of fogs polluted by the smoke of Britain's industrial revolution, a British scientist coined the term *smog* long before the 1952 event in London. Today the term is used worldwide to describe unhealthy mixtures of air pollutants that often form over urban areas. The smog that enveloped London in 1952 was what we would today call **industrial smog,** or gray-air smog. When coal or oil is burned, some portion is completely combusted, forming $CO_2$; some is partially combusted, producing CO; and some remains unburned and is released as soot, or particles of carbon. Moreover, coal contains varying amounts of contaminants, including mercury and sulfur. Sulfur reacts with oxygen to form sulfur dioxide, which can undergo a series of reactions to form sulfuric acid and ammonium sulfate (Figure 17.13a). These chemicals and others produced by further reactions, along with soot, are the main components of industrial smog, and give the smog its characteristic gray color.

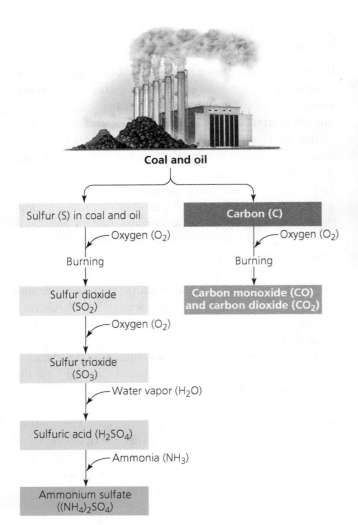

**(b) Donora, Pennsylvania, at midday in the 1948 smog event**

**FIGURE 17.13** Emissions from the combustion of coal and oil in manufacturing plants and utilities without pollution control technologies can create industrial smog. Industrial smog consists primarily of sulfur dioxide and particulate matter, as well as carbon monoxide and carbon dioxide from the carbon component of fossil fuels. Sulfur contaminants in fossil fuels when combusted create the sulfur dioxide, which in the presence of other chemicals in the atmosphere can produce several other sulfur compounds **(a).** Under certain weather conditions, industrial smog can blanket whole towns or regions, as it did in Donora, Pennsylvania, shown here in the daytime during its deadly 1948 smog episode **(b).**

**(a) Burning sulfur-rich oil or coal without adequate pollution control technologies**

Industrial smog is far less common today in developed nations than it was 50–100 years ago. In the wake of the 1952 London episode and others, the governments of most developed nations began regulating industrial emissions to minimize the external costs (▶ pp. 43–44) they impose on citizens. However, in industrializing regions such as China, India, and Eastern Europe, heavy reliance on coal burning (both by industry and by citizens heating and cooking in their homes), combined with lax air pollution controls, produces industrial smog that poses significant health risks in many urban areas.

Although coal combustion supplies the chemical constituents for industrial smog, weather also plays a role, as it did in London in 1952. A similar event occurred 4 years earlier in Donora, Pennsylvania. A thermal inversion trapped smog containing particulate matter emissions from a steel and wire factory. Twenty-one people were killed, and over 6,000 people—nearly half the town—

became ill (Figure 17.13b). In Donora's killer smog, air near the ground cooled during the night. Normally, morning sunlight warms the land and air, causing air to rise. However, because Donora is located in hilly terrain, too little sun reached the valley floor to warm and disperse the cold air. The resulting thermal inversion kept a pall of smog over the town long enough to impair visibility and cause serious health problems. Hilly topography such as Donora's is a factor in the air pollution of many other cities where surrounding mountains trap air and create inversions. This is true for the Los Angeles basin, which has long symbolized chronic smog problems in American popular culture. Modern-day Los Angeles, however, suffers from a different type of smog, one called photochemical smog.

## Photochemical smog is produced by a complex series of atmospheric reactions

A photochemical process is one whose activation requires light. **Photochemical smog,** or brown-air smog, is formed through light-driven chemical reactions of primary pollutants and normal atmospheric compounds that produce a mix of over 100 different chemicals, tropospheric ozone

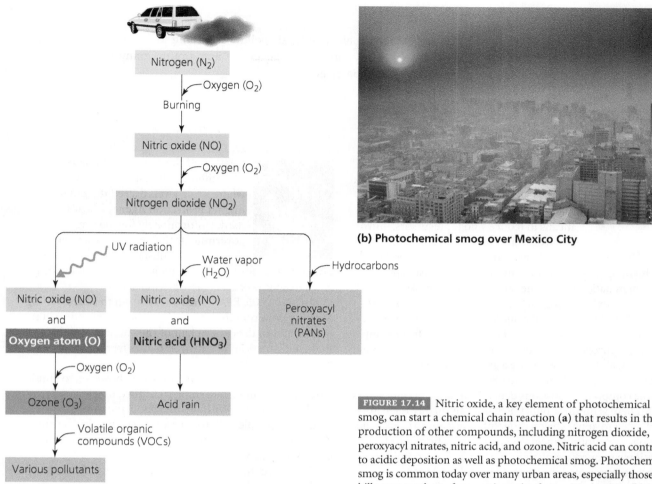

**(a) Formation of photochemical smog**

**(b) Photochemical smog over Mexico City**

**FIGURE 17.14** Nitric oxide, a key element of photochemical smog, can start a chemical chain reaction (**a**) that results in the production of other compounds, including nitrogen dioxide, peroxyacyl nitrates, nitric acid, and ozone. Nitric acid can contribute to acidic deposition as well as photochemical smog. Photochemical smog is common today over many urban areas, especially those with hilly topography or frequent inversion layers. Mexico City (**b**) is one city that frequently experiences photochemical smog.

often being the most abundant among them (Figure 17.14a). High levels of $NO_2$ cause photochemical smog to form a brownish haze over cities (Figure 17.14b). Hot, sunny, windless days in urban areas provide perfect conditions for the formation of photochemical smog. Exhaust from morning traffic releases large amounts of NO and VOCs into a city's air. Sunlight then promotes the production of ozone and other constituents of photochemical smog. Levels of photochemical pollutants in urban areas typically peak in mid-afternoon and at sufficient levels can irritate people's eyes, noses, and throats. Air pollutants called *peroxyacyl nitrates*, created by the reaction of $NO_2$ with hydrocarbons, can induce further reactions that damage living tissues in animals and plants.

Photochemical smog afflicts many major cities, especially those with topography and weather conditions that promote it. In Athens, Greece, site of the 2004 Olympics, the problem had been bad enough that the city government provided incentives to replace aging automobiles. It also mandated that cars with odd-numbered license plates be driven only on odd-numbered days, and those with even-numbered plates only on even-numbered days. According to Greek officials, smog has been reduced by 30% since 1990 as a result.

## Synthetic chemicals deplete stratospheric ozone

A pollutant at low altitudes, ozone is a highly beneficial gas at altitudes centering around 25 km (15 mi) in the lower stratosphere, where it is concentrated in the so-called *ozone layer*. Here, concentrations of ozone are only about 12 parts per million. However, ozone molecules are so effective at absorbing incoming ultraviolet radiation from the sun that this concentration is adequate to protect life on Earth's surface from the damaging effects of UV radiation.

In the 1960s, atmospheric scientists began wondering why their measurements of ozone were lower than theoretical models predicted. Researchers speculating that natural or artificial chemicals were depleting ozone finally

## Air Pollution

Despite improvements in air quality, air pollution leading to photochemical smog remains a health and environmental concern in and around many major cities. **What is needed to reduce this type of pollution?**

### A Policy Portfolio Approach to Fighting Smog

Federal and state regulations to control emissions from factories, power plants, and cars have reduced smog. Further progress will require more effective and affordable means to reduce smog "precursors," nitrogen oxides and volatile organic compounds, from old and new sources. Simply tightening the same regulations used in the past and applying them nationwide to the same sources is unlikely to significantly reduce smog for three reasons: control costs will be high and the marginal gains low for many "old" stationary sources already being regulated; emissions from many smaller sources, such as sport-utility vehicles, trucks, lawnmowers, and motorboats, are a growing concern; and the right mix of reductions in nitrogen oxide and volatile organic compound emissions depends on local circumstances.

There is no silver bullet. Regional air quality regulators will need to apply several different policy approaches, called a policy portfolio, to achieve further reductions. For large stationary sources, emissions trading is an economically attractive supplement to current technology-based regulations. Emissions trading works as follows: First, government regulators set a regional limit on nitrogen oxides. Then, regulators assign or auction to emissions sources only as many allowances (for example, one allowance equals one ton of nitrogen oxide emissions) as the overall limit (or "cap") permits. Lastly, emissions sources could take one of three actions: reduce their own emissions to stay within their allowances; sell or retire any excess allowances; or buy others' excess allowances to meet their own obligations. They would choose according to market prices, with the cheapest sources of reductions being made available first.

Small mobile sources that run on diesel fuel and gasoline are also a problem. For now, the federal government still needs to press manufacturers to build cleaner-burning vehicles and fuel makers to make cleaner fuels, as the EPA is doing. Meanwhile, regional regulators need to be given the flexibility and enforcement tools to tailor their efforts to highly variable regional climate and atmospheric conditions.

**Debra Knopman** is vice president and director of the Infrastructure, Safety, and Environment division of the RAND Corporation. This statement is based primarily on work she did at the Progressive Policy Institute, where she was director of the Center for Innovation and the Environment from 1995 to 2001.

### To Reduce Smog, States Must Take Up the Slack

Nearly half the people in this country—136 million individuals—live in areas where smog levels exceed the Environmental Protection Agency's health standard. Unfortunately for the state governments that are responsible for those areas, a substantial amount of the pollution that forms smog in their cities and valleys originates from power plants in up-wind states.

In May 2005, EPA issued a regulation to address smog-forming pollution that crosses state lines. The rule will require states in the eastern half of the country to tighten limits on emissions of nitrogen oxides from their power plants.

The prescribed limits are too weak, however, to eliminate all of the interstate smog transport, much less clean up all of the smog. Without additional measures, 20 million people will live in areas exceeding EPA's smog standard in 2015—5 years after the latest smog cleanup deadline in the Clean Air Act.

To protect their citizens from asthma attacks, hospitalizations, and missed schooldays and workdays, state governments must pick up the slack. That will require new urban planning measures to reduce vehicle miles traveled, because tailpipe emissions contribute to smog. It will also require states to impose new emissions limits—more stringent than the federally prescribed ones—on their own power plants, oil refineries, and factories.

In an attempt to avoid those new limits, large polluters in 2004 and again in 2005 convinced congressional allies to attach to the federal energy bill a provision that would have extended the Clean Air Act's smog cleanup deadlines by a decade. Fortunately, the measure was stripped from the bill after state officials made clear they were not interested in ignoring the problem. That was a good start. Now there is a lot of work to do.

**David McIntosh** is a staff attorney at the Natural Resources Defense Council in Washington, D.C. He litigates and lobbies to ensure effective implementation of clean air laws and to counter efforts aimed at weakening those laws.

Explore this issue further by accessing **Viewpoints** at www.aw-bc.com/withgott.

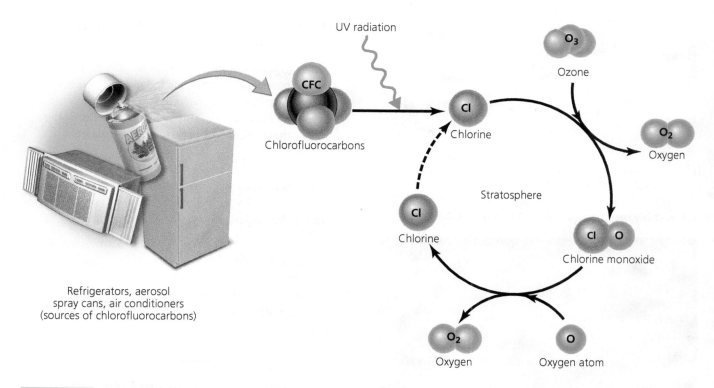

**FIGURE 17.15** Chlorofluorocarbons lead to the destruction of ozone molecules in the presence of ultraviolet radiation. A chlorine atom released from a CFC molecule reacts with an ozone molecule, forming one molecule of oxygen gas and one chlorine monoxide (ClO) molecule. The oxygen atom in the ClO molecule will then bind with a stray oxygen atom to form oxygen gas, leaving the chlorine atom to begin the destructive cycle anew. The self-perpetuating nature of this process means that one CFC molecule can destroy a great many ozone molecules.

pinpointed a group of human-made compounds derived from simple hydrocarbons, such as ethane and methane, in which hydrogen atoms are replaced by chlorine, bromine, or fluorine. One class of such compounds, **chlorofluorocarbons (CFCs),** was being mass-produced by industry at a rate of a million metric tons per year in the early 1970s, and it was growing by 20% a year.

In 1974, atmospheric scientists Sherwood Rowland and Mario Molina showed that CFCs could deplete stratospheric ozone by releasing chlorine atoms that split ozone molecules, creating from each of them an $O_2$ molecule and a ClO molecule (Figure 17.15). Three years before Rowland and Molina's study, researcher J. E. McDonald had predicted that ozone loss, by allowing more UV radiation to reach the surface, would result in thousands more skin cancer cases each year. This caught the attention of policymakers, environmentalists, and industry alike (see "The Science behind the Story," ▸ pp. 516–517).

Then in 1985, scientists from the British Antarctic Survey announced that stratospheric ozone levels over Antarctica had declined by 40–60% in the previous decade, leaving a thinned ozone concentration that was

soon dubbed the *ozone hole* (Figure 17.16). Research over the next few years confirmed the link between CFCs and ozone loss in the Antarctic and indicated that depletion was also occurring in the Arctic, and perhaps globally. Already concerned about skin cancer, scientists were becoming anxious over the possible effects of increased UV radiation on ecosystems. Research was showing a multitude of effects, including harm to crops and to the productivity of ocean phytoplankton, the base of the marine food chain.

## The Montreal Protocol addressed ozone depletion

In light of the science and the ongoing health and ecological concerns, international efforts to restrict CFC production finally bore fruit in 1987 with the **Montreal Protocol.** In this treaty, signatory nations (eventually numbering 180) agreed to cut CFC production in half. Five follow-up agreements strengthened the pact, deepening the cuts, advancing timetables for compliance, and addressing related ozone-depleting chemicals. Today the production and use

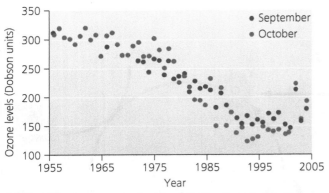

**(a) Monthly mean ozone levels at Halley Bay, Antarctica**

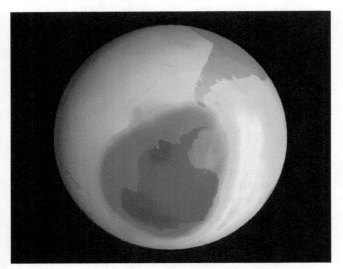

**(b) The "ozone hole" over Antarctica, September 2000**

**FIGURE 17.16** The "ozone hole" consists of a region of thinned ozone density in the stratosphere over Antarctica and the southernmost ocean regions. It has reappeared seasonally each September in recent decades. Data from Halley Bay, Antarctica **(a)**, show a steady decrease in stratospheric ozone concentrations from the 1960s to 1990. Ozone-depleting CFCs began to be regulated under the Montreal Protocol in 1987, and ozone concentrations stopped declining. Colorized satellite imagery from September 6, 2000 **(b)**, shows the "ozone hole" (blue) at its maximal recorded extent to date. Data from British Antarctic Survey.

of ozone-depleting compounds has fallen by 95% since the late 1980s, and scientists can discern the beginnings of long-term recovery of the ozone layer (although much of the 5 billion kg of CFCs emitted into the troposphere has yet to diffuse up into the stratosphere, and CFCs are slow to dissipate or break down). Industry was able to shift to alternative, environmentally safer chemicals, which have largely turned out to be cheaper and more efficient. For these reasons, the Montreal Protocol and its follow-up amendments are widely considered the biggest success story so far in addressing any global environmental problem.

Environmental scientists have attributed this success primarily to two factors:

1. Policymakers engaged industry in helping to solve the problem, and government and industry worked together on developing technological fixes and replacement chemicals. This cooperation reduced the battles that typically erupt between environmentalists and industry.
2. Implementation of the Montreal Protocol after 1987 followed an adaptive management approach (▶p. 346), altering strategies midstream in response to new scientific data, technological advances, or economic figures.

Because of its success in addressing ozone depletion, the Montreal Protocol is widely seen as a model for international cooperation in addressing other pressing global problems, such as persistent organic pollutants (▶pp. 426, 428), climate change (▶pp. 550, 552), and biodiversity loss (▶pp. 335–336).

---

**Weighing the Issues:**
## International Cooperation to Solve Global Problems

The Montreal Protocol showed how international collaboration, together with technological advances, can drastically and rapidly address a pressing environmental problem. So far, however, global problems such as organic pollutants, climate change, and biodiversity loss have not seen the same degree of targeted action. Why do you think this is? Besides the effort to halt stratospheric ozone depletion, can you name other success stories in addressing major environmental problems? Are any on the horizon?

---

## Acidic deposition represents another transboundary pollution problem

Just as the problem of stratospheric ozone depletion crosses political boundaries, so does another atmospheric pollution concern—acidic deposition. **Acidic deposition** refers to the deposition of acidic or acid-forming pollutants from the atmosphere onto Earth's surface. This can take place either by precipitation (commonly referred to as *acid rain*, but also including acid snow, sleet, and hail), by fog, by gases, or by the deposition of dry particles. Acidic deposition is one type of **atmospheric deposition,** which refers more broadly to the wet or dry deposition on land of a wide variety of pollutants, including mercury, nitrates, organochlorines, and others.

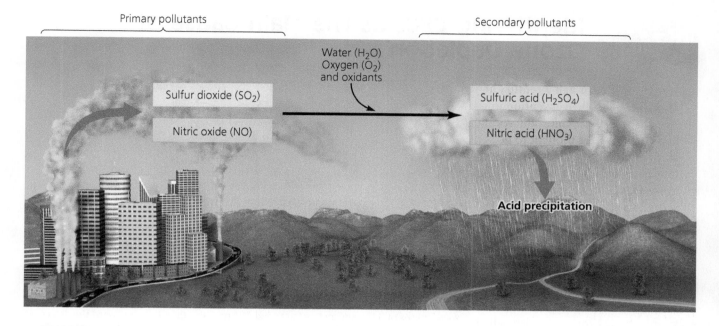

**FIGURE 17.17** Acidic deposition can have consequences many miles downwind from its source. Emissions containing sulfur dioxide and nitric oxide from industries and utilities begin the process. Sulfur dioxide and nitric oxide can be transformed into sulfuric acid and nitric acid through chemical reactions in the atmosphere, and these acidic compounds descend to Earth's surface in rain, snow, fog, and dry deposition.

Acidic deposition originates primarily with sulfur dioxide and nitrogen oxides, pollutants produced largely through fossil fuel combustion by automobiles, electric utilities, and industrial facilities. Once emitted into the troposphere, these pollutants can react with water, oxygen, and oxidants to produce compounds of low pH (▶ p. 98), primarily sulfuric acid and nitric acid. Suspended in the troposphere, droplets of these acids may travel for up to days or weeks, sometimes covering hundreds or thousands of kilometers before falling in precipitation (Figure 17.17).

Acidic deposition can have wide-ranging, cumulative detrimental effects on ecosystems and on our built environment (Table 17.1). Acids can leach basic minerals such as calcium and magnesium from soil, changing soil chemistry and harming plants and soil organisms. Streams, rivers, and lakes may become significantly acidified from runoff. In fact, thousands of lakes in Canada, Scandinavia, the United States, and elsewhere now contain water acidic enough to kill fish. Fish can die when acidic conditions cause toxic aluminum to be more readily accessible to their tissues. Elevated aluminum in the soil hinders water and nutrient uptake by plants. In some regions of the United States, acid fog with a pH of 2.3 (equivalent to vinegar) can envelop forests for extended periods. Some forests in eastern North America have experienced widespread tree die-back from these conditions.

Besides harming trees, acid precipitation also may damage agricultural crops. Moreover, it can erode stone buildings, eat away at cars, and erase the writing from tombstones. Ancient cathedrals in Europe, monuments in

| Table 17.1 | Effects of Acidic Deposition on Ecosystems in the Northeastern United States |
|---|---|

**Acidic deposition in northeastern forests has . . .**

▶ Accelerated leaching of base cations (ions that counteract acidic deposition) from soil

▶ Allowed sulfur and nitrogen to accumulate in soil

▶ Increased dissolved inorganic aluminum in soil, hindering plant uptake of water and nutrients

▶ Leached calcium from needles of red spruce, leading to tree mortality from wintertime freezing

▶ Increased mortality of sugar maples due to leaching of base cations from soil and leaves

▶ Acidified 41% of Adirondack, New York, lakes and 15% of New England lakes

▶ Lowered lakes' capacity to neutralize further acids

▶ Elevated aluminum levels in surface waters

▶ Reduced species diversity and abundance of aquatic life, and negatively affected entire food webs

*Source:* Adapted from Driscoll, C.T., et al. 2001. *Acid rain revisited.* Hubbard Brook Research Foundation.

# Identifying CFCs as the Main Cause of Ozone Depletion

For half a century after their invention in the 1920s, chlorofluorocarbons (CFCs) were thought to be useful, nontoxic, and environmentally friendly. In the early 1970s, however, scientists became concerned that CFCs could cause long-term damage to the ozone layer. By the late 1980s, evidence for such damage had become strong enough to justify a complete ban on CFC production. In their attempts to understand how CFCs influenced stratospheric ozone, scientists relied on a wide variety of data sources, including historical records, field observations, laboratory experiments, and computer models.

Stratospheric ozone and CFCs had each been the subject of much research before they were linked in the 1970s. Ozone was discovered in 1839, and its presence in the upper atmosphere was first proposed in the 1880s. In 1924, British scientist G. M. B. Dobson built what has become the standard instrument for measuring ozone from the ground. By the 1970s, the Dobson ozone spectrophotometer (see the figure) was being used by a global network of observation stations. However, scientists were unable to establish a clear picture of global trends in ozone concentrations because of

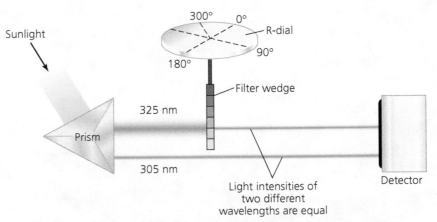

In the Dobson spectrophotometer, UV light passes through a prism that separates wavelengths of 325 nanometers (nm) and 305 nm, and then travels toward the detector. Because ozone absorbs wavelengths of 305 nm but not wavelengths of 325 nm, light that reaches the instrument after passing through the atmosphere contains more light of 325 nm wavelengths. The ratio between the intensities of the two wavelengths of light indicates the amount of ozone in the light's path between the sun and the spectrophotometer. To measure this ratio, the R-dial rotates, causing the filter wedge to block more and more 325-nm light, until the intensities of 325-nm and 305-nm light are equal. At that point, the reading on the R-dial is recorded, and a conversion is used to calculate the atmospheric ozone concentration. Figure adapted from University of Alaska, Fairbanks, http://ozone.gi.alaska.edu.

natural variations in ozone levels and the difficulty of comparing data from different stations.

Research on CFCs also had a long history. First invented in 1928, CFCs were found to be useful as refrigerants, fire extinguishers, and propellants for aerosol spray cans. Starting in the 1960s, CFCs also found wide use as cleaners for electronics and as a part of the process of manufacturing rigid polystyrene foams. Research on the chemical properties of CFCs showed that they were almost completely inert; that is, they rarely reacted with other chemicals. Therefore, scientists surmised that, at trace levels, CFCs would be harmless to both people and the environment.

However, in June 1974, chemists F. Sherwood Rowland and Mario

Washington, D.C., temples in Asia, and stone statues throughout the world are experiencing billions of dollars of damage as their features gradually wear away (Figure 17.18).

Because the pollutants leading to acid deposition can travel long distances, their effects may be felt far from their sources—a situation that has led to political bickering among the leaders of states and nations. For instance,

much of the pollution from power plants and factories in Pennsylvania, Ohio, and Illinois falls out in states to their east, including New York, Vermont, and New Hampshire, as well as in regions to the north, including Ontario, Quebec, and the maritime provinces of Canada. As Figure 17.19 shows, many regions of greatest acidification are downwind of major source areas of pollution.

Molina published a paper in the journal *Nature,* arguing that the inertness that made CFCs so ideal for industrial purposes could also have disastrous consequences for the ozone layer. More-reactive chemicals are broken down to their constituent atoms in the lower atmosphere. CFCs, in contrast, reach the stratosphere unchanged. Once CFCs reach the stratosphere, intense ultraviolet radiation from the sun breaks them into their constituent chlorine and carbon atoms. Each free chlorine atom, it was calculated, can catalyze the destruction of as many as 100,000 ozone molecules.

Rowland and Molina were the first to assemble a complete picture of the threat posed by CFCs, but they could not have reached their conclusions without the contributions of other scientists. British researcher James Lovelock had developed an instrument to measure extremely low concentrations of atmospheric gases, and American researchers Richard Stolarski and Ralph Cicerone had shown that chlorine atoms can catalyze the destruction of ozone.

Rowland and Molina's finding, which earned them the 1995 Nobel Prize in chemistry, helped spark discussion among scientists, policymakers, and industry leaders over limits on CFC production. As a result, the United States and several other nations banned the use of CFCs in aerosol spray cans in 1979. Other uses continued, however, and by the early 1980s global production of CFCs was increasing.

Then, in 1985, a new finding shocked scientists and spurred the international community to take further action. Scientists at a British research station in Antarctica had been recording ozone concentrations continuously since the 1950s. In May 1985, Joseph Farman and colleagues reported in *Nature* that Antarctic ozone concentrations had been declining dramatically since the 1970s. The decline exceeded even the worst-case predictions.

To determine what was causing the "ozone hole" over Antarctica, expeditions were mounted in 1986 and 1987 to measure trace amounts of atmospheric gases using ground stations and high-altitude balloons and aircraft. Together with other scientists, Dutch scientist Paul Crutzen, who would share the 1995 Nobel prize with Molina and Rowland, analyzed data collected on the expeditions and concluded that the ozone hole resulted from a combination of Antarctic weather conditions and human-made chemicals. In the frigid Antarctic winter, high-altitude clouds, or polar stratospheric clouds, were formed. In the spring, those clouds provided ideal conditions for CFC-derived chlorine and other chemicals to catalyze the destruction of massive amounts of ozone. The problem was exacerbated by the fact that prevailing air currents largely isolated Antarctica's atmosphere from the rest of Earth's atmosphere.

In the following years, scientists used data from ground stations and satellites to show that ozone levels were declining globally. In 1987, those findings helped convince the world's nations to agree on the Montreal Protocol, which aimed to cut CFC production in half by 1998. Within 2 years, however, further scientific evidence and computer modeling showed that more drastic measures would be needed if serious damage to the ozone layer were to be avoided. In 1990, the Montreal Protocol was strengthened to include a complete phaseout of CFCs by 2000. By 1998, the amount of chlorine in the atmosphere appeared to have leveled off, suggesting that the agreements had had the desired effect.

## Acid deposition has not been reduced as much as scientists had hoped

Reducing acid precipitation involves reducing amounts of the pollutants that contribute to it. New technology has helped; "scrubbers" that filter pollutants in smokestacks have allowed factories to decrease emissions (▸ pp. 655–656).

As a result of declining emissions of $SO_2$, average sulfate precipitation in 1996–2000 was 10% lower than in 1990–1994 across the United States and 15% lower in the eastern states. However, because of increasing $NO_x$ emissions, average nitrate precipitation increased nationally by 3% between these time periods.

**FIGURE 17.18** Acidic deposition can harm vegetation, alter soil chemistry, affect soil- and forest-dwelling animals, and even eat away at statues and buildings.

A recent report by scientists at New Hampshire's Hubbard Brook research forest, where acidic deposition's effects were first demonstrated in the United States, disputed the notion that the problem of acid deposition is being solved (see "The Science behind the Story," ▶ pp. 520–521). Instead, the report said, the effects are worse than first predicted, and the mandates of the 1990 Clean Air Act are not adequate to restore ecosystems in the northeastern United States. At Hubbard Brook, half the soil's calcium content has leached out, leaving the soil less able to neutralize future acid precipitation. This means that forests affected by acidification may take a long time to recover. An additional 80% reduction in sulfur emissions from electric utilities would be needed, the report estimates, to allow New Hampshire streams to recover in 20–25 years. The data on acid deposition show that although there have been many advances in the control of air pollution, more can clearly be done to alleviate outdoor pollution problems. The same can be said for indoor air pollution, a source of human health threats that is less familiar to most of us, but statistically more dangerous.

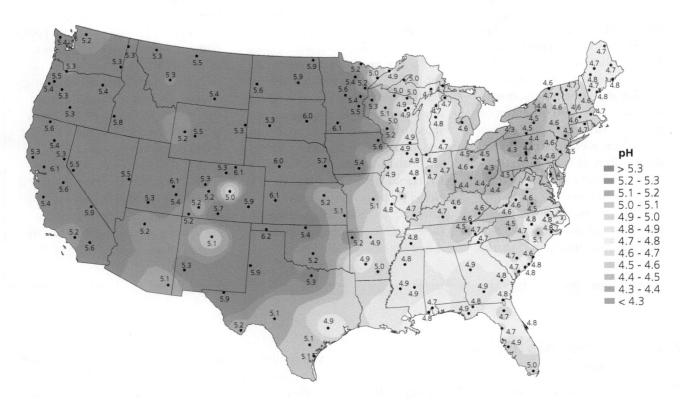

**FIGURE 17.19** This map shows pH values for precipitation throughout the United States. Acid precipitation is most serious in parts of the Northeast and Midwest, generally downwind from (roughly east of) areas of heavy industrial development. Data from National Atmospheric Deposition Program. 2005. Hydrogen ion concentration as pH from measurements made at the Central Analytical Laboratory, 2003.

**FIGURE 17.20** Indoor air pollution is an under-recognized health threat in both developed nations and developing nations. In the developing world, fires for cooking and heating are often built inside homes, as seen here in a South African kitchen (**a**), exposing family members to particulate matter and carbon monoxide. In most regions of the developing world, indoor air pollution is estimated to cause upwards of 3% of all health risks. In this graph (**b**), disability-adjusted life years (DALYs) indicate the burden of disease in total number of years of healthy life lost, including premature death and disability over a period of time, because of both indoor and outdoor air pollution. Indians suffer most severely from indoor air pollution, with approximately 650,000 years of life lost per million people, followed by sub-Saharan Africans, who suffer roughly 580,000 years loss of life per million people. *Source:* World Bank. 2002. Data from U.N. Development Programme, World Bank, Energy Sector Management Assistance Programme, 2002.

**(a) South African family cooking indoors**

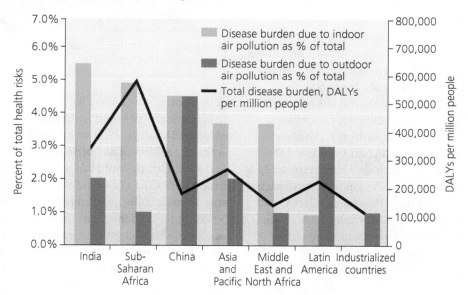

**(b) Indoor and outdoor pollution health risk statistics**

# Indoor Air Pollution

Indoor air generally contains higher concentrations of pollutants than does outdoor air. As a result, the health effects from indoor air pollution in workplaces, schools, and homes outweigh those from outdoor air pollution (Figure 17.20). One estimate, from the U.N. Development Programme in 1998, attributed 2.2 million deaths worldwide to indoor air pollution and 500,000 deaths to outdoor air pollution. Indoor air pollution alone, then, takes roughly 6,000 lives each day.

If the impact of indoor air pollution seems surprising, consider that the average U.S. citizen spends at least 90%

of his or her time indoors. Then consider that in the past half century a dizzying array of consumer products has been manufactured and sold, many of which we keep in our homes and offices and have come to play major roles in our daily lives. Many of these products are made of synthetic materials, and, as we saw in Chapter 14, novel synthetic substances are not comprehensively tested for health effects before being brought to market. Products such as insecticides and cleaning fluids can exude volatile chemicals into the air, as can solid materials such as plastics and chemically treated wood products.

In an ironic twist, some attempts to be environmentally prudent during the "energy crisis" of 1973–1974 worsened indoor air pollution in developed countries. To

## The Science behind the Story

# Acid Rain at Hubbard Brook Research Forest

The effects of acidic deposition on trees can be seen in this forest on Mount Mitchell in western North Carolina.

The effects of acidic deposition are subtle, involving incremental changes in pH levels that take place over long periods of time and affect species with long life cycles, such as trees. For this reason, no single experiment can give us a complete picture of acidic deposition's effects. Nonetheless, one long-term study conducted in the Hubbard Brook Experimental Forest in New Hampshire's White Mountains has been critically important to our understanding of acidic deposition in the United States.

Established by the U.S. Forest Service in 1955, Hubbard Brook was initially devoted to research on hydrology, the study of water flow through forests and streams. In 1963, in collaboration with scientists at Dartmouth University, Hubbard Brook researchers broadened their focus to include a long-term study of nutrient cycling in forest ecosystems. Since then, they have collected and analyzed weekly samples of precipitation. The measurements make up the longest-running North American record of acid precipitation and have helped shape U.S. policy on sulfur and nitrogen emissions.

At Hubbard Brook, only one form of acidic deposition—wet deposition—has been measured regularly. Wet deposition is the deposition of rain, snow, fog, or sea spray with low pH onto soil, plants, or water. Dry deposition, in contrast, is the deposition of airborne acidic particles. Throughout Hubbard Brook's 3,160 ha (7,800 acres), small plastic collecting funnels, 30 cm (1 ft) in diameter at their openings, channel precipitation into clean bottles, which researchers retrieve and replace each week. Hubbard Brook's laboratory measures acidity and conductivity, which indicates the amount of salts and other electrolytic contaminants dissolved in the water. Concentrations of sulfuric acid, nitrates, ammonia, and other compounds are measured elsewhere.

By the late 1960s, ecologists Gene Likens, F. Herbert Bormann, and others had found that precipitation at Hubbard Brook was several hundred times more acidic than natural rainwater. By the early 1970s, a number of other studies had corroborated their findings. Together, these studies indicated that precipitation from Pennsylvania to Maine had pH values averaging around 4, and that individual rainstorms showed values as low as 2.1—almost 10,000 times more acidic than ordinary rainwater.

reduce heat loss and improve energy efficiency, building managers sealed off most ventilation in existing buildings, and building designers constructed new buildings with limited ventilation and with windows that did not open. These steps may have saved energy, but they also worsened indoor air pollution by trapping stable, unmixed air—and its pollutants—inside.

## Indoor air pollution in the developing world arises from fuelwood burning

Indoor air pollution has the greatest impact in the developing world. Millions of people in developing nations burn wood, charcoal, animal dung, or crop waste inside their homes for cooking and heating with little or no

Over the past 40 years, precipitation at the Hubbard Brook Experimental Forest has become slightly less acidic. However, it is still far more acidic than is natural precipitation. Data from Likens, G. E. 2004. *Ecology* 85: 2355–2362.

In 1978, the National Atmospheric Deposition Program was launched to monitor precipitation and dry deposition across the United States. Initially consisting of 22 sites, including Hubbard Brook, the program now comprises more than 200, each of which gathers weekly data on acidic deposition and deposition of other substances. By the late 1980s, this program had produced a nationwide map of pH values. The most severe problems were found to be in the Northeast, where prevailing west-to-east winds were blowing emissions from fossil-fuel-burning power plants in the Midwest. Scientists hypothesized that when sulfur dioxide, nitrogen oxides, and other pollutants arrived in the Northeast, they were absorbed by water droplets in clouds, converted to acidic compounds such as sulfuric acid, and deposited on farms, forests, and cities in the form of rain or snow.

To some extent, the Clean Air Act of 1970 helped reduce acidic deposition in the Northeast. The accompanying figure shows the pH record for an area of Hubbard Brook known as Watershed 6. Between 1965 and 1995, average pH increased slightly, from about 4.15 to about 4.35. In 1990, as a consequence of the Hubbard Brook study and the nationwide research that followed, the Clean Air Act of 1970 was amended to further restrict emissions of sulfur dioxide and other acid-forming compounds. Nonetheless, acidic deposition continues to be a serious problem in the Northeast.

Some of the long-term consequences of acidic deposition are now becoming clear. In 1996, researchers reported that approximately 50% of the calcium and magnesium in Hubbard Brook's soils had been leached out. Meanwhile, acidic deposition had increased the concentration of aluminum in the soil, which can prevent tree roots from absorbing nutrients. The resulting nutrient deficiency slows forest growth and weakens trees, making them more vulnerable to drought and insects. It also reduces the ability of soil and water to neutralize acidity, making the ecosystem increasingly vulnerable to further inputs of acid.

In October 1999, researchers used a helicopter to distribute 50 tons of a calcium-containing mineral called wollastonite over one of Hubbard Brook's watersheds. Their objective was to raise the concentration of base cations to estimated historical levels. Over the next 50 years, scientists plan to evaluate the impact of calcium addition on the watershed's soil, water, and life. By providing a comparison to watersheds in which calcium remains depleted, the results should provide new insights into the consequences of acid rain and the possibilities for reversing its negative effects.

ventilation. In the process, they inhale dangerous amounts of soot and carbon monoxide. In the air of such homes, concentrations of particulate matter are commonly 20 times above U.S. EPA standards, the World Health Organization (WHO) has found. Poverty forces fully half the population and 90% of rural residents of developing countries to heat and cook with indoor fires.

Some people will burn almost any available fuel, even discarded plastic, in indoor fires. In doing so, these people are in effect subjecting themselves to a daily dose of London's smog of 1952. Indoor air pollution from fuelwood burning, the WHO estimates, kills 1.6 million people each year, comprising over 5% of all deaths in some developing nations and 2.7% of the entire global disease burden.

Many people who tend indoor fires are not aware of the health risks. They do not have access to the statistics showing that chemicals and soot released by burning coal, plastic, and other materials indoors can increase risks of pneumonia, bronchitis, allergies, sinus infections, cataracts, asthma, emphysema, heart disease, cancer, and premature death. Many who are aware of the health risks are too poor to have viable alternatives.

Even in the developed world, recognizing indoor air pollution as a problem is still quite novel. Fortunately, scientists have identified the most deadly indoor threats. Particulate matter and chemicals from wood and charcoal smoke are the primary health risks in the developing world. In developed nations, the top risks are cigarette smoke and radon, a naturally occurring radioactive gas.

## Tobacco smoke and radon are the most dangerous indoor pollutants in the developed world

The health effects of smoking cigarettes are well known in developed countries, but only recently have scientists quantified the risks of inhaling secondhand smoke. Secondhand smoke, or environmental tobacco smoke, is smoke inhaled by a nonsmoker who is nearby or shares an enclosed airspace with a smoker. Secondhand smoke has been found to cause many of the same problems as directly inhaled cigarette smoke, ranging from irritation of the eyes, nose, and throat, to exacerbation of asthma and other respiratory ailments, to lung cancer. This hardly seems surprising when one considers that environmental tobacco smoke consists of a brew of over 4,000 chemical compounds, many of which are known or suspected to be toxic or carcinogenic.

Women living with a spouse who smokes have a 24% greater chance of developing lung cancer from secondhand smoke, one study has indicated. Fortunately, the popularity of smoking has declined greatly in the United States and some other nations in recent years. The exposure of young children in the United States has decreased by almost half. A 1998 study found that 20% of young children had been exposed, as compared to 39% in 1986.

After cigarette smoke, radon gas is the second-leading cause of lung cancer in the United States, responsible for an estimated 20,000 deaths per year. Worldwide, the WHO estimates that radon may account for 15% of lung cancer cases. As we saw in Chapter 14 (▸p. 405), radon is a radioactive gas resulting from the natural decay of uranium in soil, rock, or water, which seeps up from the ground and can infiltrate buildings. Radon is colorless and odorless, and it can be impossible to predict where it will occur without knowing details of an area's underlying geology (Figure 17.21). As a result, the only way to determine whether radon is entering a building is to measure radon with a test kit. Testing in 1991 led the EPA to estimate that 6% of U.S. homes exceeded the EPA's maximum recommended level for radon. Since the mid-1980s,

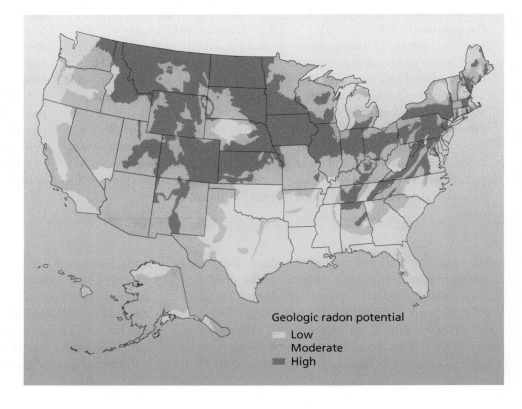

**FIGURE 17.21** The risk from radon depends largely on underground geology. This map shows relative levels of risk from radon across the United States, but there is much fine-scale geographic variation from place to place not evident on the map. Testing your home for radon is the surest way to determine whether this colorless, odorless gas could be a problem in your home. Data from U.S. Geological Survey. 1993. Generalized geological radon potential of the United States, 1993.

Geologic radon potential
Low
Moderate
High

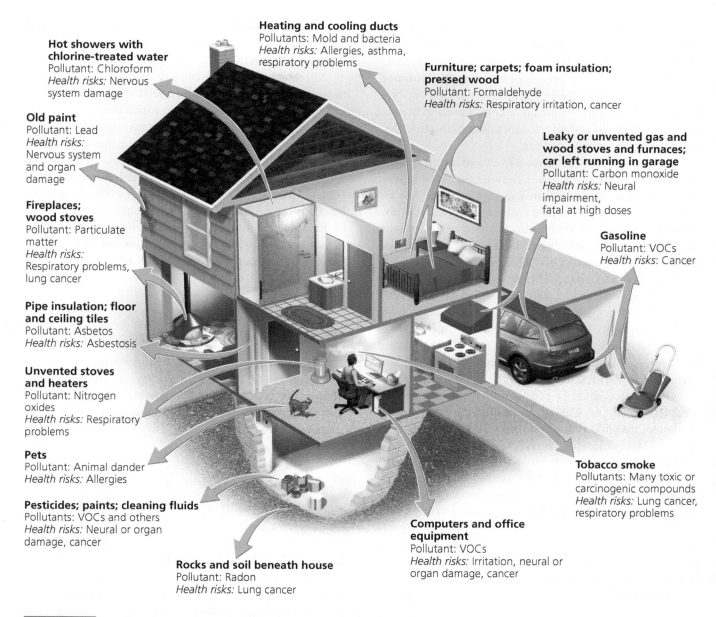

**Heating and cooling ducts**
Pollutants: Mold and bacteria
*Health risks:* Allergies, asthma, respiratory problems

**Hot showers with chlorine-treated water**
Pollutant: Chloroform
*Health risks:* Nervous system damage

**Furniture; carpets; foam insulation; pressed wood**
Pollutant: Formaldehyde
*Health risks:* Respiratory irritation, cancer

**Old paint**
Pollutant: Lead
*Health risks:* Nervous system and organ damage

**Leaky or unvented gas and wood stoves and furnaces; car left running in garage**
Pollutant: Carbon monoxide
*Health risks:* Neural impairment, fatal at high doses

**Fireplaces; wood stoves**
Pollutant: Particulate matter
*Health risks:* Respiratory problems, lung cancer

**Gasoline**
Pollutant: VOCs
*Health risks:* Cancer

**Pipe insulation; floor and ceiling tiles**
Pollutant: Asbetos
*Health risks:* Asbestosis

**Unvented stoves and heaters**
Pollutant: Nitrogen oxides
*Health risks:* Respiratory problems

**Pets**
Pollutant: Animal dander
*Health risks:* Allergies

**Tobacco smoke**
Pollutants: Many toxic or carcinogenic compounds
*Health risks:* Lung cancer, respiratory problems

**Pesticides; paints; cleaning fluids**
Pollutants: VOCs and others
*Health risks:* Neural or organ damage, cancer

**Computers and office equipment**
Pollutant: VOCs
*Health risks:* Irritation, neural or organ damage, cancer

**Rocks and soil beneath house**
Pollutant: Radon
*Health risks:* Lung cancer

**FIGURE 17.22** The typical U.S. home contains a variety of potential sources of indoor air pollution. Shown are some of the most common sources, the major pollutants they emit, and some of the health risks they pose.

18 million U.S. homes have been tested for radon, and 700,000 have undergone radon mitigation. New homes are now being built with radon-resistant features—over a million such homes since 1990.

## Many volatile organic compounds pollute indoor air

In our daily lives at home, we are exposed to many indoor air pollutants (Figure 17.22). The most diverse indoor pollutants are VOCs. These airborne carbon-containing compounds are released by everything from plastics to

oils to perfumes to paints to cleaning fluids to adhesives to pesticides. VOCs evaporate from furnishings, building materials, color film, carpets, laser printers, fax machines, and sheets of paper. Some products, such as chemically treated furniture, release large amounts of VOCs when new and progressively less as they age. Other items, such as photocopying machines, emit VOCs each time they are used.

Although we are surrounded by products that emit VOCs, they are released in very small amounts. EPA and European surveys have both measured overall levels of VOCs in buildings and have found them to be nearly always less than 0.1 part per million (ppm). This is, however, a substantially greater concentration than is generally found outdoors. When the EPA conducted a survey of U.S. office buildings between 1994 and 1998, it found 34 of the 48 VOCs it tested for, and found at least one type in 81% of buildings. All of these compounds existed at higher levels indoors than outdoors, suggesting that they originated from indoor sources.

The implications for human health of chronic exposure to VOCs are far from clear. Because they exist in such low concentrations and because individuals regularly are exposed to mixtures of many different types, it is extremely difficult to study the effects of any one pollutant. An exception is formaldehyde, which does have clear and known health impacts. This VOC, one of the most common synthetically produced chemicals, irritates mucous membranes, induces skin allergies, and causes other ailments. Formaldehyde is used in numerous products, but health complaints have mainly resulted from its leakage from pressed wood and insulation. The use of plywood has decreased in the last decade because of health concerns over formaldehyde.

VOCs also include pesticides, which we examined in Chapters 10 and 14. Three-quarters of U.S. homes use at least one pesticide indoors during an average year, but most are used outdoors. Thus it may seem surprising that the EPA found in a 1990 study that 90% of people's pesticide exposure came from indoor sources. Households that the agency tested had multiple pesticide volatiles in their air, at levels 10 times above levels measured outside. Some of the pesticides found had apparently been used years previously against termites, and then seeped into the houses through floors and walls. DDT, banned 15 years before the study, was found in five of eight homes, probably having been brought in on the soles of occupants' shoes from outdoors.

## Living organisms can pollute indoor spaces

Tiny living organisms can be or produce indoor pollutants. In fact, they may be the most widespread source of indoor air pollution in the developed world. Dust mites and animal dander can exacerbate asthma in children. Some fungi, mold, and mildew (in particular, their airborne spores) can cause potentially severe health problems, including allergies, asthma, and other respiratory ailments. Some airborne bacteria can cause infectious disease. One example is the bacterium that causes Legionnaires' disease. Of the estimated 10,000–15,000 annual U.S. cases of Legionnaires' disease, 5–15% are fatal. Heating and cooling systems in buildings make ideal breeding grounds for microbes, providing moisture, dust, and foam insulation as substrates, as well as air currents to carry the organisms aloft.

Microbes that induce allergic responses are thought to be a major cause of building-related illness, a sickness produced by indoor pollution in which the specific cause may not be identifiable. When the cause of such an illness is a mystery, and when symptoms are general and nonspecific, the illness is often called *sick-building syndrome.* The U.S. Occupational Safety and Health Administration (OSHA) has estimated that 30–70 million Americans have suffered ailments due to the environment of the building in which they live. We can reduce the prevalence of sick building syndrome by using low-toxicity building materials and ensuring that buildings are adequately ventilated.

-------------------------------------------------------
**Weighing the Issues:**
## How Safe Is Your Indoor Environment?

Think about the amount of time you spend indoors. Name the potential indoor air quality hazards in your home, work, or school environment. Are these spaces well-ventilated? What could you do to make the indoor spaces you use safer?
-------------------------------------------------------

## We can reduce indoor air pollution

Using low-toxicity material, monitoring air quality, keeping rooms clean, and providing adequate ventilation are the keys to alleviating indoor air pollution in most situations. In the developed world, we can try to limit our use of plastics and treated wood where possible and to limit our exposure to pesticides, cleaning fluids, and other known toxicants by keeping them in a garage or outdoor shed rather than in the house. The EPA recommends that we test our homes and offices for radon. Because carbon monoxide is so deadly and so hard to detect, many homes are equipped with detectors that sound an alarm if incomplete combustion produces dangerous levels of CO. In addition, keeping rooms and air ducts clean and free of mildew and other biological pollutants will reduce potential irritants and allergens. Finally, it is important to keep our indoor spaces as well ventilated as possible to minimize concentrations of the pollutants among which we live.

Remedies for fuelwood pollution in the developing world include drying wood before burning (which reduces the amount of smoke produced), cooking outside, shifting to less-polluting fuels (such as natural gas), and replacing inefficient fires with cleaner stoves that burn fuel more efficiently. For example, the Chinese government has invested in a program that has placed more fuel-efficient stoves in millions of homes in China. According to WHO studies, this is a relatively cost-efficient means of reducing the health impacts of indoor biomass combustion. Installing hoods, chimneys, or cooking windows can increase ventilation for little cost, alleviating the majority of indoor smoke pollution.

# Conclusion

Indoor air pollution is a potentially serious health threat. However, by keeping informed of the latest scientific findings and taking appropriate actions, we as individuals can significantly minimize the risks to our families and ourselves. Outdoor air pollution has been addressed more effectively by government legislation and regulation. In fact, reductions in outdoor air pollution levels in the United States and other developed nations represent some of the greatest strides made in environmental protection to date. Much room for improvement remains, however, particularly in reducing acidic deposition and the photochemical smog resulting from urban congestion. Fortunately, developed nations no longer experience the type of pollution that Londoners suffered in their 1952 killer smog. Nevertheless, avoiding such high pollutant levels in the developing world will continue to pose a challenge as less-wealthy nations industrialize.

## REVIEWING OBJECTIVES

**You should now be able to:**

**Describe the composition, structure, and function of Earth's atmosphere**

▶ The atmosphere consists of 78% nitrogen gas, 21% oxygen gas, and a variety of permanent and variable gases in minute concentrations. (p. 498)

▶ The atmosphere includes four principal layers: the troposphere, stratosphere, mesosphere, and thermosphere. Temperature and other characteristics vary across these layers. Ozone is concentrated in the stratosphere. (pp. 498–499)

▶ The sun's energy heats the atmosphere, drives air circulation, and helps determine weather, climate, and the seasons. (pp. 500–501)

▶ Weather is a short-term phenomenon, whereas climate is a long-term phenomenon. Fronts, pressure systems, and the interactions among air masses influence weather. (pp. 501–503)

▶ Global convective cells called Hadley, Ferrel, and polar cells create latitudinal climate zones. (pp. 504–505)

**Outline the scope of outdoor air pollution and assess potential solutions**

▶ Natural sources such as windblown dust, volcanoes, and fires account for much atmospheric pollution, but human activity can exacerbate some of these phenomena. (pp. 505–506)

▶ Human-emitted pollutants include primary and secondary pollutants from point and non-point sources. (p. 506)

▶ To safeguard public health, the U.S. EPA regulates six criteria pollutants (carbon monoxide, lead, nitrogen dioxide, tropospheric ozone, sulfur dioxide, and particulate matter), as well as volatile organic compounds and 188 toxic air pollutants. (pp. 506–509)

▶ Emissions in the United States have decreased substantially since the Clean Air Act of 1970, and ambient air quality is much improved. (pp. 508–509)

▶ Industrial smog like that which blanketed 1952 London is produced by fossil fuel combustion and is still a problem in urban and industrial areas of many developing nations. (pp. 509–510)

▶ Photochemical smog is created by chemical reactions of pollutants in the presence of sunlight. It impairs visibility and human health in urban areas. (pp. 510–511)

**Explain stratospheric ozone depletion and identify steps taken to address it**

▶ CFCs destroy stratospheric ozone, and thinning ozone concentrations pose dangers to life because they allow more ultraviolet radiation to reach Earth's surface. (pp. 511, 513–514, 516–517)

▶ The Montreal Protocol and its follow-up agreements have proven remarkably successful in reducing emissions of ozone-depleting compounds. (pp. 513–514, 517)

**Define acidic deposition and illustrate its consequences**

▶ Acidic deposition results when pollutants such as $SO_2$ and NO react in the atmosphere to produce strong acids that are deposited on Earth's surface. (pp. 514–515)

▶ Acidic deposition may occur a long distance from the source of pollution. (pp. 516, 518)

▶ Water bodies, soils, trees, and ecosystems all experience negative impacts from acidic deposition. (pp. 515–518, 520–521)

**Characterize the scope of indoor air pollution and assess potential solutions**

▶ Indoor air pollution causes far more deaths and health problems worldwide than outdoor air pollution. (p. 519)

▶ Indoor burning of fuelwood is the developing world's primary indoor air pollution risk. (pp. 519–522)

▶ Tobacco smoke and radon are the deadliest indoor pollutants in the developed world. (pp. 522–523)

▶ Volatile organic compounds and living organisms can pollute indoor air. (pp. 523–524)

▶ Using low-toxicity building materials, keeping spaces clean, monitoring air quality, and maximizing ventilation are some of the steps we can take to reduce indoor air pollution. (pp. 524–525)

## TESTING YOUR COMPREHENSION

1. About how thick is Earth's atmosphere? Name one characteristic of each of the four atmospheric layers.
2. Where is the "ozone layer" located? How and why is stratospheric ozone beneficial for people, and tropospheric ozone harmful?
3. How does solar energy influence weather and climate? How do Hadley, Ferrel, and polar cells help to determine long-term climatic patterns and the location of biomes?
4. What factors led to the deadly smog in London in 1952? Describe a thermal inversion.
5. Name three natural sources of outdoor air pollution and three sources caused by human activity.

6. What is the difference between a primary and a secondary pollutant? Give an example of each.
7. What is smog? How is smog formation influenced by the weather? By topography? How does photochemical, or brown-air, smog differ from industrial, or gray-air, smog?
8. How do chlorofluorocarbons (CFCs) deplete stratospheric ozone? Why is this depletion considered a long-term international problem? What was done to address this problem?
9. Why are the effects of acidic deposition often felt in areas far from where the primary pollutants are produced?
10. Name five common sources of indoor pollution. For each, describe one way to reduce one's exposure to this source.

## SEEKING SOLUTIONS

1. Consider London's "killer smog" of 1952 and modern urban pollution by photochemical smog. Describe several factors that make it particularly difficult to study causes of air pollution and to develop solutions.
2. How may human activity sometimes exacerbate natural forms of air pollution? Discuss two examples and potential solutions.
3. Describe how and why emissions of major pollutants have been reduced by over 50% in the United States since 1970, despite increases in population and economic activity.
4. International regulatory action has produced reductions in CFCs, but other transboundary pollution issues, including acidic deposition, have not yet been addressed as effectively. What types of actions do you feel are appropriate for pollutants that cross political boundaries?

5. Consider volatile chemicals, such as formaldehyde and VOCs, that may be emitted at very low levels over long periods of time from manufactured products. What do you think are the best ways to lessen the health impacts of such indoor pollutants?
6. You have just become the head of your county health department, and the EPA has informed you that your county has failed to meet the national ambient air quality standards for ozone, sulfur dioxide, and nitrogen dioxide. Your county is partly rural but is home to a city of 200,000 people and 10 sprawling suburbs. There are several large and aging coal-fired power plants, a number of factories with advanced pollution control technology, and no public transportation system. What steps would you urge the county government to take to meet the air quality standards? Explain how you would prioritize these steps.

## INTERPRETING GRAPHS AND DATA

Since the Clean Air Act of 1970, total emissions of carbon monoxide, sulfur dioxide, nitrogen oxides, VOCs, lead, and particulate matter have dropped by over 50% while U.S.

population, energy consumption, and economic productivity have all increased. As you learned from the "Interpreting Graphs and Data" feature in Chapter 3 (▶ pp. 86–87), lead emissions resulted mostly from the combustion of leaded gasoline and dropped precipitously once leaded gasoline was phased out. Consider the other pollutants listed above as you interpret the data in the graph.

1. Relative to 1970, what are the percentage changes by 2004 for each of the five variables graphed above? What are the percentage changes in the per capita values of each variable over this time period?
2. Fossil fuel combustion is the major source of most of the pollutants above. What is the percentage change in aggregate emissions of the six principal pollutants per unit of energy consumed in 2004, compared to 1970?
3. Do you think that additional reductions in emissions are likely to result primarily from changing technology (e.g., hybrid cars, advanced catalytic converters) or from changing behavior (e.g., driving fewer miles per person per year)? Use the data above to support your claim.

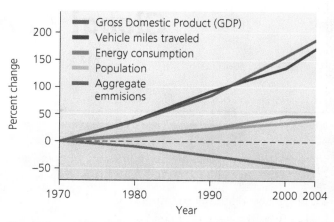

Trends from 1970 to 2004 in economic production, vehicle miles traveled, energy consumption, population, and aggregate emissions of the six principal air pollutants monitored by the EPA. Data from U.S. EPA. 2004. *Air emission trends: Continued progress through 2004.*

## CALCULATING ECOLOGICAL FOOTPRINTS

According to EPA data, emissions of nitrogen oxides in the United States in 2000 were 24,899,000 tons, of which 13,251,000 tons were from the transportation sector. Of this amount, 8,150,000 tons came from on-road vehicles, with 5,859,000 tons of this total coming from light-duty cars and trucks. The U.S. Census Bureau estimated the nation's population to be 282,192,162 at mid-year in 2000 and projects that it will reach 300,000,000 by early 2007. Considering these data, calculate the missing values in the table below (1 ton = 2,000 lb).

| | Total $NO_x$ emissions (lb) | $NO_x$ emissions due to light-duty vehicles (lb) |
|---|---|---|
| You | | |
| Your class | | |
| Your state | | |
| United States | | |

Data from U.S. EPA. 2003. *National air quality and emissions trends report 2003,* Appendix A4.

1. By what percentage is the U.S. population projected to increase between 2000 and 2007? Do you think that $NO_x$ emissions will increase, decrease, or remain the same over that period of time? Why? (You may want to refer to Figure 17.11.)
2. If you reduced by half the vehicle miles traveled for which you are responsible, how many pounds of $NO_x$ emissions would you prevent? What percentage of your total $NO_x$ emissions would that be?
3. How might you reduce your vehicle miles traveled by 50%? What other steps could you take to reduce the $NO_x$ emissions for which you are responsible?

## Take It Further

Go to www.aw-bc.com/withgott or the student CD-ROM where you'll find:

▶ Suggested answers to end-of-chapter questions
▶ Quizzes, animations, and flashcards to help you study
▶ *Research Navigator*™ database of credible and reliable sources to assist you with your research projects

▶ **GRAPHit!** tutorials to help you master how to interpret graphs
▶ **INVESTIGATEit!** current news articles that link the topics that you study to case studies from your region to around the world

# 18 Global Climate Change

Muratti Island of the Maldives

## Upon successfully completing this chapter, you will be able to:

▶ Describe Earth's climate system and explain the variety of factors influencing global climate

▶ Characterize human influences on the atmosphere and global climate

▶ Delineate modern methods of climate research

▶ Summarize current consequences and potential future impacts of global climate change

▶ Evaluate the scientific, political, and economic debates concerning climate change

▶ Suggest potential responses to climate change

Fishermen of the Maldives

# Central Case: Rising Temperatures and Seas May Take the Maldives Under

**"The impact of global warming and climate change can effectively kill us off, make us refugees. . . ."**
—Ismail Shafeeu, Minister of Environment, Maldives

**"More people enjoy health and prosperity now than ever, and a warmer environment . . . should sustain life better than the current one does."**
—Oil and Gas Journal, February 2001

A nation of low-lying coral islands, or atolls, in the Indian Ocean, the Maldives is known for its spectacular tropical setting, colorful coral reefs, and sun-drenched beaches. For visiting tourists it is a paradise, and for 320,000 Maldives residents it is home. But residents and tourists alike now fear that the Maldives could soon be submerged by the rising seas that are accompanying global climate change.

Nearly 80% of the Maldives' land area of 300 km² (116 mi²) lies less than 1 m (39 in.) above sea level. In a nation of 1,190 islands whose highest point is just 2.4 m (8 ft) above sea level, rising seas could be a matter of life or death. The world's oceans rose 10–20 cm (4–8 in.)

during the 20th century as warming temperatures expanded ocean water and as melting icecaps discharged water into the ocean. Current projections are that sea level will rise another 9–88 cm (3.5–35 in.) by the year 2100.

Higher seas are expected to flood large areas of land in the Maldives and to cause salt water to intrude into drinking water supplies. Moreover, if climate change produces larger and more powerful storms, these could worsen flooding and damage the coral reefs that are so crucial to the nation's tourism- and fishing-driven economy. Because of such concerns, the Maldives government has evacuated residents from several of the lowest-lying islands in recent years.

On December 26, 2004, the nation got a taste of what could be in store in the future. The massive *tsunami,* or tidal wave, that devastated coastal areas throughout the Indian Ocean hit the Maldives particularly hard. One hundred people were killed and 20,000 lost their homes, while schools, boats, tourist resorts, hospitals, and transportation and communication infrastructure were destroyed or badly damaged. On a per capita basis, the

Maldives suffered a greater economic shock from the tsunami than any other nation. The World Bank estimates that direct damage in the Maldives totaled $470 million, an astounding 62% of the nation's gross domestic product (GDP). Soil erosion, saltwater contamination of aquifers, and other environmental damage will result in still greater long-term economic losses.

The tsunami was caused *not* by climate change, but by an earthquake. Yet as sea level rises, the damage that such natural events—or ordinary storm waves—can inflict increases considerably. Maldives islanders are not alone in their predicament. Other island nations, from the Galapagos to Fiji to the Seychelles, are also fearing a future in which they may be constantly battling encroaching seawater. Mainland coastal areas of the world, such as the hurricane-battered coasts of Florida and Louisiana, will face similar issues. In one way or another, global climate change seems certain to affect each and every one of us for the remainder of our lifetimes.

# Earth's Hospitable Climate

As we learned in Chapter 17, *weather* describes an area's short-term atmospheric conditions (over hours or days), including temperature, moisture content, wind, precipitation, barometric pressure, solar radiation, and other characteristics. *Climate* is an area's long-term pattern of atmospheric conditions. **Global climate change** describes changes in Earth's climate, involving aspects such as temperature, precipitation, and storm frequency and intensity. Although people often use the term *global warming* synonymously in casual conversation, *global warming* refers specifically to an increase in Earth's average surface temperature and thus is only one aspect of global climate change.

Our planet's climate has never been entirely stable and unchanging. However, the climatic changes taking place today are unfolding at an exceedingly rapid rate. Moreover, most scientists agree that human activities, notably fossil fuel combustion and deforestation, are largely responsible for the current modification of Earth's atmosphere and climate. Climatic changes will likely have adverse consequences for ecosystems and for millions of people, including residents of the Maldives, Florida, Louisiana, and other regions. For this reason, increasing numbers of scientists, policymakers, and ordinary citizens are seeking to take action to minimize and mitigate our impacts on the climate system.

## The sun and the atmosphere keep Earth warm

Three factors exert more influence on Earth's climate than all others combined. The first is the sun. Without it, Earth would be dark and frozen. The second is the atmosphere. Without it, Earth would be as much as 33 °C (59 °F) colder on average, and temperature differences between night and day would be far greater. The third is the oceans, which shape climate by storing and transporting heat and moisture.

The sun is the source of most of the energy that Earth receives. Earth's atmosphere, clouds, land, ice, and water together reflect about 30% of incoming solar radiation back into space. The remaining 70% is absorbed by molecules in the atmosphere, clouds, or by land, water, or ice at Earth's surface (Figure 18.1).

## "Greenhouse gases" warm the lower atmosphere

As Earth's surface absorbs solar radiation, the surface increases in temperature and emits radiation in the infrared portion of the spectrum (▶ pp. 105–106). Some atmospheric gases absorb infrared radiation released from Earth's surface very effectively. These include water vapor, ozone, carbon dioxide ($CO_2$), nitrous oxide ($N_2O$), methane ($CH_4$), and halocarbons. Halocarbons are a diverse group of gases that include chlorofluorocarbons (CFCs; ▶ pp. 513, 516–517) and hydrochlorofluorocarbons (HFCs). Such gases that absorb infrared radiation from Earth's surface are known as **greenhouse gases.** These gases subsequently re-emit infrared energy of slightly different wavelengths, warming the atmosphere (specifically the *troposphere*; ▶ pp. 498–499) and the planet's surface. This warming of the troposphere and Earth's surface is known as the **greenhouse effect.** Despite its wide usage, the term *greenhouse effect* is actually a bit of a misnomer. The greenhouses we use for growing plants hold heat in place by preventing warm air from escaping. Atmospheric greenhouse gases, in contrast, do not trap air, but instead absorb, transform, and radiate heat.

The greenhouse effect is a natural phenomenon, and greenhouse gases (with the exception of the anthropogenic halocarbons) have been present in the atmosphere for billions of years. However, human activities have increased the concentrations of many greenhouse gases in the past 250–300 years, and we have thereby enhanced the greenhouse effect.

Not all greenhouse gases are equally effective in warming the troposphere and surface. *Global warming potential*

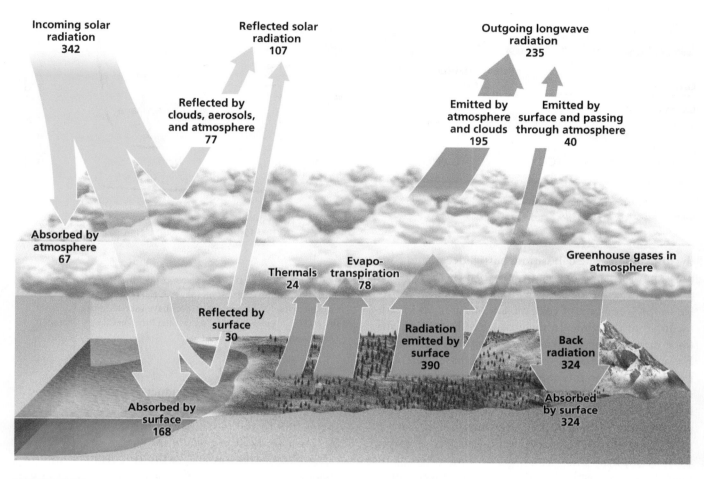

**Incoming solar radiation** 342

**Reflected solar radiation** 107

**Outgoing longwave radiation** 235

**Reflected by clouds, aerosols, and atmosphere** 77

**Emitted by atmosphere and clouds** 195

**Emitted by surface and passing through atmosphere** 40

**Absorbed by atmosphere** 67

**Greenhouse gases in atmosphere**

**Thermals** 24

**Evapo-transpiration** 78

**Reflected by surface** 30

**Radiation emitted by surface** 390

**Back radiation** 324

**Absorbed by surface** 168

**Absorbed by surface** 324

**FIGURE 18.1** Earth's climate system is in rough equilibrium; our planet emits about the same amount of energy that it receives from the sun. As greenhouse gases accumulate in the atmosphere, however, they increase the amount of radiation that is emitted from the atmosphere back toward the surface. This illustration shows major pathways of energy flow in watts per square meter. Data from Kiehl, J. T., and K. E. Trenberth. 1997. Earth's annual global mean energy budget. *Bull. Amer. Meteorol. Soc.* 78: 197–208.

refers to the relative ability of one molecule of a given greenhouse gas to contribute to warming. Table 18.1 shows the global warming potential for several greenhouse gases. Values are expressed in relation to carbon dioxide, which is assigned a global warming potential of 1. Thus, a molecule of methane is 23 times as potent as a molecule of carbon dioxide, and a molecule of nitrous oxide is 296 times as potent as a $CO_2$ molecule.

## Carbon dioxide is the primary greenhouse gas

Although carbon dioxide is not the most potent greenhouse gas on a per-molecule basis, its abundance in the atmosphere relative to gases such as methane and nitrous oxide means that it contributes more to the greenhouse

effect. For this reason, changes in the atmospheric concentration of $CO_2$ are important. Human activities have contributed to a significant increase in the atmospheric concentration of carbon dioxide, from around 280 parts per million (ppm) as recently as the late 1700s to 316 ppm in 1959 to 378 ppm in 2004 (Figure 18.2). The atmospheric $CO_2$ concentration is now at its highest level in at least 400,000 years, and likely the highest in the last 20 million years. Moreover, it is increasing faster today than at any time in at least 20,000 years.

What has changed since the 1700s to cause the atmospheric concentration of this greenhouse gas to increase so rapidly? As you may recall from our discussion of the carbon cycle in Chapter 7 (▶ pp. 195–197), and as we will see further in Chapter 19 (▶ pp. 561–562), a great deal of carbon is stored for long periods in the upper layers of

| Table 18.1 | Global Warming Potentials of Four Greenhouse Gases |
|---|---|
| **Greenhouse gas** | **Relative heat-trapping ability (in $CO_2$ equivalents)** |
| Carbon dioxide | 1 |
| Methane | 23 |
| Nitrous oxide | 296 |
| Hydrochlorofluorocarbon HFC-23 | 12,000 |

Data from Intergovernmental Panel on Climate Change, 2001. *Climate change 2001: The scientific basis.*

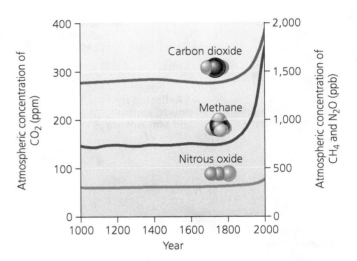

**FIGURE 18.2** Global atmospheric concentrations of carbon dioxide ($CO_2$; top curve), methane ($CH_4$; middle curve), and nitrous oxide ($N_2O$; bottom curve) have increased dramatically since 1800. Data from Intergovernmental Panel on Climate Change. 2001. *Third assessment report.*

the lithosphere. The deposition, partial decay, and compression of organic matter (mostly plants) that grew in wetland or marine areas during the Carboniferous Period led to the formation of coal, oil, and natural gas in sediments from that time. In the absence of human activity, these carbon reservoirs would be practically permanent. However, over the past two centuries we have been burning increasing amounts of fossil fuels in our homes, factories, and automobiles. In so doing, we have transferred large amounts of carbon from one reservoir (the underground deposits that stored the carbon for millions of years) to another (the atmosphere). This flux of carbon from lithospheric reservoirs into the atmosphere is the main reason atmospheric carbon dioxide concentrations have increased so dramatically in such a short time.

At the same time, people have cleared and burned forests to make room for crops, pastures, villages, and cities. Forests serve as carbon sinks (▸ p. 195), and their removal, especially in areas where they are slow to recover, can reduce the biosphere's ability to absorb carbon dioxide from the atmosphere. Therefore, deforestation has also contributed to increasing atmospheric carbon dioxide concentrations.

## Other greenhouse gases add to warming

Carbon dioxide is not the only greenhouse gas increasing in the atmosphere. Methane is also on the rise. We release methane into the atmosphere by tapping into fossil fuel deposits, raising livestock that release methane as a metabolic waste product, disposing of organic matter in landfills, and growing certain types of crops, especially rice. Since 1750, atmospheric methane concentrations have increased by 151% (see Figure 18.2), and the current concentration is the highest in at least 400,000 years.

Nitrous oxide is another greenhouse gas whose atmospheric concentration has increased because of human activities. This gas, a by-product of feedlots, chemical manufacturing plants, auto emissions, and use of nitrogen fertilizers in modern agricultural practices, has risen by 17% since 1750 (see Figure 18.2).

Ozone concentrations in the troposphere have increased by 36% since 1750 as a result of processes described in Chapter 17 (▸ pp. 507, 510–511). Halocarbon gases add greatly to the atmosphere's heat-absorbing ability on a per-molecule basis (see Table 18.1). Their overall contribution to global warming, however, has begun to slow because of the Montreal Protocol and subsequent controls (▸ pp. 513–514).

Emissions of greenhouse gases from human activity in the United States consist mostly of carbon dioxide. Even after accounting for the greater global warming potential of other gases, carbon dioxide remains the major contributor to warming (Figure 18.3).

Water vapor is the most abundant greenhouse gas in the atmosphere. Its concentration varies, but if tropospheric temperatures continue to increase, the oceans and other water bodies should transfer increasingly more water vapor into the atmosphere. Such a positive feedback mechanism could amplify the greenhouse effect. Alternatively, increased water vapor concentrations could give rise to increased cloudiness, which might, in a negative feedback loop, slow global warming by reflecting more incoming solar radiation back into space. Depending on whether low- or high-elevation clouds resulted, they could either shade and cool Earth (negative feedback) or

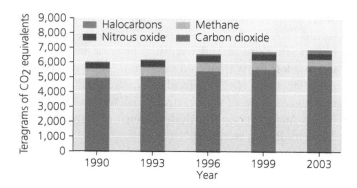

**FIGURE 18.3** Emissions of six main greenhouse gases in the United States increased by 13.3% between 1990 and 2003. Even after accounting for the greater global warming potentials of methane, nitrous oxide, and three types of halocarbons, carbon dioxide accounts for nearly 85% of potential warming. Data from U.S. Environmental Protection Agency. 2005. *Inventory of U.S. greenhouse gas emissions and sinks: 1990–2003*. 430-R-05-003. Washington, D.C.: U.S. EPA.

else contribute to warming and accelerate evaporation and further cloud formation (positive feedback). Because of feedback loops (▶pp. 184–185), minor modifications of minor components of the atmosphere can potentially lead to major changes in climate.

## Aerosols and other elements may exert a cooling effect on the lower atmosphere

Whereas greenhouse gases exert a warming effect, *aerosols*, microscopic droplets and particles, can have either a warming or cooling effect. Generally speaking, soot aerosols, also known as black carbon aerosols, can cause warming, but most tropospheric aerosols lead to climate cooling. Sulfate aerosols produced by fossil fuel combustion may slow global warming, at least in the short term. When sulfur dioxide enters the atmosphere, it undergoes a number of reactions, some of which lead to acid precipitation (▶p. 515). These reactions, along with volcanic eruptions, also contribute to the formation of a sulfur-rich aerosol haze in the upper atmosphere. Such a haze may reduce the amount of sunlight that reaches and heats Earth's surface. Major volcanic eruptions and the aerosols they release can also exert short-term cooling effects on Earth's climate on the scale of a few years.

## The atmosphere is not the only factor that influences climate

Although the atmosphere shapes climate, the amount of energy released by the sun, as well as changes in Earth's rotation and orbit, also affect climate.

**Milankovitch cycles** During the 1920s, Serbian mathematician Milutin Milankovitch described three kinds of changes in Earth's rotation and orbit around the sun. These variations, now known as **Milankovitch cycles,** result in slight changes in the relative amount of solar radiation reaching Earth's surface at different latitudes over the long term (Figure 18.4). As these cycles proceed, they change the way solar radiation is distributed over Earth's surface. This, in turn, contributes to changes in atmospheric heating and circulation that have triggered climate variation, such as periodic glaciation episodes.

**Oceanic circulation** The oceans also shape climate. Ocean water exchanges tremendous amounts of heat with the atmosphere, and ocean currents move energy from one place to another. In equatorial regions, such as the area around the Maldives, the oceans receive more heat from the sun and atmosphere than they emit. Near the poles, the oceans emit more heat than they receive. Because cooler water is denser than warmer water, the cooling water at the poles tends to sink, and the warmer

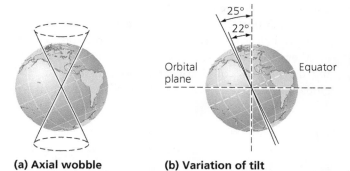

**(a) Axial wobble**　　　　**(b) Variation of tilt**

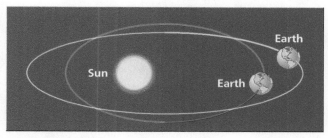

**(c) Variation of orbit**

**FIGURE 18.4** There are three types of Milankovitch cycles. The first is an axial wobble (**a**) that occurs on a 19,000- to 23,000-year cycle. The second is a 3-degree shift in the tilt of Earth's axis (**b**) that occurs on a 41,000-year cycle. The third is a variation in Earth's orbit from almost circular to more elliptical (**c**), which repeats itself every 100,000 years. These variations affect the intensity of solar radiation that reaches portions of Earth at different times, creating long-term changes in global climate.

surface water from the equator moves to take its place. This is one of the principles explaining global oceanic circulation (▸pp. 470–471).

The best-known interaction among ocean circulation, atmospheric circulation, and global climate involves the phenomena named El Niño and La Niña (see "The Science behind the Story," ▸pp. 536–537). **El Niño** conditions are triggered when equatorial winds weaken and allow warm water from the western Pacific to move eastward, preventing cold water from welling up in the eastern Pacific. In **La Niña** events, cold surface waters extend far westward in the equatorial Pacific. Both these events affect temperature and precipitation patterns around the world in complex ways. Scientists are exploring whether globally warming air and sea temperatures may be increasing the frequency and strength of El Niño events.

Another way in which climate and ocean currents interact involves the northern Atlantic Ocean. Here, warm surface water moves from the equator northward, carrying heat to higher latitudes, and keeping Europe much warmer than it would otherwise be. As the surface water of the North Atlantic releases heat energy and cools, it becomes denser and sinks. The deep part of this circulation pattern is called the *North Atlantic Deep Water (NADW)*. Figure 18.5 portrays this circulation pattern as a sort of conveyor belt that moves water and heat from one place to another. Recently, scientists have realized that interrupting the NADW could trigger rapid climate change. If global warming causes large portions of the Greenland Ice Sheet to melt, freshwater runoff into the North Atlantic would increase. Surface waters would become less dense from such dilution and warming, because warm freshwater is less dense than cold salt water. This could potentially stop the NADW circulation, shutting down the northward flow of warm equatorial water. The entire North Atlantic region, including much of Europe, could cool rapidly as a result.

# Methods of Studying Climate Change

To understand how climate is changing today, and to predict future changes, scientists must have a good idea of what climatic conditions were like thousands or millions of years ago. Environmental scientists have developed a number of methods to decipher clues from the past to learn about Earth's climate history.

## Proxy indicators tell us about the past

Earth's ice caps and glaciers hold clues about past climate. Over the ages, these huge expanses of snow and ice have accumulated to great depths, preserving within them tiny bubbles of the ancient atmosphere (Figure 18.6). Scientists can examine these trapped air bubbles by drilling into the ice and extracting long columns, or cores. From

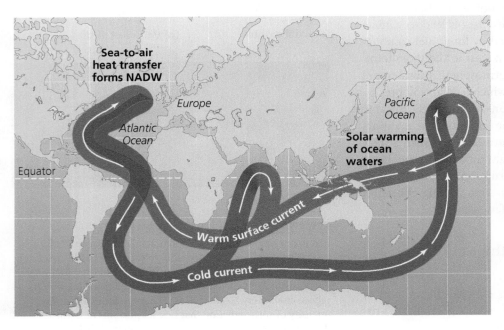

**FIGURE 18.5** The atmosphere and the oceans interact. Warm surface currents carry heat from equatorial waters north toward Europe and Greenland, where they release heat into the atmosphere, then cool and sink into the deep ocean. This is how North Atlantic Deep Water (NADW) is formed. Melting of the Greenland Ice Sheet could potentially interrupt the flow of heat from equatorial regions and lead to rapid cooling of the North Atlantic and much of Europe.

**(a) Ice core**

**(b) Micrograph of ice core**

**FIGURE 18.6** In Greenland and Antarctica, scientists have drilled deep into ancient ice sheets and removed cores of ice like this one **(a),** held by Dr. Gerald Holdsworth of the University of Calgary, to extract information about past climates. Bubbles (black shapes) trapped in the ice **(b)** contain small samples of the ancient atmosphere.

these ice cores, scientists can determine atmospheric composition, greenhouse gas concentrations, temperature trends, snowfall, solar activity, and even (from trapped soot particles) frequency of forest fires.

Scientists also drill cores into beds of sediment beneath bodies of water. Sediments often preserve pollen grains and other remnants from plants that grew in the past, and as we saw with the study of Easter Island (▶ pp. 8–9), the analysis of these materials can reveal a great deal about the history of past vegetation. Because the types of plants that grow in an area depend on the area's climate, knowing what plants occurred in a given location can tell us much about the climate at that time (see "The Science behind the Story," ▶ p. 538). Sources of data such as pollen from sediment cores and air bubbles from ice cores are known as **proxy indicators**, types of indirect evidence that serve as proxies for direct measurement and that indicate the na-

ture of past climate. Other types of proxy indicators include data culled from coral reefs and the tree rings of long-lived trees.

## Direct atmospheric sampling tells us about the present

Studying present-day climate is more straightforward, because scientists can directly measure atmospheric conditions. The late Charles Keeling of the Scripps Institution of Oceanography in La Jolla, California, documented trends in atmospheric carbon dioxide concentrations starting in 1958 (Figure 18.7). Keeling collected four air samples from five towers every hour from his monitoring station at the Mauna Loa Observatory in Hawaii. Keeling's data show that atmospheric carbon dioxide concentrations have increased from 315 ppm to 378 ppm since 1958. Today Keeling's colleagues are continuing these measurements, building upon the single best long-term dataset we have of direct atmospheric sampling of any greenhouse gas.

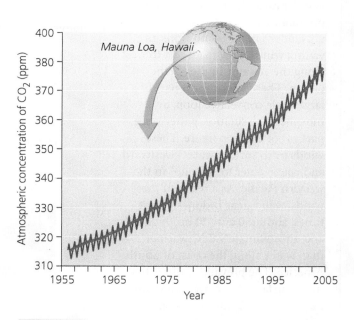

**FIGURE 18.7** Atmospheric concentrations of carbon dioxide have risen steeply since 1958, when Charles Keeling began collecting these data at the Mauna Loa Observatory in Hawaii. The jaggedness apparent within the overall upward trend of the so-called "Keeling curve" represents seasonal variation caused by the Northern Hemisphere's vegetation, which absorbs more carbon dioxide during the northern summer, when it is more photosynthetically active. Go to **GRAPHit!** at www.aw-bc.com/withgott or on the student CD-ROM. Data from National Oceanic and Atmospheric Administration, Climate Prediction Center, 2005.

# Understanding El Niño and La Niña

Some scientists suspect that the warming of global air and ocean surface temperatures is increasing the frequency of the phenomenon known as El Niño. *El Niño* was originally the name that Spanish-speaking fishermen gave to an unusually warm surface current that sometimes arrived near the Pacific coast of South America around Christmastime. El Niño literally means "the little boy" or "the Christ child," and the current received this name because of its holiday arrival time. El Niño later became the term for the warming of the eastern Pacific that occurs every 2 to 7 years and depresses local fish and bird populations.

Under normal conditions, prevailing winds blow from east to west along the equator in the Pacific Ocean. These winds form part of a large-scale convective loop, or atmospheric circulation pattern; see part (a) of the first figure. These winds push surface waters westward and cause water to "pile up" in the western Pacific. As a result of these winds, water near Indonesia is, at times, about 50 cm (20 in.) higher and approximately 8 °C warmer than water along the coast of South America. The prevailing winds that move surface waters westward also make it possible for deep, cold, nutrient-rich water to form a nutrient-rich upwelling (▶ p. 471) along the coast of Peru.

When prevailing winds weaken, the warm water that has collected in the western Pacific flows "downhill" and eastward toward South America; see part (b) of the first figure. The influx of warm surface water and the

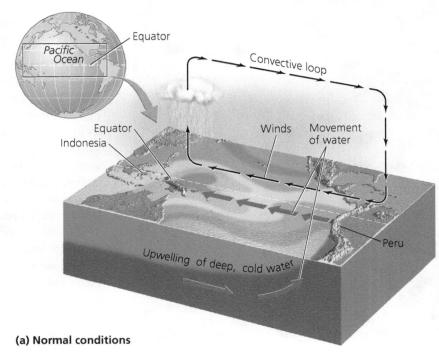

**(a) Normal conditions**

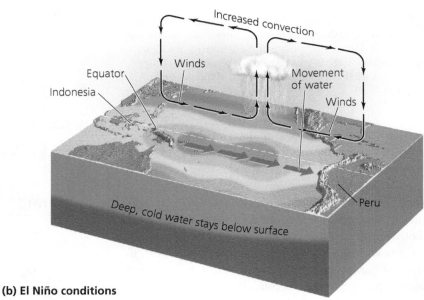

**(b) El Niño conditions**

In this view, Indonesia is on the left and Peru is on the right. During normal conditions **(a)**, prevailing winds push warm surface waters toward the western Pacific. In this diagram, red and orange water is warmer than blue and green water. The red and orange waters in the west are also at a higher elevation than those in the east. During El Niño conditions **(b)**, the prevailing winds weaken and no longer hold the warm surface waters in the western Pacific. As the warmer water "sloshes" back across the Pacific toward South America, precipitation patterns change.

absence of the normal prevailing winds suppress the upwelling along the coast of Peru, shutting down the delivery of nutrients that support the region's marine life and fisheries. This effect is felt along the entire Pacific Coast of the Americas, and it alters weather patterns around the world. Because warm surface water shapes weather by giving rise to heavy precipitation, its movement across the Pacific can create unusually intense rainstorms and floods in areas that are generally dry, and can cause drought and fire in regions that typically experience wet weather.

Scientists monitor the development of El Niño events with an array of wind- and temperature-sensing buoys, known as the Tropical Atmosphere Ocean Project, or TAO/TRITON, that are anchored across the equatorial Pacific; see part (a) of the second figure. These buoys measure temperature profiles during normal conditions (b) and El Niño events (c). Scientists use such data to determine the extent and severity of El Niño events. Awareness of El Niño conditions can enable governments and individuals to better prepare for extreme weather events and changes in ocean conditions.

*La Niña*, or "the little girl," is the opposite of El Niño and exerts impacts trending in the opposite direction. It is characterized by the presence of colder-than-normal surface water in the equatorial Pacific Ocean; see part (d) of the second figure. Scientists have made great strides recently in understanding El Niño and La Niña, but a great deal remains to be understood about their causes, their connections

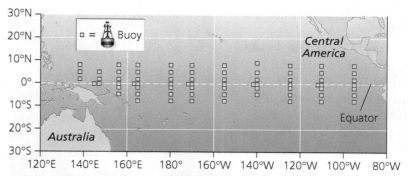

**(a) Temperature-sensing buoys: TAO/TRITON array**

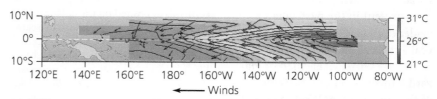

**(b) Temperature during normal conditions (Dec. 1993 averages)**

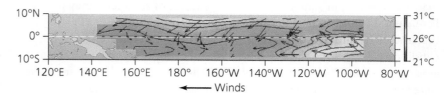

**(c) Temperature during El Niño conditions (Dec. 1997 averages)**

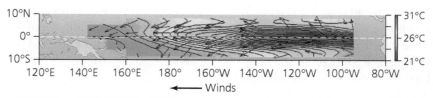

**(d) Temperature during La Niña conditions (Dec. 1998 averages)**

Scientists gather climate data in the Pacific Ocean by using anchored monitoring stations. These buoys (**a**) are distributed across the Pacific. During normal conditions (**b**), cold water reaches the surface of the eastern Pacific via an upwelling, represented by the blue tongue at the right of the graph. During an El Niño event (**c**), warmer water, shown in orange and red, is present in the eastern Pacific and the cold, blue tongue is absent. During a La Niña event (**d**), colder-than-normal water is present in the equatorial Pacific Ocean. Data from National Oceanic and Atmospheric Administration, Tropical Atmospheric Ocean Project, 2001.

to climate change, and their effects on other environmental systems. They clearly show, however, that the atmosphere, oceans, and regional and global climate are tightly integrated systems.

# Scientists Use Pollen to Study Past Climate

Scientists can learn about climate by studying the types of vegetation that grew in particular places in the past. Cores taken from the sediments that collect at the bottoms of lakes and ponds contain pollen and other clues to the plants that lived in those locations at the time each layer was deposited. Tropical plant fossils and pollen tell scientists that warm, wet conditions were present in the past, whereas evidence of cold-loving plants reveal a cooler climate history.

In 1995, J. S. McLachlan of Harvard University and L. B. Brubaker of the University of Washington published a study on the past climate of Washington state's Olympic Peninsula. The researchers found that as climate and hydrological conditions changed, so did the area's vegetation. Their conclusions were based on the characteristics of pollen, fossils, and charcoal that had accumulated over time on the bottom of a small lake and in a cedar swamp, coupled with regional climate data from other sources. Such sediment deposits serve as a timeline. As scientists dig down through

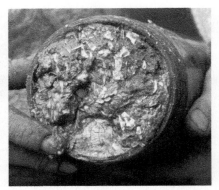

Pollen and larger plant parts preserved in sediments deposited on the bottoms of lakes and ponds over thousands of years can tell scientists about past plant communities and, by extension, about past climates. This sediment core sample was taken from Chesapeake Bay in Maryland.

the layers of sediment, they peer farther back in time.

The research team used a long metal cylinder to pull a 1,811-cm (59.4-ft) core of sediment from the middle of Crocker Lake and a 998-cm (32.7-ft) core of sediment from the middle of the cedar swamp. They wrapped the two cores in plastic and aluminum foil and stored them in large freezers at 4 °C (39.2 °F) to prevent decomposition. The team then began removing 1-mm

thick slices every 10–30 cm (4–12 in.) along the length of the cores and analyzing the pollen and charcoal content of each slice. Pollen is easily transported by the wind and thereby can indicate the types of vegetation that occur over a fairly large area. Pollen, therefore, serves as a clue to regional climate.

The researchers identified between 300 and 1,000 pollen grains to genus and species within each slice. Larger plant fossils, such as those of cones, tree stems, and bark, were also classified. Because these items are not as easily transported as pollen, they are considered to indicate the vegetational and climatological history of smaller, more local, areas. Similarly, fine particles of charcoal, which, like pollen, are easily transported through the atmosphere, tell of the history of forest fires on a regional scale, whereas larger pieces suggest fire occurrence in the immediate area.

In combination with other available information, these clues enabled researchers to piece together a record of the general plant and climate history of the Olympic Peninsula.

## Coupled general circulation models help us understand climate change

To understand how climate systems function, and to predict future climate change, scientists attempt to simulate climate processes with sophisticated computer programs. *Coupled general circulation models (CGCMs)* are computer programs that combine what is known about weather patterns, atmospheric circulation, atmosphere-ocean interactions, and feedback mechanisms to simulate climate processes (Figure 18.8). They couple, or combine, climate influences of the atmosphere and oceans in a single simu-

lation. This requires manipulating vast amounts of data and complex mathematical equations—a task not possible until the advent of the supercomputer.

Over a dozen research labs around the world operate CGCMs. The models have been tested to see how closely they simulate known climate patterns when fed the appropriate historical data. In other words, if modelers enter past climate data, and the models produce accurate predictions of current climate, we have reason to believe the models may be realistic and accurate. Figure 18.9 shows temperature results from three such simulations.

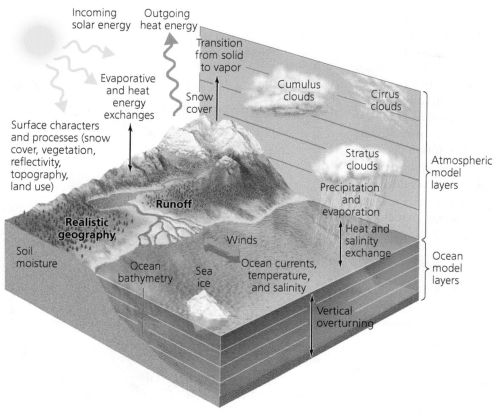

**FIGURE 18.8** Modern climate models incorporate many factors, including processes involving the atmosphere, land, oceans, ice, and biosphere. Some of these factors are shown graphically here, but the actual models deal with them as mathematical equations in computer simulations.

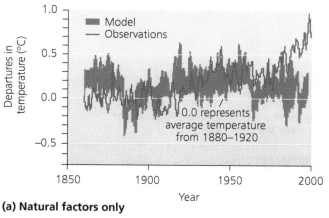

**(a) Natural factors only**

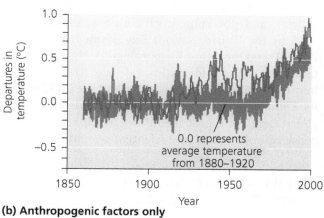

**(b) Anthropogenic factors only**

**FIGURE 18.9** Scientists can test their climate models by entering climate data from past years and comparing model predictions (blue areas) with actual observed data (red line). Models that incorporate only natural factors (**a**) or only human-induced factors (**b**) do a mediocre job of predicting real climate trends. Models that incorporate both natural and anthropogenic factors (**c**) are most accurate. Data from the Intergovernmental Panel on Climate Change. 2001. *Third assessment report.*

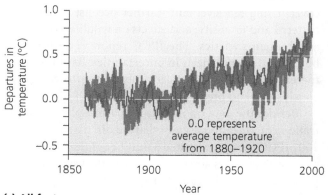

**(c) All factors**

The results in Figure 18.9a are based on natural climate-changing factors alone (such as volcanic activity and variation in solar energy). The results in Figure 18.9b are based on anthropogenic factors only (such as human greenhouse gas emissions and sulfate aerosol emissions). The results in Figure 18.9c are based on natural and anthropogenic factors combined, and this produces the closest match between predictions and actual climate. Results such as those in Figure 18.9c support the notion that both natural and human factors contribute to climate dynamics, and they also indicate that CGCMs can produce reliable predictions. As computing power increases and our ability to glean data from proxy indicators of past climate improves, CGCMs become increasingly reliable.

# Climate Change Estimates and Predictions

The most thoroughly reviewed and widely accepted collection of scientific information concerning global climate change is a series of reports issued by the **Intergovernmental Panel on Climate Change (IPCC).** This international panel of atmospheric scientists, climate experts, and government officials was established in 1988 by the United Nations Environment Programme (UNEP) and the World Meteorological Organization. Its task is to assess information relevant to questions of human-induced climate change. In 2001 the IPCC released its *Third Assessment Report.* This summary of current global trends and probable future trends represents the consensus of atmospheric scientists around the world.

## The IPCC report summarizes evidence of recent changes in global climate

The IPCC report's major conclusions concerning recent climate trends address surface temperature; snow and ice cover; rising sea level and warmer oceans; precipitation patterns and intensity; and effects on wildlife, ecosystems, and human societies. The IPCC report is authoritative but, like all science, deals in uncertainties. Its authors have therefore assigned statistical probabilities to each of its conclusions and predictions.

Besides the data on increases in atmospheric concentrations of greenhouse gases that we discussed earlier, the 2001 IPCC report presented a number of findings on how climate change has already influenced the weather, Earth's physical characteristics and processes, the habits of organisms, and our economies. The report concluded, for

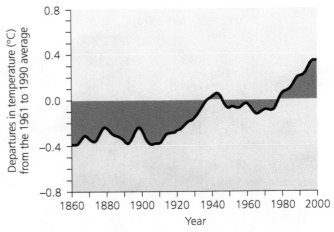

**(a) Global temperature measured over the past 140 years**

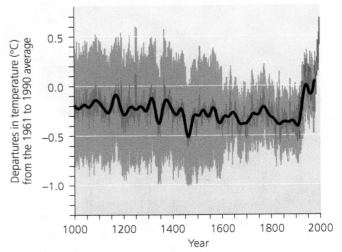

**(b) Northern Hemisphere temperature over the past 1,000 years**

**FIGURE 18.10** Data from thermometers (**a**) show changes in Earth's average surface temperature since 1860. In (**b**), proxy indicators (blue line) and thermometer data (red line) together show average temperature changes in the Northern Hemisphere over the past 1,000 years. The gray-shaded zone represents the 95% confidence range. This record shows that 20th-century warming has eclipsed the magnitude of change during both the "Medieval Warm Period" (10th–14th centuries) and the "Little Ice Age" (15th–19th centuries). Go to **GRAPHit!** at www.aw-bc.com/withgott or on the student CD-ROM. Data from the Intergovernmental Panel on Climate Change, 2001. *Third assessment report.*

instance, that average surface temperatures had increased by 0.6 °C (1.0 °F) during the 20th century (Figure 18.10). It inferred that glaciers, snow cover, and ice caps were melting worldwide. It found that hundreds of species of plants and animals were being forced to shift their

| Table 18.2 Major Findings of the IPCC Third Assessment Report, 2001 |
| --- |

**Weather indicators**

▶ Earth's average surface temperature increased 0.6 °C (1.0 °F) during the 20th century (90–99% certainty)

▶ Cold and frost days decreased for nearly all land areas in the 20th century (90–99% certainty)

▶ Continental precipitation increased by 5–10% during the 20th century in the Northern Hemisphere (90–99% certainty), but it decreased in some regions

▶ The 1990s were the warmest decade of the past 1,000 years (66–90% certainty)

▶ The 20th-century Northern Hemisphere temperature increase was the greatest in 1,000 years (66–90% certainty)

▶ Droughts increased in frequency and severity (66–90% certainty)

▶ Nighttime temperatures increased twice as fast as daytime ones (66–90% certainty)

▶ Hot days and heat index increased (66–90% certainty)

▶ Heavy precipitation events increased at northern latitudes (66–90% certainty)

**Physical indicators**

▶ Average sea level increased 10–20 cm (4–8 in.) during the 20th century

▶ Rivers and lakes in the Northern Hemisphere were covered by ice 2 weeks less from the beginning to the end of the 20th century (90–99% certainty)

▶ Arctic sea ice thinned by 10–40% in recent decades, depending on the season (66–90% certainty)

▶ Mountaintop glaciers retreated widely during the century

▶ Global snow cover decreased by 10% since satellite observations began in the 1960s (90–99% certainty)

▶ Permafrost thawed in many regions

▶ El Niño events became more frequent, persistent, and intense in the past 40 years in the Northern Hemisphere

▶ Growing seasons lengthened 1–4 days per decade in the last 40 years in northern latitudes

**Biological indicators**

▶ Geographic ranges of many plants, insects, birds, and fish shifted toward the poles and upward in elevation

▶ Plants are flowering earlier, migrating birds are arriving earlier, animals are breeding earlier, and insects are emerging earlier in the Northern Hemisphere

▶ Coral reefs are experiencing bleaching more frequently

**Economic indicators**

▶ Global economic losses due to weather events rose 10-fold over the past 40 years, partly because of climate factors

Data from Intergovernmental Panel on Climate Change. 2001. *Third assessment report.*

geographic ranges and the timing of their life cycles. These findings and many more were based on the assessment of thousands of scientific studies conducted worldwide over many years, judged by the world's top experts in these fields. Some—but by no means all—of the report's major findings are shown in Table 18.2.

## Sea-level rise and other changes interact in complex ways

Few of the processes and impacts examined in the IPCC report function in isolation, because Earth's environmental systems are connected and interact. For instance, warming temperatures are causing glaciers to shrink and disappear in many areas around the world. For the same reason, polar ice shelves that have been intact for millennia are breaking away and melting. As glaciers and ice shelves melt, an increased flow of water into the oceans is causing a rise in sea level. Sea level is also rising because ocean water is warming, and water expands in volume as its temperature increases. In fact, most sea-level rise is calculated to result from thermal expansion of seawater, rather than from runoff from melting glaciers and ice shelves.

Higher sea levels lead to beach erosion, coastal flooding, intrusion of saltwater into aquifers, and other impacts. In 1987, unusually high waves struck the Maldives and triggered a campaign to build a large seawall around Male, the nation's capital city. Known as "The

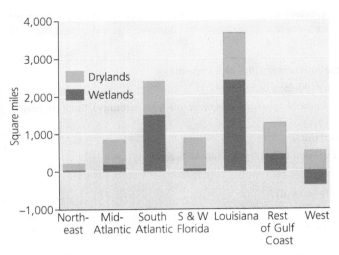

(a) U.S. coastal lands at risk from a 51-cm (20-in.) sea-level rise

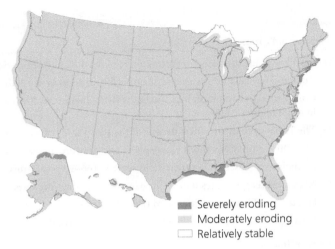

(b) Annual shoreline change

(c) Rescue from floodwaters of Hurricane Katrina

**FIGURE 18.11** The United States will lose coastal areas as a result of a rise in sea level. A 51-cm (20-in.) sea level rise would inundate wetlands (red) and drylands (orange) on portions of all coasts (**a**). Coastal areas around the nation (**b**) are at risk of increased erosion due to sea-level rise. Rescues like this one (**c**) from the floodwaters of Hurricane Katrina's storm surge in coastal Mississippi in 2005 could become more frequent in a future world of higher sea levels. Data (a, b) from National Assessment Synthesis Team, U.S. Global Change Research Program. 2001. *Climate change impacts on the United States: The potential consequences of climate variability and change: Foundation.* Cambridge, U.K.: Cambridge University Press and USGCRP.

Great Wall of Male," the seawall is intended to break up incoming waves and dissipate their energy to prevent the destruction of buildings and roads during storm surges. A *storm surge* is a temporary and localized rise in sea level brought on by the high tides and winds associated with storms. The higher that sea level is to begin with, the further inland a destructive storm surge can reach. "With a mere 1-meter rise [in sea level]," Maldives' President Maumoon Abdul Gayoom warned in 2001, "a storm surge would be catastrophic, and possibly fatal to the nation."

The Maldives is not the only nation with such concerns. In fact, among island nations, the Maldives has fared better than many others. It saw sea level rise about 2.5 mm per year throughout the 1990s, but most Pacific islands are experiencing greater changes. Different regions experience different amounts of sea level change because land elevations may be rising or subsiding naturally, depending on local geological conditions.

The United States is not immune from coastal impacts—and 53% of U.S. residents live within the 17% of the nation's land that lies in coastal areas. Figure 18.11a shows the amounts of wetlands and dry lands in the United States that would be inundated by a 51-cm (20-in.) sea-level rise. Figure 18.11b shows coastal areas in the United States that are eroding because of sea-level rise and other factors. The vulnerability of parts of the nation to coastal flooding due to storm surges became tragically apparent in 2005 when Hurricane Katrina struck New Orleans and the Gulf Coast, followed shortly thereafter by Hurricane Rita. The flooding that devastated the region (Figure 18.11c) could have been even worse had sea level been higher.

The levees surrounding New Orleans that were breached by Katrina's floodwaters are now repaired, but large portions of the city will always remain below sea level. Areas that are now 2.1 m (7 ft) below sea level may be as much as 3.3 m (10 ft) below sea level by 2100, as the land subsides and sea level rises. Just outside the city, marshes of the Mississippi River delta are being lost rapidly, as dams upriver hold back the silt that used to maintain the delta, as land subsides due to the extraction of petroleum deposits, and as rising seas eat away at coastal vegetation. Approximately 2.5 million ha (1 million acres) of Louisiana wetlands have become open water since 1940. Continued loss of these wetlands will mean that New Orleans will have less protection against future storm surges. And coastal Louisiana is not the only U.S. region with these concerns. Houston, Texas, and Charleston, South Carolina are among the major cities most likely to be affected by increased sea level. In southern Florida, coastal wetlands and mangroves are being submerged, and salt water has intruded into aquifers, killing trees and threatening drinking water supplies.

Moreover, the record number of hurricanes and tropical storms in 2005—Katrina and 22 others—left many people wondering if global warming was to blame. Are warmer ocean temperatures spawning more hurricanes, or hurricanes that are more powerful or long-lasting? Scientists are not yet sure of the answers to these questions, but evidence from a number of recent studies indicates that warmer sea surface temperatures are likely increasing the destructive power of storms, and possibly their duration, but are apparently not increasing their frequency.

## The IPCC and other groups project future impacts of climate change

Because the consequences of climate change could be substantial, the IPCC and other groups have attempted to predict future climate changes and their potential impacts. One such group is the U.S. Global Change Research Program (USGCRP), created by Congress in 1990 to coordinate federal climate research. In 2000–2001, the USGCRP issued a report highlighting the past and future effects of global climate change on the United States, where annual average temperatures increased by 0.6 °C (1.0 °F) during the 20th century.

The report used CGCMs to develop a series of predictions on impacts of climate change in the United States (Table 18.3). These models, such as the Hadley model designed by British researchers and the Canadian model designed by British Columbian researchers, allowed scientists

| Table 18.3 Some Predicted Impacts of Climate Change in the United States |
| --- |

▶ Average U.S. temperatures will increase 3–5 °C (5–9 °F) in the next 100 years

▶ Droughts and flooding will worsen, and snowpack will be reduced

▶ Drought and other factors could decrease crop yields, but longer growing seasons and enhanced $CO_2$ could increase yields

▶ Water shortages will worsen

▶ Greater temperature extremes will increase health problems and human mortality. Some tropical diseases will spread north into temperate latitudes

▶ Forest growth may increase in the short term, but in the long term, drought, pests, and fire may alter forest ecosystems

▶ Alpine ecosystems and barrier islands will begin disappearing

▶ Southeastern U.S. forests will break up into savanna/grassland/forest mosaics

▶ Northeastern U.S. forests will lose sugar maples

▶ Loss of coastal wetlands and real estate due to sea level rise will continue

▶ Melting permafrost will undermine Alaskan buildings and roads

Adapted from National Assessment Synthesis Team, U.S. Global Change Research Program. 2000. *Climate change impacts on the United States: The potential consequences of climate variability and change: Overview.* Cambridge, U.K.: Cambridge University Press and USGCRP.

to present unique graphical depictions summarizing predicted impacts of climate change on particular geographic areas (Figure 18.12).

**Agriculture and forestry** Drought and temperature extremes are among the threats that climate change may pose for farms and forests worldwide. Croplands presently near the limits imposed by heat stress and water availability could be pushed beyond their ability to produce food. If average temperatures increase by more than 3–4 °C, most tropical and subtropical areas will likely see decreased crop production, and midlatitude farmlands may also begin to see significant declines.

Conversely, warmer temperatures and longer growing seasons at higher latitudes could potentially increase agricultural productivity there. In fact, of 16 crops in the United States, the USGCRP's agricultural assessment team in 2002 predicted that yields of 13 would increase and only 1 would decrease because of climate change. The overall effect of a warmer climate on agricultural productivity is difficult to predict. Agricultural productivity might remain somewhat stable globally while increasing in some areas and decreasing in others. For this reason,

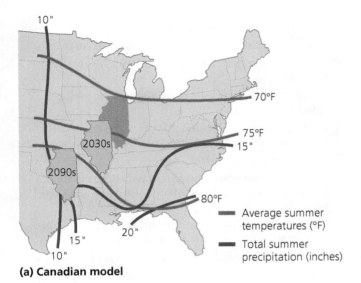

**(a) Canadian model**

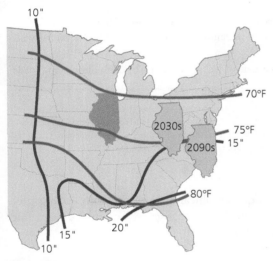

**(b) Hadley model**

**FIGURE 18.12** Using parameters of the Canadian and Hadley models, researchers were able to portray the predicted future climate of the state of Illinois. The Canadian model predicted Illinois to become warmer and drier, attaining in the 2030s a climate similar to Missouri's, and in the 2090s one similar to eastern Oklahoma's. The Hadley model predicted Illinois to become warmer and moister, attaining in the 2030s a climate similar to West Virginia's, and in the 2090s one similar to North Carolina's. Data from National Assessment Synthesis Team, U.S. Global Change Research Program. 2001. *Climate change impacts on the United States: The potential consequences of climate variability and change: Foundation.* Cambridge, U.K.: Cambridge University Press and USGCRP.

some people argue that global warming could benefit their nations, but others point out that it may increase inequities between developed and developing nations.

Research by scientists indicates that climate change could transform U.S. forests. In its 2000–2001 report, the USGCRP predicted that U.S. forests will become more productive, because additional carbon dioxide in the atmosphere will speed rates of photosynthesis. As productivity increases, however, the frequency and intensity of forest fires could increase by 10% or more. Forest communities should in general move northward and upward in elevation. Alpine and subalpine plant communities should become less common as the climate warms, because these mountaintop communities cannot move further upward in elevation. Although some forest types will likely decline, others, including oak-hickory and oak-pine forests, may expand in the eastern United States (Figure 18.13).

Effects on plant communities comprise an important component of climate change, because by drawing in $CO_2$ for photosynthesis, plants act as sinks for carbon. The widespread regrowth of forests in eastern North America (▸ pp. 350, 355) has offset an estimated 25% of U.S. carbon emissions during the past four decades. If climate change increases overall vegetative growth, this could partially mitigate carbon emissions, in a process of negative feedback. However, if climate change decreases overall growth (through drought or fire, for instance), then a positive feedback cycle could increase carbon flux to the atmosphere.

**Weighing the Issues:**
## Agriculture in a Warmer World

Some people maintain that a warmer climate would expand arable lands toward the poles and lead to greater agricultural production globally. In fact, the U.S. Corn Belt is already pushing into Canada. Locate the nations of Russia and Argentina on a world map, and hypothesize how such a poleward shift of agriculture might affect each of these nations. Now hypothesize how it might affect poorer nations near the equator that are already suffering from food shortages and agricultural problems. Thinking back to Chapters 9 and 10, name several factors that could potentially influence crop yields if climate continues changing.

**Freshwater and marine systems** In regions where climate change increases precipitation and stream flow, erosion and flooding could alter the structure and function of aquatic systems. Where agriculture and other human activities have modified the landscape, such flooding could increase pollution of freshwater ecosystems. In regions where precipitation decreases, lakes, ponds, wetlands, and streams would shrink, affecting the organisms that live in

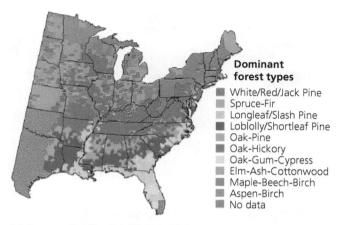

**Dominant forest types**

■ White/Red/Jack Pine
■ Spruce-Fir
■ Longleaf/Slash Pine
■ Loblolly/Shortleaf Pine
■ Oak-Pine
■ Oak-Hickory
■ Oak-Gum-Cypress
■ Elm-Ash-Cottonwood
■ Maple-Beech-Birch
■ Aspen-Birch
■ No data

**(a) Current distribution (1960–1990)**

**(b) Canadian scenario (2070–2100)**

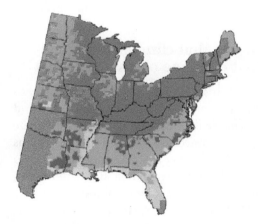

**(c) Hadley scenario (2070–2100)**

**FIGURE 18.13** While some forest types will decline, others, including oak-hickory and oak-pine forests, may expand in the eastern United States. This figure shows predicted forest cover changes based on the Canadian and Hadley models. Data from National Assessment Synthesis Team, U.S. Global Change Research Program. 2001. *Climate change impacts on the United States: The potential consequences of climate variability and change: Foundation.* Cambridge, U.K.: Cambridge University Press and USGCRP.

those habitats, as well as human health and well-being. In 2001, about 1.7 billion people were living in areas with limited water supplies. By 2025, according to the IPCC, this number will likely increase to 5 billion out of a projected world population of 8.4 billion.

The Maldives is likely to suffer from water-related stresses, because its human population is expanding rapidly while rising seas threaten to bring salt water into the nation's wells, just as the 2004 tsunami did. The contamination of groundwater and soils by seawater is particularly threatening to island nations like the Maldives and coastal areas such as the Tampa, Florida, region, which depend on small lenses of freshwater that float atop saline groundwater.

Maldives residents also worry about damage to marine ecosystems, including coral reefs (▶ pp. 474–476). Coral reefs provide habitat for important food fish, reduce wave intensity and protect fragile coastlines from erosion, and provide popular snorkeling and scuba diving sites. Damage to reefs from storm surges would depress tourism and fishing.

**Human health** As a result of climate change, people could face increased exposure to an array of health problems:

▶ Heat stress resulting from high temperatures and humidity
▶ Respiratory ailments from air pollution, as hotter temperatures promote formation of photochemical smog (▶ pp. 510–511)
▶ Expansion of tropical diseases, such as malaria and dengue fever, into temperate regions
▶ Disease and sanitation problems when floods overcome sewage treatment systems
▶ Injuries and drowning if storms become more frequent or intense
▶ Hunger-related ailments as human population grows and demands on agricultural systems increase

Figure 18.14a shows USGCRP projections regarding the 21st-century July heat index across the United States. One model predicts that the heat index—a product of temperature and humidity—will be 14 °C (25 °F) hotter in much of the southeastern United States. Heat waves can lead to high mortality rates in American cities (Figure 18.14b). In Europe, heat stress killed 35,000 people in August 2003 during a record heat wave.

At the same time, other scientists, including some IPCC contributors, have argued that a warmer world will present fewer diseases and injuries that result from cold weather. The trade-off between an increase in warm-weather ailments and a decrease in cold-weather health problems remains one of the unknowns of global climate change.

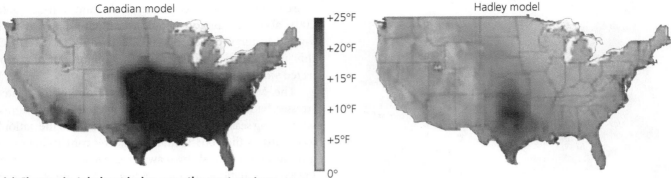

Canadian model

Hadley model

**(a) Change in July heat index over the next century**

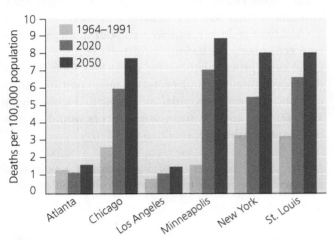

**(b) Average summer mortality rates attributed to hot weather episodes**

**FIGURE 18.14** The Canadian model and the Hadley model provide two projections of the heat index (a product of temperature and humidity) for July across the United States for the upcoming century **(a)**. The Canadian model predicts that the July heat index will be 14 °C (25 °F) hotter than that of much of the present-day southeastern United States. Past and projected future mortality rates attributed to hot weather **(b)** are shown for several U.S. cities. Data from National Assessment Synthesis Team, U.S. Global Change Research Program. 2001. *Climate change impacts on the United States: The potential consequences of climate variability and change: Foundation.* Cambridge, U.K.: Cambridge University Press and USGCRP.

# Debate over Climate Change

Virtually all environmental scientists agree that Earth's atmosphere and climate are changing. The great majority of them have concluded that human activity, particularly our emission of greenhouse gases, is the primary reason for this change. Despite this unusually strong scientific consensus, you have no doubt heard a great deal of debate over climate change. To understand why, it is most helpful to break down this debate into components that can be examined separately.

One component involves discussion within the scientific community about the details and mechanisms of climate change and the extent and nature of its likely effects on human welfare and environmental systems. This is part of the normal process of science as researchers gather evidence and test competing hypotheses, trying to get a full and complete picture of the truth. A second arena of debate involves people, primarily nonscientists, who contest the consensus findings and interpretations of the scientific community.

Some of these so-called "greenhouse skeptics" have vested interests (▸ p. 30) in continuing the widespread use of fossil fuels, and some of them have significant sway over policymakers, particularly in the United States. A third arena of debate involves how our societies should respond to climate change. This is a wide-ranging discourse among scientists, economists, business leaders, policymakers, and others.

## Scientists agree that climate change is occurring but disagree on many details

Although most scientists have concluded that our greenhouse gas emissions are altering the atmosphere and influencing climate, many details and aspects of climate change science remain uncertain, because climate systems are so complex. Climate scientists have not yet come to firm consensus on the roles played by clouds, water vapor, soot and sulfate aerosols, vegetative carbon sinks, and the oceans and NADW formation. Such uncertainties, coupled with the complexity of feedback mechanisms, make it difficult to predict the future.

Despite these uncertainties, the scientific community now feels that evidence for our role in influencing climate is strong enough that governments should take action to address greenhouse gas emissions. In June 2005, as the leaders of the "G8" industrialized nations met, the national academies of science from 11 nations (Brazil, Canada, China, France, Germany, India, Italy, Japan, Russia, the United Kingdom, and the United States) issued a joint statement urging these political leaders to take action. Such a broad consensus statement from the world's scientists was virtually unprecedented, on any issue. The statement read, in part:

> The scientific understanding of climate change is now sufficiently clear to justify nations taking prompt action. It is vital that all nations identify cost-effective steps that they can take now, to contribute to substantial and long-term reduction in net global greenhouse gas emissions. . . . A lack of full scientific certainty about some aspects of climate change is not a reason for delaying an immediate response that will, at a reasonable cost, prevent dangerous anthropogenic interference with the climate system.

## Some challenge the scientific consensus

Despite such clear statements from the scientific community about the risks posed by climate change, many people, primarily nonscientists, have ignored or disputed mainstream scientific findings and interpretations. For instance, just days after the national academies' statement, the *Wall Street Journal* ran an editorial that asked, "What Warming?" and maintained that:

> The scientific case for [climate change] looks weaker all the time. . . . Since [1997], the case for linking fossil fuels to global warming has, if anything, become even more doubtful. The Earth currently does seem to be in a warming period, though how warm and for how long no one knows. In particular, no one knows whether this is unusual or merely something that happens periodically for natural reasons. Most global warming alarms are based on computer simulations that are largely speculative and depend on a multitude of debatable assumptions.

The editorial referenced several scientific studies that contested the data shown in Figure 18.10b, as well as other key findings in climate change science. It did not make clear the extent to which studies demonstrating climate change have earned broad scientific acceptance, whereas studies that deny climate change have not been widely accepted.

The media have played a large role in the public's understanding of climate change, and the U.S. media by tradition try to portray both sides of any issue. However, they often fail to make clear when spokespeople for one side of an issue have stronger evidence or have earned wider support than spokespeople for another side. Author Ross Gelbspan has maintained in two books that the American media have portrayed the climate change debate as much more even and two-sided than it actually is. By giving greenhouse skeptics equal time with mainstream scientists, he and many scientists have argued, the media have amplified the views of greenhouse skeptics out of proportion to their prevalence in the scientific community. Moreover, he documents that the relatively few greenhouse skeptics among scientists are often funded by industries that benefit from fossil fuel use, such as the petroleum and automobile industries.

Industry lobbying has also played a part in making policymakers hesitant to enact policy to reduce carbon emissions. Attempts to improve fuel efficiency for automobiles (▶ p. 582) have repeatedly failed in the U.S. Congress, and attempts to open the Arctic National Wildlife Refuge for oil drilling (▶ pp. 557–559) have repeatedly been made.

------------------------------------------------------

**Weighing the Issues:**
### Environmental Refugees

Citizens of the Maldives need only look southward to find an omen of their future. The Pacific island nation of Tuvalu, which has been losing 9 cm (3.5 in.) of elevation per decade to rising seas, may become the first casualty of global climate change. Appeals from its 11,000 citizens were heard by New Zealand, which began accepting these environmental refugees in 2003. Do you think this refugee flow casts doubt on the arguments of those who hold that climate change is uncertain? How might the perspective of a Tuvalu resident differ from that of a U.S. oil industry executive, and why? What steps might individual people of Tuvalu or the Maldives or coastal Florida take to protect their ways of life?

------------------------------------------------------

## How should we respond to climate change?

Even if one accepts that climate change is real and poses significant ecological and economic threats, there is plenty of room for disagreement over appropriate responses. Political and economic debate over how we should respond stems from questions such as:

▶ Would the economic and political costs of reducing greenhouse gas emissions outweigh the costs of unabated emissions and resulting global climate change?

▶ Should industrialized nations, developing nations, or both take responsibility for reducing greenhouse gas emissions?

▶ Should steps to reduce emissions occur voluntarily or as a result of government regulation, political pressure, or economic sanctions?

▶ How should we allocate funds and human resources for reducing emissions and coping with climate change?

# Strategies for Reducing Emissions

Since 1990, the generation of electricity, largely through coal combustion, has produced the largest portion (34%, as of 2000) of U.S. greenhouse gas emissions (Figure 18.15). Transportation ranks second at 27%, industry produces 19%, agriculture and residential sources produce 8% each, and commercial sources account for 5%. Tackling climate change will require reducing emissions from these sources, and strategies for doing so involve scientific, technical, political, and economic approaches.

## Electricity generation is the largest source of U.S. greenhouse gases

From cooking and heating to the clothes we wear, much of what we own and do depends on electricity. Fossil fuel combustion generates over 70% of U.S. electricity. Coal alone accounts for 56%, along with most of the resultant greenhouse gas emissions. Reducing the volume of fossil fuels we burn to generate electricity would reduce greenhouse gas emissions, as would decreasing electricity consumption. There are two ways to reduce the amount of fossil fuels we use: (1) encouraging conservation and efficiency (▸ pp. 582–583, 585) and (2) switching to renewable energy sources (Chapters 20 and 21).

**Conservation and efficiency** Conservation and efficiency in energy use can arise from new technologies, such as high-efficiency lightbulbs and appliances, or from individual ethical choices to reduce electricity consumption. In one example of a technological solution, the U.S. Environmental Protection Agency (EPA) promotes energy conservation through its Energy Star Program. The Energy Star Program rates household appliances, lights, windows, fans, office equipment, heating and cooling systems, and appliances for their efficiency in using energy. Following are examples of the energy you can save by choosing Energy Star products:

▸ An Energy Star refrigerator can cut your $CO_2$ emissions by 100 kg (220 lb) annually.

▸ An Energy Star washing machine can cut your $CO_2$ emissions by 200 kg (440 lb) annually.

▸ Compact fluorescent lights can reduce the energy you use for lighting by 40%.

▸ Energy Star homes use highly efficient construction, duct work, insulation, heating and cooling systems, and windows to reduce energy use by as much as 30%.

**FIGURE 18.15** Coal-fired electricity-generating power plants, such as this one in Maryland, are the largest contributors to U.S. greenhouse emissions.

Such technological solutions are popular, and they can be profitable for manufacturers while also saving consumers money. Alternatively, consumers can opt for lifestyle choices rather than technological fixes. For nearly all of human history, people managed without the electrical appliances that most of us take for granted today. It is entirely possible for each of us to simply choose to use fewer greenhouse-gas-producing appliances and technologies or to take practical steps to use electricity more efficiently.

**Renewable sources of electricity** Technologies that generate electricity without using fossil fuels represent another means of reducing greenhouse gas emissions. These include hydroelectric power (▸ pp. 446–447 and 612–615), geothermal energy (▸ pp. 633–635), photovoltaic cells (▸ pp. 625–626), and wind power (▸ pp. 627–633). We will examine renewable energy sources in more detail in Chapters 20 and 21.

## Transportation is the second largest source of U.S. greenhouse gases

Can you imagine life without a car? Most Americans probably can't—a reason why transportation is the second largest source of U.S. greenhouse emissions. One-third of the average American city—including roads, parking lots, garages, and gas stations—is devoted to use by cars. The average American family makes 10 trips by car each day, and governments across the nation spend $200 million per day on road construction and repairs. Registered U.S. automobiles number over 220 million, and this figure is projected to surpass the human population of the country.

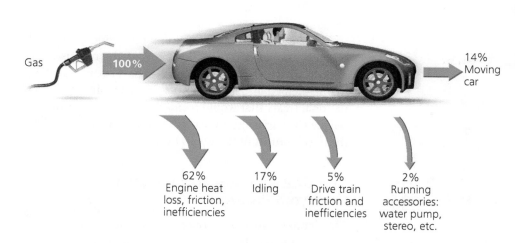

Gas  100%  14% Moving car

62% Engine heat loss, friction, inefficiencies

17% Idling

5% Drive train friction and inefficiencies

2% Running accessories: water pump, stereo, etc.

**FIGURE 18.16** Conventional automobiles are extremely inefficient. Almost 85% of useful energy is lost, and only 14% actually moves the car down the road.

Unfortunately, the typical automobile is highly inefficient. Close to 85% of the fuel you pump into your gas tank does something other than move your car down the road. According to the U.S. Department of Energy, only about 13–14% of the fuel energy actually moves the vehicle and its occupants from point A to point B (Figure 18.16). Although more aerodynamic designs, increased engine efficiency, proper maintenance, and improved tire design help to reduce these losses, gasoline-fueled automobiles may always remain somewhat inefficient.

**Automotive technology** Advancing technology, however, is making possible a number of alternatives to the traditional combustion-engine automobile. These include hybrid vehicles that combine electric motors and gasoline-powered engines for greater efficiency (▸p. 583). They also include fully electric vehicles, alternative fuels such as biodiesel and compressed natural gas (▸pp. 609–610), and hydrogen fuel cells that use oxygen and hydrogen and produce only water as a waste product (▸pp. 637–642).

**Driving less, and public transportation** Despite these novel options, the high costs of automobile ownership and concerns regarding traffic and the environmental impacts of automobiles are leading many people to make lifestyle choices that reduce their reliance on cars. For example, many people are choosing to live nearer to their place of employment. Many others use buses, subway trains, and other modes of public transportation. Still others bike or walk to work or for their errands (Figure 18.17). Unfortunately, reliable and convenient public transit is not yet available in many U.S. communities. Making automobile-based cities and suburbs more

friendly to pedestrian and bicycle traffic and improving people's access to public transportation stand as major challenges for progressive city and regional planners (▸pp. 388–391).

In a 2002 study, the American Public Transportation Association (APTA) concluded that increasing use of public transportation is the single most effective strategy for conserving energy and reducing environmental pollutants. Already, public transportation in the United States reduces fossil fuel consumption by 855 million gallons of gas (45 million barrels of oil) each year, the APTA has estimated. Yet according to the study, if U.S. residents increased their use of public transportation to the levels of

**FIGURE 18.17** Sometimes the most effective solutions are the simplest. By choosing human-powered transportation methods, such as bicycles, we can greatly reduce our individual transportation-related greenhouse gas emissions. An increasing number of people are choosing to live closer to their workplaces and to enjoy the dual benefits of exercise and reduced emissions by walking or cycling to work or school.

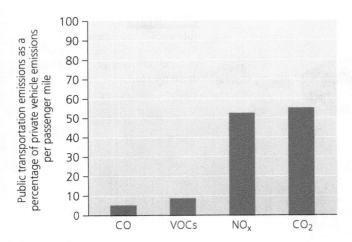

Relative to travel by private automobile, public transportation reduces almost all types of air pollution, including carbon monoxide (CO), volatile organic compounds (VOCs), nitrous oxides (NOx), and carbon dioxide ($CO_2$). Data from Shapiro, R. J., et al. 2002. *Conserving energy and preserving the environment: The role of public transportation.* American Public Transit Association.

Canadians (7% of daily travel needs) or Europeans (10% of daily travel needs), enormous amounts of energy and greenhouse emissions would be saved. These savings, the study indicated, could substantially cut air pollution, dependence on imported oil, and the nation's contribution to global climate change (Figure 18.18).

## Some international treaties address climate change

In 1992, the United Nations convened the U.N. Conference on Environment and Development Earth Summit in Rio de Janeiro. Nations represented at the Earth Summit signed five documents, including the **U.N. Framework Convention on Climate Change (FCCC)**. The FCCC outlined a plan for reducing greenhouse gas emissions to 1990 levels by the year 2000 through a voluntary, nation-by-nation approach.

By the late 1990s, it was apparent that a voluntary approach to slowing greenhouse gas emissions was not likely to succeed. Between 1990 and 2003, for example, U.S. greenhouse emissions (in $CO_2$ equivalents) increased by 13.3%.

However, some other nations have demonstrated that economic vitality does not require ever-increasing greenhouse gas emissions. For instance, Germany has the third most technologically advanced economy in the world and is a leading producer of iron, steel, coal, chemicals, automobiles, machine tools, electronics, textiles, and other goods—yet it managed between 1990 and 2003 to reduce its greenhouse gas emissions by

18.5%. In the same period, the United Kingdom cut its emissions by 13.0%.

After watching the seas rise and observing the refusal of most industrialized nations to cut their emissions, nations of the developing world—the Maldives among them—helped initiate an effort to create a binding international treaty that would *require* all signatory nations to reduce their greenhouse gas emissions. This effort led to the development of the Kyoto Protocol.

## The United States has resisted the Kyoto Protocol

The **Kyoto Protocol** is an outgrowth of the FCCC. Drafted in 1997 in Kyoto, Japan, it mandates signatory nations, by the period 2008–2012, to reduce emissions of six greenhouse gases to levels equal to or lower than those of 1990 (Table 18.4). The treaty was to take effect once nations responsible for 55% of global greenhouse emissions ratified it, and in 2005, the Kyoto Protocol at last came into force after it was ratified by Russia, the 127th nation to ratify it.

The United States, the world's largest emitter of greenhouse gases, has continued to refuse to ratify the Kyoto Protocol. U.S. leaders have called the treaty unfair because it requires industrialized nations to reduce emissions but does not require the same of developing nations, even rapidly industrializing ones such as China and India.

| Table 18.4 | Emissions Reductions Required and Achieved | |
| --- | --- | --- |
| **Nation** | **Required change,**[1] **1990–2008/2012** | **Observed change,** **1990–2003**[2] |
| Russia | 0.0% | −38.5%[3] |
| Germany | −21.0% | −18.5% |
| United Kingdom | −12.5% | −13.0% |
| France | 0.0% | −1.9% |
| Italy | −6.5% | +8.3% |
| Japan | −6.0% | +12.8% |
| United States | −7.0% | +13.3% |
| Canada | −6.0% | +24.2% |

[1]Percentage decrease in emissions (carbon-equivalents of six greenhouse gases) from 1990 to period 2008–2012, as mandated under Kyoto Protocol
[2]Actual percentage change in emissions (carbon-equivalents of 6 greenhouse gases) from 1990 to 2003. Negative values indicate decreases; positive values indicate increases.
[3]Data through 1999 (most recent available). Russia's substantial decrease was mainly due to economic contraction following the breakup of the Soviet Union.
Data from U.N. Framework Convention on Climate Change, National Greenhouse Gas Inventory Reports, 2005.

## Global Climate Change

**VIEWPOINTS**

What is scientific research telling us about global climate change and its potential consequences for our society and the environment? How should humanity respond to climate change?

### The Science Is Settled Enough to Justify Action

Many things are abundantly clear in climate change research. Human activities have undoubtedly led to the highest atmospheric levels of $CO_2$ and $CH_4$ seen in almost 1 million years, and both are powerful greenhouse gases that warm the surface of the planet. Temperatures have risen around 0.7 °C since around 1900, of which a large proportion is attributable to this enhanced greenhouse effect. The significant increases of heat in the oceans match climate model calculations of the increasing energy imbalance of the planet, and the almost global retreat of mountain glaciers is a graphic symptom of the increasing warmth of the atmosphere. Some further climate change is inevitable because the climate has yet to come into equilibrium with current greenhouse gas levels.

There are also many remaining uncertainties in climate science, particularly related to the role of aerosols and clouds. However, despite occasional claims to the contrary, the science is settled enough to justify action to reduce greenhouse gas emissions.

Due to the inertia of energy infrastructure in today's societies, $CO_2$ emissions will continue to rise for decades to come, and given the long atmospheric lifetime of $CO_2$, atmospheric concentrations will continue to increase for even longer. Model projections indicate that this could have significant and costly impacts on the environment and sea level if this continues unabated. Given the long time scales involved (in society and in climate itself), decisions made now will only start to have impacts many decades hence. Therefore, by the time serious effects are obvious, it may be too late to avoid the worst consequences.

Sensible policy approaches should combine investment in an increased resilience to climate changes, along with long-term efforts to reduce emissions. Cuts in other warming factors such as $CH_4$, black carbon, and tropospheric ozone would be positive steps for tackling both climate change and air pollution.

**Gavin Schmidt** is a climate modeller at the NASA Goddard Institute for Space Studies in New York. He is an associate editor for the *Journal of Climate* and was recently cited by *Scientific American* as one of the 50 Research Leaders of 2004.

### Climate Changes Are Mostly Natural

Climate is never constant but varies, sometimes dramatically, on timescales ranging from years to eons. On the human scale, decades to centuries, the major cause seems to be cyclical variations of solar radiation. Since the end of the most recent ice age, some 10,000 years ago, there have been many such cycles. In recent history we have seen the Medieval Warming Period when England produced wines and Vikings colonized Greenland. Then followed the Little Ice Age, which disappeared only around 1850 A.D., about the time when thermometers first became available in much of the world. The global climate then warmed strongly until about 1940, followed by a cooling until 1975 that provoked great fears of a return to an ice age. All these changes are believed to be of natural origin, even though during this time there had been a steady increase in levels of atmospheric greenhouse gases from human activities.

Since 1979, weather satellites have reported a slight warming trend, which could be partially anthropogenic, as theoretical climate models suggest. Teasing out the small human contribution from the natural "noise" is difficult and the focus of ongoing scientific debate.

Nonetheless, we can draw certain conclusions. Anthropogenic global warming is not a significant problem, amounting to less than 1 °C by 2100. On the whole, it will be beneficial, with higher levels of carbon dioxide speeding growth of crops and forests. And realistically, there is little that can be done to stem the rise of emissions, especially from nations like China and India. The best policy is one of "no regrets"—energy conservation because it pays, and strengthening our ability to adapt by fighting poverty around the world.

**S. Fred Singer** is professor emeritus of environmental science at the University of Virginia, and president of the Science and Environmental Policy Project. He was the first director of the U.S. Weather Satellite Service, and served 5 years as vice-chair of the National Advisory Committee on Oceans and Atmospheres. With Dennis T. Avery, he is the co-author of *Unstoppable Global Warming—Every 1500 Years* (Rowman & Littlefield Publishers, 2006).

 Explore this issue further by accessing **Viewpoints** at www.aw-bc.com/withgott.

Proponents of the Kyoto Protocol justify the differential requirements by pointing out that the industrialized world created the current problem and therefore should make the sacrifices necessary to solve it.

The United States' refusal to join international efforts to curb greenhouse emissions has generated resentment among its allies and has left it diplomatically isolated. In December 2005, as the world's nations met in Montreal to design a roadmap for how to build on Kyoto after 2012, the U.S. representative walked out of the meeting, and the Bush administration, according to the *New York Times,* was "repeatedly assailed by the leaders of other wealthy industrialized nations for refusing to negotiate."

Because resource use and per capita carbon dioxide emissions are far greater in the industrialized world, governments and industries in developed nations often feel they have more to lose, economically, from mandatory restrictions on emissions. Ironically, this fear neglects the equally likely probability that developed nations are the ones most likely to gain economically in such a situation. This is because they may be in the best position to invent and develop new technologies to power the world in a post-fossil-fuel era. Moreover, if an international "cap-and-trade" permit-trading system (▶ p. 73) in carbon dioxide emissions becomes successful, then U.S. industries that are left out may find themselves at a disadvantage relative to their international competitors.

Despite the U.S. government's refusal to ratify Kyoto, many state and local governments across the nation are expressing support for limits on greenhouse emissions. As of late 2005, nine states had announced voluntary commitments to emissions targets similar to those set forth by the Kyoto Protocol. These states comprised roughly one-quarter of the U.S. population and GDP. Several other states and several dozen municipalities were also poised to adopt policies to reduce their greenhouse gas emissions.

However, Kyoto Protocol critics and supporters alike acknowledge that even if every nation complied with the limits established in this treaty, greenhouse gas emissions would continue to increase—albeit more slowly than they would in the absence of the treaty.

## Some feel climate change demands the precautionary principle

With regard to global climate change, as with many other environmental issues, we may never be entirely certain of the precise outcomes of our actions until after they have occurred, and perhaps not even then. With this uncertainty in mind, the drafters of the 1992 Rio Declaration included a passage invoking the precautionary principle (▶ p. 290):

> In order to protect the environment, the precautionary approach shall be widely applied by the States according to their capabilities. Where there are threats of serious or irreversible damage, lack of full scientific certainty shall not be used as reason for postponing cost-effective measures to prevent environmental degradation.

That is, advocates of the precautionary principle assert that if a threat is reasonably suspected, we should take precautionary action without waiting for full scientific certainty regarding cause and effect.

------------------------------------------------

**Weighing** the **Issues:**
## The Precautionary Principle

Critics of the precautionary approach say that it will impede economic growth and innovation. Advocates of the precautionary principle say the stakes are too high to gamble with climate. What do you think? Is the precautionary approach an appropriate guide for dealing with climate change? What role should economics play in the discussion?

------------------------------------------------

# Conclusion

We have seen that many factors, including human activities, can shape atmospheric composition and global climate. We have also seen that scientists and policymakers are beginning to understand anthropogenic climate change and its environmental, economic, and social consequences more fully. Although many policymakers and industrial leaders express no anxiety about climate change, many scientists and other policymakers are deeply concerned. As time passes, fewer experts are arguing that the changes will be minor. Sea-level rise and other consequences of global climate change will affect far-flung places such as the Maldives, but they will also influence populated mainland areas such as coastal Florida. By becoming familiar with climate science and with potential solutions to climate-related problems, you will become better equipped to interpret the many messages you will receive regarding global climate change in the coming years.

## REVIEWING OBJECTIVES

**You should now be able to:**

### Describe Earth's climate system and explain the variety of factors influencing global climate

▶ Climate is a homeostatic system that varies naturally with time. (p. 530)

▶ The sun provides most of Earth's energy and interacts with the atmosphere, land, and oceans to drive climate processes. (pp. 530–531)

▶ Earth absorbs about 70% of incoming solar radiation and reflects about 30% back into space. (pp. 530–531)

▶ "Greenhouse gases," such as carbon dioxide, methane, water vapor, nitrous oxide, ozone, and halocarbons, warm the atmosphere by absorbing infrared radiation and re-emitting infrared radiation of different wavelengths. (pp. 530–533)

▶ Milankovitch cycles influence climate in the long term. (p. 533)

### Characterize human influences on the atmosphere and global climate

▶ By burning fossil fuels, deforesting landscapes, and manufacturing halocarbons, humans are increasing atmospheric concentrations of many greenhouse gases. Increased greenhouse gas emissions enhance the greenhouse effect. (pp. 530–532)

### Delineate methods of modern climate research

▶ Geologic records, such as cores through ice or sediments, reveal information about past climatic conditions. (pp. 534–535, 538)

▶ Direct atmospheric sampling tells us about current composition of the atmosphere. (p. 535)

▶ Coupled general circulation models (CGCMs) serve to predict future changes in climate. (pp. 538–540)

### Summarize current consequences and potential future impacts of global climate change

▶ The IPCC has comprehensively synthesized current climate research, and its periodic reports represent the consensus of the scientific community. (p. 540)

▶ Temperatures on Earth have warmed by an average of 0.6 °C (1.0 °F) over the past century. (pp. 540–541)

▶ Sea level has risen an average of 10–20 cm (4–8 in.) over the past century. (pp. 541–543)

▶ Other impacts include changes in precipitation, frequency of extreme weather events, and effects on plants and animals. (pp. 541–543)

▶ Various potential impacts of future climate change have been predicted, including physical, biological, ecological, and economic impacts. (pp. 543–546)

### Evaluate the scientific, political, and economic debates concerning climate change

▶ Many details of climate change science remain uncertain because climate systems are so complex. Yet scientists broadly agree that climate change is occurring. (pp. 546–547)

▶ Despite the remaining uncertainties, the scientific community feels that evidence for humans' role in influencing climate is strong enough to justify governments taking action to reduce greenhouse emissions. (pp. 546–547)

▶ A few scientists and many nonscientists have resisted the scientific consensus, and these "greenhouse skeptics" have enjoyed a disproportionately large voice in the public debate. (p. 547)

▶ Policymakers in the United States and some other nations have resisted confronting climate change because of fears that reducing greenhouse emissions will be economically costly. (p. 547)

### Suggest potential responses to climate change

▶ Conserving electricity, improving efficiency of energy use, and switching to renewable energy sources will help reduce fossil fuel consumption and greenhouse emissions. (p. 548)

▶ Encouraging new automotive technologies and public transportation systems should help reduce greenhouse emissions. (pp. 548–550)

▶ The Kyoto Protocol provides a first step for nations to begin addressing climate change. (pp. 550, 552)

## TESTING YOUR COMPREHENSION

**1.** What happens to solar radiation after it reaches Earth? How do greenhouse gases warm the lower atmosphere?

**2.** Why is water vapor considered a greenhouse gas? How could an increase of water vapor create a positive or negative feedback effect?

3. How do scientists study the ancient atmosphere?

4. Has simulating climate change with computer programs been effective in helping us predict climate? How do these programs work?

5. How can rising sea levels, caused by global warming, create problems for people? How may rising sea levels affect marine ecosystems?

6. How might a warmer climate affect agriculture? How might a warmer climate affect forest distribution, according to recent research?

7. What are some likely negative impacts of warmer climate on human health? Could there be beneficial consequences?

8. Do all scientists agree that climate is indeed changing? On what counts do they currently disagree?

9. What are the largest two sources of greenhouse gas emissions in the United States, and why? In what ways can we try to reduce these emissions?

10. What roles have international treaties played in addressing climate change? Give two specific examples.

---

## SEEKING SOLUTIONS

1. To determine to what extent current climate change is the result of human activity versus natural processes, which type(s) of scientific research do you think is (are) most helpful? Why?

2. As you have seen in many places in this book, people may draw dramatically different conclusions about the significance and implications of environmental change. Refer to the quotations presented at the beginning of this chapter's central case study. What questions might you ask of the editors of the *Oil and Gas Journal* and representatives of the Maldives' government to better understand their positions and their reasons for holding them?

3. Some people argue that it is appropriate, and even helpful, for former fossil fuel company executives to serve in high-level government positions where they can make decisions regarding energy policy, carbon dioxide emissions, and global climate change. Others say this presents a potential conflict of interest and should be discouraged. List some of the arguments justifying each side. What is your opinion?

4. Today, many people argue that we need "more proof," or "better science" before we commit to substantial changes in the way we live our lives. How much "science," or certainty, do you think we need before we have enough to guide our decisions regarding climate change? How much certainty do you need in your own life before you make a change? Should nations and elected officials follow a different standard? Do you believe that the precau-

tionary principle is an appropriate standard in the case of global climate change? Why or why not?

5. Describe several ways that greenhouse gas emissions from transportation can be reduced. Which approach do you think is most realistic, which approach do you think is least realistic, and why?

6. Ismail Shafeeu, the Maldives' environment minister, believes that a solution to climate change will require political leadership at the international level on the part of the United States:

> We have to strive to point out the problems that are associated with climate change and the responsibilities we feel lie with countries such as the U.S. [because the developed countries burn most of the fossil fuel], particularly the U.S. as a global leader. We would like to see the U.S. take a more constructive approach to these problems than the one they are presently taking. . . . The general impression is that the government of the United States has this sense that it's surrounded by a lot of countries trying to destroy its economy, but I don't think any country is asking of the United States something that they have not offered to do themselves.

Do you agree with Shafeeu's statements? Why or why not? Why do you think the U.S. government has chosen not to ratify the Kyoto Protocol? Do you think it should ratify the treaty?

---

## INTERPRETING GRAPHS AND DATA

We burn fossil fuels to generate electricity, to power vehicles for transportation, and as primary energy sources in the home, in businesses, and in industry. For each of these uses, trends in the emission of carbon dioxide from fossil fuel combustion in the United States are shown in the accompanying graph.

1. Calculate the approximate percentage changes in $CO_2$ emissions from transportation; electricity generation; and residential, commercial, and industrial primary energy use between 1980 and 2003.
2. Between 1980 and 2003, U.S. population increased by 28.4%, and the inflation-adjusted U.S. gross domestic product (GDP) doubled. What quantitative conclusions can you draw from these data about $CO_2$ emissions per capita? About $CO_2$ emissions per unit of total economic activity?
3. Imagine you are put in charge of designing a strategy to reduce U.S. emissions of $CO_2$ from fossil fuel combustion. Based on the data presented here, what approaches would you recommend, and how would you prioritize these? Explain your answers.

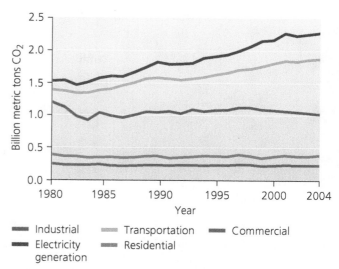

Emissions of $CO_2$ from fossil fuel combustion by end-use sector in the United States, 1980–2003. Data from U.S. Department of Energy, Energy Information Administration. 2004. *Annual Energy Review 2004*, Report No. DOE/EIA-0384.

## CALCULATING ECOLOGICAL FOOTPRINTS

U.S. energy consumption from fossil fuels currently totals 306 gigajoules per person per year. Carbon emitted from fossil fuel combustion is "sequestered" when plants take up the emitted carbon dioxide through photosynthesis and store it as organic matter. Researchers have estimated that for each 100 gigajoules of fossil fuel burned, 1 hectare of ecologically productive land is required for carbon sequestration. Considering these data, calculate the component of the ecological footprint required to sequester carbon from fossil fuel emissions, and record your results in the table.

|  | **Hectares of land to sequester carbon** |
|---|---|
| You | 3.06 |
| Your class | |
| Your state | |
| United States | |

Data from Wackernagel, M., and W. Rees. 1996. *Our ecological footprint: Reducing human impact on the earth.* Gabriola Island, British Columbia, Canada: New Society Publishers.

1. The land area of the United States is about 916 million hectares. What percentage of that land would need to be set aside to sequester all carbon from the fossil fuel consumption of 300 million Americans?
2. What is the environmental fate of carbon dioxide that is released from the combustion of fossil fuels and is not sequestered by plants? Why is this a concern?
3. Name four things you could do to lessen the modification of the global environment caused by your own personal energy consumption.

## Take It Further

Go to www.aw-bc.com/withgott or the student CD-ROM where you'll find:

▶ Suggested answers to end-of-chapter questions
▶ Quizzes, animations, and flashcards to help you study
▶ *Research Navigator*™ database of credible and reliable sources to assist you with your research projects

▶ **GRAPHit!** tutorials to help you master how to interpret graphs
▶ **INVESTIGATEit!** current news articles that link the topics that you study to case studies from your region to around the world

# Appendix A   Some Basics on Graphs

Presenting data in ways that are clear and that help make trends and patterns visually apparent is a vital part of the scientific endeavor. Scientists' primary tool for presenting data and expressing patterns is the graph. Thus, the ability to interpret graphs is a skill that you will want to cultivate early in your study of the sciences. This appendix provides basic information on four of the most common types of graphs—line plots, bar charts, scatter plots, and pie charts—and the rationale for the use of each.

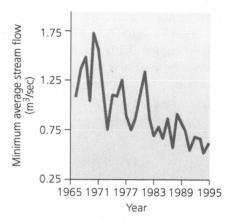

**Minimum stream flow**

## Line Plot

A line plot is drawn when a data set involves a sequence of some kind, such as a sequence through time or across distance (Figure A.1; see ▶ p. 140 and Figure 9.19, ▶ p. 266). Using a line plot allows us to see increasing or decreasing trends in the data. Line plots are appropriate when the variable measured by the *y* axis (the vertical axis) represents continuous numerical data, and when the variable measured by the *x* axis (the horizontal axis) represents either continuous numerical data or sequential categories, such as years.

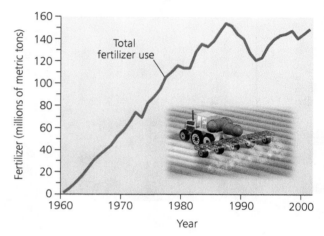

**Global fertilizer use, 1960–2002**

FIGURE A.1

One useful technique is to plot two data sets together on the same graph (Figure A.2; see Figure 6.5, ▶ p. 153). This allows us to compare trends in the two data sets to see whether and how they may be related.

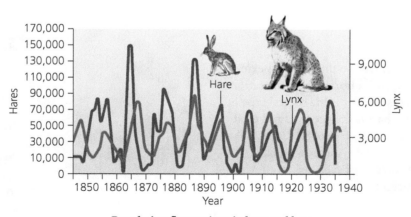

**Population fluctuations in hare and lynx**

FIGURE A.2

## Bar Chart

A bar chart is most often used when one of the variables represents categories rather than numerical values (Figure A.3; see Figure 13.10a, ▶ p. 389). Bar charts allow us to visualize how a variable differs quantitatively among categories.

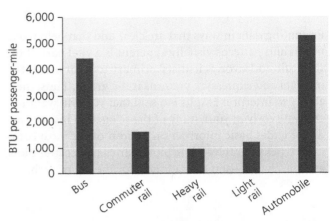

**Energy consumption for different modes of transit**

FIGURE A.3

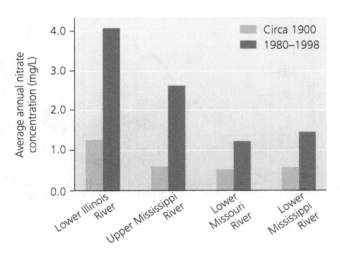

**Nitrate concentrations in portions of the Mississippi River watershed**

FIGURE A.4

It is often instructive to graph two or more variables together to reveal patterns and relationships (Figure A.4; see Figure 7.4a, ▶ p. 188). Most of the bar charts you will see in this book illustrate several types of information at once in this manner.

Bar charts are usually arrayed so that the bars extend vertically. Sometimes, however, a horizontal orientation may make for a clearer presentation. One special type of horizontally oriented bar chart is the age pyramid used by demographers (Figure A.5; see Figure 8.11, ▶ p. 226). Age categories are displayed on the y axis, with bars representing the population size of each age group varying in width instead of height.

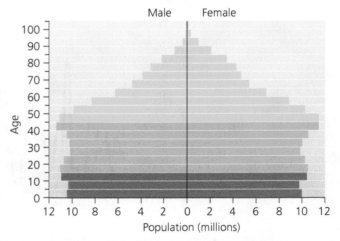

**United States age structure, 2005**

FIGURE A.5

## Scatter Plot

A scatter plot is used most often when there is no sequential aspect to the data, and each data point is independent, having no particular connection to other data points (Figure A.6; see Figure 8.15, ▸ p. 232). Scatter plots allow you to visualize a broad positive or negative correlation between variables on the two axes.

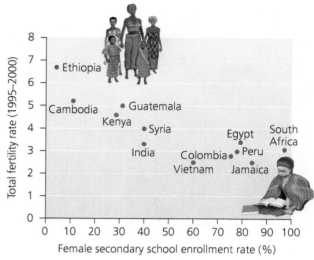

**Fertility rate and female education**

FIGURE A.6

## Pie Chart

A pie chart is used when we wish to compare the proportions of some whole that are taken up by each of several categories (Figure A.7; see Figure 9.2, ▸ p. 247). A pie chart is appropriate when one variable is categorical and one is numerical. Each category is represented visually like a slice from a pie, with the size of the slice reflecting the percentage of the whole that is taken up by that category.

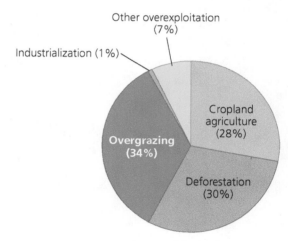

**Causes of desertification**

FIGURE A.7

But don't stop here. Take advantage of the **GRAPHit!** tutorials on the CD-ROM included with this text, or go to the Withgott/Brennan Companion Website at www.aw-bc.com/withgott. The **GRAPHit!** tutorials allow you to plot your own data, and help you further expand your comprehension of graphs.

# Appendix B  Metric System

| Measurement | Unit and Abbreviation | Metric Equivalent | Metric to English Conversion Factor | English to Metric Conversion Factor |
|---|---|---|---|---|
| Length | 1 kilometer (km) | $= 1,000\ (10^3)$ meters | 1 km = 0.62 mile | 1 mile = 1.61 km |
| | 1 meter (m) | $= 100\ (10^2)$ centimeters | 1 m = 1.09 yards | 1 yard = 0.914 m |
| | | $= 1,000$ millimeters | 1 m = 3.28 feet | 1 foot = 0.305 m |
| | | | 1 m = 39.37 inches | |
| | 1 centimeter (cm) | $= 0.01\ (10^{-2})$ meter | 1 cm = 0.394 inch | 1 foot = 30.5 cm |
| | | | | 1 inch = 2.54 cm |
| | 1 millimeter (mm) | $= 0.001\ (10^{-3})$ meter | 1 mm = 0.039 inch | |
| | 1 micrometer (μm) [formerly micron (μ)] | $= 0.000001\ (10^{-6})$ meter | | |
| | 1 nanometer (nm) [formerly millimicron (mμ)] | $= 0.000000001\ (10^{-9})$ meter | | |
| | 1 angstrom (Å) | $= 0.0000000001\ (10^{-10})$ meter | | |
| Area | 1 square meter (m$^2$) | $= 10,000$ square centimeters | 1 m$^2$ = 1.1960 square yards | 1 square yard = 0.8361 m$^2$ |
| | | | 1 m$^2$ = 10.764 square feet | 1 square foot = 0.0929 m$^2$ |
| | 1 square centimeter (cm$^2$) | $= 100$ square millimeters | 1 cm$^2$ = 0.155 square inch | 1 square inch = 6.4516 cm$^2$ |
| Mass | 1 metric ton (t) | $= 1,000$ kilograms | 1 t = 1.103 ton | 1 ton = 0.907 t |
| | 1 kilogram (kg) | $= 1,000$ grams | 1 kg = 2.205 pounds | 1 pound = 0.4536 kg |
| | 1 gram (g) | $= 1,000$ milligrams | 1 g = 0.0353 ounce | 1 ounce = 28.35 g |
| | | | 1 g = 15.432 grains | |
| | 1 milligram (mg) | $= 0.001$ gram | 1 mg = approx. 0.015 grain | |
| | 1 microgram (μg) | $= 0.000001$ gram | | |
| Volume (solids) | 1 cubic meter (m$^3$) | $= 1,000,000$ cubic centimeters | 1 m$^3$ = 1.3080 cubic yards | 1 cubic yard = 0.7646 m$^3$ |
| | | | 1 m$^3$ = 35.315 cubic feet | 1 cubic foot = 0.0283 m$^3$ |
| | 1 cubic centimeter (cm$^3$ or cc) | $= 0.000001$ cubic meter | 1 cm$^3$ = 0.0610 cubic inch | 1 cubic inch = 16.387 cm$^3$ |
| | | $= 1$ milliliter | | |
| | 1 cubic millimeter (mm$^3$) | $= 0.000000001$ cubic meter | | |
| Volume (liquids and gases) | 1 kiloliter (kl or kL) | $= 1,000$ liters | 1 kL = 264.17 gallons | 1 gallon = 3.785 L |
| | 1 liter (l or L) | $= 1,000$ milliliters | 1 L = 0.264 gallons | 1 quart = 0.946 L |
| | | | 1 L = 1.057 quarts | |
| | 1 milliliter (ml or mL) | $= 0.001$ liter | 1 ml = 0.034 fluid ounce | 1 quart = 946 ml |
| | | $= 1$ cubic centimeter | 1 ml = approx. $\frac{1}{4}$ teaspoon | 1 pint = 473 ml |
| | | | 1 ml = approx. 15–16 drops (gtt.) | 1 fluid ounce = 29.57 ml |
| | | | | 1 teaspoon = approx. 5 ml |
| | 1 microliter (μl or μL) | $= 0.000001$ liter | | |
| Time | 1 second (s) | $= \frac{1}{60}$ minute | | |
| | 1 millisecond (ms) | $= 0.001$ second | 1 second (s) | $= \frac{1}{60}$ minute |
| Temperature | Degrees Celsius (°C) | $°F = \frac{9}{5}°C + 32$ | $°C = \frac{5}{9}(°F - 32)$ | |
| Energy and Power | 1 kilowatt-hour | $= 34,113$ BTUs $= 860,421$ calories | | |
| | 1 watt | $= 3.413$ BTU/hr | | |
| | | $= 14.34$ calorie/min | | |
| | 1 calorie | $=$ the amount of heat necessary to raise the temperature of 1 gram (1cm$^3$) of water 1 degree Celsius | | |
| | 1 horsepower | $= 7.457 \times 102$ watts | | |
| | 1 joule | $= 9.481 \times 10^{-4}$ BTU | | |
| | | $= 0.239$ cal | | |
| | | $= 2.778 \times 10^{-7}$ kilowatt-hour | | |
| Pressure | 1 pound per square inch (psi) | $= 6894.757$ pascal (Pa) | | |
| | | $= 0.068045961$ atmosphere (atm) | | |
| | | $= 51.71493$ millimeters of mercury (mm hg = Torr) | | |
| | | $= 68.94757$ millibars (mbar) | | |
| | | $= 68.94757$ (hectopascal hPa) | | |
| | | $= 6.894757$ kilopascal (kPa) | | |
| | | $= 0.06894757$ bar (bar) | | |
| | 1 atmosphere (atm) | $= 101.325$ kilopascal (kPa) | | |

Representative (main group) elements

| IA | IIA | IIIB | IVB | VB | VIB | VIIB | VIIIB | | | IB | IIB | IIIA | IVA | VA | VIA | VIIA | VIIIA |
|---|---|---|---|---|---|---|---|---|---|---|---|---|---|---|---|---|---|
| 1 H 1.0079 Hydrogen | | | | | | | | | | | | | | | | | 2 He 4.003 Helium |
| 3 Li 6.941 Lithium | 4 Be 9.012 Beryllium | | | | | | | | | | | 5 B 10.811 Boron | 6 C 12.011 Carbon | 7 N 14.007 Nitrogen | 8 O 15.999 Oxygen | 9 F 18.998 Fluorine | 10 Ne 20.180 Neon |
| 11 Na 22.990 Sodium | 12 Mg 24.305 Magnesium | | | | | | | | | | | 13 Al 26.982 Aluminum | 14 Si 28.086 Silicon | 15 P 30.974 Phosphorus | 16 S 32.066 Sulfur | 17 Cl 35.453 Chlorine | 18 Ar 39.948 Argon |
| 19 K 39.098 Potassium | 20 Ca 40.078 Calcium | 21 Sc 44.956 Scandium | 22 Ti 47.88 Titanium | 23 V 50.942 Vanadium | 24 Cr 51.996 Chromium | 25 Mn 54.938 Manganese | 26 Fe 55.845 Iron | 27 Co 58.933 Cobalt | 28 Ni 58.69 Nickel | 29 Cu 63.546 Copper | 30 Zn 66.39 Zinc | 31 Ga 69.723 Gallium | 32 Ge 72.61 Germanium | 33 As 74.922 Arsenic | 34 Se 78.96 Selenium | 35 Br 79.904 Bromine | 36 Kr 83.8 Krypton |
| 37 Rb 85.468 Rubidium | 38 Sr 87.62 Strontium | 39 Y 88.906 Yttrium | 40 Zr 91.224 Zirconium | 41 Nb 92.906 Niobium | 42 Mo 95.94 Molybdenum | 43 Tc 98 Technetium | 44 Ru 101.07 Ruthenium | 45 Rh 102.906 Rhodium | 46 Pd 106.42 Palladium | 47 Ag 107.868 Silver | 48 Cd 112.411 Cadmium | 49 In 114.82 Indium | 50 Sn 118.71 Tin | 51 Sb 121.76 Antimony | 52 Te 127.60 Tellurium | 53 I 126.905 Iodine | 54 Xe 131.29 Xenon |
| 55 Cs 132.905 Cesium | 56 Ba 137.327 Barium | 57 La 138.906 Lanthanum | 72 Hf 178.49 Hafnium | 73 Ta 180.948 Tantalum | 74 W 183.84 Tungsten | 75 Re 186.207 Rhenium | 76 Os 190.23 Osmium | 77 Ir 192.22 Iridium | 78 Pt 195.08 Platinum | 79 Au 196.967 Gold | 80 Hg 200.59 Mercury | 81 Tl 204.383 Thallium | 82 Pb 207.2 Lead | 83 Bi 208.980 Bismuth | 84 Po 209 Polonium | 85 At 210 Astatine | 86 Rn 222 Radon |
| 87 Fr 223 Francium | 88 Ra 226.025 Radium | 89 Ac 227.028 Actinium | 104 Rf 261 Unnilquadium | 105 Db 262 Unnilpentium | 106 Sg 263 Unnilhexium | 107 Bh 262 Unnilseptium | 108 Hs 265 Unniloctium | 109 Mt 266 Unnilennium | 110 Uun 269 Ununnilium | 111 Uuu 272 Unununium | 112 Uub 277 Ununbium | | 114 | | 116 | | |

Transition metals

Rare earth elements

Lanthanides

| 58 Ce 140.115 Cerium | 59 Pr 140.908 Praseodymium | 60 Nd 144.24 Neodymium | 61 Pm 145 Promethium | 62 Sm 150.36 Samarium | 63 Eu 151.964 Europium | 64 Gd 157.25 Gadolinium | 65 Tb 158.925 Terbium | 66 Dy 162.5 Dysprosium | 67 Ho 164.93 Holmium | 68 Er 167.26 Erbium | 69 Tm 168.934 Thulium | 70 Yb 173.04 Ytterbium | 71 Lu 174.967 Lutetium |
|---|---|---|---|---|---|---|---|---|---|---|---|---|---|

Actinides

| 90 Th 232.038 Thorium | 91 Pa 231.036 Protactinium | 92 U 238.029 Uranium | 93 Np 237.048 Neptunium | 94 Pu 244 Plutonium | 95 Am 243 Americium | 96 Cm 247 Curium | 97 Bk 247 Berkelium | 98 Cf 251 Californium | 99 Es 252 Einsteinium | 100 Fm 257 Fermium | 101 Md 258 Mendelevium | 102 No 259 Nobelium | 103 Lr 262 Lawrencium |
|---|---|---|---|---|---|---|---|---|---|---|---|---|---|

The periodic table arranges elements according to atomic number and atomic weight into horizontal rows called periods and vertical columns called groups.

Elements of each group in Class A have similar chemical and physical properties. This reflects the fact that members of a particular group have the same number of valence shell electrons, which is indicated by the group's number. For example, group IA elements have one valence shell electron, group IIA elements have two, and group VA elements have five. In contrast, as you progress across a period from left to right, properties of the elements change, varying from the very metallic properties of groups IA and IIA to the nonmetallic properties of group VIIA to the inert elements (noble gases) in group VIIIA. This reflects changes in the number of valence shell electrons.

Class B elements, or transition elements, are metals, and generally have one or two valence shell electrons. In these elements, some electrons occupy more distant electron shells before the deeper shells are filled.

In this periodic table, elements with symbols printed in black exist as solids under standard conditions (25 °C and 1 atmosphere of pressure), while elements in red exist as gases, and those in dark blue as liquids. Elements with symbols in green do not exist in nature and must be created by some type of nuclear reaction.

# Appendix D  Geologic Timescale

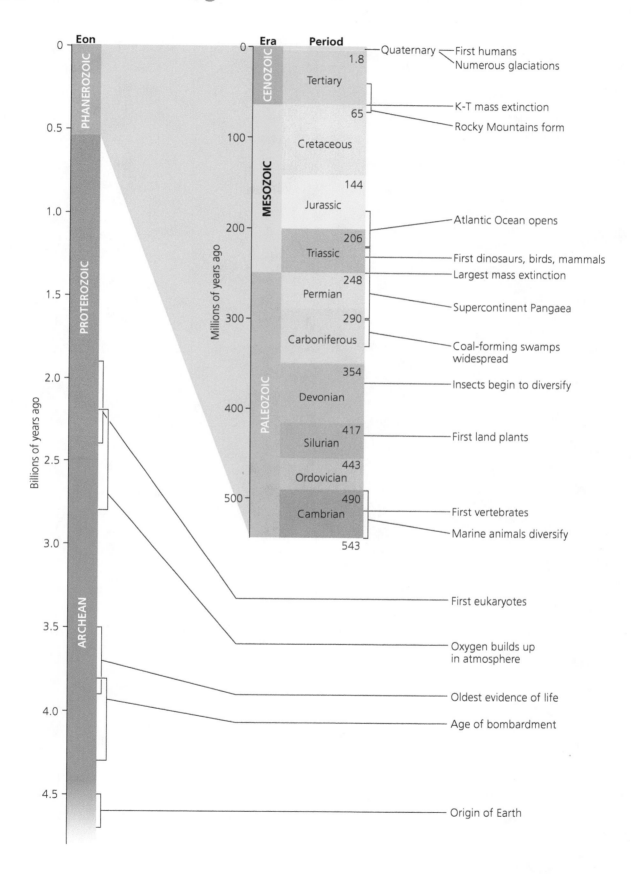

# Glossary

**abiotic factor** Any nonliving component of the *environment*. Compare *biotic factor*.

**acidic deposition** The deposition of *acidic* or acid-forming pollutants from the *atmosphere* onto Earth's surface by *precipitation*, by fog, by gases, or by the deposition of dry particles.

**acid drainage** A process in which sulfide minerals in newly exposed rock surfaces react with oxygen and rainwater to produce sulfuric acid, which causes chemical *runoff* as it *leaches* metals from the rocks. Although acid drainage is a natural phenomenon, mining can greatly accelerate its rate by exposing many new rock surfaces at once.

**acidic** The property of a solution in which the concentration of hydrogen ($H^+$) *ions* is greater than the concentration of hydroxide ($OH^-$) ions. Compare *basic*.

**active solar energy collection** An approach in which technological devices are used to focus, move, or store solar energy. Compare *passive solar energy collection*.

**acute exposure** Exposure to a *toxicant* occurring in high amounts for short periods of time. Compare *chronic exposure*.

**adaptive management** The systematic testing of different management approaches to improve methods over time.

**adaptive trait (adaptation)** A trait that confers greater likelihood that an individual will reproduce.

**affluenza** Term coined by social critics to describe the failure of material goods to bring happiness to people who have the financial means to afford them.

**aerobic** Occurring in an *environment* where oxygen is present. For example, the decay of a rotting log proceeds by aerobic decomposition. Compare *anaerobic*.

**age distribution** The relative numbers of organisms of each age within a *population*. Age distributions can have a strong effect on rates of population growth or decline and are often expressed as a ratio of age classes, consisting of organisms (1) not yet mature enough to reproduce, (2) capable of reproduction, and (3) beyond their reproductive years.

**age structure** See *age distribution*.

**agricultural revolution** The shift around 10,000 years ago from a hunter-gatherer lifestyle to an agricultural way of life in which people began to grow their own crops and raise domestic animals. Compare *industrial revolution*.

**agriculture** The practice of cultivating *soil*, producing crops, and raising livestock for human use and consumption.

**A horizon** A layer of *soil* found in a typical *soil profile*. It forms the top layer or lies below the *O horizon* (if one exists). It consists of mostly inorganic mineral components such as *weathered* substrate, with some organic matter and humus from above mixed in. The A horizon is often referred to as *topsoil*. Compare *B horizon; C horizon; E horizon; R horizon*.

**air pollutants** Gases and particulate material added to the atmosphere that can affect *climate* or harm people or other organisms.

**air pollution** The act of polluting the air, or the condition of being polluted by *air pollutants*.

**allergen** A *toxicant* that overactivates the immune system, causing an immune response when one is not necessary.

**amensalism** A relationship between members of different *species* in which one organism is harmed and the other is unaffected. Compare *commensalism*.

**anaerobic** Occurring in an *environment* that has little or no oxygen. The conversion of organic matter to *fossil fuels (crude oil, coal, natural gas)* at the bottom of a deep lake, swamp, or shallow sea is an example of anaerobic decomposition. Compare *aerobic*.

**anthropocentrism** A human-centered view of our relationship with the *environment*.

**aquaculture** The raising of aquatic organisms for food in controlled *environments*.

**aquifer** An underground water reservoir.

**artesian aquifer** See *confined aquifer*.

**artificial selection** *Natural selection* conducted under human direction. Examples include the *selective breeding* of crop plants, pets, and livestock.

**atmosphere** The thin layer of gases surrounding planet Earth. Compare *biosphere; hydrosphere; lithosphere*.

**atmospheric deposition** The wet or dry deposition on land of a wide variety of pollutants, including mercury, nitrates, organochlorines, and others. *Acidic deposition* is one type of atmospheric deposition.

**atmospheric pressure** The weight per unit area produced by a column of air.

**atom** The smallest component of an *element* that maintains the chemical properties of that element.

**autotroph (primary producer)** An organism that can use the energy from sunlight to produce its own food. Includes green plants, algae, and cyanobacteria.

**Bacillus thuringiensis (Bt)** A naturally occurring *soil* bacterium that produces a protein that kills many pests, including caterpillars and the larvae of some flies and beetles.

**background rate of extinction** The average rate of *extinction* that occurred before the appearance of humans. For example, the *fossil record* indicates that for both birds and mammals, one *species* in the world typically became extinct every 500–1,000 years. Compare *mass extinction event*.

**basic** The property of a solution in which the concentration of hydroxide ($OH^-$) *ions* is greater than the concentration of hydrogen ($H^+$) ions. Compare *acidic*.

**bedrock** The continuous mass of solid rock that makes up Earth's *crust*.

**benthic** Of, relating to, or living on the bottom of a water body. Compare *pelagic*.

**benthic zone** The bottom layer of water body. Compare *littoral zone; limnetic zone; profundal zone*.

**B horizon** The layer of *soil* that lies below the *E horizon* and above the *C horizon*. Minerals that leach out of the E horizon are carried down into the B horizon (or subsoil) and accumulate there. Sometimes called the "zone of accumulation" or "zone of deposition." Compare *A horizon; O horizon; R horizon*.

**bioaccumulation** The buildup of *toxicants* in the tissues of an animal.

**biocentrism** A philosophy that ascribes relative values to actions, entities, or properties on the basis of their effects on all living things or on the integrity of the *biotic* realm in general. The biocentrist evaluates an action in terms of its overall impact on living things, including—but not exclusively focusing on—human beings.

**biodiesel** Diesel fuel produced by mixing vegetable oil, used cooking grease, or animal fat with small amounts of *ethanol* or methanol (wood alcohol) in the presence of a chemical catalyst.

**biodiversity (biological diversity)** The sum total of all organisms in an area, taking into account the diversity of *species*, their *genes*, their *populations*, and their *communities*.

**biodiversity hotspot** An area that supports an especially great diversity of *species*, particularly species that are *endemic* to the area.

**biofuel** Fuel produced from *biomass energy* sources and used primarily to power automobiles.

**biogeochemical cycle** See *nutrient cycle*.

**biological control (biocontrol)** The attempt to battle pests and weeds with organisms that prey on or parasitize them, rather than by using *pesticides*.

**biological diversity** See *biodiversity*.

**biomagnification** The magnification of the concentration of *toxicants* in an organism caused by its consumption of other organisms in which toxicants have *bioaccumulated*.

**biomass energy** *Energy* harnessed from plant and animal matter, including wood from trees, charcoal from burned wood, and combustible animal waste products, such as cattle manure. *Fossil fuels* are not considered biomass energy sources because their organic matter has not been part of living organisms for millions of years and has undergone considerable chemical alteration since that time.

**biome** A major regional complex of similar plant *communities*; a large *ecological* unit defined by its dominant plant type and vegetation structure.

**biophilia** A hypothetical phenomenon that E. O. Wilson defined as "the connections that human beings subconsciously seek with the rest of life."

**biopower** The burning of *biomass energy* sources to generate electricity.

**bioremediation** The attempt to clean up *pollution* by enhancing natural processes of biodegradation by living organisms.

**biosphere** The sum total of all the planet's living organisms and the *abiotic* portions of the *environment* with which they interact. Compare *atmosphere*; *hydrosphere*; *lithosphere*.

**biosphere reserve** A tract of land with exceptional *biodiversity* that couples preservation with *sustainable development* to benefit local people. Biosphere reserves are designated by UNESCO (the *United Nations* Educational, Scientific, and Cultural Organization) following application by local stakeholders.

**biotechnology** The material application of biological *science* to create products derived from organisms. The creation of *transgenic* organisms is one type of biotechnology.

**biotic factor** Any living component of the *environment*. Compare *abiotic factor*.

**boreal forest** A *biome* of northern coniferous forest that stretches in a broad band across much of Canada, Alaska, Russia, and Scandinavia. Also known as taiga, boreal forest consists of a limited number of *species* of evergreen trees, such as black spruce, that dominate large regions of forests interspersed with occasional bogs and lakes.

**breeder nuclear fission** A form of *nuclear fission* that uses uranium-238 instead of uranium-235 (which is used in the conventional method to harness *nuclear energy*). Breeder fission makes better use of fuel, generates more power, and produces less waste than does conventional nuclear fission, but it is considerably more dangerous.

**Bureau of Land Management (BLM)** Federal agency that owns and manages most U.S. rangelands. The BLM is the nation's single largest landowner; its 106 million ha (261 million acres) are spread across 12 western states.

**by-catch** That portion of a commercial fishing catch consisting of animals caught unintentionally. By-catch kills many thousands of fish, sharks, marine mammals, and birds each year.

**capitalist market economy** An *economy* in which buyers and sellers interact to determine which *goods* and *services* to produce, how much of them to produce, and how to distribute them. Compare *centrally planned economy*.

**captive breeding** The practice of capturing members of threatened and endangered *species* so that their young can be bred and raised in controlled *environments* and subsequently reintroduced into the wild.

**carbohydrate** An *organic compound* consisting of *atoms* of carbon, hydrogen, and oxygen.

**carbon cycle** A major *nutrient cycle* consisting of the routes that carbon *atoms* take through the nested networks of environmental *systems*.

**carcinogen** A chemical or type of radiation that causes cancer.

**carrying capacity** The maximum *population size* that a given *environment* can sustain.

**cell** The most basic organizational unit of organisms.

**cellular respiration** The process by which a *cell* uses the chemical reactivity of oxygen to split glucose into its constituent parts, water and carbon dioxide, and thereby release *chemical energy* that can be used to form chemical bonds or to perform other tasks within the cell. Compare *photosynthesis*.

**centrally planned economy** An *economy* in which a nation's government determines how to allocate resources in a top-down manner. Also called a "state socialist economy." Compare *capitalist market economy*.

**chaparral** A *biome* consisting mostly of densely thicketed evergreen shrubs occurring in limited small patches. Its "Mediterranean" *climate* of mild, wet winters and warm, dry summers is induced by oceanic influences. In addition to ringing the Mediterranean Sea, chaparral occurs along the coasts of California, Chile, and southern Australia.

**chemical energy** *Potential energy* held in the bonds between atoms.

**chemosynthesis** The process by which bacteria in hydrothermal vents use the *chemical energy* of hydrogen sulfide ($H_2S$) to transform inorganic carbon into *organic compounds*. Compare *photosynthesis*.

**Chernobyl** Site of a nuclear power plant in Ukraine (then part of the Soviet Union), where in 1986 an explosion caused the most severe *nuclear reactor* accident the world has yet seen. As with *Three Mile Island*, the term is often used to denote the accident itself.

**chlorofluorocarbon (CFC)** One of a group of human-made *organic compounds* derived from simple *hydrocarbons,* such as ethane and methane, in which hydrogen *atoms* are replaced by chlorine, bromine, or fluorine. CFCs deplete the protective *ozone layer* in the *stratosphere.*

**C horizon** The layer of *soil* that lies below the *B horizon* and above the *R horizon.* It contains rock particles that are larger and less *weathered* than the layers above. It consists of *parent material* that has been altered only slightly or not at all by the process of *soil* formation. Compare *A horizon; E horizon; O horizon.*

**chronic exposure** Exposure for long periods of time to a *toxicant* occurring in low amounts. Compare *acute exposure.*

**city planning** The professional pursuit that attempts to design cities in such a way as to maximize their efficiency, functionality, and beauty.

**classical economics** Founded by *Adam Smith,* the study of the behavior of buyers and sellers in a free-market *economy.* Holds that individuals acting in their own self-interest may benefit society, provided that their behavior is constrained by the rule of law and by private property rights and operates within competitive markets. See also *neoclassical economics.*

**clay** *Sediment* consisting of particles less than 0.002 mm in diameter. Compare *sand; silt.*

**Clean Air Act of 1970** Revision of prior Congressional *legislation* to control *air pollution* that set stricter standards for air quality, imposed limits on emissions from new stationary and mobile sources, provided new funds for *pollution*-control research, and enabled citizens to sue parties violating the standards.

**Clean Air Act of 1990** Congressional *legislation* that strengthened *regulations* pertaining to air quality standards, auto emissions, toxic *air pollution, acidic deposition,* and depletion of the *ozone layer,* while also introducing market-based incentives to reduce *pollution.*

**clear-cutting** The harvesting of timber by cutting all the trees in an area, leaving only stumps. Although it is the most cost-efficient method, clear-cutting is also the most damaging to the *environment.*

**climate** The pattern of atmospheric conditions found across large geographic regions over long periods of time. Compare *weather.*

**climate diagram (climatograph)** A visual representation of a region's average monthly temperature and *precipitation.*

**closed system** A *system* that is isolated an self-contained. Scientists may treat a system as closed to simplify some question they are investigating, but no natural system is truly closed. Compare *open system.*

**coal** A *fossil fuel* composed of organic matter that was compressed under very high pressure to form a dense, solid carbon structure.

**cogeneration** A practice in which the extra heat generated in the production of electricity is captured and put to use heating workplaces and homes, as well as producing other kinds of power.

**cold front** The boundary where a mass of cold air displaces a mass of warmer air. Compare *warm front.*

**command and control** An approach to protecting the *environment* that sets strict legal limits and threatens punishment for violations of those limits.

**commensalism** A relationship between members of different *species* in which one organism benefits and the other is unaffected. Compare *amensalism.*

**community** A group of *populations* of organisms that live in the same place at the same time.

**community-based conservation** The practice of engaging local people to protect land and wildlife in their own region.

**community ecology** The study of the interactions among *species,* from one-to-one interactions to complex interrelationships involving entire *communities.*

**competition** A relationship in which multiple organisms seek the same limited resource.

**composting** The conversion of organic *waste* into mulch or humus by encouraging, in a controlled manner, the natural biological processes of decomposition.

**compound** A *molecule* whose *atoms* are composed of two or more *elements.*

**confined (artesian) aquifer** A water-bearing, porous layer of rock, *sand,* or gravel that is trapped between an upper and lower layer of less permeable substrate, such as *clay.* The water in a confined aquifer is under pressure because it is trapped between two impermeable layers. Compare *unconfined aquifer.*

**conservation biology** A scientific discipline devoted to understanding the factors, forces, and processes that influence the loss, protection, and restoration of *biological diversity* within and among *ecosystems.*

**conservation district** One of many county-based entities created by the Soil Conservation Service (now the Natural Resources Conservation Service) to promote practices that conserve *soil.*

**conservation ethic** An *ethic* holding that humans should put *natural resources* to use but also have a responsibility to manage them wisely. Compare *preservation ethic.*

**consumer** See *heterotroph.*

**consumptive use** *Freshwater* use in which water is removed from a particular *aquifer* or surface water body and is not returned to it. *Irrigation* for *agriculture* is an example of consumptive use. Compare *nonconsumptive use.*

**continental shelf** The gently sloping underwater edge of a continent, varying in width from 100 m (330 ft) to 1,300 km (800 mi), with an average slope of 1.9 m/km (10 ft/mi).

**contingent valuation** A technique that uses surveys to determine how much people would be willing to pay to protect a resource or to restore it after damage has been done.

**contour farming** The practice of plowing furrows sideways across a hillside, perpendicular to its slope, to help prevent the formation of rills and gullies. The technique is so named because the furrows follow the natural contours of the land.

**control** The portion of an *experiment* in which a *variable* has been left unmanipulated, to serve as a point of comparison with the *treatment.*

**controlled burn** See *prescribed burn.*

**controlled experiment** An *experiment* in which the effects of all *variables* are held constant, except the one whose effect is being tested by comparison of *treatment* and *control* conditions.

**convective circulation** A circular *current* (of air, water, magma, etc.) driven by temperature differences. In the atmosphere, warm air rises into regions of lower *atmospheric pressure*, where it expands and cools and then descends and becomes denser, replacing warm air that is rising. The air picks up heat and moisture near ground level and prepares to rise again, continuing the process.

**conventional law** International law that arises from conventions, or treaties, that nations agree to enter into. Compare *customary law*.

**Convention on Biological Diversity** An international treaty that aims to conserve *biodiversity,* use biodiversity in a *sustainable* manner, and ensure the fair distribution of biodiversity's benefits. Although many nations have agreed to the treaty (as of 2005, 188 nations had become parties to it), several others, including the United States, have not.

**Convention on International Trade in Endangered Species of Wild Fauna and Flora (CITES)** A 1973 treaty facilitated by the *United Nations* that protects endangered *species* by banning the international transport of their body parts.

**convergent plate boundary** Area where tectonic plates collide. Can result in *subduction* or mountain range formation.

**coral reef** A mass of calcium carbonate composed of the skeletons of tiny colonial marine organisms called corals.

**core** The innermost part of the Earth, made up mostly of iron, that lies beneath the *crust* and *mantle*.

**Coriolis effect** The apparent deflection of north-south air *currents* to a partly east-west direction, caused by the faster spin of regions near the equator than of regions near the poles as a result of Earth's rotation.

**correlation** A relationship among *variables*.

**corridor** A passageway of protected land established to allow animals to travel between islands of protected *habitat*.

**cost-benefit analysis** A method commonly used by *neoclassical economists,* in which estimated costs for a proposed action are totaled and then compared to the sum of benefits estimated to result from the action.

**covalent bond** A chemical bond in which the uncharged *atoms* in a *molecule* share *electrons*. For example, the uncharged atoms of carbon and oxygen in carbon dioxide form a covalent bond. Compare *ionic bond*.

**criteria pollutants** Six *air pollutants*—carbon monoxide, sulfur dioxide, nitrogen dioxide, tropospheric ozone, particulate matter, and lead—for which the *Environmental Protection Agency* has established maximum allowable concentrations in ambient outdoor air because of the threats they pose to human health.

**cropland** Land that humans use to raise plants for food and fiber.

**crop rotation** The practice of alternating the kind of crop grown in a particular field from one season or year to the next.

**crude oil (petroleum)** A *fossil fuel* produced by the conversion of *organic compounds* by heat and pressure. Crude oil is a mixture of hundreds of different types of *hydrocarbon* molecules characterized by carbon chains of different length.

**crust** The lightweight outer layer of the Earth, consisting of rock that floats atop the malleable *mantle,* which in turn surrounds a mostly iron *core*.

**culture** The overall ensemble of knowledge, beliefs, values, and learned ways of life shared by a group of people.

**current** The flow of a liquid or gas in a certain direction.

**customary law** International law that arises from long-standing practices, or customs, held in common by most *cultures*. Compare *conventional law*.

**dam** Any obstruction placed in a river or stream to block the flow of water so that water can be stored in a reservoir. Dams are built to prevent floods, provide drinking water, facilitate *irrigation,* and generate electricity.

**Darwin, Charles (1809–1882)** English naturalist who proposed the concept of *natural selection* as a mechanism for *evolution* and as a way to explain the great variety of living things. See also *Wallace, Alfred Russell*.

**data** Information, generally quantitative information.

**deep ecology** A philosophy established in the 1970s based on principles of self-realization (the awareness that humans are inseparable from nature) and *biocentric* equality (the precept that all living beings have equal value). Holds that because we are truly inseparable from our *environment,* we must protect all other living things as we would protect ourselves.

**deep-well injection** A *hazardous waste* disposal method in which a well is drilled deep beneath an area's *water table* into porous rock below an impervious *soil* layer. Wastes are then injected into the well, so that they will be absorbed into the porous rock and remain deep underground, isolated from *groundwater* and human contact. Compare *surface impoundment*.

**deforestation** The clearing and loss of forests.

**demographic transition** A theoretical model of economic and cultural change that explains the declining death rates and birth rates that occurred in Western nations as they became industrialized. The model holds that industrialization caused these rates to fall naturally by decreasing mortality and by lessening the need for large families. Parents would thereafter choose to invest in quality of life rather than quantity of children.

**demography** A *social science* that applies the principles of *population ecology* to the study of statistical change in human *populations*.

**denitrifying bacteria** Bacteria that convert the nitrates in *soil* or water to gaseous nitrogen and release it back into the *atmosphere*.

**density-dependent factor** A *limiting factor* whose effects on a *population* increase or decrease depending on the *population density*. Compare *density-independent factor*.

**density-independent factor** A *limiting factor* whose effects on a *population* are constant regardless of *population density*. Compare *density-dependent factor*.

**deoxyribonucleic acid** See *DNA*.

**dependent variable** The *variable* that is affected by manipulation of the *independent variable*.

**desalination** The removal of salt from seawater.

**desert** The driest *biome* on Earth, with annual *precipitation* of less than 25 cm. Because deserts have relatively little vegetation to insulate them from temperature extremes, sunlight readily heats them in the daytime, but daytime heat is quickly lost at night, so temperatures vary widely from day to night and in different seasons.

**desertification** A loss of more than 10% of a land's productivity due to *erosion*, *soil* compaction, forest removal, *overgrazing*, drought, *salinization*, *climate* change, depletion of water sources, or other factors. Severe desertification can result in the actual expansion of desert areas or creation of new ones in areas that once supported fertile land.

**divergent plate boundary** Area where *magma* surging upward to the surface divides tectonic plates and pushes them apart, creating new *crust* as it cools and spreads. A prime example is the Mid-Atlantic ridge. Compare *transform plate boundary* and *convergent plate boundary*.

**DNA (deoxyribonucleic acid)** A double-stranded *nucleic acid* composed of four nucleotides, each of which contains a sugar (deoxyribose), a phosphate group, and a nitrogenous base. DNA carries the hereditary information for living organisms and is responsible for passing traits from parents to offspring. Compare *RNA*.

**dose-response curve** A curve that plots the response of test animals to different doses of a *toxicant*. The response is generally quantified by measuring the proportion of animals exhibiting negative effects.

**downwelling** In the ocean, the flow of warm surface water toward the ocean floor. Downwelling occurs where surface *currents* converge. Compare *upwelling*.

**Dust Bowl** An area that loses huge amounts of *topsoil* to wind *erosion* as a result of drought and/or human impact; first used to name the region in the North American Great Plains severely affected by drought and topsoil loss in the 1930s. The term is now also used to describe that historical event and others like it.

**dynamic equilibrium** The state reached when processes within a *system* are moving in opposing directions at equivalent rates so that their effects balance out.

**ecocentrism** A philosophy that considers actions in terms of their damage or benefit to the integrity of whole ecological *systems*, including both *biotic* and *abiotic* elements. For an ecocentrist, the well-being of an individual organism—human or otherwise—is less important than the long-term well-being of a larger integrated ecological system.

**ecofeminism** A philosophy holding that the patriarchal (male-dominated) structure of society is a root cause of both social and environmental problems. Ecofeminists hold that a *worldview* traditionally associated with women, which interprets the world in terms of interrelationships and cooperation, is more in tune with nature than a worldview traditionally associated with men, which interprets the world in terms of hierarchies and competition.

**ecolabeling** The practice of designating on a product's label how the product was grown, harvested, or manufactured, so that consumers buying it are aware of the processes involved and can differentiate between brands that use processes believed to be *environmentally* beneficial (or less harmful than others) and those that do not.

**ecological economics** A developing school of *economics* that applies the principles of *ecology* and *systems* thinking to the description and analysis of *economies*. Compare *environmental economics; neoclassical economics*.

**ecological footprint** The cumulative amount of land and water required to provide the raw materials a person or *population* consumes and to dispose of or *recycle* the *waste* that is produced.

**ecological restoration** Efforts to reverse the effects of human disruption of *ecological systems* and to restore *communities* to their "natural" state.

**ecology** The *science* that deals with the distribution and abundance of organisms, the interactions among them, and the interactions between organisms and their *abiotic environments*.

**economics** The study of how we decide to use scarce resources to satisfy the demand for *goods* and *services*.

**economy** A social *system* that converts resources into *goods* and *services*.

**ecosystem** All organisms and nonliving entities that occur and interact in a particular area at the same time.

**ecosystem ecology** The study of how the living and nonliving components of *ecosystems* interact.

**ecosystem-based management** The attempt to manage the harvesting of resources in ways that minimize impact on the *ecosystems* and ecological processes that provide the resources.

**ecosystem service** An essential service an *ecosystem* provides that supports life and makes *economic* activity possible. For example, ecosystems naturally purify air and water, cycle *nutrients*, provide for plants to be *pollinated* by animals, and serve as receptacles and *recycling* systems for the *waste* generated by our economic activity.

**ecotone** A transitional zone where *ecosystems* meet.

**ecotourism** Visitation of natural areas for tourism and recreation. Most often involves tourism by more-affluent people, which may generate *economic* benefits for less-affluent communities near natural areas and thus provide economic incentives for conservation of natural areas.

**ED$_{50}$ (effective dose–50%)** The amount of a *toxicant* it takes to affect 50% of a *population* of test animals. Compare *threshold dose; LD$_{50}$*.

**E horizon** The layer of *soil* that lies below the *A horizon* and above the *B horizon*. The letter "E" stands for "eluviation," meaning "loss," and the E horizon is characterized by the loss of certain minerals through *leaching*. It is sometimes called the "zone of leaching." Compare *C horizon; O horizon; R horizon*.

**El Niño** The exceptionally strong warming of the eastern Pacific Ocean that occurs every 2 to 7 years and depresses local fish and bird *populations* by altering the marine *food web* in the area. Originally, the name that Spanish-speaking fishermen gave to an unusually warm surface *current* that sometimes arrived near the Pacific coast of South America around Christmas time. Compare *La Niña*.

**electrolysis** A process in which electrical current is passed through a *compound* to release *ions*. Electrolysis offers one way to produce hydrogen for use as fuel: Electrical current is passed through water, splitting the water *molecules* into hydrogen and oxygen *atoms*.

**electron** A negatively charged particle that surrounds the nucleus of an *atom*.

**element** A fundamental type of matter; a chemical substance with a given set of properties, which cannot be broken down into substances with other properties. Chemists currently recognize 92 elements that occur in nature, as well as more than 20 others that have been artificially created.

**emergent property** A characteristic that is not evident in a *system*'s components.

**Emerson, Ralph Waldo (1803–1882)** American author, poet, and philosopher who espoused transcendentalism, a philosophy that views nature as a direct manifestation of the divine, and who promoted a holistic view of nature among the public.

**emigration** The departure of individuals from a *population*.

**Endangered Species Act (ESA)** The primary *legislation*, enacted in 1973, for protecting *biodiversity* in the United States. It forbids the government and private citizens from taking actions (such as developing land) that would destroy endangered *species* or their *habitats*, and it prohibits trade in products made from endangered species.

**endemic** Native or restricted to a particular geographic region. An endemic species occurs in one area and nowhere else on Earth.

**endocrine disruptor** A *toxicant* that interferes with the endocrine (hormone) system.

**energy conservation** The practice of reducing *energy* use as a way of extending the lifetime of our *fossil fuel* supplies, of being less wasteful, and of reducing our impact on the *environment*.

**energy** An intangible phenomenon that can change the position, physical composition, or temperature of matter.

**entropy** The degree of disorder in a substance, *system*, or process. See *second law of thermodynamics*.

**environment** The sum total of our surroundings, including all of the living things and nonliving things with which we interact.

**environmental economics** A developing school of *economics* that modifies the principles of *neoclassical economics* to address environmental challenges. An environmental economist believes that we can attain *sustainability* within our current economic *systems*. Whereas ecological economists call for revolution, environmental economists call for reform. Compare *ecological economics; neoclassical economics*.

**environmental ethics** The application of *ethical standards* to environmental questions.

**environmental health** Environmental factors that influence human health and quality of life and the health of *ecological* systems essential to environmental quality and long-term human well-being.

**environmental impact statement (EIS)** A report of results from detailed studies that assess the potential effects on the *environment* that would likely result from development projects or other actions undertaken by the government.

**environmental justice** A movement based on a moral sense of fairness and equality that seeks to expand society's domain of ethical concern from men to women, from humans to nonhumans, from rich to poor, and from majority races and ethnic groups to minority ones.

**environmental policy** *Public policy* that pertains to human interactions with the *environment*. It generally aims to regulate resource use or reduce *pollution* to promote human welfare and/or protect natural systems.

**Environmental Protection Agency (EPA)** An administrative agency created by executive order in 1970. The EPA is charged with conducting and evaluating research, monitoring environmental quality, setting standards, enforcing those standards, assisting the states in meeting standards and goals, and educating the public.

**environmental science** The study of how the natural world works and how humans and the *environment* interact.

**environmental studies** An academic *environmental science* program that heavily incorporates the social sciences as well as the natural sciences.

**environmental toxicology** The study of *toxicants* that come from or are discharged into the *environment*, including the study of health effects on humans, other animals, and *ecosystems*.

**environmentalism** A social movement dedicated to protecting the natural world.

**epidemiological study** A study that involves large-scale comparisons among groups of people, usually contrasting a group known to have been exposed to some *toxicant* and a group that has not.

**equilibrium theory of island biogeography** A *theory* that was initially applied to oceanic islands to explain how *species* come to be distributed among them. Since its development, researchers have increasingly applied the theory to islands of *habitat* (patches of one type of habitat isolated within vast "seas" of others). Aspects of the theory include *immigration* and *extinction* rates, the effect of island size, and the effect of distance from the mainland.

**erosion** The removal of material from one place and its transport to another by the action of wind or water.

**estuary** An area where a river flows into the ocean, mixing *freshwater* with salt water.

**ethanol** The alcohol in beer, wine, and liquor, produced as a *biofuel* by fermenting biomass, generally from *carbohydrate*-rich crops such as corn.

**ethical standards** The criteria that help differentiate right from wrong.

**ethics** The study of good and bad, right and wrong. The term can also refer to a person's or group's set of moral principles or values.

**eukaryote** A multicellular organism. The *cells* of eukaryotic organisms consist of a membrane-enclosed nucleus that houses *DNA*, an outer membrane of lipids, and an inner fluid-filled chamber containing *organelles*. Compare *prokaryote*.

**European Union (EU)** Political and economic organization formed after World War II to promote Europe's economic and social progress. As of 2005, the EU consisted of 25 member nations.

**eutrophication** The process of *nutrient* enrichment, increased production of organic matter, and subsequent *ecosystem* degradation.

**evaporation** The conversion of a substance from a liquid to a gaseous form.

**even-aged** Condition of timber plantations—generally *monocultures* of a single *species*—in which all trees are of the same age. Most *ecologists* view plantations of even-aged stands more as crop *agriculture* than as ecologically functional forests. Compare *uneven-aged*.

**evolution** Genetically based change in the appearance, functioning, and/or behavior of organisms across generations, often by the process of *natural selection*.

**executive branch** The branch of the U.S. government that is headed by the president and that includes administrative agencies. Among other powers, the president may approve (enact) or reject (veto) legislation and issue executive orders. Compare *judicial branch; legislative branch*.

**experiment** An activity designed to test the validity of a *hypothesis* by manipulating *variables*. See *manipulative experiment* and *natural experiment*.

**exponential growth** The increase of a *population* (or of anything) by a fixed percentage each year.

**external cost** A negative *externality;* a cost borne by someone not involved in an economic transaction. Examples include harm to citizens from water *pollution* or *air pollution* discharged by nearby factories.

**externality** A cost or benefit of a transaction that affects people other than the buyer or seller.

**extinction** The disappearance of an entire *species* from the face of the Earth. Compare *extirpation*.

**extirpation** The disappearance of a particular *population* from a given area, but not the entire *species* globally. Compare *extinction*.

**feedback loop** A circular process in which a *system*'s output serves as input to that same system. See *negative feedback loop; positive feedback loop*.

**feedlot** A huge barn or outdoor pen designed to deliver *energy*-rich food to animals living at extremely high densities. Also called a factory farm or concentrated animal feeding operation (CAFO).

**Ferrel cell** One of a pair of cells of *convective circulation* between 30° and 60° north and south latitude that influence global *climate* patterns. Compare *Hadley cell; polar cell*.

**fertilizer** A substance that promotes plant growth by supplying essential *nutrients* such as nitrogen or phosphorus.

**first law of thermodynamics** Physical law stating that *energy* can change from one form to another but cannot be created or lost. The total energy in the universe remains constant and is said to be conserved.

**floodplain** The region of land over which a river has historically wandered and periodically floods.

**food security** An adequate, reliable, and available food supply to all people at all times.

**food web** A visual representation of feeding interactions within an *ecological community* that shows an array of relationships between organisms at different *trophic levels*.

**forestry** The professional management of forests.

**fossil** The remains, impression, or trace of an animal or plant of past geological ages that has been preserved in rock or *sediments*.

**fossil fuel** A *nonrenewable natural resource*, such as *crude oil, natural gas,* or *coal,* produced by the decomposition and compression of organic matter from ancient life.

**fossil record** The cumulative body of *fossils* worldwide, which paleontologists study to infer the history of past life on Earth.

**free rider** A party that fails to invest in controlling *pollution* or carrying out other *environmentally* responsible activities and instead relies on the efforts of other parties to do so. For example, a factory that fails to control its emissions gets a "free ride" on the efforts of other factories that do make the sacrifices necessary to reduce emissions.

**freshwater** Water that is relatively pure, holding very few dissolved salts.

**fundamental niche** The full *niche* of a *species*. Compare *realized niche*.

**gene** A stretch of *DNA* that represents a unit of hereditary information.

**gene bank** See *seed bank*.

**generalist** A *species* that can survive in a wide array of *habitats* or use a wide array of resources. Compare *specialist*.

**genetically modified (GM) organism** An organism that has been *genetically engineered* using a technique called *recombinant DNA* technology.

**genetic diversity** A measurement of the differences in *DNA* composition among individuals within a given *species*.

**genetic engineering** Any process scientists use to manipulate an organism's genetic material in the lab by adding, deleting, or changing segments of its *DNA*.

**Genuine Progress Indicator (GPI)** An *economic* indicator introduced in 1995 that attempts to differentiate between desirable and undesirable economic activity. The GPI accounts for benefits such as volunteerism and for costs such as *environmental* degradation and social upheaval. Compare *Gross Domestic Product (GDP)*.

**geothermal energy** Renewable *energy* that is generated deep within Earth. The radioactive decay of elements amid the extremely high pressures and temperatures at depth generate heat that rises to the surface in magma and through fissures and cracks. Where this energy heats *groundwater,* natural eruptions of heated water and steam are sent up from below.

**global climate change** Any change in aspects of Earth's *climate,* such as temperature, *precipitation,* and storm intensity. Generally refers today to the current warming trend in global temperatures and associated climatic changes.

**good** A material commodity manufactured for and bought by individuals and businesses.

**greenhouse effect** The warming of Earth's surface and *atmosphere* (especially the *troposphere*) caused by the *energy* emitted by *greenhouse gases*.

**greenhouse gas** A gas that absorbs infrared radiation released by Earth's surface and then warms the surface and *troposphere* by emitting *energy,* thus giving rise to the *greenhouse effect*. Greenhouse gases include carbon dioxide ($CO_2$), water vapor, ozone ($O_3$), nitrous oxide ($N_2O$), halocarbon gases, and methane ($CH_4$).

**green revolution** An intensification of the industrialization of *agriculture* in the developing world in the latter half of the 20th century that has dramatically increased crop yields produced per unit area of farmland. Practices include devoting large areas to *monocultures* of crops specially bred for high yields and rapid growth; heavy use of *fertilizers, pesticides,* and *irrigation* water; and sowing and harvesting on the same piece of land more than once per year or per season.

**green tax** A levy on *environmentally* harmful activities and products aimed at providing a market-based incentive to correct for *market failure.* Compare *subsidy.*

**Gross Domestic Product (GDP)** The total monetary value of final *goods* and *services* produced in a country each year. The GDP sums all *economic* activity, whether good or bad, and does not account for benefits such as volunteerism or for *external costs* such as *environmental* degradation and social upheaval. Compare *Genuine Progress Indicator (GPI).*

**gross primary production** The *energy* that results when *autotrophs* convert solar energy (sunlight) to energy of chemical bonds in sugars through *photosynthesis.* Autotrophs use a portion of this production to power their own metabolism, which entails oxidizing *organic compounds* by *cellular respiration.* Compare *net primary production; secondary production.*

**groundwater** Water held in aquifers underground.

**growth rate** The net change in a *population*'s size, per 1,000 individuals. Calculated by adding the crude birth rate to the *immigration* rate and then subtracting the crude death rate and the *emigration* rate, each expressed as the number per 1,000 individuals per year.

**Haber-Bosch process** A process to synthesize ammonia on an industrial scale. Developed by German chemists Fritz Haber and Carl Bosch, the process has enabled humans to double the natural rate of *nitrogen fixation* on Earth and thereby increase *agricultural* productivity, but it has also dramatically altered the *nitrogen cycle.*

**habitat** The specific *environment* in which an organism lives, including both *biotic* and *abiotic factors.*

**habitat use** The process by which organisms select and use *habitats* from among the range of options they encounter.

**Hadley cell** One of a pair of cells of *convective circulation* between the equator and 30° north and south latitude that influence global *climate* patterns. Compare *Ferrel cell; polar cell.*

**half-life** The amount of time it takes for one-half the atoms of a *radioisotope* to emit radiation and decay. Different radioisotopes have different half-lives, ranging from fractions of a second to billions of years.

**harmful algal bloom** A *population* explosion of toxic algae caused by excessive *nutrient* concentrations.

**hazardous waste** *Waste* that is toxic, chemically reactive, flammable, or corrosive. Compare *industrial solid waste; municipal solid waste.*

**herbivory** The consumption of plants by animals.

**heterotroph (consumer)** An organism that consumes other organisms. Includes most animals, as well as fungi and microbes that decompose organic matter.

**high-pressure system** An air mass with elevated *atmospheric pressure,* containing air that descends, typically bringing fair *weather.* Compare *low-pressure system.*

**homeostasis** The tendency of a *system* to maintain constant or stable internal conditions.

**horizon** A distinct layer of *soil.* See *A horizon; B horizon; C horizon; E horizon; O horizon; R horizon.*

**Hubbert's peak** The peak in production of *crude oil* in the United States, which occurred in 1970 just as Shell Oil geologist M. King Hubbert had predicted in 1956.

**hydrocarbon** An *organic compound* consisting solely of hydrogen and carbon *atoms.*

**hydroelectric power (hydropower)** The generation of electricity using the *kinetic energy* of moving water.

**hydrologic cycle** The flow of water—in liquid, gaseous, and solid forms—through our *biotic* and *abiotic environment.*

**hydropower** See *hydroelectric power.*

**hydrosphere** All water—salt or fresh, liquid, ice, or vapor—in surface bodies, underground, and in the *atmosphere.* Compare *biosphere; lithosphere.*

**hypothesis** An educated guess that explains a phenomenon or answers a *scientific* question. Compare *theory.*

**hypoxia** The condition of extremely low dissolved oxygen concentrations in a body of water.

**igneous rock** One of the three main categories of rock. Formed from cooling *magma.* Granite and basalt are examples of igneous rock. Compare *metamorphic rock; sedimentary rock.*

**immigration** The arrival of individuals from outside a *population.*

**incineration** A controlled process of burning solid waste for disposal in which mixed garbage is combusted at very high temperatures. Compare *sanitary landfill.*

**independent variable** The *variable* that the scientist manipulates in a *manipulative experiment.*

**industrial ecology** A holistic approach to industry that integrates principles from engineering, chemistry, *ecology, economics,* and other disciplines and seeks to redesign industrial *systems* in order to reduce resource inputs and minimize inefficiency.

**industrialized agriculture** A form of *agriculture* that uses large-scale mechanization and *fossil fuel* combustion, enabling farmers to replace horses and oxen with faster and more powerful means of cultivating, harvesting, transporting, and processing crops. Other aspects include *irrigation* and the use of *inorganic fertilizers.* Use of chemical herbicides and *pesticides* reduces *competition* from weeds and *herbivory* by insects. Compare *traditional agriculture.*

**industrial revolution** The shift in the mid-1700s from rural life, animal-powered agriculture, and manufacturing by craftsmen to an urban society powered by *fossil fuels* such as *coal* and *crude oil.* Compare *agricultural revolution.*

**industrial smog** Gray-air smog caused by the incomplete combustion of *coal* or oil when burned. Compare *photochemical smog.*

**industrial solid waste** Nonliquid *waste* that is not especially hazardous and that comes from production of consumer goods, mining, *petroleum* extraction and *refining,* and *agriculture.* Compare *hazardous waste; municipal solid waste.*

**industrial stage** The third stage of the *demographic transition* model, characterized by falling birth rates that close the gap with falling death rates and reduce the rate of *population* growth. Compare *pre-industrial stage; post-industrial stage; transitional stage.*

**infectious disease** A disease in which a pathogen attacks a host.

**inorganic fertilizer** A *fertilizer* that consists of mined or synthetically manufactured mineral supplements. Inorganic fertilizers are generally more susceptible than *organic fertilizers* to *leaching* and *runoff* and may be more likely to cause unintended off-site impacts.

**integrated pest management (IPM)** The use of multiple techniques in combination to achieve long-term suppression of pests, including *biocontrol,* use of *pesticides,* close monitoring of *populations, habitat* alteration, *crop rotation, transgenic* crops, alternative tillage methods, and mechanical pest removal.

**intercropping** Planting different types of crops in alternating bands or other spatially mixed arrangements.

**interdisciplinary field** A field that borrows techniques from several more traditional fields of study and brings together research results from these fields into a broad synthesis.

**Intergovernmental Panel on Climate Change (IPCC)** An international panel of *atmospheric* scientists, *climate* experts, and government officials established in 1988 by the *United Nations* Environment Programme and the World Meteorological Organization, whose mission is to assess information relevant to questions of human-induced *global climate change.* The IPCC's 2001 *Third Assessment Report* summarizes current and probable future global trends and represents the consensus of atmospheric scientists around the world.

**intertidal** Of, relating to, or living along shorelines between the highest reach of the highest *tide* and the lowest reach of the lowest tide.

**invasive species** A *species* that spreads widely and rapidly becomes dominant in a *community,* interfering with the community's normal functioning.

**inversion layer** In a *temperature inversion,* the band of air in which temperature rises with altitude (instead of falling with altitude, as temperature does normally).

**ion** An electrically charged *atom* or combination of atoms.

**ionic bond** A chemical bond in which oppositely charged *ions* are held together by electrical attraction. Compare *covalent bond.*

**ionic compound (salt)** An association of *ions* that are bonded electrically in an *ionic bond.*

**IPAT model** A formula that represents how humans' total impact (I) on the *environment* results from the interaction among three factors: *population* (P), affluence (A), and technology (T).

**irrigation** The artificial provision of water to support *agriculture.*

**isotope** One of several forms of an *element* having differing numbers of *neutrons* in the nucleus of its *atoms.* Chemically, isotopes of an element behave almost identically, but they have different physical properties because they differ in mass.

**judicial branch** The branch of the U.S. government, consisting of the Supreme Court and various lower courts, that is charged with interpreting the law. Compare *executive branch; legislative branch.*

**kelp** Large brown algae or seaweed that can form underwater "forests," providing habitat for marine organisms.

**keystone species** A *species* that has an especially far-reaching effect on a *community.*

**kinetic energy** *Energy* of motion. Compare *potential energy.*

**K–selected** Term denoting a *species* with low biotic potential whose members produce a small number of offspring and take a long time to gestate and raise each of their young, but invest heavily in promoting the survival and growth of these few offspring. *Populations* of K–selected species are generally regulated by *density-dependent factors.* Compare *r–selected.*

**Kyoto Protocol** An agreement drafted in 1997 that calls for reducing, by 2012, emissions of six *greenhouse gases* to levels lower than their levels in 1990. Although the United States has refused to ratify the protocol, it came into force in 2005 when Russia ratified it, the 127th nation to do so.

**La Niña** An exceptionally strong cooling of surface water in the equatorial Pacific Ocean that occurs every 2 to 7 years and has widespread climatic consequences. Compare *El Niño.*

**land trust** Local or regional organization that preserves lands valued by its members. In most cases, land trusts purchase land outright with the aim of preserving it in its natural condition. The Nature Conservancy may be considered the world's largest land trust.

**landscape ecology** An approach to the study of organisms and their *environments* at the landscape scale, focusing on geographical areas that include multiple *ecosystems.*

**lava** *Magma* that is released from the *lithosphere* and flows or spatters across Earth's surface.

**LD$_{50}$ (lethal dose–50%)** The amount of a *toxicant* it takes to kill 50% of a *population* of test animals. Compare *ED$_{50}$; threshold dose.*

**leachate** Liquids that seep through liners of a *sanitary landfill* and leach into the *soil* underneath.

**leaching** The process by which solid materials such as minerals are dissolved in a liquid (usually water) and transported to another location.

**legislation** Statutory law.

**legislative branch** The branch of the U.S. government that passes laws; it consists of Congress, which includes the House of Representatives and the Senate. Compare *executive branch; judicial branch.*

**Leopold, Aldo (1887–1949)** American scientist, scholar, philosopher, and author. His book *The Land Ethic* argued that humans should view themselves and the land itself as members of the same *community* and that humans are obligated to treat the land *ethically.*

**life-cycle analysis** In *industrial ecology,* the examination of the entire life cycle of a given product—from its origins in raw materials, through its manufacturing, to its use, and finally its disposal—in an attempt to identify ways to make the process more *ecologically* efficient.

**life expectancy** The average number of years that individuals in particular age groups are likely to continue to live.

**limiting factor** A physical, chemical, or biological characteristic of the *environment* that restrains *population* growth.

**limnetic zone** In a water body, the layer of open water through which sunlight penetrates. Compare *littoral zone; benthic zone; profundal zone.*

**lipid** One of a chemically diverse group of *macromolecules* that are classified together because they do not dissolve in water. Lipids include fats, phospholipids, waxes, pigments, and steroids.

**lithification** The formation of rock through the processes of compaction, binding, and crystallization.

**lithosphere** The solid part of the Earth, including the rocks, *sediment,* and *soil* at the surface and extending down many miles underground. Compare *atmosphere; biosphere; hydrosphere.*

**littoral** See *intertidal.*

**littoral zone** The region ringing the edge of a water body. Compare *benthic zone; limnetic zone; profundal zone.*

**loam** *Soil* with a relatively even mixture of *clay-, silt-,* and *sand*-sized particles.

**lobbying** The expenditure of time or money in an attempt to influence an elected official.

**logistic growth curve** A plot that shows how the initial *exponential growth* of a *population* is slowed and finally brought to a standstill by *limiting factors.*

**low-pressure system** An air mass in which the air moves toward the low *atmospheric pressure* at the center of the system and spirals upward, typically bringing clouds and *precipitation.* Compare *high-pressure system.*

**macromolecule** A very large molecule, such as a *protein, nucleic acid, carbohydrate,* or *lipid.*

**macronutrient** A *nutrient* that organisms require in relatively large amounts. Compare *micronutrient.*

**magma** Molten, liquid rock.

**malnutrition** The condition of lacking *nutrients* the body needs, including a complete complement of vitamins and minerals.

**Malthus, Thomas (1766–1834)** British economist who maintained that increasing human *population* would eventually deplete the available food supply until starvation, war, or disease arose and reduced the population.

**mangrove** A tree with a unique type of roots that curve upward to obtain oxygen, which is lacking in the mud in which they grow, and that serve as stilts to support the tree in changing water levels. Mangrove forests grow on the coastlines of the tropics and subtropics.

**manipulative experiment** An *experiment* in which the researcher actively chooses and manipulates the *independent variable.* Compare *natural experiment.*

**mantle** The malleable layer of rock that lies beneath Earth's *crust* and surrounds a mostly iron *core.*

**marine protected area (MPA)** An area of the ocean set aside to protect marine life from fishing pressures. An MPA may be protected from some human activities but be open to others. Compare *marine reserve.*

**marine reserve** An area of the ocean designated as a "no-fishing" zone, allowing no extractive activities. Compare *marine protected area.*

**marketable emissions permit** A permit issued to polluters that allows them to emit a certain fraction of the total amount of *pollution* the government will allow an entire industry to produce. Polluters are then allowed to buy, sell, and trade these permits with other polluters. See also *permit-trading.*

**market failure** The failure of markets to take into account the *environment*'s positive effects on *economies* (for example, *ecosystem services*) or to reflect the negative effects of economic activity on the environment and thereby on people (*external costs*).

**mass extinction event** The extinction of a large proportion of the world's *species* in a very short time period due to some extreme and rapid change or catastrophic event. Earth has seen five mass extinction events in the past half-billion years.

**materials recovery facility (MRF)** A *recycling* facility where items are sorted, cleaned, shredded, and prepared for reprocessing into new items.

**maximum sustainable yield** The maximal harvest of a particular *renewable natural resource* that can be accomplished while still keeping the resource available for the future.

**meltdown** The accidental melting of the uranium fuel rods inside the core of a *nuclear reactor,* causing the release of radiation.

**metamorphic rock** One of the three main categories of rock. Formed by great heat and/or pressure that reshapes crystals within the rock and changes its appearance and physical properties. Common metamorphic rocks include marble and slate. Compare *igneous rock; sedimentary rock.*

**methane hydrate** An ice-like solid consisting of molecules of methane ($CH_4$) embedded in a crystal lattice of water molecules. Methane hydrates are being investigated as a potential new source of *energy* from *fossil fuels.*

**micronutrient** A *nutrient* that organisms require in relatively small amounts. Compare *macronutrient.*

**Milankovitch cycle** One of three types of variations in Earth's rotation and orbit around the sun that result in slight changes in the relative amount of solar radiation reaching Earth's surface at different latitudes. As the cycles proceed, they change the way solar radiation is distributed over Earth's surface and contribute to changes in *atmospheric* heating and circulation that have triggered the ice ages and other *climate* changes.

**Mill, John Stuart (1806–1873)** British philosopher who believed that as resources become harder to find and extract, *economic* growth will slow and eventually stabilize into a *steady-state economy.*

**molecule** A combination of two or more *atoms.*

**monoculture** The uniform planting of a single crop over a large area. Characterizes *industrialized agriculture.*

**Montreal Protocol** International treaty ratified in 1987 in which 180 signatory nations agreed to restrict production of *chlorofluorocarbons (CFCs)* in order to forestall stratospheric ozone depletion. Because of its effectiveness in decreasing global CFC emissions, the Montreal Protocol is considered the most successful effort to date in addressing a global *environmental* problem.

**Muir, John (1838–1914)** Scottish immigrant to the United States who eventually settled in California and made the

Yosemite Valley his wilderness home. Today, he is most strongly associated with the *preservation ethic*. He argued that nature deserved protection for its own inherent values (an *ecocentrist* argument) but also claimed that nature played a large role in human happiness and fulfillment (an *anthropocentrist* argument).

**multiple use** A principle that has nominally guided management policy for national forests over the past half century. The multiple use principle specifies that the forests be managed for recreation, wildlife habitat, mineral extraction, and various other uses.

**municipal solid waste** Nonliquid *waste* that is not especially hazardous and that comes from homes, institutions, and small businesses. Compare *hazardous waste; industrial solid waste*.

**mutagen** A *toxicant* that causes *mutations* in the *DNA* of organisms.

**mutation** An accidental change in *DNA* that may range in magnitude from the deletion, substitution, or addition of a single nucleotide to a change affecting entire sets of chromosomes. Mutations provide the raw material for evolutionary change.

**mutualism** A relationship in which all participating organisms benefit from their interaction. Compare *parasitism*.

**National Environmental Policy Act (NEPA)** A U.S. law enacted on January 1, 1970, that created an agency called the Council on Environmental Quality and required that an *environmental impact statement* be prepared for any major federal action.

**national forest** Public lands consisting of 191 million acres (more than 8% of the nation's land area) in many tracts spread across all but a few states.

**National Forest Management Act** *Legislation* passed by the U.S. Congress in 1976, mandating that plans for renewable resource management be drawn up for every national forest. These plans were to be explicitly based on the concepts of *multiple use* and *sustainable development* and be subject to broad public participation.

**national park** A scenic area set aside for recreation and enjoyment by the public. The national park system today numbers 388 sites totaling 78.8 million acres and includes national historic sites, national recreation areas, national wild and scenic rivers, and other types of areas.

**national wildlife refuge** An area set aside to serve as a haven for wildlife and also sometimes to encourage hunting, fishing, wildlife observation, photography, environmental education, and other public uses.

**natural experiment** An *experiment* in which the researcher cannot directly manipulate the *variables* and therefore must observe nature, comparing conditions in which variables differ, and interpret the results. Compare *manipulative experiment*.

**natural gas** A *fossil fuel* composed primarily of methane ($CH_4$), produced as a by-product when bacteria decompose organic material under *anaerobic* conditions.

**natural rate of population change** The rate of change in a *population's* size resulting from birth and death rates alone, excluding migration.

**natural resource** Any of the various substances and *energy* sources we need in order to survive.

**natural science** An academic discipline that studies the natural world. Compare *social science*.

**natural selection** The process by which traits that enhance survival and reproduction are passed on more frequently to future generations of organisms than those that do not, thus altering the *genetic* makeup of populations through time. Natural selection acts on genetic variation and is a primary driver of evolution.

**negative feedback loop** A *feedback loop* in which output of one type acts as input that moves the *system* in the opposite direction. The input and output essentially neutralize each other's effects, stabilizing the system. Compare *positive feedback loop*.

**neoclassical economics** A *theory* of *economics* that explains market prices in terms of consumer preferences for units of particular commodities. Buyers desire the lowest possible price, whereas sellers desire the highest possible price. This conflict between buyers and sellers results in a compromise price being reached and the "right" quantity of commodities being bought and sold. Compare *ecological economics; environmental economics*.

**net primary production** The *energy* or biomass that remains in an ecosystem after *autotrophs* have metabolized enough for their own maintenance through *cellular respiration*. Net primary production is the energy or biomass available for consumption by *heterotrophs*. Compare *gross primary production; secondary production*.

**net primary productivity** The rate at which *net primary production* is produced. See *productivity; gross primary production; net primary production; secondary production*.

**neurotoxin** A *toxicant* that assaults the nervous system. Neurotoxins include heavy metals, *pesticides,* and some chemical weapons developed for use in war.

**neutron** An electrically neutral (uncharged) particle in the nucleus of an *atom*.

**new forestry** A set of *ecosystem-based management* approaches for harvesting timber that explicitly mimic natural disturbances. For instance, "sloppy clear-cuts" that leave a variety of trees standing mimic the changes a forest might experience if hit by a severe windstorm.

**new urbanism** A school of thought among architects, planners, and developers that seeks to design neighborhoods in which homes, businesses, schools, and other amenities are within walking distance of one another. In a direct rebuttal to *sprawl,* proponents of new urbanism aim to create functional neighborhoods in which families can meet most of their needs close to home without the use of a car.

**niche** The functional role of a *species* in a *community*. See *fundamental niche; realized niche*.

**nitrification** The conversion by bacteria of ammonium ions ($NH_4^+$) first into nitrite ions ($NO_2^-$) and then into nitrate ions ($NO_3^-$).

**nitrogen cycle** A major *nutrient cycle* consisting of the routes that nitrogen *atoms* take through the nested networks of environmental *systems*.

**nitrogen fixation** The process by which inert nitrogen gas combines with hydrogen to form ammonium ions ($NH_4^+$), which are chemically and biologically active and can be taken up by plants.

**nitrogen-fixing** Term describing bacteria that live in a *mutualistic* relationship with many types of plants and provide *nutrients* to the plants by converting nitrogen to a usable form.

**nonconsumptive use** *Freshwater* use in which the water from a particular *aquifer* or surface water body either is not removed or is removed only temporarily and then returned. The use of water to generate electricity in hydroelectric *dams* is an example. Compare *consumptive use.*

**nonmarket value** A value that is not usually included in the price of a *good* or *service.*

**non-point source** A diffuse source of *pollutants,* often consisting of many small sources. Compare *point source.*

**nonrenewable natural resource** A *natural resource* that is in limited supply and is formed much more slowly than we use it. Compare *renewable natural resource.*

**Northwest Forest Plan** A 1994 plan developed by the Clinton administration to allow logging of forests of western Washington, Oregon, and northwestern California with increased protection for *species* and *ecosystems.* The Northwest Forest Plan represented one of the first large-scale applications of *adaptive management.*

**nuclear energy** The *energy* that holds together *protons* and *neutrons* within the nucleus of an *atom.* Several processes, each of which involves transforming *isotopes* of one *element* into isotopes of other elements, can convert nuclear energy into thermal energy, which is then used to generate electricity. See also *nuclear fission; nuclear reactor.*

**nuclear fission** The conversion of the *energy* within an *atom*'s nucleus to usable thermal energy by splitting apart atomic nuclei. Compare *nuclear fusion.*

**nuclear fusion** The conversion of the *energy* within an *atom*'s nucleus to usable thermal energy by forcing together the small nuclei of lightweight *elements* under extremely high temperature and pressure. Developing a commercially viable method of nuclear fusion remains an elusive goal.

**nuclear reactor** A facility within a nuclear power plant that initiates and controls the process of *nuclear fission* in order to generate electricity.

**nucleic acid** A *macromolecule* that directs the production of *proteins.* Includes *DNA* and *RNA.*

**nutrient** An *element* or *compound* that organisms consume and require for survival.

**nutrient cycle** The comprehensive set of cyclical pathways by which a given *nutrient* moves through the *environment.*

**oceanography** The study of the physics, chemistry, biology, and geology of the oceans.

**ocean thermal energy conversion (OTEC)** A potential *energy* source that involves harnessing the solar radiation absorbed by tropical oceans in the tropics.

**O horizon** The top layer of *soil* in some *soil profiles,* made up of organic matter, such as decomposing branches, leaves, crop residue, and animal waste. Compare *A horizon; B horizon; C horizon; E horizon; R horizon.*

**open system** A *system* that exchanges *energy,* matter, and information with other systems. Compare *closed system.*

**organelle** A structure, such as a ribosome or mitochondrion, inside the *cell* that performs specific functions.

**organic agriculture** *Agriculture* that uses no synthetic *fertilizers* or *pesticides* but instead relies on biological approaches such as *composting* and *biocontrol.*

**organic compound** A *compound* made up of carbon *atoms* (and, generally, hydrogen atoms) joined by *covalent bonds* and sometimes including other *elements,* such as nitrogen, oxygen, sulfur, or phosphorus. The unusual ability of carbon to build elaborate molecules has resulted in millions of different organic compounds showing various degrees of complexity.

**organic fertilizer** A *fertilizer* made up of natural materials (largely the remains or wastes of organisms), including animal manure, crop residues, fresh vegetation, and compost. Compare *inorganic fertilizer.*

**overgrazing** The consumption by too many animals of plant cover, impeding plant regrowth and the replacement of biomass. Overgrazing can exacerbate damage to *soils,* natural *communities,* and the land's productivity for further grazing.

**overnutrition** A condition of excessive food intake in which people receive more than their daily caloric needs.

**ozone layer** A portion of the *stratosphere,* roughly 17–30 km (10–19 mi) above sea level, that contains most of the ozone in the *atmosphere.*

**paradigm** A dominant philosophical and theoretical framework within a scientific discipline.

**parasitism** A relationship in which one organism, the parasite, depends on another, the host, for nourishment or some other benefit while simultaneously doing the host harm. Compare *mutualism.*

**parent material** The base geological material in a particular location.

**passive solar energy collection** An approach in which buildings are designed and building materials are chosen to maximize their direct absorption of sunlight in winter, even as they keep the interior cool in the summer. Compare *active solar energy collection.*

**peat** A kind of precursor stage to *coal,* produced when organic material that is broken down by *anaerobic* decomposition remains wet, near the surface, and not well compressed.

**peer review** The process by which a manuscript submitted for publication in an academic journal is examined by other specialists in the field, who provide comments and criticism (generally anonymously), and judge whether the work merits publication in the journal.

**pelagic** Of, relating to, or living between the surface and floor of the ocean. Compare *benthic.*

**permit-trading** The practice of buying and selling government-issued *marketable emissions permits* to conduct environmentally harmful activities. Under such a system, the government determines an acceptable level of *pollution* and then issues permits to pollute. A company receives credit for amounts it does not emit and can then sell this credit to other companies.

**pesticide** An artificial chemical used to kill insects (insecticide), plants (herbicide), or fungi (fungicide).

**petroleum** See *crude oil*.

**pH** A measure of the concentration of hydrogen *ions* in a solution. The pH scale ranges from 0 to 14: A solution with a pH of 7 is neutral; solutions with a pH below 7 are *acidic,* and those with a pH higher than 7 are *basic.* Because the pH scale is logarithmic, each step on the scale represents a tenfold difference in hydrogen ion concentration.

**phosphorus cycle** A major *nutrient cycle* consisting of the routes that phosphorus *atoms* take through the nested networks of environmental *systems.*

**photochemical smog** Brown-air smog caused by light-driven reactions of *primary pollutants* with normal atmospheric *compounds* that produce a mix of over 100 different chemicals, ground-level ozone often being the most abundant among them. Compare *industrial smog.*

**photosynthesis** The process by which *autotrophs* produce their own food. Sunlight powers a series of chemical reactions that convert carbon dioxide and water into sugar (glucose), thus transforming low-quality *energy* from the sun into high-quality energy the organism can use. Compare *cellular respiration.*

**photovoltaic (PV) cell** A device designed to collect sunlight and convert it to electrical *energy* directly by making use of the *photoelectric effect.*

**phylogenetic tree** A treelike diagram that represents the history of divergence of *species* or other taxonomic groups of organisms.

**Pinchot, Gifford (1865–1946)** The first professionally trained American *forester,* Pinchot helped establish the U.S. Forest Service. Today, he is the person most closely associated with the *conservation ethic.*

**pioneer species** A *species* that arrives earliest, beginning the ecological process of *succession* in a terrestrial or aquatic *community.*

**plate tectonics** The process by which Earth's surface is shaped by the extremely slow movement of tectonic plates, or sections of *crust.* Earth's surface includes about 15 major tectonic plates. Their interaction gives rise to processes that build mountains, cause earthquakes, and otherwise influence the landscape.

**point source** A specific spot—such as a factory's smokestacks—where large quantities of *pollutants* are discharged. Compare *non-point source.*

**polar cell** One of a pair of cells of *convective circulation* between the poles and 60° north and south latitude that influence global *climate* patterns. Compare *Ferrel cell; Hadley cell.*

**policy** A rule or guideline that directs individual, organizational, or societal behavior.

**pollination** An interaction in which one organism (for example, bees) transfers pollen (male sex cells) from one flower to the ova (female cells) of another, fertilizing the female flower, which subsequently grows into a fruit.

**pollution** Any matter or *energy* released into the *environment* that causes undesirable impacts on the health and well-being of humans or other organisms. Pollution can be physical, chemical, or biological, and can affect water, air, or soil.

**polymer** A chemical *compound* or mixture of compounds consisting of long chains of repeated *molecules.* Some polymers play key roles in the building blocks of life.

**population** A group of organisms of the same *species* that live in the same area. Species are often composed of multiple populations.

**population density** The number of individuals within a *population* per unit area. Compare *population size.*

**population dispersion** See *population distribution.*

**population distribution** The spatial arrangement of organisms within a particular area.

**population ecology** Study of the quantitative dynamics of how individuals within a *species* interact with one another—in particular, why *populations* of some species decline while others increase.

**population size** The number of individual organisms present at a given time.

**positive feedback loop** A *feedback loop* in which output of one type acts as input that moves the *system* in the same direction. The input and output drive the system further toward one extreme or another. Compare *negative feedback loop.*

**post-industrial stage** The fourth and final stage of the *demographic transition* model, in which both birth and death rates have fallen to a low level and remain stable there, and *populations* may even decline slightly. Compare *industrial stage; pre-industrial stage; transition stage.*

**potential energy** *Energy* of position. Compare *kinetic energy.*

**precautionary principle** The idea that one should not undertake a new action until the ramifications of that action are well understood.

**precipitation** Water that condenses out of the *atmosphere* and falls to Earth in droplets or crystals.

**predation** The process in which one *species* (the predator) hunts, tracks, captures, and ultimately kills its prey.

**prediction** A specific statement, generally arising from a *hypothesis,* that can be tested directly and unequivocally.

**pre-industrial stage** The first stage of the *demographic transition* model, characterized by conditions that defined most of human history. In pre-industrial societies, both death rates and birth rates are high. Compare *industrial stage; post-industrial stage; transitional stage.*

**prescribed (controlled) burns** The practice of burning areas of forest or grassland under carefully controlled conditions to improve the health of *ecosystems,* return them to a more natural state, and help prevent uncontrolled catastrophic fires.

**preservation ethic** An ethic holding that we should protect the natural *environment* in a pristine, unaltered state. Compare *conservation ethic.*

**primary extraction** The initial drilling and pumping of available *crude oil.* Compare *secondary extraction.*

**primary pollutant** A hazardous substance, such as soot or carbon monoxide, that is emitted into the *troposphere* in a form that is directly harmful. Compare *secondary pollutant.*

**primary succession** A stereotypical series of changes as an *ecological community* develops over time, beginning with a lifeless substrate. In terrestrial *systems,* primary succession begins when a bare expanse of rock, *sand,* or *sediment* becomes newly exposed to the atmosphere and *pioneer species* arrive. Compare *secondary succession*.

**primary treatment** A stage of *wastewater* treatment in which contaminants are physically removed. Wastewater flows into tanks in which sewage solids, grit, and particulate matter settle to the bottom. Greases and oils float to the surface and can be skimmed off. Compare *secondary treatment*.

**producer** See *autotroph*.

**productivity** The rate at which plants convert solar *energy* (sunlight) to biomass. *Ecosystems* whose plants convert solar energy to biomass rapidly are said to have high productivity. See *net primary productivity; gross primary production; net primary production*.

**profundal zone** In a water body, the volume of open water that sunlight does not reach. Compare *littoral zone; benthic zone; limnetic zone*.

**prokaryote** A typically unicellular organism. The *cells* of prokaryotic organisms lack *organelles* and a nucleus. All bacteria and archaeans are prokaryotes. Compare *eukaryote*.

**protein** A *macromolecule* made up of long chains of amino acids.

**proton** A positively charged particle in the nucleus of an *atom*.

**proven recoverable reserve** The amount of a given *fossil fuel* in a deposit that is technologically and economically feasible to remove under current conditions.

**proxy indicator** Indirect evidence, such as pollen from *sediment* cores and air bubbles from ice cores, of the *climate* of the past.

**public policy** *Policy* that is made by governments, including those at the local, state, federal, and international levels; it consists of *legislation, regulations,* orders, incentives, and practices intended to advance societal welfare. See also *environmental policy*.

**radioisotopes** Radioactive *isotopes* that emit subatomic particles and high-*energy* radiation as they "decay" into progressively lighter isotopes until becoming stable isotopes.

**rangeland** Land used for grazing livestock.

**realized niche** The portion of the *fundamental niche* that is fully realized (used) by a *species*.

**recombinant DNA** *DNA* that has been patched together from the DNA of multiple organisms in an attempt to produce desirable traits (such as rapid growth, disease and pest resistance, or higher nutritional content) in organisms lacking those traits.

**recycling** The collection of materials that can be broken down and reprocessed to manufacture new items.

**Red List** An updated list of *species* facing unusually high risks of *extinction*. The list is maintained by the World Conservation Union.

**red tide** A *harmful algal bloom* consisting of algae that produce reddish pigments that discolor surface waters.

**refining** Process of separating the *molecules* of the various *hydrocarbons* in *crude oil* into different-sized classes and transforming them into various fuels and other petrochemical products.

**regional planning** *City planning* done on broader geographic scales, generally involving multiple municipal governments.

**regulation** A specific rule issued by an administrative agency, based on the more broadly written statutory law passed by Congress and enacted by the president.

**regulatory taking** The deprivation of a property's owner, by means of a law or *regulation*, of most or all economic uses of that property.

**relative humidity** The ratio of the water vapor contained in a given volume of air to the maximum amount the air could contain, for a given temperature.

**relativist** An ethicist who maintains that *ethics* do and should vary with social context. Compare *universalist*.

**renewable natural resource** A *natural resource* that is virtually unlimited or that is replenished by the *environment* over relatively short periods of hours to weeks to years. Compare *nonrenewable natural resource*.

**replacement fertility** The *total fertility rate (TFR)* that maintains a stable *population* size.

**reserves-to-production ratio (R/P ratio)** The total remaining reserves of a *fossil fuel* divided by the annual rate of production (extraction and processing).

**resilience** The ability of an ecological *community* to change in response to disturbance but later return to its original state. Compare *resistance*.

**resistance** The ability of an ecological *community* to remain stable in the presence of a disturbance. Compare *resilience*.

**resource management** Strategic decision making about who should extract resources and in what ways, so that resources are used wisely and not wasted.

**resource partitioning** The process by which *species* adapt to *competition* by evolving to use slightly different resources, or to use their shared resources in different ways, thus minimizing interference with one another.

**Resource Conservation and Recovery Act (RCRA)** Congressional *legislation* (enacted in 1976 and amended in 1984) that specifies, among other things, how to manage *sanitary landfills* to protect against environmental contamination.

**restoration ecology** The study of the historical conditions of *ecological communities* as they existed before humans altered them.

**revolving door** The movement of powerful officials between the private sector and government agencies.

**R horizon** The bottommost layer of *soil* in a typical *soil profile*. Also called *bedrock*. Compare *A horizon; B horizon; C horizon; E horizon; O horizon*.

**ribonucleic acid** See *RNA*.

**risk** The mathematical probability that some harmful outcome (for instance, injury, death, *environmental* damage, or *economic* loss) will result from a given action, event, or substance.

**risk assessment** The quantitative measurement of *risk*, together with the comparison of risks involved in different activities or substances.

**risk management** The process of considering information from scientific *risk assessment* in light of economic, social, and political needs and values, in order to make decisions and design strategies to minimize *risk*.

**RNA (ribonucleic acid)** A usually single-stranded *nucleic acid* composed of four nucleotides, each of which contains a sugar (ribose), a phosphate group, and a nitrogenous base. RNA carries the hereditary information for living organisms and is responsible for passing traits from parents to offspring. Compare *DNA*.

**rock cycle** The very slow process in which rocks and the minerals that make them up are heated, melted, cooled, broken, and reassembled, forming *igneous*, *sedimentary*, and *metamorphic* rocks.

**r–selected** Term denoting a *species* with high biotic potential whose members produce a large number of offspring in a relatively short time but do not care for their young after birth. *Populations* of r–selected species are generally regulated by *density-independent factors*. Compare *K–selected*.

**runoff** The water from *precipitation* that flows into streams, rivers, lakes, and ponds, and (in many cases) eventually to the ocean.

**run-of-river** Any of several methods used to generate *hydroelectric power* without greatly disrupting the flow of river water. Run-of-river approaches eliminate much of the *environmental* impact of large *dams*. Compare *storage*.

**Ruskin, John (1819–1900)** British art critic, poet, and writer who criticized industrialized cities and their *pollution*, and who believed that people no longer appreciated the *environment*'s spiritual or aesthetic benefits.

**salinization** The buildup of salts in surface *soil* layers.

**salt** See *ionic compound*.

**salt marsh** Flat land that is intermittently flooded by the ocean where the *tide* reaches inland. Salt marshes occur along temperate coastlines and are thickly vegetated with grasses, rushes, shrubs, and other herbaceous plants.

**salvage logging** The removal of dead trees following a natural disturbance. Although it may be economically beneficial, salvage logging can be ecologically destructive, because the dead trees provide food and shelter for a variety of insects and wildlife and because removing timber from recently burned land can cause severe *erosion* and damage to *soil*.

**sand** *Sediment* consisting of particles 0.005–2.0 mm in diameter. Compare *clay*; *silt*.

**sanitary landfill** A site at which solid waste is buried in the ground or piled up in large mounds for disposal, designed to prevent the waste from contaminating the *environment*. Compare *incineration*.

**savanna** A *biome* characterized by grassland interspersed with clusters of acacias and other trees. Savanna is found across parts of Africa (where it was the ancestral home of our *species*), South America, Australia, India, and other dry tropical regions.

**science** A systematic process for learning about the world and testing our understanding of it.

**scientific method** A formalized method for testing ideas with observations that involves several assumptions and a more or less consistent series of interrelated steps.

**secondary extraction** The extraction of *crude oil* remaining after *primary extraction* by using solvents or by flushing underground rocks with water or steam. Compare *primary extraction*.

**secondary pollutant** A hazardous substance produced through the reaction of substances added to the *atmosphere* with chemicals normally found in the atmosphere. Compare *primary pollutant*.

**secondary production** The total biomass that *heterotrophs* generate by consuming *autotrophs*. Compare *gross primary production* and *net primary production*.

**secondary succession** A stereotypical series of changes as an *ecological community* develops over time, beginning when some event disrupts or dramatically alters an existing community. Compare *primary succession*.

**secondary treatment** A stage of *wastewater* treatment in which biological means are used to remove contaminants remaining after *primary treatment*. Wastewater is stirred up in the presence of *aerobic* bacteria, which degrade organic pollutants in the water. The wastewater then passes to another settling tank, where remaining solids drift to the bottom. Compare *primary treatment*.

**second-growth** Term describing trees that have sprouted and grown to partial maturity after virgin timber has been cut.

**second law of thermodynamics** Physical law stating that the nature of *energy* tends to change from a more-ordered state to a less-ordered state; that is, *entropy* increases.

**sediment** The eroded remains of rocks.

**sedimentary rock** One of the three main categories of rock. Formed when dissolved minerals seep through *sediment* layers and act as a kind of glue, crystallizing and binding sediment particles together. Sandstone and shale are examples of sedimentary rock. Compare *igneous rock*; *metamorphic rock*.

**seed bank** A storehouse for samples of the world's crop diversity.

**septic system** A *wastewater* disposal method, common in rural areas, consisting of an underground tank and series of drainpipes. Wastewater runs from the house to the tank, where solids precipitate out. The water proceeds downhill to a drain field of perforated pipes laid horizontally in gravel-filled trenches, where microbes decompose the remaining waste.

**service** Work done for others as a form of business.

**sex ratio** The proportion of males to females in a *population*.

**shelterbelt** A row of trees or other tall perennial plants that are planted along the edges of farm fields to break the wind and thereby minimize wind *erosion*.

**silt** *Sediment* consisting of particles 0.002–0.005 mm in diameter. Compare *clay*; *sand*.

**sinkhole** An area where the ground has given way with little warning as a result of subsidence caused by depletion of water from an *aquifer*.

**SLOSS (Single Large or Several Small) dilemma** The debate over whether it is better to make reserves large in size and few in number or many in number but small in size.

**smart growth** A *city planning* concept in which a community's growth is managed in ways that limit *sprawl* and maintain or improve residents' quality of life. It involves guiding the rate, placement, and style of development such that it serves the *environment*, the *economy*, and the community.

**Smith, Adam (1723–1790)** Scottish philosopher known today as the father of *classical economics*. He believed that when people are free to pursue their own economic self-interest in a competitive marketplace, the marketplace will behave as if guided by "an invisible hand" that ensures that their actions will benefit society as a whole.

**social science** An academic discipline that studies human interactions and institutions. Compare *natural science*.

**soil profile** The cross-section of a *soil* as a whole, from the surface to the *bedrock*.

**soil** A complex plant-supporting *system* consisting of disintegrated rock, organic matter, air, water, *nutrients,* and microorganisms.

**source reduction** The reduction of the amount of material that enters the *waste stream* to avoid the costs of disposal and *recycling,* help conserve resources, minimize *pollution,* and save consumers and businesses money.

**specialist** A *species* that can survive only in a narrow range of *habitats* that contain very specific resources. Compare *generalist.*

**speciation** The process by which new *species* are generated.

**species** A *population* or group of populations of a particular type of organism, whose members share certain characteristics and can breed freely with one another and produce fertile offspring. Different biologists may have different approaches to diagnosing species boundaries.

**species diversity** The number and variety of *species* in the world or in a particular region.

**sprawl** The unrestrained spread of urban or *suburban* development outward from a city center and across the landscape.

**steady-state economy** An *economy* that does not grow or shrink but remains stable.

**storage** Technique used to generate *hydroelectric power,* in which large amounts of water are impounded in a reservoir behind a concrete *dam* and then passed through the dam to turn *turbines* that generate electricity. Compare *run-of-river.*

**stratosphere** The layer of the *atmosphere* above the *troposphere* and below the mesosphere; it extends from 11 km (7 mi) to 50 km (31 mi) above sea level.

**strip-mining** The use of heavy machinery to remove huge amounts of earth to expose *coal* or minerals, which are mined out directly. Compare *subsurface mining.*

**subduction** The *plate tectonic* process by which denser ocean *crust* slides beneath lighter continental crust at a *convergent plate boundary.*

**subsidy** A government incentive (a giveaway of cash or publicly owned resources, or a tax break) intended to encourage a particular activity. Compare *green tax.*

**subsistence economy** A survival *economy,* one in which people meet most or all of their daily needs directly from nature and do not purchase or trade for most of life's necessities.

**subsurface mining** Method of mining underground *coal* deposits, in which shafts are dug deeply into the ground and networks of tunnels are dug or blasted out to follow coal seams. Compare *strip-mining.*

**suburb** A smaller community that rings a city.

**succession** A stereotypical series of changes in the composition and structure of an *ecological community* through time. See *primary succession; secondary succession.*

**Superfund** A program administered by the *Environmental Protection Agency* in which experts identify sites polluted with hazardous chemicals, protect *groundwater* near these sites, and clean up the *pollution.*

**surface impoundment** A *hazardous waste* disposal method in which a shallow depression is dug and lined with impervious material, such as *clay.* Water containing small amounts of hazardous waste is placed in the pond and allowed to evaporate, leaving a residue of solid hazardous waste on the bottom. Compare *deep-well injection.*

**survivorship curve** A graph that shows how the likelihood of death for members of a *population* varies with age.

**sustainability** A guiding principle of *environmental science* that requires us to live in such a way as to maintain Earth's systems and its *natural resources* for the foreseeable future.

**sustainable agriculture** *Agriculture* that does not deplete *soils* faster than they form.

**sustainable development** Development that satisfies our current needs without compromising the future availability of *natural resources* or our future quality of life.

**sustainable forestry certification** A form of *ecolabeling* that identifies timber products that have been produced using *sustainable* methods. Several organizations issue such certification.

**symbiosis** A *parasitic* or *mutualistic* relationship between different *species* of organisms that live in close physical proximity.

**synergistic effect** An interactive effect (as of *toxicants*) that is more than or different from the simple sum of their constituent effects.

**system** A network of relationships among a group of parts, elements, or components that interact with and influence one another through the exchange of *energy,* matter, and/or information.

**Talloires Declaration** A document composed in Talloires, France, in 1990 that commits university leaders to pursue *sustainability* on their campuses. It has been signed by over 300 university presidents and chancellors from more than 40 nations.

**temperate deciduous forest** A *biome* consisting of midlatitude forests characterized by broad-leafed trees that lose their leaves each fall and remain dormant during winter. These forests occur in areas where *precipitation* is spread relatively evenly throughout the year: much of Europe, eastern China, and eastern North America.

**temperate grassland** A *biome* whose vegetation is dominated by grasses and features more extreme temperature differences between winter and summer and less *precipitation* than *temperate deciduous forests.*

**temperate rainforest** A *biome* consisting of tall coniferous trees, cooler and less species-rich than *tropical rainforest* and milder and wetter than *temperate deciduous forest.*

**temperature (thermal) inversion** A departure from the normal temperature distribution in the *atmosphere,* in which a pocket of relatively cold air occurs near the ground, with warmer air above it. The cold air, denser than the air above it, traps *pollutants* near the ground and causes a buildup of smog.

**teratogen** A *toxicant* that causes harm to the unborn, resulting in birth defects.

**terracing** The cutting of level platforms, sometimes with raised edges, into steep hillsides to contain water from *irrigation* and *precipitation.* Terracing transforms slopes into series of steps like a staircase, enabling farmers to cultivate hilly land while minimizing their loss of *soil* to water *erosion.*

**theory** A widely accepted, well-tested explanation of one or more cause-and-effect relationships that has been extensively validated by a great amount of research. Compare *hypothesis*.

**thermal inversion** See *temperature inversion*.

**Thoreau, Henry David (1817–1862)** American transcendentalist author, poet, and philosopher. His book *Walden*, recording his observations and thoughts while he lived at Walden Pond away from the bustle of urban Massachusetts, remains a classic of American literature.

**Three Mile Island** Nuclear power plant in Pennsylvania that in 1979 experienced a partial *meltdown*. The term is often using to denote the accident itself, the most serious *nuclear reactor* malfunction that the United States has thus far experienced.

**threshold dose** The amount of a *toxicant* at which it begins to affect a *population* of test animals. Compare $ED_{50}$; $LD_{50}$.

**tide** The periodic rise and fall of the ocean's height at a given location, caused by the gravitational pull of the moon and sun.

**topsoil** That portion of the *soil* that is most nutritive for plants and is thus of the most direct importance to *ecosystems* and to *agriculture*. Also known as the *A horizon*.

**total fertility rate (TFR)** The average number of children born per female member of a *population* during her lifetime.

**toxic air pollutant** *Air pollutant* that is known to cause cancer, reproductive defects, or neurological, developmental, immune system, or respiratory problems in humans, and/or to cause substantial *ecological* harm by affecting the health of nonhuman animals and plants. The *Clean Air Act of 1990* identifies 188 toxic air pollutants, ranging from the heavy metal mercury to *volatile organic compounds* such as benzene and methylene chloride.

**toxicant** A substance that acts as a poison to humans or wildlife.

**toxicology** The scientific field that examines the effects of poisonous chemicals and other agents on humans and other organisms.

**traditional agriculture** Biologically powered *agriculture*, in which human and animal muscle power, along with hand tools and simple machines, perform the work of cultivating, harvesting, storing, and distributing crops. Compare *industrialized agriculture*.

**transform plate boundary** Area where two tectonic plates meet and slip and grind alongside one another. For example, the Pacific Plate and the North American Plate rub against each other along California's San Andreas Fault.

**transgene** A *gene* that has been extracted from the *DNA* of one organism and transferred into the DNA of an organism of another *species*.

**transgenic** Term describing an organism that contains *DNA* from another *species*.

**transitional stage** The second stage of the *demographic transition* model, which occurs during the transition from the *pre-industrial stage* to the *industrial stage*. It is characterized by declining death rates but continued high birth rates. See also *post-industrial stage*. Compare *industrial stage; post-industrial stage; pre-industrial stage*.

**transpiration** The release of water vapor by plants through their leaves.

**treatment** The portion of an *experiment* in which a *variable* has been manipulated in order to test its effect. Compare *control*.

**trophic level** Rank in the feeding hierarchy of a food chain. Organisms at higher trophic levels consume those at lower trophic levels.

**tropical dry forest** A *biome* that consists of deciduous trees and occurs at tropical and subtropical latitudes where wet and dry seasons each span about half the year. Widespread in India, Africa, South America, and northern Australia.

**tropical rainforest** A *biome* characterized by year-round rain and uniformly warm temperatures. Found in Central America, South America, southeast Asia, west Africa, and other tropical regions. Tropical rainforests have dark, damp interiors; lush vegetation; and highly diverse *biotic communities*.

**troposphere** The bottommost layer of the *atmosphere*; it extends to 11 km (7 mi) above sea level. See also *stratosphere*.

**tundra** A *biome* that is nearly as dry as *desert* but is located at very high latitudes along the northern edges of Russia, Canada, and Scandinavia. Extremely cold winters with little daylight and moderately cool summers with lengthy days characterize this landscape of lichens and low, scrubby vegetation.

**turbine** A rotary device that converts the *kinetic energy* of a moving substance, such as steam, into mechanical energy. Used widely in commercial power generation from various types of energy sources.

**unconfined aquifer** A water-bearing, porous layer of rock, *sand,* or gravel that lies atop a less-permeable substrate. The water in an unconfined aquifer is not under pressure because there is no impermeable upper layer to confine it. Compare *confined aquifer*.

**undernutrition** A condition of insufficient *nutrition* in which people receive less than 90% of their daily caloric needs.

**uneven-aged** Term describing stands of trees in timber plantations that are of different ages. Uneven-aged stands more closely approximate a natural forest than do *even-aged* stands.

**United Nations (U.N.)** Organization founded in 1945 to promote international peace and to cooperate in solving international economic, social, cultural, and humanitarian problems. Several agencies within it influence *environmental policy,* most notably the United Nations Environment Programme (UNEP), created in 1972.

**United Nations Framework Convention on Climate Change (FCCC)** International agreement to reduce *greenhouse gas* emissions to 1990 levels by the year 2000, signed by nations represented at the 1992 Earth Summit convened in Rio de Janeiro by the *United Nations*. The FCCC called for a voluntary, nation-by-nation approach, but by the late 1990s it had become apparent that it would not succeed. Its imminent failure sparked introduction of the *Kyoto Protocol*.

**universalist** An *ethicist* who maintains that there exist objective notions of right and wrong that hold across cultures and situations. Compare *relativist*.

**upwelling** In the ocean, the flow of cold, deep water toward the surface. Upwelling occurs in areas where surface *currents* diverge. Compare *downwelling*.

**urban ecology** A scientific field that views cities explicitly as *ecosystems*. Researchers in this field seek to apply the fundamentals of *ecosystem ecology* and *systems* science to urban areas.

**urban growth boundary (UGB)** In *city planning*, a geographic boundary intended to separate areas desired to be urban from areas desired to remain rural. Development for housing, commerce, and industry are encouraged within urban growth boundaries, but beyond them such development is severely restricted.

**urbanization** The shift from rural to city and *suburban* living.

**variable** In an *experiment*, a condition that can change. See *dependent variable* and *independent variable*.

**volatile organic compound (VOC)** One of a large group of potentially harmful organic chemicals used in industrial processes.

**Wallace, Alfred Russell (1823–1913)** English naturalist who proposed, independently of *Charles Darwin*, the concept of *natural selection* as a mechanism for *evolution* and as a way to explain the great variety of living things.

**warm front** The boundary where a mass of warm air displaces a mass of colder air. Compare *cold front*.

**waste** Any unwanted product that results from a human activity or process.

**waste management** Strategic decision making to minimize the amount of *waste* generated and to dispose of waste safely and effectively.

**waste stream** The flow of *waste* as it moves from its sources toward disposal destinations.

**waste-to-energy (WTE) facility** An incinerator that uses heat from its furnace to boil water to create steam that drives electricity generation or that fuels heating systems.

**wastewater** Any water that is used in households, businesses, industries, or public facilities and is drained or flushed down pipes, as well as the polluted *runoff* from streets and storm drains.

**waterlogging** The saturation of *soil* by water, in which the *water table* is raised to the point that water bathes plant roots. Waterlogging deprives roots of access to gases, essentially suffocating them and eventually damaging or killing the plants.

**watershed** The entire area of land from which water drains into a given river.

**water table** The upper limit of *groundwater* held in an *aquifer*.

**weather** The local physical properties of the *troposphere*, such as temperature, pressure, humidity, cloudiness, and wind, over relatively short time periods. Compare *climate*.

**weathering** The physical, chemical, and biological processes that break down rocks and minerals, turning large particles into smaller particles.

**Whitman, Walt (1819–1892)** American poet who espoused transcendentalism. See also *Emerson, Ralph Waldo* and *Thoreau, Henry David*.

**wilderness area** Federal land that is designated off-limits to development of any kind but is open to public recreation, such as hiking, nature study, and other activities that have minimal impact on the land.

**wind turbine** A mechanical assembly that converts the wind's *kinetic energy*, or energy of motion, into electrical energy.

**wise-use movement** A loose confederation of individuals and groups that coalesced in the 1980s and 1990s as a response to the increasing success of environmental advocacy. The movement favors extracting more resources from public lands, obtaining greater local control of lands, and obtaining greater motorized recreational access to public lands.

**World Bank** Institution founded in 1944 that serves as one of the globe's largest sources of funding for *economic* development, including such major projects as *dams*, *irrigation* infrastructure, and other undertakings.

**World Trade Organization (WTO)** Organization based in Geneva, Switzerland, that represents multinational corporations and promotes free trade by reducing obstacles to international commerce and enforcing fairness among nations in trading practices.

**worldview** A way of looking at the world that reflects a person's (or a group's) beliefs about the meaning, purpose, operation, and essence of the world.

**zoning** The practice of classifying areas for different types of development and land use.

# Photo Credits

**Part Opening Photos: Part One** Bill Hatcher/National Geographic Collection **Part Two** AP Photo/Bill Haber

**Chapter 1 Opening Photo** NASA/Johnson Space Center **1.2b** Charles O'Rear/CORBIS **1.3a** Art Resource **1.3b** Bettman/CORBIS **1.4** John N. Smith **1.6** George Konig/Hulton Archive Photos **1.8** Joel W. Rogers/CORBIS **1.9a** George Bukenhofer **1.9b** Reuters New Media Inc./CORBIS **1.14** CORBIS **1.15** Reuters **1.16** Justin Sullivan/ Getty Images **The Science behind the Story: Easter Island** Richard T. Nowitz/CORBIS

**Chapter 2 Opening Photo** Reuters New Media Inc./CORBIS **Case Study** The Gundjehmi Aboriginal Corporation **2.2a, b** The Gundjehmi Aboriginal Corporation **2.5** Library of Congress **2.6** CORBIS **2.7** CORBIS **2.8** Bettmann/CORBIS **2.10** Loomis Dean/Time Life Pictures/ Getty Images **2.13** AFP/CORBIS **2.14** Larry Lee Photography/CORBIS **2.15a** Konrad Wothe/Minden Pictures **2.15b** Bill Hatcher/National Geographic Image Collection **2.15c** Bruce Forster/The Image Bank **2.15d** CORBIS **2.15e** Charles O'Rear/CORBIS **2.15f, g** Frans Lanting/ Minden Pictures **2.16** Kristin Piljay

**Chapter 3 Opening Photo** CORBIS **Case Study** Denis Poroy/ Associated Press **3.1** Lori Saldana **3.3** Annie Griffiths Belt/CORBIS **3.6** Rick Wilking/Reuters/Corbis **3.7a** Bettmann/CORBIS **3.7b** Museum of History & Industry/CORBIS **3.7c** University of Washington Libraries **3.8** Erich Hartmann/Magnum Photos, Inc. **3.9** Bettmann/CORBIS **3.10a** CWH, Associated Press **3.10b** Binod Joshi/Associated Press **3.11** Bettmann/CORBIS **3.13** Don Boroughs/The Image Works **3.14** Charles Mauzy/CORBIS **3.15** Martin Rugner/age fotostock **3.18** Lori Saldana **3.19** Jon Hrusa/AP Photo **3.20** Alex Wong/Getty Images **The Science behind the Story: Spotting Sewage via Satellite** NASA **The Science behind the Story: Assessing the Environmental Impact of Treating Transboundary Sewage** Metropolitan Wastewater Department

**Chapter 4 Opening Photo** AFP/CORBIS **Case Study** Exxon Corporation **4.1** AP Photo/Jack Smith **4.5** Digital Vision/Picture Quest **4.6a** Digital Vision/Picture Quest **4.13** Dorling Kindersley **4.16 left** Daniel Zheng/CORBIS **4.16 right** Anne-Marie Weber/Taxi **4.20** Jack Dykinga/ Stone **4.21a** Ken MacDonald/SPL/Photo Researchers, Inc. **4.21b** Woods Hole Oceanographic Institute **4.22** Chip Clark **4.23** Dorling Kindersley **The Science behind the Story: Student Chemist** Mark Burrell

**Chapter 5 Opening Photo** Michael and Patricia Fogden/CORBIS **Case Study** Michael and Patricia Fogden/CORBIS **5.1a** Nicholas Athanas/Tropical Birding **5.1b** Michael Fogden/DRK Photo **5.1c** Michael &Patricia Fogden/CORBIS **5.1d** Michael Fogden/Photolibrary **5.3** Bishop Museum, Honolulu **5.7** The National History Museum, London, painting by J. Sibbick **5.8** Chip Clark **5.9** Lynda Richardson/ CORBIS **5.11a** Wisconsin Historical Society **5.11b** G. I. Bernard/ PhotoResearchers, Inc **5.12a** Keenan Ward/CORBIS **5.12b** Art Wolfe/ The Image Bank **5.12c** PhotoDisc Green **5.18a** Mike Danzenbaker **5.18b** A. Witte/C. Mahaney/Getty Images **5.18c** John Waters/Nature Picture Library **5.19** Matthias Clamer/Stone **The Science behind the Story: Mass Extinction** Benjamin Cummings

**Chapter 6 Opening Photo** Robert Estall/Robert Harding World Imagery **Case Study** Wolfgang Polzer **6.1a** Peter Yates/Photo Researchers, Inc **6.1b** B. Runk/S. Schoenberger/Grant Heillman Photography **6.4** Michael

& Patricia Fogden/CORBIS **6.6a** Peter Johnson/CORBIS **6.6b** Tom Brakefield/CORBIS **6.6c** Michael & Patricia Fogden/CORBIS **6.7** Tom Stack **6.8** Joke Stuurman–Huitema/Foto Nat/Minden Pictures **6.9** Michael & Patricia Fogden/CORBIS **6.18a** Pat O'Hara/CORBIS **6.19a** Philip Gould/CORBIS **6.20a** Charles Mauzy/CORBIS **6.21a** David Samuel Robbins/CORBIS **6.22a** O. Alamany & E. Vicens/CORBIS **6.23a** Wolfgang Kaehler/CORBIS **6.24a** Joe McDonald/CORBIS **6.25a** Darrell Gulin/CORBIS **6.26a** Liz Hymans/CORBIS **6.27a** Charles Mauzy/CORBIS

**Chapter 7 Opening Photo** Yann Arthus-Bertrand/CORBIS **Case Study** Owen Franken/CORBIS **7.7** D. W. Schindler **7.8** NASA **7.12 left** Milos Kalab/CMSP **7.12 right** Milos Kalab/CMSP **The Science behind the Story: Biosphere 2** James Marshall/CORBIS

**Chapter 8 Opening Photo** Robert Semenvik/CORBIS **Case Study** Louise Gibb/The Image Works **8.1** Reuters New Media Inc./CORBIS **8.10c** SETBOUN/CORBIS **8.12** David Turnley/CORBIS **8.19** Tiziana and Gianni Baldizzone/CORBIS **8.21a** Elie Bernager/Stone **8.21b** Ed Kashi/IPN/AURORA **8.23** Getty Images **The Science behind the Story: Causes of Fertility Decline in Bangladesh** Mark Edwards/Peter Arnold, Inc. **The Science behind the Story: AIDS Resistance Genes and the Black Death: An Unexpected Connection?** Jean-Loup Charmet/Photo Researchers, Inc

**Chapter 9 Opening Photo** Stephanie Maze/CORBIS **Case Study** Joanna B. Pinneo/AURORA **9.8** Dorling Kindersley **9.10.** Ron Giling/Peter Arnold, Inc **9.11a** Barry Runk/Stan/Grant Heilman Photography **9.11b** Grant Heilman/Grant Heilman Photography **9.11c, d** U.S. Department of Agriculture **9.13** Library of Congress **9.14** Ted Spiegel/CORBIS **9.15a** Sylvan Wittwer/Visuals Unlimited **9.15b** Kevin Horan/Stone **9.15c** Ron Giling/Peter Arnold **9.15d** Keren Su/Stone **9.15e** Yann Arthus-Bertrand/CORBIS **9.15f** U.S. Department of Agriculture **9.16** Michael Yamashita/IPN/Aurora **9.17a** Photo Disc Blue **9.17b** Carol Cohen/CORBIS **9.18** Richard Hamilton Smith/ CORBIS **9.22** W. Perry Conway/CORBIS **9.23** Natalie Fobes/CORBIS **The Science behind the Story: Overgrazing and Fire Suppression** Malpai Borderlands Group

**Chapter 10 Opening Photo** Steve Satushek/Image Bank **Case Study** Macduff Everton/CORBIS **10.3** Alexandra Avakian/CORBIS **10.4** Art Rickerby/Time Life Pictures/Getty Images **10.6a** Jack Dykinga/ Image Bank **10.6b** Barry Runk/Stan/Grant Heilman Photography **10.8a** Department of Natural Resources, Queensland, Australia **10.8b** Department of Natural Resources, Queensland, Australia **10.10** Photo Disc **10.11** Bob Rowan, Progressive Image/CORBIS **10.15** John Schmeiser **10.16** ALEXANDER JOE/AFP/Getty Images **10.17a** Native Seeds/SEARCH **10.17b** Hal Fritts, Native Seeds/ SEARCH **10.19** Arthur C. Smith III/Grant Heilman Photography **10.23** Aqua Bounty Farms/AP **10.24** AP Wide World Photos **10.25** Martin Bourque **The Science behind the Story: Native Maize** Peg Skorpinski

**Chapter 11 Opening Photo** Maurice Hornocker **Case Study** Maurice Hornocker **11.12** Kathy Ferguson-Johnson/Photo Edit **11.15** Konrad Wothe/Photolibrary **11.19** Natalie Fobes/CORBIS **11.20** Tom & Pat Leeson/Photo Researchers, Inc. **The Science behind the Story: Amphibian Diversity** S. D. Biju **The Science behind the Story: Island Biogeography** Stock Connection, Inc./Alamy

# Selected Sources and References for Further Reading

## Chapter 1

Bahn, Paul, and John Flenley. 1992. *Easter Island, Earth island*. Thames and Hudson, London.

Bowler, Peter J. 1993. *The Norton history of the environmental sciences*. W. W. Norton, New York.

Diamond, Jared. 2005. *Collapse: How societies choose to fail or succeed*. Viking, New York.

Ehrlich, Paul. 1968. *The population bomb*. 1997 reprint, Buccaneer Books, Cutchogue, New York.

Esty, Daniel C., et al., 2005. *2005 Environmental sustainability index: Benchmarking national environmental stewardship*. New Haven, Connecticut: Yale Center for Environmental Law and Policy.

Flenley, John, and Paul Bahn. 2003. *The enigmas of Easter Island*. Oxford University Press, New York.

Goudie, Andrew. 2000. *The human impact on the natural environment*, 5th ed. MIT Press, Cambridge, Massachusetts.

Hardin, Garrett. 1968. The tragedy of the commons. *Science* 162: 1243–1248.

Katzner, Donald W. 2001. *Unmeasured information and the methodology of social scientific inquiry*. Kluwer, Boston.

Kuhn, Thomas S. 1962. *The structure of scientific revolutions*, 2nd ed., 1970. University of Chicago Press, Chicago.

Lomborg, Bjorn. 2001. *The skeptical environmentalist: Measuring the real state of the world*. Cambridge University Press, Cambridge.

Malthus, Thomas R. *An essay on the principle of population*. 1983 ed. Penguin USA, New York.

Millennium Ecosystem Assessment. 2005. *Ecosystems and human well-being: General synthesis*. Millennium Ecosystem Assessment and World Resources Institute.

Musser, George. 2005. The climax of humanity. *Scientific American* (Sept. 2005): pp. 44-47.

Ponting, Clive. 1991. *A green history of the world: The environment and the collapse of great civilizations*. Penguin Books, New York.

Popper, Karl R. 1959. *The logic of scientific discovery*. Hutchinson, London.

Porteous, Andrew. 2000. *Dictionary of environmental science and technology*, 3rd ed. John Wiley & Sons, Hoboken, New Jersey.

Redman, Charles R. 1999. *Human impact on ancient environments*. University of Arizona Press, Tucson.

Sagan, Carl. 1997. *The demon-haunted world: Science as a candle in the dark*. Ballantine Books, New York.

Schneiderman, Jill S., ed. 2003. *The Earth around us: Maintaining a livable planet*. Perseus Books, New York.

Siever, Raymond. 1968. Science: Observational, experimental, historical. *American Scientist* 56: 70–77.

Valiela, Ivan. 2001. *Doing science: Design, analysis, and communication of scientific research*. Oxford University Press, Oxford.

Van Tilburg, Jo Anne. 1994. *Easter Island: Archaeology, ecology, and culture*. Smithsonian Institution Press, Washington, D.C.

Venetoulis, Jason, et al., 2004. *Ecological footprint of nations 2004*. Redefining Progress, Oakland, California.

Wackernagel, Mathis, and William Rees. 1996. *Our ecological footprint: Reducing human impact on the earth*. New Society Publishers, Philadelphia.

World Bank. 2005. *World development indicators 2005*. World Bank, Washington, D.C.

Worldwatch Institute. *State of the world 2005: Redefining global security*. Worldwatch Institute and W. W. Norton, Washington, D.C. and New York.

Worldwatch Institute. *Vital Signs 2005*. Worldwatch Institute and W. W. Norton, Washington, D.C. and New York.

## Chapter 2

Balmford, Andrew, et al. 2002. Economic reasons for conserving wild nature. *Science* 297: 950–953.

Barbour, Ian G. 1992. *Ethics in an age of technology*. Harper Collins, San Francisco.

Brown, Lester. 2001. *Eco-economy: Building an economy for the Earth*. Earth Policy Institute and W. W. Norton, New York.

Carson, Richard T., Leanne Wilks, and David Imber. 1994. Valuing the preservation of Australia's Kakadu Conservation Zone. *Oxford Economic Papers* 46: 727–749.

Cole, Luke W., and Sheila R. Foster. 2001. *From the ground up: Environmental racism and the rise of the environmental justice movement*. New York University Press, New York.

Costanza, Robert, et al. 1997. The value of the world's ecosystem services and natural capital. *Nature* 387: 253–260.

Costanza, Robert, et al. 1997. *An introduction to ecological economics*. St. Lucie Press, Boca Raton, Florida.

Daily, Gretchen. 1997. *Nature's services: Societal dependence on natural ecosystems*. Island Press, Washington, D.C.

Daly, Herman E. 1996. *Beyond growth*. Beacon Press, Boston.

Daly, Herman E. 2005. Economics in a full world. *Scientific American* (Sept. 2005): pp. 100-107.

Elliot, Robert, and Arran Gare, eds. 1983. *Environmental philosophy: A collection of readings*. Pennsylvania State University Press, University Park.

Field, Barry C., and Martha K. Field. 2001. *Environmental economics*, 3rd ed. McGraw-Hill, New York.

Fox, Stephen. 1985. *The American conservation movement: John Muir and his legacy*. University of Wisconsin Press, Madison.

Gardner, Gary, et al. 2004. The state of consumption today. Pp. 3–23 in *State of the world 2004*. Worldwatch Institute and W. W. Norton, Washington, D.C., and New York.

Gardner, Gary, and Erik Assadourian. 2004. Rethinking the good life. Pp. 164-179 in *State of the world 2004*. Worldwatch Institute and W. W. Norton, Washington, D.C., and New York.

Goodstein, Eban. 1999. *The tradeoff myth: Fact and fiction about jobs and the environment*. Island Press, Washington, D.C.

Goodstein, Eban. 2005. *Economics and the environment*, 4th ed. John Wiley & Sons, Hoboken, New Jersey.

Gundjehmi Aboriginal Corporation. Welcome to the Mirrar site. www.mirrar.net.

Hawken, Paul, Amory Lovins, and L. Hunter Lovins. 1999. *Natural capitalism*. Little, Brown, and Co., Boston.

Kolstad, Charles D. 2000. *Environmental economics*. Oxford University Press, Oxford.

Leopold, Aldo. 1949. *A Sand County almanac, and sketches here and there*. Oxford University Press, New York.

Millennium Ecosystem Assessment. 2005. *Ecosystems and human well-being: Opportunities and challenges for business and industry*. Millennium Ecosystem Assessment and World Resources Institute.

Nash, Roderick F. 1989. *The rights of nature*. University of Wisconsin Press, Madison.

Nash, Roderick F. 1990. *American environmentalism: Readings in conservation history*, 3rd ed. McGraw-Hill, New York.

O'Neill, John O., R. Kerry Turner, and Ian J. Bateman, eds. 2001. *Environmental ethics and philosophy*. Elgar, Cheltenham, U.K.

Pearson, Charles S. 2000. *Economics and the global environment*. Cambridge University Press, Cambridge.

Ricketts, Taylor, et al. 2004. Economic value of tropical forest to coffee production. *Proceedings of the National Academy of Sciences of the USA* 101: 12579–12582.

Sachs, Jeffrey. 2005. Can extreme poverty be eliminated? *Scientific American* (Sept. 2005): pp. 56–65.

Singer, Peter, ed. 1993. *A companion to ethics*. Blackwell Publishers, Oxford.

Smith, Adam. 1776. *An inquiry into the nature and causes of the wealth of nations*. 1993 ed., Oxford University Press, Oxford.

Sterba, James P., ed. 1995. *Earth ethics: Environmental ethics, animal rights, and practical applications*. Prentice Hall, Upper Saddle River, New Jersey.

Stone, Christopher D. 1972. Should trees have standing? Towards legal rights for natural objects. *Southern California Law Review* 1972: 450–501.

Tietenberg, Tom. 2003. *Environmental economics and policy*, 4th ed. Addison Wesley, Boston.

Turner, R. Kerry, David Pearce, and Ian Bateman. 1993. *Environmental economics: An elementary introduction.* Johns Hopkins University Press, Baltimore.

Venetoulis, Jason, and Cliff Cobb. 2004. *The genuine progress indicator 1950–2002 (2004 update).* Redefining Progress, Oakland, California.

Wenz, Peter S. 2001. *Environmental ethics today.* Oxford University Press, Oxford.

White, Lynn. 1967. The historic roots of our ecologic crisis. *Science* 155: 1203–1207.

**Chapter 3**

Clark, Ray, and Larry Canter. 1997. *Environmental policy and NEPA: Past, present, and future.* St. Lucie Press, Boca Raton, Florida.

Dietz, Thomas, et al. 2003. The struggle to govern the global commons. *Science* 302: 1907–1912.

Fogleman, Valerie M. 1990. *Guide to the National Environmental Policy Act.* Quorum Books, New York.

Fox, Stephen. 1985. *The American conservation movement: John Muir and his legacy.* University of Wisconsin Press, Madison.

French, Hilary. 2000. Environmental treaties gain ground. Pp. 134–135 in *Vital Signs 2000.* Worldwatch Institute and W. W. Norton, Washington D.C., and New York.

Green Scissors. *Green Scissors 2004: Cutting wasteful and environmentally harmful spending.* Friends of the Earth, Taxpayers for Common Sense, and U.S. Public Interest Research Group.

Herzog, Lawrence A. 1990. *Where north meets south: Cities, space, and politics on the U.S.–Mexico border.* Center for Mexican-American Studies, University of Texas at Austin.

Houck, Oliver, 2003. Tales from a troubled marriage: Science and law in environmental policy. *Science* 302: 1926–1928.

Kraft, Michael E. 2003. *Environmental policy and politics*, 3rd ed. Longman, New York.

Kubasek, Nancy K., and Gary S. Silverman. 2004. *Environmental law*, 5th ed. Prentice Hall, Upper Saddle River, New Jersey.

Myers, Norman, and Jennifer Kent. 2001. *Perverse subsidies: How misused tax dollars harm the environment and the economy.* Island Press, Washington, D.C.

The National Environmental Policy Act of 1969, as amended (Pub. L. 91–190, 42 U.S.C. 4321–4347, January 1, 1970, as amended by Pub. L. 94–52, July 3, 1975, Pub. L. 94–83, August 9, 1975, and Pub. L. 97–258, § 4(b), Sept. 13, 1982). http://ceq.eh.doe.gov/nepa/regs/nepa/nepaeqia.htm.

Shafritz, Jay M. 1993. *The HarperCollins dictionary of American government and politics.* HarperCollins, New York.

Southwest Center for Environmental Research and Policy, and San Diego State University. Tijuana River Watershed Atlas Project. http://geography.sdsu.edu/Research/Projects/TWRP/tjatlas.html

Steel, Brent S., Richard L. Clinton, and Nicholas P. Lovrich. 2002. *Environmental politics and policy.* McGraw-Hill, New York.

Tietenberg, Tom. 2003. *Environmental economics and policy*, 4th ed. Addison Wesley, Boston.

Turner, R. Kerry, David Pearce, and Ian Bateman. 1993. *Environmental economics: An elementary introduction.* Johns Hopkins University Press, Baltimore.

United States Congress. House. H.R. 3378. 2000. The Tijuana River Valley Estuary and Beach Sewage Cleanup Act of 2000.

Vig, Norman J., and Michael E. Kraft, eds. 2002. *Environmental policy: New directions for the twenty-first century*, 5th ed. CQ Press, Congressional Quarterly, Inc., Washington, D.C.

Wilkinson, Charles F. 1992. Crossing the next meridian: Land, water, and the future of the west. Island Press, Washington, D.C.

**Chapter 4**

Alaska Department of Environmental Conservation. 1993. *The Exxon Valdez oil spill: Final report, State of Alaska response.* June, 1993.

Allen, K. C., and D. E. G. Briggs, eds. 1989. *Evolution and the fossil record.* John Wiley & Sons, Hoboken, New Jersey.

Atlas, Ronald M. 1995. Petroleum biodegradation and oil spill bioremediation. *Marine Pollution Bulletin* 31: 178–182.

Atlas, Ronald M., and Carl E. Cerniglia. 1995. Bioremediation of petroleum pollutants. *Bioscience* 45: 332–338.

Berry, R. Stephen. 1991. *Understanding energy: Energy, entropy and thermodynamics for every man.* World Scientific Publishing Co.

Bragg, James R., et al. 1994. Effectiveness of bioremediation for the *Exxon Valdez* oil spill. *Nature* 368: 413–418.

Campbell, Neil A., and Jane B. Reece. 2005. *Biology*, 7th ed. Benjamin Cummings, San Francisco.

Fenchel, Tom. 2003. *Origin and early evolution of life.* Oxford University Press, Oxford.

Fortey, Richard. 1998. *Life: A natural history of the first four billion years of life on Earth.* Alfred Knopf, New York.

Gee, Henry. 1999. *In search of deep time: Beyond the fossil record to a new history of life.* Free Press, New York.

Hall, David O., and Krishna Rao. 1999. *Photosynthesis*, 6th ed. Cambridge University Press, Cambridge.

Lancaster, M., 2002. *Green chemistry.* Royal Society of Chemistry, London.

Manahan, Stanley E. 2004. *Environmental chemistry*, 8th ed. Lewis Publishers, CRC Press, Boca Raton, Florida.

McMurry, John E. 2003. *Organic chemistry*, 6th ed. Brooks/Cole, San Francisco.

National Response Team. *NRT fact sheet: Bioremediation in oil spill response.* U.S. EPA, www.epa.gov/oilspill/pdfs/biofact.pdf.

Nealson, Kenneth H. 2003. Harnessing microbial appetites for remediation. *Nature Biotechnology* 21: 243–244.

Ridley, Mark. 2003. *Evolution*, 3rd ed. Blackwell Science, Cambridge, Massachusetts.

United States Environmental Protection Agency. 2003. Oil program. www.epa.gov/oilspill.

Van Dover, Cindy Lee, 2000. *The ecology of deep-sea hydrothermal vents.* Princeton University Press, Princeton.

Van Ness, H.C. 1983. *Understanding thermodynamics.* Dover Publications, Mineola, New York.

Ward, Peter D., and Donald Brownlee. 2000. *Rare Earth: Why complex life is uncommon in the universe.* Copernicus, New York.

Wassenaar, Leonard I., and Keith A. Hobson. 1998. Natal origins of migratory monarch butterflies at wintering colonies in Mexico: New isotopic evidence. *Proceedings of the National Academy of the USA* 95: 15436–15439.

**Chapter 5**

Alvarez, Luis W., et al. 1980. Extraterrestrial cause for the Cretaceous-Tertiary extinction. *Science* 208: 1095–1108.

Barbour, Michael G., et al. 1998. *Terrestrial plant ecology*, 3rd ed. Benjamin/Cummings, Menlo Park, California.

Begon, Michael, Martin Mortimer, and David J. Thompson. 1996. *Population ecology: A unified study of animals and plants*, 3rd ed. Blackwell Scientific, Oxford.

Breckle, Siegmar-Walter. 1999. *Walter's vegetation of the Earth: The ecological systems of the geo-biosphere*, 4th ed. Springer-Verlag, Berlin, 1999.

Campbell, Neil A., and Jane B. Reece. 2005. *Biology*, 7th ed. Benjamin Cummings, San Francisco.

Clark K. L., et al. 1998. Cloud water and precipitation chemistry in a tropical montane forest, Monteverde, Costa Rica. *Atmospheric Environment* 32: 1595–1603.

Crump, L. Martha, et al. 1992. Apparent decline of the golden toad: Underground or extinct? *Copeia* 1992: 413–420.

Darwin, Charles. 1859. *The origin of species by means of natural selection.* John Murray, London.

Endler, John A. 1986. *Natural selection in the wild.* Monographs in Population Biology 21, Princeton University Press, Princeton.

Freeman, Scott, and Jon C. Herron. 2003. *Evolutionary analysis*, 3rd ed. Prentice Hall, Upper Saddle River, New Jersey.

Futuyma, Douglas J. 2005. *Evolution*. Sinauer Associates, Sunderland, Massachusetts.

Krebs, Charles J. 2001. *Ecology: The experimental analysis of distribution and abundance*, 5th ed. Benjamin Cummings, San Francisco.

Lawton, Robert O., et al. 2001. Climatic impact of tropical lowland deforestation on nearby montane cloud forests. *Science* 294: 584–587.

Molles, Manuel C., Jr. 2005. *Ecology: Concepts and applications*, 3rd ed. McGraw-Hill, Boston.

Nadkarni, Nalini M., and Nathaniel T. Wheelwright, eds. 2000. *Monteverde: Ecology and conservation of a tropical cloud forest*. Oxford University Press, New York.

Pounds, J. Alan. 2001. Climate and amphibian declines. *Nature* 410: 639.

Pounds, J. Alan, et al. 1997. Tests of null models for amphibian declines on a tropical mountain. *Conservation Biology* 11: 1307–1322.

Pounds, J. Alan, and Martha L. Crump. 1994. Amphibian declines and climate disturbance: The case of the golden toad and the harlequin frog. *Conservation Biology* 8: 72–85.

Pounds, J. Alan, Michael P. L. Fogden, and John H. Campbell. 1999. Biological response to climate change on a tropical mountain. *Nature* 398: 611–615.

Powell, James L. 1998. *Night comes to the Cretaceous: Dinosaur extinction and the transformation of modern geology*. W. H. Freeman, New York.

Raup, David M. 1991. *Extinction: Bad genes or bad luck?* W. W. Norton, New York.

Ricklefs, Robert E., and Gary L. Miller. 2000. *Ecology*, 4th ed. W. H. Freeman, New York.

Ricklefs, Robert E., and Dolph Schluter, eds. 1993. *Species diversity in ecological communities*. University of Chicago Press, Chicago.

Savage, Jay M. 1966. An extraordinary new toad (*Bufo*) from Costa Rica. *Revista de Biologia Tropical* 14: 153–167.

Savage, Jay M. 1998. The "brilliant toad" was telling us something. *Christian Science Monitor*, 14 September 1998: 19.

Smith, Thomas M., and Robert L. Smith. 2006. *Elements of ecology*, 6th ed. Benjamin Cummings, San Francisco.

Ward, Peter. 1994. *The end of evolution*. Bantam Books, New York.

Williams, George C. 1966. *Adaptation and natural selection*. Princeton University Press, Princeton.

Wilson, Edward O. 1992. *The diversity of life*. Harvard University Press, Cambridge, Massachusetts.

Whittaker, Robert H., and William A. Niering. 1965. Vegetation of the Santa Catalina Mountains, Arizona: A gradient analysis of the south slope. *Ecology* 46: 429–452.

## Chapter 6

Breckle, Siegmar-Walter. 2002. *Walter's vegetation of the Earth: The ecological systems of the geo-biosphere*, 4th ed. Berlin: Springer-Verlag.

Bronstein, Judith L. 1994. Our current understanding of mutualism. *Quarterly Journal of Biology* 69: 31–51.

Chase, Jonathan M., et al., 2002. The interaction between predation and competition: A review and synthesis. *Ecology Letters* 5: 302.

Connell, Joseph H., and Ralph O. Slatyer, 1977. Mechanisms of succession in natural communities. *American Naturalist* 111: 1119–1144.

Drake, John M., and Jonathan M. Bossenbroek. 2004. The potential distribution of zebra mussels in the United States. *Bioscience* 54: 931–941.

Estes, J.A., et al. 1998. Killer whale predation on sea otters linking oceanic and nearshore ecosystems. *Science* 282: 473–476.

Ewald, Paul W., 1987. Transmission modes and evolution of the parasitism-mutualism continuum. *Annals of the New York Academy of Sciences* 503: 295–306.

Gurevitch, Jessica, and Dianna K. Padilla. 2004. Are invasive species a major cause of extinctions? *Trends in Ecology and Evolution* 19: 470–474.

Krebs, Charles J. 2001. *Ecology: The experimental analysis of distribution and abundance*, 5th ed. Benjamin Cummings, San Francisco.

Menge, Bruce A., et al. 1994. The keystone species concept: Variation in interaction strength in a rocky intertidal habitat. *Ecological Monographs* 64: 249–286.

Molles, Manuel C. Jr. 2005. *Ecology: Concepts and applications*. 3rd ed. McGraw-Hill, Boston.

Morin, Peter J. 1999. *Community ecology*. Blackwell, London.

Power, Mary E., et al., 1996. Challenges in the quest for keystones. *BioScience* 46: 609–620.

Ricklefs, Robert E., and Gary L. Miller. 2000. *Ecology*, 4th ed. W. H. Freeman and Co., New York.

Shea, Katriona, and Peter Chesson, 2002. Community ecology theory as a framework for biological invasions. *Trends in Ecology and Evolutionary Biology* 17: 170–176.

Sih, Andrew, et al. 1985. Predation, competition, and prey communities: A review of field experiments. *Annual Review of Ecology and Systematics* 16: 269–311.

Smith, Robert L., and Thomas M. Smith. 2001. *Ecology and field biology*, 6th ed. Benjamin Cummings, San Francisco.

Springer, A.M., et al. 2003. Sequential megafaunal collapse in the North Pacific Ocean: An ongoing legacy of industrial whaling? *Proceedings of the National Academy of Sciences of the USA* 100: 12223–12228.

Strayer, David L., et al. 1999. Transformation of freshwater ecosystems by bivalves: A case study of zebra mussels in the Hudson River. *BioScience* 49: 19–27.

Strayer, David L., et al. 2004. Effects of an invasive bivalve (*Dreissena polymorpha*) on fish in the Hudson River estuary. *Canadian Journal of Fisheries and Aquatic Sciences* 61: 924–941.

Thompson, John N. 1999. The evolution of species interactions. *Science* 284: 2116–2118.

Weigel, Marlene, ed., 1999. *Encyclopedia of biomes*. UXL, Farmington Hills, Michigan.

Woodward, Susan L., 2003. *Biomes of Earth: Terrestrial, aquatic, and human-dominated*. Greenwood Publishing, Westport, Connecticut.

## Chapter 7

Alling, Abigail, Mark Nelson, and Sally Silverstone. 1993. *Life under glass: The inside story of Biosphere 2*. Biosphere Press.

Capra, Fritjof. 1996. *The web of life: A new scientific understanding of living systems*. Anchor Books Doubleday, New York.

Carpenter, Edward J., and Douglas G. Capone, eds. 1983. *Nitrogen in the marine environment*. Academic Press, New York.

Committee on Environment and Natural Resources, 2000. *An integrated assessment: Hypoxia in the northern Gulf of Mexico*. CENR, National Science and Technology Council, Washington, D.C.

Ferber, Dan. 2004. Dead zone fix not a dead issue. *Science* 305: 1557.

Field, Christopher B., et al., 1998. Primary production of the biosphere: Integrating terrestrial and oceanic components. *Science* 281: 237–240.

Jacobson, Michael, et al. 2000. *Earth system science from biogeochemical cycles to global changes*. Academic Press.

Keller, Edward A. 2004. *Introduction to environmental geology*, 3rd ed. Prentice Hall, Upper Saddle River, New Jersey.

Larsen, Janet. 2004. Dead zones increasing in world's coastal waters. *Eco-economy update #41*, 16 June 2004. Earth Policy Institute, www.earth-policy.org/Updates/Update41.htm.

Mississippi River/Gulf of Mexico Watershed Nutrient Task Force. 2001. *Action plan for reducing, mitigating, and controlling hypoxia in the northern Gulf of Mexico*. Washington, D.C.

Mitsch, William J., et al. 2001. Reducing nitrogen loading to the Gulf of Mexico from the Mississippi River Basin: Strategies to counter a persistent ecological problem. *BioScience* 51: 373–388.

Montgomery, Carla. 2005. *Environmental geology*, 7th ed. McGraw-Hill, New York.

National Oceanic and Atmospheric Administration: National Ocean Service. 2000. Hypoxia in the Gulf of Mexico: Progress toward the completion of an integrated assessment. www.nos.noaa.gov/products/pubs_hypox.html.

National Science and Technology Council, Committee on Environment and Natural Resources. 2003. *An assessment of coastal hypoxia and eutrophication in U.S. waters.* National Science and Technology Council, Washington, D.C.

Rabalais, Nancy N., R. E. Turner, and D. Scavia. 2002. Beyond science into policy: Gulf of Mexico hypoxia and the Mississippi River. *Bioscience* 52: 129–142.

Rabalais, Nancy N., R. E. Turner, and W.J. Wiseman, Jr. 2002. Hypoxia in the Gulf of Mexico, a.k.a. "The dead zone." *Annual Review of Ecology and Systematics* 33: 235–263.

Raloff, Janet. 2004. Dead waters: Massive oxygen-starved zones are developing along the world's coasts. *Science News* 165: 360–362. June 5, 2004.

Raloff, Janet. 2004. Limiting dead zones: How to curb river pollution and save the Gulf of Mexico. *Science News* 165: 378–380. June 12, 2004.

Ricklefs, Robert E., and Gary L. Miller. 2000. *Ecology*, 4th ed. W. H. Freeman and Co., New York.

Schlesinger, William H. 1997. *Biogeochemistry: An analysis of global change*, 2nd ed. Academic Press, London.

Skinner, Brian J., and Stephen C. Porter. 2003. *The dynamic earth: An introduction to physical geology*, 5th ed. John Wiley and Sons, Hoboken, New Jersey.

Smith, Robert L., and Thomas M. Smith. 2001. *Ecology and Field Biology*, 6th ed. Benjamin Cummings, San Francisco.

Stiling, Peter. 2002. *Ecology: Theories and applications*, 4th ed. Prentice Hall, Upper Saddle River, New Jersey.

Takahashi, Taro. 2004. The fate of industrial carbon dioxide. *Science* 305: 352–353.

Turner, R. Eugene, and Nancy N. Rabalais. 2003. Linking landscape and water quality in the Mississippi River Basin for 200 years. *BioScience* 53: 563–572.

Vitousek, Peter M., et al. 1997. Human alteration of the global nitrogen cycle: Sources and consequences. *Ecological Applications* 7: 737–750.

Whittaker, Robert H. 1975. *Communities and ecosystems*, 2nd ed. Macmillan, New York.

**Chapter 8**

Cohen, Joel E. 1995. *How many people can the Earth support?* W. W. Norton, New York.

Cohen, Joel E. 2003. Human population: The next half century. *Science* 302: 1172–1175.

Cohen, Joel E. 2005. Human population grows up. *Scientific American* (Sept. 2005): pp. 48–55.

De Souza, Roger-Mark, et. al., 2003. *Critical links: Population, health, and the environment.* Population Bulletin 58(3), 48 pp. Population Reference Bureau, Washington, D.C.

Eberstadt, Nicholas. 2000. China's population prospects: Problems ahead. *Problems of Post-Communism* 47: 28.

Ehrlich, Paul R., and John P. Holdren. Impact of population growth: Complacency concerning this component of man's predicament is unjustified and counterproductive. *Science* 171: 1212–1217.

Ehrlich, Paul R., and Anne H. Ehrlich. 1990. The population explosion. Touchstone, New York.

Engelman, Robert, Brian Halweil, and Danielle Nierenberg. 2002. Rethinking population, improving lives. Pp. 127–148 in *State of the world 2002*, Worldwatch Institute and W. W. Norton, Washington D.C., and New York.

Greenhalgh, Susan. 2001. Fresh winds in Beijing: Chinese feminists speak out on the one-child policy and women's lives. *Signs: Journal of Women in Culture & Society* 26: 847–887.

Harrison, Paul, and Fred Pearce, eds. 2000. *AAAS atlas of population & environment.* University of California Press, Berkeley.

Hesketh, Therese, and Wei Xing Zhu, 1997. Health in China: The one child family policy: The good, the bad, and the ugly. *British Medical Journal* 314: 1685.

Holdren, John P. and Ehrlich, Paul R. 1974. Human population and the global environment. *American Scientist* 62: 282–292.

Kane, Penny. 1987. *The second billion: Population and family planning in China.* Penguin Books, Australia, Ringwood, Victoria.

Kane, Penny, and Ching Y. Choi. 1999. China's one child family policy. *British Medical Journal* 319: 992.

Mastny, Lisa. 2005. HIV/AIDS crisis worsening worldwide. Pp. 68–69 in *Vital signs 2005.* Worldwatch Institute and W. W. Norton, Washington, D.C. and New York.

Mastny, Lisa, and Richard P. Cincotta. 2005. Examining the connections between population and security. Pp. 22–41 in *State of the world 2005.* Worldwatch Institute and W. W. Norton, Washington, D.C. and New York.

McDonald, Mia, with Danielle Nierenberg. 2003. Linking population, women, and biodiversity. Pp. 38–61 in *State of the world 2003*, Worldwatch Institute and W. W. Norton, Washington D.C., and New York.

Meadows, Donella, Jørgen Randers, and Dennis Meadows. 2004. *Limits to growth: The 30-year update.* Chelsea Green Publishing Co., White River Junction, Vermont.

Notestein, Frank. 1953. Economic problems of population change. Pp. 13–31 in *Proceedings of the Eighth International Conference of Agricultural Economists.* Oxford University Press, London.

O'Brien, Stephen J., and Michael Dean. 1997. In search of AIDS-resistance genes. *Scientific American* 277: 44–51.

Population Reference Bureau. 2005. *2005 World Population Data Sheet.* Population Reference Bureau, Washington, D.C., and John Wiley & Sons, Hoboken, New Jersey.

Redefining Progress. Programs: Sustainability indicators. www.rprogress.org/newprograms/sustIndi/index.shtml.

Riley, Nancy E. 2004. *China's population: New trends and challenges.* Population Bulletin 59(2), 40 pp. Population Reference Bureau, Washington, D.C.

UNAIDS and World Health Organization. 2005. *AIDS epidemic update: December 2005.* UNAIDS and WHO, New York.

United Nations Economic and Social Commission for Asia and the Pacific. 2005. *2005 ESCAP population data sheet.* UNESCAP, New York.

United Nations Environment Programme. 2003. *Africa environment outlook: Past, present, and future perspectives.* UNEP, New York.

United Nations Population Division. 2004. *World population prospects: The 2004 revision.* UNPD, New York.

United Nations Population Fund. UNFPA, the 2005 World Summit and the millennium development goals. UNFPA. www.unfpa.org/icpd.

United Nations Population Fund. *State of world population 2005.* UNFPA, New York.

United States Census Bureau. www.census.gov.

Wackernagel, Mathis, and William Rees. 1996. *Our ecological footprint: Reducing human impact on the earth.* New Society Publishers, Philadelphia.

**Chapter 9**

Ashman, Mark R., and Geeta Puri. 2002. *Essential soil science: A clear and concise introduction to soil science.* Blackwell Publishing, Malden, Massachusetts.

Brown, Lester R. 2002. World's rangelands deteriorating under mounting pressure. *Eco-Economy Update #6*, 5 February 2002. Earth Policy Institute, www.earth-policy.org/Updates/Update6.htm.

Brown, Lester R. 2004. *Outgrowing the Earth: The food security challenge in an age of falling water tables and rising temperatures.* Earth Policy Institute, Washington, D.C.

Charman, P. E. V., and Brian W. Murphy. 2000. *Soils: Their properties and management*, 2nd ed. Oxford University Press, South Melbourne, Australia.

Curtin, Charles G. 2002. Integration of science and community-based conservation in the Mexico/U.S. borderlands. *Conservation Biology* 16: 880–886.

Diamond, Jared. 1999. *Guns, germs, and steel: The fates of human societies.* W. W. Norton, New York.

Diamond, Jared, and Peter Bellwood. 2003. Farmers and their languages: The first expansions. *Science* 300: 597–603.

Food and Agriculture Organization of the United Nations. 2001. Conservation agriculture: Case studies in Latin America and Africa. *FAO Soils Bulletin No. 78.* FAO, Rome.

Glanz, James. 1995. *Saving our soil: Solutions for sustaining Earth's vital resource.* Johnson Books, Boulder, Colorado.

Goudie, Andrew. 2000. *The human impact on the natural environment,* 5th ed. MIT Press, Cambridge, Massachusetts.

Fox, Stephen. 1985. *The American conservation movement: John Muir and his legacy.* University of Wisconsin Press, Madison.

Halweil, Brian. 2002. Farmland quality deteriorating. Pp. 102–103 in *Vital signs 2002.* Worldwatch Institute and W. W. Norton, Washington D.C., and New York.

Harrison, Paul, and Fred Pearce, eds. 2000. *AAAS atlas of population & environment.* University of California Press, Berkeley.

Jenny, Hans. 1941. *Factors of soil formation: A system of quantitative pedology.* McGraw-Hill, New York.

Larsen, Janet. 2003. Deserts advancing, civilization retreating. *Eco-Economy Update #23,* 27 March 2003. Earth Policy Institute, www.earth-policy.org/Updates/Update23.htm.

Millennium Ecosystem Assessment. 2005. *Ecosystems and human well-being: Desertification synthesis.* Millennium Ecosystem Assessment and World Resources Institute.

Morgan, R. P. C. 2005. *Soil erosion and conservation,* 3rd ed. Blackwell, London.

Natural Resources Conservation Service. 2001. *National resources inventory 2001: Soil erosion.* NRCS, USDA, Washington, D.C.

Natural Resources Conservation Service. Soils. NRCS, USDA. http://soils.usda.gov.

Pieri, Christian, et al. 2002. *No-till farming for sustainable rural development.* Agriculture & Rural Development Working Paper. International Bank for Reconstruction and Development, Washington, D.C.

Pierzynski, Gary M., et al. 2005. *Soils and environmental quality,* 3rd ed. CRC Press, Boca Raton, Florida.

Pretty, Jules, and Rachel Hine. 2001. *Reducing food poverty with sustainable agriculture: A summary of new evidence.* Center for Environment and Society, University of Essex. *Occasional Paper 2001–2.*

Richter, Daniel D. Jr., and Daniel Markewitz. 2001. *Understanding soil change: Soil sustainability over millennia, centuries, and decades.* Cambridge University Press, Cambridge.

Ritchie, Jerry C. 2000. Combining cesium-137 and topographic surveys for measuring soil erosion/deposition patterns in a rapidly accreting area. TEKTRAN, USDA Division of Agricultural Research, January 14, 2000.

Shaxson, T. F. 1999. The roots of sustainability, concepts and practice: Zero tillage in Brazil. *ABLH Newsletter ENABLE; World Association for Soil and Water Conservation (WASWC) Newsletter.*

Soil Science Society of America. 2001. Internet glossary of soil science terms. www.soils.org/sssagloss.

Stocking, M. A. 2003. Tropical soils and food security: The next 50 years. *Science* 302: 1356–1359.

Trimble, Stanley W., and Pierre Crosson. 2000. U.S. soil erosion rates—myth and reality. *Science* 289: 248–250.

Troeh, Frederick R., and Louis M. Thompson. 2004. Soil and soil fertility, 6th ed. Blackwell Publishing, London.

Troeh, Frederick R., J. Arthur Hobbs, and Roy L. Donahue 2004. *Soil and water conservation for productivity and environmental protection,* 4th ed. Prentice Hall, Upper Saddle River, New Jersey.

United Nations Convention to Combat Desertification, 2001. *Global alarm: Dust and sandstorms from the world's drylands.* UNCCD and others, Bangkok, Thailand.

United Nations Environment Programme. 2002. Land. Pp. 62–89 in *Global environment outlook 3 (GEO-3).* UNEP and Earthscan Publications, Nairobi and London.

Uri, Noel D. 2001. The environmental implications of soil erosion in the United States. *Environmental Monitoring and Assessment* 66: 293–312.

Wilkinson, Bruce H. 2005. Humans as geologic agents: A deep-time perspective. *Geology* 33:161–164.

## Chapter 10

Bazzaz, Fakhri A. 2001. Plant biology in the future. *Proceedings of the National Academy of the United States of America* 98: 5441–5445.

Brown, Lester R. 2004. *Outgrowing the Earth: The food security challenge in an age of falling water tables and rising temperatures.* Earth Policy Institute, Washington, D.C.

Buchmann, Stephen L., and Gary Paul Nabhan. 1996. *The forgotten pollinators.* Island Press/Shearwater Books, Washington, D.C./Covelo, California.

Commission for Environmental Cooperation. 2004. *Maize and biodiversity: The effects of transgenic maize in Mexico.* CEC Secretariat.

[Correspondence to *Nature*, various authors]. 2002. *Nature* 416: 600–602, and 417: 897–898.

Fedoroff, Nina, and Nancy Marie Brown, 2004. *Mendel in the kitchen: A scientist's view of genetically modified foods.* National Academies Press, Washington, D.C.

Food and Agriculture Organization of the United Nations. 2004. *The state of world fisheries and aquaculture, 2004.* FAO, Rome.

Gardner, Gary, and Brian Halweil. 2000. *Underfed and overfed: The global epidemic of malnutrition.* Worldwatch Paper #150. Worldwatch Institute, Washington, D.C.

Halweil, Brian. 2004. *Eat here: Reclaiming homegrown pleasures in a global supermarket.* Worldwatch Institute, Washington, D.C.

Halweil, Brian. 2005. Aquaculture pushes fish harvest higher. Pp. 26-27 in *Vital signs 2005.* Worldwatch Institute and W. W. Norton, Washington, D.C. and New York.

Halweil, Brian. 2005. Grain harvest and hunger both grow. Pp. 22–23 in *Vital signs 2005.* Worldwatch Institute and W. W. Norton, Washington, D.C., and New York.

Halweil, Brian, and Danielle Niereberg. 2004. Watching what we eat. Pp. 68–95 in *State of the world 2004.* Worldwatch Institute and W. W. Norton, Washington, D.C., and New York.

Harrison, Paul, and Fred Pearce, eds. 2000. *AAAS atlas of population & environment.* University of California Press, Berkeley.

International Food Information Council. 2004. Food biotechnology. IFIC, Washington, D.C. www.ific.org/food/biotechnology/index.cfm.

James, Clive. 2004. *Global status of GM crops, their contribution to sustainability, and future prospects.* International Service for the Acquisition of Agri-biotech Applications.

Kuiper, Harry A. 2000. Risks of the release of transgenic herbicide-resistant plants with respect to humans, animals, and the environment. *Crop Protection* 19: 773.

Liebig, Mark A., and John W. Doran. 1999. Impact of organic production practices on soil quality indicators. *Journal of Environmental Quality* 28: 1601–1609.

Losey, John E., Raynor, Linda S., and Carter, Maureen E. 1999. Transgenic pollen harms monarch larvae. *Nature* 399: 214.

Maeder, Paul, et al. 2002. Soil fertility and biodiversity in organic farming. *Science* 296: 1694–1697.

Mann, Charles C. 2002. Transgene data deemed unconvincing. *Science* 296: 236–237.

Manning, Richard. 2000. *Food's frontier: The next green revolution.* North Point Press, New York.

Miller, Henry I., and Gregory Conko. 2004. *The frankenfood myth: How protest and politics threaten the biotech revolution.* Praeger Publishers, Westport, Connecticut.

Nierenberg, Danielle. 2005. *Happier meals: Rethinking the global meat industry.* Worldwatch Paper #171. Worldwatch Institute, Washington, D.C.

Nierenberg, Danielle. 2005. Meat production and consumption rise. Pp. 24–25 in *Vital signs 2005.* Worldwatch Institute and W. W. Norton, Washington, D.C., and New York.

Nierenberg, Danielle, and Brian Halweil. 2005. Cultivating food security. Pp. 62–79 in *State of the world 2005*. Worldwatch Institute and W. W. Norton, Washington, D.C., and New York.

Nestle, Marion. 2002. *Food politics: How the food industry influences nutrition and health*. University of California–Berkeley Press, Berkeley.

Norris, Robert F., Edward P. Caswell-Chen, and Marcos Kogan. 2002. *Concepts in integrated pest management*. Prentice Hall, Upper Saddle River, New Jersey.

Paoletti, Maurizio G., and David Pimentel. 1996. Genetic engineering in agriculture and the environment: Assessing risks and benefits. *BioScience* 46: 665–673.

Pearce, Fred. 2002. The great Mexican maize scandal. *New Scientist* 174: 14 (15 June 2002).

Pedigo, Larry P., and Marlin E. Rice, 2006. *Entomology and pest management*, 5th ed. Prentice Hall, Upper Saddle River, New Jersey.

Pimentel, David. 1999. Population growth, environmental resources, and the global availability of food. *Social Research,* Spring 1999.

Pinstrup-Andersen, Per, and Ebbe Schioler, 2001. *Seeds of contention: World hunger and the global controversy over GM (genetically modified) crops*. International Food Policy Research Institute, Washington, D.C.

Polak, Paul. 2005. The big potential of small farms. *Scientific American* 293(3): 84–91.

Pringle, Peter. 2003. *Food, Inc.: Mendel to Monsanto—The promises and perils of the biotech harvest*. Simon and Schuster, New York.

Quist, David, and Ignacio H. Chapela. 2001. Transgenic DNA introgressed into traditional maize landraces in Oaxaca, Mexico. *Nature* 414: 541–543.

Ruse, Michael, and David Castle, eds. 2002. *Genetically modified foods: Debating technology*. Prometheus Books, Amherst, New York.

Schmeiser, Percy. Monsanto vs. Schmeiser. www. percyschmeiser.com/

Shiva, Vandana. 2000. *Stolen harvest: The hijacking of the global food supply*. South End Press, Cambridge, Massachusetts.

Smil, Vaclav. 2001. *Feeding the world: A challenge for the twenty-first century*. MIT Press, Cambridge, Massachusetts.

Stewart, C. Neal. 2004. *Genetically modified planet: Environmental impacts of genetically engineered plants*. Oxford University Press, Oxford.

Teitel, Martin, and Kimberly Wilson. 2001. *Genetically engineered food: Changing the nature of nature*. Park Street Press.

The Farm Scale Evaluations of spring-sown genetically modified crops. 2003. A themed issue from *Philosophical Transactions of the Royal Society of London B: Biological Sciences* 358(1439), 29 November 2003.

Tuxill, John. 1999. Appreciating the benefits of plant biodiversity. Pp. 96–114 in *State of the world 1999,* Worldwatch Institute and W. W. Norton, Washington D.C., and New York.

Westra, Lauren. 1998. Biotechnology and transgenics in agriculture and aquaculture: The perspective from ecosystem integrity. *Environmental Values* 7: 79.

Wolfenbarger, L. LaReesa 2000. The ecological risks and benefits of genetically engineered plants. *Science* 290: 2088.

**Chapter 11**

Balmford, Andrew, et al. 2002. Economic reasons for conserving wild nature. *Science* 297: 950–953.

Barnosky, Anthony D., et al. 2004. Assessing the causes of late Pleistocene extinctions on the continents. *Science* 306: 70–75.

Baskin, Yvonne. 1997. *The work of nature: How the diversity of life sustains us*. Island Press, Washington, D.C.

Bright, Chris. 1998. *Life out of bounds: Bioinvasion in a borderless world*. Worldwatch Institute and W. W. Norton, Washington D.C., and New York.

CITES Secretariat. "Convention on International Trade in Endangered Species of Wild Fauna and Flora. www. cites.org/

Convention on Biological Diversity. www.biodiv.org/

Daily, Gretchen C., ed. 1997. *Nature's services: Societal dependence on natural ecosystems*. Island Press, Washington, D.C.

Ehrenfeld, David W. 1970. *Biological conservation*. International Thomson Publishing, London.

Gaston, Kevin J., and John I. Spicer. 2004. *Biodiversity: An introduction,* 2nd ed. Blackwell, London.

Groom, Martha J., et al. 2005. *Principles of conservation biology,* 3rd ed. Sinauer Associates, Sunderland, Massachusetts.

Groombridge, Brian, and Martin D. Jenkins. 2002. *Global biodiversity: Earth's living resources in the 21st century*. UNEP, World Conservation Monitoring Centre, and Aventis Foundation; World Conservation Press, Cambridge, U.K.

Groombridge, Brian, and Martin D. Jenkins. 2002. *World atlas of biodiversity: Earth's living resources in the 21st century*. University of California Press, Berkeley.

Hanken, James. 1999. Why are there so many new amphibian species when amphibians are declining? *Trends in Ecology and Evolution* 14: 7–8.

Harris, Larry D. 1984. *The fragmented forest: Island biogeography theory and the preservation of biotic diversity*. University of Chicago Press, Chicago.

Harrison, Paul, and Fred Pearce, eds. 2000. *AAAS atlas of population & environment*. University of California Press, Berkeley.

Jenkins, Martin, 2003. Prospects for biodiversity. *Science* 302: 1175–1177.

Louv, Richard. 2005. *Last child in the woods: Saving our children from nature-deficit disorder*. Algonquin Books, Chapel Hill, North Carolina.

MacArthur, Robert H., and Edward O. Wilson. 1967. *The theory of island biogeography*. Princeton University Press, Princeton.

Mackay, Richard. 2002. *The Penguin atlas of endangered species: A worldwide guide to plants and animals*. Penguin, New York.

Maehr, David S., Reed F. Noss, and Jeffrey Larkin, eds. 2001. *Large mammal restoration: Ecological and sociological challenges in the 21st century*. Island Press, Washington, D.C.

Matthiessen, Peter. 2000. *Tigers in the snow*. North Point Press, New York.

Meegaskumbura, Madhava, et al. 2002. Sri Lanka: An amphibian hot spot. *Science* 298: 379.

Millennium Ecosystem Assessment. 2005. *Ecosystems and human well-being: Biodiversity synthesis*. Millennium Ecosystem Assessment and World Resources Institute.

Miquelle, Dale, Howard Quigley, and Maurice Hornocker. 1999. A habitat protection plan for Amur Tiger conservation: A proposal outlining habitat protection measures for the Amur Tiger. Hornocker Wildlife Institute.

Mooney, Harold A. and Richard J. Hobbs, eds. 2000. *Invasive species in a changing world*. Island Press, Washington, D.C.

Newmark, William D. 1987. A land-bridge perspective on mammal extinctions in western North American parks. *Nature* 325: 430.

Pimm, Stuart L., and Clinton Jenkins. 2005. Sustaining the variety of life. *Scientific American* 293(3): 66–73.

Primack, Richard B. 2004. *Essentials of conservation biology,* 3rd ed. Sinauer Associates, Sunderland, Massachusetts.

Quammen, David. 1996. *The song of the dodo: Island biogeography in an age of extinction*. Touchstone, New York.

Relyea, Rick, and Nathan Mills. 2001. Predator-induced stress makes the pesticide carbaryl more deadly to gray treefrog tadpoles. *Proceedings of the National Academy of Sciences, USA* 98: 2491–2496.

Rosenzweig, Michael L. 1995. *Species diversity in space and time*. Cambridge University Press, Cambridge.

Simberloff, Daniel S. 1969. Experimental zoogeography of islands: A model for insular colonization. *Ecology* 50: 296–314.

Simberloff, Daniel. 1998. Flagships, umbrellas, and keystones: Is single-species management passé in the landscape era? *Biological Conservation* 83: 247–257.

Simberloff, Daniel S., and Edward O. Wilson. 1969. Experimental zoogeography of islands: The colonization of empty islands. *Ecology* 50: 278–296.

Simberloff, Daniel S., and Edward O. Wilson. 1970. Experimental zoogeography of islands: A two-year record of colonization. *Ecology* 51: 934–937.

Soulé, Michael E. 1986. *Conservation biology: The science of scarcity and diversity*. Sinauer Associates, Sunderland, Massachusetts.

Takacs, David. 1996. *The idea of biodiversity: Philosophies of paradise.* Johns Hopkins University Press, Baltimore.

United Nations Environment Programme. 2002. Biodiversity. Pp. 120–149 in *Global environment outlook 3 (GEO-3).* UNEP and Earthscan Publications, Nairobi and London.

United Nations Environment Programme. 2003. Sustaining life on Earth: How the Convention on Biological Diversity promotes nature and human well-being. www.biodiv. org/doc/publications/guide.asp.

United States Fish and Wildlife Service. The endangered species act of 1973. Accessible online at http://endangered.fws.gov/esa.html.

Wilson, Edward O. 1984. *Biophilia.* Harvard University Press, Cambridge, Massachusetts.

Wilson, Edward O. 1992. *The diversity of life.* Harvard University Press, Cambridge, Massachusetts.

Wilson, Edward O. 1994. *Naturalist.* Island Press, Shearwater Books, Washington, D.C.

Wilson, Edward O. 2002. *The future of life.* Alfred A. Knopf, New York.

Wilson, Edward O., and Daniel S. Simberloff. 1969. Experimental zoogeography of islands: Defaunation and monitoring techniques. *Ecology* 50: 267–278.

World Conservation Union. 2005. IUCN Red List. www.iucnredlist.org/

## Chapter 12

British Columbia Ministry of Forests. Introduction to Silvicultural Systems. www.for.gov.bc.ca/hfd/pubs/SSIntroworkbook/index.htm. British Columbia Ministry of Forests, Victoria, B.C.

Canadian Broadcasting Corporation. 1993. A little place called Clayoquot Sound. CBC broadcast, 13 April 1993. http://archives.cbc.ca/IDC-1-75-679-3918/Science_technology/clearcutting/clip6.

Clary, David. 1986. *Timber and the Forest Service.* University Press of Kansas, Lawrence.

Food and Agriculture Organization of the United Nations. 2005. *Global forest resources assessment.* FAO Forestry, Rome.

Foster, Bryan C., and Peggy Foster. 2002. *Wild logging: A guide to environmentally and economically sustainable forestry.* Mountain Press, Missoula, Montana.

Gardner, Gary. 2005. Forest loss continues. Pp. 92–93 in *Vital signs 2005.* Worldwatch Institute and W. W. Norton, Washington, D.C., and New York.

Harrison, Paul, and Fred Pearce, eds. 2000. *AAAS atlas of population & environment.* University of California Press, Berkeley.

Haynes, Richard W. and Gloria E. Perez, tech. eds. 2001. Northwest Forest Plan research synthesis. *Gen. Tech. Rep. PNW-GTR-498.* USDA Forest Service, Pacific Northwest Research Station, Portland, Oregon.

Jacobs, Lynn. 1991. *Waste of the West: Public lands ranching.* Lynn, Jacobs, Tucson, Arizona.

Landres, Peter, David R. Spildie, and Lloyd P. Queen. 2001. GIS applications to wilderness management: Potential uses and limitations. *Gen. Tech. Rep. RMRS-GTR-80.* USDA Forest Service, Rocky Mountain Research Station, Fort Collins, Colorado.

Myers, Norman, and Jennifer Kent. 2001. *Perverse subsidies: How misused tax dollars harm the environment and the economy.* Island Press, Washington, D.C.

National Forest Management Act of 1976. October 22, 1976 (P.O. 94–588, 90 Stat. 2949, as amended; 16 U.S.C.)

National Round Table on the Environment and the Economy, Environment Canada. Clayoquot Sound Biosphere Reserve. www.nrtee-trnee.ca/eng/programs/Current_Programs/Nature/Case-Studies/Clayoquot-Case-Study-Complete_e.htm.

Natural Resources Canada. 2005. *The state of Canada's forests, 2004-2005.* Natural Resources Canada, Ottawa.

Runte, Alfred. 1979. *National parks and the American experience.* University of Nebraska Press, Lincoln.

Sedjo, Robert A. 2000. *A vision for the US Forest Service.* Resources for the Future, Washington, D.C.

Singh, Ashbindu, et al. 2001. An assessment of the status of the world's remaining closed forests. United Nations Environmental Program, UNEP/DEWA/TR 01–2l, August 2001.

Smith, David M., et al. 1996. *The practice of silviculture: Applied forest ecology,* 9th ed. Wiley, New York.

Smith, W. Brad, et al. 2004. Forest resources of the United States, 2002. *Gen. Tech. Rep.* NC-241, North Central Research Station, USDA Forest Service, St. Paul, Minnesota.

Soulé, Michael E., and John Terborgh, eds. 1999. *Continental conservation.* Island Press, Washington, D.C.

Stegner, Wallace. 1954. *Beyond the hundredth meridian: John Wesley Powell and the second opening of the West.* Houghton Mifflin, Boston.

United Nations Environment Programme. 2002. Forests. Pp. 90–119 in *Global environment outlook 3 (GEO-3).* UNEP and Earthscan Publications, Nairobi and London.

USDA Forest Service. 2001. *U.S. forest facts and historical trends.* FS-696, March 2001.

U.S. National Park Service. 2002. *National Park Service statistical abstract 2002.* NPS Public Use Statistics Office, U.S. Department of the Interior, Denver, Colorado.

## Chapter 13

Abbott, Carl. 2001. *Greater Portland: Urban life and landscape in the Pacific Northwest.* University of Pennsylvania Press.

Abbott, Carl. 2002. Planning a sustainable city. Pp. 207–235 in Squires, Gregory D., ed. *Urban sprawl: Causes, consequences, and policy responses.* Urban Institute Press, Washington, D.C.

Beck, Roy, et. al., 2003. *Outsmarting smart growth: Population growth, immigration, and the problem of sprawl.* Center for Immigration Studies, Washington, D.C.

Breuste, Jurgen, et al. 1998. *Urban ecology.* Springer-Verlag.

Cronon, William. 1991. *Nature's metropolis: Chicago and the great West.* W. W. Norton, New York.

Duany, Andres, et al. 2001. *Suburban nation: The rise of sprawl and the decline of the American dream.* North Point Press, New York.

Ewing, Reid, et al. 2002. *Measuring sprawl and its impact.* Smart Growth America.

Ewing, Reid, et al. 2003. Measuring sprawl and its transportation impacts. *Transportation Research Record* 1831: 175–183.

Girardet, Herbert. 2004. *Cities people planet: Livable cities for a sustainable world.* Academy Press.

Hall, Kenneth B. and Gerald A. Porterfield. 2001. *Community by design: New urbanism for suburbs and small communities.* McGraw-Hill, New York.

Horizon International. 2003. Efficient transportation for successful urban planning in Curitiba. www.solutions-site.org/artman/publish/printer_62.shtml.

Jacobs, Jane. 1992. *The death and life of great American cities.* Vintage.

Kalnay, Eugenia, and Ming Cai. 2003. Impact of urbanization and land-use change on climate. *Nature* 423: 528–531.

Kirdar, Uner, ed. 1997. *Cities fit for people.* United Nations, New York.

Litman, Todd. 2004. *Rail transit in America: A comprehensive evaluation of benefits.* Victoria Transport Policy Institute and American Public Transportation Association.

Logan, Michael F. 1995. *Fighting sprawl and city hall.* University of Arizona Press, Tucson.

Metro. www.metro-region.org.

New Urbanism. www.newurbanism.org.

Northwest Environment Watch. 2004. *The Portland exception: A comparison of sprawl, smart growth, and rural land loss in 15 U.S. cities.* Northwest Environment Watch, Seattle.

Portney, Kent. E. 2003. *Taking sustainable cities seriously: Economic development, the environment, and quality of life in American cities (American and comparative environmental policy).* MIT Press, Cambridge, Massachusetts.

Pugh, Cedric, ed. 1996. *Sustainability, the environment, and urbanization.* Earthscan Publications, London.

Sheehan, Molly O'Meara. 2001. *City limits: Putting the brakes on sprawl.* Worldwatch Paper #156. Worldwatch Institute, Washington, D.C.

Sheehan, Molly O'Meara. 2002. What will it take to halt sprawl? *World-Watch* (Jan/Feb 2002): 12–23.

Sprawl City. www.sprawlcity.org.

Stren, R., et al. 1992. *Sustainable cities: Urbanization and the environment in international perspective.* Westview Press, Boulder, Colorado, and San Francisco.

United Nations Environment Programme. 2002. Urban areas. Pp. 240–269 in *Global environment outlook 3 (GEO-3).* UNEP and Earthscan Publications, Nairobi and London.

United States Census Bureau. www.census.gov/

United States Environmental Protection Agency. Smart growth. www.epa.gov/smartgrowth.

Wiewel, Wim, and Jospeh J. Persky., eds. 2002. *Suburban sprawl: Private decisions and public policy.* M. E. Sharpe, Armond, New York.

**Chapter 14**

Ames, Bruce N., Margie Profet, and Lois Swirsky Gold. 1990. Nature's chemicals and synthetic chemicals: Comparative toxicology. *Proceedings of the National Academy of the USA* 87: 7782–7786.

Bloom, Barry. 2005. Public health in transition. *Scientific American* 293(3): 92–99.

Cagen, S. Z., et al. 1999. Normal reproductive organ development in wistar rats exposed to bisphenol A in the drinking water. *Regulatory Toxicology and Pharmacology* 30: 130–139.

Carlsen, Elisabeth, et al. 1992. Evidence for decreasing quality of semen during past 50 years. *British Medical Journal* 305: 609–613.

Carson, Rachel. 1962. *Silent spring.* Houghton Mifflin, Boston.

Colburn, Theo, Dianne Dumanoski, and John P. Myers. 1996. *Our stolen future.* Penguin USA, New York.

Crain, D. Andrew, and Louis J. Guillette Jr. 1998. Reptiles as models of contaminant-induced endocrine disruption. *Animal Reproduction Science* 53: 77–86.

Guillette, Elizabeth A., et al. 1998. An anthropological approach to the evaluation of preschool children exposed to pesticides in Mexico. *Environmental Health Perspectives* 106: 347–353.

Guillette, Louis J. Jr., et al. 1999. Plasma steroid concentrations and male phallus size in juvenile alligators from seven Florida lakes. *General and Comparative Endocrinology* 116: 356–372.

Guillette, Louis J. Jr., et al. 2000. Alligators and endocrine disrupting contaminants: A current perspective. *American Zoologist* 40: 438–452.

Halweil, Brian. 1999. Sperm counts dropping. Pp. 148–149 in *Vital signs 1999.* Worldwatch Institute and W. W. Norton, Washington, D.C. and New York.

Hayes, Tyrone, et al. 2003. Atrazine-induced hermaphroditism at 0.1 PPB in American leopard frogs (*Rana pipiens*): Laboratory and field evidence. *Environmental Health Perspectives* 111: 568–575.

Hunt, Patricia A., et al. 2003. Bisphenol A exposure causes meiotic aneuploidy in the female mouse. *Current Biology* 13: 546–553.

Kolpin, Dana W., et al. 2002. Pharmaceuticals, hormones, and other organic wastewater contaminants in U.S. streams, 1999–2000: A national reconnaissance. *Environmental Science and Technology* 36: 1202–1211.

Landis, Wayne G., and Ming-Ho Yu. 2004. *Introduction to environmental toxicology,* 3rd ed. Lewis Press, Boca Raton, Florida.

Loewenberg, Samuel. 2003. E.U. starts a chemical reaction. *Science* 300: 405.

Millennium Ecosystem Assessment. 2005. *Ecosystems and human well-being: Health synthesis.* World Health Organization.

Manahan, Stanley E. 2000. *Environmental chemistry,* 7th ed. Lewis Publishers, CRC Press, Boca Raton, Florida.

McGinn, Anne Platt. 2000. *Why poison ourselves? A precautionary approach to synthetic chemicals* Worldwatch Paper #153. Worldwatch Institute, Washington, D.C.

McGinn, Anne Platt. 2002. Reducing our toxic burden. Pp. 75–100 in *State of the world 2002,* Worldwatch Institute and W. W. Norton, Washington, D.C. and New York.

McGinn, Anne Platt. 2003. Combating malaria. Pp. 62–84 in *State of the world 2003,* Worldwatch Institute and W. W. Norton, Washington, D.C. and New York.

Moeller, Dade. 2004. *Environmental health,* 3rd ed. Harvard University Press, 2004.

Nagel, S.C., et al. 1997. Relative binding affinity-serum modified access (RBA-SMA) assay predicts in vivo bioactivity of the xenoestrogens bisphenol A and octylphenol. *Environmental Health Perspectives* 105: 70–76.

National Center for Health Statistics, 2004. *Health, United States, 2004, with chartbook on trends in the health of Americans.* Hyattsville, Maryland.

National Center for Environmental Health; U.S. Centers for Disease Control and Prevention. 2005. *Third national report on human exposure to environmental chemicals.* NCEH Pub. No. 05-0570, Atlanta.

Pirages, Dennis. 2005. Containing infectious disease. Pp. 42–61 in *State of the world 2005.* Worldwatch Institute and W. W. Norton, Washington, D.C., and New York.

Renner, Rebecca. 2002. Conflict brewing over herbicide's link to frog deformities. *Science* 298: 938–939.

Rodricks, Joseph V. 1994. *Calculated risks: Understanding the toxicity of chemicals in our environment.* Cambridge University Press, Cambridge.

Salem, Harry, and Eugene Olajos. 1999. *Toxicology in risk assessment.* CRC Press, Boca Raton, Florida.

Spiteri, I. Daniel, Louis J. Guillette Jr., and D. Andrew Crain. 1999. The functional and structural observations of the neonatal reproductive system of alligators exposed *in ozo* to atrazine, 2,4-D, or estradiol. *Toxicology and Industrial Health* 15: 181–186.

Stancel, George, et al. 2001. "Report of the bisphenol A sub-panel." Chapter 1 in *National Toxicology Program's report of the endocrine disruptors low-dose peer review.* U.S. EPA and NIEHS, NIH.

Stockholm Convention on Persistant Organic Pollutants. www.pops.int/

United States Environmental Protection Agency. 2003. Pesticide registration program. www.epa.gov/pesticides/factsheets/registration.htm.

United States Environmental Protection Agency. 2003. Toxic Substances Control Act. www.epa.gov/region5/defs/html/tsca.htm.

United States Environmental Protection Agency. 2003. *EPA's draft report on the environment.* EPA 600-R-03-050. EPA, Washington, D.C.

Williams, Phillip L., Robert C. James, and Stephen M. Roberts, eds. 2000. *The principles of toxicology: Environmental and industrial applications,* 2nd ed. Wiley-Interscience, New York.

World Health Organization, 2004. *World health report 2004: Changing history.* WHO, Geneva, Switzerland.

Yu, Ming-Ho, 2004. *Environmental toxicology: Biological and health effects of pollutants,* 2nd ed. CRC Press, Boca Raton, Florida.

**Chapter 15**

American Rivers. 2002. *The ecology of dam removal: A summary of benefits and impacts.* American Rivers, Washington D.C., February 2002.

British Geographical Society and Bangladesh Department of Public Health Engineering. 2001. *Arsenic contamination of groundwater in Bangladesh.* Technical Report WC/00/19, Volume 1: Summary.

De Villiers, Marq, 2000. *Water: The fate of our most precious resource.* Mariner Books.

Gleick, Peter. H. 2003. Global freshwater resources: Soft-path solutions for the 21st century. *Science* 302: 1524–1527.

Gleick, Peter. H., et al. 2004. *The world's water 2004–2005: The biennial report on freshwater resources.* Island Press, Washington D.C.

Harrison, Paul, and Fred Pearce, eds. 2000. *AAAS atlas of population & environment.* University of California Press, Berkeley.

Harvey, Charles F., et al. 2002. Arsenic mobility and groundwater extraction in Bangladesh. *Science* 298: 1602–1606.

Institute of Governmental Studies, University of California, Berkeley. Imperial Valley-San Diego water transfer controversy. www.igs. berkeley.edu/library/htImperialWaterTransfer2003.html.

Jenkins, Matt. 2002. The royal squeeze. *High Country News* 35(1), January 20, 2003.

Jenkins, Matt. 2003. California's water binge skids to a halt. *High Country News* 34(17), September 16, 2002.

Marston, Ed. 2001. Quenching the big thirst. *High Country News* 33(10), May 21, 2001.

Millennium Ecosystem Assessment. 2005. *Ecosystems and human well-being: Wetlands and water synthesis.* Millennium Ecosystem Assessment and World Resources Institute.

Nickson, Ross, et al. 1998. Arsenic poisoning of Bangladesh groundwater. *Nature* 395: 338.

Postel, Sandra. 1999. *Pillar of sand: Can the irrigation miracle last?* W. W. Norton, New York.

Postel, Sandra. 2005. *Liquid assets: The critical need to safeguard freshwater ecosystems.* Worldwatch Paper #170. Worldwatch Institute, Washington, D.C.

Postel, Sandra, and Amy Vickers. 2004. Boosting water productivity. Pp. 46–67 in *State of the world 2004.* Worldwatch Institute and W. W. Norton, Washington, D.C. and New York.

Reisner, Marc. 1986. *Cadillac desert: The American West and its disappearing water.* Viking Penguin, New York.

Sampat, Payal. 2001. Uncovering groundwater pollution. Pp. 21–42 in *State of the world 2001.* Worldwatch Institute and W. W. Norton, Washington, D.C., and New York.

Sibley, George. 1997. A tale of two rivers: The desert empire and the mountain. *High Country News* 29(21), November 10, 1997.

Smith, Lingas, Rahman. 2000. Contamination of drinking water by arsenic in Bangladesh: A public health emergency. *Bulletin of the World Health Organization,* 78(9).

Stone, Richard. 1999. Coming to grips with the Aral Sea's grim legacy. *Science* 284: 30–33.

United Nations Environment Programme. 2002. Freshwater. Pp. 150–179 in *Global environment outlook 3 (GEO-3).* UNEP and Earthscan Publications, Nairobi and London.

United Nations World Water Assessment Programme. 2003. *U.N. world water development report: Water for people, water for life.* Paris, New York, and Oxford, UNESCO and Berghahn Books.

United States Bureau of Reclamation, Lower Colorado Regional Office. www.usbr.gov/lc/region.

United States Environmental Protection Agency. 1998. *Wastewater primer.* EPA 833-K-98-001, Office of Wastewater Management, May 1998.

United States Environmental Protection Agency. 2003. *EPA's draft report on the environment.* EPA 600-R-03-050. EPA, Washington, D.C.

United States Environmental Protection Agency. 2003. *Water on tap: What you need to know.* EPA 816-K-03-007. Office of Water, EPA, Washington, D.C.

Wolf, Aaron T., et al. 2005. Managing water conflict and cooperation. Pp. 80–99 in *State of the world 2005.* Worldwatch Institute and W. W. Norton, Washington, D.C., and New York.

World Health Organization. 2000. *Global water supply and sanitation assessment 2000 report.* WHO, Geneva, Switzerland.

Youth, Howard. 2005. Wetlands drying up. Pp. 90–91 in *Vital signs 2005.* Worldwatch Institute and W. W. Norton, Washington, D.C., and New York.

## Chapter 16

Ault, J. S., Bohnsack, J. A. and G.A. Meester. 1998. A retrospective (1979–1996) multi-species assessment of coral reef fish stocks in the Florida Keys. *Fishery Bulletin* 96: 395–414.

Baker, Beth. 1999. First aid for an ailing reef: Research in the Florida Keys National Marine Sanctuary. *BioScience* 49: 173–178.

Bellwood, David R., et al. 2004. Confronting the coral reef crisis. *Nature* 429: 827–833.

Causey, Billy D., Joanne Delaney, and Brian D. Keller. 2001. *The status of coral reefs of the Florida Keys.* Florida Keys National Marine Sanctuary.

[Correspondence to *Science,* various authors]. 2001. *Science* 295: 1233–1235.

Embassy of the People's Republic of China. 2001. Fishing statistics "basically correct," ministry says. Press release, 18 December 2001. http://saup.fisheries.ubc.ca/Media/Chinese_Embassy_18_Dec_2001.pdf.

Food and Agriculture Organization of the United Nations. 2002. Fishery statistics: Reliability and policy implications. FAO Fisheries Department, Rome. www.fao.org/DOCREP/FIELD/006/Y3354M/Y3354M00.HTM.

Food and Agriculture Organization of the United Nations. 2004. *The state of world fisheries and aquaculture, 2004.* FAO, Rome.

Garrison, Tom. 2005. *Oceanography: An invitation to marine science,* 5th ed. Brooks/Cole, San Francisco.

Gell, Fiona R., and Callum M. Roberts. 2003. Benefits beyond boundaries: The fishery effects of marine reserves. *Trends in Ecology and Evolution* 18: 448–455.

Halpern, Benjamin S., and Robert R. Warner. 2002. Marine reserves have rapid and lasting effects. *Ecology Letters* 5: 361–366.

Halpern, Benjamin S., and Robert R. Warner. 2003. Matching marine reserve design to reserve objectives. *Proceedings of the Royal Society of London B:* 270: 1871–1878.

Jackson, Jeremy B. C., et al. 2001. Historical overfishing and the recent collapse of coastal ecosystems. *Science* 293: 629–638.

Larsen, Janet. 2005. Wild fish catch hits limits—Oceanic decline offset by increased fish farming *Eco-economy indicators.* Earth Policy Institute, www.earth-policy.org/Indicators/Fish/2005.htm.

Mastny, Lisa. 2001. World's coral reefs dying off. Pp. 92–93 in *Vital signs 2001.* Worldwatch Institute and W. W. Norton, Washington D.C., and New York.

Myers, Ransom A., and Boris Worm. 2003. Rapid worldwide depletion of predatory fish communities. *Nature* 423: 280–283.

National Academy of Public Administration. 1999. *Protecting Our National Marine Sanctuaries.* Center for the Economy and the Environment, NAPA, Washington, D.C.

National Center for Ecological Analysis and Synthesis (NCEAS) and Communication Partnership for Science and the Sea (COMPASS), sponsors. 2001. *Scientific consensus statement on marine reserves and marine protected areas.* Available online at www.nceas.ucsb.edu/consensus.

National Oceanic and Atmospheric Administration (NOAA). Florida Keys National Marine Sanctuary. www. fknms.nos.noaa.gov.

National Research Council. 2003. *Oil in the sea III: Inputs, fates, and effects.* National Academies Press, Washington, D.C.

Norse, Elliott, and Larry B. Crowder, eds. 2005. *Marine conservation biology: The science of maintaining the sea's biodiversity.* Island Press, Washington, D.C.

Nybakken, James W., and Mark D. Bertness. 2004. *Marine biology: An ecological approach,* 6th ed. Benjamin Cummings, San Francisco.

Palumbi, Stephen. 2003. *Marine reserves: A tool for ecosystem management and conservation.* Pew Oceans Commission.

Pauly, Daniel, et al. 2002. Towards sustainability in world fisheries. *Nature* 418: 689–695.

Pauly, Daniel, et al. 2003. The future for fisheries. *Science* 302: 1359–1361.

Pew Oceans Commission. 2003. *America's living oceans: Charting a course for sea change.* A report to the nation. May 2003. Pew Oceans Commission, Arlington, Virginia.

Pinet, Paul R. 1999. *Invitation to oceanography,* 2nd ed. Jones & Bartlett, Boston.

Roberts, Callum M., et al. 2001. Effects of marine reserves on adjacent fisheries. *Science* 294: 1920–1923.

Sumich, James L., and John F. Morrissey, 2004. *Introduction to the biology of marine life,* 8th ed. Jones & Bartlett, Boston.

Thurman, Harold V., and Alan P. Trujillo, 2004. *Introductory oceanography,* 10th ed. Prentice Hall, Upper Saddle River, New Jersey.

United Nations Environment Programme. 2002. Coastal and marine areas. Pp. 180–209 in *Global environment outlook 3 (GEO-3).* UNEP and Earthscan Publications, Nairobi and London.

United States Commission on Ocean Policy. 2004. *An ocean blueprint for the 21st century.* Final Report. Washington, D.C.

United States Department of Commerce. 1996. *Strategy for stewardship: Florida Keys National Marine Sanctuary final management plan/ environmental impact statement.* 3 vols. Dept. of Commerce, Washington, D.C.

United States Department of Commerce and United States Department of the Interior. Marine protected areas of the United States. www.mpa.gov.

Watson, Reginald, Lillian Pang, and Daniel Pauly. 2001. The marine fisheries of China: Development and reported catches. *Fisheries Centre Research Reports* 9(2). Fisheries Centre, University of British Columbia, Canada.

Watson, Reginald, and Daniel Pauly. 2001. Systematic distortions in world fisheries catch trends. *Nature* 414: 534–536.

Weber, Michael L. 2001. *From abundance to scarcity: A history of U.S. marine fisheries policy.* Island Press, Washington, D.C.

## Chapter 17

Ahrens, C. Donald. 2003. *Meteorology today,* 7th ed. Brooks/Cole, San Francisco.

Akimoto, Hajime. 2003. Global air quality and pollution. *Science* 302: 1716–1719.

Bell, Michelle L., and Devra L. Davis. 2001. Reassessment of the lethal London fog of 1952: Novel indicators of acute and chronic consequences of acute exposure to air pollution. *Environmental Health Perspectives* 109(Suppl 3): 389–394.

Bernard, Susan M., et al. 2001. The potential impacts of climate variability and change on air pollution-related health effects in the United States. *Environmental Health Perspectives* 109(Suppl 2): 199–209.

Biscaye, Pierre E., et al. 2000. Eurasian air pollution reaches eastern North America. *Science* 290: 2258–2259.

Boubel, Richard W., et al., eds. 1994. *Fundamentals of air pollution,* 3rd ed. Academic Press, San Diego, California.

Bruce, Nigel, Rogelio Perez-Padilla, and Rachel Albalak. 2000. Indoor air pollution in developing countries: A major environmental and public health challenge. *Bulletin of the World Health Organization* 78: 1078–1092.

Cooper, C. David, and F. C. Alley. 2002. *Air pollution control,* 3rd ed. Waveland Press.

Davis, Devra. 2002. *When smoke ran like water: Tales of environmental deception and the battle against pollution.* Basic Books, New York.

Davis, Devra L., Michelle L. Bell, and Tony Fletcher. 2002. A look back at the London smog of 1952 and the half century since. *Environmental Health Perspectives* 110: A734.

Driscoll, Charles T., et al. 2001. *Acid rain revisited: Advances in scientific understanding since the passage of the 1970 and 1990 Clean Air Act Amendments.* Hubbard Brook Research Foundation. Science Links™ Publication. Vol. 1, no.1.

Ezzati Majid, and Daniel M. Kammen. 2001. Quantifying the effects of exposure to indoor air pollution from biomass combustion on acute respiratory infections in developing countries. *Environmental Health Perspectives* 109: 481–488.

Gardner, Gary. 2005. Air pollution still a problem. Pp. 94–95 in *Vital signs 2005.* Worldwatch Institute and W. W. Norton, Washington, D.C., and New York.

Godish, Thad. 2003. *Air quality,* 4th ed. CRC Press, Boca Raton, Florida.

Hunt, Andrew, et al. 2003. Toxicologic and epidemiologic clues from the characterization of the 1952 London smog fine particulate matter in archival autopsy lung tissues. *Environmental Health Perspectives* 111: 1209–1214.

Jacobson, Mark Z. 2002. *Atmospheric pollution: History, science, and regulation.* Cambridge University Press, New York.

Hoffman, Matthew J. 2005. *Ozone depletion and climate change: Constructing a global response.* SUNY Press, New York.

Kunzli, Nino, et al. 2000. Public-health impact of outdoor and traffic-related air pollution: A European assessment. *Lancet* 356: 795–801.

Lelieveld, Jos, et al. 2001. The Indian Ocean experiment: Widespread air pollution from South and Southeast Asia. *Science* 291: 1031–1036.

Likens, Gene E. 2004. Some perspectives on long-term biogeochemical research from the Hubbard Brook ecosystem study. *Ecology* 85: 2355–2362.

London, Stephanie J., and Isabelle Romieu. 2000. Health costs due to outdoor air pollution by traffic. *Lancet* 356: 782–783.

Molina, Mario J., and F. Sherwood Rowland. 1974. Stratospheric sink for chlorofluoromethanes: Chlorine atom catalyzed destruction of ozone. *Nature* 249: 810–812.

Pal Arya, S. 1998. *Air pollution: Meteorology and dispersion.* Oxford University Press, Oxford.

Parson, Edward A. 2003. *Protecting the ozone layer: Science and strategy.* Oxford University Press, Oxford.

United Nations Environment Programme. Montreal Protocol. http://hq.unep.org/ozone/Treaties_and_Ratification/2B_montreal_ protocol.asp.

United Nations Environment Programme. 2002. Atmosphere. Pp. 210–239 in *Global environment outlook 3 (GEO-3).* UNEP and Earthscan Publications, Nairobi and London.

United States Environmental Protection Agency. 2003. *EPA's draft report on the environment.* EPA 600-R-03-050. Washington, D.C.

United States Environmental Protection Agency. 2003. *Latest findings on national air quality: 2002 status and trends.* EPA 454/K-03-001. Washington, D.C.

Wark, Kenneth, et al., 1997. *Air pollution: Its origin and control,* 3rd ed. Prentice Hall, Upper Saddle River, New Jersey.

World Health Organization. Indoor air pollution. WHO, Geneva, Switzerland. www.who.int/indoorair/en/index.html.

## Chapter 18

Alley, Richard B. 2000. *The two-mile time machine: Ice cores, abrupt climate change, and our future.* Princeton University Press, Princeton, New Jersey.

Burroughs, William James. 2001. *Climate change: A multidisciplinary approach.* Cambridge University Press, Cambridge.

Drake, Frances. 2000. *Global warming: The science of climate change.* Oxford University Press, Oxford.

Dunn, Seth. 2001. Decarbonizing the energy economy. Pp. 83–102 in *State of the world 2001.* Worldwatch Institute and W. W. Norton, Washington, D.C., and New York.

Dunn, Seth, and Christopher Flavin. 2002. Moving the climate change agenda forward. Pp. 24–50 in *State of the world 2002.* Worldwatch Institute and W. W. Norton, Washington, D.C., and New York.

Gelbspan, Ross. 1997. *The heat is on: The climate crisis, the cover-up, the prescription.* Perseus Books, New York.

Gelbspan, Ross. 2004. *Boiling point: How politicians, big oil and coal, journalists, and activists are fueling the climate crisis—and what we can do to avert disaster.* Basic Books, New York.

Intergovernmental Panel on Climate Change. 2001. *IPCC third assessment report—Climate change 2001: The scientific basis.* World Meteorological Organization and United Nations Environment Programme.

Intergovernmental Panel on Climate Change. 2001. *IPCC third assessment report—Climate change 2001: Impacts, adaptations, and vulnerability.* World Meteorological Organization and United Nations Environment Programme.

Intergovernmental Panel on Climate Change. 2001. *IPCC third assessment report—Climate change 2001: Mitigation.* World Meteorological Organization and United Nations Environment Programme.

Intergovernmental Panel on Climate Change. 2001. *IPCC third assessment report—Climate change 2001: Synthesis report.* World Meteorological Organization and United Nations Environment Programme.

Intergovernmental Panel on Climate Change. 2001. *Technical Summary of the Working Group 1 report.*

Intergovernmental Panel on Climate Change. www.ipcc.ch/

Kareiva, Peter M., Joel G. Kingsolver, and Raymond B. Huey, eds. 1993. *Biotic interactions and global change.* Sinauer Associates, Sunderland, Massachusetts.

Karl, Thomas R., and Kevin E. Trenberth, 2003. Modern global climate change. *Science* 302: 1719–1723.

Lomborg, Bjorn. 2001. *The skeptical environmentalist: Measuring the real state of the world*. Cambridge University Press, Cambridge.

Mastny, Lisa. 2005. Global ice melting accelerating. Pp. 88–89 in *Vital signs 2005*. Worldwatch Institute and W. W. Norton, Washington, D.C., and New York.

Mayewski, Paul A., and Frank White. 2002. *The ice chronicles: The quest to understand global climate change*. University Press of New England, Hanover, New Hampshire.

McLachlan, Jason S., and Linda B. Brubaker. 1995. Local and regional vegetation change on the northeastern Olympic Peninsula during the Holocene. *Canadian Journal of Botany* 73: 1618–1627.

National Assessment Synthesis Team. 2000. *Climate change impacts on the United States: The potential consequences of climate variability and change*. U.S. Global Change Research Program. Cambridge University Press, Cambridge.

National Research Council, Board on Atmospheric Sciences and Climate, Commission on Geosciences, Environment, and Resources. 1998. *The atmospheric sciences: Entering the twenty-first century*. National Academies Press, Washington, D.C.

National Research Council, Committee on the Science of Climate Change, Division of Earth and Life Studies. 2001. *Climate change science: An analysis of some key questions*. National Academies Press, Washington, D.C.

Nordhaus, William D. 1998. Assessing the economics of climate change: An introduction. In Nordhaus, William D., ed., *Economic and policy issues in climate change*. Resources for the Future Press, Washington D.C.

Parmesan, Camille, and Gary Yohe. 2003. A globally coherent fingerprint of climate change impacts across natural systems. *Nature* 421: 37–42.

Real Climate. www.realclimate.org.

Root, Terry L., et al. 2003. Fingerprints of global warming on wild animals and plants. *Nature* 421: 57–60.

Sawin, Janet L. 2005. Climate change indicators on the rise. Pp. 40–41 in *Vital signs 2005*. Worldwatch Institute and W. W. Norton, Washington, D.C., and New York.

Schneider, Stephen H. and Terry L. Root, eds. 2002. *Wildlife responses to climate change: North American case studies*. Island Press, Washington, D.C.

Seinfeld, John H., and Spyros N. Pandis. 2006. *Atmospheric chemistry and physics*, 2nd ed. Wiley-Interscience, New York.

Shapiro, Robert J., Kevin A. Hassett, and Frank S. Arnold. 2002. *Conserving energy and preserving the environment: The role of public transportation*. American Public Transportation Association, July 2002.

Speth, James Gustave. 2004. *Red sky at morning: America and the crisis of the global environment*. Yale University Press, New Haven, Connecticut.

Stevens, William K. 1999. *The change in the weather: People, weather and the science of climate*. Delta Trade Paperbacks, New York.

Taylor, David. 2003. Small islands threatened by sea level rise. Pp. 84–85 in *Vital signs 2003*. Worldwatch Institute and W. W. Norton, Washington D.C. and New York.

Victor, David G. 2004. *Climate change: Debating America's policy options*. U.S. Council on Foreign Relations Press, Washington, D.C.

United Nations. United Nations Framework Convention on Climate Change. http://unfccc.int/2860.php.

United Nations. Kyoto Protocol. http://unfccc.int/resource/docs/convkp/kpeng.html.

United States Congress. House Committee on Science. 2001. Climate change: The state of the science. Hearing before the Committee on Science, House of Representatives, One Hundred Seventh Congress, first session, 14 March 2001.

## Chapter 19

Association for the Study of Peak Oil and Gas. www.peakoil.net/

British Petroleum. 2005. *BP statistical review of world energy*. London, June 2005.

Campbell, Colin J. 1997. *The coming oil crisis*. Multi-Science Publishing Co., Essex, U.K.

Deffeyes, Kenneth S. 2001. *Hubbert's peak: The impending world oil shortage*. Princeton University Press, Princeton, New Jersey.

Deffeyes, Kenneth S. 2005. *Beyond oil: The view from Hubbert's peak*. Farrar, Straus, and Giroux, New York.

Douglas, D. C., P.E. Reynolds, and E. B. Rhode, eds. 2002. *Arctic Refuge coastal plain terrestrial wildlife research summaries. Biological science report*. USGS/BRD/BSR-2002-0001. United States Geological Survey, Washington, D.C.

Dunn, Seth. 2001. Decarbonizing the energy economy. Pp. 83–102 in *State of the world 2001*, Worldwatch Institute and W. W. Norton, Washington, D.C., and New York.

Energy Information Administration, U.S. Department of Energy. www.eia.doe.gov.

Energy Information Administration, U.S. Department of Energy. 1999. *Petroleum: An energy profile, 1999*. DOE/EIA-0545(99).

Energy Information Administration, U.S. Department of Energy. 2005. *Annual energy review 2004*. DOE/EIA-0384(2004). Washington, D.C.

Energy Information Administration, U.S. Department of Energy. 2005. *International energy annual 2003*. Washington, D.C.

Flavin, Christopher. 2005. Fossil fuel use surges. Pp. 30–31 in *Vital signs 2005*. Worldwatch Institute and W. W. Norton, Washington, D.C., and New York.

Freese, Barbara. 2003. *Coal: A human history*. Perseus Books, New York.

Goodstein, David. 2004. *Out of gas*. W. W. Norton, New York.

Holmes, Bob, and Nicola Jones. 2003. Brace yourself for the end of cheap oil. *New Scientist* (August 2, 2003): 9–11.

International Energy Agency. 2005. *Key world energy statistics 2005*. IEA Publications, Paris.

International Energy Agency. 2005. *World energy outlook 2005*. IEA Publications, Paris.

International Energy Agency. 2005. *Resources to reserves: Oil and gas technologies for the energy markets of the future*. IEA Publications, Paris.

Lovins, Amory B., et al. 2004. *Winning the oil endgame: Innovation for profits, jobs, and security*. Rocky Mountain Institute, Snowmass, Colorado.

Lovins, Amory B. 2005. More profit with less carbon. *Scientific American* 293(3): 74–83.

Nellemann, Christian, and Raymond D. Cameron. 1998. Cumulative impacts of an evolving oil-field complex on the distribution of calving caribou. *Canadian Journal of Zoology* 76: 1425–1430.

Pelley, Janet. 2001. Will drilling for oil disrupt the Arctic National Wildlife Refuge? *Environmental Science and Technology* 35: 240–247.

Powell, Stephen G. 1990. Arctic National Wildlife Refuge: How much oil can we expect? *Resources Policy* Sept. 1990: 225–240.

Prugh, Tom, et al. 2005. Changing the oil economy. Pp. 100–121 in *State of the world 2005*, Worldwatch Institute and W. W. Norton, Washington, D.C., and New York.

Ristinen, Robert A., and Jack J. Kraushaar. 1998. *Energy and the environment*. John Wiley and Sons, New York.

Russell, D. E. and P. McNeil. 2005. *Summer ecology of the Porcupine caribou herd*. Porcupine Caribou Management Board, Whitehorse, Yukon.

Sawin, Janet L. 2004. Making better energy choices. Pp. 24–45 in *State of the world 2004*. Worldwatch Institute and W. W. Norton, Washington, D.C. and New York.

Skinner, Brian J., and Stephen C. Porter. 2003. *The dynamic earth: An introduction to physical geology*, 5th ed. John Wiley and Sons, Hoboken, New Jersey.

United States Environmental Protection Agency. 2005. *Light-duty automotive technology and fuel economy trends: 1975 through 2005*. EPA420-R-05-001. EPA Office of Transportation and Air Quality, Washington, D.C.

United States Fish and Wildlife Service. 2001. Potential impacts of proposed oil and gas development on the Arctic Refuge's coastal plain: Historical overview and issues of concern. Web page of the Arctic National Wildlife Refuge, Fairbanks, Alaska. http://arctic.fws.gov/issues1.html.

United States Geological Survey. 2001. *The National Petroleum Reserve-Alaska (NPRA) data archive.* USGS Fact Sheet FS-024-01, March 2001.

United States Geological Survey. 2001. *Arctic National Wildlife Refuge, 1002 Area, petroleum assessment, 1998, including economic analysis.* USGS Fact Sheet FS-028-01, April 2001.

Walker, Donald A. 1997. Arctic Alaskan vegetation disturbance and recovery. Pp. 457–479 in *Disturbance and recovery in Arctic lands,* R.M.M. Crawford, ed. Kluwer Academic Publishers, Dordrecht, Netherlands.

## Chapter 20

Aeck, Molly. 2005. Biofuel use growing rapidly. Pp. 38–39 in *Vital signs 2005.* Worldwatch Institute and W. W. Norton, Washington, D.C., and New York.

British Petroleum. 2005. *BP statistical review of world energy.* London, June 2005.

Chandler, David. 2003. America steels itself to take the nuclear plunge. *New Scientist* (August 9, 2003): 10–13.

Energy Information Administration, U.S. Department of Energy. www.eia.doe.gov.

Energy Information Administration. 2005. *Annual energy outlook 2005.* Washington, D.C.

Energy Information Administration, U.S. Department of Energy. 2005. *Annual energy review 2004.* DOE/EIA-0384(2004). Washington, D.C.

Energy Information Administration, U.S. Department of Energy. 2005. *International energy annual 2003.* Washington, D.C.

European Commission/International Atomic Energy Agency/World Health Organization. 1996. One decade after Chernobyl: Summing up the consequences of the accident. Summary of the conference results. Vienna, Austria, 8–12 April, 1996. EC/IAEA/WHO.

International Energy Agency. 2005. *Key world energy statistics 2005.* IEA Publications, Paris.

International Energy Agency. 2005. *World energy outlook 2005.* IEA Publications, Paris.

International Atomic Energy Agency. 2004. *Annual report 2003.* GC(48)/3.IAEA, Vienna, Austria.

International Atomic Energy Agency. *Nuclear power and sustainable development.* IAEA Information Series 02-01574/FS Series 3/01/E/Rev.1. Vienna, Austria.

Klass, Donald L. 2004. Biomass for Renewable Energy and Fuels. In *The Encyclopedia of Energy,* Elsevier.

Lenssen, Nicholas. 2005. Nuclear power rises once more. Pp. 32–33 in *Vital signs 2005.* Worldwatch Institute and W. W. Norton, Washington, D.C., and New York.

Lovins, Amory B., et al. 2004. *Winning the oil endgame: Innovation for profits, jobs, and security.* Rocky Mountain Institute, Snowmass, Colorado.

Murray, Danielle. 2005. Ethanol's potential: Looking beyond corn. *Eco-economy Update #49,* 5 June 2005. Earth Policy Institute, http://www.earth-policy.org/Updates/2005/Update49.htm.

National Renewable Energy Lab, U.S. Department of Energy. www.nrel.gov.

Nuclear Energy Agency, OECD. 2002. *Chernobyl: Assessment of radiological and health impacts. (2002 Update of Chernobyl: Ten Years On).* OECD, Paris.

Nuclear Energy Agency. 2005. *NEA annual report 2004.* NEA, Organisation for Economic Co-operation and Development. OECD, Paris.

Office of Energy Efficiency and Renewable Energy, U.S. Department of Energy www.eere.energy.gov.

Organisation for Economic Co-operation and Development. 2000. *Business as usual and nuclear power.* OECD Publications, Paris.

REN21 Renewable Energy Policy Network. 2005. *Renewables 2005 global status report.* Worldwatch Institute, Washington, D.C.

Spadaro, Joseph V., Lucille Langlois, and Bruce Hamilton. 2000. Greenhouse gas emissions of electricity generation chains: Assessing the difference. *IAEA Bulletin* 42(2).

Swedish Bioenergy Association (SVEBIO). 2003. *Focus: Bioenergy.* Nos. 1–10. SVEBIO, Stockholm, 2003.

Swedish Energy Agency 2004. *Renewable electricity is the future's electricity.* Swedish Energy Agency, Eskilstuna, Sweden.

Swedish Energy Agency 2004. *Energy in Sweden: Facts and figures 2004.* Swedish Energy Agency, Eskilstuna, Sweden.

Swedish Energy Agency 2004. *The Swedish Energy Agency 2003.* Swedish Energy Agency, Eskilstuna, Sweden.

Swedish Energy Agency 2004. *Energy in Sweden 2003.* Swedish Energy Agency, Eskilstuna, Sweden.

U.N. Food and Agriculture Organization. *Biomass energy in ASEAN member countries.* FAO/ASEAN/EC. FAO Regional Wood Energy Development Programme in Asia, Bangkok, Thailand.

U.S. Environmental Protection Agency. Alternative fuels website. www.epa.gov/otaq/consumer/fuels/altfuels/altfuels.htm.

## Chapter 21

American Wind Energy Association. 2005. *Global wind energy market report.* AWEA, Washington, D.C.

Ananthaswamy, Anil. 2003. Reality bites for the dream of a hydrogen economy. *New Scientist,* (November 15, 2003): 6–7.

Arnason, Bragi, and and Thorsteinn I. Sigfusson. 2000. Iceland—a future hydrogen economy. *International Journal of Hydrogen Energy* 25: 389–394.

Ásmundsson, Jón Knútur. 2002. Will fuel cells make Iceland the 'Kuwait of the North?' *World Press Review,* 15 February 2002.

Burkett, Elinor. 2003. A mighty wind. *New York Times magazine.* June 15, 2003.

Chow, Jeffrey, et al. 2003. Energy resources and global development. *Science* 302: 1528–1531.

DaimlerChrysler. 2003. *360 DEGREES/DaimlerChrysler Environmental Report 2003.* DaimlerChrysler AG, Stuttgart, Germany.

Dunn, Seth. 2000. The hydrogen experiment. *WorldWatch* 13: 14–25.

Energy Information Administration, U.S. Department of Energy. www.eia.doe.gov.

Energy Information Administration, U.S. Department of Energy. 2005. *Annual energy review 2004.* DOE/EIA-0384(2004). Washington, D.C.

Energy Information Administration, U.S. Department of Energy. 2005. *International energy annual 2003.* Washington, D.C.

Flavin, Christopher, and Seth Dunn. 1999. A new energy paradigm for the 21st century. *Journal of International Affairs* 53: 167–190.

Hirsch, Tim. 2001. Iceland launches energy revolution. *British Broadcasting Corporation News,* 24 December 2001.

Hydrogen & Fuel Cell Letter. 2003. World's first commercial hydrogen station opens in Iceland. *Hydrogen & Fuel Cell Letter* May 2003.

Idaho Wind Power Working Group for the Idaho Department of Water Resources Energy Division. 2002. *Idaho wind power development strategic plan.* Boise, Idaho.

Idaho Wind Power Working Group for the Idaho Department of Water Resources Energy Division. 2002. *Wind power potential in Idaho by county.* Boise, Idaho.

International Energy Agency. 2002. *Renewables in global energy supply: An IEA fact sheet.* IEA Publications, Paris.

International Energy Agency Renewable Energy Working Party. 2002. *Renewable energy . . . into the mainstream.* SITTARD, The Netherlands.

International Energy Agency. 2005. *Renewables information 2005.* IEA Publications, Paris.

Lovins, Amory B., et al. 2004. *Winning the oil endgame: Innovation for profits, jobs, and security.* Rocky Mountain Institute, Snowmass, Colorado.

Martinot, Eric, et al. 2002. Renewable energy markets in developing countries. *Annual Review of Energy and the Environment* 27: 309–48.

Martinot, Eric, Ryan Wiser, and Jan Hamrin. 2005. *Renewable energy markets and policies in the United States.* Center for Resource Solutions, San Francisco. www.martinot.info/Martinot_et_al_CRS.pdf.

Melis, Anastasios, et al. 2000. Sustained photobiological hydrogen gas production upon reversible inactivation of oxygen evolution in the green alga *Chlamydomonas reinhardtii. Plant Physiology* 122: 127–135.

National Renewable Energy Lab, U.S. Department of Energy. www.nrel.gov.

Office of Energy Efficiency and Renewable Energy, U.S. Department of Energy www.eere.energy.gov.

Office of Energy Efficiency and Renewable Energy, U.S. Department of Energy. 2005. *Wind power today: Federal wind program highlights.* DOE/GO-102005-2115. Washington, D.C.

Randerson, James. 2003. The clean green energy dream. *New Scientist* (August 16, 2003): 8–11.

Reeves, Ari, with Fredric Beck. 2003. *Wind energy for electric power: A REPP issue brief.* Renewable Energy Policy Project, Washington, D.C.

REN21 Renewable Energy Policy Network. 2005. *Renewables 2005 global status report.* Worldwatch Institute, Washington, D.C.

Ristinen, Robert A., and Jack J. Kraushaar, 1998. *Energy and the environment.* John Wiley and Sons, New York.

Rocky Mountain Institute webpage. Energy. RMI, Snowmass, Colorado. www.rmi.org/sitepages/pid17.php.

Sawin, Janet. 2004. *Mainstreaming renewable energy in the 21st century.* Worldwatch Paper 169. Worldwatch Institute, Washington, D.C.

Sawin, Janet L. 2005. Global wind growth continues. Pp. 34–35 in *Vital signs 2005.* Worldwatch Institute and W. W. Norton, Washington, D.C. and New York.

Sawin, Janet L. 2005. Solar energy markets booming. Pp. 36–37 in *Vital signs 2005.* Worldwatch Institute and W. W. Norton, Washington, D.C. and New York.

U.S. Department of Energy National Laboratory directors.1997. *Technology opportunities to reduce U.S. greenhouse gas emissions.* DOE, Washington, D.C.

Weisman, Alan. 1998. *Gaviotas: A village to reinvent the world.* Chelsea Green Publishing Co., White River Junction, Vermont.

World Alliance for Decentralized Energy. 2005. *World survey of decentralized energy 2005.* WADE, Edinburgh, Scotland.

**Chapter 22**

Allen, G. H. and R. A. Gearheart, eds. 1988. *Proceedings of a conference on wetlands for wastewater treatment and resource enhancement.* Humboldt State University, Arcata, California.

Ayres, Robert U., and Leslie W. Ayres. 1996. *Industrial ecology: Towards closing the materials cycle.* Edward Elgar Press, Cheltenham, U.K.

Beede, David N., and David E. Bloom. 1995. The economics of municipal solid waste. *World Bank Research Observer* 10: 113–150.

Diesendorf, Mark, and Clive Hamilton. 1997. *Human ecology, human economy.* Allen and Unwin, St. Leonards.

Edmonton, Alberta, City of. 2003. Waste management. www.edmonton.ca/portal/server.pt/gateway/PTARGS_0_2_104_0_0_35/http%3B/cmsserver/COEWeb/environment+waste+and+recycling/waste/

Energy Information Administration. Municipal solid waste. EIA, U.S. Department of Energy, Washington, D.C. www.eia.doe.gov/cneaf/solar.renewables/page/mswaste/msw.html.

Gitlitz, Jenny, and Pat Franklin. 2004. *The 10-cent incentive to recycle,* 3rd ed. Container Recycling Institute, Arlington, Virginia.

Graedel, Thomas E., and Braden R. Allenby, 2002. *Industrial ecology,* 2nd ed. Prentice Hall, Upper Saddle River, New Jersey.

Integrated Waste Services Association. WTE: About waste-to-energy. www.wte.org/waste.html. IWSA, Washington, D.C.

Kaufman, Scott, et al. 2004. The state of garbage in America. *Biocycle* 45: 31–41.

Lilienfeld, Robert, and William Rathje. 1998. *Use less stuff: Environmental solutions for who we really are.* Ballantine, New York.

Manahan, Stanley E. 1999. *Industrial ecology: Environmental chemistry and hazardous waste.* Lewis Publishers, CRC Press, Boca Raton, Florida.

McDonough, William, and Michael Braungart. 2002. *Cradle to cradle: Remaking the way we make things.* North Point Press, New York.

McGinn, Anne Platt. 2002. Toxic waste largely unseen. Pp. 112–113 in *Vital signs 2002.* Worldwatch Institute and W. W. Norton, Washington D.C., and New York.

New York City Department of Planning. Fresh Kills: Landfill to landscape. www.nyc.gov/html/dcp/html/fkl/ada/about/1_0.html/

New York City Department of Planning. Fresh Kills lifescape. www.nyc.gov/html/dcp/html/fkl/fkl_index.shtml.

New York City Department of Sanitation. 2000. Closing the Fresh Kills landfill. *The DOS Report,* Feb. 2000.

Rathje, William, and Colleen Murphy. 2001. *Rubbish! The archeology of garbage.* University of Arizona Press, March 2001.

Smith, Ronald S. 1998. *Profit centers in industrial ecology.* Quorum Books, Westport.

Socolow, Robert H., et al., eds. 1994. *Industrial ecology and global change.* Cambridge University Press, Cambridge.

United Nations Environment Programme. 2000. *International source book on environmentally sound technologies (ESTs) for municipal solid waste management (MSWM).* UNEP IETC, Osaka, Japan.

United States Environmental Protection Agency. 2005. *Municipal solid waste generation, recycling, and disposal in the United States: Facts and figures for 2003.* EPA530-F-05-003, EPA Office of Solid Waste and Emergency Response.

United States Environmental Protection Agency. Municipal solid waste. www.epa.gov/epaoswer/non-hw/muncpl.

**Chapter 23**

Bartlett, Peggy, and Geoffrey W. Chase, eds. 2004. *Sustainability on campus: Stories and strategies for change.* MIT Press, Cambridge, Massachusetts.

Brower, Michael, and Warren Leon. 1999. *The consumer's guide to effective environmental choices: Practical advice from the Union of Concerned Scientists.* Three Rivers Press, New York.

Brown, Lester. 2001. *Eco-economy: Building an economy for the Earth.* Earth Policy Institute and W. W. Norton, New York.

Brown, Lester. 2006. *Plan B 2.0: Rescuing a planet under stress and a civilization in trouble.* Earth Policy Institute and W. W. Norton, New York.

Creighton, Sarah Hammond. 1998. *Greening the ivory tower: Improving the environmental track record of universities, colleges, and other institutions.* MIT Press, Cambridge, Massachusetts.

Daly, Herman E. 1996. *Beyond growth.* Beacon Press, Boston.

Dasgupta, Partha, Simon Levin, and Jane Lubchenco. 2000. Economic pathways to ecological sustainability. *BioScience* 50: 339–345.

De Graaf, John, David Wann, and Thomas Naylor. 2002. *Affluenza: The all-consuming epidemic.* Berrett-Koehler Publishers, San Francisco.

Durning, Alan. 1992. *How much is enough? The consumer society and the future of the Earth.* Worldwatch Institute, Washington, D.C.

Erickson, Jon D., and John M. Gowdy. 2002. The strange economics of sustainability. *BioScience* 52: 212.

French, Hilary. 2004. Linking globalization, consumption, and governance. Pp. 144–163 in *State of the world 2004.* Worldwatch Institute and W. W. Norton, Washington, D.C., and New York.

Gardner, Gary. 2001. Accelerating the shift to sustainability. Pp. 189–206 in *State of the world 2001.* Worldwatch Institute and W. W. Norton, Washington, D.C., and New York.

Gardner, Gary, and Erik Assadourian. 2004. Rethinking the good life. Pp. 164–179 in *State of the world 2004.* Worldwatch Institute and W. W. Norton, Washington, D.C., and New York.

Gibbs, W. Wayt. 2005. How should we set priorities? *Scientific American* 293(3): 108–115.

Hawken, Paul. 1994. *The ecology of commerce: A declaration of sustainability.* HarperBusiness, New York.

Keniry, Julian. 1995. *Ecodemia: Campus environmental stewardship at the turn of the 21st century.* National Wildlife Federation, Washington, D.C.

Mastny, Lisa. 2002. Ecolabeling gains ground. Pp. 124–125 in *Vital signs 2002.* Worldwatch Institute and W. W. Norton, Washington D.C., and New York.

McMichael, A. J., et al. 2003. New visions for addressing sustainability. *Science* 302: 1919–1921.

Mastny, Lisa. 2002. Ecolabeling gains ground. Pp. 124–125 in *Vital signs 2002.* Worldwatch Institute and W. W. Norton, Washington D.C., and New York.

McMichael, A. J., et al. 2003. New visions for addressing sustainability. *Science* 302: 1919–1921.

Millennium Ecosystem Assessment. 2005. *Ecosystems and human well-being: General synthesis.* Millennium Ecosystem Assessment and World Resources Institute.

McIntosh, Mary, et al., 2001. *State of the campus environment: A national report card on environmental performance and sustainability in higher education.* National Wildlife Federation Campus Ecology.

Meadows, Donella, Jørgen Randers, and Dennis Meadows. 2004. *Limits to growth: The 30-year update.* Chelsea Green Publ. Co., White River Junction, Vermont.

National Research Council, Board on Sustainable Development. 1999. *Our common journey: A transition toward sustainability.* National Academies Press, Washington, D.C.

National Wildlife Federation. Campus Ecology. www.nwf.org/campusecology.

Office of Management and Budget, Executive Office of the President of the United States, Washington, D.C. 2003. *Informing regulatory decisions: 2003 report to Congress on the costs and benefits of federal and unfunded mandates on state, local, and tribal entities.* Washington, D.C., September 2003.

Sanderson, Eric W., et al. 2002. The human footprint and the last of the wild. *Bioscience* 52: 891–904.

Schor, Juliet B., and Betsy Taylor, eds. 2002. *Sustainable planet: Solutions for the twenty-first century.* The Center for a New American Dream. Beacon Press, Boston.

Toor, Will, and Spenser W. Havlick. 2004. *Transportation and sustainable campus communities: Issues, examples, solutions.* Island Press, Washington, D.C.

United Nations. 2002. *Report of the World Summit on Sustainable Development, Johannesburg, South Africa, 26 August–4 September 2002.* United Nations, New York.

United Nations. 2002. *The road from Johannesburg: What was achieved and the way forward.* United Nations, New York.

United Nations Development Programme. 2002. *Human development report 2002.* Oxford University Press, Oxford.

United Nations Division for Sustainable Development. 1990. *Agenda 21.* Accessible online at www.un.org/esa/sustdev/documents/agenda21/index.htm.

United Nations Environment Programme. 2002. Outlook: 2002-2032. Pp. 319–400 in *Global environment outlook 3 (GEO-3).* UNEP and Earthscan Publications, Nairobi and London.

United States Environmental Protection Agency. 2000. *Regulatory impact analysis: Heavy-duty engine and vehicle standards and highway diesel fuel sulfur control requirements.* EPA420-R-00-026. EPA, Washington, D.C.

University Leaders for a Sustainable Future. www.ulsf.org.

Wackernagel, Mathis, Lillemor Lewan, and Carina Borgström-Hansson. 1999. Evaluating the use of natural capital with the ecological footprint. *Ambio* 28: 604.

Wilson, Edward O. 1998. *Consilience: The unity of knowledge.* Alfred A. Knopf, New York.

World Commission on Environment and Development. 1987. *Our common future.* Oxford University Press, Oxford.